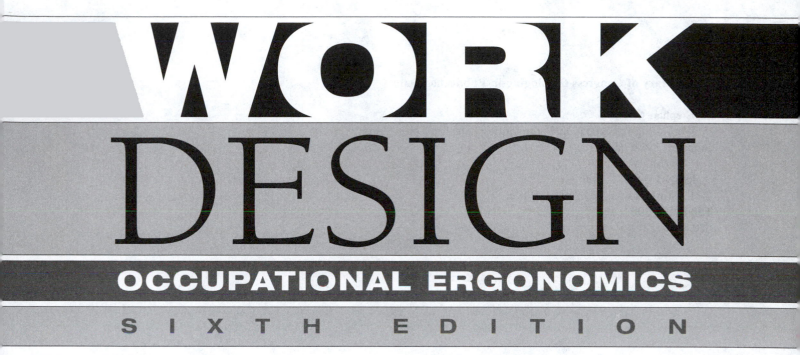

WORK DESIGN

OCCUPATIONAL ERGONOMICS

SIXTH EDITION

Stephan Konz

KANSAS STATE UNIVERSITY

Steven Johnson

UNIVERSITY OF ARKANSAS

Holcomb Hathaway, Publishers
Scottsdale, Arizona 85250

Library of Congress Cataloging-in-Publication Data

Konz, Stephan A.
    Work design : occupational ergonomics / Stephan Konz, Steven
Johnson.— 6th ed.
        p. cm.
    ISBN 1-890871-48-6
    1. Work design. I. Johnson, Steven. II. Title.
T60.8.K66 2004
620.8—dc22

                                                                    2003015549

Holcomb Hathaway, Publishers, Inc.
6207 North Cattletrack Road
Scottsdale, Arizona 85250
(480) 991-7881
www.hh-pub.com

ISBN 1-890871-48-6

10 9 8 7 6 5 4 3 2 1

BRIEF CONTENTS

CONTENTS

PART V

Work Environments

PREFACE

The world is overwhelmed by information. Each year brings new experiments, theories, articles, books. Our computers are richly interconnected to more data sources than we can count. Television offers hundreds of channels. It's no wonder many of us feel inundated with information of all types.

This book is an attempt to bring some order to one select field, ergonomics, and within ergonomics the area of work design. Despite our efforts to be selective, the information included here is likely to be more than can be covered in the typical 3 credit-hour course, and the book can in fact be used in multiple courses. (The Instructor's Manual includes course outlines from different universities. At Kansas State, we cover the entire book, but in two courses.) Whether or not the material is covered in the actual course, students benefit from having it available to them. This text is a tremendously valuable resource beyond the classroom.

Work Design is divided into seven parts: (I) Overview and History, (II) The Human Body and Design, (III) The Design Process, (IV) Ergonomic Guidelines, (V) Work Environments, (VI) Work Measurement, and (VII) Implementing the Design. The core of the book is Part IV, Ergonomic Guidelines, which includes Chapters 11 to 22. These guidelines are not laws or scientific principles but an attempt to permit a designer to "stand on the shoulders of those who have gone before."

Features of the new Sixth Edition include:

- A new chapter on organizing for ergonomics.

- A more stream-lined organization.

- Extensive revision of material with hundreds of new references.

- Numerous examples illustrating the economic value of ergonomics applications.

- A CD-ROM, ERGO, with 9 major categories: Forms (16 programs), Anthropometry (14 programs), Environment (16), Lift/Move (13), Work Physiology (8), Stat/Math (10), Time (6), and Units (18). The ninth category is quiz questions (with answers) for each chapter.

- Many website addresses (URLs) to help students utilize the vast amount of information now available on the World Wide Web.

The opening page of each chapter includes a graphic showing the relationship of that chapter to the rest of the book and listing the sub-topics within the chapter. The chapter's key concepts are also included on the opening page to alert readers to important topics. All chapters make use of extensive cross-references to other chapters and other sections within that chapter. These references allow students to relate topics to one another and follow up on areas of particular interest. Each chapter closes with Review Questions and extensive References for those readers who wish to dig deeper. The book also includes a detailed index.

The Instructor's Manual offers course outlines, lab exercises, additional review questions, and exam questions. It is available free to instructors who adopt the textbook for classroom use. Contact the publisher at sales@hh-pub.com.

Acknowledgments

We wish to thank several individuals who contributed in some way to make *Work Design* a better book. First, thank you to Steven E. Guffey of West Virginia University, who read the manuscript and offered constructive suggestions as to how it might be improved. Thanks also to the following individuals, who offered feedback regarding the book or its software: Thomas J. Albin, University of St. Thomas; James W. Barany, Purdue University; Regina Barker, Practical Ergonomics; Paul J. Componation, The University of Alabama in Huntsville; Kimberly Dunn, Oregon State University; D. L. Kimbler, Clemson University; Lt. Col. Mary Lopez, U.S. Army Center for Health Promotion and Preventive Medicine; Paul McCright, University of South Florida; James D. McGlothlin, Purdue University; Thomas W. Merritt, University of Alabama; William C. Moor, Arizona State University; Susan Murray, University of Missouri-Rolla; P. E. Patterson, Iowa State University; Marc Resnick, Florida International University; Diane Schaub, University of Florida; and Jeffrey Wolstad, Oregon State University.

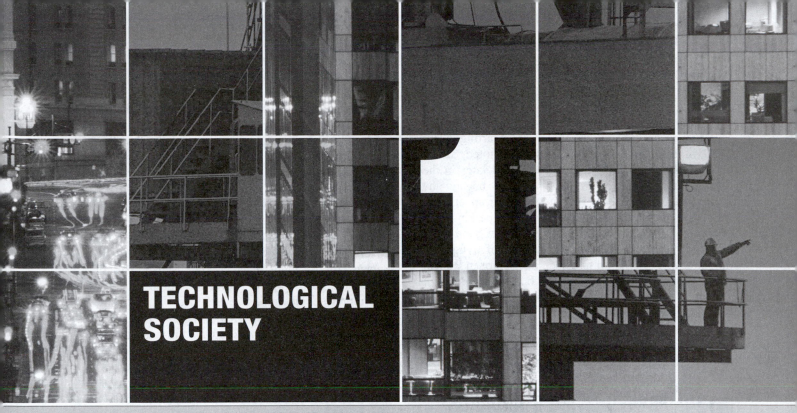

TECHNOLOGICAL SOCIETY

TECHNOLOGICAL SOCIETY

1 Historical Background
2 Improved Living Standards
3 Technological Society

Overview

The developments that make entire nations (rather than just a few individuals) rich are the pivotal developments of history. These developments have occurred both in the larger social structure and within the area of economic development (standard of living).

The eight characteristics of technological society (specialization of labor; energy from machines; standardization and interchangeable parts; use of machines; mass production and mass consumption; the assembly line; computers; and computer networks) have become part of our culture.

Key Concepts

change
Industrial Revolution
standard of living
technological society

1 HISTORICAL BACKGROUND

In the long tape of history, why have the last few inches seemed so much better? Starting about 1750 in England, about 1800 in the United States, about 1825 in northwestern Europe, and later in the rest of the world, a profound change began—the **Industrial Revolution**—the change from an agriculture- to a manufacturing-based society. The key word is **change.** Prior to that time there had been good times and bad times, but the overall standard of living was no better in 1700 than it had been in 1000 or in Roman times. Roman houses in England had bathrooms; not until the time of Queen Victoria were bathrooms again built in private houses. The rising wind of change has continued until today it is a firestorm. Slow and steady progress no longer is acceptable as people expect miracles from the great flowing rivers of technology.

2 IMPROVED LIVING STANDARDS

The following aspects of our technological society do not have any particular rank order, but are all interrelated.

2.1 Increased Knowledge
The nature of knowledge is that it is cumulative and that it diffuses. Occasionally, the reservoir has stagnated, but the general trend is upward. Many innovations require developments in related fields. For example, the cell phone required the development of mainframe computers to process the information as well as miniaturized electronics.

2.2 Diffusion of Knowledge
Literacy and education are essential. Beginning with the invention of printing (China and Korea in A.D. 800, Europe in 1400), knowledge came to be mass-produced at reasonable cost. This in turn has permitted the development of libraries throughout the world rather than in just a few major cities. The system of widely distributed professional journals ensures that specific knowledge in, say, industrial engineering, biochemistry, or electronics becomes available within a month of publication to specialists in that field in Johannesburg, Bombay, Eindhoven, and Manhattan, Kansas. On-line versions of these journals become available even more quickly. In most countries, the median years of schooling has risen dramatically in the last century. The Internet only became popular in the 1990s. Television's impact on education of the population began within the last few generations.

2.3 Freedom from War
Throughout history, people have destroyed prosperity through war, revolution, and military expenses. It is not a coincidence that the Industrial Revolution began in the United Kingdom and the United States. There was political stability; neither country was invaded; wars were fought on foreign soil (with the exception of the U. S. Civil War), and military spending was a low percentage of gross national product.

2.4 Capital
It takes money to make money. In the England of 1750 to 1850, the capital came from the work of the poor and the colonies; stories of the poverty of the working class at that time are well known (for example, Dickens and Marx). But this capital did permit "getting over the hump" so future generations could have a better life. In the United States, the country itself was virgin; the natural resources had not been picked over for tens of generations. In addition, as a country welcoming immigrants, the United States did not have the expense of raising those workers to adulthood.

Capital (deferred consumption) is needed for education, machine tools, buildings, bridges, research, and so forth, not only at the start of industrialization but also on a continuing basis. Low capital availability means few advances in the **standard of living** (the minimum of necessities, comforts, or luxuries held essential to maintaining a person or group). If a firm or country "eats its seed corn" (i.e., does not save), its long-run prosperity will be hindered.

2.5 A Development Orientation
A necessary condition of development is that a country must want to be developed. There must not be an entrenched dominant social class eager to maintain its power and the status quo. Democracy is related to economic development, as the developed countries tend to be democracies and the less-developed countries tend to be nondemocratic. A virtue of private enterprises is that they become independent sources of decision making (diffuse decision making). No single individual or authority can unilaterally veto an exploratory undertaking.

Historically, England had a merchant society eager for trade. The United States had few established social groups trying to avoid change. Japan, on the other hand, remained undeveloped—by choice—until the 1850s. Even today there are many countries illustrating Churchill's saying, "The inherent vice of capitalism is the unequal sharing of blessings while the inherent virtue of socialism is the equal sharing of miseries."

2.6 A Large Market
Many developments require a large customer base. The number of customers can be limited by technology and by politics.

In Roman times, land transport was very expensive. The Romans had not yet invented horseshoes or, more important, the horse collar; when a horse pulled a load, the horse strangled. Oxen could go only about 10 miles per day. Thus, factories were scarce because any economy of scale from manufacturing was cancelled by the cost of getting goods to market. Most transport of goods was by water. Low-cost land transport came with the train and the truck. (In 1860, there were 35,000 miles of railroad track in the United States.)

Countries traditionally have had barriers to foreign commerce. In the 1800s, Britain thrived not only due to its sea transportation but also due to its captive market (the British Empire). After World War II, Europe began to reduce internal trade barriers. Since then, there have been a number of other regional political groupings.

The largest market is the entire world. Active participation in international trade is closely associated with economic growth. Some explanations are economies of scale, keener competitive incentives, and economies of specialization.

3 TECHNOLOGICAL SOCIETY

Separate from the larger social context, **technological society** has eight key concepts:

1. specialization of labor
2. energy from machines
3. standardization and interchangeable parts
4. use of machines
5. mass production and mass consumption
6. the assembly line
7. computers
8. computer networks

3.1 Specialization of Labor

Specialization is not new. In the 1254 *Livre de Metiers (Book of Trades)* concerning the 101 Paris guilds, there were separate guilds in the leather industry for skinners, tanners, cobblers, harnessmakers, saddlers, and makers of fine leather goods; in carpentry there were guilds for chestmakers, cabinetmakers, boatbuilders, wheelwrights, coopers, and twiners. What is new is the degree of specialization throughout society. When we think of specialization, we think of an industrial worker whose sole function is to add three screws and three nuts to each assembly on the line. But other jobs also have become specialized.

In the United States, most farmers no longer raise their own food but specialize in one or two crops; ranchers who raise beef may buy the beef for their own table from the grocery store. Teachers formerly covered all grades and subjects in the "one-room school"; now they specialize by grade and subject. Physicians specialize in radiology, obstetrics, dermatology, and brain surgery. There are electrical, industrial, chemical, mechanical, ceramic, agricultural, aerospace, and many other kinds of engineers.

3.2 Energy from Machines

Before the Industrial Revolution, power came from muscles (human or animal), wind, or falling water. In 1776, the steam engine began the liberation of humans from physical effort while the Declaration of Independence began the liberation from totalitarianism—it was a very good year. Watt's steam engine, Faraday's and Henry's electric motor, and Otto's internal combustion engine permitted the enormous magnification of physical effort. Use of energy is probably the best single index of a society's standard of living.

The computer has accomplished the same magnification of mental effort. TV and print journalism (i.e., the mass media) have magnified our ability to communicate with the masses. Telephones and the Internet have magnified our ability to communicate with individuals.

3.3 Standardization and Interchangeable Parts

With galleys "as alike to another as swallows' nests," in the 16th century the 3,000-man Venetian shipyard could ready 100 galleys for battle in 60 days. The concept did not catch on in manufacturing due to the lack of accurate machine tools at that time. Around 1800, Maudslay in England made some special machines to make standardized ship components, but the real development of interchangeable parts had to await accurate machine tools. Interchangeable parts were put into use in the United States during the 1820s to 1850s in a few industries (gun manufacture, textiles, clocks) and spread gradually. Standardization tends to reduce the number of choices available to consumers (Ford's Model T was available only in black). Clever engineering can make many of the non-style parts usable on many different models and so reduce production costs drastically. However, sales departments constantly push for additional models, so there is a never-ending battle. An interesting example of the two strategies in practice is the Japanese approach of a few cars with a few models and few options versus the Detroit approach of many models with many options.

3.4 Use of Machines

The steam engine, applied to railroads and to ships, drastically reduced the effect of distance on the transport of goods and people. The internal combustion engine, applied to vehicles and airplanes, has further reduced the effect of distance. The telegraph, the telephone, the radio, television, and the Internet have reduced the effect of distance for communication.

For the production of goods, the continued development of the electric motor ("muscles") and computers ("brains") has given rise to the question: "How many machines will each human supervise?"

3.5 Mass Production and Mass Consumption

These really are chicken and egg—you can't have one without the other, although group technology is a technique that tries to achieve the benefits of mass production with low sales volumes. Without mass production, cost is high; so prices are high; so sales are low. A large poor population is not sufficient because a customer must pay for the product. That is why high productivity is important. With high productivity, high wages can be paid and workers can be good customers, enabling firms to sell their products and pay high wages, and so forth.

3.6 The Assembly Line

In construction, you move the workers and the machines to the product; in manufacturing, you move the product past stationary machines and workers. When the sequence of operations is standardized, the machines can become specialized and the flow can be arranged into an assembly line.

3.7 Computers

In the 1940s, the computer was developed. Key features are (1) stored programs (a processor for crunching numbers and a memory for storing both data and programs) and (2) the transistor. The stored programs allow the same hardware to perform a variety of tasks. Gordon Moore, the cofounder of Intel, forecast in 1965 that the processing power of a silicon chip would double every 18 months. And so it has.

Initial computers (mainframes) were large standalone central units with one input location and one output location. (The Mark I computer, which went on-line in 1944, used electromagnetic relays, was 51 feet long, and had 760,000 parts.) Gradually, it was realized that there could be multiple input stations and multiple output stations for one computer and that the input and output stations did not even have to be in the same city as the central computer. As computers grew in power (both in storage capacity and calculational speed), the desktop (personal) computer was born. By 2000, computers had shrunk so much in size and increased so much in capability that many common machines (e.g., automobiles, machine tools, TVs, telephones, toys) had computers. Motors had given machines "muscle" capability; computers gave them "brains."

The microprocessor of the year 2000 was 100,000 times faster than its 1950s ancestor and, when inflation is considered, cost 1,000 times less. Obviously, computers will become more important in our lives.

Since 1980, with the constantly decreasing cost of computers, machines have become more flexible and workers on many lines now supervise the machines instead of doing the work themselves.

3.8 Information and Communications Networks

The world has functionally gotten much smaller due to advancements in both voice and data communication. The Internet has increased the number and efficiency of communications for both individuals and corporations.

In a one-to-many network (e.g., radio, television), the value of the network rises with N, the audience size; this relationship is known as Sarnoff's Law (Sarnoff was a pioneer of radio and TV). In a many-to-many network (e.g., telephones, both fixed and mobile), the number of possible connections (excluding yourself) is $N^{(N-1)}$ or $N^2 - N$; this is known as Metcalf's Law, after the inventor of computer networking. The Internet is a special application of Metcalf's Law because users have the opportunity to form *groups*. Reed's Law, from David Reed of Lotus, says the value of the network is $2^N - N - 1$ (Anderson, 2000).

Computers (both mainframe and personal) began to be interconnected in the 1960s. At first, this interconnection was only within organizations. The Internet, a key development of the late 1970s, allowed any remote terminal to access these connected computers using the telephone network. The Internet really got going with the invention of the World Wide Web (WWW) in 1990 and web browsers in 1993.

Mobile phones connected to the Internet further increase access. It took 100 years to connect the first billion people by phone and only 10 years to connect the second billion. For example, cell phone technology is allowing China to experience rapid technological advance without the expensive and time-intensive infrastructure of land lines.

International communication using the Internet has implications for ergonomics in terms of choosing symbology that can be understood in many different cultures. Similarly, as communication devices such as hand-held computers (also referred to as PDAs, personal digital assistants) become more portable and smaller, significant ergonomic issues relate to both data input and display technologies.

Communications advances are allowing individuals to work together from many locations. The *virtual office* allows people to control their work location and schedule. This is particularly important in a global economy, where engineers in the United States can be in real-time communication with engineers and production personnel anywhere in the world. This ease of international interaction has important implications for ergonomics in the future.

Direct computer-to-computer interaction (i.e., e-commerce) allows companies to adjust delivery schedules based on individual purchases at retail stores. The software that collects data from scanners at check-out stations and adjusts the inventory database and delivery schedules is associated with point-of-sales systems. The technology has significantly affected the jobs of people throughout the supply chain, from cashiers to delivery truck drivers

Review Questions

1. Using 10–20 words for each concept, describe the eight key characteristics of technological society.

2. Is specialization of labor a development of the Industrial Revolution?

3. When did the Industrial Revolution begin?

4. What two important events occurred in 1776?

5. What is the "inherent vice of capitalism"? What is the "inherent virtue of socialism"?

6. Discuss the relation between economic development and democracy.

7. Make a list of the machines you supervise.

8. What was the greatest technological development of the last 1,000 years, in your opinion? Some candidates are: moveable type, railroads, television, computers, gunpowder, the factory system, electric motors, internal combustion engine, and eyeglasses.

References

Anderson, A. The mathematics of mayhem. *The World in 2001*, 117–118. London, England: The Economist, 2000.

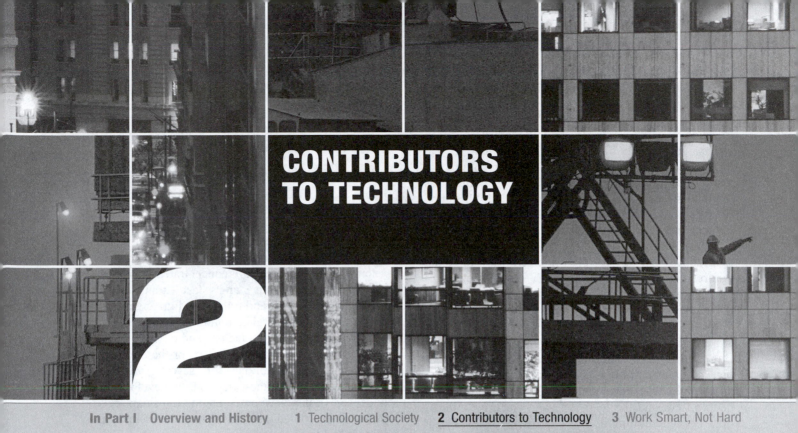

CONTRIBUTORS TO TECHNOLOGY

Overview

Machine power comes from internal and external combustion, often distributed and applied locally by electricity. We compute and communicate with machines. We have organizational concepts such as interchangeable parts, assembly lines, scientific study of work, and high pay for workers.

Our lives have been profoundly influenced by the technical culture, although most historians write only of the other culture—that of poets and politicians, the nonproducing verbalizers rather than the nonverbalizing producers.

Key Concepts

accurate machine tools	electronics	interchangeable parts	prime movers
assembly line	ergonomics	internal combustion engine	scientific study of work
Bell	factory	machine computation	Taylor
Colt	Faraday and Henry	mass consumption	Taylorism
continuous improvement	Ford	Maudslay	telephone
de Forest	Gilbreth	motion study	two cultures
Edison	Hollerith	Otto	Watt
electric illumination	incentive wages	personnel selection	Whitney
electric motor			

‖1 THE CONCEPT OF TWO CULTURES

C. P. Snow wrote of the **"two cultures"**: one of scientists and engineers and the other of poets, artists, and writers. This chapter is written so that engineers not only can understand their culture but also can appreciate the contribution their culture has made to society. As Galbraith commented: "Insist on the priority of dams, ditches, and fertilizer plants—it is these that feed poets."

Emerson said, "There is properly no history; only biography." However, the nontechnical historian ignores the people who have really changed our lives while paying extraordinary attention to the trivial behavior of politicians. For example, Barbara Tuchman's (1967) acclaimed history, *The Proud Tower: A Portrait of the World 1890–1914,* covers Europe and the United States during this period without *once* mentioning that during this time the automobile was developed, the radio was invented, people flew, and the telephone and electric illumination became common. Ford, Marconi, the Wright brothers, Bell, and Edison are not mentioned once.

Make your own list of contributors. You might consider the following in addition to those described in this chapter: Richard Arkwright, Alexander Graham Bell, John Bardeen, William Shockley, Walter Brattain, Henry Gantt, Gratt, Guglielmo Marconi, Walter Shewhart, Louis Pasteur, Johann Gütenburg, Orville and Wilbur Wright, Edwin Land, Frank Whittle, Wilhelm Roentgen, Leo Baekeland, Elias Howe, Christopher Sholes, Cyrus McCormick, Vladimir Zworykin, Elmer Sperry, Henry Bessemer, Ronald Fisher, and George Stevenson. Who can deny the importance of (in a random order) low-cost steel, railroads, the reaper, automatic controls, the transistor, mechanical spinning, analysis of variance, the typewriter, "plastics," the sewing machine, the airplane, instant photography, the jet engine, printing (European inventor), the germ theory of disease, the telephone, statistical quality control, radio, TV, production scheduling, and X-rays?

For a list emphasizing the 20th century, what were the contributions of George Washington Carver, Jonas Salk, J. C. Licklider, John Von Neumann, James Watson, Wallace Carothers, Willis Carrier, and Robert Noyce? Clues are integrated circuits, air conditioning, nylon, DNA structure, stored-program computer, polio vaccine, and agricultural technology.

The following vignettes give a brief view of some of the movers and shakers who made the world what it is.

The reasonable man adapts to the world. The unreasonable man tries to adapt the world to himself. Therefore all progress comes from unreasonable men.

G. B. SHAW

‖2 VIGNETTES

James Watt: Key Concept— A New Prime Mover, the Steam Engine

Before James **Watt** there were four basic sources of power **(prime movers):** human, animal, wind, and water. Watt's steam engine permitted the power source to be located anywhere and to be of unlimited magnitude. It permitted implementation of the **factory** system (where machines are concentrated in one central location), cheap and fast transportation (steam-powered ships and trains), and urbanization as people moved from rural communities to a new life of working and living in the factory and city.

Watt was an instrument maker for the University of Glasgow and worked for several years on Newcomen steam engines. In 1764, he developed the condenser. In the Newcomen engine the steam cylinder itself was cooled with water; then the metal of the cylinder had to be brought up to temperature again for the next stroke. Watt's design eliminated this inefficient cooling and heating, so fuel efficiency doubled.

The first engine was installed in Wilkinson's foundry in 1776. Wilkinson's invention of an accurate boring mill, upon which Watt's cylinders were machined, had made possible Watt's engine. (Wilkinson's boring mill could make a cylinder that "erred from a true circle not more than the thickness of an old shilling." His mill could bore a 50-inch diameter; a worn shilling was .050 inches thick.)

Before Watt retired, rich and famous, in 1800, he made two additional improvements. First he made the engine double-acting, which made rotary power practical and improved efficiency. Then he modified the ball governor used in flour milling by adding the critical concept of feedback so that the speed of the engine was self-regulating rather than just automatic. (Watt also invented steam heat when he heated his office in 1784.) Mining engineers in Cornwall, led by Trevithick, improved the energy efficiency of steam engines by a factor of 6 between 1810 and 1840; meanwhile, Carnot, in France, published his work on the ideal heat engine. Stevenson invented the railroad in 1814.

From 1776, it took 50–75 years until the first Industrial Revolution was firmly in place. The carding mill in the New Salem village of Abraham Lincoln (built in 1832) was powered by oxen; a census of steam engines in France in 1833 reported 947 in use; the Secretary of the Treasury reported to Congress in 1838 that there were 3,010 steam engines in the United States (800 on steamboats, 350 in locomotives, and 1,860 in factories and public works). However, the factory (Latin *facio,* to make) system was in place in England by 1830. A factory involves: (1) adoption of machinery, (2) power from machines, (3) greater use of capital, and (4) collection of scattered workers into a regulated group.

Other developments of the first Industrial Revolution include intellectual property, universal incorporation, limited liability, trade unions, cooperatives, the technical university, and daily newspapers.

Henry Maudslay: Key Concept— Accurate Machine Tools

It has already been mentioned that Watt's steam engine could not be manufactured until Wilkinson had a boring mill that could produce reasonably concentric cylinders. In a similar manner, the concept of interchangeable parts is based on the premise of each part being alike (from **accurate machine tools**); in practice, each part will not be alike unless the machines that make the parts are accurate. In 1807, Maudslay had 43 machines at Portsmouth make wooden pulleys for the British navy; each machine did one step. This was an early example of the specialized factory.

Maudslay is famous due to his improvement of the mother tool of the industrial age, the lathe (described by Farey in 1810 as "the most perfect of its kind"), and transferring his devotion to precision to the next generation of machine-tool builders. Clement, Roberts, Whitworth, and Nasmyth all worked for Maudslay at one time or another.

The heart of Maudslay's lathe was an extremely accurate regulating screw. A screw is a helix, a three-dimensional curve that twists around a cylinder at a constant inclined angle. It was probably invented by Archimedes about 230 B.C. But screws were expensive and inaccurate until British and American manufacturers learned how to make cheap, accurate screws in the early 1800s (Rybczynski, 2000). Clement improved the lathe and planer design and worked on Babbage's mechanical computers. Roberts built a metal-planing machine in 1817, improved lathe gearing, and built many drilling machines. Whitworth introduced a standard screw thread and, by manufacturing and selling standard gauges, made his influence felt worldwide. Nasmyth invented a special-purpose milling machine, the shaper, and the steam forge hammer. In Nasmyth's words:

> Illustrating his often repeated maxim that "there is a right way and a wrong way of doing everything," Maudslay would take the shortest and most direct cuts to accomplish his objects. The grand result of thoughtful practice is what we call experience: it is the power or facility of seeing clearly, before you begin, what to avoid and what to select.

His "innate love of truth and accuracy" led him to develop a bench micrometer, which could measure to one ten-thousandth of an inch. He called it "the Lord Chancellor" after the one from which there is no appeal.

Eli Whitney: Key Concept— Interchangeable Parts

Eli **Whitney** was born in 1765 and spent his youth on the family farm in Massachusetts. The Revolutionary War caused shortages, and Eli manufactured nails at the age of 14. At 23 he entered Yale. Graduating at age 27 and wanting to study law, he intended to take a job as a tutor in the South. He visited a southern plantation and within 2 weeks had invented the cotton gin.

For his next project, he turned to the federal government. In 1798 he signed a contract for 10,000 muskets for $13.40 apiece (normal price was $9.40), all to be delivered in 2 years. The key concept was that of **interchangeable parts.**

An inventive French mechanic, Honore Blanc, had developed a system of interchangeable parts for gunmaking. (Moveable type probably is the first example of completely standardized and interchangeable parts.) Thomas Jefferson had visited his shop in the 1780s, seen parts "gaged and made by machinery," and had tried to get him to move to America. Jefferson was President from 1801 to 1809, which was fortunate for Eli, as it took him 10 years to complete the 10,000 muskets. (Secretary of State Thomas Jefferson reviewed patent applications in the evening; it was he who granted Eli Whitney's cotton gin patent.)

Although Whitney emphasized interchangeable parts and even, in 1801, demonstrated a musket on which he could fit any of several locks, all of the 10,000 muskets had identifying marks on each part, something that truly interchangeable parts do not need. The Whitney muskets in the Smithsonian Institution have parts that cannot be interchanged. Simeon North (pistols) in 1799 and John Hall (rifles) in 1824 made truly interchangeable parts. Whitney, though never really achieving his objective, had good public relations and so receives the credit for the "American system of manufacture."

Michael Faraday and Joseph Henry: Key Concepts—The Dynamo, the Source of Electricity; the Motor, a New Prime Mover

Michael **Faraday,** one of a blacksmith's 10 children, did not attend school. Fortunately he was apprenticed to a bookbinder where he not only bound books but looked inside them. In 1823, he liquefied gases under pressure; in 1825 he discovered benzene; and in 1831 he had his greatest discovery, the dynamo and the electric motor. When Queen Victoria heard of the invention of the dynamo, she asked "What good is it?" Faraday replied, "Madam, someday you will tax it!"

In 1829, Joseph **Henry** made a vastly improved electromagnet that lifted 750 lbs; in 1835 he invented the electrical relay (in effect, the telegraph); in 1846 he became head of the Smithsonian Museum; and during the Civil War he founded the National Academy of Sciences. At the Smithsonian he began the policy of "publishing original research in a series of volumes and giving a copy to every major library on earth."

Technology includes social concepts such as public libraries, technical societies, and technical journals, as well as physical devices such as electric motors. If technology is an engine, then knowledge is its fuel; the fuel is becoming richer. Henry had a habit of not patenting his ideas, as he thought discoveries of science should be for the benefit of humanity. He discovered the principle of induction in 1831 but put his work aside at the end of August to be completed the following summer. Faraday published his results in November 1831.

The **electric motor** has three major advantages over the steam engine: It can be made any size (especially smaller); it can be started and stopped quickly; and it can be powered at a distance by use of wires. Somewhat surprisingly, motors were not applied until about 1880, but then their growth was rapid.

Samuel Colt: Key Concept—Assembly Line

Sam **Colt** designed a repeating pistol: "the six shooter," "Colt's Patent Pacifier," "The Difference." He opened a factory in Paterson, New Jersey, in 1835 that used the **assembly line** for production.

In 1847, the Mexican War began. General Zachary Taylor ordered 1,000 Colt 44s, and the weapon was back in production after a 5-year lull.

> The first workman would receive two or three . . . important parts and would affix them together and pass them on to the next who would add a part and pass the growing article to another who would do the same . . . until the complete arm is put together.

The National Bureau of Standards reports that the conveyor belt for assembly was not used until 1908.

Nikolaus Otto: Key Concept—The Internal Combustion Engine, a New Prime Mover

Reuleaux wrote in 1875 of the need for a small engine due to a high capital cost of steam engines: "How to make power independent of capital? . . . Engineers must provide small engines with low running costs. . . . These little engines are the true power units of the people."

In steam engines, combustion takes place outside the engine; in 1860 Jean Lenoir built the first engine in which the combustion was internal. It was powered with illuminating gas and had a very poor efficiency, but it was a start.

Then, in 1862, Nikolaus **Otto** (with his partner Eugen Langen, in a relationship much like Watt and Boulton) began work on internal combustion engines. In 1876 (100 years after the steam engine) he produced the silent Otto, the first 4-cycle engine.

Improvements by fellow Germans Karl Benz, Gottlieb Daimler, William Maybach, and Rudolf Diesel came before 1900. Advantages of the **internal combustion engine** over the steam engine were low capital cost, quick starts, and high power/weight. The advantage over the electric motor was the elimination of the tether—the wire. The age of the automobile and the airplane began.

Thomas Edison: Key Concept— Electric Illumination

Thomas **Edison** represents the classic tale of the self-made man: the poor boy who, without schooling or influence, made his way to fame and fortune by intelligence and hard work. With 1,093 patents to his name, he was the most productive inventor in the history of the United States. He also is very quotable:

> There is no substitute for hard work. Genius is 99% perspiration and 1% inspiration. We will make electric light so cheap that only the rich will be able to burn candles. [To a job applicant:] Well, we don't pay anything and we work all the time.

Early inventions of an improved telegraph and the stock market ticker permitted Edison (age 29) to found Menlo Park (an "invention factory," the first industrial research laboratory in the world—in itself one of Edison's many inventions) in 1876. He hoped to produce a new invention every 10 days! In fact, during one 4-year stretch before he became involved in finance, he obtained 300 patents, or one every 5 days.

In 1876 he improved the telephone and made it practical; in 1877 he invented the phonograph; in 1878 he announced he would tackle the problem of producing light by electricity.

Edison, who scorned theory, used the research method since then known as the Edison method—a trial of many possible alternatives. In 1879, he produced the first practical light bulb.

To apply the concept of **electric illumination,** he had to invent a host of auxiliary inventions—devices for sealing the bulbs, screw-in sockets, light switches, electric meters, safety devices—and then founded the first electric utility, Consolidated Edison, which opened in 1882. He also founded what became General Electric.

Consolidated Edison began the concept of the electrical utility. At first, electrical power was sold only for lights. But in the 1890s, electricity was used for streetcars. Steam power hung on in manufacturing, and not until 1919 did over half of manufacturing power come from electric motors.

His one contribution to science, the Edison effect, which led to the vacuum tube and electronics, he ignored.

Alexander Graham Bell: Key Concept—Long-Distance Transmission of Speech

Alexander **Bell's** father invented "visible speech"—a system of written phonetic symbols. Alex was driven to do something great. This urge for eminence led him to develop the **telephone.**

In 1874 Bell began thinking of a "speaking telegraph." This required a "sound-shaped" current. One possibility was a diaphragm armature vibrated by the voice that would induce such a current in another electromagnet. Then, in 1875, he plucked free from its electromagnet a receiver reed. Beyond a partition, another reed twanged and began vibrating. Bell recognized the implication that the motion of one reed had generated an effective current by induction. By 1876 he had a patent.

Among his other contributions were crusades to teach speech to the deaf, the first iron lung, and the original work on tetrahedral frames (later developed into geodesic domes by Fuller).

Although the telephone still is used for transmitting speech, the major traffic now is data (between computers, faxes, e-mail, and the Internet).

The cell phone permits omitting the physical wire between phones so communication now is even more available.

Herman Hollerith: Key Concept— Machine Computation

After receiving a degree in mining engineering in 1880, Herman **Hollerith** worked on statistics for the census office. Marking tallies with dip-pen and ink was just too slow. He needed a method of **machine computation** to automate the process. At first he tried edge-marked cards. Then he tried holes in paper tape. But the tape had to be wound to find the information—most likely at the end of the roll!

One day Herman took a trip to St. Louis. At this time train robbers were posing as passengers, and the government asked the railroads to keep track of everyone aboard. The conductors punched the ticket in specific places to indicate specific body characteristics—brown hair, blue eyes, medium weight—a punch-photograph.

Herman adopted the idea into the Hollerith card, the size of an 1890 dollar bill so it could fit existing file drawers. He developed a keyboard punching machine, rented his machines, and astounded the world with the speed of his census machine. IBM and the computer industry had been born.

The development of the electric motor, the assembly line, the internal combustion engine, electric illumination, the telephone, and machine computation led to the second Industrial Revolution. Some of its byproducts include governmental civil service, the modern corporation, the commercial bank, the business school, and non-menial jobs for women.

The third Industrial Revolution began with the development of the computer in the 1940s. Now, after the typical lag, we are in its midst.

Frederick Taylor: Key Concept—Scientific Study of Work

Frederick **Taylor** asked the question: "What is the best way to do this job?" He did not accept opinions; he wanted facts—evidence. The questioning scientific approach (hypothesis, experiment, evaluation of data to prove or disprove the hypothesis) is well known today. It was known then and applied to chemistry and physics but not to the design of everyday jobs. This is Taylor's primary contribution—application of the principles of science to improving jobs (the **scientific study of work**).

A famous example of this approach was his study of shoveling. In 1898, Taylor worked for Bethlehem Steel. In those days before mechanized material handling, when you wanted material moved, you shoveled it by hand. In this one plant, 400 to 600 men spent most of their time shoveling. Each man shoveled various materials each day; each man furnished his own shovel. There was no training in shoveling techniques; pay was $1.15 a day.

One thing Taylor noticed was that with a constant-volume shovel the load was only 3.5 lbs when shoveling rice coal but 38 lbs when shoveling ore. The question was: "What is the best size shovel?" For the experiment, he had material shoveled with large shovels (i.e., heavy loads) then cut a little off the end of the shovel and had the same material shoveled; cut off a little more the next day; and so on. For subjects, he used two good, experienced shovelers (i.e., he replicated his data). Taylor used as his criterion the amount shoveled per day. The results indicated that maximum material was shoveled per day when the load on the shovel was 21.5 lbs (for distances up to 4 feet and heights less than 5 feet).

Taylor instituted another concept that was quite radical for that day. He did not believe that all the benefits from increased productivity should be retained by the organization; the worker also should benefit. Therefore, he specified a standard tonnage to be shoveled for each type of material. The worker was trained in the proper work method, given the proper tools, and put to work. When he achieved standard, he received a 60% bonus above the day wage rate. If he could not achieve standard even after training, he was put on a different job. The concepts of pay-by-results (**incentive wages**) and **personnel selection** (select the best people for each job) are commonplace today; they were radical innovations then.

After these methods were applied to the yard at Bethlehem, the same amount of work was done with 140 men; material handling cost for the company (including the cost of the study, toolroom, and bonuses) was reduced from $.08/ton to $.04. Employee wages, of course, were 60% higher.

Taylor's scientific management is a good example that technology includes techniques as well as devices. Taylorism emphasizes the three S's: standardization, specialization, and simplification—basically, management of time.

The concept that the "one best way" to do a job is determined by experts (engineers) and the worker's duty is just to follow instructions is called **Taylorism.** It resulted in dramatic improvements in productivity and

the standard of living in many cultures for approximately 100 years. Instead of the static world of "one best way," however, we now have the dynamic world of **"continuous improvement"** (both the product and the process to produce the product change continuously). Continuous improvement requires more participation of the workers in job design. The educational level of the workforce, however, has risen over time (see Table 32.3), so "intelligence" now is distributed throughout the workforce, not just located in supervisors and staff. Chapter 32 provides more discussion on worker participation.

Henry Ford: Key Concepts— High Pay for Workers, Low-Cost Auto, Mass Consumption

Just as Whitney is incorrectly credited with interchangeable parts, Henry **Ford** is incorrectly credited with the auto **assembly line.** The specialization of labor, combined with use of conveyors, had been used earlier in slaughterhouses (a "disassembly" line) (see Figure 2.1). The auto, however, was the product in the public eye. Ransom Olds applied the assembly-line concept to building Oldsmobiles in 1899, 10 years before Ford installed an assembly line. By 1904, Oldsmobile production had reached 5,000/yr. Ford, however, dominated auto production. In 1924 Model Ts accounted for one-half of the world's motor vehicles. Ford's assembly line cut throughput time/car from 13 hours to 1. Formerly one man took 20 minutes to assemble a magneto by himself; using a subassembly line with 29 operators, time was cut to 13 man-minutes/unit.

F I G U R E   2 . 1

Assembly lines did not begin with the automobile, as is proven by the lithograph "Interior View of a Modern First Class Pork Packing & Canning Establishment of the United States of America" (Courtesy of the Chicago Historical Society), published in 1880. Titles under the respective pictures are: The Office; Killing Benches Nos. 3 & 4 (capacity 700 pr. hour); Fire Department (at dinner); Section No. 4 Hanging Room (capacity 10,000 hogs); Cutting Room No. 3 (capacity 5,000 pr. day); Section of Tank Room; Lard Coolers, Filling & Cooperage; Inspection & Packing for Foreign Markets; Boiler Room; Sausage Department; Curing Room No. 4 Temperature 38 Fah. Year to Year; Polishing; Canning Department Filling by Machinery, Meat Untouched by Hand, Soldering; Labelling. A question might be why it took so long to apply assembly-line technology to other industries.

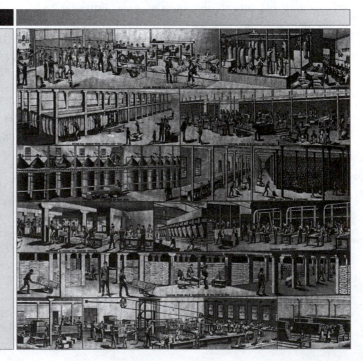

High pay for workers and a low-cost auto were implemented with Ford's decision in 1914 to pay his workers $5 for an 8-hour day when they had been getting $2.50 for a 9-hour day. In addition, he set up a $30,000,000 profit-sharing fund. How could he double wages while reducing costs? Through productivity. (High wages without accompanying productivity mean either losses or inflation.) The concept of **mass consumption** is the key to our society. When Ford's employees received low wages, they were not able to purchase cars (see Table 2.1). As long as cars were priced so that only a few people could afford them, the total output of cars was small. And, looking at the problem as a businessman, Ford saw that even though his profit/car was satisfactory, his total profit was limited due to the small number of cars he could sell because of their high price.

To maximize his total profits, Ford set up his assembly line, made a standardized product ("any color you want as long as it's black") at high volume (and thus low cost), and paid his workers well (permitted by the high volume, which was permitted by the high sales, which were permitted by the high wages and low costs, which were permitted by the high volume, which was permitted by the high sales, which were permitted . . .). The natural result was that Henry Ford became the richest man in the world.

The "main effect" of the mass consumption of automobiles may really be less important than the "side effect" of personal mobility obtained as a result of the automobile. In the United States it has increased our radius of daily travel from the limits of the streetcar to approximately 50 miles; this in turn has changed population distributions in both cities and small towns. Although at one time factories were located in the center of cities in order to obtain employees (who walked to work or took streetcars), since 1940 virtually no factories have been built in the center of cities in the United States. Trade and distribution jobs began moving out of the city center in the 1950s. The population of most American cities now resembles a doughnut with a relatively empty center

and a population living in the suburbs. It is difficult to determine in advance the main effects of developments; it is exceedingly difficult to anticipate the side effects and interactions occurring after a time lag.

Frank and Lillian Gilbreth: Key Concept—Motion Study

Frank **Gilbreth's** business was construction. A key construction job was laying brick. Frank, who had learned the bricklayer's trade as a teenager, applied his analytical skills to the study of bricklaying. He did this by studying the job in great detail—**motion study.**

In the existing method, bricks were dumped in a heap on the scaffold; the bricklayer bent over and picked up a brick. He then inspected it on all sides to select the best side for the wall face.

In Gilbreth's method, the bricks were inspected when they were unloaded from the freight car. They were placed with the best side up in packets of 90 lbs. The packets of oriented bricks were then placed on the scaffold. The scaffold was redesigned so that it could be raised or lowered easily, thereby reducing the distance the bricklayer had to reach. The mortar box and the packets were placed on the scaffold so that while the bricklayer picked up a brick with one hand, he scooped his trowel full of mortar with the other hand. The mortar was made of a standardized consistency so that the motion of tapping the brick into place with the trowel was no longer required. The number of motions/brick was reduced from 18 to 4.5. In a test of the new method, bricklayers laid 350 bricks/hour while the previous record for this type of construction had been 120 bricks/hour. However, van der Molen et al. (1998) demonstrate that there still are problems in bricklaying.

The reason Gilbreth's results attracted such attention was the task studied—bricklaying. Men had laid brick since antiquity. If there was any skill in which no more change could be anticipated, it seemed that bricklaying, with its 3,000 years of experience, cer-

	TABLE		2.1		
Prices of Fords vs. wages/hour.					
YEAR	TYPE OF MODEL T	PRICE ($)	WAGE/HOUR OF UNSKILLED LABOR IN FORD FACTORY	NORMAL HOURS/ DAY	HOURS OF WORK REQUIRED TO BUY CAR
1908	Roadster	825	.19	10	4,340
1913	Runabout	500	.26	10	1,923
1918	Runabout	434	.50	8	870
1923	Runabout	265	.75–.85	8	331

Courtesy of Ford Archives.

BOX 2.1   *The Rise of Ergonomics*

Taylor's and Gilbreth's successors were active in the management division of the American Society of Mechanical Engineers and the Society for Advancement of Management. The first Ph.D. in industrial engineering in the United States was given to Ralph Barnes by Cornell University in 1933. Barnes' book *Motion and Time Study,* first published in 1936, had its seventh edition 44 years later in 1980. The American Institute of Industrial Engineers was founded in 1948; it is now the International Institute of Industrial Engineers (Helander, 1997).

During World War II, research was conducted to maximize human performance in military applications. In 1949 the Ergonomics Research Society (now Ergonomics Society) was founded in the United Kingdom.

Murrell developed the name **ergonomics** from the Greek *erg* (work) and *nomos* (laws, study of). Over the years, this focus on "work" has expanded to cover all aspects of the human–machine interaction, not just the industrial workplace.

The International Ergonomics Association (IEA), the umbrella society of the various national societies, was founded in 1959. Table 2.2 shows the membership of the IEA-affiliated ergonomics society in each country.

Note that not all people interested in ergonomics necessarily are members of the affiliated society. For example, in the United States there are people interested in traffic ergonomics who belong to the Society of Automotive Engineers; those in agricultural ergonomics who belong to the American Society of Agricultural Engineers; people in safety who belong to the National Safety Council; and so forth.

During the 1960s, industrial ergonomics was the province of Ph.D. scientists. During the 1970s, it was taught to M.S. students and even a few B.S. students in Industrial Engineering. During the 1980s, ergonomics became "mainstream" for B.S. industrial engineering students. During the 1990s, it became more and more a technology (not just a science), being extensively taught to people without university degrees, through short courses and continuing education.

---

tainly would be it. Yet one man, by systematic study, had made a 300% improvement over the experience of 3,000 years! A powerful example.

When Frank died, his wife, Lillian, continued his work on motion study. (She is on the 40-cent stamp.) The many small elements of jobs have been named therbligs—Gilbreth spelled backward (almost). See Box 2.1 about the rise of ergonomics.

Lee de Forest: Key Concept— Three-Electrode Tube (triode)

The telegraph was a great boon to speedier communication, but it required a wire connecting the sender and receiver. Marconi developed the wireless telegraph, the sending of dots and dashes without intervening wires. Edison, who had been a telegrapher himself, had discovered the Edison effect: electrons flowed across a gap between two electrodes inside a vacuum tube. Fleming developed the concept into a device—the two-electrode tube or rectifier. In 1906, **de Forest** added the third electrode (the grid). A varying weak signal on the grid could be converted into a varying strong signal between the cathode and anode. Signals could now be continuous (rather than just discrete) and could be amplified. In 1912, he added the concept of a feedback circuit. Radio and the age of **electronics** began.

Armstrong receives credit for inventing FM radio in 1934. By analogy to waves of water, electronic noise affects wave height (amplitude) more than the spacing between waves (frequency); Armstrong developed frequency modulated (FM) radio vs. the amplitude modulation (AM) radio. Scientific discovery and technological invention (like poetry) benefits from metaphor.

Microsoft/Apple: Key Concept— Integrated Software

The previous vignettes described individual contributors. Today, however, most technical advancements are beyond individuals, requiring corporate research, development, and funding. A contributor becomes leader of a team, perhaps not even the technical leader but a managerial leader. Ford is an early example of such a leader.

The development of computers and computer networks is briefly discussed in Chapter 1. Although some may focus on the improvement of the computer itself (the "hardware"), just as important are the operating system and programs (the "software"). Initial computers were large, stand-alone computers with one input and one output station. Computers were run by specialists. Gradually computers evolved into small,

TABLE   2.2

International Ergonomic Association societies and recent full members (does not include associates, students, or retirees). If a country has more than one ergonomic society, only the IEA society is listed.

COUNTRY/REGION	FOUNDING DATE	RECENT MEMBERS DATE	RECENT MEMBERS NUMBER	POPULATION (MILLIONS)	MEMBERS/ MILLION
Federated societies					
Assoc. Espanola de Ergonomia (Spain)	88	02	151	40.0	3.8
Assoc. of Canadian Ergon.	68	02	547	31.6	17.3
All-Ukrainian Erg. Society	92	02	107	48.8	2.2
Belgian Erg. Society	86	02	179	10.3	17.4
Brazilian Erg. Society	83	02	140	174.5	0.8
Chilean Erg. Society	88	02	30	8.7	3.4
Chinese Erg. Society	89	02	450	1,273.1	0.4
Croatian Erg. Society	74	02	40	4.3	9.3
Czech Erg. Society	93	02	43	10.3	4.2
The Ergonomic Society (UK)	49	02	1024	59.6	17.2
Erg. Society of Australia	64	02	566	19.4	29.2
Erg. of FR Yugoslavia (Serbia)	73	02	50	10.0	5.0
Erg. Society of Korea	82	02	520	47.9	10.9
Erg. Society of S. Africa	84	02	45	43.6	1.0
Erg. Society of Taiwan	93	02	60	22.4	2.7
Gesell. fur Arbiets. (Germany)	58	02	487	83.0	5.9
Hellenic Erg. Society (Greece)	88	02	34	10.6	3.2
Hong Kong Ergo. Society	01	02	30	7.2	4.2
Human Factors & Ergonomic Society (USA)	57	02	3655	278.1	13.1
Hungarian Erg. Society	87	02	70	10.1	6.9
Indian Society of Ergonomics	87	02	53	1030.0	.05
Inter-reg. Erg. Society (Russia)	95	02	207	145.7	1.4
Irish Erg. Society	95	02	35	3.8	9.2
Israeli Erg. Society	82	02	38	5.9	6.4
Japan Erg. Society	64	02	2047	126.8	16.1
Nederlandse V.v. Erg.	62	02	510	16.0	31.9
New Zealand Erg. Society	86	02	117	3.9	30.0
Nordic Erg. Society		02	1596	23.5	67.9
Danish Erg. Society	72	00		5.4	
Finnish Erg. Society	85	00		5.2	
Norwegian Erg. Society	85	00		4.5	
Swedish Erg. Society	88	00		8.4	
Oest. Arb. f. Erg. (Austria)	76	02	32	8.2	3.9
Polish Erg. Society	77	02	373	38.6	9.7
Portuguese Assoc. of Erg.	92	02	104	10.1	1.0
Slovak Erg. Society	93	02	27	5.4	5.0
Soc. Colombiana de Erg.		02	30	40.4	0.7
Sociedad de Erg. de Mexico	98	02	30	101.9	0.3
Societa Italiana di Erg.	61	02	191	57.7	3.3
Societe d'Erg. Langue Francaise	63	02	680	59.6	11.4
South East Asian Erg. Society	84	02	64	250.0	0.3
Swiss Society for Ergonomics		02	63	7.3	8.6
Turkish Erg. Society		02	50	66.5	0.8
Affiliated					
Human Ergology Society	70	02	222		
TOTAL			14,145		

desktop models (and now laptops) run, for the most part, by non-experts. Microsoft Corporation and Apple Computers, along with countless others, developed a great variety of software packages (word processing, spreadsheets, presentation programs, databases, and so on). In addition to performing the designated tasks, these programs needed to be easy to use, compatible with one another, and eventually, be transferable via the Internet. As these firms and others continue to develop new programs, computer use continues to advance efficiency and flexibility worldwide

Review Questions

1. What are the "two cultures"?
2. How are accurate machine tools and interchangeable parts related?
3. Prime movers are essential to an industrial society. Why was the steam engine important? Why was the electric motor important? Why was the internal combustion engine important?
4. Describe Taylor's shovel experiment using the words *task, subjects, controlled variable, criterion, results,* and *application.*
5. Who were the Gilbreths and why were they important?
6. Ergonomics is based on what two words?

References

Helander, M. Forty years of IEA: Some reflections on the evolution of ergonomics. *Ergonomics,* Vol. 40, No. 10, 952–61, 1997.

Morrison, S. *The Oxford History of the American People.* New York: Oxford University Press, 1965.

Rybczynski, W. *One Good Turn: A Natural History of the Screwdriver and the Screw.* New York: Scribner, 2000.

Tuchman, B. *The Proud Tower: A Portrait of the World 1890–1914.* New York: Bantam, 1967.

van der Molen, H., Bulthuis, B., and van Duivenbooden, J. A prevention strategy for reducing gypsum bricklayers' physical workload and increasing productivity. *Int. J. of Industrial Ergonomics,* Vol. 21, 59–68, 1998.

Websites

Argentina
www.angelfire.com/ar/umberg

Australia
Ergonomics Society of Australia,
www.ergonomics.org.au

Austria
www.ebweb.tuwein.ac.at

Brazil
http://abergo.pep.ufrj.br

Canada
ACE, www.ace-ergocanada.ca

Chile
Chilean Ergonomic Society (SOCHERGO),
www.sochergo.ergonomia.cl

Czech Republic
Czech Ergonomics Society, www.vubp.cz

Denmark
Soc. for Work Env. and Working Conditions,
www.sam.ida.dk

Finland
Finnish Ergonomic Society,
www.occuphealth.fi/org/ery

France
SELF, www.ergonomie-self.org

Germany
GfA, www.gfa-online.de

Hong Kong
Hong Kong Ergonomic Society,
www.ergonomics.org.hk/

International Ergonomics Association
www.iea.cc

Ireland
Irish Ergonomic Society, www.UL.ie/~ies/

Italy
SIE, www.societadiergonomia.it

Japan
Japan Ergonomic Society, www.orihara.co.jp

Korea
Korean Ergonomic Society, http://esk.or.kr

Mexico
http://alebrije.uam.mx/ergonomics

Netherlands
Nederlanders Vereniging v. Erg., www.ergonoom.nl/

New Zealand
New Zealand Ergonomic Society,
www.ergonomics.org.nz

Norway
Norwegian Ergonomic Society,
www.stami.no/hotell/nef

South Africa
Ergonomic Society of South Africa,
www.ergonomics-sa.org.za

Spain
Associacion Espanola de Ergonomia,
www.prevencionintegral.com/aee

Sweden
Swedish Ergonomic Society (ESS),
www.iav.ikp.liu.se/ESS/

Taiwan
Ergonomic Society of Taiwan, www.est.org.tw

Ukraine
All-Ukraine Association, http://ukrergo.elan-ua.net

United Kingdom
Ergonomics Society, www.ergonomics.org.uk

United States
Human Factors and Ergonomic Society,
www.hfes.org

Board of Certified Professional Ergonomists,
www.bcpe.org

ErgoWeb (ergonomic standards and guidelines),
www.ergoweb.com/pub/info/infoopts.shtml

3

WORK SMART, NOT HARD

WORK SMART, NOT HARD

1 Productivity and Living Standards

2 Productivity

3 Total Time for a Job or Operation

4 Working Smart

Overview

The rich nation is the exception; techniques that make not only individuals but entire nations rich are the pivots of history. Our standard of living, which can be measured in leisure, health care, wine, or weapons, as well as consumer goods, depends on productivity. Productivity comes from efficient technology (combination of scientific, engineering, and managerial techniques) applied to land, materials, machines, and labor. The key to productivity is to WORK SMART, not to WORK HARD. The ergonomics in this book will show you how to work smart.

Key Concepts

components of productivity   pivotal events of history   work smart versus

extra work content   telecommute   work hard

PRODUCTIVITY AND LIVING STANDARDS

1.1 Benefits of Productivity   Table 3.1 gives a concise view of the change in the standard of living in the United States since the first census in 1790. What do you predict for 30 years from now? Figure 3.1 gives the output/work-hour from 1890 to 2001. Table 3.2 shows substantial differences among the countries as of 1997; the relative rankings change with the decades.

The long-term trend is to have fewer and fewer work full-time as they age. The proportion of men aged 60–64 still in the workforce is 50% in the United States, about 35% in Germany, and less than 20% in France and the Netherlands. Retirement, a concept that barely existed in 1900, now begins in the developed world at an age so early that in 2000 men spend about 36 years in employment and 36 years not in employment. However, with increased health and longevity and decreased physical requirements of work, many older people want to work part-time. Thus, designers should consider that some workers may be over 70.

People have overcome countless obstacles to successively higher levels of income. The rich nation is the exception; the techniques that made entire nations rich are the **pivotal events of history.** Was it done by working harder? No. By working more efficiently? Yes. We now are more productive—producing more output for the same input.

The benefits from increased productivity are not always taken in increased material goods; they can be spent on health care, wine, education, weapons, or increased leisure. Of course, with more productivity, there is more to share ("a rising tide lifts all boats"). The choices interact. Education may be considered a goal in itself; yet the correlation coefficient between educational level and gross national product/capita in 75 countries is .89 (Harbison, 1963).

Before 1914 the 60-h week was typical for most industrial workers in France, Germany, England, Canada, and the United States. By 1922 the 48-h week was in general practice in industry throughout Europe, Australia, New Zealand, and Latin America. In 1926 Ford introduced the 40-h week in the United States. By 1948 the 40-h week was the norm in the United States, Australia, New Zealand, and Russia. In 1953 most Western European countries and Japan worked 45–48 h/week; in 1963 it was 44–46 h/week; in 1973 it was 42–43 h/week. The decline has continued as the normal work week has become fewer than 40 hours in many countries (for example, 39 in France and 38.5 in West Germany). In 1984, manufacturing workers worked an average of 2,180 h/yr in Japan, 1,941 in the United Kingdom, 1,934 in the United States, 1,652 in West Germany, and 1,649 in France. In 1992 average annual hours/worker were 2,007 in Japan, 1,857 in the United States, 1,646 in France, and 1,519 in Germany. In the United States, average weekly hours and hourly earnings of production workers in 1970 were 37.1 h ($3.23), in 1980 were 35.3 ($7.25), in 1990 were 34.5 ($10.01), and in 2000 were 34.5 ($13.76) (World Almanac, 2001).

Although working hours/year have declined over the years, in recent years they may have started going up in the United States, especially for professional and managerial employees (Schor, 1991). Schor believes the reasons are that people prefer more income to more leisure and that the "system" now rewards employers for employing fewer people for longer hours rather than more people for shorter hours.

FIGURE   3.1

Output/work hour in U.S., 1890–2002. For the years 1000 to 1820, real annual per capita growth in the West and Japan averaged .13%. Since then it's been 1.67%, which compounded over 200 years gives a population 20 times better off (Fox, 2002). What do you predict for the future?

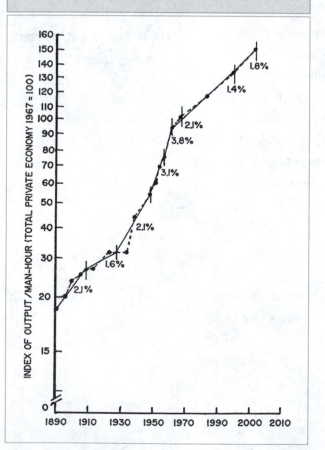

T A B L E   3 . 1

A concise view of the change in the standard of living of the average person in the United States since 1790. The changes are due to improved productivity.

INDEX	1790	1860	1930	1970	2000
Population	4,000,000	31,000,000	123,000,000	213,000,000	273,000,000
Housing	Single-family log cabin.	Frame houses. 93% of dwellings single family.	Frame houses. 67% of dwellings single family. Multi-story of brick with steel frame. 3.8 population/ dwelling unit; 4.8 rooms /dwelling unit (median).	Frame houses. Apartments, condominiums. 63% own their own home. 3.1 population/dwelling unit; 5.0 rooms/ dwelling unit.	67% own own home; 5.3 rooms/dwelling unit.
House furnishings and equipment	Homemade furniture. No running water. Privy. Fireplace heat. Illumination by candle.	Factory-made furniture. Hot and cold running water in homes of rich. Stove (wood, coal). Illumination by kerosene and gas lamps. Matches.	Factory-made furniture. 　　　　　　　Urban　Rural Electricity　96%　31% Indoor toilet　92　11 Running 　water　92　18 Mech.refrig.　56　15 Central heat　58　10 6,000,000 pianos	*% of Dwelling Units* Flush toilet + 　H & C water + 　　bath or shower　94% Running water　98 Telephone　94 TV　99+ Air conditioning　45 Home freezer　32	*Per 100 households* TV　99% Microwave　83 AC　71 Phone line　66 Computer　62 Dishwasher　50 Mobile 　phone　44
Food and drink	Local supply, little variety. Preserve by salt, pickling, and smoking.	Regional supply. Preserve also with ice. 2 cans of food/yr/capita. 178 lbs red meat/ yr/capita (carcass weight).	Regional and world supply. Mech. refrig. in transport and home. 54 cans of food/yr/capita. 141 lbs red meat/yr/capita.	Regional and world supply. Fresh at all seasons, frozen, freeze dried, convenience foods. 101 cans of food/yr/ capita. 129 lbs red meat/ yr/capita (49 fowl, 11 fish). Food cost = 16% of disposable income.	116 lbs red meat/yr/capita (49 fowl, 15 fish). 10.6% of personal income for food.
Clothing	Made at home. Linen, wool, leather.	Some factory clothing, especially men's. Cotton and wool.	Factory-made for men and women. Rayon and silk plus cotton and wool.	Factory-made for all. Synthetic fabrics. Fabric treatments (permapress, soil and water resistant).	
Health	Life expectancy at birth = 36. Doctors trained as apprentices. First hospital (1750). First medical school (1765). No public responsibility for health or sanitation.	Life expectancy at birth = 40. 149 hospitals; .0009 beds/capita (1873). 40 medical schools. 175 doctors, 18 dentists, 26 nurses/ 100,000 pop. First comprehensive water and sewer system (Chicago).	Life expectancy at birth = 60. 6,150 hospitals; .009 beds/capita. 125 doctors /100,000 pop.	Life expectancy at birth = 71. 7,100 hospitals; .0075 beds/ capita. 174 doctors, 57 dentists, 353 nurses/100,000 pop. 36% of pop. have major medical insurance. Medicare.	286 doctors, 55 dentists, 828 nurses/ 100,000 pop. Medicaid. Health spending = 12.9% of GPD. Life expectancy at birth = 74.6 (males), 80.4 (females)
Transportation and communication	Postal expense = $.01yr/capita. No public roads.	Roads by local government. 35,000 miles of RR track.	227 pieces of mail/yr/capita. 200,000 miles of RR track. 53% of families own a car (1937). Some commercial air transport.	409 pieces of mail/yr/ capita. .6 telephones/ capita. 204,000 miles of RR track. 3,700,000 mi. of highway. 83% of families own 1 or more cars (.47 cars & .1 truck/capita). 150,000,000 air passengers/yr. Man on moon.	3,900,000 mi. of highway. 614,000,000 air passengers/ year.

T A B L E	3 . 1

Continued.

INDEX	1790	1860	1930	1970	2000
Work and leisure	Child labor; work until death; dawn to dark; 6-day week; no vacations.	65-70 h/wk for city and factory workers; no vacations. Circus, vaudeville, nonprofessional baseball. Newspaper circulation = .05/day/capita.	40 h/wk or less for 50% of wage earners. Begin work at 16-18; retire without pay before death; some vacations. Unions 15% of workers; 30% white collar (1940). 90,000,000/wk movie attendance. Radio. 6000 golf courses. Baseball and football pro sports.	56% of people over 16 hold at least one job. 40 h/wk or less average for entire work force. Retire at 65 (Social Security and company benefits). 6 or more paid holidays for 97% of work force; 15 days paid vacation after 15 years for 93%. Unions 23% of workers; 50% white collar. Newspaper circulation = .29/day/capita. 6600 radio, 707 TV stations; 1463 symphony orchestras, 713 opera companies, 763 museums, 11,000 golf courses. 100% of homes have TV. 3.7 visits/yr/capita to federal parks or recreation areas.	Unions 9% for private employers; 37% for government. Internet; cable TV (many with >100 channels); cell phones; photocopiers, CDs, VCRs and DVDs; express mail, fax, bar codes; personal video cameras; electronic cameras.
Education	No public education	Some tax-supported libraries. 80% literacy. Average schooling = 434 days. First land grant university (Kansas State University).	Education (including secondary and college) government responsibility. Free education for 12 grades. Median school completed by pop. over 25 = 8.0 yr. 96% literacy. School expense = 3.1% of GNP. 6200 public libraries.	Median school completed by population over 25 = 12.2 years. Literacy = 99%. School expense = 8.0% of GNP. 7109 public libraries.	9,800 public libraries. Education spending = 5.0% of GDP.
Government	New York City government expense/yr/capita = $1.87.	150 public and private water supply systems. New York City government expense/yr/capita = $10.52.	New York City government expense/yr/capita = $189 (1935). Taxes = 10% of GNP. Government (all levels) workers = 9.7% of all workers.	Federal $729, state and local $731 expense/yr/capita (nationwide). NYC government expense/yr/capita = $1207. Taxes = 31% of GNP. Public responsibility for unemployment and recreation. Government (all levels) workers = 19.3% of all workers (1975).	Federal government 21% of GDP.

T A B L E		3 . 2	
Average hours worked/yr per person employed.			

COUNTRY	1980	1990	2000
United States	1830	1830	1820
Italy	1730	1680	1600
France	1800	1660	1590
Germany	1740	1560	1490

Of the over 50% of the U. S. workforce now in "office" jobs, a substantial number **telecommute.** In the United States in 2000, an estimated 24 million telecommuted regularly or occasionally (Voigt, 2001). Technology (e.g., computers, pagers, cell phones, voice-mail, instant messaging) has put us in a sea of work with no boundaries between work time and personal time. Using these devices, people work not only at the office and at home but also in cars, airports, hotels, and so forth. There were 110 million mobile phones in the United States in 2000; the prediction for 2005 is 184 million.

2 PRODUCTIVITY

2.1 Components of Productivity
Productivity is the ratio between input and output. One definition of output gives four essentials (**components of productivity**): labor, materials, energy, and information. The special character of a technical society is that the materials, energy, and information replace labor. There are four classic factors: land, materials, machines, and labor. (Sometimes materials and machines are called *capital*.) Overriding these four factors is a fifth factor—technology (the combination of scientific, engineering, and managerial techniques).

Improved productivity from *land* might involve using better seed to grow 10% more corn/acre or better trees, which will mature in 20 years instead of 25. Fertilizer or insecticides may increase crop yield. Output/unit of land increases. (For the industrialized countries, the farm population has shrunk to less than 5% of the population due to the high productivity of farmers.)

Improved productivity from *materials* might be the use of a collector container to catch the drips from barrels of viscous chemicals so that 99.7% of a container's contents are used instead of 98.5%, or the use of a noncorrosive material to extend the life of a bridge or truck. Insulation reduces the need for fuel oil. Output/unit of material increases. Shields on the top of semi-trailer cabs reduce the coefficient of drag and thus save energy. (Other examples of drag reduction are air bubbles on airplane wing tips and the below-the-water bulb in the front of tankers.)

Improved productivity from *machines* might be scheduling a truck to haul materials both going and coming rather than returning empty, or using a ceramic cutting tool in a lathe to enable a higher speed, or using e-mail rather than regular mail. Increasingly, machines are used to process information, not just materials in the "information economy." And electronic communication (phone, fax, e-mail) can replace transported mail. A machine's physical life might be 36,000 h. Use of 1 shift (1,800 h/yr) would allow the machine to be used 20 years. Two shifts (3,600 h/yr) improve machine utilization and decrease the risk of obsolescence. (Because the problems of shift work are social rather than physiological, shift work may not be utilized if public transport or recreation or shopping is closed during part of the day.) Output/unit of machine time increases.

Improved productivity from *labor* might be improvement in the work methods of a nurse to permit attending to more patients, or a simplified form so a clerk could calculate more vouchers/h. The use of a fixture to hold parts can permit assembly with two hands instead of one. Output/unit of time increases.

Although the examples assume the same input with an increase in output, productivity also can improve by decreasing input for the same output, by increasing output faster than input, or by decreasing input more than output. Productivity should be recorded in nonmonetary units so comparisons are not distorted by inflation. Example indices are vouchers/week from the accounts payable office, number of student credit hours/teacher, and area cleaned/day by the janitors.

Productivity is a mixture of the factors of land, materials, machines, and labor. Later-developing nations have an advantage in that they can selectively accept ideas from an ever-larger store of global knowledge. This knowledge is not just physical hardware but also social knowledge (e.g., Quality Circles, interlibrary loans, double-entry bookkeeping, agricultural extension agents). The popular press often writes as if only reduction in labor costs is meaningful and ignores improved productivity for the other factors. Historically, the developed countries have substituted cheap energy and materials for labor. As the developed countries have become "information societies," the per capita use of materials has decreased. In the United States labor costs now dominate, while in the less-developed countries a shortage of foreign exchange or surplus of labor makes material cost or machine cost dominant.

2.2 Uses of Productivity

The standard of living/capita is the product of working smart and working hard; typically it is defined numerically by:

$$GDP = HGDP(H)$$

where GDP = Gross domestic product/capita

$HGDP$ = Hourly gross domestic product/capita

H = Hours worked/year/capita

Some values for $HGDP$ in 1997 (Doyle, 2000) (where U. S. = 100) are: Belgium 107, France 103, Germany 88, England 83, Canada 81, and Japan 68.

H depends on (1) the labor force participation rate and (2) the average hours worked by each person per year. The labor force participation rate depends on the age when people enter the workforce, the age when people leave the workforce, and the unemployment rate. The values for H tend to be higher for the United States than the rest of the developed countries because of higher participation rates (e.g., 64% in the United States in 1997 versus 48% in France and Germany) and more hours worked/year. The average hours worked/year depends upon full- versus part-time work, vacation and holiday time, and overtime.

Assume a worker enters the labor force at 18 and retires at 63—giving 45 years of work. Assume that work on 5 days/week times 52 weeks gives 260 days/year; reduce this number by 10 days vacation and 10 holidays to get 240 working days/year. Assume an 8-h/day minus two breaks of 15 min to get a 7.5-h/day. Then, $45 \times 240 \times 7.5 = 81,000$ h/lifetime.

The approximation of 81,000 h is affected by absenteeism, strikes, illness, unemployment (voluntary or involuntary), overtime, second jobs, more or less schooling, and early or late retirement. The 81,000 h must support not only the worker's needs for food, furniture, and frivolity but also support the children, aged, blind, and other nonproducers (either directly or through taxes). In this book we will discuss "how to increase the size of the cake" rather than "how to cut the cake"—that is, how to multiply, not how to divide.

The output from the 81,000 h can be increased by working efficiently (**work smart**) or by working with more effort (**work hard**). Work smart is the desirable alternative because (1) there is more potential for improvement through reducing the excess work than through making the worker work harder, and (2) people don't like to work hard and therefore resist efforts to make them do so.

3 TOTAL TIME FOR A JOB OR OPERATION

How can expensive American labor compete with low-cost labor from Asia? By substituting capital (i.e., machinery) for labor. Figure 3.2 shows that this tech-

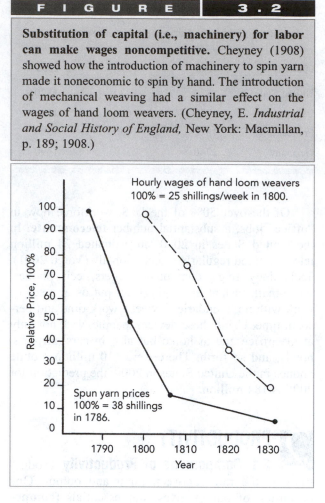

F I G U R E   3 . 2

Substitution of capital (i.e., machinery) for labor can make wages noncompetitive. Cheyney (1908) showed how the introduction of machinery to spin yarn made it noneconomic to spin by hand. The introduction of mechanical weaving had a similar effect on the wages of hand loom weavers. (Cheyney, E. *Industrial and Social History of England*, New York: Macmillan, p. 189; 1908.)

nique has been known for several centuries. In 1970, the manufacturing wage/h ($3.36) and the price of a barrel of oil ($3.18/barrel) were almost equal. Although there certainly will be fluctuations in the ratio of a barrel of oil to manufacturing labor in the future, the long-run tendency will be to increase the relative cost of oil and, thus, oil-based energy costs. Therefore, energy from other sources (such as coal) and conservation should become relatively more important.

In some countries there is a great surplus of labor, and thus the relative price of labor is low. In some countries foreign exchange is limited, which may cause energy or materials to be relatively expensive. Capital may be relatively expensive or cheap in various countries. Capital has been relatively cheap in Japan, so Japan has tended to substitute capital for labor more rapidly than other countries. In addition, some industries are labor-intensive, some skill-intensive, and some knowledge-intensive. Thus engineers in different countries and organizations will have different objectives.

3.1 Who Gets Benefits?

Any program to raise productivity by reducing time/unit must consider the workers' fears (1) that they will work themselves out of a job and (2) that employers will receive all the benefits of the higher productivity. Policies to ensure adequate employment and satisfactory distribution of the benefits of the productivity are not merely desirable parts of productivity programs—they are the foundation. (The good of the whole conceals the cost to the few.)

Reducing time/unit has costs: (1) erosion of individual skills and experience, (2) the need for some workers to change their jobs and perhaps their place of residence, and (3) the inability of some individuals to make the changes required. Thus workers, individually and collectively, must have the costs of improved productivity not fall too heavily on any one person. In the United States, employers attempt to use normal turnover and expansion of sales to cushion layoffs; severance pay and unemployment pay are backup systems.

People also differ on who should receive the benefits of higher productivity: the workers through higher wages, the society through lower prices, or the person who risks the capital through greater profits. Wars have been fought over this issue. When political rhetoric is brushed aside, the answer is that benefits must be split among the three. Naturally there is always discussion on the amount of the split. Samuel Gompers expressed labor's opinion concisely when asked what labor wanted: "More." Table 3.3 demonstrates how productivity relates to cost of living.

3.2 Extra Work Content

Extra work content is defined as work that is not essential. Extra work content can be due to the basic concept of the customer and the service to the customer. Consider a restaurant. The standard restaurant gives: (1) the customer a selection from a wide variety of food items, (2) service of individual portions, (3) a specified amount of food for a specified price, (4) personal service to the customer, and (5) service within a limited portion of the 168 h of the week. What are some alternative strategies?

A popular strategy is to minimize the labor cost of the server. One possibility is automation—a vending machine. Another strategy is to minimize the menu selection—fast food. The strategy of self-service has two options with no table service: a cafeteria (limited portion of food) and buffet (unlimited portion of food).

The following examples emphasize manufacturing, although the extra work concept can be applied to retailing, health services, transportation, and so forth. For simplicity, productivity is assumed to depend only on the time required for the person or the machine.

T A B L E   3 . 3

"Low cost of living" is made possible by changes in productivity (Cox, 1998), decreasing the cost to the consumer and increasing the wage. The product also has quality and performance improvements, so the table understates the benefits of productivity.

EARLY YEAR	PRODUCT	Early cost ($)	1970 cost ($)	1997 cost ($)
			Average labor h needed to buy	
1908	Automobile	4,696	1,397	1,385
1915	Refrigerator	3,162	112	68
1915	Long-distance call	90	.4	.03
1917	Movie ticket	.48	.47	.32
1919	Air travel (1000 mi)	221	18	11
1919	Chicken, 3-lb fryer	2.6	.4	.2
1947	Microwave oven	2,467	176	15
1954	Color TV	562	174	23
1971	Soft contact lenses	95	n/a	4
1972	VCR	365	n/a	15
1984	Cellular phone	456	n/a	9
1984	Computing (1,000,000 instructions/second)	57	n/a	.4

Source: Reprinted with permission of the Federal Reserve Bank of Dallas and *The Wall Street Journal.* © 1998 Dow Jones & Company, Inc. All rights reserved.

3.2.1 *Poor product design*

Five types of poor product design are as follows.

Improper design. For example, don't design a product to be composed of weldments when a casting is more economical. (In some cases, weldments are better than castings.) Don't design for the use of slot-head screws instead of Phillips head screws. Design for easy maintenance. Coat steel used in corrosive atmospheres. If truckloads are weight-limited, use aluminum instead of steel on the trucks so they can carry more payload. Reduce the cost of shipping also by using stackable containers and thereby utilizing the cube.

Yokogawa Electric used die casting of a plastic recorder cover instead of an assembly of 31 pieces; cost of materials was reduced 90%, and assembly time was reduced 96%.

One firm had an "ergonomic" problem of cumulative trauma when making flywheels; part of the solution was to improve flywheel forging specifications and thereby reduce flywheel weight by 2 lbs. (This example points out that reducing "ergonomic" problems often leads to reduced material and labor expenses.) As another example, Milton Bradley

(Marcotte and Kessler, 1997) had a problem of "excessive wrist movements." The solution, coordinated with Packaging Engineering, resulted in a packaging change that not only reduced wrist movements 50% but also achieved a cost savings of more than $1,000,000, and the company decided not to discontinue the product!

Table 3.4 summarizes "design for assembly." Design for easy maintenance is another possibility. For example, fasteners for access covers/panels should be captive (so they don't get lost), minimum type and number (to minimize the number of tools required), and robust (using coarse threads and large heads to avoid stripping).

Nonstandardization. Use standard materials, not special materials. Use standard parts, not special parts. For example, can a standard washer, bracket, screw, or bolt, be used instead of a special? Lack of standardization splits the production volume between the parts, increases paperwork, and makes supply of spare parts more expensive and difficult.

A key factor in cost of assembly is the number of components that have to be assembled. A popular strategy is to reduce the number of components. Can a nut and washer set be replaced by a single integrated part? GM had 80–90 parts/bumper in its 1980s cars; the late 1990s cars have bumpers with 15–20 parts. Ford has cut the number of types of car horns from 30 to 3, the number of types of batteries from 40 to 14, and the number of types of steering wheels from 50 to 11. The company also expects to save 7% on trunk carpeting by installing a single material and color in all Ford vehicles. It saved $1.50 on the Taurus by using a part from a Lincoln to reinforce the seats.

Incorrect quality standards. The quality specified can be too low or too high. An example of low quality might be a plastic part instead of a metal part, or a container that allows the product to be damaged. An example of too-high quality is using precision threads when standard threads are sufficient. In overdesign

---

T A B L E   3 . 4

Design for manufacturability (DFM) guidelines for assembly (adapted from Helander, 1995). Note that DFM aids both manual and robotic assembly.

GUIDELINE	COMMENTS
1. Use a base part as the product and fixture	■ Insert fasteners from one direction (above or in front) to minimize wrist deviations and simplify tool use. ■ Have the product have a flat bottom and simple shape, permitting ease of transport. This allows use of roller and wheel conveyors without parts carriers and minimizes weight lifted.
2. Eliminate or minimize different types or sizes of fasteners	■ Combine parts if: —no relative motion between the parts —parts are made of the same material ■ Eliminate fasteners. For example, use "snap and insert" assembly. ■ Minimize number, types, and sizes of screws; this means fewer bins, handtools, errors, and spare parts. ■ Don't use separate washers. Use components in which the washer is part of the screw.
3. Facilitate handling of parts	■ Use parts that are easy to grip. ■ Avoid flexible parts (wires, cables, belts), as they are difficult to handle. ■ Avoid parts that nest or tangle. Consider coiled springs with closed (not open) ends. ■ Avoid weak or fragile parts that bend, chip, or crack.
4. Facilitate orientation of parts	■ Use symmetrical parts. ■ For nonsymmetrical parts, provide orientation aids (shape such as lugs or notches, color). ■ Consider parts feeders (magazines, vibratory bowl feeders [see Figure 13.19]).
5. Facilitate assembly	■ Use self-locating parts (chamfers, notches, guides, tapers) (see Figure 3.3). Reduce tolerances in part mating. For example, can a slotted hole replace a circular hole? ■ Use torx screws to eliminate the push force to keep the drive bit in; avoid cross-recess drivers (Phillips screws); avoid drill point screws (push force can be >40 lbs).

Source: From M. Helander, *A Guide to the Ergonomics of Manufacturing.* Chapter 17. © Copyright 1995 by Taylor & Francis. Reprinted by permission.

("goldplating"), each engineer designs for the "worst case" rather than "real world." It is nice to have good quality, but not everyone can afford a Mercedes.

Material wastage. A stamping pattern might be fitted poorly on the strip of a coil-fed press (see Figure 3.3). An office form might use a large sheet of paper when a small piece would do. For faxes, cover sheets usually can be omitted; if they are used, they do not have to be 8.5 x 11 inches; this saves on phone bills as well as paper. (See Box 3.1.)

Many firms now are designing for "product end of life" to minimize the problems of recycling. As examples, don't use bleached cartons for packaging; make the plastics in a product a single-resin type; make plastic parts with integral finishes (eliminates painting as well as easing end-of-life processing); and use resins and paints that do not have polybrominated biphenyls (PBBs), polybrominated biphenyl ethers (PBBEs), lead, cadmium, or mercury metal.

Energy wastage. One example of inefficiency is a standard electrical motor used in place of a high-efficiency motor. A truck or car may have an engine with poor fuel economy; a semitrailer may not have a shield on the cab top to streamline air flow. A PC may not power down (have a "sleep mode") when not in use.

F I G U R E	3 . 3

Layout of items within a strip to reduce waste. Two good strategies are changing nonfunctional perimeter shape and reversing the item.

Extra energy can be wasted because of poor usage patterns. For example, turn off the lights when no one is in the room; turn off conveyor motors during lunch breaks.

3.2.2 *Poor methods*   Four poor methods are the following.

Poor macro method. For example, a person might play "telephone tag" instead of using voice-mail, a fax, or e-mail. A cellular phone in a vehicle permits executives, maintenance people, and sales people to call from a vehicle instead of having to stop and look for a public phone. Further examples are data being entered by hand instead of by scanner and bar code; a factory not being organized for "lean production" and, therefore, having many uncorrected problems; a machine cutting one item at a time instead of 60 at a time; and a product being sent by rail when using a truck would be better (or vice versa).

Poor micro method. For example, a waitress might have to enter orders on a form with handwriting instead of circling preprinted information, or the wrong type or size of screwdriver, pliers, or other tool may be used.

Assembly time depends not only on how the parts of a product are designed, but also on how the parts are stored and presented to the operator, and how the parts are moved to the point of assembly. See Table 3.5 and Figure 3.4.

Poor arrangement. Examples are machines arranged in a job-shop layout when a flow-line arrangement is better (or vice versa), supplies located in a crib when storage at the machine is better (or vice versa), or a bin at a workstation that is not conveniently located. Ground maintenance depends on location of trash containers. Disney found people reluctant to carry trash more than 28 paces (about 60 ft) and so places containers accordingly.

Poor equipment use. The equipment may not be used properly if the worker is not properly trained. Training should include not only the main person assigned to the task but all people who do the task as well. The thrust has been to multiskilled workers so they can do all tasks (cross-training).

3.2.3 *Poor management*   Five types of poor management are as follows.

Too many product models. Are your customers really more interested in increased selection or in lower price? Sales groups are always pushing for a wide variety of models to fulfill the needs of any possible customer. Unfortunately, this tends to fragment the market and results in very low volumes for each product and, thus, high cost/unit. If many different models must be produced for marketing reasons,

T A B L E	3 . 5		

"Best case" versus less efficient alternatives, using MTM-1 classifications (Helander and Willen, 1999). See Chapter 29 for information on MTM.

MOTION	BEST CASE	LESS EFFICIENT	% TIME SAVING OF BEST CASE
Reach	To fixed location (case A)	To variable location (case B)	30
		To small or jumbled objects (case C)	40
Grasp: pickup	Easily grasped (1A)	Object on flat surface (1B)	75
		Small object (1C2)	400
Grasp: select	Large jumbled objects (4A)	Object smaller than 1 x 1 x 1 inch (4B, 4C)	50
Move	Against a stop or to other hand (A)	To exact location without a stop or barrier (C)	15
Position: symmetrical	Symmetrical (S)	Semi-symmetrical, 45° turn typical (SS)	20
		Non-symmetrical, 75° turn typical (NS)	30
Position: depth of insertion	No depth	4-inch insertion	100
Position: pressure to fit	Gravity, no pressure (1)	Light pressure (2)	210
		Heavy pressure (3)	500
Disengage 2 parts: class of fit	Loose	Tight	500
Disengage: ease of handling	Easy	Difficult	40

F I G U R E	3 . 4	

Gripping aids for assembly. (A) Self-feeding container. (B) Container with inclined opening. (C) A ring holder with smaller bottom diameter. (D) Use of vacuum gripper. (E) Tweezers or tongs used against a rippled table surface. (F and G) Gripping against a soft surface (Luczak, 1993).

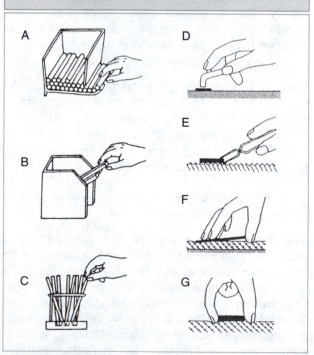

insist that nonstyle components such as screws, washers, motors, brackets, clips, and so forth be standardized so they, at least, can have reasonable production quantities and ease of spare parts supply.

Poorly designed product. The product may not be designed to withstand the stresses of normal use. The customer will be unhappy and will tend to refuse to buy more products from that organization, thereby killing the organization in the long run. Rework, repair, and warranty expenses will be high.

Poor production scheduling. Poor scheduling can increase setup time, cause missed customer shipment dates, and require overtime and layoffs. A unit train hauling coal shows how scheduling a shipment all at once instead of in small amounts can improve transportation efficiency.

Poor maintenance. Equipment breakdowns annoy everyone. In addition to loss of production, product quality may suffer.

Poor safety and health. Safety pays. In addition to the moral responsibility of organizations to have safe working conditions, safety can be justified just from the economic benefits. (See Chapters 7 and 20.)

3.2.4 Poor workers Not all the excessive work is the fault of management. Some is caused by workers. Workers can fail to start on time, quit early, and stretch breaktimes; they can be absent and thus cause

BOX 3.1 *Waste Minimization*

Three ways to minimize waste involve the product, the supplies, and the packaging.

Product Minimize product waste by changing product materials and reducing manufacturing waste.

Changing product materials. Reduce use of chemicals for cleaning through mechanical agitation (air or water jets, brushes, ultrasonics). Kill insects with bug zappers instead of insecticides. Make wastes nonhazardous (e.g., use inks without cadmium).

Reducing manufacturing waste. As examples of saving trees: Photocopy on both sides of a sheet of paper, replace letters and envelopes with electronic communication (e-mail, faxes), file correspondence electronically rather than with photocopies, and reuse envelopes for internal correspondence. A plant found that it was throwing away several pounds of varnish per drum because it was not allowing the drum to drain long enough.

Supplies Consider solvents, coolants and lubricants, metal finishing, and painting and coating.

Solvents. Reduce "dirt" and thereby use fewer solvents for cleaning (e.g., use less lubricant on dies, and use electrostatic painting). If the item is cleaned before the contaminant has had time to harden, less solvent is needed (just think of dishes being washed in a dishwasher).

Coolants and lubricants. Extend the life of coolants and lubricants by reducing contamination (e.g., using a biocide to kill bacteria in the coolant) and removing contaminants, thereby permitting reuse of coolant (e.g., use of settling tanks or centrifuges).

Metal finishing. Some examples are reducing impurities entering the plating solution (drag in) and loss of solution from the tank (drag out). Some drag-out approaches are increasing drip time to allow liquid to drain from the part; minimizing pockets, cavities, and depressions that can bail from a tank; decreasing solution viscosity (e.g., increase solution temperature); and decreasing surface tension (add wetting agents).

Painting and coating. Avoid conventional spray painting, which deposits only 40% of the paint on the product; use electrostatic or powder coating.

Packaging Consider reduction, reuse, and recycling/disposal.

Reduction. Minimize the weight (volume) of the package in relation to the product. Can the box hold 10 units instead of 5? Or can the product be shrunk (e.g., concentrate the product and the customer adds water)? Can more cartons be placed on a pallet (additional layer or larger pallet)?

Reuse. One example is reusable pallets. Another is returned containers (it helps if they can nest when being returned).

Recycling/disposal. Design packaging to be recycled. For example, minimize corrugated paper stapled to wood or glued to foam (staples and foam prevent reuse of cardboard). Eliminate ink containing hazardous materials (any hazardous material, regardless of its percent of the total, makes the entire container of material hazardous).

Source: Facility Design: Manufacturing Engineering, 3rd ed., by S. Hanna and S. Konz (Scottsdale, AZ: Holcomb Hathaway, 2004).

---

extra work for their coworkers. They can cause poor quality—although most quality problems result from poor product design, poor tools, poor procedures—in short, from poor management.

In most operations or jobs, the effect of the worker in causing extra work is relatively minor compared to the extra work caused by poor design, work methods, or management. Obtaining better productivity (the benefits to be shared among the workers, the society, and the providers of capital) thus is a shared responsibility.

WORKING SMART

The importance of better productivity and the method to achieve it can be demonstrated with a pegboard. Figure 3.5 is a photograph of the pegboard task: "work smart" in front, "work hard" at the right. The

task is to put 30 pegs into the 30 holes. Figure 3.6 gives a left-hand/right-hand chart of the method the instructor used in demonstrating condition A: blunt end of peg into nonchamfered hole. The students should time the instructor doing one assembly to the instructions, "Work at a pace you can maintain for 8 hours; assume you are paid by the hour." For reference, when 51 students assembled 10 boards, their mean time for 10 boards for condition A was 1.02 min.

Condition B demonstrates "work fast." Use the method for condition A but with instructions "Work at a pace you can maintain for 8 hours; assume you are paid by the piece." Mean time/assembly for 10 assemblies for the 51 students was .81 min—a reduction of 21%.

Condition C demonstrates "work smart"—that is, reduce the excess work content. For *product design*

F I G U R E   3 . 5

Pegboard task. "Work smart, not hard" can be demonstrated with assembly of pegs into a pegboard.

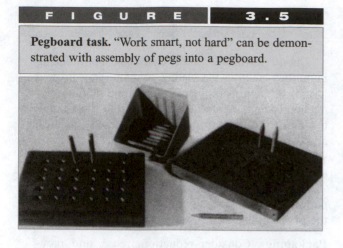

changes, use chamfered holes instead of nonchamfered holes (turn board over) and insert the pointed end of the peg instead of the blunt end. For *manufacturing methods* changes, use two parts bins and two hands instead of one and fill the center holes first to avoid moving the hands over a barrier. Preorient the pegs in the bins. (Preorientation involves a cost, but cost would be low if it could be done by the previous operator or by a vibratory feeder.) Working at the pace of condition A, the mean time/assembly for 10 assemblies was .47 min—a reduction of 54%.

The effect of better management can be demonstrated by long production runs. To save demonstration time, use the learning curve rate of 94% calculated by Youde, who timed 300 consecutive assemblies of the pegboard (Youde, 1947). The 94% means that every time output is doubled, the new time is 94% of the previous time. Thus, if time for 10 is .47, time for 20 would be .94 (.47) = .4418; time for 40 would be .94 (.4418) = .4153; time for 80 would be .94 (.4153) = .3908, and so on.

The potential improvement for better product design, manufacturing methods, and management is unlimited. The potential improvement for working

---

F I G U R E   3 . 6

Left-hand/right-hand chart of method. Detailed analysis of the pegboard assembly shows that the right-hand activity includes only the acts of get and place, whereas the left-hand activity has only inactivities of wait. (Acts are get, place, and dispose; inactivities are hold, wait, process, and drift.) The analyst "worked smart" by using G for get, P for place, and W for wait. The analysis is typed for clarity—normally it would be handwritten.

ACT BREAKDOWN

SKETCH

Study File No. _____ Date _____
Oper. Name-Equip. Description _____
  Pegboard Assembly—Method A & B

Tools Used _____ 1 bin for pegs

Part Description pegboard with non-
beveled holes (30)-3/8 D 5/16 D peg
Part No. _____
Routing Hrly. Cap. _____

Study Hrly. Cap. _____
Analysis By _____ SK

Step No.	LEFT HAND DESCRIPTION	OBJECT	ACT	ACT	OBJECT	RIGHT HAND DESCRIPTION	
1			W	G	peg	in bin	Repeat
2			W	P	peg	in hole—column 6	5 times
3			W	G	peg	in bin	Repeat
4			W	P	peg	in hole—column 5	5 times
5			W	G	peg	in bin	Repeat
6			W	P	peg	in hole—column 4	5 times
7			W	G	peg	in bin	Repeat
8			W	P	peg	in hole—column 3	5 times
9			W	G	peg	in bin	Repeat
10			W	P	peg	in hole—column 2	5 times
11			W	G	peg	in bin	Repeat
12			W	G	peg	in hole—column 1	5 times
13							
22							
23							
24							
25							
26							

03080-219 - 12-86 -- IE-74-1   (OVER)

hard is only about 20%. In addition to the small potential improvement for working hard, convincing workers to work harder is difficult. Sweat, as they know, is inversely related to wealth.

In 1812 the British posted a guard on the cliffs of Dover to watch for an invasion by Napoleon. The job was abolished in 1935. They should have worked smart, not hard! Effort is no substitute for knowledge.

Review Questions

1. Briefly discuss the change in hours of work over the last century. What do you predict the typical hours of work/yr will be when you are 40? Give assumptions.
2. Briefly discuss the concept of increasing the size of the cake versus dividing the cake.
3. Discuss replacing transportation with communication.
4. Give the two reasons why it is more important to work smart than to work hard.

References

Cheyney, E. *Industrial and Social History of England.* New York: Macmillan, 189, 1908.

Cox, M. The low cost of living. *Wall Street Journal,* 9 April 1998.

Doyle, R. Productivity. *Scientific American,* Vol. 282, 34, May 2000.

Fox, J. But don't forget the silver lining. *Fortune,* September 2, 2002.

Hanna, S. and Konz, S. *Facility Design: Manufacturing Engineering,* 3rd ed. Scottsdale, AZ: Holcomb Hathaway, 2004.

Harbison, F. Education for development. *Scientific American,* Vol. 209, 140–47, September 1963.

Helander, M. *A Guide to the Ergonomics of Manufacturing,* Ch. 17. London: Taylor and Francis, 1995.

Helander, M. and Willen, B. Design for human assembly (DHA). In *The Occupational Ergonomics Handbook,* W. Karwowski and W. Marras (eds.). Boca Raton, FL: CRC Press, 1999.

Luczak, H. *Arbeitswissenschaft,* Berlin: Springer-Verlag, 1993.

Marcotte, A. and Kessler, J. Ergonomic improvement in games manufacturing: Leveraging one initial success into an integrated self-sustaining ergonomics effort. *Proceedings of the Human Factors and Ergonomics Society,* 707–11, 1997.

Schor, J. *The Overworked American.* New York: Basic Books, 1991.

Tanner, J. Earlier maturation in man. *Scientific American,* Vol. 218, 20–27, January 1968.

Voigt, K. For extreme telecommuters, remote work means really remote. *Wall Street Journal,* B1, 31 January 2001.

World Almanac 2001. Mahwah, NJ: K–111 Corp, 147, 2001.

Youde, L. A study of the training time for two repetitive operations. Master's thesis, State University of Iowa, 1947.

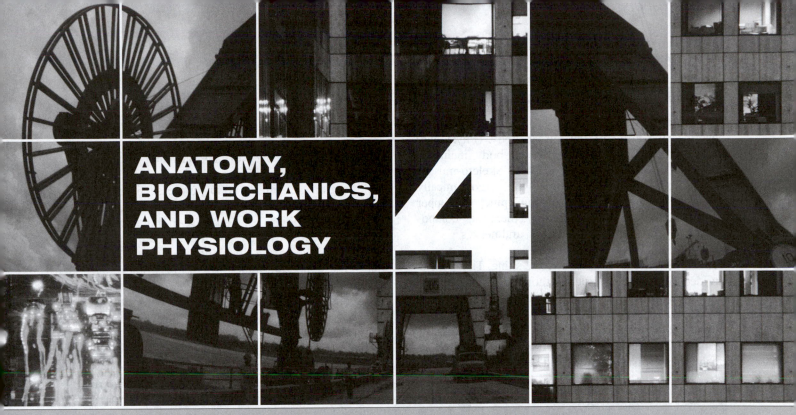

ANATOMY, BIOMECHANICS, AND WORK PHYSIOLOGY

ANATOMY, BIOMECHANICS, AND WORK PHYSIOLOGY

1 Musculoskeletal Anatomy

2 Biomechanics of Muscular Movement

3 Cardiovascular Anatomy

4 Metabolism

5 Response to Exercise

6 Cardiovascular Limits

7 Responses to Mental Work

Overview

Anatomy is given for three ergonomically interesting subassemblies of the body: the spine, the upper extremity, and the foot. Joints, tendons, muscles, and nerves are described briefly. Biomechanics is covered briefly, focusing on the ergonomic aspects. Sections 1 and 2 focus on the human as a physical engine.

The cardiovascular system and its responses to exercise are discussed. The measurement of physical capacity and recommended limits are given, as well as the effects of gender, age, and training. Due to the overall decline in heavy physical work, the information is most relevant to older workers; that is, those with lower physical abilities.

Key Concepts

activity metabolism
aerobic vs anaerobic
age effects
artery–vein differential
basal metabolism
blood pressure
bursa
cardiovascular system
cartilage
digestion metabolism
edema

electromyogram (EMG)
gender effects
heart rate cost of work
heat acclimatization
isoinertial
isometric
isotonic
isovelocity
joints
kyphosis
levers, skeletomuscular

ligaments
lordosis
maximum oxygen uptake ($\dot{V}O_2$max)
maximal voluntary contraction (MVC)
measuring heart rate
mental load
muscles
nerves

oxygen debt
proportion of capacity
pulmonary/systemic circulation
rating of perceived exertion (RPE)
response to exercise
scoliosis
stroke volume
tendons
venous pooling

33

MUSCULOSKELETAL ANATOMY

Anatomy (*anatomia,* Greek, to cut up) describes the build of the human body. (Physiology deals with the functions of the living body, including the physical and chemical processes.) Skeleto-muscular anatomy is divided into the ergonomically important "subassemblies" of the spine, the upper extremity, and the lower extremity; then, the "components" of joints, tendons, muscles, and nerves.

1.1 Spine   Figure 4.1 shows the spine. The spine is divided into the cervical, thoracic, lumbar, and sacrum regions. The low back, Lumbar 4 and Lumbar 5 (abbreviated L4 and L5) is the problem area. Note how these discs angle downward instead of being horizontal. The weight of the torso therefore tends to push these discs forward. The disc pressure is 50–100% higher when sitting than standing, especially when sitting with a slumped back. Reduce that pressure by using chairs with armrests (the armrests support some of the torso weight).

The spine is concave backward in the cervical and lumbar region; it is concave forward in the thoracic region. **Lordosis** is an increase in lumbar curvature—a swayback posture, with the stomach protruding. **Kyphosis** is an increase in thoracic curvature—a hunchback posture, with the shoulders rolling forward and the person slouching. **Scoliosis** is a bending of the spine to the side (i.e., from a front view).

Due to cumulative compressive loading on the discs, body stature shrinks about 1.1% during the day. However, sleep restores the shrinkage. Krag et al. (1990) found the change was relatively rapid; 26% of the 8-h loss occurred in the first hour upright and 41% of the 4-h recovery occurred in the first hour recumbent.

Figures 4.2 and 4.3 show how the vertebrae and discs are held together with **ligaments.** There are many "low-back" problems due to the narrow width of the rear ligament in the low back. Figure 4.4 shows how the discs separate the bony segments; Figure 4.5 shows a detail of a disc. Note the ringlike structure of the disc, which gives great strength. In the young adult, the discs are so strong that when violence is applied to the vertebral column (e.g., parachutist whose chute didn't open), the bones usually give way rather than the discs.

Discs fail because they wear out. "Normal daily activities ultimately exact their toll in the form of microscopic stretching, tearing, and raveling of the

---

FIGURE 4.1

The spine is divided into cervical, thoracic, lumbar, and sacrum areas.

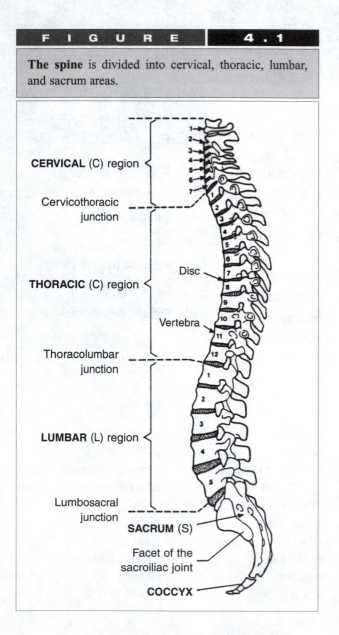

FIGURE 4.2

Two ligaments hold the vertebrae together.

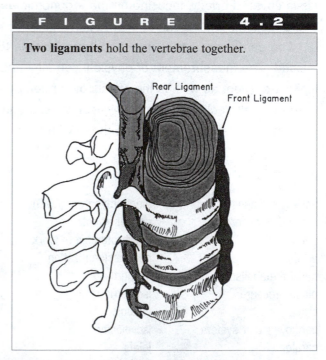

Source: L. Ring, *Facts on Backs.* Copyright © 1981 by Institute Press, Loganville, GA. Reprinted with permission of L. Ring.

F I G U R E   4 . 3

The rear ligament narrows as it descends. In the lumbar region, the ligament width is only half its original width, exposing unprotected discs on either side.

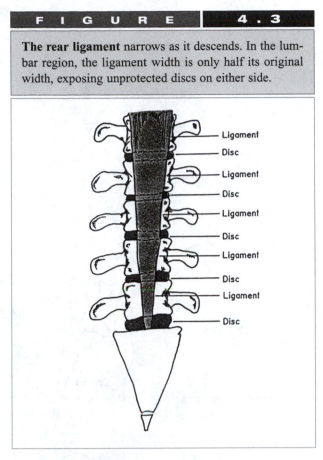

Source: L. Ring, *Facts on Backs.* Copyright © 1981 by Institute Press, Loganville, GA. Reprinted with permission of L. Ring.

casing fibers. The increments of microdamage become cumulative until, finally, the casing is no longer capable of containing the packing material. Usually, slow leaks of the fluid of the gel occur from time to time and the disc begins to narrow and gradu-

F I G U R E   4 . 4

Discs separate bony facets.

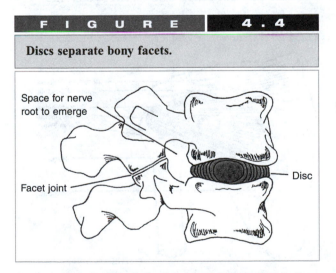

Source: L. Ring, *Facts on Backs.* Copyright © 1981 by Institute Press, Loganville, GA. Reprinted with permission of L. Ring.

F I G U R E   4 . 5

Discs have a ringlike structure surrounding a sac of fluid (Ring, 1981).

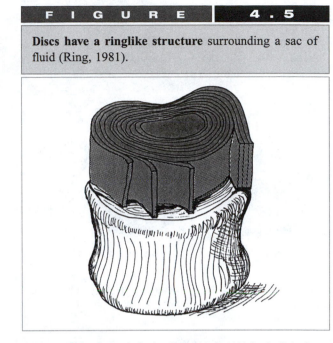

Source: L. Ring, *Facts on Backs.* Copyright © 1981 by Institute Press, Loganville, GA. Reprinted with permission of L. Ring.

ally go flat. Less commonly, the weakened casing may bulge [see Figure 4.7] or a sudden blowout may occur" (Rowe, 1985, p. 140).

The two load-bearing structures (the facets, excluding the synovial membrane, and the intervertebral discs) do not have nociceptors, the peripheral pain nerves. *Thus, one can injure them without experiencing pain* (Garg, 1992); low-back pain may be the culmination of a series of point-in-time painless injuries. Disc problems are shown in Figure 4.6 (side view) and 4.7 (top view)—emphasizing the pinching of the nerve.

F I G U R E   4 . 6

Disc degeneration reduces the space available for the nerve to emerge, possibly causing pinching of the nerve (Ring, 1981).

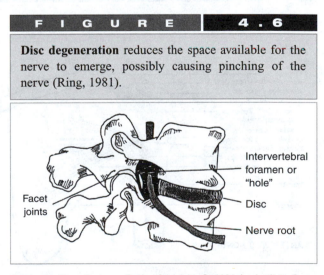

Source: L. Ring, *Facts on Backs.* Copyright © 1991 by Institute Press, Loganville, GA. Reprinted with permission of L. Ring.

F I G U R E	4 . 7

Normal disc (left) and prolapsed (herniated, ruptured) disc (right). A prolapsed disc (incorrectly called a "slipped disc") pinches the nerve (Ring, 1981).

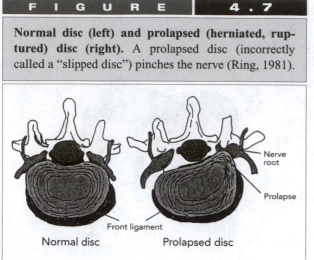

Normal disc   Prolapsed disc

Source: L. Ring, *Facts on Backs.* Copyright © 1991 by Institute Press, Loganville, GA. Reprinted with permission of L. Ring.

Although the back is complex, mathematical models of the spine have been developed. Three-dimensional models have been developed that predict lumbar compression as well as shear and torsional forces during various activities.

1.2 Upper Extremity   This section is divided into shoulder, arm, and hand.

1.2.1 *Shoulder*   Figure 4.8 shows an overview of the bones of the upper extremity. Figure 4.9 shows some detail of the shoulder. The clavicle and scapula form the shoulder itself. The shoulder, designed for mobility instead of stability, is stabilized almost exclusively by

F I G U R E	4 . 8

Bones of the upper extremity (Putz-Anderson, 1988). The clavicle and scapula form the shoulder. The humerus is the single bone in the upper arm. The radius and ulna are the two bones in the forearm. The metacarpals and phalanges form the hand.

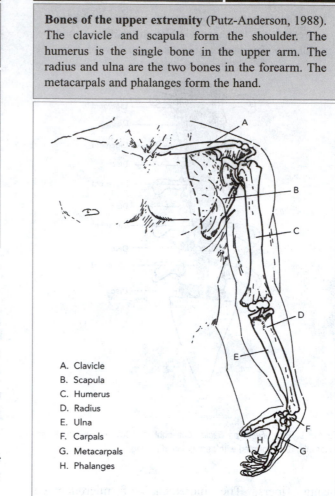

A. Clavicle
B. Scapula
C. Humerus
D. Radius
E. Ulna
F. Carpals
G. Metacarpals
H. Phalanges

Source: V. Putz-Anderson, (ed.). *Cumulative Trauma Disorders.* Copyright © 1988 by Taylor and Francis, London. Reprinted with permission.

F I G U R E	4 . 9

Right views of the shoulder (Rowe, 1985).

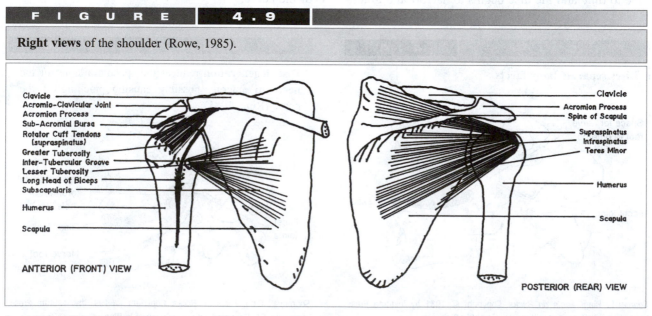

Clavicle
Acromio-Clavicular Joint
Acromion Process
Sub-Acromial Bursa
Rotator Cuff Tendons
  (supraspinatus)
Greater Tuberosity
Inter-Tubercular Groove
Lesser Tuberosity
Long Head of Biceps
Subscapularis

Humerus

Scapula

ANTERIOR (FRONT) VIEW

Clavicle
Acromion Process
Spine of Scapula

Supraspinatus
Infraspinatus
Teres Minor

Humerus

Scapula

POSTERIOR (REAR) VIEW

tendons instead of the mechanical fit of opposing bones or snug ligaments. The round end of the upper arm bone (humerus) fits into a shallow groove in the scapula (like a golf ball rests on a tee). Only about 1/3 of the ball surface engages the socket. In the more-stable hip socket, over 1/2 of the ball surface is engaged.

The rotator cuff is the cojoined sheet of three tendons (supraspinatus, infraspinatus, and teres minor); it is surrounded by connective tissue (the shoulder capsule). Some shoulder problems include: tendinitis (rotator cuff tendons inflamed or damaged), bursitis (inflammation of the bursa between the tendons and the shoulder bone), tendon or muscle tear, and frozen shoulder (adhesive capsulitis—inflammation of the shoulder capsule.

1.2.2 *Arm* The upper arm has a single bone—the humerus, followed by the lower arm's two bones—radius and ulna. Figures 4.10 and 4.11 show palm views of the arm muscles. Figures 4.12 and 4.13 show back-of-the-hand views of the muscles. Table 4.1 lists the functions of forearm muscles.

F I G U R E   4 . 1 0

Flexing the wrist (right palm view) is done by the three flexor muscles (Luttgens, et al., 1992). There are 19 muscles to control the fingers and thumb. The 10 entirely within the hand are called intrinsic muscles; the 9 in the forearm (with tendon attachments to the thumb or fingers) are called extrinsic muscles.

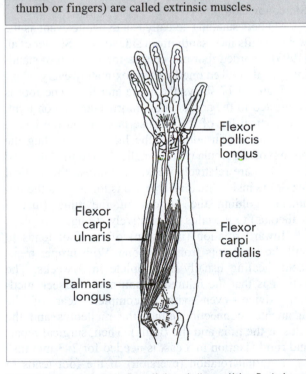

Source (Figures 4.10–4.13): From Kathryn Luttgens, Helga Deutsch, and Nancy Hamilton, *Kinesiology: Scientific Basis of Human Motion,* 8th ed. Copyright © 1992 Wm. C. Brown Communications, Dubuque, IA. Used by permission of The McGraw-Hill Companies.

F I G U R E   4 . 1 1

Extending the wrist (back of right hand, anterior view) is done by combinations of muscles (Luttgens et al., 1992). Radial flexion of the wrist (abduction) is produced by the flexor carpi radialis (Fig. 4.10), flexor carpi radialis longus (Fig. 4.13), and the abductor pollicis longus of the thumb.

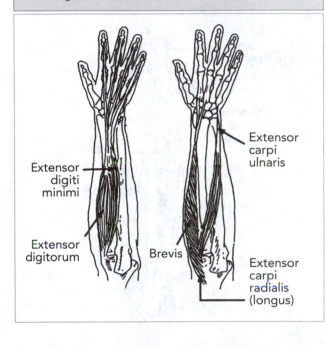

F I G U R E   4 . 1 2

Closing (flexing) the fingers (right palm view) is done with muscles in the forearm (Luttgens et al., 1992); see Table 4.1. The closing muscles have over twice the strength of the opening (extensor) muscles.

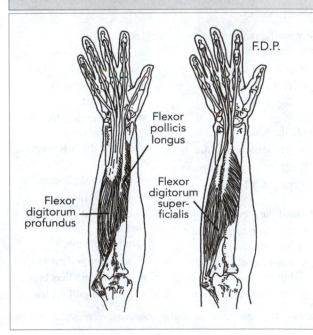

F I G U R E **4 . 13**

Opening (extending) the fingers (back of right hand, anterior view) is done with two sets of muscles (Luttgens et al., 1992); see Table 4.1. Ulnar flexion (adduction) of the wrist is produced by the extensor carpi ulnaris, extensor carpi radialis longus, and extensor carpi radialis brevis.

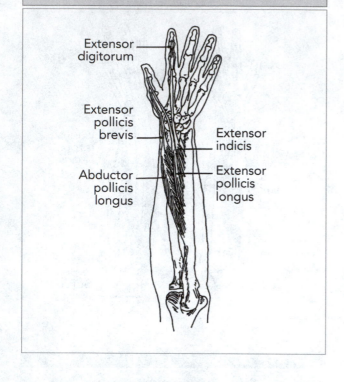

Extensor digitorum

Extensor pollicis brevis

Abductor pollicis longus

Extensor indicis

Extensor pollicis longus

T A B L E **4 . 1**

Functions of forearm muscle.

WRIST	DIGITS
Rotate the radius on the ulna:	Flex the digits:
▪ pronator teres	▪ flexor digitorum superficialis
▪ pronator quadratus	▪ flexor digitorum profundus
▪ supinator	▪ flexor pollicis longus
Flex the hand:	
▪ flexor carpi radialis	Extend the digits (except thumb):
▪ flexor carpi ulnaris	▪ extensor digitorum
▪ palmaris longus	▪ extensor indicis
	▪ extensor digiti minimi
Extend the hand:	
▪ extensor carpi radialis longus	Extend the thumb:
▪ extensor carpi radialis brevis	▪ adductor pollicis longus
	▪ extensor pollicis brevis
▪ extensor carpi ulnaris	▪ extensor pollicis longus

1.2.3 *Hand* The bones of the wrist are followed by the bones of the hand and fingers. Figure 4.14 shows a cross-section of the wrist. Figure 4.15 shows the parts of the fingers.

1.3 Lower Extremity From an ergonomics viewpoint, the bones of the hip, upper leg (femur), knee, and lower leg (tibia and fibula) present relatively few problems. Problems are in the ankle and in the foot. However, Figure 4.16 shows that unequal leg lengths can present back pain problems.

The mean distance between the inside of the two feet, when standing, is about 100 mm; between foot centerlines, it is about 200 mm; and between the outside edges, it is about 300 mm (Rys and Konz, 1994). The mean height for males is 1750 mm; thus, there is a base of only 200–300 mm for a structure of 1750 mm. (The base can be increased if the person stands with one foot forward; one foot forward also reduces twisting stress if the turn is to the side opposite the forward foot.)

This structure has two supports (legs) up to the waist and then one support (the spine). Thus, there is sway—especially front to back. When standing, the center of gravity passes from the ear opening forward of the spine (even L4–L5) so the body normally has a forward-bending moment, counteracted by ligament and back muscle forces and soleus muscles of the calf. At elevation (>4 m eye height), sway increases in both lateral and front–back directions (Hsiao and Simeonov, 2001).

"Quiet" standing actually is a dynamic event as the weight shifts incessantly from side to side. Satzler et al. (1993) recorded foot movements for 120 min of standing; people moved one foot approximately every 90 s.

Figure 4.17 shows the ankle and foot. The foot is connected to the ankle with a mortise-and-tenon joint. The vertical leg of the mortise is short on the lateral side (outside); in addition, the ligaments holding the bottom of the fibula (lateral malleolus) to the talus and calcaneus are relatively weak. In contrast, the vertical leg of the inside (medial) mortise is longer and the ligaments holding the bottom of the tibia (medial malleolus) to the talus are relatively strong.

Inward rotation (inversion) of the foot tends to pull the ligaments from the bone. With proper treatment, healing usually is complete in 3 weeks. The danger is that the injured person may not seek medical advice—even with a complete tear of the ligaments (connecting either the malleolus and the talus or the tibia and the fibula). Then, surgical repair and rigid fixation in a cast is needed for 2–3 months.

External rotation (eversion) of the foot tends to break one of the malleoli bones (vertical part of the mortise). The person tends to recognize this serious injury and go to a physician.

Section of right wrist (looking toward fingers). Note that the shape of the median nerve conforms to the available tunnel space (Tanaka and McGlothlin, 1993).

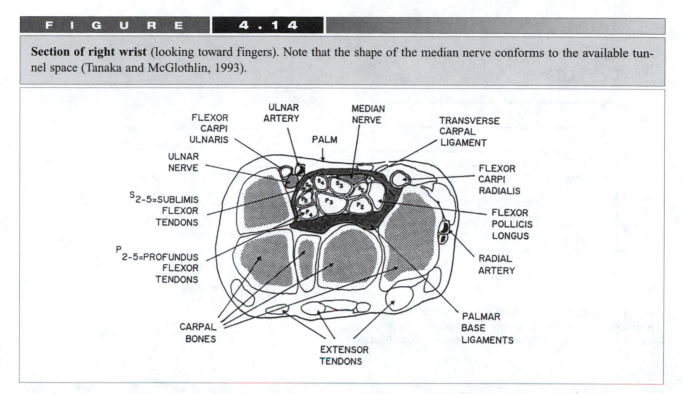

Source: S. Tanaka and J. McGlothlin, "A Conceptual Quantitative Model for Prevention of Work-Related Carpal Tunnel Syndrome (CTS)," *Int. J. of Industrial Ergonomics,* Vol. 11, pp. 181–93. Copyright © 1993 by Elsevier Science, Amsterdam, Netherlands. Reprinted with permission.

Approximately 80% of all foot fractures involve the toes. Almost all could be prevented by safety shoes, as the fractures lie within the area protected by the metal toe cap.

The toes (foot fingers) are divided into *metatarsals* and three *phalanges* (except for the big toe, which has only two phalanges). In supporting the body, the *calcaneus* (heel) supports 50% of the weight; the first and second metatarsals 25%; and the third, fourth, and fifth metatarsals 25%. In between are two arches: (1) the medial arch (the calcaneus; the talus; the navicular; the cuneiform bones; and the first, second, and third metatarsals), and (2) the lateral arch (the calcaneus, the talus, the cuboid, and the fourth and fifth metatarsals). The plantar fascia is a fibrous tissue that forms the arch underneath your foot from the heel to the toes. If it weakens, the fascia can cause pain to either the heel end or the toe end.

Under the heel (calcaneus) is an important shock absorber, the heel pad (about 1.8 cm thick). The bottom of the calcaneus is spherical but has two small "mountains"; the pad reduces the pressure on these mountains, and thus on the ankle, knee, and back.

1.4 Joints   Joints are formed by two or more bones that are connected by thick tissues. The bone ends are covered with cartilage to prevent bone-to-

Parts of the fingers. The five fingers are the thumb, index, middle, ring, and little. The thumb has a metacarpal and a proximal and distal phalanx. However, the other fingers have a metacarpal plus three phalanx (proximal, middle, and distal).

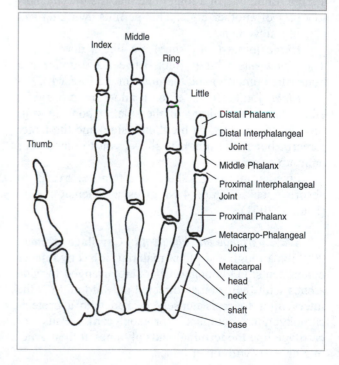

Leg-length discrepancy affects back pain (Contreras, Rys, and Konz, 1993).

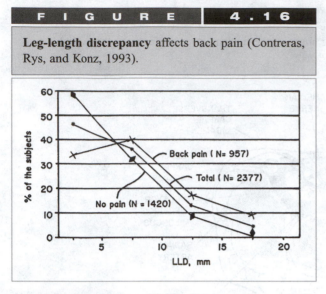

Source: R. Contreras, M. Rys, and S. Konz. "Leg Length Discrepancy," *The Ergonomics of Manual Work*, W. Marras, W. Karwowski, J. Smith, and L. Pacholski (eds.). Copyright © 1993 Taylor and Francis, London. Reprinted with permission.

bone contact. Most joints are enclosed by a capsule, lined with the tissue synovium. Synovium produces a lubricant fluid. Arthritis is a disease that causes joint inflammation.

1.4.1 *Types of joints*   Joint design can emphasize mobility (e.g., shoulder) or stability (e.g., ankle). The body has four types of joints: ball-and-socket, hinge, pivot, and fixed.

Ball-and-socket joints (e.g., hips, shoulders) have a large round end of a long bone that fits into the hollow part of another bone. This permits swinging and rotating movements.

Hinge joints (e.g., knee) are like a door hinge. The elbow has a hinge joint between the upper arm bone (the humerus) and the ulna (in the forearm).

Pivot joints (e.g., elbow) allow rotation. The elbow has a pivot joint of the smaller bone in your forearm (the radius, on the thumb side) and the larger forearm bone (the ulna); it allows you to place your palm up or down.

Fixed joints (e.g., skull) don't move, except to absorb shock. Figure 4.18 gives a schematic joint (Kumar, 2001).

1.4.2 *Cartilage and ligaments*   Cartilage (Kumar, 2001) is a tough and pliant material; it has two major components: (1) collagen fibers are arranged in wide arches with their domes directed outward and (2) the intervening space is densely packed with a protein-carbohydrate complex (proteoglycan). Pads of cartilage line the terminal ends of bones at their articulating ends with other bones.

Bones of the ankle and foot. The right foot is viewed from below (top left) and the outside (middle); the left ankle (bottom) is viewed from the front.

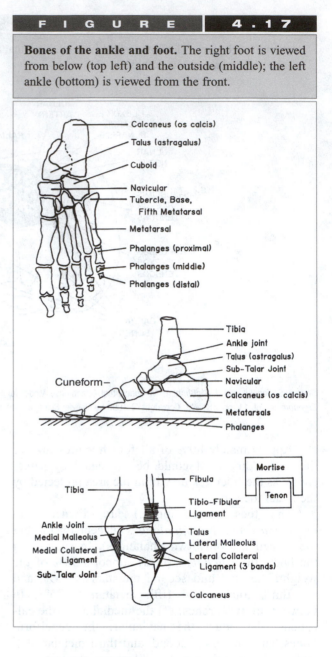

Joint capsules are sheets of collagen fibers surrounding the entire joint from all sides. The collagen fibers are laid in a bed of proteoglycan that binds the fibers together—much like concrete and metal rods or wire mesh.

Synovial fluid is present in the capsules of all articulated joints; it acts as a dynamic lubricant. Its velocity is shear-rate dependent. In slow motions, it maintains a high viscosity, however, in rapid motions, its viscosity drops instantly to allow appropriately thinned lubrication.

Where ligaments are subject to friction, a lubricating device called a **bursa** (a small, flat, fluid-filled sac lined with synovial membrane—the body has about 200 of them) shields the structure from rubbing against the bone. An inflamed bursa is called *bursitis*.

FIGURE	4.18

Schematic joint (Kumar, 2001).

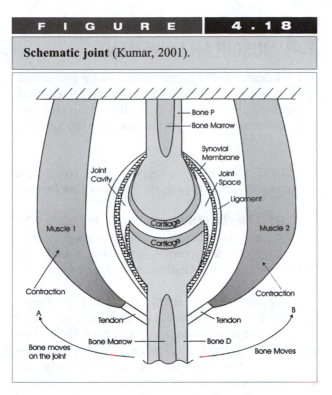

Source: Kumar, 2001. Reprinted with permission of the author.

FIGURE	4.19

Tendons connect muscles to bones (Putz-Anderson, 1988).

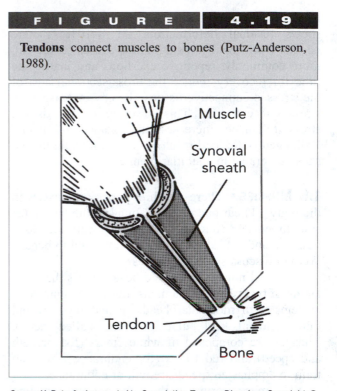

Source: V. Putz-Anderson, (ed.). *Cumulative Trauma Disorders.* Copyright © 1988 by Taylor and Francis, London. Reprinted with permission.

Both ligaments and tendons are made from the same protein—collagen. Ligaments are a flat sheet with a small number of collagen fibers in different directions. Ligaments are well supplied with blood vessels and nerve fibers. Tendons, however, are a "rope" with densely packed collagen fibers running in one direction. They are less vascular. Ligaments provide joint support and stability. They accommodate the normal range of joint motion.

A sprain is a tearing of ligament or muscle—within itself or from the bone.

1.5 Tendons

Tendons, which transmit force from muscles to bones, have a very high modulus of elasticity (close to mild steel!) and very high tensile strength (45 to 125 N/m^2). See Figure 4.19. Synovial sheaths, containing a lubricant called synovial fluid, often (but not always) surround the tough, ropelike tendon. A tendon in a sheath is like a wire in a soda straw. A *strain* is the tearing apart of tendon fibers (akin to fraying a rope). *Tendinitis* (also called tendonitis) is the inflammation of the tendon. *Tenosynovitis* (also called tendosynovitis, tendovaginitis, and peritendinitis) results when the sheath produces excessive synovial fluid, making the sheath swollen and painful. Tendons have virtually no blood supply, and thus, they heal very slowly. An inflammatory reaction may begin in the damaged tendon area. The inflamed tissue carries

with it a blood supply for tendon repair, but it also has a nerve supply that can cause severe pain.

If the tendon sheath constricts (stenosis) , it is called *stenosing tenosynovitis.* The most common example is DeQuervsain's disease, affecting the long abductor and short extensor tendons on the side of the wrist and base of the thumb. The person is unable to "bridge a wide span" (spread thumb and index finger apart) and may have difficulties with a combination firm grip and forearm roll (wringing motion).

If a tendon becomes locked in a swollen sheath, the movement will be snappy or jerky. In a finger, this is called *trigger finger.* This often occurs with extended use of sharp-edged tools. A sheath that swells with fluid may form a ganglionic cyst (a bump).

The unsheathed tendons in the elbow can get tendinitis. The humerus bone of the upper arm splits into two condyles at the elbow; the epicondyle is the outside protrusion on each condyle. Medial epicondylitis (golfer's elbow) is on the inside (medial side) of the elbow; it often occurs when the forearm is rotated when the wrist is bent. Lateral epicondylitis (pitcher's elbow, bowler's elbow, tennis elbow) is on the outside (lateral side) of the elbow; it often occurs when the arm is used for impact or jerky throwing motions.

Tendons and many ligaments have a reversible range of deformation of 4–6% (Kumar, 2001).

Deformation beyond this, even upon full recovery, shows residual deformation. At 8–10%, rupture occurs. Occasionally, a single load causes failure but, more commonly, repetitive exertions and inadequate time for recovery reduce the cross-sectional area of the stressed connective tissues, thereby increasing the stress concentration. This lowering of the tissue's stress tolerance increases the chance of injury. Prolonged static load results in creep, making the tissues vulnerable in a similar manner.

1.6 Muscles   There are three types of **muscles** in the body: (1) cardiac muscle (found in the heart), (2) smooth muscle (internal organs and walls of blood vessels), and (3) skeletal muscles (attached to bones). We will discuss skeletal muscles.

Skeletal muscle is striated because it is the interlacing of two types of filaments: thick filaments (long proteins with molecular heads, called myosin) and thin filaments (globular proteins, called actin). Muscles are composed of white fibers (for strength and speed) and red fibers (for endurance). You can train to emphasize speed/strength or endurance.

The muscle origin is the proximal end (pointing toward the body center); the muscle insertion is the distal end (moving with the moving body segment). The muscle motor units are controlled by neurons. Fine control (e.g., eyeball rotation) may have only 7 motor units/neuron, while gross control may have 1,000 motor units/neuron.

Muscles usually are attached to bones in a paired arrangement. The action (agonist, protagonist) muscles perform the main movement of the body segment; the opposer (antagonist) muscles act as the controller. For example, the agonist muscle initially contracts to provide rotation about a joint; a short time later, the antagonist muscle slows or stops the motion.

Arteries furnish nutrients, oxygen, and hormones to the muscles; veins remove the waste products. The exchange takes place in the capillaries.

1.7 Nerves   Nerves are divided into the central nervous system (brain and spinal cord) and the peripheral nervous system. Peripheral **nerves** supply the communication within the body. Motor nerves bring messages (efferent signals) from the brain to the muscles. Sensory nerves bring messages (afferent signals) from the body (e.g., muscles, pain transducers, pressure transducers) to the brain. Autonomic nerves control various functions, such as sweat production.

In addition to the nervous system (electrical, instantaneous, point-to-point), communication occurs with the hormonal system (chemical, slow and prolonged, to entire body).

2 BIOMECHANICS OF MUSCULAR MOVEMENT

Box 4.1 describes the biomechanics of leg movement. See Section 5.4 of Chapter 15 for a brief discussion of biomechanical software. This section is divided into lever systems; force capability; and gender, age, and training effects.

2.1 Lever Systems   Muscles and bones are arranged into three types of **skeletomuscular levers.**

2.1.1 *First-class levers*   As shown in Figure 4.20, the fulcrum is in the middle, which is good for fine positional control. Common examples outside the body are the seesaw, scissors, and platform balance.

2.1.2 *Second-class levers*   As shown in Figure 4.21, the fulcrum is at one end. The force is exerted through a longer moment arm than the resistance so the force has a mechanical advantage over the resistance. Common examples outside the body are wheelbarrows and refrigerator doors.

2.1.3 *Third-class levers*   As shown in Figure 4.22, the fulcrum is at one end. However, the force is exerted through a shorter moment arm than the resis-

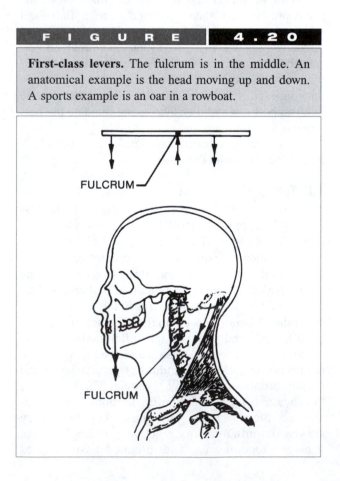

F I G U R E   4 . 2 0

First-class levers. The fulcrum is in the middle. An anatomical example is the head moving up and down. A sports example is an oar in a rowboat.

FULCRUM

FULCRUM

BOX   **4.1**   *Biomechanics of Walking, Running, and Stepping*

Walking

(Konz, 1999)

When walking, the activity of one leg has a shorter swing phase (when the foot is being passed forward) and a longer support (stepping, contact) phase (when the foot is on the ground). The support phase starts at heel strike and ends at toe-off; it has an early passive section and a later active (propulsion) section.

At heel strike, the forward-moving heel hits the ground (causing deceleration). Continued forward motion of the body results in the forefoot contacting the ground, and propulsion (acceleration) begins. The heel rises and the foot is pushed backward under the body. This tendency is resisted by friction under the sole; the body is propelled forward. The foot is everted, increasing forefoot contact on the inner side, until only the skin around the big toe is in ground contact. Finally, the contact ceases and the cycle repeats.

Because the swing phase is shorter than the support phase, heel strike of the opposite limb occurs during the propulsion part of the support phase. At heel strike, horizontal velocity decreases from about 450 cm/s to 20 cm/s; heel angle to the floor changes from about 20° prior to heel contact to 0° at 100 ms after contact (Redfern and Rhoades, 1996). During a slip, instead of stopping, the heel continues to move and the leading foot moves out in front of the body.

Running

Walking changes to running, for normal size adults, at about 2.5 m/s (6 miles/h), since it uses less energy (for the same speed).

Running differs from walking in that both feet are off the ground for part of the stride. In addition, the heel strike should be renamed the "foot strike," since the initial contact probably will be forward of the heel. After foot strike (usually on the outside edge of the foot), the foot rolls inward and flattens out (pronation). Then the foot rolls through the ball and rotates outward (supination).

Peak force is about 3 (body weight) at about .1 s after contact. For running, the average contact duration is .29 s. In contrast, it is .48 s for walking (Scanton and McMaster, 1976).

Stepping

Descending stairs demands a gait quite different from ascent (Templer, 1992).

For descent, the leading foot swings forward over the nosing edge and stops its forward motion when it is directly over the tread below; the toe is pointed downward. Meanwhile, the heel of the rear foot begins to rise, starting a controlled fall downward toward the tread. The heel of the forward foot then is lowered and the weight is transferred to the forward foot. The rear foot then begins to swing forward.

We tend to hold our center of gravity as far back as possible by leaning backward. Problems are overstepping the nosing with the forward foot, catching the toe of the forward foot, and snagging the heel of the rear foot on the nosing as it swings past. Falls tend to be down the stairs.

For ascent, the leading foot has a toe-off, swing, and first contact with the upper step. The foot is approximately horizontal. The ball of the foot is well forward of the tread; the heel may or may not be on the tread. The rear foot then rises on tiptoes, pushing down and back. The rear leg then begins the swing phase. The primary problem is catching the toe, foot, or heel of either foot on the stair nosing. Another problem is the rear foot slipping when it pushes backward. Falls tend to be upward.

See Box 4.6 for the energy costs of walking, running, and carrying.

tance so the resistance has a mechanical advantage over the force. Thus, there is a higher internal force in the body than external force outside the body. Most levers in the limbs are third-class levers. A example outside the body is a forceps.

Assume the muscle is inserted .025 m from the fulcrum and the weight is .30 m from the fulcrum. If the weight is 2 kg, then the weight's external torque is .3 (2) = .6 kg-m; the internal force is .6/.025 = 24 kg. Note that the internal moment arm (the .025 m in the example) becomes smaller as the forearm is raised or lowered from a 90° angle, thus increasing the internal force. (The internal moment arm is quite low when the upper and lower arms are aligned—as in a long reach.) In addition, as the length of the muscle changes from the 90° value, the resulting tension drops.

In reality, there is an additional weight involved. Assume the forearm plus hand weight is 2.3% of body weight; assume its center of gravity is .15 m from the fulcrum. Then, a 70-kg person would have an additional torque of .023 (70) (.15) = .24 kg-m to overcome.

The above static analysis ignores the effect of accelerations, momentum, and friction, but it shows that good design minimizes these moments by using lighter tools and loads and reducing reach distances.

F I G U R E	4.21

Second-class levers. The fulcrum is at one end; the force has a mechanical advantage over the resistance. An anatomical example is the ankle joint when walking. A sports example is a pole in a pole vault, when the pole is bent downward just before the athlete springs off the ground.

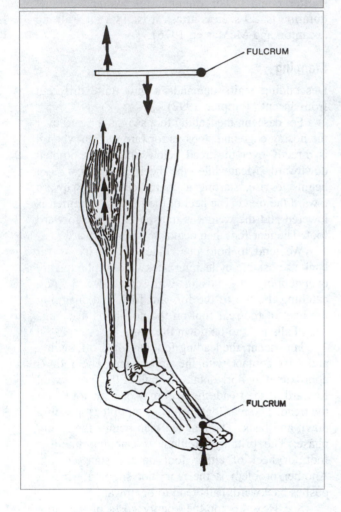

F I G U R E	4.22

Third-class levers. The fulcrum is at one end; the resistance has a mechanical advantage over the force. An anatomical example is holding a weight in the hand. A sports example is movement of the arm when throwing.

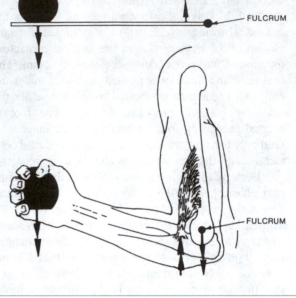

Ferguson and Mason (1988) studied force capability using wrenches. They told designers: (1) at fastener heights below .5 m above the floor, don't require downward movement of the wrench; (2) at heights above .5 m above the floor, don't have horizontal movement of the wrench unless the workers can brace themselves; and (3) at heights above 1 m, move the wrench up or down but not horizontally. Jorgensen et al. (1989) recommended that, when cutting meat with knives, cuts be made pulling toward the body and the knife edge should be down, not up.

Haselgrave et al. (1997a) reported foot placement can have large effects on exertable force. Haselgrave et al. (1997b) reported that exertions are stronger when kneeling on one knee than when kneeling on two knees.

2.2 Force Capability   Force capability is divided into posture factors and individual factors.

2.2.1 *Posture factors*   Table 4.2 and Figure 4.23 show the effect, for seated males, of elbow angle and movement direction. Warwick et al. (1980) reported that their subjects could push (using both hands) with a force of 29.8 kg (100%), pull back with a force of 17.3 (58%), push right with 15.9 (53%), and push left with 17.0 (57%). They could lift up with 39.4 (132%) and push down with 34.7 (116%). Haselgrave et al. (1987), studying maintenance postures, defined pushing horizontally while standing as 100%; most forces while lying supine or working overhead while standing ranged from 35% to 45%, although some angles and positions had values of 140% to 240%.

2.2.2 *Individual factors*   Strength varies greatly with individuals. Note the 42% coefficient of variation in Table 4.2. That is, for a standardized lab experiment using college males, the standard deviation was 42% of the mean. Thus, to include 2 sigma in each direction (i.e., 95% of the people), the range would be (+84% of the mean to –84% of the mean! Industrial workers doing real work probably would vary even more. See Section 2.3 for the effects of gender, age, and training.

T A B L E	4 . 2				

Variables in arm strength. Forces (kg) exertable on a vertical handgrip with the right arm at various elbow angles (Damon et al., 1966, citing Hunsicker, 1955). Arm strength depends upon the angle, the direction, the arm, and the individual. See Figure 4.23. $N = 55$ college males. The mean coefficient of variation was 42%.

	ELBOW ANGLE, DEGREES					
Movement	60	90	120	150	180	Left arm, % of Right
Pull	28.6	40.0	47.3	55.5	54.5	.94
Push	41.8	39.1	46.8	55.9	62.7	.92
Move right	19.1	16.8	15.5	15.0	15.5	1.30
Move left	23.6	22.7	24.1	24.5	22.7	.60
Up	22.3	25.5	27.3	25.5	19.5	.92
Down	23.2	24.1	26.4	21.4	18.6	.88

Strength also varies greatly with time exerted. See Figures 21.1 and 21.2. **Maximum voluntary contraction (MVC),** the maximum sustained force of a muscle, declines exponentially with time. The asymptote at which a force can be held indefinitely is about 10% of MVC.

2.2.3 *Strength measurement* Testing types are isometric, isoinertial, and isovelocity. If the muscle length does not move (there is a balance between muscle torque and external torque), the test is isomet-

ric. If there is a constant mass being moved, it is **isoinertial.** If movement is constant, it is **isovelocity. Isotonic** (concentric) contractions have a constant internal force of the muscle, but the muscle shortens.

Isovelocity testing is recommended due to its greater predictive ability as well as greater safety for the person being tested. Also see Kroemer et al. (2001).

Muscle activity can be evaluated with an **electromyogram** (see Box 4.2).

2.3 Gender, Age, and Training Effects Three individual variables are gender, age, and training.

2.3.1 *Gender* The average female has less muscular strength than the average male, although individual females may be stronger than individual males. The most simple approximation is that females have 2/3 the strength of males. However, there are differences by muscle groups. Laubach (1976) reported 56% for upper body strength, 72% for lower extremity strength, 64% for trunk strength, and 69% for dynamic strength. The differences are primarily due to the smaller size (shorter lever arms) and muscle masses of women rather than gender itself. Franson and Winkel (1991) reported that 35% of the gender differences in hand strength are due to hand size differences.

Females have less muscle mass than males but also lighter arms. Hence, rhythmic work performed by the arms (such as most bench work), may result in a higher risk of musculoskeletal disorders because females are working at a higher percent of their capacity.

2.3.2 *Age* Figure 4.24 shows the effect of age on muscle strength for males and females. Figures

F I G U R E	4 . 2 3

Arm muscle strength versus angle. Table 4.2 shows how strength varies greatly with elbow angle.

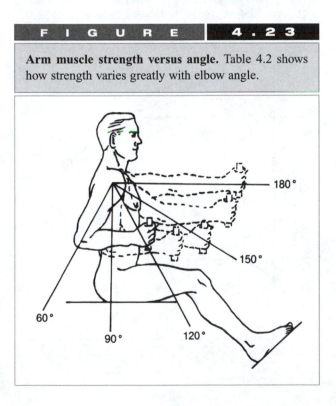

BOX   **4.2**   *Electromyography (EMG)*

For heavy work, the measurement of the cardiovascular system's oxygen capability is of interest. However, for lighter, more repetitive work, specific muscles may be of interest. Using an electromyogram (EMG), electrodes are taped on the skin above the specific muscles of interest. An EMG can provide information about:

- whether the muscle was in use (on/off)
- a relative activity level
- force generation (under special conditions)
- muscle fatigue

To improve the "signal/noise" ratio of the EMG, the raw EMG can be normalized. One approach is to express the signal as a ratio of the percent of maximum voluntary contraction (MVC). However, MVC is a voluntary measure, based on the subject's own evaluation of his/her maximum power; thus, MVC varies between and within subjects.

An alternative is to normalize, using the mean and standard deviation of each subject (Udo et al., 2000).

$$SEMG = (AEMG - SAEMG)/SDEMG$$

where

$SEMG$	=	Standardized EMG at a time, ratio
$AEMG$	=	Average EMG over a short period, such as 5 min, uV
$SAEMG$	=	Mean of a subject's EMG over a longer period, such as one hour, uV
$SDEMG$	=	Standard deviation of a subject's EMG over the longer period, uV

The energy content of the muscle activity is proportional to the root-mean-square (RMS) value.

Fatigue is estimated by the decrease in frequency. Kim and Jung (1998) reported that mean power frequency was superior to median frequency at 30% to 75% of MVC. Fatigue also can be quantified by the slope of frequency versus time. However, Kumar (1997) reported that different muscles had different median frequencies, and, for the same muscle, frequency differed between males and females, and between holding upright and stooping.

4.28 and 4.29 show more age effects. Speed of movement decreases with age; older people slow down most on more difficult movements (Brogmus, 1991). Roozbahar et al. (1979) give grip strength as:

$$GS = 608 - 2.94\,AGE$$

where

GS	=	Grip strength of dominant hand, N
AGE	=	Age, years

Rhodes (1983), in a review of the relation between age and job performance, indicated that approximately 1/3 of the studies report that job performance increases with age, 1/3 say it remains the same, and 1/3 say it decreases. See also Waldman and Avolio (1986).

2.3.3 Training   With the same type of muscle training, strength increases faster and to a greater extent for males; thus, training may increase gender differences.

For industrial jobs, training should emphasize strength, endurance, and flexibility. A short, intensive training program can substantially improve muscular strength and endurance. To improve strength, the training load should be >50% of the person's initial dynamic strength. Increased endurance time in a job

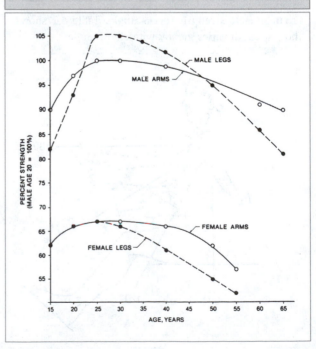

F I G U R E   **4.24**

Isometric strength of arms and legs. Strength varies with gender, with limb, and with age (Asmussen and Heebøll-Nielsen, 1962). Male strength at age 20–22 is set as 100%.

is partially due to the person's improved micromotions and neuromuscular coordination.

3 CARDIOVASCULAR ANATOMY

Work physiology deals primarily with the response of the **cardiovascular system** to exercise. Thus, we will begin with an introduction to the anatomy of the cardiovascular system. (For skeletomuscular anatomy, see the beginning of this chapter.) The discussion will cover the overall system and then local systems.

3.1 Overall System
Figure 4.25 shows an "engineer's view" of the cardiovascular system.

Pulmonary circulation starts at the right atrium (*little room,* Latin) and goes through a valve to the right ventricle (the pump itself). Systole is the contraction of the heart muscle; it ends with blood ejection from the heart (aortic valve opens). Diastole is the relaxation of the heart (aortic valve closes). At 75 beats/min, systole takes about .3 s and diastole about .5 s. At 150 beats/min, both take about .2 s; thus, an increase in heart rate takes place primarily by decreasing diastole. When the blood returns from the lungs (with more oxygen and less carbon dioxide), it enters the **systemic circulation.**

After passing through the left atrium and ventricle, the blood enters the arteries, goes through the capillaries, and then returns in the veins. The circulating blood has not only transferred gases and compounds (including enzymes and hormones) around the body; it has also transferred heat. It also stores gases and compounds.

Blood volume is divided into plasma (55%, mostly water) and solids (45%). The solids are primarily red cells, white cells, and platelets. Hematocrit is the percent of red cell volume in the total blood volume.

Box 4.3 describes cardiac output and Box 4.4 describes blood pressure.

3.1.1 *Legs* Three venous systems drain the lower limbs: (1) a deep central system drains the muscles, (2) a superficial system drains the foot and skin of the leg, and (3) a perforating system connects the deep and superficial systems.

The veins store the body's blood. If the legs don't move, the blood from the heart tends to go down to the legs and stay there **(venous pooling).** This causes more work for the heart, as, for a constant supply of blood, when blood/beat is lower, then there must be more beats. Venous pooling causes swelling of the legs **(edema)** and varicose veins.

Venous pressure in the ankle of sedentary people is approximately equal to the hydrostatic pressure from the right auricle. Pollack and Wood (1949) gave a mean ankle venous pressure of 56 mm Hg for sitting and 87 for standing. Nodeland et al. (1983) gave 48 for sitting and 80 for standing. Pollack and Wood reported that walking about 10 steps drops ankle venous pressure to about 23 mm Hg; Nodeland et al. (1983) reported 21.

A fall occurs because the calf muscles contract while taking the next step before venous filling is complete. Thus, additional blood is pumped out of the leg, causing a further drop in pressure when the calf muscles relax. The drop stabilizes in about 10 steps when the incoming flow to the veins from the capillaries equals the flow out of the leg.

Thus, walking can compensate partially for standing posture. For example, Nodeland et al. (1983) reported that standing benchwork (i.e., with occasional steps around the area) had ankle pressure approximately equal to sitting at a desk (48 mm Hg).

Walking aids blood circulation through the "milking action" of the leg muscles; this reduces the work of the heart. Active standing (walking 2–4 min every 15 min) results in less discomfort than standing without walking (Konz et al., 1988). Also see Table 4.3.

3.1.2 *Thermal regulation* During heat stress, the body may heat acclimatize. In brief, because acclimatized people sweat more, there is less need for peripheral blood flow, and thus, less work by the heart. See Box 4.3 and Chapter 25 for more on the

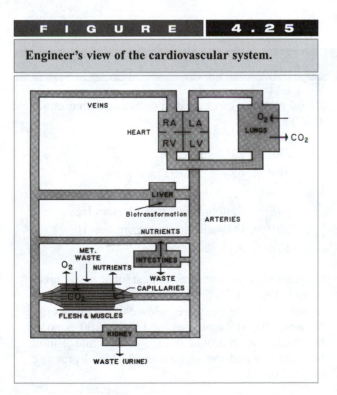

F I G U R E   4 . 2 5

Engineer's view of the cardiovascular system.

| BOX | 4.3 | *Cardiac Output* |

Cardiac output is the output of the left ventricle:

$$CO = HR (SV)$$

where

CO = Cardiac output, liters/min
HR = Heart rate, beats/min
SV = Stroke volume, liters/beat

Cardiac output, for a resting young man, is about 5 liters/min. Maximum, for a normally sedentary young man, is about 25 and, for a world-class athlete, is about 35.

Cardiac output can be predicted from formulas. Basal cardiac output is (Guyton, 1961):

$$COBASL = CI (DBSA)$$

where

$COBASL$ = Basal cardiac output, liters/min
CI = Cardiac index, liters/(min - m²)
= $4.29 - .029\ AGE + .003\ AGE^2$
$(5 < AGE < 70)$
AGE = Age, years
$DBSA$ = DuBois surface area, m²

Activity cardiac output is (Astrand and Rohdahl, 1986):

$$COACT = CLMW (TOTMET)$$

where

$COACT$ = Activity cardiac output, liters/min
$CLMW$ = Conversion from liters of blood to watts
= .166 for $TOTMET$ <700 W
= .114 for $TOTMET$ >700 W

Activity cardiac output increases (up to 18 times basal flow) primarily in the muscles.

Skin cardiac output (Stolwijk, 1970) is .4 liters/min for basal conditions. For tasks with $TOTMET$ <.2 $\dot{V}O_2$max, any increase in skin blood flow comes from $COBASL + COACT$ rather than an increase in CO—that is, a redistribution of blood flow rather than an increase (Rowell, 1974).

However, with vasodilation, skin cardiac output can reach 1.6 liters/min. This vasodilation circulation bypasses the muscles as the blood flows from the small arteries (arterioles) to the small veins (venules) through bypasses (arteriovenous anastomoses). This high-resistance flow increases heart rate.

However, if people are accustomed to heat **(heat acclimatization),** they have an enhanced ability to sweat (losing heat by evaporation). Thus, they do not have to lose heat by vasodilation and the blood does not use the high-resistance paths. Acclimatized people have lower heart rates in heat stress than do unacclimatized people.

| BOX | 4.4 | *Blood Pressure* |

Blood pressure (the pressure blood puts on the blood vessel walls) commonly is measured with a sphygmomanometer. The cuff is applied to the upper arm and while it is being tightened, one listens to the sound of the blood flowing in the artery below the cuff. After the cuff is tight, there is no sound because no blood is flowing in the artery. As the cuff is loosened, blood begins to flow turbulently and a noise is heard. This first sound indicates systolic blood pressure. As the cuff is loosened further, the turbulence decreases until the flow becomes laminar and the sound disappears. The disappearance of the sound indicates diastolic blood pressure, the minimum or base pressure exerted by the blood on the artery walls.

Pulse pressure = Systolic pressure – diastolic pressure

Blood pressure can be estimated (Roozbahar et al., 1979) as:

$$SBP = 101.3 + .68\ AGE$$
$$DBP = 63.7 + .36\ AGE$$

where

SBP = Systolic blood pressure, mm Hg
DBP = Diastolic blood pressure, mm Hg
AGE = Age, years

Life insurance studies indicate that blood pressures below 110/70 are optimal for a long life span. Resting diastolic pressure below 90 is satisfactory, from 90–100 is suspicious, and above 100 is poor. In 2003, the National Heart, Lung, and Blood Institute lowered the recommended blood pressure to 120/80.

T A B L E	4 . 3		
Cardiovascular effects of sitting and standing for 16 adults between 18 and 51 with mean age of 30 (Ward et al., 1966).			

CRITERION	STAND (A LITTLE WALKING)	SIT	SIT/STAND %
Cardiac output, L/min	5.1	6.4	125
Stroke volume, mL/beat	54.5	78.3	144
Mean arterial pressure, torr	107.0	87.9	82
Heart rate, beats/min	97.2	84.9	87
Total peripheral resistance, dynes/cm²-s.	1820.0	1207.0	66

physiology of thermal regulation and techniques to overcome its challenges.

4 METABOLISM

The cardiovascular system primarily responds to changes in metabolism. In some cases, heart response is affected by emotions and by heat stress. In industry, metabolism usually is determined from tables and formulas; see below and the ERGO disk. In a laboratory, metabolism can be determined from oxygen consumption (indirect calorimetry), which gives the total of basal, activity, and digestion metabolism.

Table 4.4 gives some of the possible units and their conversions. The standard power unit is watts, abbreviated *W*. The energy content of food is given in kcal (commonly spoken of as Calories rather than the technically correct kilocalories.) Table 4.5 gives metabolic rate as a function of exertion level.

Metabolic rate is divided into three parts: basal, activity, and digestion.

4.1 Basal Metabolism

Basal metabolism maintains body temperature, body functions, and blood circulation.

$$BSLMET = BSMET\ (WT)$$

where

$BSLMET$ = Basal metabolic rate, W

$BSMET$ = 1.28 W/kg for males
1.16 W/kg for females

WT = Body weight, kg

BSMET is lower for females because females tend to have a higher percentage of fat than males (see Box 4.5). Fat has a limited metabolism.

The ERGO disk also has a more complex formula that considers a person's age (from 5 to 70). Children have a higher basal metabolic rate/kg because they have a higher surface area/volume (thus, requiring more heat to maintain body temperature) and because growth takes energy.

T A B L E	4 . 4		
Energy conversions.			

MULTIPLY UNITS BY 1	TO EQUAL UNITS	MULTIPLY UNITS BY 1	TO EQUAL UNITS
Joule	1.0 Nm		
Joule	.000239 kcal		
Watt	1.0 J/s		
Watt	.85885 kcal/h	kcal/h	1.163 W
Watt	3.413 BTU/h	BTU/h	.293 W
Watt	.00134 HP	HP	746.0 W
Watt	6.116 (kg-m)/min	(kg-m)/min	.1635 W
Watt/sq m	.01718 mets	met	58.2 W/sq m
Watt/sq m	10.764 W/sq ft	W/sq ft	.0929 W/sq m
Kcal	3.968 BTU	BTU	.252 kcal
		BTU	776.65 ft-lb

T A B L E	4 . 5		
Metabolism as a function of exertion. Moderate (for a 70 kg male) includes playing the piano, carpentry, walking 3 km/h, and dancing the waltz. ILO 8996 (1990) considers very light work to be <100 W/m², light work to be 100 to 165, and moderate to heavy to be ≥165.			

EXERTION LEVEL	TOTAL METABOLISM RATE	
	Watts	Kcal/h
Light	Up to 230	Up to 189
Moderate	230 to 350	189 to 300
Heavy	Over 350	Over 300

BOX 4.5   *Percent Fat*

Percent fat can be determined by (1) underwater weighing (most accurate, but requires special facilities) or (2) by using formulas. (The formulas are in the ERGO disc.)

Formulas for fat

Cowgill (1957) gave a formula for adult males:

$$DENSTY = .161 + .8 \, (HT)^{.242}/(1000 \, WT)^{.1}$$

where

$DENSTY$	=	Density of the human body, g/mL
HT	=	Height, cm
WT	=	Weight, kg

Dividing the body into a fat compartment with a mean *DENSTY* of .9 for fat and 1.1 for the lean body (rest of the body), the typical female will have a *DENSTY* of 1.03, with a male's *DENSTY* being 1.06 (population range of 1.02 to 1.08).

The next step is to calculate percent fat (Brozek et al., 1963):

$$PERFAT = ((4.570/DENSTY) - 4.142) \, 100$$

where

$PERFAT$ = Percent of the body that is fat

Wilmore and Behnke (1969) recommend the following for adult males:

$$PERFAT = 74 \, WACIRC/WT - 4464/WT - 8.2$$

where

$WACIRC$ = Waist circumference, cm

The U. S. Army (1987) has formulas to predict percent fat for both males and females. For males:

$$PERFAT = -8.4 + 3.75 \, (A - N) - .045 \, (A - N)^2 - .417 \, HGT$$

where

A	=	Abdomen (belly button) circumference, in.
N	=	Neck (below Adam's apple) circumference, in.
HGT	=	Height (barefoot), in.

For females:

$$PERFAT = WTF - HTF + HPF - FF - NF - WRF$$

where

WTF	=	Weight factor = $86.1 + .633 \, WHT - .001 \, (WHT)^2$
WHT	=	Weight (clothed, no shoes), lb
HTF	=	Height factor = $.02 + 1.31 \, HGT$
HPF	=	Hip factor = $8.84 + .0054 \, HP$
HP	=	Hip circumference (max) (where buttocks protrude the most), in.
FF	=	Forearm factor = $18.4 + .196 \, F$
F	=	Forearm circumference (max), in.
NF	=	Neck factor = $1.35 \, N$
N	=	Neck (below Adam's apple) circumference, in.
WRF	=	Wrist factor = $2.34 + .025 \, WR$
WR	=	Wrist circumference, in.

Fat indices

A number of body mass indices combine weight (W, kg) and height (H, m)—but with large errors. Two examples are Quetelet's index (W/H^2) and the ponderal index ($W^{.33}/H$). A Quetelet's index from 19 to 25 is "healthy," from 25 to 29 is "moderately overweight," and above 29 is "severely overweight."

Fat distributions

Fat distributed around the waist (apple shape) increases the risk of heart attack, stroke, diabetes, breast cancer, high blood cholesterol, and high blood pressure; weight around the hips and thighs (pear shape) is not as bad. Using a flexible tape, measure your waist at its narrowest point. Then, measure your hips around the fullest part of the buttocks. An acceptable waist/hip ratio for men is <1.0; for women, <.80.

The amount of fat increases with age. Garn and Harper (1955) reported that although lean body weight changes little from age 20 to 60, fat increases from 16% of body weight at ages 20–30 to 22% of body weight at ages 50–60.

About 3% of body weight is "essential" fat (cell membranes, nerve tissue, tissue in and around various organs). Women have sex-specific fat (primarily breasts and hips) of 9–12%. Thus, anything over 3% for men and 15% for women is storage fat.

4.2 Activity Metabolism **Activity metabolism** provides the energy for activities. See Table 4.6 for some examples. Working in a contorted posture (kneeling, bent over) increases metabolic rate (Freivalds and Bise, 1991). Box 4.6 gives the metabolic cost for walking/running/carrying. For lifting, Garg et al. (1978) give the equation:

$$LFTMET = .0109 \, BWLB + F \, (LOADF)$$

where

$LFTMET$	=	Lifting metabolism, kcal/min
$BWLB$	=	Body weight, lb
F	=	Frequency of lifts, lifts/min

T A B L E	4 . 6

Activity cost for various activities. For total energy cost, add the basal metabolism and, if appropriate, the cost of digestion. See Box 4.6 for equations for walking, carrying, and running.

W/KG	ACTIVITY
.4	Crocheting, eating, reading aloud, sitting quietly, writing
.6	Playing cards, standing relaxed
.7	Paring potatoes, standing office work, standing at attention, violin playing
.8	Dressing and undressing, knitting a sweater
.9	Singing in a loud voice
1.0	Driving a car
1.2	Dishwashing
1.4	Washing floors
1.5	Cello playing, light laundry
1.6	Riding a walking horse, sweeping floor with broom
1.7	Golfing, organ playing, painting furniture with brush
1.9	Sweeping with hand (push) carpet sweeper
2.7	Doing heavy carpentry
3.0	Cleaning windows
3.1	Cleaning with upright vacuum cleaner
3.5	Dancing the waltz
4.1	Ice skating
4.5	Weeding a garden
5.0	Horseback riding (trot)
5.1	Playing ping pong
5.8	Dancing rhumba, playing tennis
6.6	Sawing wood (handsaw)
7.9	Playing football
8.9	Fencing

$LOADF$ = Load factor

= $LFBW (BWLB) + LF (W) + GENF (W)$

$LFBW$ = Lift factor: body weight = .0002 for arm lift, .0012 for stoop, .0019 for squat

LF = Lift factor: load = .0103 for arm lift, .0052 for stoop, .0081 for squat

$GENF$ = Gender factor = $-.0017\ G$ for arm lift, .0028 G for stoop, and .0023 G for squat

G = Gender (female = 0; male = 1)

W = Object weight, lb

In industrial applications, estimate metabolism from tables or formulas as in the ERGO disk. But remember that most work is not continuous as people take microbreaks. Estimate the time of each activity from a videotape.

The body burns additional Calories after the exercise stops so exercise benefits weight loss more than you might calculate.

4.3 Digestion Metabolism   Digestion metabolism (also called specific dynamic action) accounts for transformation of food within the body. We burn:

4 kcal/g of carbohydrate

9 kcal/g of fat

4.3 kcal/g of protein

For reference, there are 7 kcal/g for alcohol. Alcohol is a problem as it decreases lipid (fat) oxidation about 33% (Suter et al., 1992). For the typical carbohydrate/fat/protein mixture of the U. S. diet and disregarding time following the meal:

$$DIGMET\ =\ .1\ (BSLMET + ACTMET)$$

4.4 Calories Required   Metabolism is related to calories and body weight.

Assume a 70 kg male spent 24 h in bed without eating. Then, basal metabolism would be (70)(1.28) = 89.6 W. To convert this rate to an amount/hour, multiply by .86. Then, for a 24 h period, this 70 kg male would require 89.6 W (.86 kcal/W-h)(24 h) = 1849 kcal (1000 calories = 1 kcal = 1 Cal).

Hopefully, he will move during the day! Assume activity metabolism is .7 W/kg for 16 waking hours. Then, .7 (70) (.86) (16) = 674 kcal would be needed, or a total of 2523 kcal. Assuming 10% for digestion of food, this means he could eat 1.1 (2,523) = 2,773 kcal/day without gaining or losing weight.

If you eat more or less than your equilibrium amount, you will gain or lose weight. There are 3,500 kcal/lb, 7,700 kcal/kg. If you eat 20 kcal less per day (or increase exercise by 20 kcal/day), you will lose 7,300 kcal/year or 2.1 pounds/year or 21 lbs in 10 years. Small changes in eating or exercise can have large cumulative effects!

As a side note, Klieber (1961) determined the following formula for a variety of animals (dove, rat, pigeon, hen, dog, sheep, human, cow, and steer):

$$DAYMET\ =\ 70\ WT^{3/4}$$

where

$DAYMET$ = Metabolism during a day, kcal

WT = Weight, kg

The exponent could have been predicted to be 2/3 since surface area increases by a power of 2 and volume increases by a power of 3. Peters (1989) says the difference is due to the differing shape of animals as the size increases.

BOX **4.6** *Metabolic Cost of Walking/Running/Carrying*

Box 4.1 discusses the biomechanics of walking, running, and stepping.

Pace

For many time studies, the concept of a normal pace is walking 3 mph (4.84 km/h; 1.39 m/s). The speed that minimizes energy expenditure is 2.2 mph (3.6 km/h) (Bunc et al., 2000).

The pace of Methods-Time-Measurement (MTM) is 3.57 miles/h (1.64 m/s) at a stride of 34 inches (.86 m)—.000015 h/stride. It is based on studies of 125 people walking a variety of paces (Maynard et al., 1948). MTM uses .000015 h/stride for climbing stairs. For carrying a load of up to 16 kg, MTM uses .000015 h/stride, but .76 m strides. For walking through obstructed areas, MTM uses .000017 h/stride and .86 m strides.

The length of stride *(L)* divided by stature height *(h)* varies linearly with velocity; L/h = .67 at v = .8 m/s and L/h = .9 at 1.7 m/s (Alexander, 1984). Thus, for the same velocity, a short person takes more steps. L decreases as floor slipperiness and weight carried increase (Myung and Smith, 1997).

Walking: Metabolic cost

Pandolf et al. (1976) gave the metabolic cost (total) of walking without a load as:

$$WLKMET = C (2.7 + 3.2 (v - .7)^{1.65})$$

where

$WLKMET$ = Walking metabolism (total), W/kg of body weight

C = Terrain coefficient

= 1.0 for blacktop road, treadmill

= 1.1 for dirt road

= 1.2 for light brush

= 1.3 for hard-packed snow; C = 1.3 + .082 (foot depression, cm)

= 1.5 for heavy brush

= 1.8 for swamp

= 2.1 for sand

v = velocity, m/s (for v >.7 m/s [2.5 km/h, 1.56 miles/h])

Walking stooped requires more energy: 12% more for a 10% stoop (90% of stature height), 51% more for a 20% stoop, and 91% more for a 30% stoop (Morrisey et al., 1981).

A person walking on a treadmill swings the arms and legs, so the effective air movement is not zero but about .9 m/s (Nishi and Gagge, 1970).

Running: Metabolic cost

The cost of running (Van der Walt and Wyndham, 1973) is:

$$RUNMET = -142/WT + 11 + .04 \, V^2$$

where

$RUNMET$ = Running metabolism (total), W/kg

V = Velocity, km/h

WT = Weight, kg

Carrying/standing: Metabolic cost

The metabolic cost of carrying (walking with a load) depends on the load location. Soule and Goldman (1980) reported that loads on the head used 1.2 times the energy of carrying a kg of your own body weight; in the hands, loads required 1.4 to 1.9 times as much; on the feet, loads required 4.2 to 6.3 times as much.

As a general guide for carrying, minimize the load's moment arm—both in the frontal and transverse axes. See also Section 4, Chapter 15.

Pandolf et al. (1977), for carrying very slowly or standing, give:

$$WLKMETT = 1.5 \, WT + 2 \, (WT + WTL) \, (WTL/WT)^2 + C \, (WT + WTL) \, (1.5 \, v^2 + .35 \, vG)$$

where

$WLKMETT$ = Metabolic rate (total) for walking slowly, W

WT = Body weight, kg

WTL = Weight of a load on the shoulders, kg

v = velocity of walking, m/s (v <1 m/s)

C = Terrain coefficient (see above)

G = Grade, %

The first term (1.5 WT) is the metabolic cost of standing without a load (1.5 W/kg). The second term is the cost of bearing a load while standing. Walking on the level is $C \, (WT + WTL) \, (1.5 \, v^2)$. The cost of walking up a grade is $C \, (WT + WTL) \, (.35 \, vG)$.

5 RESPONSE TO EXERCISE

The cardiovascular system has five **responses to exercise:** (1) heart rate, (2) stroke volume, (3) artery–vein differential, (4) blood distribution, and (5) going into debt.

5.1 Heart Rate For light and medium workloads (see Table 4.7), heart rate is a good predictor of metabolic rate. Three exceptions are:

1. *Emotions.* Emotions increase heart rate. The effect is relatively larger when the metabolic rate is low.
2. *Vasodilation.* In heat stress, unacclimatized people vasodilate, while acclimatized people sweat more and thus need less vasodilation and fewer heart beats.
3. *Heavy exercise.* In heavy exercise, other cardiovascular responses such as stroke volume and artery–vein differential may reduce the need for some of the increase in heart rate.

There are four ways of **measuring heart rate:**

1. *Light* can be used by shining it on an artery in the earlobe. A photocell on the far side of the earlobe sees the light during "ebb tide" between beats. Another model works by reflecting light on the finger. Both the earlobe and the finger techniques are sensitive to body movement, so they work best with a stationary person.
2. *Sound* through a stethoscope is used by physicians.
3. *Palpation* is the detection, with the fingers, of the surge of blood that follows each beat. Common locations are the arteries in the wrist and neck. Count the number of beats during 10 or 15 s and multiply by 6 or 4. In working situations, this is done after the work stops—that is, you measure recovery pulse.
4. *Electronics* is the most common and only practical technique for a nonstationary person. The recording unit is about the size of pack of ciga-

rettes and is belt-mounted. The output can be sent immediately or stored for later analysis.

Heart rate can be estimated by asking a person for his/her **rating of perceived exertion (RPE).** The scale is a column of numbers from 6 to 20. The person votes his/her perceived exertion as a number, using accompanying words for guidance; the heart rate is estimated by multiplying the rating by 10. For example, the words accompanying level 9 are "Very light" and the word with 11 is "Light." If the person identifies his/her exertion as "Light," the heart rate would be estimated as 10(11) = 110 beats/min. The concept has been validated by many experimenters for many tasks. Ljunggren (1986) reported it is not even necessary to have the individual's own perceived exertion—the exertion can be estimated by an observer.

Maximum heart rate can be estimated by:

$$HRMAX = 220 - AGE$$

where

$HRMAX$ = Maximum heart rate, beats/min

AGE = Age, years

The standard deviation of the prediction is 10 beats/min. Thus, an average person age 20 would have a maximum heart rate of 200 beats/min, with 95% of that age having from 180 to 220 beats/min. Maximum heart rate is relatively unaffected by physical fitness. (When exercising for physical fitness, initially exercise at 60–70% of $HRMAX$. An experienced exerciser can use 75–85% of $HRMAX$.)

A predictor equation of heart rate for light and medium workloads (Andrews, 1969) is:

$$INCHR = K + .12\ INCMET$$

where

$INCHR$ = Increase in heart rate, beats/min

K = Constant

= 2.3 for arm work (cranking)

= −11.5 for leg work (walking) or arm and leg work (The 13.8 difference in the coefficient for the legs is due to venous pooling in the legs.)

$INCMET$ = Increase in metabolism, W

Figure 4.26 shows how the heart rate (primarily determined by aerobic oxygen supply) responds to constant-intensity exercise. At the start of exercise, the **aerobic response** (and therefore heart rate) lags. (**Aerobic** refers to reactions using oxygen from the lungs.) The resulting deficit (Figure 4.26, area A) is replaced by anaerobic oxygen. **Anaerobic** (without oxygen) reactions use oxygen stored as compounds in the blood. The anaerobic supply is composed of alactate (energy equivalent of 1.9 L of oxygen) and lactate (equivalent of 3.1 L). During recovery (Figure 4.26,

T A B L E		4 . 7
Oxygen uptake and heart rate as a function of exertion.		

EXERTION LEVEL	OXYGEN UPTAKE, L/MIN	HEART RATE, BEATS/MIN
Light	<.5	<90
Moderate	0.5–0.99	90–110
Heavy	1.0–1.49	110–130
Very heavy	1.5–2.00	130–150
Extremely heavy	>2.0	150–170

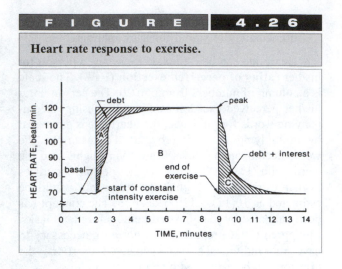

Heart rate response to exercise.

WT = Weight, kg

$TOTMET$ = Total metabolism, W. For $TOTMET$ over 500 W, add .000 025 ($TOTMET$ – 500) to the SV equation.

Stroke volume also depends on body posture, exercise, and physical fitness. For sitting and standing, stroke volume of .08 liters/beat is typical but, for lying down, the value may be .12. Exercise with the legs improves venous return; stroke volume may increase. Arm exercise permits venous pooling in the legs, so stroke volume changes little.

Physical fitness affects maximum stroke volume. Maximum SV = .135 for excellent cardiovascular fitness, .120 for good, .100 for fair, .090 for poor, and .085 for very poor. See Table 4.8 for maximum oxygen uptake values for these fitness levels. Stroke volume peaks at about 40% of maximum oxygen consumption.

area C), the anaerobic oxygen used from the blood is replaced; however, the replacement process itself uses oxygen ("interest"), so area C is larger than area A. For task cost, use areas B + C.

The **heart rate cost of work** can be determined three ways. The simplest is to subtract an individual's basal heart rate from the peak. For example, Joe's peak of 110 and basal of 70 give a task cost for him of 40 beats/min. This assumes that the peak represents the work heart rate—that is, that the top of the curve in Figure 4.26 is flat.

Determining the basal is more complex than it might seem. People subconsciously increase their heart rate just before exercise. Measure basal 5 to 10 min before beginning the exercise.

A second way is to determine area B under the curve in Figure 4.26. However, this assumes that the heart rate instantaneously accelerates and decelerates at the start and stop of work. Thus, use a third method, totaling areas B + C (Chen and Lee, 1998).

5.2 Stroke Volume   The heart also can adjust oxygen supply to the body through changing **stroke volume,** the amount of blood pumped by the left ventricle.

$$SV = STROVB + .000\ 050\ (TOTMET - 200)$$
$$TOTMET \leq 500$$

where

SV = Stroke volume, liters/beat

$STROVB$ = Basal stroke volume, liters/beat (females = .9 male)

= SI ($DBSA$)/1,000

where

SI = Stroke index, ML(beat-m^2)

= 53.45 + .194 AGE

AGE = Age, years

$DBSA$ = DuBois surface area, m^2

= .007 184 $HT^{.725}$ $WT^{.425}$

HT = Height, cm

5.3 Artery–Vein Differential   A third method of adjusting oxygen supply to the body is **artery–vein differential.**

$$OXUPTK = CO\ (AVDIF)$$

where

$OXUPTK$ = Oxygen uptake, $\dot{V}O_2$ at standard temperature (0°C) and pressure (760 torr) dry (STPD), liters of oxygen/min. See Box 4.7.

CO = Cardiac output, liters of blood/min

$AVDIF$ = Arterial-venous oxygen differential, liters of oxygen/liter of blood

While resting, the arterial oxygen content is 19 mL/100 mL of blood, while the venous oxygen content is 15 mL/100 mL. That is, for every 100 mL of blood passing through the muscles, the muscles get 4 mL of oxygen. In an emergency (e.g., fleeing from a tiger), the veins drop to 6 mL and the $AVDIF$ becomes 13 mL. The coronary blood supply, even under normal circumstances, has an $AVDIF$ of 17. Therefore, more oxygen for the heart must come from more blood, not an increase in the $AVDIF$.

5.4 Blood   Distribution   Redistribution is the fourth way of getting more blood to a muscle. During exercise, capillary density increases from a resting 200/mm^2 to 600. Muscle blood flow can increase from 2 mL/100 mL of tissue to 14 mL. Blood stored in the lungs can change from 500 mL to 1500. As exercise increases, the kidneys and intestines have less blood since it has been sent to the skin and muscles. If food is present in the stomach, cramps may result.

5.5 Debt   If "underdeposited" for aerobic oxygen, the body goes into oxygen debt. The muscles then draw upon the anaerobic oxygen stored in the blood (**oxygen**

| BOX | 4.7 | *Oxygen Uptake and Pulmonary Ventilation* |

In some circumstances, the response of an individual may be measured.

$$TOTMET = 60\ ENERGY\ (OXUPTK)$$

where

$TOTAL$ = Total metabolism, W

$ENERGY$ = Energy equivalent of 1 liter of oxygen, W-h/liter

Energy depends on the respiratory quotient (RQ), which in turn depends on the proportion of fat versus carbohydrate metabolized during the exercise.

= 5.36 for RQ = .83 (rest)

= 5.66 for RQ = .86 (exercise up to 60% of maximum rate)

= 6.40 for RQ = 1.00 (100% of maximum oxygen uptake)

$OXUPTK$ = Oxygen uptake, $\dot{V}O_2$, liters of oxygen/min

Pulmonary ventilation is:

$$PULVNT = (LAPLOX)\ (OXUPTK)$$

where

$PULVNT$ = Pulmonary ventilation, liters of air/min

$LAPLOX$ = Liters of air/liter of oxygen

= 20–25 at rest and for work less than 1.5 L/min

= 30–35 during maximal work

See the ERGO disk for calculations.

---

debt). However, the anaerobic supply is limited and it must be repaid—with "interest." See Figure 4.26.

6 CARDIOVASCULAR LIMITS

There are two questions: (1) How can one determine an individual's work capacity? and (2) What proportion of the capacity should be used?

6.1 Capacity   An individual's cardiovascular capacity is determined from **maximum oxygen uptake, $\dot{V}O_2$max**, mL/kg-min. $\dot{V}O_2$max is a product of cardiac output and A–V differential. Table 4.8 shows five fitness categories for U. S. males. Females typically have $\dot{V}O_2$max 15–30% below that of males so their critical values would be about 75% of males'. A male under age 30 in fair shape would have a value of 33 mL/kg-min. But a female under age 30 with a value of 33 would compare with 33/.75 = 44 and be in good shape.

How is $\dot{V}O_2$max determined? Four possibilities are given. The most accurate test (requires trained staff and equipment) is to do a maximal test on a treadmill or bicycle ergometer. The person exercises until exhaustion.

A submaximal test is the step test. There are two 5-min sessions of stepping up and down on a 40-cm step with 15 cycles/min for the first test and 25 cycles/min for the second test. The heart pulse is measured from 30 to 60 s after work stops, from 90 to 120 s, and from 150 to 180 s.

The last two tests use the distance a person can walk/run in a time period. The first is:

$$\dot{V}O_2max = -10.3 + 35.3\ DIST$$

where

$\dot{V}O_2max$ = Maximum oxygen uptake, mL/kg-min

$DIST$ = Distance run in 720 s, miles

Bunc (1994) recommends standardizing the distance at 2 km and recording the time:

$$\dot{V}O_2max = 85.7 - 251.3\ T\ \text{(for males)}$$
$$= 61.9 - 124.2\ T\ \text{(for females)}$$

where

T = Time to run 2 km, h

It should be mentioned that testing an individual's capability for screening purposes has become controversial in the United States due to discrimination laws.

| T A B L E | 4 . 8 |

Maximum oxygen consumption $\dot{V}O_2$max, mL/(kg-min) for U. S. males with various ages and degrees of cardiovascular fitness (Cooper, 1970).

| Cardiovascular | AGE, YEARS | | | |
Fitness	Under 30	30–39	40–49	50+
Very poor	<25.0	<25.0	<25.0	—
Poor	25.0–33.7	25.0–30.1	25.0–26.4	25.0
Fair	33.8–42.5	30.2–39.1	26.5–35.4	25.0–33.7
Good	42.6–51.5	39.2–48.0	35.5–45.5	33.8–43.0
Excellent	51.6+	48.1+	45.1+	43.1+

Source: The New Aerobics by Kenneth H. Cooper. Copyright © 1970 by Kenneth H. Cooper. Used by permission of Bantam Books, a division of Random House, Inc.

6.2 Proportion of Capacity

For an individual, what **proportion of capacity** is reasonable for work?

The general concept is to avoid anaerobic metabolism. Jorgensen (1985) recommends 50% for trained workers and 33% for untrained. If the task is primarily upper body work, the maximum should be about 30% less.

Mital et al. (1993) give lifting guidelines of 21–23% of uphill treadmill aerobic capacity or 28–29% of bicycle aerobic capacity. Note that lifting has static as well as dynamic components.

For shorter or longer periods, see Figure 4.27. Kodak recommends 33% for an 8-h shift, 30.5% for a 10-h shift, and 28% for a 12-h shift (Kodak, 1986; their Figures 11.1 and 14.1). Mital et al. (1993) reduce their 28–29% for bicycle capacity for 8 h to 23–24% for 12 h. Mital et al. (1994) reported that workers in an air-cargo firm's package handling section, hired for only a 2-h shift, worked at 43–50% of their maximum capacity.

Assuming you wish to exclude only a small percentage of the population, the above criteria are about 350 W, 5 kcal/min, and 100–120 heartbeats/min. Wisner (1989) states, "It is more or less universally admitted that heartbeat rates should not exceed 110 beats/min during the working day. During more intensive work periods, 130 beats/min should not be exceeded." Kroemer and Grandjean (1997) give, for extended periods of work, a maximum of 35 beats/min over resting level.

The fact that people can work hard does not mean they should. High-metabolic rate jobs are prime candidates for mechanization. After all, although scientists may be interested in physiology, engineers should be interested in productivity.

Reduce cardiovascular stress with both engineering and administrative solutions.

The primary engineering solution is to use a motor. For material handling, consider the use of forklifts, hoists, and powered conveyors. Workers should slide rather than lift objects (horizontal transfer rather than vertical transfer); lower objects instead of lifting them; use wheeled transfer (carts and dollies) instead of carrying loads; and use powered handtools. Balancers and manipulators can reduce static load. See Chapter 15.

Two administrative solutions are job rotation and part-time work. With job rotation, people periodically shift jobs during the day. With part-time work, the job is split among several people, each of whom works part of a shift. For example, Joe works for 4 h in the morning and Pete for 4 h in the afternoon. Or hire a large number of people so the entire task is done in part of a shift. For example, package handling for delivery services often is done in 2–3 h.

When setting work standards, industrial engineers usually add fatigue allowances. See Chapter 27.

6.3 Gender, Age, and Training Effects

6.3.1 *Gender* Physical work has **gender effects** on performance. The average female has a $\dot{V}O_2$max 15–30% lower than that of males because of a higher percent of body fat and a lower hemoglobin level. Since fat tissue has little blood, blood volume for an adult male averages 75 mL/kg and 65 for a female (it is 60 for a child). For the same age and body weight, females have lung volumes about 10% lower than males. Females also have lower hemoglobin content than males (13.9 vs 15.3), lower hematocrit (42 vs 47), and lower arterial oxygen content (16.7 mL/100 mL vs 19.2). Therefore, for submaximal work (oxygen uptake of <1.5 L/min), females need 9 liters of cardiac output to transport 1 liter of oxygen, while males require only 8.

Although these figures help explain the difference in athletic performance, in industrial work, cardiovascular differences between average males and females should have little importance since most industrial tasks should not be designed to require maximum cardiovascular output.

6.3.2 *Age* The body's physical performance peaks sometime around ages 25–30. After that, it is all "downhill" **(age effects)**. See Figures 4.28 and 4.29.

For the specific index of $\dot{V}O_2$max, Dehn and Bruce (1972) reported, from three studies by others, declines of 1.04, .94, and .93 mL/kg-min/year; in their own study, the decline was 1.32 for habitually inactive males and .65 for active males. Astrand et al. (1973) reported declines for Swedish physical education instructors, over a 21-year period, of .64 for males and .44 for females. Illmarinen (1992) says that the decline in $\dot{V}O_2$max after ages 20–25 is 1–2%/year, but there are large individual variations.

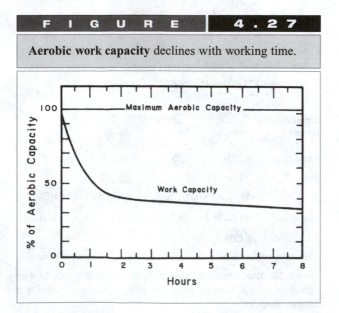

F I G U R E   4 . 2 7

Aerobic work capacity declines with working time.

Age effect on 9 physiological variables (Shock, 1962). Originally, we have surplus capacity but, as age increases, capacity eventually declines below requirements. (If you wish to calculate your life expectancy, select "Health Profile" at healthcentral.com.)

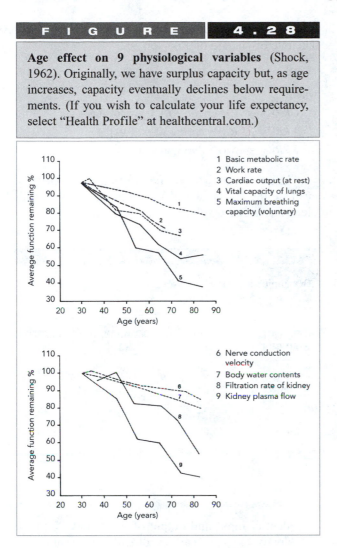

Age effect on 21 physiological variables (Astrand and Rodahl, 1986). Heart rate, oxygen pulse, and blood pressure are reported for a total metabolism of 100 W.

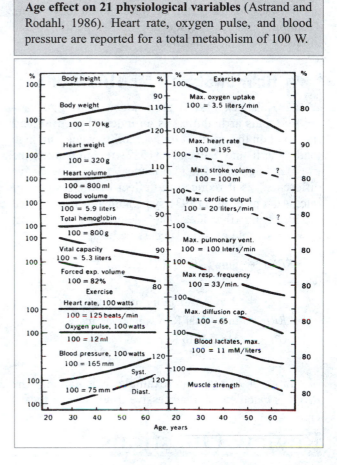

Bunc (1994) reports for European subjects:

$$\text{Male } \dot{V}O_2 max = 57.7 - .404 \, AGE$$
$$\text{Std. dev.} = 8.8 \text{ mL}$$
$$\text{Female } \dot{V}O_2 max = 46.6 - .344 \, AGE$$
$$\text{Std. dev.} = 6.4 \text{ mL}$$

where

$\dot{V}O_2 max$ = Mean maximum oxygen uptake, mL/kg-min

AGE = Age, years

Schacherer et al. (1992) used the variables of gender, age, and fat to predict treadmill VO_2max:

$$\text{Male } \dot{V}O_2 max = 66.734 - .315 \, AGE - .678 \, FAT$$
$$\text{Female } \dot{V}O_2 max = 58.094 - .356 \, AGE - .494 \, FAT$$

where

$PFAT$ = Body fat, percent

Jackson et al. (1992) emphasize that most of the decline is due to physical activity level and percent body fat, not aging. The aging effect was just .27 mL/kg-min/year.

$$\text{Male } \dot{V}O_2 max = 47.9 - .27 \, AGE + 3.41 \, SRPA - .20 \, PFAT - .09 \, (SRPA)(PFAT)$$

where

$SRPA$ = Self-report of physical activity

What does this decline in oxygen uptake mean for jobs? In summary, cardiovascular capacity to perform light to moderate physically exhausting work is not grossly age-dependent up to age 65, although capacity for hard, exhausting work is strongly age-dependent, with maximum capacity between ages 20 and 25.

6.3.3 Training Fitness has dimensions of cardiovascular endurance, muscle strength, and flexibility. Specific training techniques are more appropriately found in books on kinesiology or athletics. However, two statements can be made: (1) For training the cardiovascular system for cardiac output, train with large-muscle groups and (2) for training the strength of specific muscles, train the specific muscles. Some exercises strengthen weak muscles (work hardening, work conditioning), and other exercises stretch tight muscles and ligaments. If the work loads the muscles dynamically, relax and stretch them. If the work loads the muscles statically, the exercise should move them. Training variables include duration (repetitions) and intensity (weight, resistance).

7 RESPONSES TO MENTAL WORK

Kalsbeek (1968) proposed a heart rate variability (sinus arrhythmia) as an index of **mental load** (the load on the brain). Low variability went with high load. Sharit and Salvendy (1982) recommended the use of a "high pass filter" (the mean square successive difference) as it reduced the effect of the respiratory rate. Atsumi et al. (1993) systematically investigated the high pass filter idea. They determined it was best to use a sample of three successive beats:

$$RRV3 = \text{Sum } (RRI_i - RRI_m)^2/3$$

where

$RRV3$ = R to R variability of 3 beats, (ms)^2

RRI_i = Individual R to R interval, ms

RRI_m = Mean R to R interval for 3 successive beats, ms

Table 4.9 gives an example calculation. The $RRV3$ is calculated on successive triads of heartbeats, adding a new value and dropping the oldest value. The rate of change of a person is:

$$CRRV3 = (WRRV3 - RRRV3)/RRRV3$$

where

$CRRV3$ = Change in $RRV3$, proportion

$WRRV3$ = $RRV3$ during work, (ms)^2

$RRRV3$ = $RRV3$ during rest, (ms)^2

Atsumi, who worked for Toyota, used $RRV3$ to evaluate the stress caused by operating various vehicle controls and displays during driving.

T A B L E			4 . 9
Example calculation of *RRV3*.			

HEART RATE, BEATS/MIN	RRI, MS	DEVIATION, MS	DEVIATION SQUARED (MS)^2
91	659	−8	64
90	667	0	0
89	674	7	49
Mean	667		37.7

Review Questions

1. Where in the body do you have each of the following types of joints: ball and socket, hinge, pivot, and fixed?
2. What is a bursa?
3. Why is a prolapsed disc bad?
4. Sketch a 1st-, 2nd-, and 3rd-class lever for the human body.
5. Briefly describe how an electromyogram is obtained.
6. Sketch a schematic of the cardiovascular system, showing pulmonary and systemic circulation. Identify input and output of the following to the blood: oxygen, carbon dioxide, nutrients, and metabolic wastes.
7. Oxygen supply to a muscle is adjusted in what five ways?
8. List four ways by which heart rate can be measured.
9. Define cardiac output using a formula.
10. What is A–V differential?
11. Discuss the effect of age on the ability to do work.
12. What can you use as an index of mental load?

References

Alexander, R. Stride length and speed for adults, children and fossil hominids. *Am. J. Physical Anthropology,* Vol. 63, 23–27, 1984.

Andrews, R. The relation between measures of heart rate and measures of energy expenditure. *Am. Institute of Industrial Eng. Transactions,* Vol. 1, 1, 2–10, 1969.

Asmussen, E. and Heebol-Nielsen, K. Isometric muscle strength in relation to age in men and women. *Ergonomics,* Vol. 5, 167–69, 1962.

Astrand, P., Astrand, I., Hallbeck, I., and Kilbohm, A. Reduction in maximal oxygen uptake with age. *J. Applied Physiology,* Vol. 35, 5, 649–54, 1973.

Atsumi, B., Sigura, S., and Kimura, K. Evaluation of mental workload in vehicle driving by analysis of heart rate variability. *Proc. of Human Factors and Ergonomics Society,* 574–77, 1993.

Borg, G. Psychophysical scaling with applications in physical work and the perception of exertion. *Scand. J. Work Environ. Health,* Vol. 16 (Supplement 1), 55–58, 1990.

Brogmus, G. Effects of age and sex on speed and accuracy and hand movements and the refinements they suggest for Fitt's law. *Proc. of the Human Factors Society,* 208–12, 1991.

Brozek, J., Grande, F., Anderson, T., and Keys, A. Densitometric analysis of body composition: Revision of some quantitative assumptions. *Annals of N.Y. Academy of Science,* Vol. 110, 113–40, 1963.

Bunc, V. A simple method for estimating aerobic fitness. *Ergonomics,* Vol. 37, 1, 159–65, 1994.

Bunc, V., Segetova, J., and Safarikova, L. Walking in visually handicapped children and its energy cost. *Ergonomics,* Vol. 43, 10, 1571–77, 2000.

Chen, Y. and Lee, Y. Effect of combined and static workload on heart rate recovery cost. *Ergonomics,* Vol. 41, 1, 29–38, 1998.

Contreras, R., Rys, M., and Konz, S. Leg length discrepancy. In *The Ergonomics of Manual Work,* Marras, W., Karwowski, W., Smith, J., and Pacholski, L. (eds.). London: Taylor and Francis, 1993.

Cooper, K. *The New Aerobics.* New York: Bantam Books, 1970.

Cowgill, G. A formula for estimating the specific gravity of the human body. *Am. J. of Clinical Nutrition,* Vol. 5, 601–11, 1957.

Damon, A., Stoudt, H., and McFarland, R. *The Human Body in Equipment Design,* 226–27. Cambridge, MA: Harvard University Press, 1966.

Dehn, M. and Bruce, R. Longitudinal variations in maximum oxygen intake with age and activity. *J. of Applied Physiology,* Vol. 33, 805–07, 1972.

Ferguson, C. and Mason, S. Design strategies for maximizing human force capability when using spanners. *Int. J. of Industrial Ergonomics,* Vol. 2, 251–58, 1988.

Franson, C. and Winkel, J. Hand strength: The influence of grip span and grip type. *Ergonomics,* Vol. 34, 7, 881–92, 1991.

Freivalds, A. and Bise, C. Metabolic analysis of support personnel in low-seam coal-mines. *Int. J. of Industrial Ergonomics,* Vol. 8, 147–55, 1991.

Garg, A. Occupational biomechanics and low-back pain. In *Ergonomics: Low Back Pain, Carpal Tunnel Syndrome, and Upper Extremity Disorders in the Workplace,* Moore, J. and Garg, A. (eds.). Philadelphia: Hanley and Belfus, 1992.

Garg, A., Chaffin, D., and Herrin, G. Prediction of metabolic rates for manual material handling jobs. *American Ind. Hygiene Association J.,* Vol. 39, 661–74, 1978.

Garn, S. and Harper, R. Fat accumulation and weight gain in the adult male. *Human Biology,* Vol. 27, 1, 39–49, 1955.

Guyton, A. *Textbook of Medical Physiology.* Philadelphia: W. B. Sanders, 1961.

Haselgrave, C., Tracy, M., and Corlett, N. Industrial maintenance tasks involving overhead working. In *Contemporary Ergonomics 1987,* Megaw, E. (ed.). London: Taylor and Francis, 1987.

Haselgrave, C., Tracy, M., and Corlett, N. Force exertion in awkward working postures—Strength capability while twisting or working overhead. *Ergonomics,* Vol. 40, No. 12, 1335–62, 1997a.

Haselgrave, C., Tracy, M., and Corlett, N. Strength capability when kneeling. *Ergonomics,* Vol. 40, No. 12, 1363–79, 1997b.

Hsiao, H. and Simeonov, P. Preventing falls from roofs: A critical review. *Ergonomics,* Vol. 44, 5, 537–61, 2001.

Hunsicker, P. Arm strength at selected degrees of elbow flexion. *WADC Technical Report 54–548.* Wright Patterson AFB, OH, 1955.

Illmarinen, J. Job design for the aged with regard to decline in their maximal aerobic capacity: Part II The scientific basis for the guide. *Int. J. of Industrial Ergonomics,* Vol. 10, 65–77, 1992.

ILO 8996. *Ergonomics—Determination of Metabolic Rate.* Geneva, Switzerland: ILO, 1990.

Jackson, A., Beard, A., Wier, L., and Stuteville, A. Multivariate model for defining changes in maximal physical working capacity of men, ages 25 to 70 years. *Proc. of the Human Factors Society,* 171–74, 1992.

Jorgensen, K. Permissible loads based on energy expenditure measurements. *Ergonomics,* Vol. 28, 1, 365–69, 1985.

Jorgensen, M., Riley, M., Cochran, D., and Bishu, R. Maximum forces in simulated meat cutting tasks. *Proc. of the Human Factors Society,* 641–45, 1989.

Kalsbeek, J. Measurement of mental workload and of acceptable workload: Possible applications in industry. *Int. J. of Production Research,* Vol. 7, 1, 33–45, 1968.

Kim, J.-Y. and Jung, M.-C. The measurement of sensitivity of numerical parameters in quantification of local muscle fatigue. *Proc. of the HFES,* 936–39, 1998.

Klieber, M. *The Fire of Life.* New York: Wiley, 1961.

Kodak, E. *Ergonomic Design for People at Work: Vol. 2.* New York: Van Nostrand-Reinholt, 1986.

Konz, S., Rys, M., and Harris, C. The effect of standing barefoot on a hard tile surface. *Proc. of 10th Int. Ergonomics Association.* London: Taylor and Francis, 1988.

Konz, S. Ergonomics of the foot. *The Industrial Ergonomics Handbook.* Boca Raton, FL: CRC Press, 1999.

Kroemer, K. and Grandjean, E. *Fitting the Task to the Man,* 5th ed. London: Taylor and Francis, 1997.

Kroemer, K., Kroemer, H., and Kroemer-Elbert, K. *Ergonomics,* 2nd ed. Upper Saddle River, NJ: Prentice Hall, 82–86, 2001.

Kumar, S. The effect of sustained spinal load on intra-abdominal pressure and EMG characteristics of trunk muscles. *Ergonomics,* Vol. 40, 12, 1312–34, 1997.

Kumar, S. Theories of musculoskeletal injury causation. *Ergonomics,* Vol. 44, 1, 17–47, 2001.

Krag, M., Cohen, M., Haugh, L., and Pope, M. Body height change during upright and recumbent posture. *Spine,* Vol. 15, 3, 202–07, 1990.

Laubach, L. Comparative muscular strength of men and women: A review of the literature. *Aviation, Space and Environmental Medicine,* Vol. 47, 5, 534–42, 1976.

Ljunggren, G. Observer ratings of perceived exertion in relation to self-ratings and heart rate. *Applied Ergonomics,* Vol. 17, 2, 117–25, 1986.

Luttgens, K., Deutsch, H., and Hamilton, N. *Kinesiology: Scientific Basis of Human Motion,* 8th ed. Dubuque, IA: Brown and Benchmark, 1992.

Maynard, H., Stegmerten, G., and Schwab, J. *Methods-Time Measurement.* New York: McGraw-Hill, 1948.

Mital, A., Nicholson, A., and Ayoub, M. M. *A Guide to Manual Material Handling.* London: Taylor and Francis, 1993.

Mital, A., Hamid, F., and Brown, M. Physical fatigue in high and very high frequency manual material handling: Perceived exertion and physiological factors. *Human Factors,* Vol. 36, 2, 219–31, 1994.

Morrisey, S., Ayoub, M., George, C., and Ramsey, J. Male and female responses to stoopwalking tasks. *25th Proc. of Human Factors Society,* 445–49, 1981.

Myung, R. and Smith, J. The effect of load carrying and floor contaminants on slip and fall parameters. *Ergonomics,* Vol. 40, 2, 235–46, 1997.

Nishi, Y. and Gagge, A. Direct evaporation of convective heat transfer coefficient of naphtalene sublimation. *J. Applied Physiology,* Vol. 29, 830, 1970.

Nodeland, H., Inemansen, R., Reed, R., and Aukland, K. A telemetric technique for studies of venous pressure in the human leg during different positions and activities. *Clinical Physiology,* Vol. 3, 573–76, 1983.

Pandolf, K., Giovani, B., and Goldman, R. Predicting energy expenditure with loads while standing or walking very slowly. *Applied Physiology: Respirat. Environ,* Vol. 43, 4, 577–81, 1977.

Pandolf, K., Haisman, M., and Goldman, R. Metabolic energy expenditure and terrain coefficients for walking on snow. *Ergonomics,* Vol. 19, 683–90, 1976.

Parenmark, G., Malmkvist, A., and Ortengren, R. Ergonomic moves in an engineering industry: Effects on sick leave frequency, labor turnover and productivity. *Int. J. of Industrial Ergonomics,* Vol. 11, 291–300, 1993.

Peters, R. *The Ecological Implications of Body Size.* Cambridge, MA: Cambridge University Press, 1989.

Pollack, A. and Wood, E. Venous pressure in the saphenous vein at the ankle in man during exercise and changes in posture. *J. Applied Physiology,* Vol. 1, 649–62, March 1949.

Putz-Anderson, V. (ed.) *Cumulative Trauma Disorders.* London: Taylor and Francis, 1988.

Redfern, M. and Rhoades, T. Fall prevention in industry using slip resistance testing. In *Occupational Ergonomics,* Bhattacharya, A. and McGloughlin, J. (eds.), 463–76. New York: M. Decker, 1996.

Rhodes, S. Age-related differences in work attitudes and behavior—A review and conceptual analysis. *Psychological Bulletin,* Vol. 93, 328–67, 1983.

Ring, L. *Facts on Backs.* Loganville, GA: Institute Press, 1981.

Roozbahar, A., Bosker, G., and Richardson, M. A theoretical model to estimate some ergonomic parameters from age, height, and weight. *Ergonomics,* Vol. 22, 1, 43–58, 1979.

Rowell, L. Human cardiovascular adjustments to exercise and thermal stress. *Physiological Reviews,* Vol. 54, 1, 75–159, 1974.

Satzler, L., Satzler, C., and Konz, S. Standing aids. *Proc. of the Ayoub Symposium,* Texas Tech University, Lubbock, TX, 29–31, 1993.

Scanton, P. and McMaster, J. Momentary distribution of forces under the foot. *J. Biomechanics,* Vol. 9, 45–48, 1976.

Schacherer, C., Rowe, A., and Jackson, A. Development of prediction models for physical work capacity: Practical and theoretical implications. *Proc. of the Human Factors Society,* 674–78, 1992.

Sharit, J. and Salvendy, G. External and internal attentional environments II: Reconsideration of the relationship between sinus arrhythmia and information load. *Ergonomics,* Vol. 25, 2, 121–32, 1982.

Shock, N. The physiology of aging. *Scientific American,* Vol. 206, 100–10, 1962.

Soule, R. and Goldman, R. Energy cost of loads carried on the head, hands, or feet. *J. of Applied Physiology,* Vol. 27, 687–90. Nov. 1980.

Stolwijk, J. Mathematical model of thermoregulation. In *Physiological and Behavioral Temperature Regulation,* Chapter 48, J. Hardy, A. Gagge, and J. Stolwijk (eds.). Springfield, IL: Charles C. Thomas, 1970.

Suter, P., Schutz, Y., and Jequier, E. The effect of ethanol on fat storage in healthy subjects. *New England J. of Medicine,* Vol. 326, 983–87, 1992.

Tanaka, S. and McGlothlin, J. A conceptual quantitative model for prevention of work-related carpal tunnel syndrome (CTS). *Int. J. of Industrial Ergonomics,* Vol. 11, 181–93, 1993.

Templer, J. *The Staircase: Studies of Hazards, Falls and Safer Design.* Cambridge, MA: MIT Press, 1992.

Udo, H., Otain, T., Udo, A., and Yoshinaga, F. An electromyographic study of two different types of ballpoint pens. *Industrial Health,* Vol. 38, 47–56, 2000.

U. S. Army. *AR 600-9 (Section III Weight Control).* 13 Feb 1987.

Van der Walt, W. and Wyndham, C. An equation for prediction of energy expenditure of walking and running. *J. of Applied Physiology,* Vol. 34, 5, 559–63, 1973.

Waldman, D. and Avolio, B. A meta-analysis of age differences in job performance. *J. of Applied Psychology,* Vol. 71, 1, 33–38, 1986.

Ward, R., Danziger, F., Bonica, J., Allen, G., and Tolas, A. Cardiovascular effects of change in posture. *Aerospace Medicine,* (now *Aviation Space and Environmental Medicine*), Vol. 37, 257–59, March 1966.

Warwick, D., Novak, G., Schultz, A., and Berkson, M. Maximum voluntary strengths of adult males in some lifting, pushing, and pulling activities. *Ergonomics,* Vol. 23, 1, 49–54, 1980.

Wilmore, J. and Behnke, A. An anthropometric estimation of body density and lean body weight in young men. *J. of Applied Physiology,* Vol. 7, 1, 25–31, 1969.

Wisner, A. Variety of physical characteristics in industrially developing countries—Ergonomic consequences. *Int. J. of Industrial Ergonomics,* Vol. 4, 117–38, 1989.

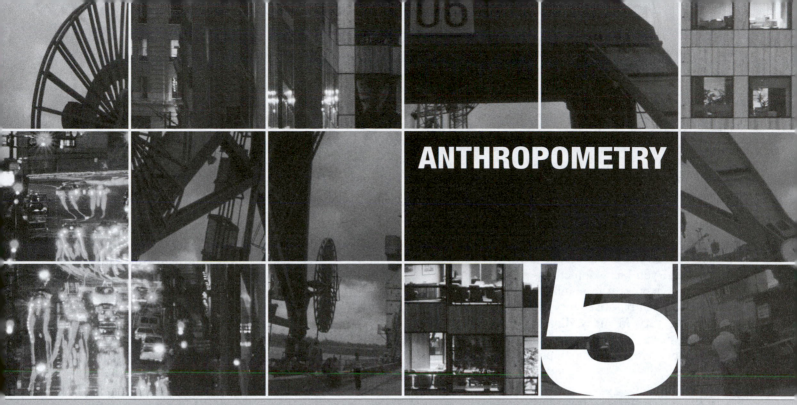

ANTHROPOMETRY

ANTHROPOMETRY

1 Fit the Job to the Person
2 Population Values
3 Statistical Calculations

Overview

Anthropometric data permit the designer to design to fit the individual. Design to include as large a proportion of the population as possible—that is, minimize the number of people excluded by your design.

Key Concepts

anthropometry

DuBois surface area

ergonomics

exclude few

population percentile

principle of similitude

selection/job modification

surface area/volume

FIT THE JOB TO THE PERSON

1.1 Variability   **Anthropometry,** from the Greek *anthropos* (man) and *metrein* (to measure), explains how people vary. **Ergonomics** also comes from the Greek: *erg* (work) and *nomos* (study of). A more formal definition of ergonomics is "a body of knowledge about human abilities, human limitations, and other human characteristics that are relevant to design."

This chapter will quantify human variability—put it into numbers. As Lord Kelvin said, "When you can measure what you are speaking about and express it in numbers, you know something about it; but when you cannot express it in numbers, your knowledge is of a meager and unsatisfactory kind."

People vary in many dimensions, for example, initiative, needs, dexterity, intelligence, visual acuity, imagination, determination, upper back strength, age, and leg length.

1.2 Selection Versus Job Modification

Assume a heavy box is to be moved from point A to point B. Realizing that people vary, there are two basic strategies.

One alternative is to use **selection.** That is, from the population of workers, select a strong person. This alternative can be labeled *fit the person to the job.* The other alternative is **job modification** so that almost everyone can do it. This alternative can be labeled *fit the job to the person* or, more personally, *fitting the job to you.* In general, follow the second alternative, as the key to our improved living standard has been to challenge the environment and make the environment adjust to people rather than people adjust to the environment.

Given the decision to modify the job, one question is how much modification is necessary. That is, how much weight can employees lift? Or in other jobs, how far can they reach? How much space do they need?

1.3 Exclude as Few as Possible

Sometimes you need to design for a "special population"; for example, Morrissey (1998) gives recommendations for pregnant workers. (Pregnant women are like the canary in a mine. Whatever is affecting them also affects the workforce as a whole. They are the most vulnerable.) Nevertheless, designers should design to **exclude few** so that as many people as possible can do the job. Not only does this minimize the number of people excluded but also this design strategy tends to make the job easier—benefiting everyone, not just the person who might have been excluded.

The percent of people to exclude depends on the tradeoff between the seriousness of exclusion versus the cost of inclusion. The more serious the exclusion, the smaller the percent that are excluded. For exam-

ple, if a button is outside the normal reach distance but the operator can reach it by stretching, it is not good but it may still be allowed. However, if a control requires more strength to operate than the operator can exert, that is not allowable.

The cost of including a larger percent of the population may be negligible or it may be high. In most applications a taller door (so people don't hit their heads) adds little expense; however, if the door is in a warship and weakens the structure, the cost may be high. In a fighter airplane, a taller, heavier pilot requires a larger cockpit, which increases the cross-section, which may incur severe performance penalties. Thus, most military organizations have a height restriction on fighter pilots.

Or consider the weight of a tote pan to be used in a factory. If the weight is so low that a very high percentage of the population can move it easily, more tote pans/day must be moved. That is, 50 pans each weighing 10 kg are moved instead of 40 pans each weighing 12.5 kg. The engineer will have to balance the benefits of less weight/pan versus more pans to move.

An excluded **population percentile** can be the upper, lower, or both upper and lower portions of the population. For example, a door might exclude the tallest .1% of the population. For manual dexterity, a test might exclude those with the least dexterity. For a factory job, a firm might exclude those who score low on an intelligence test (who can't learn how to do the job) *and* those who score high (who may become bored and quit).

Note that if the design is for the mean (50th percentile) instead of, for example, the 1st or 99th percentile, many are eliminated. This is most obvious for reach distances. For example, if a pedal is designed so the average person can barely reach it, 50% can't reach it. Because of the relatively low coefficient of variation of human dimensions (about 5%), however, accommodating more people doesn't require much change in physical dimensions.

1.4 Design Recommendations

While this chapter focuses on dimensions of the human body, later chapters and the ERGO disk give design data.

POPULATION VALUES

2.1 Dimensions   Figures 5.1 and 5.2 give technical descriptions for body postures. Designers should not design using their personal dimensions or capabilities. Only slightly better is designing using the dimensions/capabilities of the people in the designer's department; although using a variety of people gives some variability, mean and variability of fellow engineers is unlikely to be the mean and variability of users. Thus, the first step is to define the user popula-

F I G U R E	5 . 1

Terminology for body position descriptions.

PLANES	DESCRIPTION
Sagittal:	Divides body into left and right
■ Medial (Y):	Close to center
■ Lateral (+Y or −Y):	Away from medial on left (+Y) or right (−Y)
Coronal:	Divides body into front and back
■ Anterior (+X):	Front or ventral side
■ Posterior (−X):	Back or dorsal side
Transverse:	Divides body into top and bottom
■ Superior (+Z):	Closer to head
■ Inferior (−Z):	Closer to feet

LIMBS	
Proximal:	Closer to torso
Distal:	Farther from torso

WRIST/HAND MOTIONS

Flexion (bend hand down; palm toward front of wrist) versus **extension** (bend hand up; palm toward back of wrist)
Radial deviation (bend horizontal hand toward thumb) versus **ulnar deviation** (bend horizontal hand toward little finger)
Pronation (rotation toward palm down) versus **supination** (rotation toward palm up)

tion. The focus of this book is on the individual at work. See Kroemer et al. (2001) for a detailed discussion of children and of seniors. Pheasant (1996) has tables for infants and children of various ages as well as tables for adults from England and other countries.

Chaffin and Faraway (2000), in a study of vehicles, showed that movement of the shoulder and torso can have great effects on reach distances; the following data do not consider shoulder and torso movements.

Table 5.1 gives some useful physical dimensions of the nude U. S. adult civilian population (Kroemer et al., 1994). The data were gathered in 1988 using U. S. Army personnel (Gordon et al., 1989).

F I G U R E	5 . 2

Terminology for hand movements and positions. Radial/ulnar deviation (radial toward the thumb, ulnar toward the little finger) and flexion/extension (flexion toward the palm, extension toward the back of the hand) occur in the wrist joint. Pronation/supination is a function of the radius rotating around the ulna in the forearm. Pronation is "thumbs down"; supination is "thumbs up."

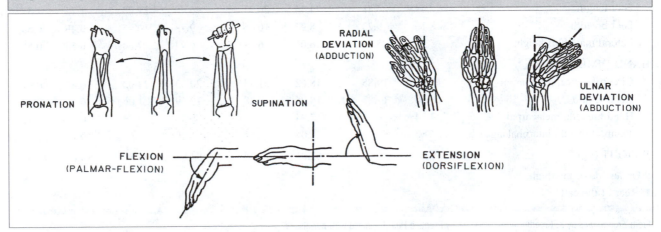

T A B L E	5 . 1

Body dimensions (cm) of nude U. S. adult civilians (Kroemer et al., 1994). Average height in the U. S. has been reasonably stable since the 1960s.

	\multicolumn{6}{c}{PERCENTILES}		
	\multicolumn{2}{c}{5th}	\multicolumn{2}{c}{50th}	\multicolumn{2}{c}{95th}	\multicolumn{2}{c}{Standard Deviation}
	Fem.	Male	Fem.	Male	Fem.	Male	Fem.	Male
HEIGHTS (Above Floor)								
Stature (height)	152.78	164.69	162.94	175.58	173.73	186.65	6.36	6.68
Eye height	141.52	152.82	151.61	163.39	162.13	174.29	6.25	6.57
Shoulder (acromial) height	124.09	134.16	133.36	144.25	143.20	154.56	5.79	6.20
Elbow height	92.63	99.52	99.79	107.25	107.40	115.28	4.48	4.81
Wrist height	72.79	77.79	79.03	84.65	85.51	91.52	3.86	4.15
Crotch height	70.02	76.44	77.14	83.72	84.58	91.64	4.41	4.62
HEIGHTS (Above Seat)								
Height (sitting)	79.53	85.45	85.20	91.39	91.02	97.16	2.49	3.56
Eye height (sitting)	68.46	73.50	73.87	79.20	79.43	84.80	3.32	3.42
Shoulder (acromial) height (sitting)	50.91	54.85	55.55	59.78	60.36	64.63	2.86	2.96
Elbow height (sitting)	17.57	18.41	22.05	23.06	26.44	27.37	2.68	2.72
Thigh height (sitting)	14.04	14.86	15.89	16.82	18.02	18.99	1.21	1.26
Knee height (sitting)	47.40	51.44	51.54	55.88	56.02	60.57	2.63	2.79
Popliteal height (sitting)*	35.13	39.46	38.94	43.41	42.94	47.63	2.37	2.49
DEPTHS								
Forward (thumbtip) reach	67.67	73.92	73.46	80.08	79.67	86.70	3.64	3.92
Buttock-knee distance (sitting)	54.21	56.90	58.89	61.64	63.98	66.74	2.96	2.99
Buttock-popliteal distance (sitting)**	44.00	45.81	48.17	50.04	52.77	54.55	2.66	2.66
Elbow-fingertip distance	40.62	44.79	44.29	48.40	48.25	52.42	2.34	2.33
Chest depth	20.86	20.96	23.94	24.32	27.78	28.04	2.11	2.15
BREADTHS								
Forearm-forearm breadth	41.47	47.74	46.85	54.61	52.84	62.06	3.47	4.36
Hip breadth (sitting)	34.25	32.87	38.45	36.68	43.22	41.16	2.72	2.52
HEAD DIMENSIONS								
Head circumference	52.25	54.27	54.62	56.77	57.05	59.35	1.46	1.54
Head breadth	13.66	14.31	14.44	15.17	15.27	16.08	0.49	0.54
Interpupillary breadth	5.66	5.88	6.23	6.47	6.85	7.10	0.36	0.37
FOOT DIMENSIONS								
Foot length	22.44	24.88	24.44	26.97	26.46	29.20	1.22	1.31
Foot breadth	8.16	9.23	8.97	10.06	9.78	10.95	0.49	0.53
Lateral malleolus height	5.23	5.84	6.06	6.71	6.97	7.64	0.53	0.55
HAND DIMENSIONS								
Circumference, metacarpal	17.25	19.85	18.62	21.38	20.03	23.03	0.85	0.97
Hand length	16.50	17.87	18.05	19.38	19.69	21.06	0.97	0.98
Hand breadth, metacarpal	7.34	8.36	7.94	9.04	8.56	9.76	0.38	0.42
Thumb breadth, interphalangeal	1.86	2.19	2.07	2.41	2.29	2.65	0.13	0.14
WEIGHT (kg)	39.2	57.7	62.01	78.49	84.8	99.3	13.8	12.6

*Underside of the thigh.
**Rear of the calf.

From *Ergonomics* by K. Kroemer et al., © 1994 by Prentice Hall. Reprinted with permission.

Marras and Kim's (1993) data on Midwestern U. S. industrial workers (384 males, 124 females) showed that the army data were a good representation of the industrial workforce except for weight and abdominal dimensions. Mean male weight was 182.3 lbs (versus 173.0 for the army); mean female weight was 139.2 lbs (versus 136.7). For adjustment of nude data, they recommend:

- Shoe height adds 1 in. (2.5 cm) for males and .6 in. (1.5 cm) for females.
- Clothing increases torso breadths by .3 in. (.8 cm).
- Clothing increases torso circumferences by .6 in. (1.5 cm).
- Shoes add 2.0 lb (.9 kg) of weight.
- Clothing (except shoes) adds 1.0 lb (.45 kg) of weight.

Annis and McConville (1996) add, for normal industrial clothing, 4.7 cm for stature, 1.9 cm for sitting height, and 3.4 cm for knee height. Add 6.5 cm for chest depth, 13.0 cm for forearm-forearm breadth, and 14.3 for hip breadth, sitting. Add 3.4 cm for foot length and 1.1 cm for foot breadth.

Females tend to be smaller than males. But, if you compare the 50th percentile male versus female in Table 5.1, the ratio is not constant for various dimensions; for sitting hip breadth, females are larger than males.

Military populations tend to be selected (young, healthy, fit), and so are biased estimators of the civilian population. Americans are clearly, on average, taller than Japanese and Chinese. (See Juergens et al. [1990] and the computer program accompanying this book for 19 dimensions on 143 populations.) That is, design for an American population may not be appropriate for a non-American population. However, the U. S. population certainly is not homogeneous. In addition to the male–female difference, there are ethnic differences (people of Swedish descent are taller than those of Mexican descent), racial differences (African Americans are taller than Asians; African Americans of a given stature have longer limbs than white Americans), occupational differences (farmers are stronger than bookkeepers), and so forth. Naturally, adults differ from children. In addition, older (e.g., over 50) people tend to be weaker than those age 30; after 30, people even begin to shrink in height (due to changes in spinal disc thickness). In addition, clothing will increase many of the dimensions, especially with winter outdoor clothing.

A large part of the variation in human stature is in the length of the legs; the torso is relatively constant in height (White, 1975). There is a desire to predict various body dimensions from a person's height. Unfortunately, most body dimensions have coefficients of determination versus height of less than 50%—that is, the statistical relationship is poor. However, approximations sometimes may be useful. Annis and McConville (1996) give, for the ratio of the dimension to stature height, 128% for maximum overhead reach, 122% for fist height for overhead reach, 74% for kneeling height, and 64% for squatting height.

Note that because a person is tall does not mean that the person has high intelligence. A short person does not necessarily have low manual dexterity. That is, because a person is average in one characteristic does not mean the person is average in another characteristic—even if all the characteristics are dimensions. For example, a person who is at the 50th percentile in height may be 40% in reach distance and 75% in weight.

If only male anthropometric data for a population are available, the female dimensions can be estimated as 93% of the corresponding male dimensions; males and females differ primarily in leg length rather than torso or arm length (van Schoor and Konz, 1996; Annis, 1996).

Between species, however, there is a general relationship between size and shape—the **principle of similitude.** See Box 5.1 for the principle of similitude.

2.2 Strengths On average, females have 63% of the isometric strength of males, but the ratio depends on part of the body (60% for the arms, 64% for the trunk, and 72% for the legs). For equal lean body weights, females average 90% of male strengths (Annis, 1996). The 63% value means that women are far more exposed to risk of injury when muscular work is required.

Strengths for a specific muscle group vary greatly. Expect the coefficient of variation (standard deviation/mean) to be 50% or more. Strengths are greatly affected by the limb (arm versus leg), by direction exerted, and, for arms, by whether it is the preferred hand. The average difference in muscular strength between symmetrical muscle groups is 5%–11%.

Table 4.2 gives arm strengths. Tables 16.1 and 16.8 give handgrip strengths, and Table 16.2 gives finger strengths. Figures 17.2 and 17.11 give leg strengths. Figure 4.24 shows the effect of age.

To summarize: (1) The leg is approximately 3 times stronger than the arm. (2) Direction is very important, with arm force at the nonoptimum angles being 50%–80% of the force at the optimum angle. (3) The nonpreferred arm averages 60%–150% of the strength of the preferred arm, depending on the angle and direction. (4) There seems to be no appreciable difference between the strength of the left and right legs.

BOX	5.1	*Principle of Similitude*

The basic concept of the principle of similitude is that, due to the ratio of **surface area/volume,** for every volume, there is an optimum shape (Haldane, 1928).

- For a cylinder's (tube, pipe) ratio of surface area/volume (ignoring ends):

$$2 \, (pi) \, rL/((pi) \, r^2 \, L = 2/r = 4/d \qquad (1)$$

- For a sphere's ratio:

$$4 \, (pi) \, r^2 \, / \, (4/3)(pi) \, r^3 = 3/r = 6/d \qquad (2)$$

- For a cube's ratio:

$$6L^2/L^3 = 6/L \qquad (3)$$

To minimize surface area/volume, use a sphere. Within a cylinder, sphere, or cube, smaller diameters have more area in proportion to volume. Greater areas maximize exchange with the "environment."

What if you scale a specific shape up or down? Consider a man 2 m tall. If you made him a giant of 20 m, then his weight would increase by 10 (for height) × 10 (for width) × 10 (for thickness) = 1000. However, his leg bone cross-section increases only by 10 × 10 = 100, so with every step, the stress on the leg is 10 times what it would be in a normal-size human. So, when he runs, his leg breaks! If trees increase in size, their limit is approximately 100 m, due to the stress of the wind on their increased surface area.

Consider the giant grasshoppers often found in grade D movies. Grasshoppers breathe through their skin. Giant grasshoppers would increase oxygen intake by the square and mass by the cube and so would die of oxygen starvation. Klieber's Rule, for a variety of animals, is that metabolic rate = k (body weight)$^{3/4}$. The exponent is 3/4, not 2/3, as larger animals have different shapes than smaller animals.

Roberts (1975) reported that people living in cold climates tend to be "spherical," which minimizes their surface area-to-volume ratio. However,

in the tropics you want to be more like a radiator than a boiler, so long arms and legs are good. Elephants increase their surface area through "fins"—commonly known as ears. Gloves (i.e., separate fingers) lose more heat than mittens, due to their greater surface area/volume. The surface area/volume of the hand as a whole is 1.1, but individual fingers have a surface area/volume of around 2.0 (Mignano and Konz, 1994).

From a biomechanics viewpoint, big people not only have larger muscles (increasing by the cube) but also a longer moment arm (length of arm or leg), and so they can exert much more force or torque than small people.

For buildings occupied by people, the sphere is not generally used, even though it minimizes surface area in relation to volume. But the sphere is popular for storage of liquids and gases because it minimizes material cost and energy exchange with the environment. A popular compromise is a cylinder (e.g., for storage of pressurized gas). A dome minimizes material use for volume enclosed and strongly resists external pressure (although weaker for internal pressure); thus, it finds applications in military bunkers and igloos.

The cube is an efficient enclosure for cartons and boxes.

The shape used for industrial buildings is the square or rectangle with a wall height of about 15 feet (low bay) or about 30 feet (high bay). For heating and ventilating ducts, for the same air flow, round ducts have less perimeter than rectangular ducts; this results in less friction (i.e., smaller fans and thus lower energy costs) and heat transfer to the environment.

See Hanna and Konz (2004) for a more extensive discussion of surface area/volume and of perimeter/area.

2.3 Other Characteristics

2.3.1 *Weight and center of mass* See Table 5.2. Kaleps et al. (1984) give mass distribution properties of the head.

2.3.2 *Manual dexterity* In general, for "simple" tasks (such as manual handling), the range of performance from the least qualified to the most qualified is small (say 2); for the entire population the range might be 4 or 5. For complex tasks (such as computer programming), the performance range of those qualified for the job would be much larger (say 50).

2.3.3 *Surface area* Body surface area from the DuBois formulas (based on 5 subjects) is:

$$DBSA = .007\,184 \, (HT)^{.725} \, (WT)^{.425}$$

where

$DBSA$ = **DuBois surface area,** m^2

HT = Height, cm

WT = Weight, kg

Mitchell et al. (1971) recommend a corrected formula (based on an improved measurement technique and 16 subjects):

T A B L E	5 . 2

Weight and center of mass for various body segments in adult males (Clauser et al., 1969).

BODY SEGMENT	WEIGHT OF SEGMENT/ TOTAL BODY WEIGHT	STANDARD ERROR	LOCATION OF CENTER OF MASS AS RATIO OF SEGMENT SIZE
Head	7.28	.16	.46 (top of head/ht of head)
			.40 (back of head/head length)
Trunk	50.70	.57	.38 (suprastern/trunk length)
Hand	0.65	.02	.18 (meta 3/styl-meta 3 length)
			.56 (med aspect/hand breadth)
Forearm	1.61	.04	.39 (radiale/rad-styl length)
			.49 (ant aspect/ap at cm)
Forearm + hand	2.27	.06	.63 (radiale/rad styl length)
			.52 (ant aspect/ap at cm)
Upper arm	2.63	.06	.51 (acrom/acrom-rad length)
			.51 (ant aspect/ap at cm)
Total arm	4.90	.09	.41 (acromion/arm length)
Both arms and hands	9.80		
Foot	1.47	.03	.45 (heel/foot length)
			.54 (sole/sphyrion height)
Calf	4.35	.10	.37 (tibiale/calf length)
			.42 (ant aspect/ap at cm)
Calf + foot	5.82	.12	.47 (tibiale/tibiale height)
			.33 (ant aspect/ap at cm)
Thigh	10.27	.23	.37 (trochanterion/thigh length)
			.53 (ant aspect/ap at cm)
Total leg	16.10	.26	.38 (troc/trochanteric height)
			.63 (ant aspect/ap at cm)
Both legs and feet	32.20		
	99.98		

An improved estimate can be made for some segments using the following equations where X is total body weight, kg:

SEGMENT	EQUATION	STANDARD ERROR
Trunk	$.551 X - 2.837$	1.33
Head and trunk	$.580 X + .009$	1.36
Total arm	$.047 X + .132$	.23
Upper arm	$.030 X - .238$	.14
Thigh	$.120 X - 1.123$	.54
Foot	$.009 X + .369$	.06

$$SA = .208 + .945\ DBSA \text{ or}$$
$$= .208 + .006\ 789\ (HT)^{.725}\ (WT)^{.425}$$

where

SA = surface area, m^2

$DBSA$ = DuBois surface area, m^2

Van Graan (1969) reported that the total body area can be apportioned into two arms and hands = 18.1% (hands 5.1% and arms 13.0%), the two legs and feet = 35.9% (legs 29.8%, feet 6.1%), the trunk = 37.5%, and head and neck = 8.5%. Some people remember the division by the "rule of 9s": head and neck = 9%, each hand–arm = 9%, each leg–foot = 18%, and trunk = 36%. Mignano and Konz (1994) reported one clenched fist is 1.6% of body surface area, one hand open with fingers joined is 2.7%, and one hand open with fingers spread is 3.1%.

2.3.4 *Age* Box 5.2 discusses the effect of age.

5.2   *Age of Workforce*

Life expectancy (and the number of older people) has been going up for 300 years. But the decline in the number of young people is something new. The replacement birth rate is 2.1/woman (the extra .1 allows for deaths before child bearing). In 2000, it was 1.3 in both Japan and Germany; rates are similar in most of Europe. The U. S. rate is 2.1.

Thus, the workers will have to come from immigration and/or people working longer. Working longer could be more hours/year or more years/life-time. Both seem to be occurring. The more hours/year is occurring especially in the managerial and professional workforce. The more years/lifetime, contrasted with the desire of some to retire "early," has resulted in a blurring of the traditional retirement age of 65. Some people retire before 65 and some work into their 70s—especially in part-time work. Thus, ergonomists will have to consider older workers in their job designs.

2.3.5 *Personal space*   The space around an individual, called "personal space," has four zones:

- Intimate (0–18 inches)
- Personal (18–48 inches)
- Social (4–12 ft)
- Public (>12 ft)

The exact boundaries vary with nationalities, gender (females are comfortable with smaller zones), and how well you know the other person. A related concept is territoriality (from animals who mark out their territory); personal space is a temporary rather than long-term occupancy of space. Thus, the amount of space required for groups of individuals depends not only on the physical size of the individuals but, perhaps more important, on their personal space and territory.

2.3.6 *Aisles/corridors and doors*   Aisle width depends upon whether the aisle is for people only or for people plus vehicles (Hanna and Konz, 2004). For one-way traffic and people only, 3 ft is a minimum. Use 6 ft if there is a door opening *into* the aisle from one side; use 8 ft if doors open into the aisle from both sides. For two-way traffic, double the dimensions. If doors open *from* the aisle into individual offices, use 6 ft. Aisles for people only (such as in offices) need not be straight; aisles for vehicles plus people should be straight.

Corridors are aisles with walls. Because people can step outside of aisles to avoid oncoming traffic, aisles can be narrower than corridors. Shoulder width is the key factor. See Table 5.3.

For doors, see Table 5.4. See Hanna and Konz (2004) for more on aisles and doors.

2.4 Anthropometric Sources   For anthropometric techniques, see Kroemer et al. (1994) and Roebuck (1995). For data, see Gordon et al. (1989) and the computer program accompanying this book.

STATISTICAL CALCULATIONS

3.1 Normal   Distribution   Probably the most useful single descriptor is the population mean. Although many anthropometric characteristics are not precisely fitted by a normal distribution, the normal distribution will give answers that are close enough, and so the normal distribution is used. Assuming the normal distribution allows us further to state that the mean is equivalent to the 50th percentile. The normal distribution has the further useful characteristic of being symmetrical.

The absolute variability of a population is given by the standard deviation, abbreviated S.D. The relative variability of a population is given by the coefficient of variation, which is the standard deviation/mean. For example, in Table 5.1 the mean height of females is 162.94 cm and the standard deviation is 6.36 cm. The coefficient of variation is 6.36/162.94 = 3.9%.

See Figure 5.3 for how to sketch the normal distribution of a characteristic. Table 18.6 is a table of the normal distribution. The coefficient of variation (COV) of "bony" dimensions, such as stature, is on the order of 3.5% to 5%. Then ± 2 sigma of the data

T A B L E		5 . 3

Recommended corridor widths (inches) for people-only traffic.

NUMBER OF PEOPLE	SITUATION	MINIMUM	BETTER
1	Avoid touching equipment or hitting switches	20	24
2	Passing one person standing with back to wall	30	36
3	All three walking abreast in same direction	60	72

T A B L E	5 . 4	

Considerations in door design.

1. DOOR'S PURPOSE (e.g., security, fire, noise, climate control, insects)	2. CONDITIONS/USERS	3. SOLUTIONS

■ Door for people or vehicles or both?
 	
■ One-way or two-way passage? Panic bar OK?
 	
■ Will door be locked? How will door/lock be actuated/opened?
 	
■ Will door slide or be hinged? If hinged and not locked, push plate may suffice.
 	
■ How often will door be used (e.g., per 24 h)?
 	
■ Are esthetics an issue?
	■ Will the door be used by adults, children, aged? Design force for 1% female adult?
	
	■ Will people in wheelchairs use the door?
	
	■ What will be the posture of door user (e.g., seated, standing, holding objects)?
	
	■ Will users wear gloves?
	
	■ What is the lighting on the door?
	
	■ Is the door indoors or outdoors?
		■ Eliminate door.
		
		■ Use a motorized door. Consider various triggers.
		
		■ For manual opening, a lever is a better choice than a knob:
		
		  a. Can be opened by small children (little force).
		
		  b. Can be opened by elbow.
		
		A "return curve" on lever will reduce snagging.

F I G U R E	5 . 3	

Normal distribution of male stature height. From Table 5.1, the mean is 176.6 cm with std. deviation = 6.7 cm. Using the normal curve (discussed numerically in Table 18.6):

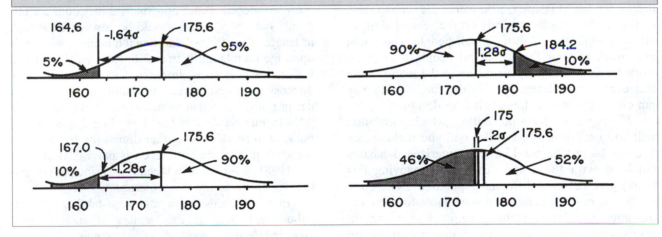

(1) Put the mean at 175.6.

(2) Draw the curve concave downward between the mean and ±1 standard deviation; that is, 175.6 − 6.7 = 168.9 and 175.6 + 6.7 = 182.3. These are the inflection points of the curve.

(3) Draw the curve upward outside this range.

(4) Have the curve approach the axis at the mean ±3 standard deviations; that is, at 175.6 + 20.1 = 155.5 and 175.6 + 20.1 = 195.7.

For the vertical scale, if the height of the mean is 1.0, then the height of the curve at ±1 standard deviation = .58, at ±2 standard deviations = .12 and at ±3 standard deviations = .01.

The 5th percentile height is 175.6 − 1.64 (6.7) = 164.6. The 10th percentile height is 175.6 − 1.28 (6.7) = 167.0. The 90th percentile height is 175.6 + 1.28 (6.7) = 182.2.

If you wish to determine what percentile is below 175 cm, this is 175 − 175.6 = −0.6 cm/6.7 cm/S. D. = .09 S. D. below the mean. From a table of the normal distribution, 46% of the U. S. male population is below 175 cm.

for height is within ± 8% of the mean (Kreifeldt and Nah, 1996).

Assume you wish to calculate your percentile height. See Figure 5.3. If you are male and have a height of 170 cm, then you are 175.58 minus 170.0 = 5.58 cm below the mean. Next you will have to convert from cm to standard units. The conversion factor is 1 standard deviation = 6.68 cm, so you are 5.58/6.68 = .84 standard units below average in height. From a table of the normal distribution, this is the 20th percentile. That is, 20% of the population is shorter than you and 80% of the population is taller than you.

Assume you wish to calculate the 99th percentile of the male population (that is, you are going to exclude the largest 1% of the population). Then, from a normal table, 99% is 2.33 standard deviations above the mean. Converting from standard units to cm makes the distance above the mean equal to 2.33 (6.68) = 15.6 cm. Adding this to 175.58 gives 191.2 cm. If you wish to calculate the 1st percentile, subtract 15.6 from 175.58 to get 159.98 cm.

3.2 Designing for a Population/Person

Assume you wish to design a workstation, a handtool, gloves, or whatever. There are a number of steps.

3.2.1 *Population or person?*

Are you going to design for Joe Velasquez, who works the second shift, or for all the people presently on the second shift, or all the people on all shifts, or all people who might ever work at your facility, or all people who might work for your company anywhere in the world? Note that even if you design specifically for Joe, Joe may put on weight and no longer fit your design.

If you design for a population, which population will you use? What percentiles will you include (see Section 14 in Chapter 13)? Computerized databases (such as with the ERGO disk accompanying this book) give data for different populations. There are many computer programs now available to show the designer the consequences (e.g., vision, reach, access) of various decisions. Some programs are

COMBIMAN, CREW CHIEF, and JACK. Cardboard mock-ups are another alternative.

Designing for a specific individual usually is done through equipment adjustability. Conveyor height can be adjusted by turning screws on the conveyor legs. Chairs can be adjusted in height.

The adjustment may not be continuous; there may be discrete sizes. For example, clothing often comes in a variety of sizes. Sometimes the device sizes may adjust automatically (clothing in which "one size fits all"); one-size-fits-all tends to yield lower manufacturing and inventory costs but relatively poor fit. Although salespeople emphasize "ease of adjustment," it may not be important if the adjustment is made rarely.

3.2.2 *Sizes*

The number of sizes needed varies with several factors. *First,* how much does the population vary along the relevant dimension? For example, for shoes, feet may vary in length from 21 cm (1st percentile) to 29 cm (99th percentile). *Second,* how well can a specific size fit part of the population? Sizes near the mean will fit better; sizes at the extreme will fit less well. Also, how much mismatch is acceptable at a given size? For example, a foot 25 cm long might be fitted only by a shoe from 25 to 26 cm in length. If a greater mismatch is accepted, fewer sizes are needed. *Third,* how many dimensions are relevant? For shoes, width should be considered as well as length. The effect of additional dimensions depends upon the correlation between dimensions (Haber and Haber, 1997). That is, in cases where more than one dimension is relevant (such as clothing design, cockpit design), it is important to realize that a person who is 90% in one dimension (such as shoulder height) is unlikely to be 90% in another dimension (such as hip breadth); that is, the correlation is not 1.0. Hudson et al. (1998) comment on a technique (principal components analysis) to use in such cases.

In many cases, sizes and adjustability interact. Adjustability reduces the number of sizes needed; sizes reduce the needed adjustment range.

Review Questions

1. If you design a footpedal for the distance an average person can reach, what percent of the population will not be able to reach the pedal?

2. Contrast the two opposing strategies of selection and job design.

3. Discuss what percentage of the employees you would exclude from a manual material handling job.

4. If King Kong (the giant gorilla) had really lived, why would he have had to be hollow?

5. Design a tote pan that 95% of the employees can lift. Assume the mean for what a person can lift is 20 kg and 1 standard deviation is 5 kg.

6. Select another person in your class. How would you design that person's office workstation so the person's elbow is even with the bottom of the keys? Would your design change if the workstation were used on two shifts?

References

Annis, J. Men and women; anthropometric comparisons for the ergonomist. *Advances in Occupational Ergonomics and Safety,* A. Mital, H. Krueger, S. Kumar, M. Menozzi, and J. Fernandez (eds.). Cincinnati, OH: *Int. Society for Occ. Ergonomics and Safety,* 60–65, 1996.

Annis, J. and McConville, J. Anthropometry. In *Occupational Ergonomics,* A. Bhattacharya and J. McGloughlin (eds.). New York: Dekker, 1996.

Chaffin, D. and Faraway, J. Stature, age, and gender effects on reach motion postures. *Human Factors,* Vol. 42, 3, 408–420, 2000.

Clauser, C., McConville, J., and Young, J. *Weight, Volume, and Center of Mass of the Human Body,* AMRL-TR-70. Dayton, OH: Aerospace Medical Research Laboratory, 1969.

Gordon, C., Churchill, T., Clauser, C., Bradtmiller, B., McConville, J., Tebbets, I., and Walker, R. *1988 Anthropometric Survey of U. S. Army Personnel.* Natick, MA: U. S. Army Natick Research, Development and Engineering Center, 1989.

Haber, R. and Haber, L. One size fits all? *Ergonomics in Design,* 10–17, Vol. 5, No. 1, Jan. 1997.

Haldane, J. *Possible Worlds.* New York: Harper, 1928. Also reprinted in Newman, J., (ed.), *The World of Mathematics,* 952–57. New York: Simon and Schuster, 1956.

Hanna, S. and Konz, S. *Facility Design: Manufacturing Engineering,* 3rd ed. Scottsdale, AZ: Holcomb Hathaway, 2004.

Hudson, J., Zehner, G., and Meindl, R. The USAF multivariate accommodation method. *Proc. of Human Factors and Ergonomic Society,* 722–26, 1998.

Juergens, H., Aune, I., and Pieper, U. *International Data on Anthropometry.* Geneva: International Labour Organization, 1990.

Kaleps, I., Clauser, C., Young, J., Chandler, R., Zehner, G., and McConville, J. Investigation into the mass distribution properties of the human body and its segments. *Ergonomics,* Vol. 12, 1225–37, 1984.

Kreifeldt, J. and Nah, K. The relative sizes of percentiles. *Proc. of Human Factors and Ergonomics Society,* 394–97, 1996.

Kroemer, K., Kroemer, H., and Kroemer-Elbert, K. *Ergonomics,* 2nd ed. Upper Saddle River, NJ: Prentice-Hall, 2001.

Marras, W. and Kim, J. Anthropometry of industrial populations. *Ergonomics,* Vol. 36, No. 4, 371–78, 1993.

Mignano, B. and Konz, S. The surface area and volume of the hand. *Proc. of Human Factors and Ergonomics Society,* 608–10, 1994.

Mitchell, D., Strydom, N., van Graan, C., and van der Walt, W. Human surface area: Comparison of the DuBois formula with direct photometric measurement. *Pflugers Archieves,* Vol. 325, 188–90, 1971.

Morrissey, S. Work place design recommendations for the pregnant worker. *Int. J. of Industrial Ergonomics,* Vol. 21, 383–95, 1998.

Pheasant, S. *Bodyspace,* 2nd ed. London: Taylor and Francis, 1996.

Roberts, D. Population differences in dimensions. In *Ethnic Variables in Human Factors Engineering,* A. Chapanis (ed.), Ch. 2. Baltimore: Johns Hopkins University Press, 1975.

Roebuck, J. *Anthropometric Methods: Designing to Fit the Human Body.* Santa Monica, CA: Human Factors and Ergonomic Society, 1995.

Stevenson, M. and Baidya, K. Some guidelines on repetitive work design to reduce the dangers of tenosynovitis. In *Readings in RSI,* M. Stevenson (ed.). Kensington, NSW: New South Wales University Press, 1987.

van Graan, C. The determination of body surface area. *South African Medical J.,* Vol. 3, 952–59, August 1969.

van Schoor, H. and Konz, S. Males/females: An anthropometric comparison for modeling missing data. *Int. J. of Industrial Ergonomics,* Vol. 17, 437–40, 1996.

White, R. Anthropometric measurements on selected populations of the world. In *Ethnic Variables in Human Factors Engineering,* A. Chapanis (ed.), Ch. 3. Baltimore: Johns Hopkins University Press, 1975.

6

CRITERIA

CRITERIA

1 Organizations

2 Employees

3 Work Design Criteria

Overview

Work design requires a tradeoff of multiple criteria. The criteria are vague, and no explicit tradeoff equations are available. Six design criteria are given.

Key Concepts

Americans with Disabilities
   Act (ADA)
criteria of job design
ego needs
enlargement/enrichment
foundations of job design

goals
knowledge-based pay
limits (restraints)
machines as slaves
Maslow's hierarchy of
   needs

physical needs
security needs
self-actualization
social needs

73

ORGANIZATIONS

1.1 Goals   Organization **goals** include survival and growth, among others. *Survival* is the first rule of any organism, whether bacterium, insect, human, corporation, or state. Carrying the analogy further, the organism must have sufficient nutrition. To an organization, money is the food. A surplus of income over outgo (called profits in capitalist countries and net favorable balance in socialist countries) is necessary in the long run. In the short run, a "diet" will not kill the patient, if the diet is not too severe or prolonged. Normally, organizations set prices at a level that more than covers costs. If the price charged is higher than the market can bear or than the government permits, either costs must be reduced or starvation begins. One exception is transfusions of public funds; this, in effect, has the taxpayer (a nonuser of the goods or services) pay some of the cost of the goods or services.

Growth is the second rule of an organism. Biological organisms, however, mature, stop growth, and die. Social organisms, such as auto manufacturers, universities, hospitals, and governments, are composed of "replaceable parts" and attempt to grow, grow, grow. Isn't a university with 15,000 students better than one with 7,000? Isn't a firm with 20,000 employees better than one with 10,000? Isn't a hospital with 500 employees better than one with 250? Isn't a bureau with 1,000 employees better than one with 500?

Although some may not believe that bigger is better, more employees do give more power, prestige, status, and income to higher managers of an organization than do smaller numbers. Since the higher managers set the organization's goals, their rewards are what count. Thus, number of employees is an important managerial criterion. Although this is not even admitted to exist as a criterion, it is a rare manager who would not prefer to supervise 2,000 rather than 1,000.

In the United States, a publicly proclaimed goal is a larger net income; profits of $1,000,000 are considered better than profits of $200,000. A more sophisticated criterion is net income/assets; return on investment of 10% is better than return of 5%. See Table 7.5 for returns on investment of some firms. Note that the return is not the same in all countries.

1.2 Limits   There are often **limits** (external **restraints**) imposed by society (usually governments and unions; see Box 6.1) but sometimes by public opinion or religious/moral values. The public influences and changes decisions through laws concerning pollution, safety, or other issues. These restraints can be quite different in developed and developing countries; they can be quite different in Judeo-Christian, Moslem, and Buddhist countries; and they can be quite different in capitalist and socialist countries.

Regulations (and enforcement) can be quite different concerning threshold limit values for toxic compounds. Environmental regulations can vary greatly, as do wage and employment regulations.

Japan provides an example of a religious/moral limit. The major firms (although not the small firms) have a "lifetime" employment policy for men (although not for women). Since labor is considered a fixed cost, there is tremendous pressure to continue producing product no matter what the price at which it can be sold. For example, as long as a car can be sold for a price exceeding the cost of purchased components, it will be cheaper to make it than not to make it. Finding a local market may be a problem, so the Japanese export. Thus, prices in Japan often are considerably higher for products made in Japan than for the same product exported to other countries. Maintaining employment is a higher priority than profits to Japanese firms.

EMPLOYEES

The organizational goals are affected by the goals of the employees. These goals are divided into physiological and psychological–social.

2.1 Physiological   Employees naturally want to work with the least stress.

2.2 Psychological–Social   **Maslow's hierarchy of needs** in Figure 6.1 gives perspective to this concept. Maslow proposed a hierarchy of individual needs. **Physical needs,** at the lowest level, concern basics such as the need for food, shelter, and health. Once these physical needs have been satisfied, the second level of needs, **security (safety) needs,** becomes important. In job terms, security needs might be having seniority on a job or having a supervisor who doesn't threaten you. The third level, **social needs,** becomes important after the second level is satisfied. Work examples of social needs are having a job with status, a job you enjoy, a job with friendly coworkers, or working in a physical location in which you can talk with fellow workers while working.

The fourth level, **ego (esteem) needs,** concerns challenge and achievement. Does the job challenge you? Do you have a feeling of contribution, or are you "just a number"? The fifth level, **self-actualization,** concerns personal fulfillment and realization of potential. For example, is the organization "serving humanity," or are you merely making common items such as soap, autos, or chairs? Satisfying the fifth level may call for a "missionary" type of endeavor such as ecology, religion, or

BOX 6.1 *Americans with Disabilities Act (ADA)*

The **Americans with Disabilities Act (ADA)** became law in 1990, although the starting date for some actions was postponed a few years. The ADA has 5 sections: (1) access to employment, (2) public services, (3) public accommodation, (4) telecommunications, and (5) miscellaneous provisions.

We will focus on Title 1: access to employment. Title 1 was designed to prohibit discrimination in employment against "qualified individuals with disabilities." (There are 10 regional Disability and Technical Assistance centers to help businesses comply with the law. The service is free; call 1-800 949 4232.)

The law incorporates several key terms (Olsheski and Breslin, 1996; Montgomery, 1996; EEOC, 1992).

Individual with a disability. This is any individual who has physical or mental impairment that substantially limits one or more major life activities (walking, speaking, breathing, performing manual tasks, seeing, hearing, learning, caring for oneself, and working).

Qualified individual with a disability. First, the individual must satisfy the requisite skill, experience, education, and other job-related requirements. Second, the person has to be able to perform the "essential functions" of the job, with or without reasonable accommodations.

Essential functions. The ADA does not specifically define essential functions.

Reasonable accommodation. This is "any modification to a job, an employment practice, or the work environment that makes it possible for an individual with a disability to enjoy an equal opportunity." Reasonable accommodation to perform essential functions may include any type of modification of the work environment (including work devices, the manner in which the job is performed, or administrative policies). Reasonable accommodation may include:

- Making facilities readily accessible and usable
- Restructuring a job by reallocating or redistributing marginal job functions
- Altering when or how an essential job function is performed
- Part-time or modified work schedules
- Obtaining or modifying equipment or devices
- Modifying examinations, training materials, or policies
- Providing qualified readers and interpreters
- Reassignment to a vacant position
- Permitting use of accrued paid leave or unpaid leave for necessary treatment
- Providing reserved parking space (if mobility is impaired)
- Allowing the employee to provide devices that an employer is not required to provide.

The U.S. Supreme Court has decided that: (1) the ADA does not cover most correctable conditions (such as eyesight problems that can be corrected with glasses), (2) states cannot be sued by their employees under the ADA, (3) ordinarily an employer does not have to bend its seniority system to make sure a disabled worker can stay on the job, (4) an employer can bar employment to a person if the job might endanger the person's health, and (5) the ADA does not cover carpal tunnel syndrome (a temporary condition). Pregnant women are not covered by the ADA since pregnancy is a temporary condition; however, good standard practice uses special accommodations for them such as restricted lifting and minimizing prolonged standing or sitting.

The Kansas State University Telecommunications Department is in a building that is not handicapped accessible. If a disabled person has to go to the department's office, the accommodation is that a person from the office meets the disabled person in an accessible location.

Accommodation for low back pain for sitting workers can involve lumbar rolls and back cushions as well as more frequent standing. Consider making "light duty" into "transitional duty." That is, light duty should be considered temporary, not permanent. The intent is that the employee is moving in the direction of full-time duty. For example, start work 2 h/day, then 4 h/day, 6 h/day, then 8 h/day. Or do 80% of job 1 and 20% of job 2, then 90% of job 1 and 10% of job 2, and so forth. Or set up an on-site rehabilitation facility and count rehabilitation time as part of duty time.

Traditionally, the focus on people with disabilities has been on the individual (a "medical" orientation). The ADA focus is on the environment (an "ergonomic" orientation).

Initially many employers were concerned with the ADA's effect on hiring of employees; however, the majority of complaints filed so far concern current or former workers. Typically, they have been considered "disabled" and have received Worker Compensation. Now they want to return to work. (This has caused

BOX **6.1** *Americans with Disabilities Act, continued*

some conflicts with physicians as, for Worker Compensation, they want to be as disabled as possible [maximum medical restrictions] and, for ADA, they want to have minimum medical restrictions.)

Disabilities have been broadly defined. In 1993, the top 10 impairments were back ailments (19%), followed by mental illness, heart impairment, diabetes, neurological impairment, hearing impairment, vision impairment, drug addiction, speech impairment, and high blood pressure (Litvan, 1994).

The worker (plaintiff, claimant) has the burden of proof. Juries, however, tend to sympathize with individuals rather than employers. In addition, the ADA is designed to favor people with disabilities.

A key is that the worker must perform the essential functions of the job. Reasonable accommodation does not contemplate hiring an additional individual to do the essential function. A reasonable accommodation must not impose an "undue hardship" on the employer. The employer need not create a new position or vacancy, fundamentally change the nature of the job, or place the employee in a higher position.

Ergonomists will have to define the essential functions of each job in a job description. If there is a complaint, reasonable accommodations must be investigated. Some job characteristics to document are:

- Time of observation
- Location of job site
- Worker identity
- Level of supervision
- Interactions with others
- Physical requirements

- Mental and training requirements
- Environment (light, noise, chemicals, and so on)
- Output criteria (quantity, quality)

Physicians often are asked to make a determination of a worker's employability. One example is the post-offer/preplacement exam. (Under the ADA, employers may not conduct medical exams or make disability-related inquiries of applicants before they are extended a conditional offer of employment.) The employer may withdraw the conditional job offer ONLY if the employer can show one of the following:

1. The individual cannot perform the essential functions of the job offered despite reasonable accommodations.

2. The individual poses a "direct threat" to self or others in the position that cannot be reasonably accommodated. The direct threat risk must be significant (highly probable) and the potential harm must be substantial (severe).

3. Other federal laws or regulations (such as Department of Transportation regulations) require the employer to withdraw the offer because of the medical condition.

Physician examinations tend to be subjective. It is better if objective information is obtained. Estimates of work risk are more valid if the physician has work materials, a videotape of work activities, and measured weights and distances.

Note that reducing the "stress" of a job benefits all people doing the job, not just those filing complaints.

---

its secular equivalent, politics. Some find it in teaching, music, or running their own businesses.

One question is how relevant these needs are to job design. Which of them, if any, are to be satisfied by the job and which outside of the job? As was pointed out in Chapter 3, males in the United States tend to work about 81,000 h during their lifetimes. In general, from the earnings of these 81,000 h, they may support a family as well as provide for themselves and their wives during retirement. (In the United States, increasing participation of women in the employed labor force probably has added 30,000 to 40,000 h/family.)

Employees may prefer income from a monotonous, boring, dirty, dead-end job if they can own a sailboat and a Mercedes. Others may prefer less income but enjoy the status of a white-collar job.

Should an engineer be concerned with satisfying higher wants on the job? Some points for discussion are as follows.

1. There are dead-end jobs that must be done by someone. Idealists, perhaps with sounder hearts than heads, proclaim they would not be willing to work on an assembly line; this is true due to self-selection. Their opinions do not seem to be shared by those who actually work on assembly lines, probably because assembly-line work is well paid and the workers are willing to trade satisfaction off the job for satisfaction on the job.

2. More and more, societies over the world guarantee the basics of life (food, shelter, clothing) whether an individual works or not. In the United

FIGURE   6.1

Adaptation of Maslow's hierarchy of needs.

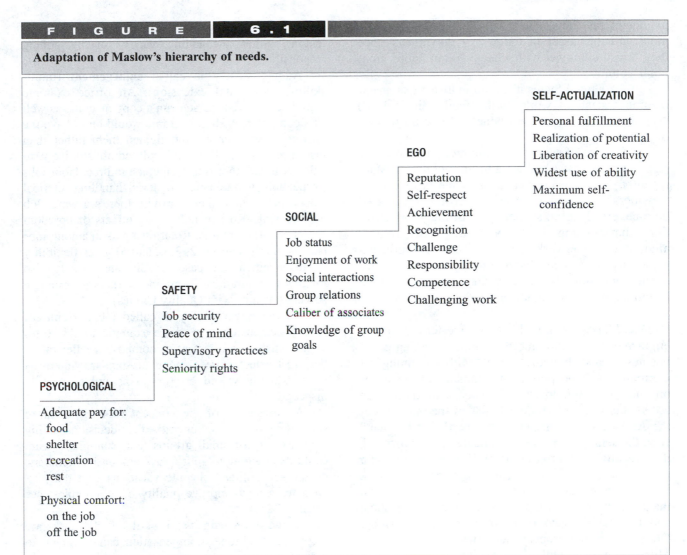

SELF-ACTUALIZATION

Personal fulfillment
Realization of potential
Liberation of creativity
Widest use of ability
Maximum self-
  confidence

EGO

Reputation
Self-respect
Achievement
Recognition
Challenge
Responsibility
Competence
Challenging work

SOCIAL

Job status
Enjoyment of work
Social interactions
Group relations
Caliber of associates
Knowledge of group
  goals

SAFETY

Job security
Peace of mind
Supervisory practices
Seniority rights

PSYCHOLOGICAL

Adequate pay for:
  food
  shelter
  recreation
  rest

Physical comfort:
  on the job
  off the job

States, in 1996, government transfer payments were 10% of all income. In addition, net income of the unemployed (due to tax policies and benefits available to those not working) often is 70% to 90% of working income after taxes. This has led to *high*-seniority workers demanding that they be laid off first. Thus, if a job is dirty, boring, monotonous, dead-end, *and low paid,* finding employees is becoming more and more difficult.

3. A satisfied want does not motivate. With job enrichment, it may be possible to design jobs to motivate workers; the motivated workers may work harder. However, unions in general oppose the concept of motivation. They favor working smart, not working hard.

4. Unfortunately, extensive research shows that satisfied workers do not necessarily have improved safety or productivity (Helander, 1997). On the other hand, if we design for safety and productivity, we may be able to get satisfaction at no additional cost.

2.3 Satisfying Higher Wants   Higher wants will be discussed in sequence.

2.3.1 Security wants   In different cultures, managements have different approaches to job security. Large Japanese firms, for example, hire males at age 18 to work without layoffs until they are 55 (nenkō policy); their labor is considered a fixed cost. Since pensions don't start until age 60, many hire back into their jobs at 55 as "temporary" workers (at 2/3 pay). Production fluctuations thus do not affect the permanent workers but do affect women, temporary workers, and subcontractors. The workers, in return, shift jobs freely (wages depend upon age, not the specific job), make methods and quality analyses during off-job hours to improve their jobs, and often return early from vacations. A side effect is that since most costs except material are fixed costs, Japanese firms continue production almost regardless of the sales volume or price/unit. Japanese managers say they cannot afford to discharge their most valuable asset in temporary downturns since they must compete with cheap Asian labor from other countries.

In the United States, the auto industry guarantees income instead of work. If the worker is laid off, "supplemental employment benefits" pay up to 95% of wages for a year.

In the area of supervisory practices and seniority rights, unions have had a traditional concern. More recently, U. S. governmental agencies have exerted considerable pressure for less discrimination based on race, creed, color, sex, or age. Although organizations have complained about the extraordinary amount of paperwork now required, and although some arbitrary and discriminatory practices still occur occasionally, supervisory practices have become a relatively minor problem.

2.3.2 *Social wants*

In some Western societies, employees are gaining more say in the running of the business. Most dramatic is the "Mitbestimmung" of Germany, the concept of joint command, of two hands on the tiller. Employees of firms with more than 2,000 employees elect almost 50% of the members of the Aufsichsrat, the supervisory board that hires and fires the senior executives who make up the Vorstand, the executives who run the firm. Workers also elect a Betriebsrat (works council); it, rather than the union, is the focus of shop-floor grievances, negotiates with management on changes in production organization, and has certain veto rights over hiring and firing. Other northern European countries have a form of Mitbestimmung with a smaller proportion of employee representatives. In England, where there is a strong "us vs. them" feeling, unions and management both reject Mitbestimmung as it requires cooperation rather than confrontation. Japanese organizations have a decentralized decision-making procedure with many different individuals "fixing their seal" on a proposal. There is a strong attempt to modify a proposal until 100% agreement is reached.

In the United States there has been little formal sharing of authority between employees and management but considerable informal sharing due to the changing nature of work. In 1999, managerial and professional specialties comprised 30.3% of the U. S. workforce, and technical, sales, and administrative support comprised 29.1%—a total of 59.4%. Precision production, craft, and repair comprised 10.9%, and operators, fabricators, and laborers comprised 13.6%—a total of 24.5%. Managements traditionally have shared more decision making with white-collar employees than with blue-collar employees. Changing skill levels are shifting the shape of the workforce from a pyramid to a diamond.

2.3.3 *Ego wants*

Work can be made more challenging either by adding variety or by adding responsibility.

Adding variety is called **enlargement** (multi-skilling, horizontal extension). An office example would be to have a person run a copy machine as well as a computer. A shop example would be to have the operator insert screws and tighten them rather than just insert them. It is difficult administratively to enlarge direct labor jobs to include indirect labor jobs (inspection, maintenance, material handling, clerical work), but "where there's a will, there's a way." Job enlargement also can reduce the effects of boredom and cumulative trauma. Rotating a person among jobs (say assembly stations 2, 3, 4, and 5) gives flexibility to management in case of absenteeism. It also improves communication among workers for problem solving (such as with Quality Circles).

Adding responsibility is called job **enrichment** (vertical extension). An office example would be for an administrative assistant to compose a letter rather than just select from a menu of standard letters. A shop example would be for an assembler also to inspect.

An extension of the concept of enrichment of specific jobs is to enlarge the decision-making responsibility of small groups. For example, a team could decide how to split a task among its members, do the scheduling, schedule vacations, and the like. Or a team may improve quality or ergonomics; see Chapter 22.

If the knowledge and skill of the task are increased, additional compensation can be given to individuals who have more knowledge and skill, called **knowledge-based pay.** Thus some "career advancement" can be offered without adding supervisory responsibilities.

Do workers want job enlargement and enrichment? Job enrichment is contrary to the traditional union approach of standard jobs, working conditions, and pay. Advocates of job enrichment often state that the workers will be more motivated and thus more productive. This "work hard, not smart" philosophy is irritating to unions.

Job enlargement (less specialization, more variety) is not as controversial. Less specialization gives management more flexibility in job assignments and reduces union jurisdiction problems. Job rotation also can reduce the effects of cumulative trauma. Spreading the work among different tasks, and thus different body parts, reduces the strain. Salvendy (1978) commented that some people like to work at enlarged jobs, others prefer simplified jobs, and still others do not like work in any form.

Bennett (1973) divided jobs into four categories: physical (carry, lift), procedural (operate, follow procedures), social (talk, answer), and cognitive (decide, answer). Job enrichment seems most interesting to social and cognitive workers. Physical and procedural workers tend to be uninterested in more challenge and responsibility on the job; they tend to focus their lives on their off-work hours rather than the minority of hours they spend on the job. It may be just as well because truly challenging work for everyone may be an impossible dream.

2.3.4 Self-actualization In relatively few organizations do workers "throw in their whole selves." Japanese industry may be an exception. In 1974, the Matsushita Electric workers' song "Love, Light, and a Dream" (see excerpt) replaced the previous song, "For the Building of a New Japan," which had been written in 1946, when rehabilitation of the war-devastated economy was the national goal.

> Love, Light, and a Dream
> A bright heart overflowing
> With life linked together,
> MATSUSHITA DENKI.
>
> Lyrics by Shoji Miyazawa
> Music by Kozaburo Hirai

The song is sung at the morning meeting, which was begun in 1933. Each section (10–20 people) has its own meeting, which lasts 10–15 min. On each day, one employee, in turn, goes up to the platform and reads the company creed and 7 objectives, which all the others recite. Then he or she makes a 3–5 min speech on any subject (hobbies, family, job, and so on). Anyone else who wants to talk can then do so.

The meeting is closed by singing the company song. The purpose is to (1) start the day with a refreshed recognition of the company mission, (2) have everyone learn to speak thoughts in public, (3) improve communication among the group, and (4) improve group members' knowledge of each other.

Another technique is the Quality Circle movement, discussed in Chapter 32.

3 WORK DESIGN CRITERIA

3.1 Foundations Eight **foundations of job design** (underlying trends) will set the stage (Konz, 1987).

- *Foundation 1: People vary.* Variation in people in many dimensions (height, strength, training, and so on) is not new. However, more and more data have become available to designers to quantify this variation for different populations. See Chapter 5, as well as the ERGO program accompanying this book.

- *Foundation 2: People are more educated.* Median years of schooling at age 25 in the United States is now over 12, in comparison to Taylor's time, when it was 8.2. The same trend has occurred worldwide. Management has recognized that the workforce is educated and now encourages worker participation. See Box 6.2.

- *Foundation 3: People want a say.* Democracy has increased not only at the political level but also at the industrial level—at least in the developed countries. See Chapter 32 for a discussion of small-group activities.

- *Foundation 4: The world is becoming smaller.* Not physically smaller, of course, but changes in communication and transportation have had that effect. Consider telephone (voice, fax) and computer networks (e-mail, the Internet), jet travel, interstate highway systems, and so forth. Multinational firms now manufacture on an international basis, not a national or regional basis.

BOX 6.2   *Productivity Versus Stress Reduction*

Frederick Taylor, working around 1900, advocated "scientific management" to improve productivity. He improved handtools (such as shovels), gave better training, advocated rest breaks to reduce fatigue, and made other innovations. Taylor basically considered people as machines and aimed to improve the output of those machines. He did recognize the importance of motivation and advocated incentive wages. Taylor lived in a time when the educational level of workers as well as the level of technology were low.

However, the level of education has risen and the level of technology has advanced. Using a biological analogy, technology has advanced in "muscles" (motors, prime movers), in "nerves" (wired and wireless communication), and in "brains" (computers). The organizational design and management (ODAM) literature now emphasizes the individual, stress (physical and mental) reduction, social democracy, and quality of life. The ODAM writers tend to think of ergonomic improvements as micro-solutions and their emphasis as macro-solutions.

■ *Foundation 5: Machines are becoming more capable.* Machines have become more capable in power, control, and memory. Computers became commercially available in the 1940s. Their costs and capabilities have continued to improve. For example, in 1971, the 4004 chip had 27,000 transistors and ran at 5 MHz. In 1985, the 386 had 275,000 transistors and ran at 33 MHz. In 2002, the Pentium 4 had 55,000,000 transistors and ran at 3060 MHz. In contrast, labor costs have continued to increase—generally around 2–5%/year.

■ *Foundation 6: Safety and health are more important.* The annual occupational death rate in the United States was 11.6/100,000 workers in 1933; in 1997 it was 4. The death rate for all accidents was 72.4/100,000 people in 1933; in 1996 it was 35.2. The American Industrial Hygiene Association had 160 members in 1940, and in 2000 it had 4,711. The Human Factors and Ergonomics Society was founded in 1957; in 1998 it had 4,930 members. The worldwide increase in the number and membership of ergonomics societies reflects increased concern for the worker.

■ *Foundation 7: Job specialization is changing.* In developed countries, specialization in cognitive and social jobs (engineers, supervisors, teachers, and so on) has increased. Specialization in physical and procedural jobs (assembly line and clerical work) has decreased due to computeriza-

tion and the movement of high-labor-content jobs to developing countries. In an information society, machines have replaced most physical labor.

■ *Foundation 8: Jobs are more interrelated.* With increasing technology, "No man is an island, entire of himself." More and more, "everything touches" and very few jobs stand alone. See Box 27.2. Figure 6.2 shows a conceptual work system.

3.2 Criteria The eight foundations lead to six ergonomic **criteria of job design:**

■ *Criterion 1: Safety is first.* No job design that endangers the worker's safety or health is acceptable. However, life does not have infinite value. Management must take reasonable precautions. Naturally the definition of "reasonable" is debatable. As pointed out above, we are putting increased emphasis on safety. After designing for safety, design for performance, then worker comfort, and finally consider higher wants.

■ *Criterion 2: Make the machine user-friendly.* The machine is to adjust to the worker, not the converse. If the system does not function well, redesign the machine or procedure rather than blame the operator.

■ *Criterion 3: Reduce the percent excluded by the design.* Permit any person to use the machine or procedure. Gender, age, strength, or other physi-

---

FIGURE 6.2

Conceptual work system. Individuals should be the focus of a work system (Smith, 1997). Everything affects everything else.

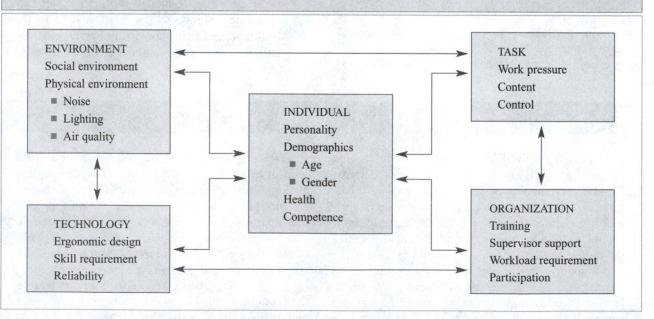

Source: From M. Smith, Psychosocial Aspects of Working with Video Display Terminals (VDTs) and Employee Physical and Mental Health, *Ergonomics,* Vol. 40, No. 10, pp. 1001–1015. Copyright © 1997 by Taylor & Francis, London. Used by permission. www.tandf.co.uk/journals

cal attributes should not prevent people from participating in work or leisure activities.

- *Criterion 4: Design jobs to be cognitive and social.* Physical and procedural work now can be done by machines. Manufacturing jobs in the developed countries will take a smaller percent of the workforce. At present, over 50% of all jobs in the developed countries are in offices.

- *Criterion 5: Emphasize communication.* We communicate to machines with controls and receive information from machines by displays. We also need to improve communication among people to increase output and, perhaps equally important, reduce errors.

- *Criterion 6: Use machines to extend human performance.* The choice is not worker *or* machine; it is which machine to use. Workers reduce their own effort by using **machines as slaves.** Small machines (such as a word processor or electric drill) tend to have costs (total of capital, maintenance, and power) of less than $.25/h. Even large machines (such as automobiles and lathes) tend to cost only $1–2/h. Labor costs, however, run $8–25/h. Thus, the real question is how many machines the human will supervise and how to design the system to use the output of the machines.

Review Questions

1. Does the ADA focus on the individual or the environment? Explain.
2. List the five levels of Maslow's hierarchy of needs; give examples for each level.
3. What is the difference between job enlargement and job enrichment? Why should any organization use either?
4. List the six work design criteria.

References

Bennett, C. The human factors of work. *Human Factors,* Vol. 15, No. 3, 281–87, 1973.

EEOC, *Title 1 of the Americans with Disabilities Act,* Technical Assistance Manual, Jan. 26, 1992.

Helander, M. Forty years of IEA: Some reflections on the evolution of ergonomics. *Ergonomics,* Vol. 40, No. 10, 952–61, 1997.

Konz, S. Ergonomic job design. *International J. of Industrial Ergonomics,* 307–15, 1987.

Litvan, L. The disabilities law: avoid the pitfalls. *Nations Business,* Vol. 82, 25–27, Jan. 1994.

Montgomery, J. Legal aspects of ergonomics. In *Occupational Ergonomics,* Bhattacharya, A. and McGloughlin, J., eds. New York: Marcell Dekker, 1996.

Olsheski, J. and Breslin, R. The Americans with Disabilities Act: implications for the use of ergonomics in rehabilitation. In *Occupational Ergonomics,* Bhattacharya, A. and McGloughlin, J., eds. New York: Marcell Dekker, 1996.

Salvendy, G. An industrial engineering dilemma: simplified vs. enlarged jobs. *Proceedings of 4th Int. Conference on Production Research* (Tokyo). London: Taylor and Francis, 1978.

Smith, M. Psychosocial aspects of working with video display terminals (VDTs) and employee physical and mental health. *Ergonomics,* Vol. 40, No. 10, 1002–15, 1997.

ENGINEERING DESIGN

ENGINEERING DESIGN

1 Scientific Method

2 Engineering Design

3 Cost Allocation

4 Return on Investment

5 Cost Analysis

Overview

Engineering design differs from the scientific method in that there is not just one design solution; you must select the optimum design from the alternatives. Cost is an important criterion in this selection.

Key Concepts

annual savings	data versus theory	optimum solution	satisfiers
benchmarking	direct labor	overhead (burden)	scientific method
cost centers	life of the application	prerelease review	standard cost
DAMES	one-time costs	return on investment	

1 SCIENTIFIC METHOD

If asked to list important inventions, the ordinary citizen tends to list devices such as the wheel, the transistor, and the electric motor. Just as important, however, and perhaps even more important, are *concepts*. Examples of important concepts are technical societies, public libraries, the scientific method, and fast food (the restaurant as a factory).

Mowrer (1960) stated the importance of research:

In plants change occurs almost entirely by means of the evolutionary mechanism; but in animals there is the capacity for another kind of "evolution" of change; namely learning. Learning by actual doing involves hazards. A still higher level of advantage accrues to organisms which can explore their environments not only in terms of actual performance but also perceptually.

The **scientific method** (see Table 7.1) is an efficient method of doing research (learning by doing). It becomes even more useful if combined with another concept, education (perceptual exploration of the environment).

We can use a formula to predict when a beam will break; we do not need to build the beam. We can use a model to predict the best production schedule; we do not actually need to use all possible schedules. We can predict the amount of material handling required for a proposed plant; we do not need to build all possible plants. Nothing is so practical as a good theory. But, if we are going to trust the output of the formula (or model/theory) and not physically evaluate alternatives, it is essential that the formula (model/theory) is valid for the conditions of use.

Table 7.1 gives the five steps of scientific method as well as an example application to the optimum height for a keyboard. The essence of the scientific method is the feedback of **data versus theory.** The ancient Greeks were good at the first three steps, but they considered it beneath their dignity to see if their theories checked with the reality. Mere data gathering without an underlying theory also is not very useful. The powerful combination is theory plus data with a comparison of the data versus theory until the error is acceptable: a negative-feedback control circuit.

2 ENGINEERING DESIGN

Engineering design, although related to the scientific method, differs from it. Remember the five steps of engineering design with the acronym **DAMES,** where D = Define the problem, A = Analyze, M = Make search, E = Evaluate alternatives, and S = Specify and sell solution. See Table 7.2. Box 7.1 gives an overview of the steps in releasing a part for manufacturing.

2.1 Define the Problem Broadly Usually the designer is not given the problem but instead is confronted with the existing solution. The current solution is not the problem but just one solution among many possible solutions. The broad, detail-free

---

T A B L E	7 . 1

Scientific method. The scientific method has five steps. Step 5, the critical step, compares data to the prediction.

STEP	EXAMPLE
1. Clearly state the problem you are trying to solve.	1. What is the optimum height at which a keyboard should be placed?
2. Construct a hypothesis or model.	2. Speed and accuracy of keying depend upon fatigue.
3. Apply analysis to the model. From the analysis, predict what will happen in various conditions.	3. Fatigue is caused primarily by supporting the arm weight; the higher the hand is held, the greater the torque that must be resisted and the greater the fatigue. Since the keystroker is assumed to be seated, the optimum keyboard position will be in the keystroker's lap (i.e., at the lowest feasible position).
4. Design and perform an experiment with the real situation. Compare to the model.	4. Have a number of individuals key the same material at a number of heights. Record their speed, accuracy, and preferred work heights.
5. Compare data from the real situation to the model's predictions: a. If the difference between the prediction and the data (called error) is acceptable, accept the model. b. If the error is too large, revise the experiment or model until the error is acceptable.	5. See Section 3 of Chapter 13.

T A B L E	7 . 2

DAMES. The five steps of the engineering design procedure can be remembered by the acronym DAMES (define, analyze, make search, evaluate, specify and sell).

STEP	COMMENTS	EXAMPLE
Define the problem broadly.	Make statement broad and detail-free. Give criteria, number of replications, schedule.	Design within 5 days, a workstation for assembly of 10,000/yr of unit Y with reasonable quality and low mfg cost.
Analyze in detail.	Identify limits (constraints, restrictions). Include variability in components and users. Make machine adjust to person, not converse.	Obtain specifications of components and assembly. Obtain skills/availability of people; obtain capability/availability of equipment. Get restrictions in fabrication and assembly techniques and sequence. Obtain more details on cost accounting, scheduling, and tradeoffs of criteria.
Make search of solution space.	Don't be limited by imagined constraints. Try for optimum solution, not feasible solution. Have more than one solution.	Seek a variety of assembly sequences, layouts, fixtures, units/h, handtools, etc.
Evaluate alternatives.	Trade off multiple criteria. Calculate benefit/cost.	Alt. A: installed cost $1000; cost/unit = $1.10. Alt. B: installed cost $1200; cost/unit = $1.03.
Specify and sell solution.	Specify solution in detail. Sell solution. Accept a partial solution rather than nothing. Follow up to see that design is implemented and that design reduces the problem.	Recommend Alt. B. Install Alt. B1, a modification of B suggested by the supervisor.

statement of the problem should include the number of replications, the criteria, and the schedule. Using the example of Table 7.2, the replications are "10,000/yr," the criteria are "reasonable quality and low manufacturing cost," and the schedule is "within 5 days." Putting in too much detail makes you start by defending your concept rather than opening minds (yours and your clients') to new possibilities. At this stage, the number of replications should be quite approximate (within ± 500%). The importance of giving criteria is that there usually are multiple criteria (cost, quality, simplicity, etc.) rather than just one criterion. (Nadler, on the other hand, recommends that you start with an ideal—extreme—solution and then "back off.") The schedule identifies priorities and allocation of resources that can be used both in the design process and in the replication of the products from the design.

Job design has a large sociopolitical element. Be sure to get input and feedback from those affected by the design both early and often.

An important distinction between science and engineering is that the scientist wants a precise answer while the engineer is willing to settle for a practical answer.

2.2 Analyze in Detail
Amplify step 1 (defining the problem) with more detail on replications, criteria, and schedule:

- Who is affected by the design (operators, supervisors, other departments, maintenance)?
- What are the needs of the design users (productivity, style, comfort, accuracy, esthetics)?
- What should the design achieve?
- What are the design limits (also called constraints and restrictions)?
- What are the characteristics of the population using the design? For example, for an office workstation, the users would be adults within certain ranges (age from 18 to 65, weight of 50 to 100 kg).

The design should consider not only the main activities (e.g., the assembly) but also the "get ready" and "put away" and support activities such as setup, repairs, maintenance, quality, material handling, utilities, training, and so forth.

Since people vary, designers can follow two alternatives. (1) *Make the design with fixed characteristics and make the people adjust to the device.* One exam-

BOX **7.1** *Releasing a Part for Manufacturing*

Product life has four overlapping stages: (1) product design, (2) process design (how to make the product), (3) process build/installation, and (4) production. Because the cost of a change increases exponentially with each stage, the benefits of change decrease exponentially with the stage. Thus, make changes early; making changes once the product is in production is expensive.

The following expands on the first three steps.

1. Prerelease review. Before design engineering releases a part number to manufacturing, representatives from manufacturing should have a formal conference with design engineering. (A **prerelease review,** intended to reduce manufacturing problems, is a special case of a "useability review," which has the goal of reducing customer problems.) Typical representation would be industrial engineering, tool engineering, inspection, quality assurance, scheduling, and purchasing. The participation of purchasing is very important. The group challenges the details on the drawings. For example, can a specially designed item be replaced by a low-cost consumer item? Can standard threads replace precision threads? Can existing part numbers replace

new part numbers? Should component tolerances be increased (to help component manufacturing) or be decreased (to help assembly)? Designers still may be willing to consider changes at this stage but "set their feet in concrete" once the drawing is officially released for production.

2a. Process design: Outline. The manufacturing engineering group needs to decide on the general production concept. What machines will be used? Approximately what batch size? Job shop or production line?

2b. Process design: Detail. Now specific tools and fixtures have to be designed. What feed and speeds will be used? Will the operator use one or two hands? Will the operator sit or stand? What will the layout be? Will the conveyor feed from the left or the right?

3. Process installation. Concepts now have to be turned into reality. Translating drawings into reality often requires adjustments. Time/unit has to be established for cost accounting, planning, scheduling, and so forth. (See Chapter 27.) Operators and supporting staff need to be trained.

ple would be a fixed-dimension chair and selecting people to fit the chair; another would be a machine-paced assembly line and forcing each worker to work at the speed of the master cam. (2) *Fit the task to the worker.* The design adjusts to varying characteristics of the users. One example would be a chair that adjusts to individuals of different dimensions; another would be a human-paced assembly line with buffers so that all workers work at their own paces.

2.3 Make Search of Solution Space

At this stage the engineer designs a number of alternatives. (One of the key distinctions between science and engineering is that in science there is only one solution while in engineering there are a number of solutions.)

It is important for the engineer to try to get potential design ideas from many sources: workers, supervisors, vendors, suppliers, other staff people, other engineers, etc. Progress in technology can change formerly expensive solutions into good solutions. For example, previously, voice input/output and robots were expensive, unproven technologies; now they are applied routinely. In general, anything related to computers is much cheaper than it was 5 years ago. Benchmarking (see Box 7.2) is a technique of obtaining ideas from other organizations.

As shown later in Figure 32.2, the solution space will be cut down by various economic, political, esthetic, and legal constraints. Of the many feasible solutions (solutions that work), however, the engineer should try to get the best one—the **optimum solution.** The best will be a tradeoff of the various criteria, which also change from time to time, so the designer must be careful not to eliminate alternative designs too early.

Another problem is the tendency of designers to be **satisfiers** rather than optimizers. That is, designers tend to stop designing as soon as they have one feasible solution, when they have satisfied the problem. For example, when designing an assembly line, the engineer may stop as soon as there is a solution; when laying out the factory, the designer may stop as soon as one satisfactory layout is made. To get an optimum design, there must be a number of alternatives to select from. Alternatives also suggest further alternatives, so stopping too soon can severely limit the solution quality and acceptance.

2.4 Evaluate Alternatives

Consider trying out various alternatives with mockups, dry runs, pilot experiments, and simulations. This should give you better data for your evaluation.

BOX   **7.2**   *Benchmarking*

If you stand on someone's shoulders, you can see farther than that person can. The key concept of **benchmarking** is to learn from the experience of others and then apply the knowledge of someone else's product or process to your own product or process.

Product Ford provides an example of benchmarking using a product. To build a better car, Ford compiled a list of 400 features that customers said were important, looked at how its competitors did each of these features, and then picked the one to beat. For example, Ford benchmarked door handles versus Chevy Lumina, halogen headlamps versus Honda Accord, fuel economy (Lumina), front bench seats (Lumina), easy-to-change tail lamp bulbs (Nissan Maxima), express window control (Maxima), tilt wheel (Accord), remote radio controls (Pontiac Grand Prix), and so forth.

Process Firms often compare designs of their own processes at different plants of their own firm, but the big improvements come from seeing how strangers do it. A key point here is that the stranger may be in a different country or industry. For example, Ford benchmarked handling of accounts payable versus Mazda in Japan; Xerox benchmarked its order picking versus L. L. Bean.

Some guidelines for benchmarking follow:

- *Select a specific target.* After defining the problem, study your own process in detail before evaluating the approach of others.
- *Have people who make the decisions see the alternatives.* Senior decision makers often refuse to believe the teams and say "We can't be that bad."
- *Exchange information.* Be prepared to allow others to benchmark you also.
- *Avoid legal problems.* Benchmarking is not industrial espionage. Focus on existing products and processes, especially from noncompetitors.
- *Respect confidentiality.* Firms usually don't want their names used or data going to competitors.

A scientist tends to look for the single formula that describes one criterion of a situation; the engineer must trade off multiple criteria, usually without any satisfactory trade-off values. For example, one design of an assembly line may require .11 min/unit while another design may require .10 min/unit; however, the first design may give more job satisfaction to the workers. Which assembly line design should be used? How do you quantify job satisfaction? Even if you can put a numerical value on it, how many "satisfaction units" equal a 10% increase in assembly labor cost?

A simple ranking of alternatives (good, better, best) is sufficient in some cases. More precise is a numerical ranking, using a single criterion with an equal interval scale. (Method A requires 1.1 min/unit while method B requires 1.0 min/unit; design A requires 50 m^2 of floor space while design B requires 40 m^2 of floor space.) Most managers, however, prefer a comparison combining all the various costs and benefits in terms of money.

Even if the various costs and benefits can be put in such terms, they may be "different kinds" of money. For example, you must add operating costs (such as labor cost/unit), capital costs (machine purchase costs), maintenance costs (machine lubrication costs), product quality costs (reduced product failures in the field after 3 years of use), environmental costs (CO concentration in the work area reduced from 40 ppm to 30 ppm), and so on. Table 9.7 shows one approach.

Another technique is the "Disagree and Commit" method used at Intel. Normally, consensus is used for proposed solutions. But, when consensus cannot be achieved, design team members are given time to research a given issue and bring their recommendations to the team for discussion and review. Dissenters then agree to support the majority opinion.

2.5 Specify and Sell Solution Your abstract concept must be translated into "nuts and bolts"—detailed specifications. In addition, the installation has to be planned in detail (who does what and when). This is a relatively straightforward, although time-consuming, process.

First, however, you must convince decision makers to accept the proposal. Since the Amount of change = (Proposal quality)(Proposal acceptance), a low acceptance means little change. Thus, acceptance is critical.

Chapter 32 goes into more depth on resistance to change and how to overcome it. The key is input from others (especially users and decision makers) early in the design stage (steps 1, 2, and 3). At the meeting where the final proposal is presented, there should be no "surprises"; the participants should feel that you are presenting material they have already seen, commented on, and approved. That is, the "selling" is done early, not late; if they did not buy your approach then, you have modified it until it is acceptable. If you are modifying a previous design, the person who did the earlier design may feel you are challenging his or her work and thus resist any change. One common modification is partial change instead of full change; a "test market approach" instead of "immediate national rollout"; change of some of the machines in the department instead of all the machines.

The installation plan will have to be approved at a second meeting. It also should have preapproval by everyone before the decision meeting. During the installation itself, be flexible, as improvements may become apparent from suggestions of supervisors, operators, skilled-trade workers, and so on. The implementation should include training of direct and indirect workers, quality checks, debugging of equipment and procedures, and the like. Evaluate the project only after allowing time for operator learning and equipment/procedure debugging.

For firms with similar applications at multiple sites, follow the "Alpha site" project with a "Beta site" implementation before implementing at all sites (national rollout).

Finally, document the results. A documentary video and photos give opportunities to praise all the contributors (and may even reduce resistance to your next project).

Although some of the difficulties of engineering design are presented, engineering is a very satisfying profession. Herbert Hoover expressed it well:

> It is a great profession. There is the fascination of watching a figment of the imagination emerge through the aid of science to a plan on paper. Then it moves to realization in stone or metal or energy. Then it brings jobs and homes to men. Then it elevates the standards of living and adds to the comforts of life. That is the engineer's high privilege.

3 COST ALLOCATION

Organizations allocate costs into various categories to aid decision making. Table 7.3 gives a hypothetical cost breakdown of an electric fan. Different organizations, industries, and countries will have different categories and different ratios of costs in the categories depending on the product, industry, amount of competition, and so forth. A monopoly, for example, may have a higher profit/unit.

Direct materials and **direct labor** (also called "touch" labor because they touch the product) are the most easily allocated costs. Of course, there may be difficulties, such as when multiple products use

---

TABLE   7.3

Hypothetical cost breakdown of an electric fan. Although the percent of each cost varies widely by product and industry, a rule of thumb is direct labor cost = 10% of manufacturing cost; operating indirect labor = 100%–150% of direct labor; clerical/technical indirect labor = 100%–250% of direct labor cost. These same ratios apply to the vendor who furnishes purchased components.

CATEGORY	EXAMPLE		COST/FAN ($)
Raw materials (need more work)	Steel for fan blades		.80
Purchased parts and assemblies (used as is)	Motor, bearings, knobs		4.00
Direct labor	Time to stamp out blades, paint blades, assemble knob to shaft		1.00
		Prime Cost	**5.80**
Indirect labor burden	Fork truck drivers, industrial engineers		4.00
Indirect materials burden	Toilet paper, light bulbs		.50
Capital burden	Depreciation for machines, conveyors, building		.72
		Manufacturing Cost	**11.02**
Selling cost	Warranties, sales salaries		2.00
		Total Cost at Factory	**13.02**
Profit	Interest, risk		.98
		Factory Selling Price	**14.00**
Distribution cost	Shipping, distribution chain expenses and profit		6.00
		Consumer Price	**20.00**

the same material or the same worker is assigned to work on many different products. For managerial control, firms usually keep raw material costs separate from purchased components costs; their total is the direct material cost. *Direct material + direct labor = prime cost.*

Overhead (burden) is the next level of costs to be allocated. It can be divided into indirect labor, indirect materials, and capital costs. Indirect labor includes the salaries and wages of the clerks, engineers, technicians, supervisors, inspectors, and others. Indirect materials burden includes the cost of the electricity, water, and other utilities and the cost of various supplies such as paper clips, pencils, lubricating oil, degreasing compounds used before painting, grinding wheels, and toilet paper. Capital burden includes the cost of the fork trucks, conveyors, machine tools, the building, property taxes, and so forth.

Progressive firms now are allocating portions of overhead costs to local organizational units called **cost centers** to encourage the reduction of waste. For example, a department could be charged $200/yr/desk for utilities, $100/yr for PC computer maintenance, $100/person/yr for janitorial support, or $20,000 for every lost-time back injury. *Prime cost + factory burden = manufacturing cost,* the cost of getting an item to the factory door.

In most circumstances customers are not standing outside your door in the rain clamoring to buy your product. To sell a product requires catalogues, product warranties, and so forth, as well as wages for those concerned with this work. *Manufacturing cost + selling cost = total cost at the factory.*

Next is the cost of capital (interest) and the cost of risk of the capital. They are usually totaled and called *profit.* For example, income taxes on the firm will be built into the cost structure and thus really are passed on to the customer; corporate income taxes really are a concealed sales tax. In the long run these expected costs and risks must be built into the product price in both capitalist and socialist organizations. If these costs are not included in the product price, the organization loses money, which must come either from the owner's assets or the taxpayer's assets. *Total cost + profit = selling price at the factory.*

Since in normal circumstances the customer does not come to the door, there are additional costs for distribution of the product. They include shipping and expenses of the retailing organization. *Factory price + distribution cost = consumer price.*

Within the factory, the engineer probably will deal mostly with the manufacturing cost of $11.02. Actually, fans probably will not cost $11.02 each day because on some days more scrap is made, on some days more or less labor is used, and so forth. The $11.02 is not the real cost but is a **standard cost.** Standard costs incorporate assumptions about things such as the standard amount of material, a standard price/unit of material, a standard amount of labor, a standard price/unit of labor, a standard amount of scrap, a standard cost of each type of defect, a standard use of energy/unit, a standard amount of overhead/unit.

Unfortunately it is difficult to keep standard costs accurate over time as conditions change. For example, standard labor cost may be based on prorating the setup cost over 10,000 units/yr. Over the years, however, production may have changed to 5,000/yr or 15,000/yr, causing an error in the standard setup hours/unit and thus an error in the standard cost. Another common problem is that the standard labor hours/unit (say, painting time of 10 s/unit) may not be the actual time (painting time may be 9 s or 12 s). When making a cost analysis, try to use actual costs instead of standard costs.

When jobs are designed, a common criterion is the cost/unit; that is, we judge workstation A to be better than workstation B because labor cost/unit is lower for workstation A. Labor cost/unit should never be the sole criterion because material and overhead costs also are important. The following section discusses some of the important money costs to consider.

4 RETURN ON INVESTMENT

Do the benefits of a design outweigh the costs? Oxenburgh (1991) has written an excellent book giving 61 case studies of the economic benefits of ergonomic improvements. See Box 7.3.

Making the benefit/cost comparison (determining the **return on investment**) requires three steps:

1. determining what is changed due to the design (e.g., product quality is better)
2. putting the changes into monetary units (e.g., improved quality is worth $.02/unit)
3. calculating the total benefits versus costs (e.g., all the changes totaled give benefits of $4,700/yr; all the costs total $1,400/yr)

Most errors in decision making are due to poor data for steps 1 and 2; engineers and accountants tend to "overkill" step 3 with exotic formulas and complex calculations to four decimal places when they have errors of ±50% in steps 1 and 2. Spend approximately 90% of your time in steps 1 and 2 and 10% in step 3; you will make better decisions than the person who reverses the ratio. The secret is valid data. Leave out judgments and opinions unless supported by data and quantified into dollars.

BOX **7.3** *Justifying Ergonomics*

Some people think ergonomics does not have to be justified economically because "it is the right thing to do." How could anyone be against improving health and safety of the workers? Managers, although predisposed to "do good deeds," have to be able to justify them financially—at least in general, even if not every specific application has to be cost-justified.

One approach is "success stories" (case studies). Oxenburgh (1991) shows 61 case studies; he calls this the "100,000,000 blowflies can't be wrong method." Hendrick (1996) has more examples. Success stories also can be used as parables, teaching general guidelines. This book has many short examples scattered through the various chapters.

AT&T Global in San Diego had 800 employees. The company made computers and identified three types of frequent injuries: lifting, fastening, and keyboarding (Hendrick, 1997). After ergonomic analyses and changes, annual Worker Compensation cost dropped from $400,000 to $94,000. After a second round of changes, the Worker Compensation cost dropped to $12,000 annually. Lost workdays due to injury dropped from 298 in year 0 to 0 in both years 3 and 4. The savings in 4 years was $1,480,000.

Red Wing Shoes in Minnesota implemented an ergonomics program (Hendrick, 1997). In a 6-year period, Worker Compensation premiums dropped 70% for a savings of $3,100,000; annual OSHA-reportable lost-time injuries per 100 workers dropped from 75 to 19.

Helander and Burri (1995) reported that, at IBM, 250,000 h had been devoted to ergonomics training. "Ergonomics improvements have resulted in cost savings of approximately $130,000,000."

MacLeod and Morris (1996) reported that a paper manufacturer initiated a comprehensive ergonomics program. Investment was $2,500,000, and total benefits were $3,500,000. They concluded that ergonomics programs should be instituted just for the cost savings, even if there were no government regulations. In their experience, the average productivity improvement of an ergonomics change was 25%.

Three examples from 3M (Albin, 1997) are:

- A 3M "ergo-team" modified molds to reduce the wrist-intensive effort required to remove flash (waste material). This resulted in an approximate annual cost saving of $250,000 for an initial investment of $85,000.

- A 3M "ergo-team" redesigned a work area to reduce repetitive motion while packing cans. The redesign decreased costs, repetitive motion, and space requirements. Benefits were $350,000/yr at an initial cost of about $300,000.

- A 3M "ergo-team" redesigned a production line to reduce awkward wrist postures during assembly. The improvements resulted in more comfort and productivity gains worth $10,000/yr at a one-time cost of $5,000.

Everyone will be happier if ergonomics can be justified financially. (Note that other staff people, such as product designers, cost accountants, and maintenance personnel, are all in the same boat as ergonomists; they occasionally will have to justify their job.) This justification is much easier if you will collect **your** success stories and be able to show a good return on investment on at least some of your projects. Oxenburgh (1991; 1997) shows how to justify ergonomic projects; there is a heavy emphasis on overhead and indirect costs such as overtime, turnover (replacement workers), training, and supervisory expenses.

Riel and Imbeau (1995a, 1995b) divide health and safety costs into (1) insurance costs (disability payments, legal and medical expenses), (2) work-related costs (from work performed in less than optimal conditions), and (3) perturbation costs (costs from accidents and diseases). Although it may be obvious, since return on investment is a ratio of benefits/expenses, it is a great help to keep expenses (primarily capital costs) low. Everyone wants a "low-cost" solution; however, this is not always a low capital-cost solution. If a solution has a high capital cost (say $100,000) but a quick payback (say .5 year), then it is certainly a low-cost solution as you are talking about a 200% return on investment!

When calculating the "bottom line," don't ignore inflation. For example, Moore and Garg (1998) reported that year 7 Worker Compensation expenses in a meat products firm were, if inflation was considered, 16% of year 1; but, if inflation was ignored, 31% of year 1. Inflation for your firm may not be the same as for the U. S. economy. Also, different people may be interested in different bottom lines; for example, Moore and Garg (1998) said that, for this firm, the sale of 35,000 pounds of product was required to balance $1,000 of extra cost.

From a "big-picture" viewpoint, consider ergonomics, productivity, quality, and "yield." Ergonomics changes may be justified by improve-

BOX | **7.3** | *Justifying Ergonomics, continued*

ments only in safety and health and reduced stress on the worker. Ergonomic changes, however, usually improve productivity and quality as well. If maintenance access time for a specific repair is improved from 10 min to 5 min, this increases machine "uptime" by 5 min. This can be quite important for expensive or bottleneck equipment.

As an example of yield, Moore and Garg (1998) reported that, when deboning operations were modified to improve ergonomics, the firm not only got better quality meat but also more meat/pig.

Thus, when justifying ergonomic projects, don't ignore the productivity and quality benefits. Also, when doing quality or productivity projects, don't forget to include ergonomic benefits.

A good procedure is to require all process modifications and capital project modifications to be evaluated for "ergonomic concerns"; require a sign-off before the project is released for implementation.

Table 7.4 shows how Boeing prioritizes ergonomic projects.

5 COST ANALYSIS

Figure 7.1 gives a cost analysis that emphasizes steps 1 and 2. It is oriented to metal-working manufacturing, but you can adapt it to your own industry. The example evaluates use of a special-purpose screwdriver for use in making automobile tune-ups in a garage. Key information required is: (1) project life, (2) annual savings, and (3) one-time cost.

5.1 Life of the Application The top of the form starts with basic information such as project, part name, part number, and where used. The first item is **life of the application,** which can be limited either by the life of the equipment (say a lathe would be worn out in 5 years) or by life of the product (say a fixture

made obsolete by an anticipated change in product design in 3 years). Good practice is to use a project life of 20 years or less. It is very hard to predict the future; a project life of 30 or 40 years is highly unlikely. Assume the screwdrivers have an application life of 5 years.

The volume/yr is important. Be careful to calculate pcs/h and pcs/day by dividing by the proper number of days the product is made/yr; most products are *not* made continuously, so the rate/h usually cannot be multiplied by 1,800 hours/yr to obtain annual output. In many cases volume/h may change over the life of the application. Estimate volume/yr for each year; for a simple level of analysis (such as with this form), use the average; for a more precise analysis, use each year's estimate to calculate the benefits/cost

T A B L E		7 . 4		

Matrix to determine ergonomic benefit (Faville, 1995). Ergonomists evaluate both ergonomic risk and ergonomic improvement on a low, medium, and high scale; the result is low, medium, and high benefit. Additional calculations are made of: the number of people affected (few, some, many), development time required (low = <1 week, medium = 1 week to 6 months, high = >6 months), and estimated implementation cost (low, medium low, medium, medium high, and high). Numerical values are assigned to the four factors: ergonomic benefit, number of people affected, development time, and implementation cost. The scores then are added. Historically, Boeing has used a double weight for ergonomic benefit. The ranking then is presented to management.

ERGONOMIC IMPROVEMENT	ERGONOMIC RISK		
	Low	**Medium**	**High**
Low	Low Benefit	Low Benefit	Medium Benefit
Medium	Low Benefit	Medium Benefit	High Benefit
High	Medium Benefit	High Benefit	High Benefit

Source: From B. Faville, One approach for an ergonomics program in a large manufacturing environment. In *Advances in Industrial Ergonomics and Safety VII.* A. Bittner and P. Champney, Eds. © Copyright 1995 by Taylor & Francis, London. Reprinted with permission.

FIGURE   7.1

Example cost analysis. Cost analysis forms reduce the risk of omitting relevant data. The data shown are for a proposed specialized screwdriver to be used for automobile tune-ups. Costs can be given for two alternatives; for example, for direct labor, the cost is $.111 for the existing method and $.083 for the best manual proposal. The costs also can be given as a change from the reference value; for example, for pain and suffering, the existing method is the reference and the best manual proposal will save $.010/unit.

Project _____ Superdriver _____

Part name _____ Part number _____ Used in dept. ____ Tune-up ____

Volume ___ 800 ___ pcs/yr _____ pcs/day _____ pcs/h _____ h/pc

Labor cost/h ___ $20.00 ___ Engineer ___ SK ___

A. Life of Application _____ 5 _____ yrs

B. Annual Cost on the Controlling Operation

	Existing Method	Best Manual Proposal	Best Mechanized Proposal
Direct labor, $/unit	.111	.083	
Relief labor, $/unit			
Downtime, $/unit			
Maintenance, $/unit			
Direct material, $/unit	reference	0	
Indirect material, $/unit	.007	.009	
Perishable tools, $/unit			
Tool regrind (repair), $/unit			
Utilities, $/unit			
Inspection, $/unit	reference	0	
Product quality, $/unit	reference	−.010	
Rework and scrap, $/unit	.005	.002	
Absenteeism cost, $/unit			
Safety and health, $/unit			
Turnover of workers, $/unit			
Other (specify) _pain_ $/unit	reference	−.010	
TOTAL, $/unit and suffering	.123	.074	
TOTAL, $/year			
Line 1 Savings/year (Col. 2 or 3 − Col. 1)		$39.20	

C. One-Time Cost, $

Equipment, $	reference	3.00	
Jigs, fixtures for equipment, $	−	−	
Installation, $	−	−	
Operator retraining, $	reference	1.67	
Engineering, $	reference	90.00	
Line 2 Total one-time cost, $	reference	$94.67	

D. Benefit/Cost Calculations

Line 3 Total savings during application life	= $	196.00	(Line 1 × yrs)
Line 4 One-time cost	= $	94.67	(Line 2)
Line 5 Net savings	= $	101.23	(Line 3 − Line 4)
Line 6 Net savings/year	= $	20.27	(Line 5 ÷ application yrs)
Line 7 Return on investment before taxes, %	=	21%	(Line 6 × 100 / Line 4)

for each year (see an engineering economics text such as Newman and Lavelle [1998] for the solution techniques). In our example, assume 800 tune-ups/yr with an average time of 1.0 h/tune-up.

An important question is the labor cost/h. Most cost reductions are justified by labor savings; the question is what is the proper labor-cost rate to use. A worker may be paid $14/h. Because of fringe benefits (insurance, pension, Social Security, holidays, vacations, etc.), the cost to the organization will be higher, perhaps 30–40% higher. Thus, use cost of (for example) $20/h instead of $14/h. The burden in the factory may be allocated in proportion to direct labor cost (e.g., at 300% of direct labor), so cost/h may be given as $20 + 3(20) = $80/h. Use the direct labor cost ($20/h) rather than direct labor plus burden ($80/h). If labor cost is reduced, there is no reason to believe that burden cost will be reduced; in fact, burden expense often increases (e.g., for more electrical power). Even for a constant burden cost, a lower amount of direct labor will mean that the burden rate/direct labor-hour will increase. Be suspicious of cost-reduction proposals that use cost rates including burden. Burden changes can be listed separately. These imprecise cost estimates may be important in finely balanced decisions. In our case, assume labor cost of $20/h.

Next, record information for three alternatives: the existing solution, the best manual proposal, and the best mechanized proposal. The reason for requiring the best manual proposal is that engineers love machines and devices and, thus, often have a bias toward solutions that involve machines and devices. In our example, only simple handtools seem feasible, so the mechanized alternative will not be considered.

Two additional types of information are needed. These are annual savings and one-time costs.

5.2 Annual Savings

When calculating benefits of an ergonomic change, you need to implement the change at other similar workstations at the same facility as well as other facilities of the organization. This transfer of technology is not automatic; the firm has to have a "lessons learned" procedure to implement the ideas within the facility and between facilities. Also, you need to remember the improvements over time so the engineers do not "reinvent the wheel."

Annual savings, the second key item, is determined by calculating the savings/unit and then multiplying by annual volume. (Most items are not produced continuously, so it is not valid to multiply the daily rate by 240 days/yr.) In some situations, it may be easier to calculate annual savings for each subcategory directly:

■ Direct labor is the cost of labor exerted specifically on this particular operation. An existing screwdriver for auto tune-ups may require 20 s/tune-up versus 15 s/tune-up for a proposed screwdriver. In the example, existing cost would be (20/3600) (20) = $.111/tune-up, while proposed cost is $.083.

■ Relief cost is the cost for substitute labor on an assembly line (e.g., seven workers may work at six stations). In this auto tune-up example, there are no relief costs.

■ Downtime is the cost of idle equipment or workers at this or other workstations. On tightly linked jobs, downtime becomes very important since downtimes add. In the screwdriver example we will assume that other workers are not tightly linked to this job and downtime is zero for both alternatives.

■ Maintenance is the cost of equipment maintenance. Assume zero maintenance for both screwdrivers.

■ Direct material is material used in the product. Assume $12 for materials with either tool (no cost difference).

■ Indirect materials cover miscellaneous supplies and materials. Assume that the existing tool causes one stripped setscrew/50 tune-ups but the proposed tool, because it permits more torque, will probably have one stripped setscrew/40 tune-ups. Assume a setscrew costs $.10 plus $.25 for the labor required to get the replacement screw from the stockroom. Thus the existing tool cost is $.35/50 = $.007/tune-up while the proposed cost is $.009.

■ Perishable tools (tool bits, grinding wheels, etc.) are used up by the process. Assume zero for both screwdriver alternatives.

■ Tool regrind (repair) is the repairing, resharpening, or reworking of tools. Assume neither screwdriver will need repair.

■ Utility costs include electricity, water, heat, and light. Assume no change in utility costs occurs with either screwdriver.

■ Inspection costs include inspection both by the worker and by separate inspectors. Assume inspection cost of $1/tune-up regardless of the screwdriver used.

■ Product quality is the improvement (degradation) in the product as expressed in warranties, lost customers, good will, lawsuits, and so forth. A product can be defective due to (1) a design defect (improper design, perhaps because the engineer did not anticipate how the product would be used) or (2) a manufacturing defect (item not made to specification). Legal costs are difficult to predict, but just defending a firm can cost hundreds of thousands of dollars; if you lose, it may cost much more. One aspect of injuries that often is not considered in the cost of accidents is the lower quality work by the replacement worker, as a "rookie" makes many mistakes. Assume that the proposed tool will give a very slightly better tune-up; estimated value of $.01/tune-up.

- Rework and scrap is the cost of the product quality before it leaves the department. These costs are notoriously underestimated, because people do not want to call attention to their errors. (See Figure 8.5.) Assume the existing tool requires rework in 1/70 tune-ups while the proposed tool will require rework for 1/140; the rework time is estimated as 60 s. Then existing cost is (60/3600) (1/70) (20) = $.005/tune-up while the proposed cost is $.002.

- Absences can be planned (holidays, vacation) or unplanned. Unplanned absenteeism can be voluntary or involuntary. Involuntary absenteeism typically comes from sickness, accidents, and cumulative trauma. Payment (plus fringe benefits) goes to the absent person as well as to the replacement worker, and so costs are approximately doubled. Estimate the absenteeism rate for each alternative and the number of hours/yr absent. Multiply by the cost of an absent hour. Assume equal absences for both screwdrivers.

- Safety and health costs include medical costs and paperwork costs. Many doctors charge hundreds or even thousands of dollars/hour, and therefore costs become extraordinary. Estimate the cost of a safety/health problem and multiply it by the probability of its occurring for the various alternatives. Costs for a firm can be estimated from Workers Compensation records (medical costs and disability costs) plus costs incurred that Workers Compensation does not cover. Probability of occurrence can be estimated from the OSHA 200 logs (which record all on-the-job illnesses and injuries). A job might have an incidence of 8/200,000 hours. (The 200,000 is based on 100 people working 2,000 hours/yr.) If you estimate that incidence would be cut to 6, there would be a savings of 2/200,000 h or 1 case/ 100,000 h. Assume equal health and safety costs for both screwdrivers.

- Turnover of workers should include (1) acquisition costs such as recruiting, selecting, hiring, and induction of employees; (2) development costs such as orientation, on- and off-the-job training, and loss in productivity due to incomplete training; and (3) separation costs such as severance pay and vacant position costs. Assume equal turnover for both screwdrivers.

- Other costs are any additional costs you find relevant. Assume, in this case, that the proposed

screwdriver will cause less fatigue, less muscle pain, and fewer cracked knuckles; you value this as $.01/tune-up.

The total cost considered for the existing screwdriver then is .111 + .007 + .005 = $.123/tune-up while for the proposed tool it is .083 + .009 − .01 + .002 − .01 = $.074/tune-up. Thus, savings/tune-up is $.49/tune-up; annual savings are .49 × 800 = $39.20/year.

5.3 One-Time Costs Next consider the **one-time costs**, the third key item, which include the following:

- Equipment cost is the purchased cost (including tax and delivery) of the equipment to your receiving dock. In this example, assume the existing tool costs $1 while the proposed tool costs $3. However, the existing tool will last the application life and its cost already has been paid, so consider its cost as zero. For a more expensive tool it may be worth considering its decline in value over the application life; that is, the difference between what you could sell it for now and what you could sell it for at the end of the application life.

  Many pieces of support equipment, such as tables, chairs, and jigs, can be made by a firm's existing staff; these people are already on the payroll so the equipment gets costed at out-of-pocket costs such as material; labor and overhead costs are ignored. Thus, the reported capital cost is very low.

- Jigs and fixtures often are required for equipment use. Assume as zero in the screwdriver example.

- Installation costs refers to the costs of getting the equipment from your dock installed and working. Typical expenses are for millwrights, electricians, and plumbers. Assume as zero in this example.

- Operator retraining refers to the loss in output while the operators adjust to the new procedure, tool, or device. Assume retraining for the proposed tool will require about 5 min; thus, its one-time costs would be (5/60) (20) = $1.67.

- Engineering costs (often forgotten in cost analyses) include time to investigate the new method, determine alternatives, calculate costs, sell recommendations, and install the new method, if accepted. For our example, assume it took the engineer 3 h to read about the proposed tool, talk to people, and make this estimate. Assume the engineer's wages are 150% of the mechanic's wages/h, so engineering cost is 3 ($30/h) = $90.

Thus, total one-time costs for the existing alternative are $0; one-time costs for the proposal are $3 + $1.67 + $90 = $94.67.

TABLE	7.5

Return on investment and return on sales of selected organizations in 2002. Each year *Fortune* magazine reports the results for the 500 largest corporations.

NAME	SALES RANK	SALES	ASSETS (000,000,000 omitted)	NET INCOME	PERCENT RETURN ON SALES	ASSETS
Wal-Mart	1	246.5	94.5	8.0	3.3	8.5
Abbott Lab	100	17.7	24.3	2.8	15.8	11.5
Pepsi Bottling	200	9.2	10.0	0.4	4.6	4.3
Apple Computer	300	5.7	6.3	0.065	1.1	1.0
Cablevision Sys.	400	4.0	10.3	0.090	2.3	0.9
Neiman Marcus	500	2.9	1.9	0.100	3.4	5.2
The 500 median					3.1	2.3

5.4 Benefit/Cost Calculations

Total gross savings/yr, during the application life of 5 years, give total gross savings of $39.20 \times 5 = \$196$. Subtracting the one-time expenses ($94.67) gives net benefits of $196 - \$94.67 = \$101.33$. Returning to a yearly basis, this is $101.33/5 = \$20.27$. The return on investment is $20.27 \times 100/94.67 = 21\%$.

In some cases it is difficult to estimate the amount of savings from a project. A useful technique is to calculate the savings for several alternatives, such as a 1%, a 2%, and a 5% improvement in productivity. The question then becomes not the exact improvement but whether the improvement is likely to be greater than the minimum required.

For example, for a person costing $20/h (including fringes), the annual cost (assuming an 1,800 h workyear) is $36,000. A 1% change would be $360, a 2% = $720, and a 5% = $1,800. Then a new chair costing $180 and improving output 1% (5 min/day; $360) would pay for itself in $180/360 = .5$ years. If it were to improve output .1%, it would pay for itself in 5 years (i.e., a 20% return on investment). The question that management then has to answer (assuming 20% is satisfactory) is, "Do you think an improved chair will improve output at least 30 s/day?"

For professional/office occupations, it often is difficult to count output. Substitute "time spent at work" for "work output." For example, if an engineer has back pain and loses 18 h of work in an 1,800 h year, the engineer has a productivity loss of 1%.

Organizations usually require new projects to have a proposed return on investment greater than they presently are making. Table 7.5 gives some example returns on investments for firms on an overall basis. The return needed for individual projects depends on the organization. This "expected minimum" rate might be modified in some situations. For example:

Category 1: laboratories, safety equipment, recreation facilities, etc., where no direct return is available, so return on investment is not used

Category 2: new projects with expectation of growth

Category 3: old products with a short life that may require greater return on investment

Review Questions

1. Give the five steps of engineering design (DAMES).
2. Give three industrial applications of "fighting giants."
3. What is an OSHA 200 log?
4. Discuss benchmarking an office operation.
5. What is a typical return on investment, after taxes, for a 1-year certificate of deposit in a bank (i.e., a risk-free investment)? What is a typical return on investment of U. S. manufacturing industry (i.e., a risky investment)?
6. Why should cost reductions include an analysis for "best manual proposal" as well as "best mechanized proposal"?

References

Albin, T. Personal communication, Sept. 1997.

Andersson, E. Economic evaluation of ergonomic solutions: Part I—Guidelines for the practitioner. *Int. J. of Industrial Ergonomics,* Vol. 10, 161–71, 1992.

Faville, B. One approach for an ergonomics program in a large manufacturing environment. In *Advances in Industrial Ergonomics and Safety VII,* A. Bittner and P. Champney, eds. London: Taylor and Francis, 1995.

Helander, M. and Burri, G. Cost effectiveness of ergonomics and quality improvements in electronics manufacturing. *Int. J. of Industrial Ergonomics,* Vol. 15, 137–51, 1995.

Hendrick, H. The ergonomics of economics is the economics of ergonomics. *Proceedings of HFES,* HFES: Santa Monica, CA, 1996.

Hendrick, H. The economics of ergonomics. *Advances in Occupational Ergonomics and Safety II,* B. Das and W. Karwowski, eds. Cincinnati: IOS Press and Ohmsha, 3–8, 1997.

MacLeod, D. and Morris, A. Ergonomics cost benefits case study in a paper manufacturing company. *Proc.*

of Human Factors and Ergonomics Society, 698–701, 1996.

Moore, S. and Garg, S. The effectiveness of participatory ergonomics in the red meat packing industry. *Int. J. of Industrial Ergonomics,* Vol. 21, 47–58, 1998.

Mowrer, O. *Learning Theory and the Symbolic Process.* New York: Wiley & Sons, 1960.

Newman, D. and Lavelle, J. *Engineering Economic Analysis,* 7th ed. Austin, TX: Engineering Press, 1998.

Oxenburgh, M. *Increasing Productivity and Profit Through Health and Safety.* Chicago: CCH International, 1991.

Riel, P. and Imbeau, D. Economic justification of investments for health and safety interventions—Part I: A cost typology. *Int. J. of Industrial Engineering,* Vol. 2, No. 1, 45–54, 1995a.

Riel, P. and Imbeau, D. Economic justification of investments for health and safety interventions—Part II: Applying activity based costing to the insurance cost. *Int. J. of Industrial Engineering,* Vol. 2, No. 1, 55–64, 1995b.

SEARCH FOR SOLUTIONS

SEARCH FOR SOLUTIONS

1 Unstructured Search

2 Structured Search: Systematic

3 Structured Search: SEARCH

Overview

Searching for the best job design is divided into three categories. The first category is unstructured search, typified by brainstorming. Both the second and third categories are structured search. The second category is checklists. The third category uses the acronym SEARCH, where S = Simplify, E = Eliminate, A = Alter sequence, R = Requirements, C = Combine, and H = How often.

Key Concepts

alter sequence

autoconfrontation

brainstorming

checklists

combine operations

critical examination form

eliminate unnecessary
  work

exception principle

group technology

groupware

how often

initial versus continuing
  costs

nominal group technique

prerelease review

red, yellow, and green
  operations

requirements

self-service

simplify operations

unstructured search

As discussed in Chapter 7, engineering design requires DAMES:

- definition of the problem
- analysis
- making a search for a solution
- evaluation of alternatives
- specification and selling of the solution

This chapter discusses the search for a solution. Edison, who had more inventions than anyone else in the history of the world, expressed it well: "Genius is 1% inspiration and 99% perspiration." What are some of the techniques for searching?

UNSTRUCTURED SEARCH

When trying to solve a problem, we may focus too narrowly. That is, we reject possible solutions in our own minds due to assumptions, which, if considered carefully, turn out to be not limiting. What is desirable is obtaining many possible solutions; reducing them later is easy compared to the problem of getting a "large solution space."

In **unstructured search,** ideas (green-light thinking) are encouraged and criticism (red-light thinking) is discouraged, because criticism may discourage contributions. Avoid "groupthink," the drive for consensus that suppresses disagreement and prevents the appraisal of alternatives.

Three techniques are described to encourage inspirations: brainstorming, the nominal group technique, and groupware. All three techniques are used with groups of people.

1.1 Brainstorming In the **brainstorming** technique, the discussion leader states the problem clearly and then asks for oral suggestions from the group. The leader displays the idea publicly (say, on a chalkboard) using different words if possible. (Paraphrasing the ideas is a useful technique to be sure the leader understands the idea.) The public display of the idea encourages the person contributing and also may serve as a springboard to other ideas by other people. No criticism is permitted of any idea. Ideas are not identified with their contributors. This reduces social pressure to accept or reject an idea because it came from someone with high or low status.

The leader, knowing the tendency of some individuals to be extroverts, should discourage one or two individuals from dominating the session by recognizing others in the group first. In some cases it may be necessary to recognize shy individuals purposefully and say, "What do you think, Joe?" Another technique for encouraging participation is to take ideas from people in sequence. Ten minutes is sufficient for most brainstorming sessions.

After the brainstorming is complete, the group begins evaluating the ideas. If there are many ideas, rank the "top 5" or "top 10." A more complex procedure is to vote on the square root of the number of alternatives displayed.

1.2 Nominal Group Technique There is some evidence that group participation *inhibits* creative thinking, because some people dominate and some just sit there. Another technique is the **nominal group technique,** in which the participants are only nominally a group. They act more as individuals than as a group. This technique uses the following steps:

1. The leader states the problem.
2. In small groups, the leader gets suggestions from each person in turn. Participants cannot make a suggestion until their turn comes. In larger groups, each person makes suggestions on a sheet of paper. The idea is to force everyone to contribute, preventing one or two people from dominating the discussion. No criticism is allowed.
3. The leader publicly displays the ideas. If there are many, it may be worthwhile to consolidate them to fewer ideas.
4. The merit (importance) of the ideas is evaluated by selecting the best ideas rather than eliminating the worst. If there are 9 alternatives, vote for 3. The best would have a vote of 3; the second, 2; and the third, 1.
5. The leader publicly tallies the number of votes for each alternative. For example, alternative 1 got 8 points, alternative 2 got 10 points, and so forth. Select the alternatives with the highest points (perhaps 3 or 4) for further discussion.

1.3 Groupware **Groupware,** for use with computer networks, allows multiple computers to communicate simultaneously with each other. Technically, what everyone does is communicate to central "bulletin boards," one for each topic. The bulletin board can hold not only comments but also databases. Thus, communication is not one-to-one but many-to-many. In this approach, the nominal group need not even be at the same physical location. Because the responses are anonymous, social pressure does not restrain comments. Some remarks, therefore, can be quite blunt: "The company policy is stupid!" This behavior goes by the picturesque label of "flaming."

Since nearly everyone in the company has access to the bulletin board, the information on the board is much more widely available than traditional sources of information. And, because the information that supports decisions is now widely available to all levels of the organization, decisions (both good and bad) are fair game for comments by many people. This trend has profound consequences for organizations that emphasize authority over democracy.

Although groupware can speed communication, it also increases the mass of information available to everyone and thus may cause information overload. At one time, people responded to every letter and phone call. This is less feasible when a person receives hundreds of messages every day.

1.4 Videotape Analysis   A trained mind can find many possible problems and solutions through a simple "walk through" of the facility. Even better is to record the operations on videotape (see Box 14.3) and then have a team (supervisors, engineers) observe the tape in a quiet conference room. The videotape permits backing up, repeating the actions, viewing in slow motion, freezing the frame, and so on. The team permits multiple people with multiple backgrounds to interact. **Autoconfrontation,** where the operator explains the video to the team, gives a deeper understanding of the task because the operator can explain the mental and managerial aspects of the task, as well as the physical aspects. The results of the meeting can be potential solutions to problems or indications of where further analysis is desirable.

2 STRUCTURED SEARCH: SYSTEMATIC

Most people think that, rather than depending upon inspiration, they should follow a more systematic approach. Why not follow tried-and-true techniques used by people who have previously worked on this type of problem?

Table 8.1 gives such a systematic approach. The basic concept is that good information leads to good decisions. In addition, "before" information can be compared to "after" information.

Step 1 is to identify management's perception of the problem. Although it may not be the real problem, it is a start. For example, management may consider that there is a quality problem, or an ergonomics problem, or a labor cost problem. Your goal is to get the best combination of ergonomics, quality, and other factors. (The project also may be triggered by ergonomics teams, Quality Circles, and many other possibilities.) For preliminary statistics, get time/unit, process yield, error rate (ideally with types of errors), and job descriptions.

Step 2 is to see for yourself. **Checklists** help you remember what to look for. (Note that questions not on the checklist tend to be forgotten!)

Victor Morales developed the **critical examination form** shown in Figure 8.1. The boxes ask suggestive questions about the rows of purpose, place, sequence, person, and means. The first column describes the existing situation. The second and third columns try to get you to think of alternatives by bringing out disadvantages of the present method and advantages of alternatives. The fourth column asks for a decision.

Beardsley (1980) gives another technique, based on the "5 W's and an H." Taking 6 pieces of paper, write WHO, WHAT, WHY, WHERE, WHEN, and HOW, one on the top of each sheet. Then, on the sheet

		TABLE 8.1	

Procedure for ergonomics and productivity assessment (Helander and Burri, 1995). If possible, for comparison, obtain measures before and after the change.

SOURCE OF INFORMATION	METHOD	DATA COLLECTED
1. Management	Unstructured interview Collect statistics	Manufacturing measures of productivity, yield throughput, types of defects; job descriptions; injury and absenteeism rates
2. Plant walk-through	Ergonomics checklist	Investigator observes ergonomics and productivity; verified by operator
3. Operators	Unstructured interview Questionnaires Task analyses Videos	Comments on ergonomics, productivity; task analyses; job descriptions
4. First-line supervisors	Unstructured interviews	Current problems in mfg. process; housekeeping
5. Field measurements	Light, sound meters; tape measures	Ambient environment; workstation dimensions

Source: Reprinted from *Int. J. of Industrial Ergonomics,* Vol. 15. M. Helander and G. Burri. "Cost Effectiveness of Ergonomics and Quality Improvements in Electronics Manufacturing." Copyright © 1995, pp. 137–51, with permission from Elsevier Science.

FIGURE   8.1

Morales's critical examination form.

Situation Studied _____	Date _____
Why Studied _____	Study by _____
Where _____	_____ minutes/occurrence
How Often Repeated per Year _____	_____ minutes/year

	1	2	3	4
Purpose	What is achieved?	What would happen if it weren't done?	What could be done and still meet requirements?	What should be done?
Place	Where is it done?	Disadvantages of doing it there:	Where else could it be done? Advantages of doing it elsewhere:	Where should it be done?
Sequence	When is it done? After:	Disadvantages of doing it then:	Advantages of doing it sooner: Advantages of doing it later:	When should it be done?
Person	Who does it?	Why that person?	List two others who could do it.	Who should do it?
Means	What equipment and methods are used? Equipment: Method:	Disadvantages of equipment: Method:	How else could it be done? Advantages:	How should it be done?

with WHO, write down all questions concerning WHO and the problem. Examples are:

WHO should do it?

WHO should bring the materials?

WHO should supervise?

WHO should inspect?

Then, on the sheet with WHAT, write down all questions concerning WHAT and the problem. Continue with WHY, WHERE, WHEN, and HOW. Don't worry about the sequence of questions. At this stage you are just generating ideas.

The second stage is to answer one of the questions on one of the sheets. For example, Joe Roberts should bring the material. Now write JOE ROBERTS on the top of a sheet of paper and make up 6 questions con-

cerning Joe Roberts, starting with WHO, WHAT, WHERE, WHY, WHEN, and HOW. Examples are:

WHO is Joe Roberts?

WHAT exactly should Joe bring?

WHERE should Joe bring it?

WHY did I select Joe?

WHEN should Joe bring it?

HOW should Joe bring it?

Then go on to the next question on the initial sheets. Answer it, and ask WHO, WHAT, WHERE, WHY, WHEN, and HOW.

The third stage is to review your sheets for ideas to solve the problem. The "5 W's and an H" can be expanded into "5 W's and 2 H's" if HOW MUCH (i.e., capital cost) is added.

There are also many specific checklists for ergonomics, such as those shown in Tables 8.2, 8.3, and 8.4. Some musculoskeletal disorder checklists are given in Box 14.4 and Tables 14.4, 14.5 and 14.6.

Step 3 of Table 8.1 is to obtain information from the operator. Although the analyst may have a university degree and specialized training, the operator has thousands of hours of experience with that specific job.

Step 4 involves information from the supervisor.

Step 5 is for measurements of light, noise, dimensions, and so on.

Now that you have the information, the next step in DAMES is to consider alternatives.

3 STRUCTURED SEARCH: SEARCH

This section describes some alternatives using the acronym SEARCH, where:

S = Simplify operations
E = Eliminate unnecessary work and material
A = Alter sequence
R = Requirements
C = Combine operations
H = How often

(Eliminate really should be done first, but the SEARCH acronym is easy to remember.)

T A B L E	8 . 2	

Ergonomics checklist (Kellerman et al., 1963).

A. Dimensions

1. Has a tall person enough room?
2. Can a petite person reach everything?
3. Is the work within normal reach of arms and legs?
4. Can the worker sit on a good chair? (height, seat, back)
5. Is an armrest necessary, and (if so) is it a good one? (location, shape, position, material)
6. Is a footrest required, and (if so) is it a good one? (height, dimensions, shape, slope)
7. Is it possible to vary the working posture?
8. Is there sufficient space for knees and feet?
9. Is the distance between eyes and work correct?
10. Is the work plane correct for standing work?

B. Forces

1. Is static work avoided as much as possible?
2. Are vises, jigs, conveyor belts, etc., used wherever possible?
3. Where protracted loading of a muscle is unavoidable, is the muscular strength required less than 10% of the maximum?
4. Are technical sources of power employed where necessary?
5. Has the number of groups of muscles employed been reduced to the minimum with the aid of counter-support?
6. Are torques around the axis of the body avoided as far as possible?
7. Is the direction of motion as correct as possible in relation to the amount of force required?

8. Are loads lifted and carried correctly, and are they not too heavy?

C. Noise

1. Is noise reduced to the minimum by means of technical measures at the source?
2. Are the sources of noise so insulated that they hinder as few people as possible?
3. Is reflected noise reduced to the minimum by provisions on walls and ceilings?
4. Are the noisiest apparatuses located as far as possible from the ears?
5. Can sound signals and verbal instructions be readily distinguished from the ambient noise?

D. Lighting

1. Is the lighting adequate for the nature of the work?
2. Has the fact that old lamps emit less light than new ones been taken into account?
3. Has glare on account of naked light sources, windows, or their reflection in shiny surfaces been avoided?
4. Has too great a brightness contrast between work position and surroundings been avoided?
5. Is reading of meters not impeded by reflection of light sources?

E. Climate

1. Are the surroundings where the work is done not too warm or too cold for the nature of the work?
2. Have effective measures been taken to prevent a high radiation temperature?

(continued)

Continued.

3. Can the humidity of the air be kept within acceptable limits?

4. Are processes calling for a high degree of humidity insulated to the greatest possible extent?

5. Are drafts avoided and, at the same time, is there adequate ventilation?

F. Information

1. Is the quantity of information the worker receives adequate and yet confined to essentials?

2. Does the information arrive in good time, and is it perceived through the correct sense?

3. Is the information clear and unambiguous?

4. Is urgent information given via the ears?

5. Particularly in the case of lengthy inspection tasks, is seeing replaced by hearing?

6. Can sound signals having different meanings be readily distinguished from each other?

7. Can prealignment, assembly, and setting be carried out rapidly and efficiently by touch?

8. Can the positions of components, control knobs, control buttons, and tools be perceived by touch?

G. Displays

1. Can the meter be read quickly and correctly, according to a measure immediately suitable for use and with the required degree of accuracy?

2. Is the desired degree of accuracy really necessary?

3. Is the type of meter selected efficient?

4. Is the scale graduated properly and as simply as possible?

5. Are the letters, figures, and graduate marks clearly visible at the required range?

6. Is the pointer simple and distinct, and does it pass close to the scale without concealing the figures?

7. Are reading errors caused by parallax avoided?

8. If the meter fails, is a warning given?

H. Controls

1. Have the knobs, wheels, grips, and pedals been adapted to the specific requirements of fingers, hands, and feet (location, dimensions, shape, direction of motion, counterpressure)?

2. Have the controls been located logically, in the sequence of operation, and can they be easily recognized by shape, dimensions, marking, and color?

3. Are pedals avoided for standing work and confined to two for sedentary tasks?

4. Are all the selected controls efficient?

I. Panels

1. Is positioning of the controls logical in relation to the displays?

2. Is the relation between the direction of motion of the control and that of the deflection of the pointer or the reaction of the apparatus (e.g., On–Off) logical?

3. Has the panel the correct shape and dimensions in connection with sitting posture, grasping range, and direction of vision?

4. Are the meters, knobs, and buttons that are most important and most frequently employed appropriately located?

5. Are the meters so grouped and positioned in relation to each other that they can be read quickly and faultlessly?

6. Do the scale divisions and subdivisions of different meters correspond as far as possible?

7. Have larger panels been made easier to scan through separation of groups of meters?

8. If possible, is the process represented on the panel in the form of a diagram?

9. Are warning lamps clear, and have they been located in the central part of the field of vision?

J. Paced Work

1. Are at least three vacant positions available at any moment?

2. Is the component to be mounted supplied ready-aligned?

3. Are the assembly positions equipped with ample guides for the feed movements? (holes, stops, etc.)

4. Are faulty components removed on the basis of preliminary inspection?

5. If the answers to questions 2, 3, and 4 are negative, are there at least six vacant positions?

a. Might it be useful to make a mockup of the machine or work setup?

b. Might it be useful to discuss the work setup with the operator concerned, the supervisor, or the departmental manager?

c. Might it be useful to discuss the work setup with your liaison for ergonomic matters?

T A B L E	8 . 3	

The "eleven commandments" (van Wely, 1970).

I AIM AT MOVEMENT

Use muscles, but not for holding or fixation.

Movement reduces monotony.

II USE OPTIMUM MOVEMENT SPEEDS

Too-quick or too-slow movements are fatiguing and inefficient; try to find the specific optimum speed of each movement.

III USE MOVEMENTS AROUND THE MIDDLE POSITIONS OF THE JOINTS

Long duration or frequent use of extreme positions of a joint, especially under load, are harmful and have poor mechanical advantage; yet occasional extreme positions, while not loaded, are desirable.

IV AVOID OVERLOADING OF MUSCLES

Keep dynamic forces to less than 30% of the maximum force that the muscle can exert; up to 50% is OK for up to 5 minutes.

Keep static muscular load to less than 15% of the maximum force the muscle can exert.

V AVOID TWISTED OR CONTORTED POSTURES

Do not use pedals in standing work.

Use arm supports only when the upper arms cannot relax and be approximately perpendicular to the floor.

Bending the head backward causes glare and a sore neck.

VI VARY THE POSTURE

Any fixation causes problems in muscles, joints, skin, and blood circulation. Do not use pedals in microscope work.

VII ALTERNATE SITTING, STANDING, AND WALKING

Continuous sitting for more than 1 hour and continuous standing for more than 1/2 hour are, in the long run, too fatiguing.

Standing for more than 1 hour a day is fatiguing and causes physical abnormalities. Concrete floors are fatiguing; elastic supports such as wood, rubber, or carpet are better.

VIII USE ADJUSTABLE CHAIRS

For sitting longer than 1/2 hour continuously or longer than 3 hours a day, use adjustable chairs and footrests (if necessary). When adjusting, remember:

a. Seat so elbows are at about the height of the working plane

b. Footrest so no pressure is applied to the back of the knees

c. Backrest so the lower back is supported and the working plane adjustable; a platform for the short person is a simple solution.

IX MAKE THE LARGE PERSON FIT AND GIVE HIM ENOUGH SPACE; LET THE SMALL PERSON EASILY REACH

For standing it is essential that the working plane be adjustable; a platform for the short person is a simple solution.

Keep the working plane within 50 mm of elbow height. Note: The working plane height is usually above the table height.

X TRAIN IN CORRECT USE OF EQUIPMENT: FOLLOW UP

People must be instructed and trained in good working postures; sitting, standing, and especially lifting are often done incorrectly.

XI LOAD PEOPLE OPTIMALLY

Neither maximum nor minimum is optimum.

An optimum load (physical and mental) gives better performance, more comfort, less absenteeism, and less harm.

3.1 Eliminate Unnecessary Work and Material

Eliminate unnecessary work is discussed under four subcategories: (1) eliminate unneeded work, (2) eliminate work where costs are greater than benefits, (3) use the exception principle, and (4) use self-service.

3.1.1 *Eliminate unneeded work* One example of eliminating unneeded work would be that, when duplicating class handouts, the teacher uses both sides of a sheet of paper. This not only reduces the amount of paper used but also reduces the page assembly task (eliminating assembly altogether for a two-page handout).

Another example is pruning mailing lists and internal distribution lists. Once each year send a letter saying that unless the person completes the form and returns it, the person will be taken off the list. Another technique is to make the continuation form page 2 or 3 of the report so you can see who *really* reads the report. Check your list by address so you aren't sending the same report to several people at the same address or one person for whom you have multiple spellings of the name. Another example of eliminating unneeded work is the use by the airlines of an electronic ticket in place of a paper ticket. A final example is the use of left-justification of date and signature on a business letter instead of requiring an additional tabulation to the right side of the page.

Of course, errors cause much work. Perhaps a deburring operation can be eliminated by initially

T A B L E	8 . 4

Guidelines to reduce repetitive strain (cumulative trauma) injuries (adapted from Stevenson and Baidya, 1987). See Figure 5.2 for wrist terminology.

GUIDELINE	COMMENT
1. Minimize the number and angular range of wrist extension movements in a repetitive cycle.	Sharp bending of the wrist often accompanies tossing motions. Avoid prolonged holding of the wrist in an extended position.
2. Minimize ulnar deviation of the wrist, particularly for longer portions of the work cycle or with force applications.	Consider bent-handle tools and tilted work surfaces. Give careful attention to keyboard heights so the home row is even with the elbow.
3. Minimize radial deviation of the wrist.	Can occur with poorly chosen handtools, especially with poor workstations and postures.
4. Avoid highly flexed wrists, particularly when combined with finger flexion.	Grip strength decreases rapidly when wrist flexion increases.
5. Keep hand and arm movements at the mid-position of their range.	See Figure 4.23.
6. Don't repetitively decelerate the wrist rapidly.	Repeated shock-loading has a large cumulative effect (for example, hammering, tugging wires tight).
7. Avoid excessive finger and hand extension.	The grip becomes weaker as it becomes wider. Avoid thumb triggers and thumb buttons. "Scissors grip" motions (wide extension combined with resistance) are bad.
8. Avoid grasps and hand movements of heavy objects with a pronated (palm-down) hand.	Check picking of objects from a conveyor or pallet. The effect is much worse if the object's center of gravity is beyond the hand. Can sliding replace lifting?
9. Avoid excessive squeezing force.	The typical female has only 50%–60% of male grip strength. For cutting with handtools, use motors instead of human force. See the "4th commandment" in Table 8.3.
10. Decrease gripping force and duration.	Replace pinch grips with power grips. Reduce duration by using tools with each hand alternately.
11. Minimize stress from tool handles.	Handles can be too short, too sharp, or too grooved (fit only a few hands). See Chapter 16.
12. Work at elbow height.	Reduce static loading or holding up the upper arm and forearm. Hand blood supply is reduced when the hands are above the heart.

using sharper tools or tools with a different rake angle. Chapter 19 focuses on error reduction techniques.

3.1.2 *Eliminate work where costs are greater than benefits* Consider eliminating backup and "just-in-case" procedures. Often much expense is incurred to protect against a rare event. For example, when one of the authors worked for a midwestern firm, the department making springs found one batch defective due to faulty material. He instituted a policy of testing each coil of material received. At the time, it seemed a good policy. With hindsight, the persistent cost of the inspection far outweighs the cost of the rare defective material.

Another example of excessive zeal is the expense-account paperwork some firms require. Few expenses are reduced, but the time spent processing paperwork is great. Another example is staffing of a service facil-

ity such as a tool crib. What would happen if there were no attendant and self-service were used? The reply might be, "They would steal us blind," "People wouldn't return items," and the like. The key question is whether the staffing cost exceeds the benefits of the reduced thefts and improved neatness. Perhaps a compromise is possible in which the facility is open only part of a shift or is restricted to key employees or supervisors. Most retail businesses have decreased staff and allow self-service, while restricting access to high-value items. Some restaurants have even eliminated serving a portioned container of beverage (soft drink, coffee); instead, they allow free refills, believing the additional good will and decreased serving costs offset the increased cost of the beverage.

3.1.3 *Use the exception principle* The idea of the **exception principle** is to take action only in "exceptional" circumstances. As a first example, consider a reserved parking stall with a strange car in it. Normally the police would give a ticket. Using the exception principle, the police give a ticket only if the stall owner complains. This reduces police work and allows the owner to lend the stall to someone else if the owner is not using it that day. Membership cards from most societies are sent to members at the same time the dues bill is sent. This saves the organization a great deal of paperwork.

3.1.4 *Use self-service* Eliminating may involve having the customer do the task at no cost to you, the seller; this is known as **self-service.** Filling stations have eliminated attendants pumping your gas; retail stores have eliminated clerks picking out your merchandise; manufacturers have eliminated product assembly (the item now comes "ready to assemble using simple tools"). Another good use of others is to have them sort for you. The post office does this with local and out-of-town mailboxes; organizations can do this with multiple mail bins such as "company—this building," "company—other buildings," and "U. S. mail." The U. S. Postal Service also uses group mail distribution points—one group of mailboxes for multiple customers (instead of a mailbox for each customer's location). The customers come to the common point instead of the carrier going to multiple points. Sorting of trash can make recycling worthwhile. For example, put a separate container for aluminum cans next to other trash containers so people will sort aluminum cans from other trash. (You may have to use a lid with a can-sized hole to reduce the insertion of paper trash by absent-minded people.)

Ford Hospital in Detroit treated about 250 chemotherapy cases/year with cisplatin. But cisplatin had a side effect of damaging the kidneys. The hospital routinely admitted the patients a day early to "tank up" on water. Now it has the patients tank up at home (saving 1 day's hospital stay); the patient keeps a diary of liquid intake for the nurse to check upon admittal.

3.2 *Simplify Operations* There are many examples of how to **simplify operations.** When giving directions (hotel, car rental, receptionist), use a map the individual can take instead of just verbal instructions.

A wide variety of jigs and fixture designs can be used to simplify machining operations. When ejecting parts from a machine, use drop delivery instead of precise placement of the parts. Even better, if possible, is to use automatic ejection—either mechanically or with compressed air.

Shift from counting to sampling and statistics. Register keys in fast-food restaurants can be keyed to specific items rather than price. Not only does this

reduce errors but the information also can be communicated automatically to the kitchen.

Figure 8.2 shows an office form in which a checkmark substitutes for short, standard phrases. Writing a letter takes considerable time. Can you write your answer on the other person's inquiry, make a photocopy for your files, and mail back the original? Many firms have form letters that are individually typed but the computer stops at the appropriate place for insertion of specific details such as name and address. Word processors permit easy modification of the output if necessary. Use of e-mail greatly reduces communication costs. Consider, for example, the savings in using the "reply" option versus typing a postal address on an envelope. What other savings can you achieve with e-mail? Perhaps writing is not necessary at all and a phone call, with its advantages of speed and two-way interaction, can be used in place of written communication. Long-distance phone calls using a wide area telephone system (WATS) typically cost less than 10 cents/min for a phone call anywhere in the United States. Certainly this compares favorably with the managerial and secretarial cost of typing a letter.

FIGURE 8.2

Sample office form to simplify operations. Substitute a quick checkmark for writing phrases, such as "please see me" or "note, sign, return."

Kansas State University
Department of Industrial Engineering
Manhattan, Kansas

To:

_____ ( ) See Me
_____ ( ) Type
_____ ( ) File
_____ ( ) Signature
_____ ( ) Refer
_____ ( ) Necessary Action
_____ ( ) Comment
_____ ( ) Information
_____ ( ) Note, Sign, Return
_____ ( ) Per Conversation
_____ ( ) _____

Comments:

Date: _____ Signature: _____

Simplify pollution and waste disposal problems by generating less waste. For example, in metal-finishing operations (electroplating, anodizing, conversion coating, chemical etching, chemical milling) the products are rinsed after processing. The rinse water becomes contaminated with "drag-in." Reduce drag-in by allowing products to drain sufficiently before entering the rinse tank (5 to 10 s over the processing tank is sufficient). Rotate the product to aid dripping from concave surfaces and blind holes.

A related example is reclaiming cutting oil in machining operations by giving the chips time to drain. Reducing the variety of cutting oils and coolants not only simplifies inventory control but also simplifies recycling of the oils and coolants. Some firms color-code chip bins—one for each type of oil or coolant.

In a Japanese steel mill, certain parts had to be cleaned. A robot could not do a satisfactory job, so the company decided to let the robot do 90% of the cleaning (preliminary cleaning) and have a human do the last 10%.

3.3 Alter Sequence

To **alter sequence,** (1) simplify other operations, (2) reduce idle/delay time, and (3) reduce material handling costs.

3.3.1 *Simplify other operations*

Cleaning and deburring operations sometimes may be omitted if the operation sequence is changed; machining before hardening is easier than machining after hardening. Distance between holes can be controlled more easily if holes are drilled after assembly than if they are drilled in the components.

Formerly, boxes went down two lines, one automatic and one manual. On the automatic line, the boxes were weighed and the weight was printed on the box with a jet printer. However, on the manual line, the boxes had to be pulled from the line, put on the scale, and the weight handwritten on the box. This physically demanding task was eliminated by moving the scale upstream to just after case sealing and *before* the lines split. Then all the boxes could be weighed and marked automatically. Figure 8.3 shows how modifying *when* something is done can reduce physical strain on the operator.

Some time is more valuable than other time. Customers at a hotel usually are in more of a hurry when they leave than when they check in. Use of a charge card when checking in reduces checkout time.

3.3.2 *Reduce idle/delay time*

Travel agents can issue you a boarding pass for a flight when you pick up your ticket instead of your obtaining one at the airport.

"Do it now" is a customer service concept that saves money and gives faster customer service. When a customer (who may be an employee of your own firm) calls on the phone, the customer receives the answer during the same phone call. Implementing this concept requires (1) empowering employees to make a decision (instead of referring it to others) and (2) using good information resources (usually on-line access to computer databases).

"Do it later" may be best. For example, maintenance might best be done during the evening and night shifts. The operator of the maintained equipment would be immediately shifted to other work rather than wait until the item is fixed during the day shift.

Another concept is "inside machine time." Many machines are semiautomatic. Once loaded, they process automatically, or loading/unloading is automatic and processing is manual. During the automatic portion, the operator can perform other tasks. For example, if machine 1 is automatically processing, spend the time loading machine 2. If a copy machine has a document feeder, do some filing while it is copying. Semiautomatic operations can be combined.

F I G U R E   8 . 3

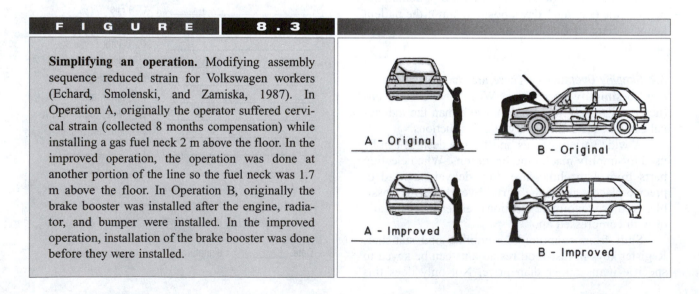

Simplifying an operation. Modifying assembly sequence reduced strain for Volkswagen workers (Echard, Smolenski, and Zamiska, 1987). In Operation A, originally the operator suffered cervical strain (collected 8 months compensation) while installing a gas fuel neck 2 m above the floor. In the improved operation, the operation was done at another portion of the line so the fuel neck was 1.7 m above the floor. In Operation B, originally the brake booster was installed after the engine, radiator, and bumper were installed. In the improved operation, installation of the brake booster was done before they were installed.

A - Original

B - Original

A - Improved

B - Improved

For example, at fast-food restaurants, soft drink dispensers are semiautomatic (fill automatically on a trigger), allowing the employee to do other things (such as get lids) while the cup fills. Have service personnel process two lines of customers sequentially to minimize delay while the customer goes away and a new one arrives. Examples are bank drive-ins and cafeteria checkout.

One cause of delays is absenteeism. The most successful method of curbing absenteeism is to lump vacation, personal time, and sick time together; thus, sick time is not considered "extra vacation." Firms also can use a "carrot": permit accumulation of sick days with payment for unused days when the person is no longer employed (quits, is laid off, or retires).

Another delay is the time for maintenance workers to arrive at a machine that requires maintenance. One approach is to install a red light above each machine; the operator turns it on when help is needed. A more sophisticated approach involves a large maintenance board (similar to a baseball scoreboard) showing the status of multiple machines. Each operator can key multiple requests (red = machine stopped, yellow = supplies low, blue = need info from supervisor, and so forth). See also Section 3 in Chapter 11.

Another concept involves simultaneous versus sequential. For example, can the operator reposition a part in the fingers while moving it, or must the operations be done sequentially? Another "simo" example involves cleaning an airplane between flights. Typically, this would be done on the ground after the passengers have left. However, if the flight attendants collect newspapers from passengers just before landing, there is less work for the ground-based cleanup.

Central versus local storage provides another example. If items are stored locally, there is less delay in obtaining them. Central storage, however, probably gives better control, less theft, and reduced inventory because storage is at one location instead of many. For example, New York City formerly had central storage of parts for sanitation department trucks. By decentralizing storage, the city reduced delays in repairing trucks and, thus, truck downtime. However, the total stored increased (20 local stores, each with 5 units, versus 1 central store with 50 units); there also were more places for theft.

Consider fast-food restaurants that have you pay your bill while the meal is being assembled or cooked. When serving breakfast, a good server will bring coffee to the table on the initial trip. A standard sequence also simplifies training and reduces errors. At McDonald's, for example, the standard sequence for order taking is drinks, sandwiches and pies, french fries, and ice cream.

3.3.3 Reduce material handling costs

Formerly, the U. S. mail was sorted by hand in each town. Now the mail from the smaller towns is sent unsorted (unless deposited in "local" boxes) to larger centers so it can be sorted by machine. Then the sorted mail for the town is sent back to the local post office. This approach actually increases material handling costs but at the advantage of reduced processing costs.

Grouping similar parts into "parts families" and scheduling "relatives" together is known as **group technology.** It not only reduces material handling and paperwork but also obtains the benefits of similar tooling and manufacturing skills.

Material handling costs can be reduced by modifying the sequence of when items are moved, using a bus system instead of a taxi system. See Figure 12.4. The "taxi" goes from point to point quickly, but at high cost. If speed is not critical, the "bus," although it travels a longer distance, may be cheaper.

In the home, you can save steps if you don't bring wastebaskets to the trash barrel in the garage. Take an empty trash bag to the wastebaskets and empty each wastebasket into the bag in turn; then take the bag to the garage.

3.4 Requirements

Two aspects of **requirements** must be determined: (1) quality (capability) costs and (2) initial versus continuing costs.

3.4.1 *Quality (capability) costs* Figure 8.4 shows the general shape of the cost versus quality (capability) curve. Beyond a certain point, additional quality (precision, capability) has a high cost. The question then becomes: Is the quality used or specified the appropriate quality? (Remember the old joke that a

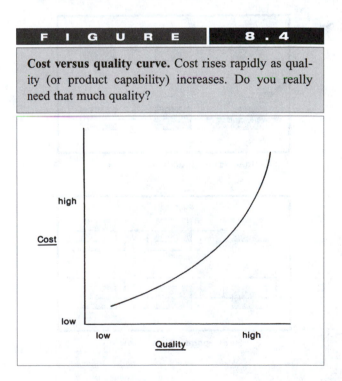

F I G U R E   8 . 4

Cost versus quality curve. Cost rises rapidly as quality (or product capability) increases. Do you really need that much quality?

tolerance is the smallest number that a design engineer can think of.)

It is important to have manufacturing people review design tolerances with the design engineer *before* the unit is released for production. Engineers tend to be reasonable at the **prerelease review** (see Box 7.1), but once the drawing becomes official, everything becomes "set in concrete." Material costs can be reduced along with manufacturing costs. For example, Emerson Electric saved $485,000/yr when it replaced some steel items with aluminum items in electric baseboard heaters. Thus, it is good to have a purchasing department representative in the prerelease review meeting.

Many requirement costs are concealed because they do not show up in the standard cost system. Figure 8.5 shows that the ideal flow of items through a factory is considered to be a river, but more realistically is a river with "eddies." These eddies are rework. Most rework is done "under the table." For example, if you were to tell your boss that you had 10% scrap today, the boss might rant and rave. So you don't report it; you just fix the defectives, quietly, with no official paperwork.

Indirect materials, supplies, and utility costs often receive less attention than they should. One firm

found it was gold-plating electronic parts too thickly. The company found out about it because people are conscious of gold.

One of the authors experienced a wastage of brightener in a motor plant. The supervisor had commented to the operator that the parts coming out of plating didn't seem very bright. So the operator put three times the required amount of brightener in the tank. The parts became bright, but at quite a cost, since the brightener was very expensive.

DuPont found that a process was using 20,000 lb/h of steam although the requirement was 14,000 lb/h. It replaced the instructions "turn the valve about three turns" with a meter.

An electric motor manufacturer used varnish on the motor coils. When the varnish on the coils was weighed and compared with the varnish purchased, there was a 10% shortage. It turned out that the varnish was purchased in 55-gallon drums. When the drums were emptied, they had been turned right side up and disposed of when there was still considerable product left inside. The solution was a stand that permitted the varnish to drip out of the drum over a period of hours.

Another requirements issue is the cost of components versus the cost of assembly. The standard procedure for over 100 years has been interchangeable parts—that is, high-precision components to make assembly easy. But in some cases, selective assembly may give lower total costs. In selective assembly, the component is made to a lower tolerance and then sorted into sizes, such as small, medium, and large. Thus, instead of each bushing fitting on each shaft, you would have three piles of bushings and three piles of shafts. You assemble small bushings on the small shafts, and so forth. The savings in component cost may outweigh the cost of additional sorting and more difficult assembly. Note, however, that if parts are not interchangeable, spare components cannot be sold, only spare assemblies.

3.4.2 Initial versus continuing costs

A common tendency is to focus on **initial costs** and ignore **continuing costs** (operating and maintenance costs). Many maintenance, operating, and utility costs are not even known. However, the optimum decision is to minimize life-cycle costs (total of purchase, operating, utility, and maintenance costs over the item's life) rather than the conventional minimizing of initial purchase cost.

An example is provided by the bracket on a car's air cleaner. The bracket was too thin, but it reduced the material cost of the bracket to the manufacturer by a fraction of a penny. However, it broke every 10,000 miles—forcing the owner to buy new brackets. Yet the auto companies have found that people are reluc-

---

F I G U R E   8 . 5

Ideal flow of product through a factory. A more realistic flow is shown below. Rework will cause "eddies in the river," substantially increasing the number of items processed at each station.

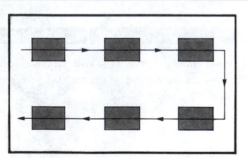

Idealized production flow

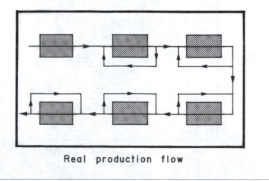

Real production flow

tant to pay attention to any cost of a car except first cost. Do you know what the maintenance cost or operating cost of your car will be over a 5-year period? Most people don't even think about it.

For military aircraft, the government found that the maintenance cost over a plane's life is 30 times the initial cost.

In fish farming, when high-initial-cost cupro-nickel cages replaced nylon nets (which must be cleaned often due to algae fouling), there were large maintenance savings. An electronics firm found that using titanium plating baskets for acid dipping was better than using steel baskets due to the much longer life of the titanium. However, it was a "hard sell" due to the high initial cost of the titanium baskets.

If cost is ignored, expect noneconomic behavior. For example, the Los Angeles motor pool formerly sent out a truck to refuel vehicles at the worksite with no charge for the service. The popularity of this practice dropped sharply when the departments were billed for the extra cost of $1.17/gallon to pay for the truck and driver.

Serving customers in a restaurant provides some examples of initial versus continuing costs. To minimize continuing costs (repeated visits by the server), (1) bring water on the initial server visit, (2) have a large enough glass of water so it rarely needs refilling (or have a carafe of ice water on the table), (3) serve a carafe of coffee instead of a cup, (4) have the water container for hot tea large enough that repeated visits are not necessary, and (5) give the check when serving the food.

3.5 Combine Operations

Often, **combine operations** can be thought of as an argument for general purpose versus special purpose. Sometimes the general purpose is best, and sometimes the special purpose.

For materials, consider waxing your car. You can buy two separate compounds to clean and wax or one special-purpose compound that will allow cleaning and waxing in one operation. Farmers can combine seed, fertilizer, and insecticide in one pass through the field. Figure 8.6 shows a drilling example. Instead of drilling the hole in one operation and countersinking in a second operation, the hole is drilled and counter-sunk in one operation. A pencil and eraser is a combined tool used in sequence rather than simultaneously. Another example is the cogeneration of electricity and heat. Formerly, many firms generated heat for their industrial processes or space heating but bought electricity from the power company. A number of years ago, the government changed the rules and required the utilities to buy all the electricity you want to sell to them at the highest price they pay for their own generation of power. Thus, many firms have found it good to generate electricity for the utility

F I G U R E   8 . 6

Example of combining operations. Special-purpose equipment (a combined drill and countersink) makes it possible to drill and countersink in one operation instead of two; the engineer must trade off the extra capital cost versus the reduced operating cost.

while generating heat for themselves. Another energy saver is to preheat intake air from exhaust air.

The approach to job design once was to have a specific job description—a specialist. One person was a carpenter, another an electrician A, another an electrician B, a welder, and so on. Although this allows a logical and organized workforce, it also tends to be inefficient, as it is difficult to find enough work to keep each and every specialist busy for a full day, day after day after day. One new automotive plant has only four job titles: operator, inspector, maintenance, and clerical. For more on job specialization, see Chapter 33.

Even the hooks on conveyors can be made single-purpose or multiple-purpose. The more expensive multiple-purpose hooks permit carrying multiple identical or even different items. As an example of special-purpose equipment, McDonald's grills hamburgers on both sides simultaneously.

Advances in communications (faxes, e-mail, computer networks, express mail) now permit one central department to furnish service to a variety of local facilities—resulting in many economies of scale. For example, do you need a travel agent for each plant site? When there is sufficient volume (from many sites), agents often give discounts. Can you combine accounting functions of various local facilities? Other types of services? Note that local supervisors often resist consolidation because they measure their own status by the number of people they supervise.

3.6 How Often

"When" questions can be divided into "time," "sequence," and "how often." A formal way of considering **how often** is to use economic lot size calculations. For "make" items, the tradeoff is setup cost versus inventory (capital, spoilage) cost. For "buy" items, the tradeoff is purchasing cost versus inventory cost. For example, when preparing a meal, should a large portion be prepared and part frozen for use later? Technologies change the answer over time. Freezers and microwave ovens have decreased the storage problem and thus encouraged cooking larger batches. In manufacturing, computer-controlled machine tools, cell layouts, and group technology have encouraged smaller batches due to their lower setup costs. Inventories also have been divided into A, B, and C categories with close attention being paid to the inventories of the expensive A items. The inexpensive C items (nuts, bolts, washers, screws, etc.) have relatively little inventory cost but a large out-of-stock cost; thus a 6- to 12-month supply is ordered for them to keep purchasing costs low.

The question of "what frequency" also can be applied to sales. For example, assume it costs $100 to call personally on a potential customer. Then, if profit is 5% of sales, the sales/call should be $2,000. If sales/call are lower, the sales effort should be redirected; perhaps direct mail or phone contact could be used.

Should information be sent via next day service, two-day service, or U. S. mail? The "how often" ques-tion is especially relevant to maintenance, service, and inspection activities. Should a machine be oiled once an hour, a week, or a month? Should failed fluo-rescent lamps be replaced immediately or once a week, or relamped only in groups? Should you pick up the mail once an hour, twice a day, or four times a day? Should the cash be taken to the bank once a day, twice a day, or what? Should the solution pH be tested once an hour, once a shift, or once a week? Should all suppliers receive equal attention, or should some get more inspection than others? Should wastebaskets be emptied once per day? (Every other day may require larger baskets.)

One way of concentrating your resources where they will do the most good is to label operators or operations or vendors as "red," "yellow," and "green" **(red, yellow, and green operations)**. A green vendor is OK and inspection may even be omitted; a yellow vendor means caution and requires inspection; a red vendor signals trouble and perhaps requires 100% inspection of all characteris-tics of all items.

Review Questions

1. What are the three unstructured search tech-niques?
2. Discuss the autoconfrontation concept.
3. Describe Beardsley's five W's and an H tech-nique.
4. Relate the short phrases that SEARCH stands for.
5. Give an example of how "inside machine time" can be used.

6. Briefly discuss the concept of the prerelease review meeting.
7. Show flow of product through a factory as a river with eddies. Why don't people report rework?
8. Briefly discuss selective assembly.
9. Why would vendors be labeled red, yellow, and green?

References

Beardsley, J. Ingredients of successful Quality Circles. *Transactions of 2nd Annual International Association of Quality Circles,* 139–45, 1980.

Echard, M., Smolenski, S., and Zamiska, M. Ergonomic considerations: Engineering controls at Volkswagen of America. In *Ergonomic Interventions to Prevent Musculoskeletal Injuries in Industry,* 117–31. Chelsea, MI: Lewis Publishers, 1987.

Helander, M. and Burri, G. Cost effectiveness of ergonomics and quality improvements in electronics manufacturing. *Int. J. of Industrial Ergonomics,* Vol. 15, 137–51, 1995.

Kellerman, F., van Wely, P., and Willems, P. *Vademecum: Ergonomics in Industry.* Eindhoven, Netherlands: Philips Technical Library, 1963.

Stevenson, M. and Baidya, K. Some guidelines on repet-itive work design to reduce the dangers of tenosynovitis. In *Readings in RSI,* Stevenson, M. (ed.). Kensington, NSW: New South Wales University Press, 1987.

van Wely, P. Design and disease. *Applied Ergonomics,* Vol. 1, 262–69, 1970.

OPERATIONS ANALYSIS

OPERATIONS ANALYSIS

Overview

Engineers can explore physically (i.e., trial and error in a physical situation). However, the engineer also can explore conceptually, using formulas and mathematical models. This chapter presents some tools of the trade for job design (see Table 9.16 for a summary). Be sure not to make final decisions based solely on the calculations. The techniques are aids to decision making, not the decisions themselves. The techniques give a first draft; only rarely is the first draft the final decision.

Key Concepts

active observation	Evolutionary Operation of	passive observation	rework
activity relationship diagram	Processes (EVOP)	PERT	satisfiers/optimizers
adjective scales	fish diagrams	process charts	semantic differential
body discomfort map	flow diagrams	protocol	slack
Borg vote	from–to table	rating of perceived exertion	subjective
cost versus distance	kitting	(RPE)	Systematic Layout
critical path	locating one item	relationship chart	Procedure (SLP)
decision structure tables	multi-activity chart	relative versus absolute	
double tooling	Pareto (ABC)	rating	

This chapter presents analysis techniques for the "big picture" (analysis of several operations or tasks) and then the "little picture" (analysis of an individual job). For the "miniature picture" (analysis of specific motions), see Chapters 13 and 29. For more on location of one item, systematic layout, and line balancing, see Hanna and Konz (2004).

LOCATION OF ONE ITEM

1.1 Problem
Locating one item in a network of customers is a fairly common problem (see Table 9.1). The item can be a person, a machine, or even a building. The network of customers can be people, machines, or buildings. The criterion minimized can be distance moved by people or product, the amount of energy lost, or even time to reach a customer.

Typically, a user is interested in finding the location that minimizes the weighted distances moved—a minisum problem. (An example would be to locate a copy machine in an office.) Another possible objective is to minimize the maximum distance—a minimax or "worst-case" problem. (An example minimax problem would be to locate an ambulance so that everyone could be reached in no more than 15 minutes.)

There is extensive analytical literature on "planar single-facility location problems." See Chapter 4 in Francis, McGinnis, and White (1992) for an excellent discussion of the analytical techniques.

The following material is not elegant math but "brute force" calculations. The reason is that with a computer or even a hand calculator, the engineer can solve all reasonable alternatives in a short time, perhaps 20 minutes. Then the engineer uses the material-handling cost calculations to gain insight

into the location problem and, using this as one criterion (other criteria might be capital cost, maintenance cost, etc.), makes a recommended solution.

1.2 Solution
In the following example, consider (1) the item to be located as a machine tool, (2) the network of customers (circles in Figure 9.1) as other machine tools with which the machine tool will exchange product, and (3) the criterion to be minimized as distance moved by product.

In most real problems, there are only a few possible places to put the item; the remaining space is

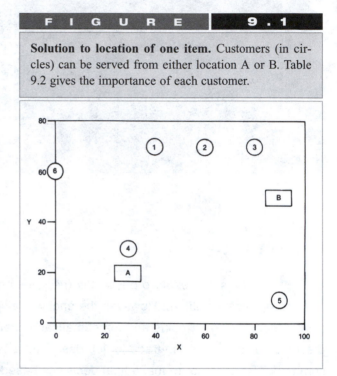

F I G U R E   9 . 1

Solution to location of one item. Customers (in circles) can be served from either location A or B. Table 9.2 gives the importance of each customer.

T A B L E   9 . 1

Examples of locating an item in an existing network of customers with various criteria to be minimized.

NEW ITEM	NETWORK OF CUSTOMERS	CRITERION MINIMIZED
Machine tool	Machine shop	Movement of product
Tool crib	Machine shop	Walking of operators
Time clock	Factory	Walking of operators
Inspection bench	Factory	Movement of product or inspectors
Copy machine	Office	Movement of people
Warehouse or store	Market	Distribution cost
Factory	Warehouses	Distribution cost
Electric substation	Motors	Power loss
Storm warning siren	City	Distance to population
IIE meeting place	Locations of IIE members	Distance traveled
Fire station	City	Time to fire

already filled with other machines, building columns, aisles, and so forth. In the example problem, the first solution will be based on the assumption that there are only two feasible locations (A and B) for the new item. They are the rectangles in Figure 9.1.

Travel between a customer and A or B can be (1) straight line (e.g., conveyors), (2) rectangular (e.g., fork trucks down an aisle), or (3) measured on a map (e.g., fork trucks using one-way aisles, conveyors following aisles or connecting several machines, conveyors following nondirect paths). In real problems, travel may be a mixture of the three types.

Some customers are more important than others. Thus, the distance must be weighted. In a factory, a common index would be pallets moved/month. If the problem is location of a fire station, the weight of a customer might depend on the fire risk of the customer or the number of people occupying the site.

The operating cost of locating the item at a specific feasible location is:

$$MVCOST = WGTK\,(DIST) \qquad (9.1)$$

where $MVCOST$ = index of movement cost for a feasible location

$WGTK$ = weight (importance) of the Kth customer of N customers

$DIST$ = distance moved

$$MVCOST = \sum_{k=1}^{n} (|X_{i,j} - X_k| + |Y_{i,j} - Y_k|)$$
$$\text{(for rectangular)} \quad (9.2a)$$

$$MVCOST = \sum_{k=1}^{n} \sqrt{(X_{i,j} - X_k)^2 + (Y_{i,j} - Y_k)^2}$$
$$\text{(for straight line)} \quad (9.2b)$$

For the two locations given in Table 9.2, Table 9.3 shows the $MVCOST$. Movement cost at B is about $67,954/53,581 = 126\%$ of A.

T A B L E   9 . 2

Importance of each customer. Customers 1 to 6 can be served either from location A ($X = 30$, $Y = 20$) or from location B ($X = 90$, $Y = 50$). Which location minimizes movement cost?

Customer	COORDINATE X	Y	Weight or Importance	Movement Type	
1	40	70	156	Straight line	
2	60	70	179	Straight line	(a)
3	80	70	143	Straight line	
4	30	30	296	Rectangular	
5	90	10	94	Rectangular	(b)
6	0	60	225	Rectangular	

T A B L E   9 . 3

Cost of locating a new machine at location A or B. Since $WGTK$ was pallets/month and $DIST$ was in meters, $MVCOST =$ meter-pallets/month.

Customer	Weight, Pallets/Month	SITE A Distance, Meters	Cost, M-Pallets/Month	SITE B Distance	Cost, M-Pallets/Month
1	156	51	7,956	54	8,424
2	179	58	10,382	36	6,444
3	143	71	10,153	22	3,146
4	296	10	2,960	80	23,680
5	94	70	6,580	40	3,760
6	225	70	15,750	100	22,500
			53,781		67,954

Assume you wish to know the cost at locations other than A and B for the above problem. By calculating costs at a number of points, a contour map can be drawn. This indicates that the best location is $X = 42$ and $Y = 40$ with a value of 32,000. Thus, Site A is 6,000 from the minimum and Site B is 13,000 from the minimum.

The example, however, made the gross simplification that movement cost per unit distance is constant. Figure 9.2 shows a more realistic relationship of **cost versus distance,** where most of the cost is loading and unloading (starting and stopping) or paperwork, and where cost of moving, when "acceleration and deceleration" are omitted, is very low. More realistically:

$$DIST = L_k + C_k (|X_{i,j} - X_k| + |Y_{i,j} - Y_k|)$$
(for rectangular)   (9.3a)

$$DIST = L_k + C_k \sqrt{(X_{i,j} - X_k)^2 + (Y_{i,j} - Y_k)^2}$$
(for straight line)   (9.3b)

where L_k = load + unload cost (including paperwork) per trip between the kth customer and the feasible location

C_k = cost/unit distance (excluding L_k)

Assume for customers 1, 2, and 3 that $L_k = \$.50$/trip and $C_k = \$.001$/m; for customers 4, 5, and 6, $L_k = \$1$/trip and $C_k = \$.002$/m. Then the cost for alternative A = \$854 + \$79.07 = \$933.07 while the cost of B = \$854 + \$117.89 = \$971.89. Thus, B has a movement cost of 104% of A. When making the decision where to locate the new item, use not only

the movement cost but also installation cost, capital cost, and maintenance cost. Note that the product *(WGTK) (DIST)* (that is, the \$854) is independent of the feasible location; it just adds a constant value to each alternative.

Cost need not be expressed in terms of money. Consider locating a fire station where the customers are parts of the town and the weights are expected number of trips in a 10-yr period. Then load might be 1 min to respond to a call, travel is 1.5 min/km, and unload might be 1 min; the criterion is to minimize mean time/call.

Note also that the distance cost may rise by a power of 2—the *inverse square law*—for problems such as location of a siren or a light.

2 SYSTEMATIC LAYOUT OF MULTIPLE ITEMS

In contrast to the previous section on location of one item in a network of customers, this section discusses arrangement of the entire facility.

Systematic Layout Procedure (SLP) was developed by Richard Muther and is based on his extensive consulting work in plant layout (Muther and Hales, 1980). SLP deals with arrangement of entire facilities and can be used at the "block" (department) level or the "detail" (machine) level. When used to arrange displays within a panel, it may be called "link analysis."

The following is a concise, simplified version of Muther's approach.

Step 1. The goal is to group the departments within a factory (or machines within a department). Grouping is based on relationships.

Depending on the problem, divide the area into departments (office, lathes, drill press, etc.) or machines (lathe 1, lathe 2, drill 1, etc.). Then establish the product relationships using a from–to table (Table 9.4); establish service relationships using a relationship chart (Table 9.5).

Table 9.4, a **from–to table,** summarizes the flow from one department (or machine) to another. The information in the top portion comes from the various routing sheets and the production schedule. The information in the bottom portion summarizes the flow from the top portion. Note that the two sides of the diagonal are not identical; that is, the loads from A to B are not the same as the loads from B to A. The from–to table combines the movement of several products. Thus, the numbers added must be expressed in a common unit (pallets/week or tote boxes/day) rather than mixed units (pieces of product A, pieces of product B). As a refinement, you may wish to consider some pallets easier to move than others and multiply each type

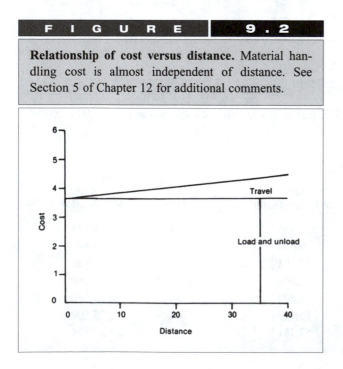

F I G U R E   9 . 2

Relationship of cost versus distance. Material handling cost is almost independent of distance. See Section 5 of Chapter 12 for additional comments.

T A B L E	9 . 4

From–to table quantifying the relationships between departments (or machines). The top portion of the table gives the product sequence and importance; use standard units such as pallets/week. If the flow "backtracks" (goes from B to A, not A to B), in the lower table it will be below the diagonal. The 15 in the lower table is the sum of 10 (from product 1) and 5 (from product 2).

PRODUCT	DEPT. FLOW	PALLETS/WEEK
1	ABC E	10
2	AB E	5
3	BCDE	8
4	B DE	3

FROM	A	B	C	D	E
A	–	15			
B		–	18	3	5
C			–	8	10
D				–	11
E					–

T A B L E	9 . 5

Relationship chart. Step 1 of systematic layout. Identify the desired closeness between areas with a letter grade. Give reasons for letters A, B, and E. Thus, B/2 for drill press—lathes indicates a B importance for reason 2.

AREA NUMBER	AREA NAME	OFFICE 1	LATHES 2	DRILL PRESS 3	PUNCH PRESS 4	PLATING 5	SHIPPING 6	DIE STORAGE 7
1	Office							
2	Lathes	D						
3	Drill Press	D	B/2					
4	Punch Press	E/5	D	B/2				
5	Plating	D	C	D	D			
6	Shipping	C	D	D	C	B/2		
7	Die Storage	D	D	D	A/4	D	B/4	

of pallet by a different difficulty factor. When there is difficulty in quantifying the relationships between departments, use a **relationship chart** (Table 9.5).

In addition, you may have design concepts such as:

- truck docks on rear perimeter of the building
- executives on top floor of multi-floor building
- windows (view) for those with status
- cafeteria and toilets centrally located
- U-shaped flow (if shipping and receiving are one department or adjacent)
- storage kept together
- utilities grouped together (a building "spine") to minimize utility distribution costs

Step 2. Assign floor space to each activity area, along with physical features and restrictions (see Table 9.6). However, just as every closet in a home becomes filled, inventories expand into whatever space is available, regardless of the need for the

T A B L E	9 . 6

Step 2 of simplified SLP. Specify the amount of space (including about 20%–30% for aisles) for each area. Give physical features and restrictions.

	AREA NAME	DESIRED M²	RESTRICTIONS
1	Office	50	Air conditioning
2	Lathes	40	Minimum of 10 m long
3	Drill press	40	
4	Punch press	50	Foundation
5	Plating	30	Water supply, fumes, wastes
6	Shipping	20	Outside wall
7	Die Storage	50	Crane
		280	

inventory. If the layout is a group of machines within an area, add space to the space for the machine alone. Consider space for the operator, for maintenance access, for movement of parts of the machine, and for local storage of product and supplies.

Step 3. Make an **activity relationship diagram** (see Figure 9.3). First, list all the A relationships from the relationship chart, then the B's, C's, D's, and E's. Then make a diagram with just the A's. Then add the B's, keeping in mind the E restrictions. (For E's, walls and other barriers permit physical closeness while reducing visual and auditory distraction.) Then add the C's; then the D's.

Step 4. Make a scaled layout of at least two trials from Step 3, using the areas and restrictions of Step 2

(see Figure 9.4). First, use pieces of stiff paper for each department. Sketches tend to get "set into concrete" too soon. An alternative is a computer-aided design (CAD) system, in which areas can be rotated, moved, and so on. Don't forget that both areas and shapes of the departments can be adjusted. Some areas may be fixed in a specific location—for example, the shipping dock or the punch press department.

The reason for at least two layouts is that engineers are **satisfiers** rather than **optimizers**—they tend to stop designing as soon as they have a solution that works instead of continuing to search for the best solution. (When the decision maker is satisfied to the point that it is not worth further effort to find something better, it is called *satisficing*.)

Note that E relationships do not have to be satisfied with distance. Walls and other barriers permit physical closeness while preventing the passage of noise, fumes, and other distractions.

Note also that A relationships do not have to be satisfied with closeness. For example, if the reason for the A is communication, the communication medium may be telephones, computer lines, faxes, video, or even pneumatic tubes; a distance of 50 or 500 ft is irrelevant. If the A is for product movement on a conveyor, again a distance of 100 or 500 ft is relatively insignificant.

Step 5. Evaluate the alternatives (see Table 9.7). The relevant criteria and their weights will change from situation to situation. Grade each layout (A = Excellent = 4; B = Good = 3; C = Average = 2; D = Fair = 1; F = Bad = 0). Calculate the layout's "grade-point" (grade × weight). If there is an existing layout, include it as one alternative. Defining the best as 100%, calculate the percent for each alternative. Have the affected people sign off on the evaluation form.

F I G U R E   9 . 3

Step 3, the activity relationship diagram. This first groups the A's, B's, C's, and E's (left side of figure). (It may help to think of the lines as rubber bands pulling areas together. More bands make them closer together. The wavy line for the E's is a "spring" keeping them apart.) Then group all the A's (right side of figure), add the B's to the A's (remembering the E's), and then add the remainder. D's are not used.

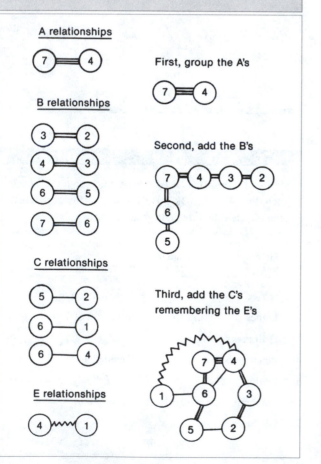

F I G U R E   9 . 4

Step 4, scaled layout. This step results in several alternative arrangements. It may be desirable to modify slightly some of the desired areas or total plant area from Step 2 (to keep the building shape regular). A square (or nearly square) building shape minimizes wall perimeter and thus construction and energy costs.

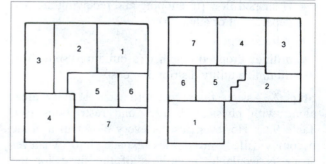

TABLE		9.7					

Step 5, evaluate the alternatives. Criteria and weights depend upon specific management goals.

CRITERION	WEIGHT	PRESENT		ALTERNATIVE 1		ALTERNATIVE 2	
Minimum investment	6	A	24	B	18	A	24
Ease of supervision	10	C	20	C	20	B	30
Ease of operation	8	C	16	C	16	C	16
Ease of expansion and contraction	2	C	4	C	4	B	6
Total points			64		58		76
Relative merit (best = 100%)			84%		76%		100%

Then go back and select features from the alternatives to get an improved set of designs.

Step 6. Detail the layout (make a working drawing, using a 1:50 scale or possibly a 1:100 scale). At this step, replace the department boundary lines with exterior walls (with doors), interior walls (with doors), and no walls (just department boundaries). Refine the estimate of the number of machines and operators (through detailed analyses of run and setup time, production schedules, consideration of alternative staffing patterns, use of simulation, and so on). Determine material handling and aisles. Locate machines and operators. Show operators as ovals so their shoulder orientation is specified. Detail utilities (electricity, water, compressed air, and communications) and service areas (offices, toilets, breakrooms, toolrooms, nurse's office, and the like).

Present the alternatives to management for approval. After any modifications, install the final design.

3 IMPORTANT ITEMS FIRST (PARETO)

Engineering time is a valuable resource; don't waste time on unimportant problems. Allocate design time to the important problems; neglect the minor problems. To check quickly whether a project is worth considering, calculate (1) savings/yr if material cost is cut 10% and (2) savings/yr if labor cost is cut 10%.

The concept of the **Pareto distribution** may help you find the important problems (see Figure 9.5). Lorenz also used curves to demonstrate the concentration of wealth, but Vilfredo Pareto's name is now associated with the concept of "the insignificant many and the mighty few" (Figure 9.6). Cause (x axis) and effect (y axis) are not related linearly; the Pareto curve (also called the ABC curve) can be approximated by a log-normal distribution. The key

FIGURE		9.5	

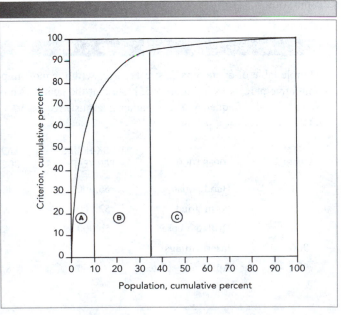

Pareto distribution. Many populations have a Pareto distribution, in which a small proportion of the population has a large proportion of the criterion. Inventories, for example, can be classified by the ABC system. "A" items may comprise 10% of the part numbers but 70% of the inventory cost. "B" items may comprise 25% of the part numbers and 25% of the cost; so the total of A + B items comprise 35% of the part numbers but 95% of the cost. "C" items thus comprise the remaining 65% of the part numbers but only 5% of the cost. The concept is to concentrate your effort on "A" items so you don't use gold cannons to kill fleas.

F I G U R E   9 . 6

While engineers fight the "mighty few" (large problems) have quality circle groups fight the "insignificant many" (small problems).

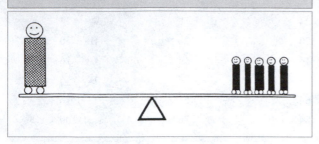

concept is that the bulk of the problem (opportunity) is concentrated in a few items, for example:

A few

products	produce	most of the direct labor dollars.
products	have	most of the storage requirements.
products	produce	most of the profit.
operations	produce	most of the quality problems.
machines	use	most of the energy.
operations	produce	most of the cumulative trauma problems.
time studies	cover	most of the direct labor hours.
routes	have	most of the customers.
days	have	most of the outgoing or incoming orders.
individuals	drink	most of the beer.
salespersons	sell	most of the product.

Pareto diagrams are just a special form of histograms (frequency counts); the key difference is that the categories are put in sequence of largest first (instead of a random order) and the cumulative curve is plotted. Table 9.8 shows an example table of operations arranged in order of largest annual cost first. This then is translated into a cumulative figure such as in Figure 9.5. For examples that show the bars as well as the cumulative curve, see Figures 32.4, 32.5, and 32.7.

Therefore, using the Pareto concept, if your design concerns crime, it should concentrate on the few individuals who cause most of the crimes; if your design is to affect food consumption at a party, it should concentrate on the few individuals who eat the most; if it is to improve quality, it should concentrate on the few components that cause most of the problem, and so on.

To maximize your design productivity, work on several projects at the same time rather than spending all your time on one project and then going on to the second project (i.e., parallel projects, not series projects). Not only will your time be spent more effectively, but the idea quality also will be better.

4 FLOW DIAGRAMS AND PROCESS CHARTS

In contrast to the systematic layout and the location of one new item procedure, **flow diagrams** and their associated **process charts** combine in a technique for visually organizing and structuring a problem rather than providing a solution. Gilbreth designed this tool to give an overview ("mountaintop" view) of the problem. Although a good engineer should be able to notice what is important in a problem and make corrections without the aid of a flow diagram and process chart, visually organized solutions become more obvi-

T A B L E   9 . 8

Example table of operations. List categories with the most important one first and the least important last. Then plot the cumulative percent as in Figure 9.5. Note that the cumulative cost (h × cost/h) is plotted, not the cumulative work-hours (h); that is, plot frequency × cost rather than just frequency.

ITEM NUMBER	OPERATION	WORK-HOURS PER YEAR	LABOR COST/H	LABOR COST/YR	PERCENT OF TOTAL ANNUAL COST	CUMULATIVE PERCENT
1	Hand polish	65,000	8.75	568,750	15.7	15.7
2	Form grind	52,000	9.30	483,600	13.4	29.1
3	Drill and bore	56,000	8.25	462,000	12.8	41.9
906	Insert fittings	120	8.00	960	.0	99.9
907	Apply nameplates	60	8.50	510	.0	100.0
				3,600,000	100.0%	100.0%

ous with them. (Another technique for communicating and recording work methods is videotaping an operation.) After the task is analyzed, the results often are put in a routing sheet (see Table 31.9) to systematically record all of the decisions about the process.

Figure 9.7 shows a single-object process chart (the single object can be a person or an object). Figure 9.8 shows a flow diagram for Joe Smith, who is making a complex job of fixing a snack in his apartment.

Figure 9.9 gives the five standard symbols for process charts: operations are circles, transportations or moves are arrows, inspections are squares, storages are triangles (upside down piles?), and delays (unplanned storage) are capital D's. A circle inside a square is a combined operation and inspection. Some people put a number inside each symbol (identifying operation 1, 2, 3, or inspection 1, 2, 3) while others don't. Some people darken the circle for "do" operations but not "get ready" or "put away" operations; if "do" operations are eliminated, "get ready" and "put away" operations are eliminated automatically. Since a process chart is primarily a tool for concise communication to yourself, take your choice. Since inspection without change was a square, inspection with change (an operation) is a circle inside a square.

At the end of the analysis, summarize the number of operations, moves, inspections, storages, and delays, and total the distance moved. Estimate times for storages and delays. Usually it is not worthwhile to determine or record operation or inspection times since this between-operations analysis usually is not concerned with within-operations methods. Process charts, because they give a "bird's-eye view" of the operation, often serve as methods documentation for others; you may wish to make a polished copy for them.

Expense account paperwork was simplified at Intel by cutting 25 steps to 14 with the aid of a process chart. Steps 5 and 7 were eliminated by having the accounts payable clerk, instead of the cash receipts clerk, collect unused refunds or advances. Steps 8, 10, and 11 were eliminated because another department also did these steps. Step 14 was eliminated as costing more than it saved. Step 19 proved unnecessary. The

FIGURE 9.7

Single-object process charts. The chart follows a single object or person—in this example, an object. For good communication, give time and distance. (Also see Figure 9.11, an assembly process chart.)

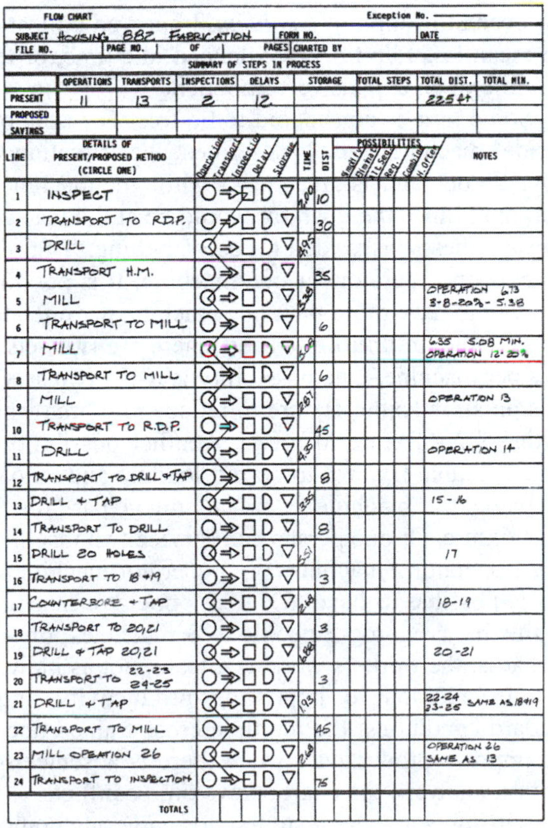

FLOW CHART — Exception No. ———

SUBJECT Housing 882 Fabrication | FORM NO. | DATE

FILE NO. | PAGE NO. | OF | PAGES | CHARTED BY

SUMMARY OF STEPS IN PROCESS

	OPERATIONS	TRANSPORTS	INSPECTIONS	DELAYS	STORAGE	TOTAL STEPS	TOTAL DIST.	TOTAL MIN.
PRESENT	11	13	2	12			225 ft	
PROPOSED								
SAVINGS								

LINE	DETAILS OF PRESENT/PROPOSED METHOD (CIRCLE ONE)	Operation / Transport / Inspection / Delay / Storage	TIME	DIST	POSSIBILITIES: Simplify / Eliminate / Alt. Seq. / Req. / Combine / H. Often	NOTES
1	INSPECT	○ ⇒ □ D ▽	2.00	10		
2	TRANSPORT TO R.D.P.	○ ⇒ □ D ▽		30		
3	DRILL	○ ⇒ □ D ▽	4.95			
4	TRANSPORT H.M.	○ ⇒ □ D ▽		35		
5	MILL	○ ⇒ □ D ▽	3.38			OPERATION 6.73 3-8-20%-5.38
6	TRANSPORT TO MILL	○ ⇒ □ D ▽		6		
7	MILL	○ ⇒ □ D ▽	3.08			6.35 5.08 MIN. OPERATION 12·20%
8	TRANSPORT TO MILL	○ ⇒ □ D ▽		6		
9	MILL	○ ⇒ □ D ▽	2.87			OPERATION 13
10	TRANSPORT TO R.D.P.	○ ⇒ □ D ▽		45		
11	DRILL	○ ⇒ □ D ▽	4.35			OPERATION 14
12	TRANSPORT TO DRILL & TAP	○ ⇒ □ D ▽		8		
13	DRILL & TAP	○ ⇒ □ D ▽	3.35			15-16
14	TRANSPORT TO DRILL	○ ⇒ □ D ▽		8		
15	DRILL 20 HOLES	○ ⇒ □ D ▽	5.51			17
16	TRANSPORT TO 18 & 19	○ ⇒ □ D ▽		3		
17	COUNTERBORE & TAP	○ ⇒ □ D ▽	2.68			18-19
18	TRANSPORT TO 20,21	○ ⇒ □ D ▽		3		
19	DRILL & TAP 20,21	○ ⇒ □ D ▽	6.88			20-21
20	TRANSPORT TO 22-23 24-25	○ ⇒ □ D ▽		3		
21	DRILL & TAP	○ ⇒ □ D ▽	1.93			22-24 23-25 SAME AS 18 & 19
22	TRANSPORT TO MILL	○ ⇒ □ D ▽		45		
23	MILL OPERATION 26	○ ⇒ □ D ▽	2.68			OPERATION 26 SAME AS 13
24	TRANSPORT TO INSPECTION	○ ⇒ □ D ▽		75		
	TOTALS					

FIGURE 9.8

Flow diagram. This is a graphical communication device used with process charts.

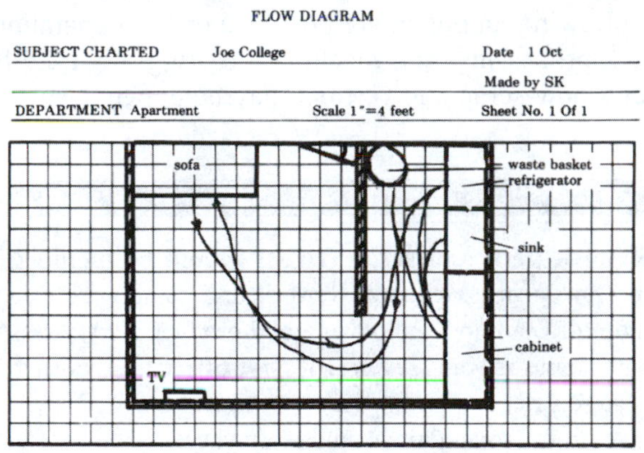

FIGURE 9.9

Five standard symbols for process charts: a circle (operation), arrow (move), square (inspection), triangle with point down (storage), and D (delay). A circle in a square is a combined operation and inspection.

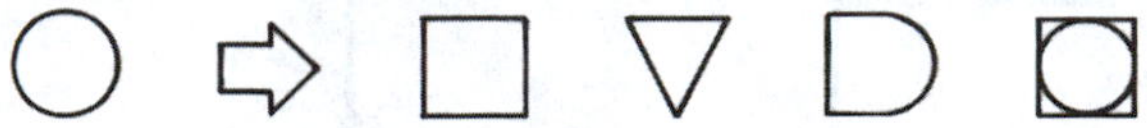

delays (steps 2, 6, 9, and 18) were cut. Expense accounts now are processed in days instead of weeks. Expense accounts less than $100 just require a petty cash voucher and a visit to the cashier. When the job was analyzed, the process chart was arranged horizontally and displayed on large horizontal strips of paper in a conference room (use of the "wall technique"). Each step then was questioned in detail by a group.

In hospitals, flow charts have helped reduce the length of patient stays. For example, large doses of narcotics were easy to administer, but these doses impaired patient digestion and therefore delayed discharge. Now patients receive smaller doses of narcotics and are discharged sooner. Some hospitals give physicians an additional fee to make an additional bedside visit late in the day. As a result, many patients are discharged late in the day instead of the next morning. Detailed analysis of flow charts can yield an improved standard procedure—a **protocol.**

Draw—not to drafting standards—the flow diagram to scale on cross-section paper. It serves as a communication aid and shows overall relationships.

The three types of flow diagrams are: single object, assembly, and action-decision. Figures 9.7 and 9.8 showed the single-object type. Either an operator or an object is followed. Examples of following a person are vacuuming an office, making a bed, stocking shelves, changing a tire, unloading a semitrailer, handling material in the sandblast room, waiting on tables, and loading/unloading a dishwasher. Examples of following an object are purchase order preparation, check processing, and machining casting. Figure 9.10 shows how scrap and **rework** may be drawn.

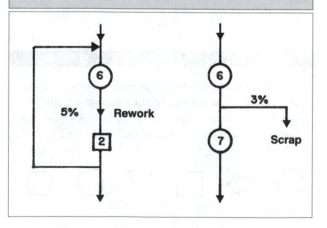

F I G U R E 9.10

Rework (left) and scrap (right) should be included in flow process charts. Rework and scrap often are more difficult to handle than good product. Most items have some rework—even if it isn't officially reported. Material removal scrap occurs in machining and press operations; scrap units occur everywhere.

Figure 9.11 shows the second type, an assembly process chart. Assembly flow diagrams tend to point out the problems of disorganized storage. Other examples are making a pizza, assembling a switch, potting plants, making a whiskey sour, analyzing a blood sample, and reloading shotgun shells. There also are disassembly charts, useful in some situations (packing beef, portioning pie). See Figure 9.12.

Figure 9.13 shows an action-decision flow diagram for a checkout operator in England using a laser scanner. Note that in England the operator sits and the customer not only pays for the bag but also bags the groceries.

The purpose of flow diagrams and process charts is to focus your thinking. Use them with critical examination forms and checklists (see Chapter 8).

5 MULTI-ACTIVITY CHARTS

Figure 9.14 shows a **multi-activity chart.** In different forms it has different names. If the columns represent people, it may be called a gang chart; if some columns are people and some machines, it may be called a man–machine chart. If one column represents the left hand and one the right, it may be called a left-hand right-hand chart. See Figure 9.15.

There can be two or more columns. The time axis (drawn to a convenient scale) can be seconds, minutes, or hours. The goal of a multi-activity chart is improved utilization of a *column.* Improved utilization can mean less idle time, rebalanced idle time, or less idle time of an expensive component.

Some time is considered to be free. For example, "inside machine time" describes the situation in which an operator is given tasks while the machine is operating. Since the operator would be at the machine anyway, these tasks don't cost anything. But this assumes one operator for one machine. It is possible, however, to have more than one machine per operator. For example, in **double tooling,** there are two sets of tools per machine. One possibility is using two sets of tools on an indexing fixture to reduce idle time while waiting for a fixture to rotate. Another possibility is to have double fixtures to permit loading and unloading while the machine is processing a part on the other fixture. Or one person can service two machines (i.e., 1 operator/2 machines or .5 operator/machine). It also is possible to have .67 or .75 operator/machine. Do this by assigning 2 people to 3 machines, or 3 to 4. That is, the workers work as a team, not as individuals. In addition to improving productivity under standard conditions, the multiple cross-trained operators improve productivity when there is absenteeism. For task analysis, the chart shows time conflicts.

Kitting is a general strategy of gathering components before assembly to minimize search-and-select

Assembly process charts. Useful for methods analysis, these charts point out the relationships among components and help emphasize storage problems. Each column is an item with the assembly on the right. (Figure 9.7 depicts a single-object flow chart.)

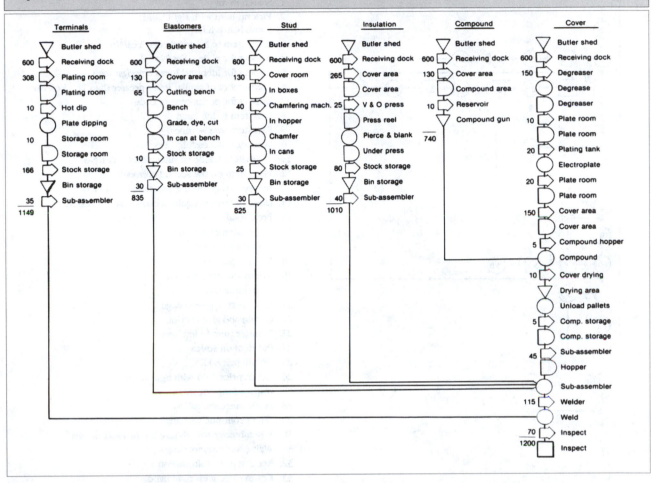

Disassembly process chart.

USE DRILL

REMOVE DRILL BIT

INSPECT FOR BIT SIZE

STORE DRILL   STORE WRENCH   STORE BIT

operations and to ensure that there are no missing parts. Subassemblies also may be useful. For example, McDonald's Big Mac has a special sauce. It is just a combination of relish and mayonnaise, pre-mixed to ensure consistency.

For each column, give cycles/yr, cost/min, and percent idle. Make the idle time distinctive by cross-hatching, shading, or coloring red.

A disadvantage of the multi-activity chart is that it requires a standardized situation. Nonstandardized situations are difficult to show. For them, use computer simulation.

Example charts and columns might be: make lead molds (operator, machine, cooler); milling casting (operator, machine); cash checks (cashier, customer 1, customer 2); and serve meals (customer, server, cook).

6 FISH DIAGRAMS

Fish diagrams (see Figure 9.16), the "cause" side of cause-and-effect diagrams, are also known as Ishikawa diagrams; they were developed in 1953 by Kaoru Ishikawa while on a quality control project for Kawasaki Steel. They graphically depict a multidimensional list. Fish diagrams are widely used in

FIGURE   9.13

Action-decision flow diagram for checkout operator in England using laser scanner (Wilson and Grey, 1984).

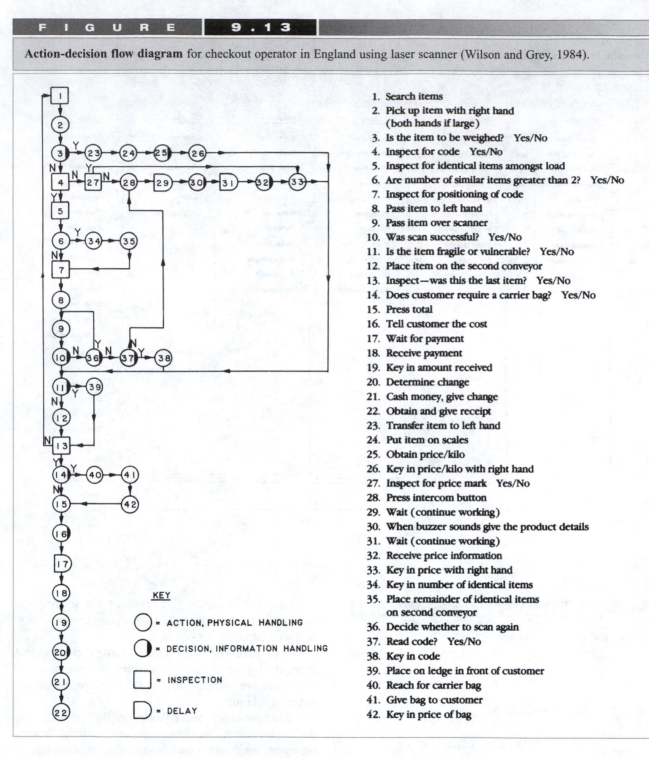

1. Search items
2. Pick up item with right hand
   (both hands if large)
3. Is the item to be weighed?   Yes/No
4. Inspect for code   Yes/No
5. Inspect for identical items amongst load
6. Are number of similar items greater than 2?   Yes/No
7. Inspect for positioning of code
8. Pass item to left hand
9. Pass item over scanner
10. Was scan successful?   Yes/No
11. Is the item fragile or vulnerable?   Yes/No
12. Place item on the second conveyor
13. Inspect—was this the last item?   Yes/No
14. Does customer require a carrier bag?   Yes/No
15. Press total
16. Tell customer the cost
17. Wait for payment
18. Receive payment
19. Key in amount received
20. Determine change
21. Cash money, give change
22. Obtain and give receipt
23. Transfer item to left hand
24. Put item on scales
25. Obtain price/kilo
26. Key in price/kilo with right hand
27. Inspect for price mark   Yes/No
28. Press intercom button
29. Wait (continue working)
30. When buzzer sounds give the product details
31. Wait (continue working)
32. Receive price information
33. Key in price with right hand
34. Key in number of identical items
35. Place remainder of identical items
    on second conveyor
36. Decide whether to scan again
37. Read code?   Yes/No
38. Key in code
39. Place on ledge in front of customer
40. Reach for carrier bag
41. Give bag to customer
42. Key in price of bag

KEY

◯ = ACTION, PHYSICAL HANDLING

◖ = DECISION, INFORMATION HANDLING

▢ = INSPECTION

◖ = DELAY

Japanese Quality Circle meetings (meetings of about 10 production workers on their own time to try to improve their jobs; by 1979 there were 6,000,000 people in 600,000 such groups in Japan [Aoki, 1979]).

Start with the "effect," a "fishhead," a specific problem. Then add the "cause," the "fish body," composed of a backbone and other bones. A good diagram will have three or more levels of bones (backbone, major bones, minor bones on the major

bones). There are various strategies for defining the major bones. You may want to use the 4M's: manpower, machines, methods, materials. Or use the 4P's: policies, procedures, people, plant. Or be creative. The diagram gives an easily understood overview of a problem and tends to trigger suggestions.

Figure 9.16 has improved grinding efficiency for the "head" and excessive grinding, working environment, method, machine, and manpower as the "major

Multi-activity chart. The basic concept is to have two or more columns using a common, *scaled* time axis. The chart may show idle time on a particular column, allowing activities to be moved between columns. It can show whether one operator can run two machines or three operators run four machines, or two operators run three machines, when the operators are in a cell layout.

Left-hand right-hand chart, a type of multi-activity chart.

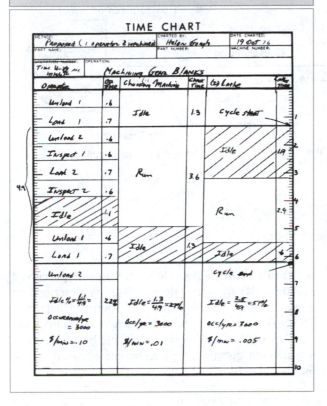

bones." Figure 9.17 was used at Bridgestone to reduce the variability of the viscosity of the splicing cement used in radial tires. Figure 9.18 shows the variability of the four operators before and after the Quality Circle studied the problem. For other examples, consider defective berry boxes as the head, and equipment, material, workers, box design, and delays as the major bones; making a better pie shell (flour, fat, shaping shell, tools used, water, mixing ingredients, and baking); drilling a well (drill bit grinding, working environment, method, machine, operator); bartending serving efficiency (method, materials, operator, environment, and cash register); improved physiology lab teaching (skeletons, manuals, rats, cadavers, exams, instructor, assistants, visual aids, and handouts); barber shop utilization (sales promotion, environment, work policies, method, and man); and stabilizing the rice price in Indonesia (market monitoring, harvest forecasting, stock reporting, procurement operation, storage system, sales operation, and stock movement).

7 DECISION STRUCTURE TABLES

Decision structure tables are a version of *if* statements in computer programs; they also are known as protocols or *contingency* tables (see Tables 31.5, 31.7, and 31.8 for examples). They unambiguously describe complex, multirule, multivariable decision systems.

The discussion in Chapter 31 emphasizes making better quality decisions due to (1) better decision analysis (higher quality personnel make the decision, using complex analysis techniques if necessary) and (2) less time pressure at the time the decision is made. They are a "game plan" worked out in advance, not in the "heat of the battle." The educated guesses have been made and tested. However, in addition, decision structure tables are a good tool for methods analysis since they make the analyst consider all possibilities and they enforce thoroughness. They also are good training aids.

A common example of a two-way decision structure table is a schedule with days as columns and hours, people, or machines as rows. A comput-

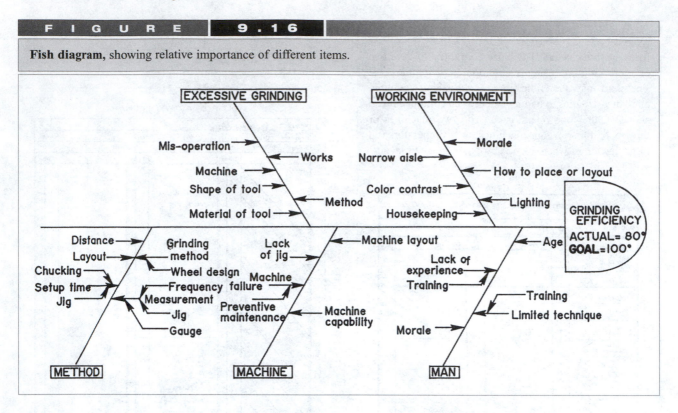

F I G U R E   9.16

Fish diagram, showing relative importance of different items.

erized version of a decision structure table is a spreadsheet. A spreadsheet is especially valuable in showing the results of "what if" decisions that have many effects.

The Federal Aviation Administration has a "playbook" of typical responses to a dozen common storm patterns. By knowing that playbook, the airlines can better adjust their schedules to minimize disruption for passengers.

Some example applications are spot welding, bowling prices, firewood prices, library checkout procedure, refund policy, spare parts prices, hiring policy, food scoop equivalents, bowling position for spares, CO_2 level for furnace, and flight scheduling.

 SUBJECTIVE OPINIONS

When evaluating alternatives, the criterion can be performance-related (e.g., time, errors), physiological (e.g., heart rate, electromyogram [EMG]), or **subjective** (vote, opinion). In addition, data is history; to speak of the future, you need subjective opinion.

Rather than just asking someone's opinion, it is better to shape the question so that the answer you get is more precise and quantified (psychophysical scaling). See Hill et al. (1992) and Muckler and Seven (1992) for some comments on subjective evaluations. Four techniques are the Borg vote, body discomfort map, absolute adjective scales, and relative votes.

8.1 Borg Vote The Borg **rating of perceived exertion (RPE)** vote (Borg, 1990) is described in more detail in Cardiovascular Response, Chapter 4. The basic concept of the **Borg vote** is to estimate the heart rate of 30- to 50-year-old people by asking them a structured question. The technique is based on the psychophysical power law:

$$R = a + c (S-b)^n$$

where: R = response intensity

a = constant for threshold (starting point)

c = constant for measure (proportionality constant)

S = stimulus intensity

b = constant for threshold (starting point)

n = power exponent

Although the Borg RPE scale was developed to estimate heart rate, it has become quite popular as a general index of stress. For example, Hagen (1993) demonstrated that a .09 m longer lifting hook used by forestry workers was better by assessing heart rate, oxygen consumption, and force plate measurements as well as RPE. The RPE was compatible with the more complex measurements.

Freivalds and Eklund (1993) used multiple criteria to evaluate powered nutrunners. The perceived exertion votes were good estimators of the peak torque of the nutrunners. That is, rather than measure the torque of the nutrunner or the EMG of the fore-

F I G U R E	9 . 17

Fish diagrams used at Bridgestone Tire to reduce cement viscosity variance. The four main categories were raw materials, operating methods, equipment, and human. The problem turned out to be an improper standard method as variability was greater for those who followed the standard procedure. See Figure 9.18.

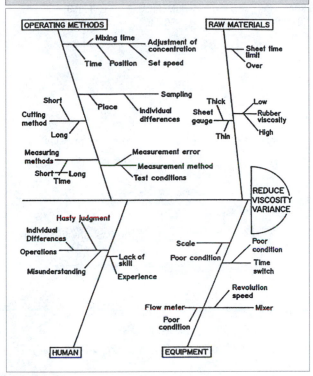

Source: Robert Cole, *Work, Mobility and Participation: A Comparative Study of American and Japanese Industry.* Copyright © 1979, University of California Press, Berkeley. Reprinted with permission.

F I G U R E	9 . 18

Distribution curves of four operators before and after the Quality Circle project (Cole, 1979). Reducing variability is an excellent quality improvement technique, as the effects of various changes are seen much more clearly for processes with little variability. For another process improvement technique, see EVOP (Section 9).

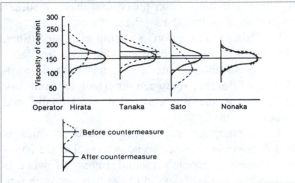

arm muscles, an engineer can have operators use alternative tools and give their opinion of their perceived exertion on the tools; the tools then can be selected from the perceived exertion vote.

8.2 Body Discomfort Map   The **body discomfort map** shows a number of body locations (Corlett and Bishop, 1976); some body maps are more detailed (e.g., for the hand, wrist, arm, etc.). The amount of discomfort at any location can be quantified by a scale such as Table 9.9 or the Borg (1990) category ratio scale (CR-10) included in Figure 9.19. The CR-10 scale gives .5 for "extremely weak" and 10 for "extremely strong"; people also are permitted to go below .5 and above 10. (A 10 is defined as the strongest value a person has experienced, but since a person can imagine something even stronger, the absolute maximum could be 12, 13, or even higher.) Use the body map of Figure 9.19 with the scale of Table 9.9. Of course, don't administer the body discomfort survey if you won't respond to the results!

8.3 Adjective Scales (Absolute)   In the **adjective scales** measure, a person provides an opinion about a product or environment by ranking it on a scale between two opposite adjectives such as hot–cold,

F I G U R E	9 . 19

Body discomfort map.

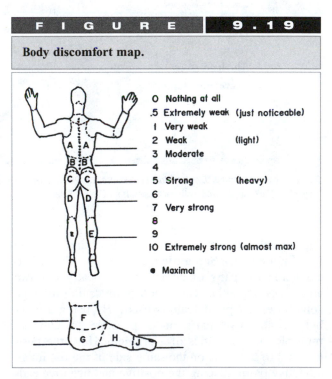

Source: Figure from N. Corlett and R. A. Bishop, "A Technique for Assessing Postural Discomfort," *Ergonomics,* Vol. 19, pp. 175–82. Copyright © 1976 by Taylor & Francis, London. Reprinted with permission. Scale from G. Borg, "Psychophysical Scaling with Applications in Physical Work and the Perception of Exertion," *Scand. J. Work Environ. Health,* Vol. 16, Suppl. 1, pp. 55–58. Copyright © 1990 by *Scand. J. Work Environ. Health,* Helsinki, Finland. Reprinted with permission.

T A B L E	9 . 9

Body discomfort scale. A category partitioning scale (CP 50) has high discriminability and high consistency (Shen and Parsons, 1997). The subject (1) selects from "no effect" or the five common divisions of very low, low, medium, high, and very high, and then (2) fine-tunes the vote by using the 5 numbers on either side of the adjective. The example shown was used to test seated pressure/discomfort. A person might say an alternative had "high pressure" and then vote exactly with a 38.

NUMERICAL SCALE	VERBAL DESCRIPTION	NUMERICAL SCALE	VERBAL DESCRIPTION	NUMERICAL SCALE	VERBAL DESCRIPTION
52		30		10	
51		29		9	
50		28		8	
49		27		7	
48		26		6	
47		25	medium pressure/	5	very low pressure/
46		24	discomfort	4	discomfort
45	very high pressure/	23		3	
44	severe discomfort	22		2	
43		21		1	
42		20		0	no pressure/discomfort
41		19			
40		18			
39		17			
38		16			
37		15	low pressure/		
36		14	discomfort		
35	high pressure/	13			
34	severe discomfort	12			
33		11			
32					
31					

Source: Reprinted from *Int. J. of Industrial Ergonomics,* Vol. 20. W. Shen and K. Parson. "Validity and Reliability of Rating Scales for Seated Pressure Discomfort." Copyright (1997, pp. 441–46, with permission from Elsevier Science.

comfortable–uncomfortable, good–bad, and so forth (see Figure 9.20). **Semantic differential** is the technical name for pairs of adjectives. Typically, the two adjectives peg either end of a 9-point scale (although sometimes a 7-point scale is used). By using a number of adjective pairs, it is possible to consider multiple characteristics of a problem. Have the positive end of the scale on the same side of the list for all adjective pairs. Placing the positive and negative ends randomly on both sides confuses people and gives less reliable results (Konz, Bennett, and Miller, 1986). Add the scores for the various pairs arithmetically to get an overall evaluation.

A more precise technique is to use a statistical technique called "factor analysis," which weights the contribution of each pair to the total. Rohles and Laviana (1985) recommend retaining eigenvalues greater than or equal to 1 and using a varimax rotation, then retaining descriptors that have loadings greater than .7 or less than –.7.)

If a "single dimension" is being evaluated, Shen and Parsons (1997) recommend the scale in Table 9.9. Some advantages are that it has high discriminability (difference between alternatives) and low variability (people are consistent individually and between persons).

The assumption underlying adjective scales is that it is possible to pick two adjectives that are opposites. However, people's mental image of what is opposite may not correspond to the two words chosen

FIGURE   9.20

Adjective scale. Multiple pairs aid in evaluation of multiple dimensions of the situation.

satisfied	____:____:____:____:____:____:____:____:____	dissatisfied
comfortable	____:____:____:____:____:____:____:____:____	uncomfortable
pleasant	____:____:____:____:____:____:____:____:____	unpleasant
acceptable	____:____:____:____:____:____:____:____:____	unacceptable

for the scale (Konz et al., 1986). One way to minimize this problem is to use only one end of the scale instead of both ends. For example, an office could be rated in the categories of air movement, aisle space, amount of dust, and so forth. The person would evaluate each with an acceptability vote:

6 = very acceptable

5 = acceptable

4 = somewhat acceptable

3 = somewhat unacceptable

2 = unacceptable

1 = very unacceptable

8.4 Relative (Paired) Votes   In Section 8.3, the person voted (using multiple criteria) for alternative A or B. For example, the person would vote concerning handtool A and then concerning handtool B; this is absolute rating. However, it is well known that a relative rating is more sensitive. That is, the person looks at the two items side by side and picks the preferred item. But relative rating does not allow determination of the strength of the preference.

FIGURE   9.21

Relative ranking scale. Used by (1) first selecting which member of the pair is preferred and then (2) indicating the degree of preference. Decimal votes (e.g., 3.5) are permitted.

10	——	
9	——	absolutely better
8	——	
7	——	significantly better
6	——	
5	——	much better
4	——	
3	——	somewhat better
2	——	
1	——	equal to

Considering the problem of **relative versus absolute rating**, Saaty (1980) developed a procedure that (1) allows the preference strength to be indicated also, and (2) allows the resulting data to be compared statistically. Figure 9.21 shows the relative ranking scale. The person selects which member of the pair is preferred and the degree of preference. The data now have two values: preference and amount.

Then the data are reduced (Liu et al., 1990; Mitta, 1993) to one value, an eigenvector. Assume three lighting conditions were to be evaluated. Each person compares the pairs of conditions, indicating which condition is preferred and by how much. An example showing the result for one subject is given in Table 9.10.

Next the data are normalized and a single value *(w)* is calculated (see Table 9.11). This single value then can be entered into standard statistical analyses such as analysis of variance.

Note that since the alternatives have to be paired for evaluation, the number of pairings rises rapidly with the number of alternatives. Thus, if 4 tools are to be compared, there are 6 pairings.

TABLE   9.10

Pairwise comparison matrix for one subject. The matrix is filled in three steps. Step 1 is to enter 1.0 on the diagonal. Step 2 is to enter the preference scores at the intersections. Here, condition 1 is preferred over condition 2 and the preference score is 2.5. (A fractional score can occur either from the person using a decimal when voting or from averaging the results of several trials.) The third step is to enter the reciprocals for the corresponding conditions. For example, 1/2.5 = .4.

Lighting Condition	Lighting Condition		
	1	2	3
1	1.0	2.5	3.5
2	.4	1.0	3.5
3	.29	.29	1.0
Sum	1.69	3.79	8.0

T A B L E	9 . 1 1

Normalized preferences for the subject in Table 9.10. The columns are normalized by dividing each entry by the column total. For example, 1/1.69 = .592. Then the eigenvector *(w)* is calculated by determining the row mean. The 1.001 grand total is approximately equal to 1. Condition 1 (score .563) is best.

Lighting Condition	Lighting Condition			Row Mean (w)
	1	2	3	
1	.592	.660	.437	.563
2	.237	.264	.437	.313
3	.172	.077	.125	.125
				1.001

9 EVOLUTIONARY OPERATION OF PROCESSES (EVOP)

When designing, there are major decisions and minor decisions to be made—that is, major and minor in their effect on the outcome. Through trial and error, experimentation, luck, prototypes, pilot projects, and so forth, the engineer designs a process. Eventually there comes a stage in which the job "goes into production." There are still possibilities for improvement, but each individual change has only a small improvement potential. Yet, your firm has a goal of "continuous improvement." Individual changes are not considered worthy of spending additional engineering resources to investigate them and delay production.

For example, consider painting part 123 in Department A. Considering that we could vary paint-thinner ratio, distance of part 123 from the paint nozzle, the nozzle diameter, the air pressure, the paint temperature, the temperature of part 123, and so forth, what is the optimum value of each of these variables? Or consider drilling holes in part 345 in Department C. Considering that we could vary drill rake angle, drill material, drill rpm, drill feed rate, coolant type, coolant volume, and so forth, what is the optimum value of each of these variables? To experiment would seem to require too much engineering time and expense.

You could use **passive observation** to examine the process through control charts. That is, you could examine control charts and hope to see a pattern that would allow you to guess the important trends. But the process is not just what occurs; it is subject to modification. That is, you could actively investigate possible variables—that is, do an experiment: **active observation.**

EVOP has the simple, yet powerful concept that a process produces two things: (1) items for sale, and (2)

information about the process. That is, while we are painting part 123, we also are generating information about the effects of the variables affecting the painting. In other words, we have been running an experiment—we just didn't realize it and collect and analyze the data!

Box and Hunter (1959) proposed that, to minimize the engineering expense and to study the process in its "production" version, the "experiment" be run by the plant operation personnel (the painter or drill press operator) on the production machines, thus eliminating the cost of the experimenter and the cost of the lab.

In most experiments, the experimental design attempts to maximize the amount of information obtained from the experiment, usually by minimizing the effects of "noise" (variability due to the process or the measurement of the process). This can be visualized as "cutting the weeds" (see Figure 9.22). The normal experiment tries to "cut the weeds" so the "crop" can be observed. However, there is an alternate strategy. Repeat the experiment over and over until the signal appears through the noise. Using the crop analogy, that means that if you watch long enough, eventually the crop rises above the weeds. **Evolutionary Operation of Processes (EVOP)** follows this second strategy, using the assumption that experimentation costs nothing since the process is producing product for sale.

Box and Hunter said that if the experiment is to be run by "shop" personnel (i.e., no college, no statistical training) and the primary objective of producing products for sale is not to be endangered, the experiments must be simple and cautious so as to cause no scrap. The

F I G U R E	9 . 2 2

"Cutting the weeds" design. Traditional experimental design reduces the noise level to detect the effect—"cutting the weeds to detect the crop." EVOP uses another approach, continued experimentation until the signal shows through—"letting the crop grow above the weeds."

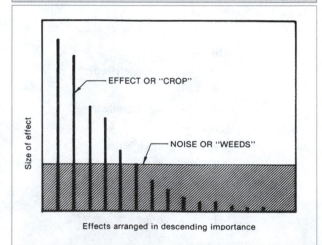

technique is called Evolutionary Operation of Processes since it follows the two essentials of evolution: (1) small variations and (2) selection of favorable variants.

Table 9.12 gives some possible applications of EVOP. In most applications, the criterion is the *yield* of the process. EVOP usually is used to maximize quality or the use of material or energy rather than to minimize the cost of labor. Box and Draper (1969) wrote an excellent text on EVOP, which not only gives administrative procedure for EVOP to apply trial and error systematically but also gives simple and elegant statistical techniques. EVOP is really another version of the operations research problem of "hill climbing"; EVOP, however, deals with a "noisy" signal.

Assume that a stainless steel bushing is being machined. We will use as the criterion the machining cost/bushing. Since we are looking for a minimum, look for the "bottom of the valley" rather than the "top of the mountain." The present feed and speed were selected from a handbook so we probably are close to but not at the bottom. For this specific bushing with its specific type of stainless steel and required type of cut, made on this specific machine, with a specific brand of cutting fluid at a specific volume, etc., what is the optimum value of each variable?

An EVOP committee (composed of, perhaps, a manufacturing engineer, a quality control engineer, the supervisor, and the lathe operator) decides to vary feed and speed. At present, feed = .140 mm/rev and speed = 30 m/min; cost = $.25/unit. The committee members set up a "search pattern" of four perimeter points around the center point (see Figure 9.23). The operator machined bushings for one day at each point, keeping track of output and tool life. The .16 and 31 point looked good as cost was $.22/unit. Should they shift to this point and run a new search; should they continue

the search using the existing pattern; or should they try a different variable, such as volume of cutting fluid?

In our example, they decided to continue at the same five points for another week. After 3 weeks, they shifted to .14 and 32 as a center point and started a new search pattern. In general, it is good practice to overlap search areas as it helps to prevent "falling off a cliff." Eventually, after some months, the data shown in Figure 9.24 were available. They decided, as the new standard for feed and speed on this bushing, to machine the bushing with a feed of .16 mm/rev and a speed of 31 m/min for an anticipated savings of $.03/piece. EVOP savings, though worthwhile, rarely are spectacular.

In statistical terms, what has been described is a "full factorial design"; that is, data are gathered at each point. A fractional factorial design (data at only certain selected points) can be used for preliminary (screening) work. An example would be to determine which of eight potential variables is important. The

---

TABLE   9.12

Example applications of EVOP.

APPLICATION	CRITERION	SOME VARIABLES
Turning	Machining cost Surface finish	Feed, speed, tool geometry
Welding	Weld strength	Cooling rate, amps, rod type
Painting	Scrap rate	Paint-thinner ratio, gun distance
Casting	Yield	Pouring temperature, additive percentages, sand additive percentages
Chemical processes	Yield	Time, temperature, percentages of constituents and catalysts

---

FIGURE   9.23

Search pattern. The focus is an initial center point (at .14 mm/rev and 30 m/min) with four perimeter points. Initial cost = $.25/unit.

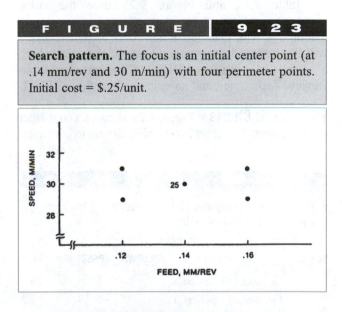

FIGURE   9.24

Feed and speed decision. Optimum values of feed and speed selected are .16 mm/rev and 31 m/min, respectively, for an estimated savings of $.03/unit.

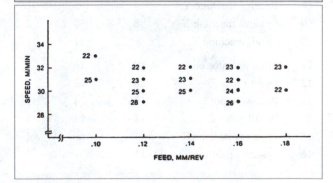

reduction of data points can be substantial, but only main effects (not interactions) are considered and someone quite knowledgeable in statistics would be needed to set up and analyze the data.

10 PROJECT SCHEDULING

Project planning is simple in concept but difficult in execution. It has two stages: (1) plan the work, and (2) work the plan.

In the first stage (a) list the project *tasks,* (b) list the *sequence* (precedence) requirements of the tasks, and (c) allocate resources to the tasks to determine task *time.* Then the tasks, sequences, and times are combined into a plan.

The second stage is to execute the plan. As the project progresses, the time, sequence, and even the tasks themselves change; thus, the plan needs to be continually revised and updated.

Table 9.13 and Figure 9.25 give the tasks, sequence, and times for a small project—replacing machine X with machine Y and robot Z. The example will be used to demonstrate the use of the Gantt chart, a simplified version of **PERT** (Program Evaluation Review Technique), and an enhanced version of PERT.

10.1 Gantt Charts
Figure 9.26 shows a Gantt chart of the project. The chart is relatively simple to construct;

T A B L E				9 . 1 3

Tasks, precedence, and time for replacing machine X with machine Y and robot Z.

NUMBER	ACTIVITIES	FOLLOWS	PRECEDES	DAYS
1	Get cost of machine X		4	3
2	Get cost of machine Y		4	2
3	Get cost of robot Z		4	8
4	Compare X to Y + Z	1, 2, 3	5	2
5	Decide on Y + Z	4	6	1
6	Get approval on Y + Z	5	7, 12	6
7	Order machine Y	6	8	1
8	Receive machine Y	7	9	41
9	Remove machine X	8	10	2
10	Install machine Y	9	11	1
11	Train operator on Y	10	16	1
12	Order robot Z	6	13	2
13	Receive robot Z	12	14	35
14	Install robot Z	13	15	6
15	Train operator on Z	14	16	4
16	System operational	11, 15		

F I G U R E   9 . 2 5

Tasks, sequence, and times for example project. Tasks of Table 9.13 are shown as "nodes" (circles, events, milestones). Task times (not drawn to scale) are on the arrows (lines) following the nodes. (There is an alternative graphical technique in which the tasks are placed on arrows.) The network shows task precedence (left to right); it is assumed that it cannot start until its predecessors have been completed. The number above each node is the cumulative time to reach that node. Node 4 shows that when several paths join in a node, the node time is the maximum of the path times. Node 6 shows how one task time can affect more than one node.

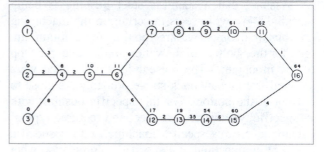

many vendors sell wall-mounted units with pegs, tapes, and magnetic bars in a variety of colors. The Gantt chart is useful not only for planning the work but also for working the plan. It forces a plan to be made, shows the situation (planned versus done) at a glance, and is easy to modify; modifications do not require computers or complicated mathematics. Gantt charts are used more often than either simplified or enhanced PERT.

10.2 Simplified PERT
An extension of the Gantt chart, PERT, is especially useful for very large projects (say, more than 100 tasks). (PERT stands for Program Evaluation Review Technique, but people rarely use the words; they simply say PERT.) The key concept here is the **critical path,** the path on which the "bottleneck" tasks are located. Tasks on the critical path require special attention. Conversely, tasks not on the critical path need less attention. Thus PERT helps the analyst decide which tasks need attention.

Figure 9.25 showed the tasks, sequence, and times for the machine/robot project. Where is the critical path? To find the critical path, you need an additional step. Figure 9.25 now is known as the forward pass. Figure 9.27 shows the critical path, which is revealed when a backward pass is added to the forward pass. The difference between the forward pass and the backward pass is **slack.** When slack is zero, the task is on the critical path. (There can be multiple critical paths.)

The knowledge of which tasks are on the critical path is useful in stage 2—working the plan. Consider expediting. Expediting shortens total time only when

F I G U R E	9 . 2 6

Gantt chart representation of Figure 9.25 and Table 9.13. There is one row for each task. The horizontal axis is *scaled* time. The tasks are located to show the beginning and finish time for each task—they are *scaled*. Hanging from the top of the chart is a movable cord or bar showing today's date. In the figure, "today" is November 22.

As tasks are completed, they are shaded. In this figure, tasks 1, 2, 3, 4, 5, 6, 7, and 12 have been completed. Task 8 is about 5 days behind schedule; task 13 is about 3 days ahead of schedule.

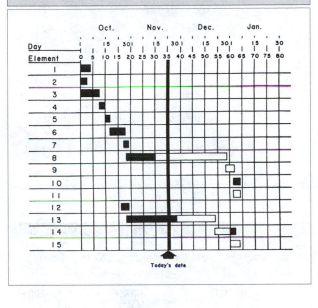

F I G U R E	9 . 2 7

Forward and backward paths are shown in one figure (Figure 9.25 shows just the forward path). From the forward pass, the total at the final task (64 days) is put on the bottom of the final node. Then, working backward, subtract task time from the total, and enter it at the bottom of the node to the left. When two paths converge (as at node 6), the smaller number is entered. The difference between the forward pass time (above the node) and the backward pass time (below the node) is *slack* time. When slack time is zero, the task is on the *critical path*.

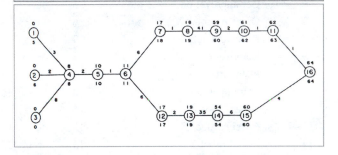

In simplified PERT, only one estimate is made of the task time. In enhanced PERT, three time estimates are used: (1) an "optimistic" task completion time, (2) a "most likely" time, and (3) a "pessimistic" time. Table 9.14 shows the three time estimates for the example problem. The PERT computer programs calculate the weighted average of the three times (expected time) using the following formula:

$$t_e = (t_o + 4t_m + t_p)/6$$

where

t_e = expected time

t_o = optimistic time

t_m = most likely time

t_p = pessimistic time

There are two assumptions.

1. The most likely time should have weight of 4, and the other two times have a weight of 1.

2. The estimator will give the t_p value such that it is farther from t_m than t_o is from t_m. That is, the time distribution is assumed to have a positive skew.

The net result is that t_e will be larger than t_m. Since it is a longer schedule (and people work toward goals), working your plan may take longer just because of the techniques used to plan your work. Table 9.14 gives the times for the machine/robot example.

Three time estimates instead of one give another possibility. They permit an estimate of time variability. In addition to the two above assumptions, four additional assumptions are made:

---

the expedited tasks are on the critical path. Expediting tasks not on the critical path, as long as there is sufficient slack time, is probably a waste. This information is not available from a Gantt chart.

Some advantages of PERT are: (1) putting the tasks, sequences, and times into the network shows potential problems while the project is still in the planning stage, (2) it shows which tasks should and should not be expedited, (3) it sets up progress checkpoints, and (4) it tends to be self-fulfilling since people work toward known schedules. Disadvantages are: (1) PERT takes time and effort to set up and (especially) to maintain and (2) the times may be too long. That is, since there is a PERT analysis, the project may take longer. This is because people work to the schedule.

In addition, at the beginning when people are asked how long a task will take, they tend to give an inflated estimate. That is, if you can do the task in 3 weeks, to be on the safe side, you tell the boss 4 weeks. Then, when 4 weeks goes into the formal schedule, you take 4 weeks.

10.3 Enhanced PERT   Two enhancements will be discussed: (1) time variability and (2) time/cost tradeoffs.

T A B L E   9.14

Tasks, precedence, and four times for replacing machine X with machine Y and robot Z.

Number	Activities	Follows	Precedes	Optimistic	Most Likely	Pessimistic	Expected
					TIME (DAYS)		
1	Get cost of machine X		4	2	3	5	3
2	Get cost of machine Y		4	1	2	4	2
3	Get cost of robot Z		4	6	8	9	8
4	Compare X to Y + Z	1, 2, 3	5	2	2	3	2
5	Decide on Y + Z	4	6	1	1	2	1
6	Get approval on Y + Z	5	7, 12	4	6	8	6
7	Order machine Y	6	8	1	1	2	1
8	Receive machine Y	7	9	30	41	60	42
9	Remove machine X	8	10	2	2	3	2
10	Install machine Y	9	11	1	1	2	1
11	Train operator on Y	10	16	1	1	3	1
12	Order robot Z	6	13	2	2	4	2
13	Receive robot Z	12	14	31	35	60	38
14	Install robot Z	13	15	5	6	10	6
15	Train operator on Z	14	16	3	4	6	4
16	System operational	11, 15					

3. The range of the times (optimistic minus pessimistic) equals 6 standard deviations.

4. The expected time for a node is the sum of the times of the path for that node.

5. The variability of each task is independent of the variability of all other tasks (i.e., task times are independent).

6. The distribution of the cumulative variances can be approximated by a normal distribution.

For example, the variance of task 3 is $(3/6)^2 = .25$ day^2. The variance of task 4 is $(1/6)^2 = .03$ day^2. Then the variance of the time to node 5 is $.25 + .03 = .28$ day^2; the standard deviation is .53 days. Then, using the normal distribution, 95% of the times would fall between $1.96(.53) = 1.04$ days of the mean. Rounding off 1.04 to 1.0, it might be said that the 95% confidence limit for node 5 is $10 - 1 = 9$ days to $10 + 1 = 11$ days. (You can turn the problem around and ask what the probability is of accomplishing node 5 by 9 or 11 days.)

The computer printout looks impressive (especially when it prints the prediction to several decimal places). But don't bet any money that prediction equals reality.

The second capability of enhanced PERT, PERT/COST, permits a tradeoff of various task times against cost. It requires four estimates for each task: (1) a normal time, (2) the task cost for the normal time, (3) a "crash" (expedited) time, and (4) the task cost for the crash time. Table 9.15 shows values for the example project.

T A B L E   9.15

PERT times and costs for example problem.

TASK	NORMAL TIME (DAYS)	NORMAL COST ($)	CRASH TIME (DAYS)	CRASH COST ($)	EXPEDITED COST/DAY ($/DAY)
1	3	50	2	100	50
2	2	50	1	75	25
3	8	125	6	150	12
4	2	60	1	90	30
5	1	40	1	40	–
6	6	100	3	50	17
7	1	40	1	40	–
8	41	4500	35	4000	83
9	2	400	1	600	200
10	1	200	1	200	–
11	1	40	1	40	–
12	2	50	1	60	10
13	35	600	32	900	100
14	6	1200	5	1400	200
15	4	150	3	190	40

The last column of Table 9.15 shows the cost of saving a day for each task. The three assumptions are:

1. The times are accurate.
2. The costs are accurate.
3. The tradeoff between time and cost is linear.

Naturally it is worthwhile to expedite only those tasks on the critical path. If it is decided to cut the project completion time from 64 to 63 days, tasks 3, 4, 5, 6, 12, 13, 14, and 15 are on the critical path. Since it will cost only $10 to crash task 12, it is the best bet. Note that changing the time for task 12 from 2 days to 1 day not only makes the total time 63 days but also makes the upper branch a critical path. That is, when you expedite a task, the critical path may change.

Table 9.16 summarizes the analysis techniques presented in this chapter.

T A B L E	9 . 1 6	
A summary of the analysis techniques given in this chapter.		

ANALYSIS TECHNIQUE	PURPOSE OF TECHNIQUE	TYPICAL CRITERION
Between Operations		
Location of one new item	Locate one new item in an existing facility.	Minimize material handling costs.
Arrangement of entire facility	Rearrange all items in a facility.	Minimize material handling cost.
Flow diagrams and process charts	Get overview of a task.	Eliminate unnecessary operations, movements, and inspections.
Pareto	Prioritize tasks.	Reduce annual costs.
Multi-activity charts	Study coordination problems: between hands, people, and machines.	Reduce delay time.
Project scheduling	Plan the work: work the plan.	Reduce project time, cost.
Within an Operation		
Fish diagrams	Organize cost-reduction analysis.	Reduce costs, improve quality.
Decision structure tables	Have better quality decisions by workers; better communication of procedures.	Improve quality of procedure implementation.
EVOP	Improve efficiency.	Improve process yield, quality.
Subjective opinions	Decide which procedure to use.	Choose among alternatives.

Review Questions

1. Discuss the Pareto concept.
2. What are the three types of flow diagrams?
3. In a flow diagram and process chart, what are the standard symbols for an operation, transportation, inspection, delay, and storage?
4. What is the purpose of a multi-activity chart?
5. What is "inside machine time" used for?
6. What is "kitting"?
7. How is a body discomfort map used?
8. Give an example of a semantic differential question.
9. In the EVOP concept, what two things does a process produce?
10. Is EVOP an active or a passive observation of the process?
11. What is a critical path in PERT?
12. Sketch a Gantt chart.

References

Aoki, J. Japanese productivity: What's behind it? *Modern Machine Shop,* Vol. 52, No. 4, 117–25, 1979.

Borg, G. Psychophysical scaling with applications in physical work and the perception of exertion. *Scandinavian J. Work Environ. Health,* Vol. 16 (Supplement 1), 55–58, 1990.

Box, G. and Draper, N. *Evolutionary Operation: A Method of Increasing Industrial Productivity.* New York: Wiley, 1969.

Cole, R. *Work, Mobility, and Participation: A Comparative Study of American and Japanese Industry.* Berkeley: University of California Press, 1979.

Corlett, N. and Bishop, R. A technique for assessing postural discomfort. *Ergonomics,* Vol. 19, 175–82, 1976.

Francis, R., McGinnis, L., and White, J. *Facility Layout and Location: An Analytical Approach.* Englewood Cliffs, NJ: Prentice Hall, 1992.

Freivalds, A. and Eklund, J. Reaction torques and operator stress while using powered nutrunners. *Applied Ergonomics,* Vol. 24, No. 3, 158–64, 1993.

Hagen, K. Longer lifting hooks for forestry workers: An evaluation of ergonomic effects. *Int. J. of Ind. Ergonomics,* Vol. 12, 165–75, 1993.

Hanna, S. and Konz, S. *Facility Design: Manufacturing Engineering,* 3rd ed. Scottsdale, AZ: Holcomb Hathaway, 2004.

Hansen, D. and Taylor, S. Optimal production strategies for identical production lines with minimum operable production rates. *IIE Transactions,* Vol. 14, No. 4, 288–95, December 1982.

Hill, S., Iavecchia, H., Byers, J., Bittner, A., Zaklad, A., and Christ, R. Comparison of four subjective workload rating scales. *Human Factors,* Vol. 34, No. 4, 429–39, 1992.

Konz, S., Bennett, C., and Miller, B. Task lighting at a VDT workstation. *Proceedings of the Human Factors Society,* 192–96, 1986.

Liu, T., Narayanan, S., Subramanian, V., and Konz, S. Relative versus absolute rating. *Proceedings of the Human Factors Society,* 1229–32, 1990.

Mitta, D. An application of the analytic hierarchy process: A rank-ordering of computer interfaces. *Human Factors,* Vol. 35, No. 1, 141–57, 1993.

Muckler, F. and Seven, S. Selecting performance measures: "Objective" vs. "subjective" measurement. *Human Factors,* Vol. 34, No. 4, 441–55, 1992.

Muther, R. and Hales, L. *Systematic Planning of Industrial Facilities (SPIF),* Vols. I and II. Kansas City, MO: Management and Industrial Research Publications, 1980.

Rohles, F. and Laviana, J. Quantifying the subjective evaluation of occupied space. *Proceedings of the Human Factors Society,* 706–10, 1985.

Saaty, T. *The Analytic Hierarchy Process.* New York: McGraw-Hill, 1980.

Shen, W. and Parsons, K. Validity and reliability of rating scales for seated pressure discomfort. *Int. J. of Industrial Ergonomics,* Vol. 20, 441–61, 1997.

Wilson, J. and Grey, S. Reach requirements and job attitudes at laser-scanner checkout stations. *Ergonomics,* Vol. 1, No. 27 [12], 1247–66, 1984.

Website

Success stories for root cause analysis, www. taproot .com

10

OCCURRENCE SAMPLING

Overview

Occurrence sampling is a technique of gathering and analyzing data to aid decision making. After deciding how much accuracy and confidence are desired, a representative sample is gathered. The results then can provide information for decisions.

Key Concepts

confidence

control chart

diminishing returns

discrete/continuous
   sampling

influence

p chart

periodicity

random sample

randomization with
   restrictions

relative/absolute accuracy

reuse of data

stratification

time standards

PROBLEM

Assume that in your organization material is moved with a fork truck. There seem to be long delays. Upon what do you base your opinion? The question is asked, "Do we need another truck or is the present one idle too much?" This leads to a more specific question: "What is the present utilization of the truck?" It is important to remember that the purpose of occurrence sampling is to obtain information in order to make decisions; the purpose is not to demonstrate knowledge of statistical theory.

We might have someone follow the truck for a specific time period—say, 20 working days—and record the following type of information for each day:

0700	Went to shipping dock
0706	Parked outside supervisor's office
0711	Left office with orders
0712	Entered first freight car with load

This would be a continuous time study. It gives a complete picture of the situation while it is studied, assuming the past is the same as the future. The problem is the expense of the study.

To cut the expense of the study, the truck might be observed for only 5 days, or 1 day, or even half a day. The expense has been cut, but we now have the problem of a representative sample. Perhaps the Monday morning on which we made the study is not representative of the entire month. We could reduce the problem by following the truck for 2 h on Monday morning and 2 h on Tuesday morning. We still might worry about idleness in the afternoon. However, we could observe for 1 h on Monday morning, 1 h on Monday afternoon, 1 h on Tuesday morning, and 1 h on Tuesday afternoon. We still might worry about before and after breaks; about Wednesday, Thursday, and Friday; about the first week of the month versus the second week, and so forth.

The end result is a sample composed of a large number of very short intervals: **discrete sampling** instead of **continuous sampling.** All time studies are samples from a population. The conventional time study (a "movie") is a continuous sample of *n* cycles (assuming underlying statistical distribution is normal). Occurrence sampling (a series of "snapshots") is a technique in which there are gaps of occurrences between the sample readings (assumed underlying statistical distribution is binomial). Although the statistical calculations are valid even if there are no gaps between the events sampled, continuous recording of occurrences does present questions as to whether the sample represents the population.

Occurrence sampling of times was first used by Tippett in the British textile industry in the early 1930s; it was introduced to the United States about 1940 under the name "ratio delay" since it is often used to study the ratios of various delays. It also is known as *work sampling* since the times sampled often are times of people working. More correct, however, is *occurrence sampling* since what are sampled are occurrences of various types of events. These events can be delays (such as in equipment utilization), work–task ratios (such as the proportion of material handling labor that is direct labor or the proportion of time spent on the telephone), or other ratios (such as the proportion of loads that are damaged). Work- and ratio-delay are poor adjectives since no connotation of work or delay is needed to use the technique.

Let us return to the fork truck problem. If we observe the fork truck many times (say, 1,000), we will be quite confident in the information. If we observe the fork truck a few times (say, 10), our confidence will be much less. But there is a large difference in the cost of obtaining the information—the historic conflict between information and cost of obtaining information. You must make a tradeoff. A small sample gives a low cost of information but a high risk that the sample is not representative of the population. A large sample gives a high cost of information but a low risk that the sample is not representative of the population. (See Figure 10.1.)

The sampling problem then becomes:

1. obtaining a sample whose size gives the desired tradeoff between cost and risk

2. obtaining a sample representative of the population

The sample size problem will be discussed first.

F I G U R E   1 0 . 1

Sampling tradeoff. Trading off information (which increases with $\sqrt{n}$) versus cost of information (which increases with *n*) is a common engineering problem.

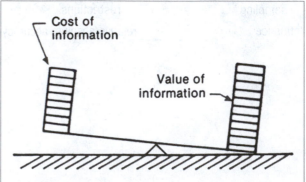

Cost of information

Value of information

REQUIRED NUMBER OF OBSERVATIONS

There is a general principle of statistics that the information obtained from a sample is a function of the square root of the sample size, n. (It comes from the standard deviation of the error having that square root.) That is, if we get 2 units of information from a sample size of 4, then to get a total of 4 units of information, we need a sample size of 16; to get 8 units of information, we need a sample size of 64. The cost of obtaining information, however, generally increases directly with the sample size, n, rather than the square root of n.

In ordinary words, it is the law of **diminishing returns.** As n increases, there comes a point beyond which additional information is not worth the additional cost. Assume we can decide whether to buy a new fork truck if we know that the present truck is idle between 6% and 8% of the time. Then additional samples telling us that the idle percent is between 7.06% and 7.07% are not worth the additional cost.

How many observations should you make? It depends on:

A = Desired absolute accuracy

p = Proportion of occurrence

c = Confidence level desired

First, the standard deviation of a proportion, σ_p, is:

$$\sigma_p = \sqrt{\frac{p(1-p)}{n}}$$

where p = Proportion (decimal) of occurrence

n = Number of observations

Second, since sample sizes generally will be large (over 30), the normal distribution is assumed. See Figure 10.2.

T A B L E	1 0 . 1
Confidence level for z values of equation $A = z\sigma_p$.	

Z, NUMBER OF STANDARD DEVIATIONS	CORRESPONDING CONFIDENCE LEVEL, %
±1.0	68
±1.64	90
±1.96	95
±2.0	95.45
±3.0	99.73

F I G U R E	1 0 . 2

Normal distributions are symmetrical. The proportion of the total distribution included by a number of standard deviations does not depend on the value of the mean (see Table 10.1). See Table 18.6 (the normal distribution) for the area included for other numbers of standard deviations. (Note: It gives area from $-\infty$ to z, not area within $\pm z$.)

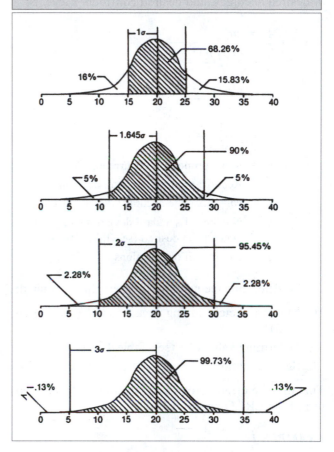

Third, make the distinction between **relative accuracy** and **absolute accuracy.** This simple distinction, if not made, will cause much grief. If the mean proportion of occurrence, $\overline{p}$ = 40%, then 10% relative accuracy is (.1)(.4) = 4% absolute accuracy; 20% relative accuracy is 8% absolute accuracy; and 30% relative accuracy is 12% absolute accuracy. We need to use absolute accuracy in the calculations, but most people think in terms of relative accuracy. Be sure management understands the distinction when it makes a statement such as, "Make the study accurate to within ±10%." The confusion arises because both the criterion and accuracy are in percentages. If 10% accuracy on 25 lb is requested, then the 10% relative accuracy must not be confused with the 2.5 lb absolute accuracy.

Fourth, how confident do you wish to be in your conclusions? Quite confident, very confident, or absolutely confident is not precise enough, so confidence must be expressed in numbers—70%

confident, 90% confident, 99.9% confident. What **confidence** expresses is the *long-run* probability that the sample mean is within the accuracy limits.

The probability calculations are similar to flipping a "true" coin; 8 of 10 heads or tails is possible; 80 of 100 is very unlikely. It is the *number* of occurrences, not the percent, that is critical.

The formula to show the relationship between p, n, desired accuracy, and desired confidence level is:

$$A = z\sigma_p$$

$$\text{or } A = z\sqrt{\frac{p(1-p)}{n}}$$

$$\text{or } n = \frac{z^2 p(1-p)}{A^2}$$

$$n = \frac{z^2(1-p)}{s^2 p}$$

where p = Mean proportion occurrence, decimal

s = Relative accuracy desired, decimal

A = sp = Absolute accuracy desired, decimal

z = Number of standard deviations for confidence level desired (see Table 10.1)

n = Number of observations

To determine the number of observations required:

1. Make a sketch, giving mean and A (see Figure 10.3).
2. Determine value of z (see Table 10.1).
3. Solve equation.

This may be clearer from some examples or repeated use of the ERGO program.

EXAMPLE 1

Given	Estimated idle percent of fork truck = 40%
	Relative accuracy desired = ±10%
	Confidence level desired = 68%
To Find	How many observations, n, are required?
Solution	(.1) (.4) = .04 = 4% (see Figure 10.3) 68% confidence equals ±1 standard deviation (from Table 10.1)

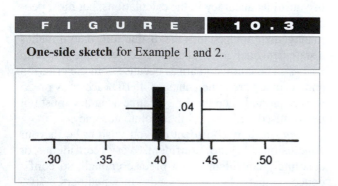

FIGURE 10.3

One-side sketch for Example 1 and 2.

Therefore:

$$.04 = 1\sigma_p$$

$$.04 = 1\sqrt{\frac{(.4)(.6)}{n}}$$

$$.04 = \sqrt{\frac{(.4)(.6)}{n}}$$

$$.0016 = \frac{.2400}{n}$$

$$n = .2400/.0016 = 150$$

Statement If the sample average of 150 observations is 40%, you can say with 68% confidence that the long-run idle percentage is between 36% and 44% with 40% being the most likely estimate, if the situation does not change.

EXAMPLE 2

Given	Estimated idle percent of fork truck = 40%
	Relative accuracy desired = ±10%
	Confidence level desired = 95%
To Find	How many observations, n, are required?
Solution	(.1) (.4) = .04 = 4% (see Figure 10.3) 95% confidence equals ±1.96 standard deviations

Therefore:

$$.04 = 1.96\sigma_p$$

$$.04 = 1.96\sqrt{\frac{(.4)(.6)}{n}}$$

$$.0016 = 3.8416\left(\frac{.24}{n}\right)$$

$$n = .922/.0016 = 576$$

Statement If the sample average of 576 observations is 40%, you can say with 95% confidence that the long-run idle percentage is between 36% and 44% with 40% being the most likely estimate, if the situation does not change.

EXAMPLE 3

Given	Estimated percent of people wearing sweaters = 40%
	Relative accuracy desired = ±20%
	Confidence level desired = 68%
To Find	How many observations, n, are required?
Solution	(.2) (.4) = .08 (see Figure 10.4)

$$.08 = 1\sigma_p$$

$$.08 = \sqrt{\frac{(.4)(.6)}{n}}$$

$$.0064 = \frac{.2400}{n}$$

$$n = .2400/.0064 = 37.5$$

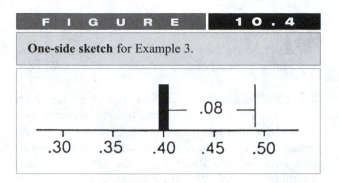

FIGURE 10.4

One-side sketch for Example 3.

Statement   If the sample average of 38 observations is 40%, you can say with 68% confidence that the long-run percentage of people wearing sweaters is between 32% and 48% with 40% being the most likely estimate, if the situation does not change.

EXAMPLE 4

Given   Estimated percent of overcast days = 25%
Relative accuracy desired = ±5%
Confidence level desired = 95%

To Find   How many observations, *n*, are required?

Solution $(.05)(.25) = .0125 = 1.25\%$ (see Figure 10.5)

$$.0125 = 1.96 \sqrt{\frac{(.25)(.75)}{n}}$$

$$n = 4,618$$

In Example 4, we required "considerable" accuracy (5%) for a "small" target (1.25%). To see that it is easier to aim at a big target, consider Example 5.

EXAMPLE 5

Given   Estimated percent of days that are not overcast = 75%
Relative accuracy desired = ±5%
Confidence level desired = 95%

To Find   How many observations, *n*, are required?

Solution $(.05)(.75) = .0375$ (see Figure 10.5)

$$.0375 = 1.96 \sqrt{\frac{(.25)(.75)}{n}}$$

$$n = (1.96)^2(.25)(.75)/(.0375)^2 = 512$$

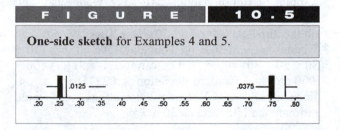

FIGURE 10.5

One-side sketch for Examples 4 and 5.

TABLE 10.2

Relationship between *p* and *n* when a requirement of 5% relative accuracy and 95% confidence is imposed regardless of *p*.

p (DECIMAL)	5% OF *p*	RESULTING RANGE ABOUT *p* (TARGET)	REQUIRED NUMBER OF OBSERVATIONS
.01	.0005	.0095 to .0195	158,400
.02	.0010	.0190 to .0210	78,400
.03	.0015	.0285 to .0315	51,700
.04	.0020	.0380 to .0420	38,400
.05	.0025	.0475 to .0525	30,400
.10	.0050	.0950 to .1050	14,400
.15	.0075	.1425 to .1575	9,070
.20	.0100	.1900 to .2100	6,400
.30	.0150	.2850 to .3150	3,730
.40	.0200	.3800 to .4200	2,400
.50	.0250	.4750 to .5250	1,600
.60	.0300	.5700 to .6300	1,070
.70	.0350	.6650 to .7350	685
.80	.0400	.7600 to .8400	400
.90	.0450	.8550 to .9450	175
.95	.0475	.9025 to .9975	85

Table 10.2 shows the relation between *p* and *n* for a 5% value of *relative* accuracy and 95.45% confidence level. The table displays numerically the importance of not shooting at a small target. If we require ±5% relative accuracy about an occurrence with a mean of 1%, then we need 158,400 "shots" to hit the target (which has a width from .95% to 1.05%).

Examples 4 and 5 pointed out the importance of a precise statement of the problem. Contrast, from the table, the number of observations required for an occurrence with *p* = .1 (*n* = 14,400) versus a nonoccurrence of *p* = .9 (*n* = 175).

Example 6 works the problem after gathering the data, with accuracy being the unknown and *z* being specified since *p* and *n* are by then known. You could specify *A* and calculate *z* if you wish.

EXAMPLE 6

Given   In a completed study:

Machines idle	1,400
Machines working	2,600
Total observations	4,000

To Find   If you must be 95.45% confident of the answer, what is

a. The absolute accuracy level?

b. The relative accuracy level of percent idle?

Solution $\bar{p} = 1,400/4,000 = .35 = 35\%$

$$A = 2 \sqrt{\frac{(.35)\,(.65)}{4,000}}$$

$= \pm.015 = \pm1.5\%$ absolute accuracy

Relative accuracy $= .015/.35$

$= \pm4.3\%$ on machines idle

$= .015/.65 = \pm2.3\%$ on machines working

Statement From the sample of 4,000 observations, you are 95.45% confident that the long-run idle percent is between 33.5% and 36.5% with 35% being the most likely estimate, if the situation does not change.

EXAMPLE 7

Given Estimated percent of idle = 30%

Estimated percent of operating = 55%

Estimated percent of maintenance = 15%

Relative accuracy desired = $\pm10\%$

Confidence level desired = 95%

To Find How many observations, *n*, are required?

Solution $(.10)\,(.030) = .30 = 3.0\%$

$(.10)\,(.55) = .055 = 5.5\%$

$(.10)\,(.15) = .015 = 1.5\%$

$n = 896, 314,$ and 2176

Statement You can use 2176 observations and determine that maintenance is between 13.5% and 16.5% (assuming the true percent is 15%); you will get higher accuracy for idle and operating; or use 896 and get higher accuracy for idle and lower accuracy for maintenance; or use 314 and get lower accuracy for idle and maintenance.

Assume there are two shifts and you want to complete the study in a week; there are 10 shifts and 3 operators. If you use 300 observations, this is 10 samples/shift (observing all 3 operators at a specific sampling time). Or, to improve your accuracy a little, you might use 12 samples/shift to get 360 observations.

The above procedure is based on the sequence of: plan study, do study, analyze data. If you are willing to analyze the data as you gather them (i.e., sequential sampling), the sample size can be reduced in some situations.

If there are several events to be studied (e.g., on a machine, you are interested in percent setup time, percent idle time, and percent rework time), you will get different *n* for the different percents. You will have to decide which percent and *n* to use—perhaps making several calculations and then compromising on some of the initial desires for confidence and accuracy.

3 REPRESENTATIVE SAMPLE

There are three problems in obtaining a representative sample: stratification, influence, and periodicity.

3.1 Stratification

If you are taking a sample on political opinion, it is desirable to keep separate data from different strata (Kansas vs. New York, old vs. young, rich vs. poor, male vs. female, city vs. rural) This is called **stratification.** In the same way, when sampling for work design purposes, it is desirable to stratify your sample. Sample from morning and afternoon, first and second shift, Monday and Thursday, and so on. Data can always be combined.

The same item of information can belong simultaneously to several strata. A political poll could identify the same person as belonging to the male stratum, the Kansas stratum, the college graduate stratum, and others. By proper planning and by identifying the data, it is possible to "reuse" the data—that is, predict votes for males, for Kansas, for college graduates, and so forth. Data on the fork truck could belong to several strata: the morning stratum, the first shift stratum, and so on.

If the sample is not properly stratified, you will fail to obtain potentially important information. More important, your sample will not faithfully represent the universe, and the risk of making incorrect assumptions about the population is greatly increased. The sampled population should be a good representation of the target population—the population to which your decision will apply.

An example might help. In 1936 the *Literary Digest* took a poll to see whether Landon or Roosevelt would win the presidential election. The magazine took a random sample of the people listed in the phone book. The poll predicted a Landon victory! Roosevelt won big, because people who weren't able to afford a phone voted heavily for Roosevelt. The sample had been unbiased, but it also had not been representative.

Stratified samples have a higher efficiency (a smaller number of observations is required for a given risk) than nonstratified samples. More precisely, if the percent of occurrence is constant in all strata, efficiency is the same for stratified and nonstratified sampling. The higher efficiency is due to the lower variance (error) when strata are used. Stratification might not help, but it can't hurt.

Using the fork truck example, assume you took samples of 100 on Monday, Tuesday, Wednesday, and Thursday. Assume further that the truck was idle 10% of the time on Monday, 30% on Tuesday, 50% on Wednesday, and 30% on Thursday. Overall, $\bar{p} = (10 + 30 + 50 + 30)/400 = .3$. The variance is $(.3)\,(.7)/400 = .000\ 525$ and standard deviation $= .023$. Using a confidence band of ±2 standard deviations, you would estimate the idle time as 30% $\pm5\%$.

If you had kept your data stratified, you could predict idle times of .1, .3, .5, and .3. Variances would be .000 900, .002 100, .002 500, and .002 100; standard deviations would be .030, .046, .050, and .046. Your estimate of idle time then would be 10% ±6% on Monday, 30% ±9.2% on Tuesday, 50% ±10% on Wednesday, and 30% ±9.2% on Thursday.

3.2 Influence   The second problem of a representative sample is **influence.** The event being sampled must not change its behavior because it is being sampled. In many situations, changing behavior is not a problem. If you are observing the color of passing automobiles, the auto will not change from green to red because you looked at it. When recording freethrow percentage in a basketball game, the player will not make or miss the shot because you are keeping score in the stands.

But, if Harry Nairdowell can see you coming on your sampling round, he may start working just before you record your observation. Even if Harry can't see you coming but can anticipate your presence since you always come at a specific time (you are periodic), the occurrence is not likely to be representative of the population.

3.3 Periodicity   Both the situation studied and the sample of the situation can be periodic or nonperiodic. **Periodicity** describes a situation in which a given behavior occurs regularly. For convenience we will call nonperiodic situations random even though they don't satisfy a mathematical definition of randomness. For engineering purposes they are sufficiently random.

The worst combination is a periodic situation and periodic sample with the same period length and initial point. For example, assume that Bill Kukenburger, the fork truck driver, every hour on the hour, drives by the desk on the shipping dock where Lisa Nimtz works, and checks the time on his watch versus the clock above her desk. If Sam Helal, your time study technician, observed Bill only every hour on the hour, his study would show that Bill did nothing but set his watch. If Sam observed Bill only at 14 minutes after the hour, he would never know the importance Bill attaches to having his watch set correctly.

Fortunately, although some machine cycles such as cam-controlled machines are completely periodic, most situations are not. But the possibility of a periodic situation, although rare, should be considered.

The most common technique of avoiding problems of influence and periodicity is to make the sample have no pattern. The easiest way to make a sample without a pattern is to make the sample random.

3.4 Sampling Procedure   Three sampling possibilities are random samples, random samples with restrictions, and periodic samples.

3.4.1 *Random samples*   Random samples are samples without a pattern. Assume that it has been calculated that we need 10 observations on the first shift on Monday. That shift runs from 7:00 A.M. to 3:30 P.M. with 10-min coffee breaks at 9:00 and 1:30 and a 30-min lunch at 11:30. That is 480 minutes plus 30 minutes for lunch, or 510 total. Label the minutes of the shift from 1 to 509. We need a representative sample from 1 to 119, no sample from 120 to 129, a sample from 130 to 269, no sample from 270 to 299, a sample from 300 to 389, no sample from 390 to 399, and a sample from 400 to 509.

Don't randomize over the entire day—stratify first by hours and then randomize within the hours. That is, label the hours from 1 to 8 and randomly select 10 numbers from a random number table such as Table 10.3. Although the table is printed in blocks of three, the sequence is without pattern, so the digits can be used in blocks of two, three, four, nine, or whatever.

To be precise, close your eyes and touch the table with a pencil; this selects the first number. Then, if the first digit is odd, work up in the table; if it is even, work down. If you are not a purist, start in the upper left-hand corner and work down. The sequence will be random, but it also will be the same sequence every day.

Let's assume your pencil touched the ninth number from the top of column 6. The number is 413. The digit 4 indicates hour 4. Since the first digit, 4, was even, work down in the table. The next number is 1, then 6, 8, 6, 1, 9 (which will be skipped since there is no hour 9), 3, 9 (skip), 6, 1, and 3. Now you know you will take 3 samples in hour 1, 2 in hour 3, 1 in hour 4, 3 in hour 6, and 1 in hour 8.

Next decide on the minute at which you will start your round of observation in each hour. Starting at the first time could be 41, then 16, skip 67, skip 80, skip 66, 10, and so on. The result is: 1 + 41 = 7:41, 6 + 16 = 12:16, etc. If the interval between rounds is not sufficient for you to complete the round before a new round is scheduled to start, toss out the starting time and select another random time. A sampling program is included in the ERGO software accompanying this book.

In addition to randomization of times, it is feasible to randomize the direction of approach to a situation. For example, sometimes you come from the left, sometimes right. It also is feasible to have different people do the observing at different times. These additional randomizations can be done by computer or simple coin flips, but the results probably should be recorded on a tour log such as Figure 10.6 so everything can be organized.

Simple randomization over the complete sampling period really is not very practical. In addition, it is inefficient.

T A B L E	1 0 . 3

Random numbers: For generation of random numbers or letters, see the ERGO program.

055	946	090	448	484	262	866	709	215	965
377	581	299	769	989	571	093	274	080	345
237	314	819	383	771	826	432	461	290	888
426	456	446	502	940	674	067	984	296	147
058	314	689	338	028	326	355	013	649	130
604	693	293	677	885	237	010	607	790	854
328	936	541	717	374	919	214	734	912	564
798	775	751	834	129	780	432	725	086	256
451	370	364	974	131	413	863	702	462	622
206	720	296	942	836	168	233	219	872	571
679	552	230	488	685	679	177	806	287	646
865	692	160	848	614	807	929	802	832	944
667	018	105	282	789	660	445	003	735	862
551	514	984	310	208	101	432	620	094	792
235	587	038	871	121	942	074	328	623	632
414	337	184	222	776	380	271	105	779	582
093	586	647	215	391	907	499	906	809	678
902	721	537	183	856	687	118	632	834	231
989	222	232	477	170	171	712	650	011	654
742	979	974	710	082	326	884	474	392	281
118	501	436	502	856	956	883	429	643	548

F I G U R E	1 0 . 6

Tour log. Tour logs help organize all the times, entry points, observers, and other details.

Date	Time	Entry point	Observer
8/16	8:07	A	J
8/16	8:33	C	J
8/16	8:51	C	J
8/16	9:43	A	J
8/16	9:46	B	J
8/16	12:26	A	M
8/16	12:56	A	M

3.4.2 *Randomization with restrictions* Stratified random sampling has three advantages over nonstratified random sampling: (1) It is more efficient. (2) It is easier to calculate the observation schedule than with a purely random sample. Using the fork truck example, it is easier to determine 20 sampling times on each of 10 days than to determine 200 sampling times randomized over the 10 days. (3) It is easier to modify a stratified plan. For example, if on day 3 you find that you have a meeting on the morning of day 4, and thus can't use the morning samples, you can change the schedule just for day 4. If randomization was over the entire 10 days, the schedule couldn't be changed since some of the times had already passed. If the plan is stratified, it also is easy to add or drop a day.

Randomization with restrictions can be used to encourage a representative sample. These restrictions are more important for small (e.g., n less than 30) sample sizes. For example, you might require that half of the observations occur before and half after the midshift break or that 20% occur on each of the 5 days of the week. (By chance, random times could occur disproportionally more or less in a specific time slot.)

You also may wish to have a specified minimum time between observations if you are making multiple observations at a point. For example, if you are making observations of 10 different machines at each sampling time, you may wish that times between samples be at least 5 min so you can complete the observations on the 10 machines.

You might restrict the sampling schedule to match your schedule. For example, you may have a department meeting every Thursday from 9 to 10 and thus schedule no sampling during that time. This gives a small systematic bias of your sample versus the population. Engineering judgment must be used in these situations. The goal is not a statistically perfect sample, but it is obtaining reasonably valid information with reasonable cost of information gathering, allowing valid decisions to be made.

A random number (and thus time) may occur twice during the sampling period. This is valid. Just count that observation as two when it is done. Technically this is a situation with the minimum interval between samples equal to zero. The other extreme is where the interval between samples becomes quite large.

For maximum statistical efficiency, Moder and Kahn (1980) recommend a procedure, restricted random sampling, based on having a specified maximum interval between observation rounds—that is, no long, "uncovered" gaps in sampling are permitted.

3.4.3 *Periodic samples*

We use the random sample when there are problems of periodicity or influence. Yet random samples are a lot of bother to calculate and tend to disrupt the observer's day by breaking it into segments of various lengths. Observers would like to use periodic samples.

The typical assumption is that the people being observed get tired of modifying their behavior if observed for a long enough time, so periodic samples can be used. An assumption! The periodicity of the situation and its phase relationship with the periodicity of the sample are also matters for engineering judgment. If you know the periods and their phases accurately, there is little need for the occurrence sampling study. Periodic samples also can be used when the thing being studied cannot be influenced by being observed.

Nonetheless, if there is a very large number of observations, say 1,000, periodic sampling may be satisfactory. Our recommendation is to avoid periodic sampling since it introduces an additional possible error to the data. Your basic desire is to get clean data rather than "probably" clean data.

4 DATA GATHERING

4.1 Person or Machine?

The first question is whether the data will be gathered by a person or a device. Historically, the answer has been to use a person, as devices did not have the capability to do the sampling. However, this has changed, and devices now, in some cases, can do the sampling. The people being observed, however, may resent being "spied upon" by a camera. In addition, the camera field of view is relatively narrow, making it difficult to get a good view of events unless they are in a relatively small, fixed location. Carayon (1993) discusses worker stress caused by electronic monitoring.

One possibility is to mount a videocamera to survey an area that has a clock displayed in the scene. An observer then can watch the tape at leisure. If there is a desire to save tape, the tape can be used repeatedly or the camera turned on only occasionally. An alternative is to record continuously but stop the video player at predetermined sampling times to obtain the "snapshot."

Another possibility is to connect an event recorder to a machine. That is, it could record the times the machine was running or the time the machine was stopped. Such devices now are attached routinely to long-haul trucks to continuously record speed and time the engine was running. In this way, the firm can identify how many times the driver exceeded the speed limit, how long the driver stopped for breaks, or other behaviors.

Another example is having a word processor operator monitored by a computer. The computer can record micro events (such as keystrokes/h) or macro events (files accessed/day). Clearly, in either situation, detailed information is available about the operator's performance. Strictly speaking, this electronic surveillance really is not sampling; rather, it is continuous observation.

Assuming a person will do the study, the next question is *who*. The answer may depend on the study duration. If the study is relatively short-term (a week or so), it may be worthwhile to hire casual labor full-time (at minimum wage) to study the situation relatively intensely. Of course, there will be some training time (perhaps a day) for the novice to become familiar with the task and the situation being studied. If the study is long-term (a month or more, depending on the situation studied, which varies considerably), using people already on the payroll (such as the supervisor or an engineer) for a portion of the day may be better. Another possibility is to use a person who has been injured and is on "light duty." The assumption is that this person can fit in a given number of observations/day (perhaps 10–15) among other duties. Of course, the wage cost will be considerably higher than minimum wage, but the training time should be minimal.

4.2 Reuse Data?

For many situations, a simple cumulative data form, such as in Figure 10.7, is satisfactory. The observer simply puts a tally mark in the appropriate place. At the end of the study, the total

FIGURE	10.7

Cumulative data form. Combining data simplifies analysis but allows only one use of each entry.

Situation _____ Clark Fork Truck _____   Observer _____ SK _____   Date _____ 8/15/04 _____

	TALLY			TOTAL			PERCENT		
Period	Working	Idle		Work	Idle (absent)	Idle (present)	Work	Idle (absent)	Idle (present)
		Driver absent	Driver present						
1	1111	111	1	4	3	1	50	37	12
2	1111 111			8			100		
3	1111 111			8			100		
4	1111 111			8			100		
5	1111 111			8			100		
6	1111 111			8			100		
7	1111 111			8			100		
8	1111 111			8			100		
9	1111 111			8			100		
10	1111		1	4	3	1	50	37	12
Total				72	6	2	90.0	7.5	2.5

and percentages are calculated. Raw data, calculations, and final answer are all on the same sheet.

The big disadvantage of cumulative recording is that the data are used only once. **Reuse of data,** in contrast, allows the data to be examined in terms of multiple criteria. Consider a political survey in which a 50-year-old male, living in Manhattan, Kansas, who is a registered Republican, agreed with a statement on a particular issue. A 25-year-old female, living in Topeka, Kansas, and a registered Democrat, disagreed with the statement. Using cumulative tallies, this would be one for and one against. But the information is much more useful if the percent for and against can be identified by age, by town, by political preference, and other characteristics. In the same way, it is better to keep a fork truck observation so that it can be identified as occurring on Monday, in Dept. X, with driver Y, at time XXX, and so forth. Recorded this way, the data can be "reused" many times.

For example, Steiner et al. (1998) used work sampling to record 20 different locations around a machine that operators used during extended cut mining. These locations then were compared with many variables (operator, time of cut, type of mine, and so forth) to identify why unsafe practices were sometimes used.

Standard programs such as SAS (Statistical Analysis System) are widely available. See Box 10.1 for an example SAS program for use on a mainframe.

5 DATA ANALYSIS

If you have stratified your sample, you can use two different data analysis techniques. If you have no strata (subgroups), you cannot use these two techniques.

5.1 Strata Comparison   It may be desirable to compare the occurrences between two different strata to see if there is a statistically significant difference. The following procedure assumes that the total observations are the same for both strata. See Natrella (1963) also for tables for unequal sample sizes. Allen and Corn (1978) present a chi-square procedure that can be used for unequal sample sizes.

Put the data in the following format:

Class I   Class II

Sample from strata A r_a S_a r = number of occurrences

Sample from strata B r_b S_b s = number of nonoccurrences

n = $r + s$ = number of observations

For $n_a = n_b$

EXAMPLE 1

Given $n_a = n_b = 16$

BOX 10.1   *SAS Program for Occurrence Sampling*

See Figure 10.8 for an example output. In the actual program, data were entered for different days and a series of tables was generated for each machine. In addition, the data were re-sorted and tables printed by time of day versus activity and by shift versus activity, as well as by product versus activity. Note how the analyst can enter a code such as M21 and the computer will print May 21. Note how the analyst can enter a time and the computer will categorize it by hour.

Code
```
DATA MAY 21;
INPUT DATE$ 1–4 SHIFT 5–6 PRODUCT
7–9 TIME 10–14 TIMES$ 15–24 STATION$
25–29 OPERATORS$ 30–34 ACTIVITIES
35–39 COMMENTS$ 40–65;
IF TIME GE 0900 AND TIME LE 0959
THEN BLOCK = "0900–0959";
PROC FORMAT;
    VALUE $D M21 = "MAY 21";
    VALUE $A TPL = "PALLET TOT:LVR"
DATA GE:
    SET MAY 21;
    IF STATION = "GE";
PROC SORT DATA = GE OUT=GENEW;
    BY DATE PRODUCT;
PROC FREQ DATA = GE;
    TABLES PRODUCT * ACTIVITY;
    FORMAT PRODUCT $P.;
    FORMAT ACTIVITY $A.;
    FORMAT DATE $D.;
    TITLE "GRINDER EAST";
RUN;
```

Comment
Data set is called May 21.

Input of date, shift, etc., in the specified columns.

Items with $ are alphanumeric.

Blocks readings into hourly groups.

Expands input of date M21 into May 21 on output.
Expands activity input.

Data set for east grinder is called GE.

Sort data set GE, create a new data set GENEW.
   Sort the new set by date, then product.

Do frequency analysis on data set GE with a table of product × activity. Title it *Grinder East.*

Strata	Times Idle	Times Working
Monday	9	7
Tuesday	1	15

To Find Is there a difference between Monday's and Tuesday's data?

	Procedure	Number
Solution	1. Pick the smallest of the four numbers.	1
	2. Select the other number in the same column.	9
	3. Calculate "observed contrast."	9 – 1 = 8
	4. On Table 10.4, enter at sample size row, go across to the smaller number of steps 1 and 2, or, if it is not given, the end of the row. Then go up to "minimum contrast"; 16 to 1 to 6 require contrast of at least 6.	
	5. Compare observed versus minimum.	8 > 6

Therefore, Tuesday's data are different from Monday's data ($\alpha < .05$).

EXAMPLE 2
Given $n_a = n_b = 75$

Strata	Times Phone Busy	Times Phone Not Busy
1st Shift	45	30
2nd Shift	15	60

To Find Is there a difference between the data for the first shift and the second shift?

	Procedure	Number
Solution	1. Pick the smallest of the four numbers.	15
	2. Select the other number in the same column.	45
	3. Calculate "observed contrast."	45 – 15 = 30
	4. On Table 10.4, enter at sample size row, go across to the smaller number of steps 1 and 2, or, if it	

F I G U R E   1 0 . 8

Example SAS output. SAS output gives four numbers within each block. The top number is the number of the event occurring, the second is the percent of the overall total, the third is the percent of the row total, and the fourth is the percent of the column total.

SHIFT	ACTIVITY					
	Cleaning	Feeding Lids	Idle	Remove Lid Pack	Work Misc.	Total
1						
	1	11	5	2	1	20
FREQUENCY %	3.03	33.33	15.15	6.06	3.03	60.61
ROW %	5.00	55.00	25.00	10.00	5.00	
COLUMN %	100.00	64.71	50.00	66.67	50.00	
2						
	0	6	5	1	1	13
FREQUENCY %	0.00	18.18	15.15	3.03	3.03	39.39
ROW %	0.00	46.15	38.46	7.69	7.69	
COLUMN %	0.00	35.29	50.00	33.33	50.00	
TOTAL	1	17	10	3	2	33
	3.03	51.52	30.30	9.09	6.06	100.00

is not given, the end of the row. Then go up to "minimum contrast." There is no row for 75, so use 70 and 80 and interpolate, 70 to 13 to 18, 80 to 12 to 15. Thus, minimum contrast is 12.

5. Compare observed to minimum: 30 > 12

Therefore, first shift differs from second shift ($\alpha < .05$)

5.2 Control Charts

This test evaluates the effect of time (sequence) for your various strata (subgroups). A special form of analysis of variance, called a **control chart,** was developed by Walter Shewhart during the 1930s. It has been used extensively in quality assurance work. A typical application in quality assurance would be monitoring a quality characteristic (say percent of parts with scratched paint). The percent of parts with scratched paint depends on many influences (operator, machine, type of paint, etc.), so you might think that an analysis of variance is desirable. However, in practice, there is a very strong relationship to sequence or time. That is, if you can identify *when* something occurred, you can do the detective work to find out *where* and *why* it happened. The control chart helps identify *when* the process changes.

The same reasoning applies to occurrence sampling. Although attribute control charts and measurement control charts are used in quality assurance, occurrence sampling records the data in a discrete manner (yes–no, working–not working), so we use an

attribute control chart. In fact, we use only one of the various types of attribute control charts—the percentage chart or **p chart.**

The first step in constructing a p chart is to plot the center line of the chart, $\bar{p}$. The average percentage is calculated by totaling the number of occurrences and dividing by the total number of observations.

The second step is to estimate the variability from the average that could occur by chance. The spread of the distribution is quantified by the standard deviation of p, symbolized σ_p. (Note that the n used for calculating the spread uses the sample size, not the total n of the study.) If all the individual readings were "slid along a wire parallel to the center line," they would form a histogram (see Figure 10.9).

The histogram describes the variability that could occur by chance. Variability beyond the histogram is assumed to occur not by chance but from a cause.

How far does the histogram spread? In theory, from negative infinity to positive infinity. However, the odds get quite small once we get out a ways from the center. If we go out $\pm 3\sigma_p$ in either direction from the mean percentage, there are very few chance occurrences; if we go out $\pm 2\sigma_p$ there are few; if we go out $\pm 1.5\sigma_p$ there are some, and so on.

First let's define "very few," "few," and so on. Although it's not statistically correct to use the normal as an approximation to the binomial for small sample sizes, the normal is commonly used because it is simple to use and gives answers that are close enough. Limits including $\pm 3\sigma_p$ include 99.7% of the chance occurrences; limits including $\pm 2\sigma_p$ include 95.45%

TABLE 10.4

Relationships of sample size, smallest number (in table), and "minimum contrast" for tests between two percentages. Binomial distribution is used. Significance level of .05 for 2 tails; .025 for 1 tail.

MINIMUM CONTRAST FOR STATISTICAL SIGNIFICANCE

Sample Size $n_a = n_b$	4	5	6	7	8	9	10	11	12	13	14	15	16	17	18
4–5	0														
6		0													
7–9		0–1													
10–11		0	1–2												
12–13		0	1–3												
14		0	1–2	3											
15–16		0	1	2–4											
17–19		0	1	2–5											
20			1	2–5	6										
30			0	1–2	3–5	6–10									
40			0	1–2	3–4	5–7	8–15								
50			0	1	2–3	4–6	7–10	11–19							
60			0	1	2–3	4–5	6–8	9–13	14–24						
70			0	1	2–3	4–5	6–8	9–12	13–18	19–28					
80				1	2–3	4–5	6–7	8–11	12–15	16–23	24–33				
90			0	1	2–3	4–5	6–7	8–10	11–14	15–20	21–31	32–37			
100			0	1	2–3	4	5–7	8–10	11–13	14–18	19–25	26–42			
150			0	1	2	3–4	5–6	7–9	10–12	13–15	16–19	20–25	26–32	33–41	42–66
200			0	1	2	3–4	5–6	7–8	9–11	12–14	15–18	19–22	23–27	28–33	34–41
300			0	1	2	3–4	5–6	7–8	9–10	11–13	14–17	18–20	21–24	25–29	30–35
400			0	1	2	3–4	5	6–8	9–10	11–13	14–16	17–20	21–24	25–28	29–33
500			0	1	2	3–4	5	6–8	9–10	11–13	14–16	17–19	20–23	24–27	28–32

Sample Size	19	20	21	22	23	24	25	26	27	28	29	30	31	32
200	42–51	52–65	66–89											
300	36–41	42–48	49–56	57–66	67–68	69–95	96–137							
400	34–38	39–44	45–51	52–58	59–67	68–76	77–87	88–100	101–117	118–141	142–185			
500	33–37	38–42	43–48	49–55	56–62	63–70	71–79	80–89	90–100	101–113	114–128	129–147	148–172	173–234

F I G U R E   1 0 . 9

An example control chart. Control charts are a specialized form of analysis of variance showing the effect of time. Without the time scale it is a histogram (figure on right). The control limits indicate how much variability is likely to occur by chance. If a point falls outside $\pm 2\sigma$ limits, the odds are about 5% that nothing is different from the typical situation and about 95% that something has changed.

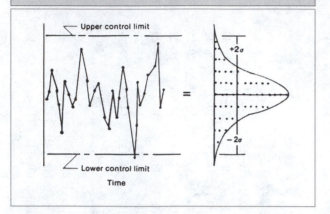

(usually rounded to 95%); limits including $\pm 1.645\sigma_p$ include 90%. The tradeoff is looking for trouble where none exists versus not looking for trouble when it does exist. Quality assurance limits commonly are $\pm 3\sigma_p$ although the chemical industry uses $\pm 2\sigma_p$ since the consequences of a change in the process are

severe in the chemical industry. If a point is beyond the $3\sigma_p$ limits, the odds are 3/1,000 that the point is beyond the limit due to chance and 997/1,000 that the sample differs from the population.

For occurrence sampling, our recommendation is $\pm 2\sigma_p$ or even $\pm 1.645\sigma_p$ limits. If a point is beyond $2\sigma_p$ limits, the odds are 1/20 that chance has occurred and 19/20 that the sample differs from the population. The odds are still very good for $\pm 1.645\sigma_p$ limits: 1/10 for chance, and 9/10 for cause.

Figure 10.10 shows an example chart. In constructing the chart, use all the observations to calculate the average, $\bar{p}$. *But* the standard deviation for the limits uses the sample size n. That is, for a plot of 10 days, each an average of 50 occurrences, use $n = 500$ for the calculation of $\bar{p}$ but $n = 50$ for the calculation of σ_p. If n varies from sample to sample (e.g., 50 on sample 1, 52 on sample 2, 48 on sample 3, and so on), in theory the control limits should be calculated differently for each sample size. In practice, just use the average sample size. Note also that the limits cannot exceed 0% or 100%. Thus if $\bar{p} = 60\%$ and $2\sigma_p = 70\%$, the upper limit would be 100% and the lower limit 0%.

All of the discussion has emphasized the use of control *limits*—that is, the process is out of control (i.e., changed) only if a point is beyond the limit. However, in addition, an analyst can use *runs*. For example, eight events in a row that are all above the average (but not beyond the limit) have the same statistical significance as 1 point beyond the limit.

F I G U R E   1 0 . 1 0

Example control chart for occurrence sampling. These should use limits either 1.645 or 2σ from the mean rather than the 3 used in statistical quality control, as the cost of a type 1 error (looking for a problem when none exists) is much lower in occurrence sampling. Use all the observations in calculating the mean, but only the sample size for the limits.

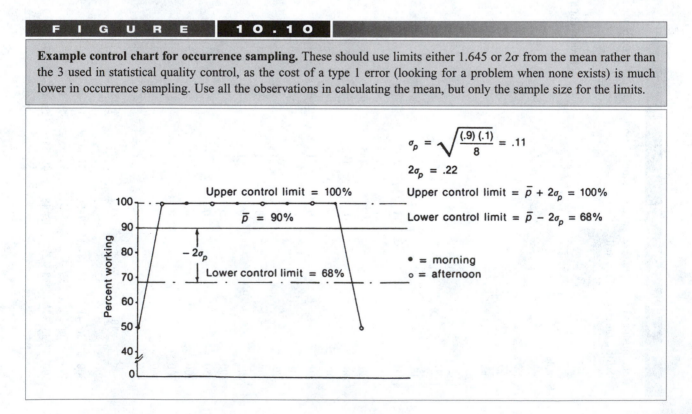

6 APPLICATIONS OF OCCURRENCE SAMPLING

The most common application is to provide information for management decisions. Examples might be work versus idle time of inspectors, nurses, doctors, teachers, supervisors, setup operators, or material handling equipment. In many studies, the categories of activity and of the items observed are not split into 2 or 3, but 10 to 20. That is, you might observe 10 different nurses and divide their activities into 18 different categories rather than observe just 1 nurse and divide the nurse's activity into 2 categories.

A slightly different application is to set **time standards,** which requires a count of the units produced during the time period as well as the occurrence sample.

Assume you have the data for an administrative assistant shown in Table 10.5. From the sample, percent of time times 40 h gives the third column, the estimated hours spent on the activity. Then the fifth column, estimated h/unit, can be calculated by dividing by output. Note that standards need not be set on the entire list of activities during the week. Note that the worker's work method is assumed to be good; that is, we are setting time standards, not improving productivity.

An advantage of time standards from occurrence sampling is that the study can cover a large number of cycles of varied work (e.g., maintenance work, rework, office work). A disadvantage in the example data is that no performance rating was used. Performance rating of a crude nature can be done if the observer, when making the observation (allocating the activity to phone calls, typing letters, responding to e-mail, typing forms, and so on), simultaneously estimates a performance rating (90%, 120%, etc.). It should be recognized that the accuracy of the resulting standard will be improved only slightly by using this type of performance rating since instantaneous rating necessarily must be crude. Use a conventional time study with performance rating for the important activities and use occurrence sampling for the minor activities. The rating from the important activities (e.g., 90%) is assumed to be valid also for the occurrence sampling activities.

See Box 10.2 for a summary of the steps in making an occurrence sample.

T A B L E	1 0 . 5			
Example data showing how occurrence sampling data can be used to determine time standards.				
ACTIVITY	**PERCENT OF TIME SPENT ON ACTIVITY**	**ESTIMATED HOURS/WEEK ON ACTIVITY**	**OUTPUT FOR ACTIVITY**	**ESTIMATED HOURS/UNIT**
Phone calls	12	4.8	147	.033
Letters/E-mail	28	11.2	48	.233
Form A	3	1.2	121	.010
Form B	3	1.2	12	.100
Other	54	21.6		

Review Questions

1. What is the purpose of occurrence sampling?
2. Does information from a sample increase proportionally to sample size?
3. The number of observations to take in occurrence sampling depends upon what three things?

4. Briefly describe the three problems in obtaining a representative sample.
5. Discuss how a time standard could be set using occurrence sampling.

10.2 *Steps to Make an Occurrence Sample*

Steps in making an occurrence sampling study:

Step	*Example*
1. State the problem:	Determine idle percent for fork trucks in Dept. 8.
a. Give application of data.	Aid decision whether to buy new fork truck.
b. Determine categories.	Truck will be considered to be: ■ working ■ idle—driver absent ■ idle—driver present
2. Calculate sample size required.	Estimated percentages are: ■ working 75% ■ idle—driver absent 10% ■ idle—driver present 15% At this stage, estimates are just the best guess. $A = 5\%$ (plus and minus) on all three c = confidence = 68% on all three Required n are 75, 36, and 51, respectively, so use $n = 75$.
3. Plan to obtain a representative sample.	Take study during one entire week; half before lunch, half after. Divide week into 10 periods of 4 hours each. For simplicity, take 8 observations per period for 80 total observations. Make up random times for 10 periods. Walk into observation area by one of the three entrances—specific entrance chosen randomly. Make up data form.
4. Make study.	
5. Analyze results: a. Strata	a. See Figure 10.10. $\bar{p} = .90$; $A = .034$. Does not seem to be a morning versus afternoon effect even though all idleness does occur on only 2 of the 5 days. The observed contrast is 4; required contrast is 5.
b. Time	b. See Figure 10.10. It seems there is a problem at the beginning and end of the week as points are beyond the control limits. The $2\sigma = 95\%$ assumption is not valid for small samples; our n was 8, not the 30 needed for the assumption of normality. A check shows production control was unorganized at beginning of the week due to a late computer printout; not enough work was scheduled on Friday due to lack of knowledge of what would be made the following week.
6. Make conclusion.	You are 68% confident that the long-run working percent is between 87% and 93%, with 90% the most likely estimate, if nothing changes.

7. Make decision.	Make two decisions:
	  a. Get production control organized.
	  b. Don't buy new fork truck.

References

Allen, D. and Corn, R. Comparing productive activities at different times. *Industrial Engineering,* Vol. 13, No. 3, 40–43, 1978.

Carayon, P. Effects of electronic performance monitoring on job design and worker stress: Review of the literature and conceptual model. *Human Factors,* Vol. 35, No. 3, 385–95, 1993.

Moder, J. and Kahn, H. Selection of work sampling observation times: Part II—Restricted random sampling. *AIIE Transactions,* Vol. 12, No. 1, 32–37, March 1980.

Natrella, M. *Experimental Statistics,* Chapter 8, Handbook 91. Washington, DC: Supt. of Documents, 1963.

Steiner, L., Cornelius, K., Turin, F., and Stock, D. Work sampling applied to a human factors analysis of mine worker positioning. *Proc. of Human Factors and Ergonomic Society,* 1103–07, 1998.

MACRO ERGONOMICS

MACRO ERGONOMICS

1 Plan the Work, Then Work the Plan

2 Reward Results

3 Optimize System Availability

4 Minimize Idle Capacity

5 Use Filler Jobs or Filler People

6 Communicate Information

Overview

Design jobs at the macro ergonomics level as well as the micro ergonomics level. Six guidelines give some of the "big-picture" concepts to complement the micro ergonomics guidelines given in the other chapters.

Key Concepts

availability	financial and nonfinancial motivation	job sharing	pools
core time		life-cycle costs	preventive maintenance
double tooling	fixed costs and variable costs	modularization	revising schedules
downtime		not one on one	staggered work times
duplicate components	flex time	off-peak	standby
filler job	hours/year	part-time workers	temporary workers
filler people	idle low-cost components	plan the work; work the plan	uptime

PLAN THE WORK, THEN WORK THE PLAN

If a sailor does not know
to which port he is sailing,
no wind is favorable.

Seneca

Much blue-collar work is repetitive with a countable output. The goals are set by others. White-collar work, on the other hand, tends to be self-directed, with a great variety of tasks. Self-directed people need to determine their desired direction and then work toward the goal—**plan the work; work the plan.**

1.1 Plan the Work   There are four steps to planning the work.

1.1.1 *List goals*   First you need to set long-range, lifetime major goals. It is convenient to divide these into work-related and nonwork-related goals. Examples of work-related goals are to get a 10% raise in salary, to be promoted, to transfer from a line to a staff job (or vice versa). Example nonwork goals are to get married, to buy a new car (house, take a vacation), to spend more time with your spouse (children, parents), to become more religious. It may help you to focus your thinking to ask, "If I were to die in a plane crash in six months, what would I do until then?"

1.1.2 *Set goal priorities*   Now prioritize your work and nonwork goals by assigning an A, B, or C priority to each goal.

1.1.3 *Make a "to do" list*   This list is of *activities* to reach the goal. For example, a nonwork goal might be to spend more time with your spouse. Example activities might be to go to a movie, go out to dinner, or be home by 6:00. A work goal might be to get a report done by the first of the month. Example activities might be to make a rough draft of figures, set up a table on the spreadsheet, and get cost figures from accounting. The "to do" list should be written. If you have accomplished no activities toward the goal within a week, either add activities or consider revising the goal.

1.1.4 *Set activity priorities*   Next to each activity, mark an A, B, or C. You now are ready to work your plan.

1.2 Work the Plan   There are three approaches to working the plan.

1.2.1 *Start with A's, not with C's*   The concept here is to start the work period working on your A

goals. The reason is that in the day you really have little free time because most of it will be taken up with required duties (answer phone, go to meetings, eat lunch, drive to work, handle the mail); so work on your A goals first. Using the Pareto concept, only 20% of your activities will have a high payoff, so concentrate your efforts on the larger tasks and put off the smaller ones as long as possible. Perhaps some of the tasks can be eliminated, delegated, or simplified. For example, instead of writing a letter, can you use e-mail? Can a phone call replace a letter?

1.2.2 *Do it now*   Avoid procrastination. It may help to standardize the location of free time for your A activities. For example, lock the door of your office and don't answer phone calls for the first 30 min while working on your A's. Spend Saturday afternoon working on your nonwork A's.

1.2.3 *Cut big activities into bits*   Big goals may seem overwhelming, so they are put off. However, each journey of a thousand miles begins with a single step. Assume your A goal is to get a 10% raise and among the activities leading toward that goal is to have a monthly report done on time. However, you won't be able to complete it today. Get started on it and do as much as you can.

REWARD RESULTS

Work smart, not hard is the primary message of this book. However, reasonable effort cannot be ignored. The challenge is to get people to work hard *and* smart.

2.1 Types of Motivation   Very briefly, motivation can be divided into positive and negative. Positive motivation can be internal (self-motivation) or external. External can be divided into **financial and nonfinancial motivation** (pay versus other incentives).

2.2 Financial Rewards   Figure 11.1 shows four different financial reward plans.

2.2.1 *Pay independent of output*   Curve A, the horizontal line, shows that pay has no relation to performance. Who would use such a plan? Most organizations! Pay by the month (salary) is an example; workers are paid even if they don't come to work (within limits). Salary often is used when an individual's specific contribution is difficult to count. Examples are administrative and technical jobs such as deans, researchers, accountants, engineers. Sometimes there is a countable output, but it is irregular and of unknown quality. Examples might be patents or designs from an engineer or articles pub-

Four financial reward plans. Curve A shows pay as being independent of output. Most people are paid according to curve A. Curve B shows pay as being independent of output but with a step function after a delay (e.g., a 5% raise at the end of the year). Curve C shows incentive pay with a guaranteed base. Curve D shows incentive pay with no guarantee. Pay versus output depends on the pay plan.

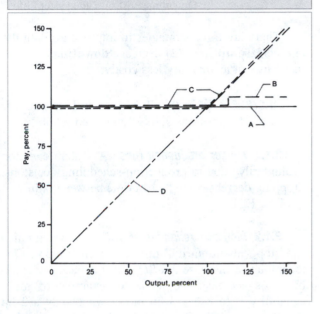

lished or classes taught by a professor. Salary also is used for situations where there is an undefined relationship between effort expended and the value of the contribution. Examples might be classroom teaching or TV news announcing.

A variation on curve A is pay by the hour. The worker is not paid unless physically present at the workplace. Pay-by-the-hour plans range from pay for the entire day (once you arrive at work) to plans that pay to the nearest 10th of an hour for time clocked in. Although physical presence on the premises does not guarantee a useful contribution, it has better odds than not being there at all!

2.2.2 *Pay independent but step function*   Curve B shows pay independent of output but there is a delayed step-function response by the organization. For example, if a professor does a good job, there may be a larger raise at the end of the year. Motivation is increased and longer lasting when the size of the step function is larger, the relationship between the behavior and the reward is clearer, and the reward is automatic (i.e., does not depend upon someone's judgment).

For example, if someone works paid overtime or receives a bonus, pay this in a separate check. (Some people feel that the regular paycheck is to be shared

with the spouse but the bonus is theirs.) Pay it quickly—say within 24 h.

There has been a growing trend to give a special one-time payment to reward current performance—that is, in response to the question "What have you done for me lately?" Five advantages are (1) it can be given for a specific contribution, (2) it can be substantial (not being spread out over a year), (3) it can be awarded soon after the specific contribution, (4) it does not make the extra pay permanent, and (5) it increases compensation flexibility.

Many firms give an annual bonus to all employees, depending upon the firm's success. This can range from a bonus of $100 to each worker at a retail store that achieved the goal of preventing shrinkage from theft, to a bonus of $1,000 to all employees of Ford Motor when company profits are high. Although the Ford employees like the money, there is very little relation between an individual's performance and the firm's profit.

2.2.3 *Piecework with a guaranteed base*   Curve C shows piecework with a guaranteed base. Just coming to work gives the guaranteed hourly rate. But for every 1% increase in output, there is a 1% increase in pay. Although the organization's direct labor cost per unit stays constant with greater output, total cost per unit declines because fringe costs (holidays, health costs) decline on a per-unit basis. In addition, overhead (burden) per unit declines. Thus, the employee wins and the firm wins.

For more on incentives, see Box 27.2.

2.2.4 *Piecework without a guarantee*   Curve D pays you what you are worth. The self-employed (doctors, dentists) are in this situation, as are people on commissions (stockbrokers, insurance agents). Curve D is rare in the industrial workforce.

2.3 Nonfinancial Motivation   Pay is a great motivator, but it is not the only motivator. An interesting phenomenon is the "Pygmalion" effect. It is based on the play *Pygmalion,* later made into the movie *My Fair Lady.* It concerns Eliza Doolittle, a poor flower girl adopted by an eccentric professor. When treated like a lady, she acted like a lady. The point is that if you expect your workers to do well, praise them, and trust them, they will do well and will deserve your trust. If you criticize people, don't trust them, and so forth, they will do poorly and not deserve your trust.

There are many nonfinancial motivators.

2.3.1 *Positive rewards*   Positive rewards generally work better than negative rewards—perhaps because negative rewards are difficult to implement fruitfully in the real world.

Some examples of positive rewards might be stars on the helmets of football players for good plays, a reserved parking place for perfect attendance, public recognition, praise. (Don't ignore the power of public praise and recognition; the military has found that soldiers will die for such praise.)

Excellent organizations work hard at creating opportunities to shower awards of pins, buttons, badges, and medals on employees. Titles are cheap, so distribute them generously. Publicity is powerful; even better than an award is an award accompanied by a photograph.

Positive rewards need not be restricted to individuals. Teams crave them also. Consider the motivation in sports of "conference champion," "Top Ten," and "Super Bowl ring." To improve machine availability, a Japanese firm instituted a program to improve maintenance. Two of the awards were: (1) the president's total preventive maintenance award, general class, to the unit or group that made the most remarkable improvement and (2) decoration of outstanding *machine*. Gold, silver, and bronze medals were given to machines that had zero failures for 3, 2, or 1 month. "These machines were the pride of the workplace" (Tachibana, Naniwada, and Salvendy, 1994).

2.3.2 *Negative rewards* Some negative rewards are verbal abuse by a supervisor (coaches do this a lot) and penalty points for tardiness and absenteeism. For example, late for work = .5 point, unexcused absence = 3 points, sick with a doctor's excuse = 2 points for first day only. All points are dropped to zero every 4 months. When 9 points are accumulated, you get an oral warning, 12 points is written warning, 14 points is termination.

3 OPTIMIZE SYSTEM AVAILABILITY

This guideline discusses improving the availability of a service channel; Guidelines 4 and 5 discuss matching service channel availability and requirements.

$$\text{Availability} = \frac{\text{Uptime}}{\text{Total Time}}$$
$$= \frac{\text{Uptime}}{\text{Uptime} + \textbf{Downtime}}$$
$$= \frac{MTBF}{MTBF + MTR}$$

where $MTBF$ = Mean time between failures (reliability)
MTR = Mean time to repair (maintainability)

In a year there are 525,600 minutes. "Three nines" (availability of .999) has uptime of 525,074 min and downtime of 525.6 min (8.76 h/year). "Four nines" has downtime of 52.56 min/year. The famous "five nines" permits only 5.26 min/year. To get "six nines," you have to limit downtime to .53 min/year.

In calculating optimum system availability, use life-cycle costing (rather than just initial cost).

Life-cycle cost = Initial capital cost
+ Operating cost over the system life
+ Maintenance cost over the system life
+ Downtime cost over the system life

There are three strategies to improve availability: (1) increase **uptime,** (2) decrease **downtime,** and (3) make loss of availability less costly.

3.1 Increase Uptime   Two possibilities are (1) longer production runs and (2) increased reliability.

3.1.1 *Longer production runs* A system can stop "voluntarily" due to production-scheduling decisions. Stopping decreases the "mean time between failures"; see Box 12.1.

3.1.2 *Increase reliability (MTBF)* A system also can stop "involuntarily" due to system failure. One technique to increase *MTBF* is to increase the capability or decrease the load. An example of more capability is to use a 3 hp motor when only a 2 hp motor is needed. The additional capability makes failure less likely (although with additional capital and operating costs). A lower load would be using special controls to reduce starting problems as well as operating the motor in a less stressful (cooler, cleaner) environment.

Another possibility is to consider **series versus parallel arrangements;** in a series arrangement, the system works if *every* component in a path works; in a parallel arrangement, the system works if *any* path works. Also see Box 20.3.

$$R_{\text{series}} = R_1 R_2$$
$$R_{\text{parallel}} = 1 - U_1 U_2$$
$$U_1 \text{ (unreliability)} = 1 - R_1$$
$$U_2 = 1 - R_2$$

For example, if $R_1 = .9$ and $R_2 = .8$, then in a series system the system reliability is .9(.8) = .72. In a parallel system, the system reliability is $1 - .1(.2) = .98$.

For example, in a truck, two batteries could be installed in parallel; if one fails, the other does the job. In addition, life should be longer since there is less stress on the two batteries than one. Redundancy in people generally is quite expensive and isn't used very much, although copilots in aircraft are one example. A critical item could be inspected by two independent people and accepted only if both pass it.

For series systems, reduce the number of components and/or steps because each is a possible source of failure. For example, when making a request for a hotel wake-up call, contact the operator directly rather than requesting that the desk clerk give the message to the operator.

Another possibility is to use a standby circuit. For example, in a boat if you run out of fuel you could switch to the standby tank. If the power screwdriver fails at the assembly station, you replace it with a new power screwdriver. If the air conditioner fails, you use the fan. In a car, if you have a flat tire, you switch to the spare tire. Standby people are quite common, ranging from the utility operator on a flow line to a relief pitcher in baseball.

Modularization is a variation of the standby concept. Instead of the original unit being repaired, it is discarded and the standby unit replaces it. An example is small electric motors, which are no longer repaired, just replaced. Automobile spark plugs rarely are cleaned and reused anymore; they are just discarded. Modules permit relatively quick switching and can be done by less skilled people. In addition, it may not be either technically feasible or economic to repair the unit locally.

Note that, in a standby system, there generally is some time and effort involved in switching, and the system may not return to normal. The switching itself may have a failure rate—for example, you forgot the jack so you can't change the tire! Or the baseball manager may not make the switch to the relief pitcher in time! Or the relief pitcher may fail.

Critical systems (such as electricity, fuel, and computers) need **standby** (backup) systems. At a minimum, if the system goes down, it should be fail-safe. That is, no damage or injury should result from the downtime.

3.2 Decrease Downtime

Two alternatives are (1) decrease voluntary downtime and (2) increase maintainability *(MTR)*.

3.2.1 *Decrease voluntary downtime*

Assuming the downtime is "voluntary" because it is due to machine setup, work to reduce setup time. Strive for "single-minute" setup; see Table 11.1 and Box 12.1. Have a quick-change team—complete with coaches, practices, videotapes, competitions, T-shirts, team banquets, team photos, and so forth.

Box 11.1 gives some tips on how to reduce waiting.

3.2.2 *Increase maintainability (MTR)*

If the downtime is "involuntary" (that is, due to failure), there are some approaches to reduce the *MTR*.

T A B L E	1 1 . 1

Categories of maintenance tasks (Ostrofsky, 1977). Relative to direct labor expense (which has been analyzed intensively for over half a century), maintenance has many opportunities for improved methods and cost reductions. Smith (1993) gives a systematic procedure for evaluating maintenance costs.

TASK	COMMENT
Troubleshoot	Isolating a fault or failure to keep the desired level in the system.
Inspect	Observing or testing to determine the condition or status of the system (or component of the system).
Calibrate (or adjust)	Regulating or bringing the condition or status of the system (or component of the system) to the desired level.
Remove	Removing a desired portion of the system.
Repair	Restoring a given level of the system to operating condition.
Replace	Replacing the desired portion of the system, given that a removal has occurred.
Service	Replenishing consumables needed to keep a given level of the system in operating condition.

Downtime = Fault detection time
(time to find the device doesn't work)

+ Fault location time
(time to find the problem)

+ Logistics time
(time to get repair parts)

+ Repair time (time to fix unit)

A standby unit has only fault detection time; it is working (perhaps not returning the system to 100% performance) while fault location, logistics, and repair time occur. For equipment, this requires good planning for spares. For people, this requires good planning for cross-training of personnel.

Fault location time can be reduced. For example, maintenance personnel can be given beepers and service vehicles can have radios; this reduces the time until help arrives. Diagnostic aids and test points aid in locating faults. Some automatic testing equipment is computerized. The "diagnostic aid" can be offsite. For example, advice can be given to the local person who furnishes the "hands" to the remote "brain." This can permit very specialized expertise to be applied nationwide.

11.1   *Reduce Waiting*

Avoid queue:

- Get service at non-peak times.
- Schedule truck/ship/plane deliveries at receiving docks so trucks/ships/planes don't have to wait; also, dock personnel won't have overloads and underloads.
- Preprocess customers to avoid queue or minimize time in queue.

Faster queue processing:

- Increase machine speed (modem, printer, copier, lathe).
- Use express mail/packages (UPS, FedEx, post office) instead of regular mail.

- Use fax and e-mail whenever possible.
- Use address memories (speed dial) for phone, e-mail, radio stations, and so on. UPS stores for two years the addresses of all people you send packages to; thus, you do not have to write these addresses a second time.
- Have waiters use wireless handhelds to communicate orders to the kitchen.
- Increase service capability (more clerks or machines, faster clerks or machines, more toilets, more parking spaces).
- Limit products sold (fast food).

Logistics time also can be reduced by administrative procedures. For example, good records allow people to find the supplier for a replacement part quickly. Low-level authorization for ordering parts is quicker than requiring lots of paperwork and multiple signatures. Establishing relationships with vendors so that a telephone call instead of a letter is sufficient reduces the ordering time. Having a rotatable pool of spare components allows the item to be repaired at leisure while the replacement is immediately available. Stocking spares at a number of locations may help, although nationwide 24-hour delivery courier services have made distance less important.

Ideally, if the product is "designed for maintenance," the maintainer should be able to work with a "friendly" posture (not lying on the side or back, not reaching overhead, and so on).

For ease of repair (as well as fault location), provide for reach accessibility and visibility accessibility.

Once there is access, maintainers can do a better job if they are not "blind." Thus, provide light. One approach is to permanently mount light fixtures inside machines. Consider painting the *inside* of housings to aid light reflection. Clearly label service and test points; use color-coding. Perhaps a mirror can be mounted inside to show non-visible locations.

Both logistics and repair time require a maintenance budget (funds for parts and funds for personnel); see Guideline 3 in Chapter 19.

Repair time is usually a small portion of downtime. It can be cut by **modularization,** in which the repair involves merely switching units. Maintenance personnel do more than just repair items. Table 11.1 gives some standard maintenance tasks. Maintenance and repair tasks tend to present more safety problems than production operations. This is due to: (1) less structured tasks, (2) highly variable performance of personnel, (3) sometimes unfriendly environments, and (4) time pressures.

3.3 Make Loss of Availability Less Costly   There are two possibilities: (1) preventive maintenance and (2) partial function.

Preventive maintenance is scheduled maintenance. You pick the time you don't need the availability and then do the maintenance. This probably will increase your maintenance expenses over an "if it ain't broke, don't fix it" philosophy.

Partial function may not be too much of a problem—if the partial function is temporary and the "partial" is closer to full capacity than to zero. For example, on an assembly line, two identical stations could do a job in parallel. Then if one station fails (equipment failure, employee absence, or whatever), the remaining stations can get by. Firms often split orders between vendors rather than having one vendor as the sole source. The decision to go multiple source or sole source for equipment, vendors, operators, and others should be considered in detail.

Note that not all maintenance is done "at the machine." Modules may be removed from a machine to be repaired/adjusted at a central location. In addition, large items (such as jet engines and locomotives) may be overhauled periodically. This is really "low-volume production" but with non-standard tasks (similar to construction).

4   MINIMIZE IDLE CAPACITY

Minimizing idle capacity has two divisions: **fixed costs and variable costs.**

11.2 *Maintenance Access*

Design/location: (Adapted from Corlett and Clark, 1995; Helander, 1995).

- Use hinged covers and quick release fasteners. Put hinges at the bottom. Consider the removal of the entire panel/cover.
- Note that the maintainer may be using gloves.
- Consider quick disconnects of utilities.
- Access ports should not expose the maintainer to hot surfaces, electrical currents, or sharp edges.
- Locate access apertures on the same side of the machine as related displays, controls, and test points.
- Access apertures on top surfaces can collect debris and water; when opened, the machine becomes contaminated.
- If a fastener is close to the floor, locate it on the horizontal plane; at high heights, locate it on the vertical plane at the rear. Avoid having fasteners on the plane perpendicular to the right side of the opening as they are difficult for right-handed operators to manipulate.

Size:

- Access ports must (1) provide clearance for tools and (2) allow the insertion/removal of machine components.
- Aperture size depends upon (1) height off the floor and (2) depth of reach.
- Consider visual accessibility and reach accessibility.
- For tool access, allow straight-line access to fasteners/components.
- If the tool is inserted "deep" into the machine, allow room for the hand/arm to move. The hand/arm in the aperture may block vision. Avoid aperture widths of less than 25 cm— especially for depths over 30 cm.
- For inserting/removing a component (two-hand insertion), have aperture width = component width + 8 cm. If the forearms are inserted, have aperture width = component width + 16 cm.

4.1 Fixed Costs

This is divided into problem and solutions.

4.1.1 *Problem*

Annual cost of many machines and people varies little with output.

Equipment depreciation (i.e., capital cost), for example, usually depends more on equipment age than equipment hours of use. Think of used car prices; they depend more on the model year than on whether the car has been driven 60,000 miles or 80,000 miles. The capital cost and property taxes of a factory or warehouse will not vary whether it is used 8, 16, or 24 h/day, or 5, 6, or 7 days/week.

An airline's cost for an airplane flight is about the same whether there are 50 or 150 passengers. A professor will receive the same pay whether there are 20 or 40 students/class; a hospital's cost will be approximately the same whether there are 70 or 100 patients; a hotel's cost will be approximately the same whether there are 300 or 500 guests. The reason is that direct labor cost is a small percentage of total cost.

Even if direct labor is a high proportion of job cost, the wages, especially salaries, vary little with output. A cook receives the same pay whether cooking for 50 or 100; a bus driver receives the same pay whether there are 10 or 40 on the bus.

Even for hourly wages, costs are relatively fixed, because employers are reluctant to lay off people for minor ups and downs. Part of this is because of the economic cost of the layoff (increased unemployment taxes on the employer, disruption of the existing workforce, slowdowns by the existing workforce, and so on), and part is due to the natural desire of managers not to cause economic problems for their employees.

Thus, a desirable social goal is to get more use from the existing capacity. This also has good economic benefits for the firm since the incremental cost of using the existing capacity is low.

4.1.2 *Solutions*

Four solutions are to operate more hours/yr, use pools, revise work schedules, and encourage off-peak use.

Operate more hours/yr. More **hours/yr** may spread a constant number of customers over more hours, thus requiring fewer facilities. For example, if a machine shop were to run for two shifts instead of one, fewer machines would be required (for the same total daily output).

The longer hours may attract more customers. Service facilities often use this strategy. Examples are resorts open more than one season, fast-food restaurants open for breakfast, and discount stores open in the evenings.

Use pools. **Pools** are based on the concept that peaks (or valleys) in one group don't coincide with peaks (or valleys) in another group. For example, assume the secretarial requirements of 10 individuals go to one secretary and the requirements of 10 other individuals go to another secretary. The pool concept is that work from any of the 20 might go to either of the secretaries.

Motor pools are an example for vehicles. Other pool examples are technicians, computers, printers, copiers, and lift trucks. You trade off reduced buying of duplicate staff or equipment against loss of specialized services. Pools do not have to be within an organization. Rental cars are an example of a pool among organizations.

Revise schedules. It may be that you have control of when the output is due. If so, **revising schedules** by dividing or joining categories can minimize idle time.

This technique can be extended. The State of Kansas divides all automobile licenses into 12 months, depending on the last name; thus it divides the load into 12 groups. Many firms formerly sent out bills on the first of the month. Now they divide the month into 20 working days and divide their bills into 20 categories, depending on the customer's last name.

Your purchasing department can schedule shipments to the dock for all days of the week and all weeks of the month instead of Mondays and the first of the month.

Hospitals have found that it is not necessary to do all surgeries during the morning only; thus they can do more operations with fewer operating rooms and less staff.

Be sure to do maintenance and inventory work during slow periods rather than peaks. However, Kansas State University saves over $100,000/yr in lighting costs by having custodial work done during the day instead of the night; it also is easier to recruit custodial staff.

Encourage off-peak use. Even if you don't have full control of when the service is to be performed, you can encourage customers to be serviced **off-peak,** that is, in the valleys. One example is the "demand ratchet charge" of utilities in which electrical use in peak periods is very severely penalized; this results in the utility requiring less generating plant. Telephone companies charge less for long-distance calls during nonbusiness hours. Airlines and hotels charge less for use during slack times. Courier services charge less for 2-day delivery than 1-day delivery. Thus, your sales or specials should be timed to fill in the valleys of demand rather than amplifying the peaks.

4.2 Variable Costs

4.2.1 *Problem* Consider the relation among the resources. The general concept is to improve utilization among members of a team. The concept is that some team members are more expensive than others; thus it is more important to keep some parts of the team busier than other parts.

The term *team* is defined broadly. Team members include machines, tools, and facilities as well as people. For example, a lift truck driver and the lift truck will be considered to be a team. Imada and Stawowy (Hendrick, 1996) redesigned two food-service stands at Dodger Stadium in Los Angeles. Total cost was $40,000. However, the average customer transaction time was reduced 8 s, giving an increase in productivity of $1,200/game; payback was 33 games. Modifying the remaining 50 stands cost $12,000/stand; payback was 20 games.

In the United States, the expensive part of the team generally is human labor. Labor cost (including fringes such as holidays, vacations, and social security) ranges from $8/h to more than $20/h. Although work hours/yr vary, assume 1,800 h/year. Thus, an operator being paid $10/h probably has a cost (assuming 30% fringes) of $13/h, or $23,400/year.

A machine's costs are for capital, utilities, and maintenance.

Capital cost usually is the most important. With a 10-yr life, an $18,000 machine (such as a lift truck) would be $1,800/yr, or $1/h; an $1,800 machine (such as a PC workstation) would be $.10/h; a $1,000 machine (conveyors, a workbench with handtools) would be $.05/h.

Utility costs are primarily power, of which most is electricity. At 7 cents/kWh, even a big motor (1 hp or .75 kW) costs only $.05/h.

Maintenance varies, but few machines require $1,000/yr for maintenance; that is, $.50/h. A value of $.25/h seems more representative.

Thus, if capital is $.25/h, utilities are .05, and maintenance is .25, this is only $.55/h. Few machines cost over $1/h. In sum, in the United States the important thing is to maximize use of the person, the expensive part of the system.

4.2.2 *Solutions* Three possibilities are duplicate components, idle low-cost components, and not one on one.

Duplicate components. To maintain utilization of the high-cost components, have low-cost **duplicate components** (substitutes). For example, if one printer on the network fails, perhaps the printing can be routed to another printer. There might be more than one printer. On a production line, there might be a spare power handtool in case one fails. Since people are flexible, if the computer breaks down, it might be possible to shift the worker to another task, such as filing or duplicating. If one person in a group "fails" (e.g., by being absent), perhaps a substitute worker can be used (assuming cross-training).

Idle low-cost components. You may decide that part of the system, the low-cost part, will be idle and not worry too much about it. In **double tooling,** two duplicate tools are used as **idle low-cost components**—generally on a semiautomatic machine. For example, while the part in fixture B is being machined, the operator unloads the part from fixture A and loads a new part. Then, while the part in fixture A is being machined, fixture B is unloaded and loaded.

Another example is two Coke dispensers at McDonald's to reduce serving time. McDonald's is more concerned with minimizing time of the server and the customer than utilizing inexpensive pop dispensers. An example with people is an executive and secretary. It is more important to reduce idle time of the executive than of the secretary. (However, for some unknown reason, the advent of e-mail and word processors has resulted in expensive staff people answering hundreds of e-mails/day and doing their own word processing instead of having lower-paid assistants do it. The world is not always logical!) On a production line, the supervisor may keep 30 workers when there is work for only 29 so that illness and other absences don't stop the line.

Duplicate service lines for a single-queue server permit faster customer service and reduce worker idle time. An example would be a bank drive-in teller servicing two car lanes. After the first customer is served, the teller can begin serving a customer in the other lane while the first lane is "unloaded" and then "loaded" with a new customer. The same concept can be used for cafeteria checkout and any other situation where customer movement takes appreciable time. Graphically, where C = Customer and S = Server:

```
C        |S|        C
C                   C
C                   C
```

Not one on one. A common assumption is that there is one worker for one machine. But as shown above there can be double tooling—two for one. The numbers need not be integers, however. You can have fractions—2/3 worker/machine or 3/4 worker/machine. How can this be done? You can't cut a person into pieces! With full-time workers, 2/3 worker per machine can be achieved by assigning 2 workers to 3 machines, which results in 2/3 worker/machine or 3/2 machines/worker. The worker simply walks back and forth among the machines (many machines are semiautomatic or automatic and need only occasional tending). Often this is called a cell layout, and it illustrates **not one on one.**

Machines and people also can be shared between functions. For example, a lift truck driver (or vehicle) can work for Department A for 4 h, B for 2 h, and C for 2 h. A mechanic, secretary, or technician can be shared between Departments E and F. Although supervisors like to "own" people and equipment (it increases their status as well as making their job easier by giving them complete control), from the organization's viewpoint the system is suboptimal.

5 USE FILLER JOBS OR FILLER PEOPLE

The problem is to match worker time to job requirement time. For example, a fast-food restaurant may have a need for workers primarily at meal times; so what does it do with the worker during the middle of the afternoon? In a factory, a maintenance worker may be scheduled to work until 4:00 but finishes a job at 3:15. What should be done for the remaining 45 minutes? Many workers have idle time while a machine is "on automatic" and is either loading/unloading or operating. "Machine time" examples are numerical control operators while the machine processes parts, disk jockeys while the song is being played, and a cook while the food is cooking.

The two general strategies to minimize idle time are to (1) adjust the workload but keep the workforce constant and (2) adjust the workforce but keep the workload constant.

5.1 Adjust Workload   Use **filler jobs** to adjust the workload. It is easier to minimize idle time when the work idle time is in relatively large blocks. For example, a job with 25% idle time could work 6 h and then be idle for the last 2 h of the shift. It also could have 225 cycles of 2 min—with each cycle having .5 min idle time. It is more difficult to find an additional job (filler job) for the idle time when the time is in short segments. Thus, try to concentrate the idle time.

It is important to have broadly defined job descriptions so that transferring workers from task to task is not a problem. See Chapter 33.

5.1.1 Short jobs   Longer jobs can be broken down into shorter jobs. Consider the task of waxing a car—it might take 6 h. If you have just Saturday afternoon to work, you might be reluctant to start and leave unfinished work. Try to think of it as 4 jobs, each taking a shorter time (wax top, wax hood and fenders, wax door and sides, and wax rear); now work will not be "unfinished." Now you can do 2 jobs this Saturday, 1 Monday, and 1 Tuesday. Or consider a university secretary who has an exam to key, duplicate, and assemble. If the entire job takes 40 min, the secretary may be reluctant to start it 20 min before quitting time. Think of it as three jobs: keying, duplicating, and assembling. Then do just the keying before quitting time.

Make a list of short, low-priority jobs that can be done in the idle time. Many routine maintenance and clerical tasks fit this category. Opening the mail and returning phone calls are good filler jobs. Don't do these low-priority, "machine-time" tasks during "prime" time; reserve them for idle time, end-of-shift time, or while the machine is operating. Service personnel (receptionists, toolroom clerks, and so on) often have considerable time between customers.

A receptionist could do copying and answer the telephone. A toolroom clerk could sharpen tools. As another example, police officers in Manhattan, Kansas, formerly reported back to the police station approximately 30 min before the end of the shift to dictate reports. Now each officer has a battery-operated tape recorder. Whenever a report is needed, the officer parks the car in a prominent place and dictates into the recorder. Thus, not only can the officer complete the report while the topic is still fresh, but the officer can also remain visible and thus act as a deterrent—increasing useful time/shift. One of the guidelines at McDonald's is, "If there is time to lean, there is time to clean."

5.1.2 *Scheduling*

Scheduling may increase or decrease idle time. For example, if a meeting starts 15 min after the start of work, most people will waste the 15 minutes. (However, if the meeting is of supervisors, it may be best to allow them 15 min to get their people organized for the day.) In addition, meetings tend to fill the time available. To shorten meetings, have an agenda and schedule the meeting partly on the participants' time rather than on the organization's time (i.e., schedule them to overlap lunch or quitting time). If possible, schedule meetings for a time of reduced workload (a less busy time of the day, week, or month).

Supervisors should assign more work to subordinates than subordinates have time to do. The reason is the variability of the estimated time and the variability of the actual time for each job. No one wants to come to the boss and say, "I'm out of work." What they will do is "stretch" the job as much as possible.

5.2 Adjust Workforce

Use **filler people** to adjust the workforce. Three possible ways are to use staggered work times, temporary workers, and part-time workers.

5.2.1 *Staggered work times*

Make an analysis of the work requirements versus time. The most efficient staffing pattern may have **staggered work times,** with varied starting and stopping times for different workers.

For example, in a restaurant, the dishwasher can start after the waiters; the waiters need not stay as long as the dishwasher. In a mail-order business, people opening the mail should arrive before those filling the orders. Hospital emergency rooms have periods of peak demand that should have peak staffing and periods of low demand that should have low staffing. Staggered schedules spread the demand on production facilities (workstations) but also the demand on service facilities (parking lots, toilets, food-service facilities, and so on).

When people do the same task, staggering their work hours permits keeping the business open for more hours at no additional cost. For example, if Mary goes to lunch from 11:30 to 12:00 and Sam goes from 12:00 to 12:30, someone can always be present to answer the phone. If Mary works from 7:30 to 4:30 and Sam works from 8:30 to 5:30, customers can be served from 7:30 to 5:30 instead of 8 to 5. Staggered hours often are popular with employees also, as it may simplify their personal life.

A greater modification is changing the work from the standard 8 h/day, 5-day week pattern. There are many alternatives. They are called "compressed" plans, as they compress the number of days worked, although expanding the number of hours/day. One plan is 7 shifts of 12 h each during a 14-day period; another is 4 shifts of 10 h during each week. Flexible schedules tend to be popular with employees because they give employees greater control of their personal lives. Firms with flexible schedules usually have less absenteeism and tardiness.

Note that flexible schedules imply greater cross-training of workers since the business must be able to continue when a specific individual is not there. Some firms reduce this problem by defining certain time as **core time** (a time when everyone must be there) and **flex** (i.e., flexible) **time** (a time in which some but not all people are present).

Over the longer period of the year, most organizations have busy times and slack times. Require vacations to be taken during slack times, not busy times.

5.2.2 *Temporary workers*

Short-term workers **(temporary workers)** have a long history. Farmers have hired daily and seasonal labor for thousands of years. Construction firms traditionally have had a small core staff and many temporary people hired for a specific job. Many firms hire students and faculty for work during the summer. Starting about 50 years ago, special firms began furnishing temporary secretaries and office help. They furnished trained workers for the amount of time needed. Gradually this service has spread to other jobs such as warehouse labor.

Within the technical and executive areas, however, the concept was to consider all workers as core workers. (Some business was subcontracted out to consulting firms and freelancers, such as professors.)

More recently, however, the practice of hiring temporary executives, engineers, accountants, and other professionals has grown considerably. They tend to cost more than the permanent staff (even though they don't get as many fringe benefits). The big advantage for the organization is that it can staff for the bottom of the business cycle and have a no-layoff policy for its core staff. (The famous Japanese "life-time employee policy" applies only to a core staff of males and excludes temporary workers and females.) The temporary executives and engineers can be removed from the payroll very quickly and with no problems or trauma to the organization. The temporary workers (freelancers) are like entrepreneurs. They have freedom, mobility, and possibly high income but little security.

5.2.3 *Part-time workers* People can be hired for less than 8 h/day, 5 days/week—**part-time workers.** In 2000, 13% of workers in the United States worked part-time (less than 30 h/week); women make up about 70% of part-timers (*The Economist*, 2001). Part-time workers are relatively rare in manufacturing but are large percentages of services and retail trade. There are a number of advantages to the organization:

- The organization may be able to match work requirements and worker availability better (e.g., part-time workers for McDonald's at meal times).

- The organization, for the same hourly rate, may be able to get a better quality part-time than full-time person. For example, a part-time college student may work for $8/h but wouldn't consider working full-time for $8/h.

- The part-time worker may work boring, tedious, or fatiguing work part-time but would not do it full-time.

- Labor costs will be lower. Fringe benefits costs probably will be lower. Pension costs should be lower since most part-time workers quit before retirement. In addition, part-time workers tend to be under 30, so their medical costs tend to be lower. The wage itself tends to be lower as the worker has little experience and thus is in the bottom of the wage bracket, not the top.

- Increasing or decreasing work hours often is quite easy with part-time workers. For example, you can ask them to work 20 h this week instead of 15 (33% increase) or tell them they will work only 15 h this week instead of 20. It is difficult to cut hours of full-time people, and an extra 8 h/week (20% change) is the usual maximum increase.

- By using temporary workers, part-time workers, and overtime, labor can be made a variable cost instead of a fixed cost.

Job sharing, that is, two people each working part time to fill one position, also provides benefits to management: (1) It allows for an expanded range of skills and experience; (2) both employees may work extra hours during peak loads; (3) noncoverage of the job (due to vacations, illnesses, absenteeism) becomes minimal; and (4) if one person leaves, the other provides coverage until a new person is hired.

There are many part-time plans. Part-time can be (1) part-time within a day or (2) full-time within a day but part-time within the week or month. For example, one Kansas firm has a monthly peak load. It hires people to work only the first 2 weeks of the month. People also can be hired to work only weekends or Wednesdays or whatever. See Burns (2001) for more on alternatives to the 8-h, 5-day work schedule.

6 COMMUNICATE INFORMATION

Figure 17.1 shows the flow of information in the human–machine system. The information flows from the person to the machine through controls. The information flows from the machine to the person through displays. In addition, in the larger system, information flows (it is hoped) among people. Long-term information can be considered job instruction and training. Short-term information can be considered "command and control."

6.1 Job Instruction/Training A work method in the mind of the engineer must be transferred to the mind of the operator. The worker can memorize this information (be trained) or can look it up each time (have job aids). See Chapter 31 for more details.

6.2 Command and Control The concept of command and control is of relatively short messages that trigger behavior patterns. See Chapter 18 for techniques for improving communication of alphanumeric information as well as information from instruments. Box 20.4 discusses the problem of warnings. The problem of noise and speech interference is discussed in Chapter 24.

Review Questions

1. Sketch the reward-versus-output curve for a person on salary.
2. Give the formula for availability. What is availability if mean time between failure = 1,000 h and mean time to repair is 10 h?
3. Give an example of a standby system in baseball.
4. Four solution techniques are given for minimizing fixed costs. Give the four and an example of each.
5. Why should a queue server have two queues?

References

Burns, R. Personnel scheduling. In *Handbook of Industrial Engineering,* Salvendy, G. (ed.), Chapter 64. New York: Wiley, 2001.

Corlett, E. and Clark, T. *The Ergonomics of Workspaces and Machines.* London: Taylor and Francis, 1995.

Helander, M. *A Guide to the Ergonomics of Manufacturing.* London: Taylor and Francis, 1995.

Hendrick, H. Good ergonomics is good economics. *Proceedings of the Human Factors and Ergonomics Society.* Santa Monica, CA: HFES, 1–10, 1996.

Ostrofsky, B. *Design, Planning and Development Methodology.* Englewood Cliffs, NJ: Prentice Hall, 1977.

Smith, A. *Reliability Centered Maintenance.* New York: McGraw-Hill, 1993.

Tachibana, M., Naniwada, M., and Salvendy, G. Operational model for increasing quality, productivity, and profitability in maintenance. *Design of Work and Development of Personnel in Advanced Manufacturing,* G. Salvendy and W. Karwowski, eds. New York: Wiley, 1994.

The Economist, p. 90, July 28, 2001.

12 ORGANIZATION OF WORKSTATIONS

Overview

Nine guidelines are given concerning the organization of workstations.

Key Concepts

assembly line
balance-delay percentage
balance-delay time
balanced line
balancing flow lines
bottleneck station
buffer
bus/taxi
capital costs
carrier
cellular manufacture
cycle time
decoupling
distance insensitive

elements
element sharing
environmental stimulation
families
fixed cost/trip
flow lines
get and put-away times
get ready, do, put away
group technology
help your neighbor
just-in-time
lean production
more places than people
multi-function

non-progressive
   assembly
one-worker line
on-line/off-line buffers
operation-only line
order-picking line
paired station
precedence diagram
progressive assembly
rocks in the river
special-purpose
   equipment
station blockage
station starvation

task stimulation
transportation/
   communication
type 1/type 2
utility operator

ORGANIZATION OF WORKSTATIONS

1 Use Specialization Even Though It Sacrifices Versatility

2 Consider Group Technology

3 Consider Both Non-Progressive and Progressive Assembly

4 Balance Flow Lines

5 Minimize Material Handling Cost

6 Decouple Tasks

7 Make Several Identical Items at the Same Time

8 Combine Operations and Functions

9 Vary Environmental Stimulation Inversely with Task Stimulation

USE SPECIALIZATION EVEN THOUGH IT SACRIFICES VERSATILITY

Specialization is a key to progress. Use special-purpose equipment, material, labor, and organization. Seek the simplicity of specialization; thereafter distrust it, but first seek it.

1.1 Equipment

Special-purpose equipment, designed for unique tasks, has the advantages of greater capability and lower production cost/unit. It has the disadvantages of slightly higher capital cost and less flexibility.

Special-purpose equipment often can perform functions that general-purpose equipment cannot. As the designer designs specialized equipment and the user uses it, design restrictions of general-purpose equipment are eliminated and major improvements often result. For example, an ordinary grinder is used to remove very little material and give a high surface finish. A special-purpose grinder may be able to remove large amounts of material (rough cuts) as well as leave a good finish so that the job may be done on one machine in one setup instead of on two machines.

A general-purpose cash register will have numbers on the keys so any price product can be registered. A special-purpose register has special keys for each item (hamburger, small drink) instead of prices; pressing the key actuates the proper price and perhaps may even display the complete order on a screen for the employee to use for order picking. When McDonald's cooks hamburgers, a special-purpose grill cooks the hamburger on both sides simultaneously.

Lower production cost/unit results from the specialized nature of the machine's components. The components run at higher speed, have less variability, require less labor time to operate, or have other unique features.

In theory, special-purpose equipment has fewer components since many of the components needed to make general-purpose equipment general purpose are not needed. Fewer components should mean a simpler machine and thus a lower capital cost. However, the number of copies of each special-purpose machine is small, so design and build costs must be spread over a few machines instead of many. Thus, special-purpose equipment usually has a higher capital cost than general-purpose equipment.

A penalty of special-purpose equipment is its lack of flexibility. It does one job very well—but only one job. What if you don't have just one job?

1.2 Material

Specialized materials have the same types of advantages and disadvantages as specialized equipment with the most common tradeoff being higher material cost versus greater capability.

For example, when you use tool steel for dies instead of the cheaper low-carbon steel, you trade off greater capability and longer die life for a higher material cost. A titanium basket in the plating department trades longer life and less maintenance for higher initial material cost. A throw-away syringe in the hospital trades better sanitation and elimination of cleaning costs for higher initial cost/syringe. A rug in the office trades lower maintenance costs for higher capital costs (than tile).

1.3 Labor

Labor specialization affects both labor quality and quantity.

1.3.1 Quality

Quality of output of a specialist is potentially high due to the skill being in the tool and due to practice. When specialization is high, the specialist develops or purchases special-purpose machines and tools—thus the statement "the skill is in the tool."

With special-purpose tools, many hours spent at the same task, and a more restricted variety of skills required, quality should be better for the specialist. At least in theory, a Ford carburetor tune-up operator should be more skilled at tune-ups of Ford carburetors than a carburetor tune-up operator who works on all models of cars or a tune-up operator who works on all aspects of the field. The specialist may be much farther out on the learning curve; that is, the specialist may have tuned 7,500 Ford carburetors while the mechanic may have tuned 150. The brain surgeon may have operated on 1,000 brains while the general surgeon may have operated on 1.

1.3.2 Quantity

Quantity of output/time usually is higher for a specialist (that is, labor time/unit is lower) for the same reasons that quality is higher. With a restricted range of skills, training time is less for the specialist.

Since the individual is trained deeply rather than broadly, the general rationale has been that a less talented individual is required and so a lower rate of pay is justified. In most industries, the generalist (tool and die maker) is paid more than the specialist (turret lathe operator). Therefore, specialized labor costs less—both because of its greater productivity/unit and its lower wages/h.

From the individual viewpoint, specialized work may be repetitive and monotonous. It has been difficult to recruit workers for monotonous jobs if they have low pay. If the job has high pay, many workers can be found whether the job is monotonous or not.

1.4 Job Organization

Adjectives that describe specialization are *rigidly structured, inflexible, disci-*

plined, and *machinelike.* The overwhelming characteristic is the need for high volume of a standardized product. Levitt mass-produced homes by breaking home construction into 26 steps and reversing the assembly line (the product stood still and the worker moved). If you are going to do nothing but brain surgery, you need many patients requiring brain surgery; if all you do is tune up Ford carburetors and it takes 30 min/carburetor, you need about 15 Fords/day to keep busy.

If, instead of time/unit of 30 min, time/unit = 1 min, then output/day is 450 (allowing for breaks), output/month is about 10,000, and output/yr is about 120,000. Can you sell 120,000 identical units/yr? For time/unit of .1 min (6 s), output is 1,200,000/yr. Can you sell that many?

Most firms don't have that volume and can use specialization only as a desirable goal. One approach finding growing favor is **group technology,** which attempts to get the benefits of mass production from batch production.

2 CONSIDER GROUP TECHNOLOGY

2.1 Concept
Flow line advantages and challenges are discussed elsewhere in this chapter. However, many items do not have sufficient production volume to justify a flow line. How can you get the benefits of a flow line with low volume?

In a flow line, each item is identical. The concept of **group technology** is to form **families** of items that are almost identical. The closer the items are to identical, the more closely we can imitate a flow line and shift the fixed costs of the flow line (tooling, machines, conveyors, procedures) to the *process* instead of the item. That is, find common solutions to common problems.

2.2 Benefits of Product Families
Benefits fall into two categories: (1) product design and (2) common manufacturing.

2.2.1 Product design
Reducing the number of items made (standardization, variety reduction) has many benefits. Consider a simple washer. In the past, the firm's engineers may have designed hundreds of washers for many models of many products. When a new product is designed, it would be better if an existing washer could be used rather than add another part number to the system. Three justifications of variety reduction are:

1. *Hit.* An existing part can be used in place of a proposed new part.
2. *Modify.* An existing part, suitably modified, can replace a new part.

3. *Design information.* The existing part can be analyzed for specifications, tolerances, and material to aid in the design of the new part.

2.2.2 Common manufacturing
There are office and shop-floor advantages. Comparing the similar parts—designed, planned, and costed over a period of years by a variety of people—brings out many anomalies in the processing, tooling, time standards, and cost estimates. Studying these anomalies can reduce the cost of previous approaches as well as benefit new approaches.

Another benefit is the use of existing tooling. Either the existing die or fixture can be used directly or the tool can be modified (e.g., with an insert) to produce the new part.

Manufacturing benefits are increased when the family members are manufactured not only close in time but also close in space. Close-in-time benefits include a setup cost reduction and the minimization of operator forgetfulness. Space proximity is implemented through cells; see Section 2.4.

2.3 Family Formation
At the macro level, a focused factory can specialize in a particular type of part or assembly. At the micro level, families can be based on similarities in part geometry (e.g., group shafts, flat parts, gears) or in the process (e.g., group castings, forgings, sheet metal parts, printed circuits). At the heart of the grouping (clustering, classification, pattern) process is the problem of coding (numerical classification).

2.4 Cells
Manufacturing items close together in space is called cell layout. (If the cell is automated, it may be called a flexible manufacturing system, adaptive manufacturing system, or versatile manufacturing system.) This section will discuss the cell concept, cell advantages and disadvantages, and cell layout.

2.4.1 Cell concept
Manufacturing the related items in a parts family should require almost the same steps. Therefore, all similar machines and skills are located in one area—a cell. Machines and skills include not only the machines and people but also jigs, fixtures, measuring equipment, material handling equipment, and so forth.

2.4.2 Cell advantages and disadvantages
Advantages include specialization, minimum material handling, simpler production control, shorter throughput times, and lower work-in-process inventory.

Specialization in a cell is by product family; each operator runs a mixture of machines (lathe, drill, inspection gauge). In a job shop, an operator runs a variety of products on the same machine; in a cell, the operator runs the same product on a variety of machines. Since the cell machines can be specialized to produce only what is needed on that family, output/h should be higher.

Material handling cost in the cell is minimal since material handling paperwork is zero and distances (1 to 5 m) are small.

Production control is *to* the cell, not *within* the cell. Within the cell, the routing is fairly standardized and at the operator's discretion. Shorter throughput times result from the simplified flow pattern and the eliminated paperwork.

Work-in-process within the cell is small since the buffers between machines are small. The policy of running similar parts together to maximize productivity within the cell means that due dates have reduced importance. That is, an item is scheduled because it is similar rather than overdue. In addition, the ability to produce similar items together requires raw materials to be available before they are needed from a due-date viewpoint. Cell inventories are minimized at the expense of larger inventories before and after the cell. Thus, total inventories may or may not increase.

Disadvantages of a cell versus a job shop include lower equipment utilization, loss of flexibility, and the cost of setting up and maintaining the family and cell concept.

Since a cell has to be capable of doing all of the necessary operations, it will duplicate machines in other cells. Some low-cost machines (e.g., drill presses, deburring benches) may even be duplicated within the same cell. Specialized processes such as heat treating, painting, and plating are called *exceptional* elements and may be "subcontracted" outside the cell.

Since the cell has dedicated equipment, people, and procedures, new products must meet the family characteristics or they cannot be produced in the cell.

The capital cost of the group technology includes the cost of setting up and maintaining the parts family information as well as the duplicate equipment in the cells.

The benefits of group technology and cells are primarily in *avoided* costs: extra parts are not designed, extra jigs are not purchased, more efficient processing. Unfortunately, *these avoided costs do not show up in the cost-accounting system.* Managers who are evaluated on their short-term performance may resist implementing group technology because reported expenses will increase and reductions will not appear in the reported costs.

2.4.3 *Cell layout* A flow line usually is linear (although it can be L or U shaped), but cells usually are circular or U shaped. This arrangement minimizes the transportation distance within the cell and encourages multiple machines per operator. See Figure 12.1.

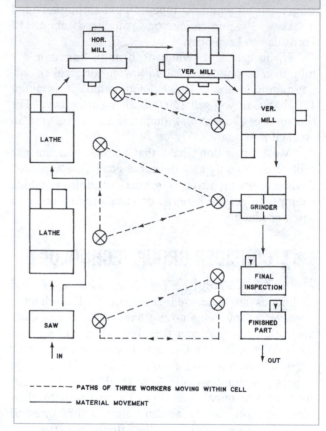

FIGURE 12.1

Cell layout example (Black, 1983). Note that multi-skilled operators tend multiple machines; the machines need not be in the production sequence. It also is relatively easy to add or subtract workers if production requirements change.

------ PATHS OF THREE WORKERS MOVING WITHIN CELL
———— MATERIAL MOVEMENT

Three important concepts are:

- *Multiple machines/operator.* Most machines are automatic or semiautomatic, resulting in considerable idle time for the machine operators. In the conventional job shop, there is 1 operator for 1 machine. Group technology, with its multiple machines/operator, can substantially increase labor productivity. As shown in Figure 12.1, the second and third machines in the production sequence need not be assigned to the first operator. The additional machines also do not have to be the same type of machine. This flexibility ensures that the operator will be busy—whether cell production requirements increase or decrease.

- *Teamwork.* People near each other will talk to each other. Problems (such as quality and rework) can be discussed immediately.

- *Minimum movement.* The distances for the movement of people, products, and tools are minimized.

CONSIDER BOTH NON-PROGRESSIVE AND PROGRESSIVE ASSEMBLY

3.1 Problem   Consider an assembly of N elements with sufficient product demand to require m people to work. Should each worker do all N elements—**non-progressive assembly,** a complete workstation, "job enlargement," multi-skilling—or should the job be split so each person does N/m elements—**progressive assembly,** an assembly line, a flow line, "job simplification," Taylorism? Workstations need not be entirely progressive or non-progressive. Assume $N = 60$ elements and $m = 5$ people. In addition to 5 stations doing all 60 elements or 5 stations each doing 12 elements, there could be other combinations such as 3 workstations with 2 persons at station 1, 2 at station 2, and 1 at station 3. For some alternatives, see "one-worker line" and "cellular manufacturing" in Sections 2 and 5.

The work also can be organized so that all workers in the department can do all jobs, or most workers can do most jobs, some workers can do multiple jobs, or each person can do only one.

In addition, jobs can be defined more broadly. The first level of additional jobs would be to include material handling, and packaging and dispatching of finished articles. An even broader scope would include production scheduling and routine clerical work. Even routine supervisory work can be included.

What of inspection? One possibility is that Joe produces and Sam inspects and Pete repairs the defects. But Sam's and Pete's job can be combined, or Joe's and Pete's, and even Joe's, Sam's, and Pete's.

3.2 Advantages and Disadvantages   The discussion will be grouped into advantages, neutral characteristics, and disadvantages.

3.2.1 *Advantages of non-progressive*   Five advantages involve balance delay, scheduling flexibility, shocks, musculoskeletal disorders, and satisfaction.

Balance delay time is eliminated. Since each worker does a complete job, the job does not have to be divided into equal time segments. On progressive lines, if these segments are not equal (balanced), there is idle time—**balance delay time**—which tends to be 5% to 15% of the work times. Balance delay is increased by more stations, smaller buffers, shorter cycle times, longer element times, and increasing precedence requirements.

Scheduling flexibility is increased. Non-progressive stations can make multiple products at the same time (different stations make different products).

Making multiple products at the same time results in many scheduling, inventory, and marketing advantages. In addition, a non-progressive station working "off-line" (see Section 5) can use intermittent, non-paced work; examples are trainees, repair work, and rehabilitation (light work). Flow lines work best with steady, uninterrupted production of a single product. However, it is possible to design flow lines to make multiple products at the same time; see Section 5.

Shocks do not have multiple effects. When using non-progressive stations, shocks (machine breakdowns, interruptions, absenteeism) affect only a single operator or station. On flow lines, a shock affects multiple stations; see Section 6 for some techniques for reducing shock effects on flow lines.

Musculoskeletal disorders are less of a problem because individuals have greater variety in motions. The greater variety allows one muscle to rest while another works (working rest). The greater autonomy permits more control over rest breaks. However, the greater job complexity makes mechanization or automation more difficult.

Satisfaction may increase. Each worker has the satisfaction of completing an entire unit, not just a piece. There is more autonomy and less monotony. In addition, when elements are divided, some are more desirable than others; non-progressive treats each worker equally (more "fairly"). This higher satisfaction would tend to result in less absenteeism and less turnover. Oxenburgh (1991) reported (in Case 4) that two companies (A organized with assembly line, B organized with non-progressive) were compared. Employee absenteeism and turnover were much greater in company A; this led to higher production costs as new workers, although paid the same as experienced workers, had considerably lower productivity. The high turnover also led to considerable quality problems.

3.2.2 *Neutral characteristics*   Quality, material handling, space, and walking can favor non-progressive or progressive designs.

Quality may be higher or lower. Doing all steps at a single station allows that operator to adjust later stages to the results of the previous stages; feedback of information within one person is simple and direct. In a line, adjustment of later operations is restricted, as the feedback occurs to other people and after a time delay. A line station is often simple and automated, so quality resides in the equipment; when it's good, it's very good and when it's bad, it's horrid. Lines also tend to conceal responsibility, because many people handle each item, making it difficult to identify exactly which person or station is responsible for an error.

Material handling at non-progressive stations is simpler since everything is at one station. However, there may not be enough space for bulky equipment or parts; in this case the station may be "spread out," with the operator walking a few feet. There will be multiple complete stations; components will have to be furnished to each of these locations, assembled units and rejects taken away. For a line, only a few components will be furnished to each station; assembled units are taken from just one location. Thus, non-progressive makes it more difficult to use specialization and mechanization.

Space requirements could favor either alternative. Individual workstations of a line will tend to be smaller, but space for conveyors may increase the total.

Walking may be required. If the non-progressive station is "large" and requires some walking, there is a time requirement for walking. For example, at a Swedish ABB plant making motors, one worker makes a complete motor but does the work at 3 adjacent workstations. He walks 20 ft between the stations once every 15 min. The Methods-Time-Measurement predetermined time system gives .2 s/ft for walking. The walking takes 4 s out of every 900 s, for a penalty of $4/900 = .4\%$. From a fatigue viewpoint, occasional walking is superior to constant standing.

If an assembly takes "considerable" time, non-progressive stations can be used with multiple operators. For example, at Volvo's Uddevalla plant, cars were assembled by teams of 8–10 people. Each person was responsible for a thorough knowledge of 1/7 of the process and a working knowledge of 3/7. Cars were assembled in cells with 4 cars in a cell at a given time; 3 people worked on each of 3 cars. Since the 48 teams worked on 3 cars at a time, many product varieties could be assembled in a shift. In addition, if a car must be retained in the cell, it could be kept without disturbing the flow. However, this plant since has been shut down and no other auto manufacturers have used this concept.

3.2.3 *Disadvantages of non-progressive* Disadvantages are direct labor cost/unit, skill requirements, equipment capital cost, in-process inventory, and supervision.

Direct labor cost/unit will be higher for non-progressive since the operator will not be as specialized and will not have as much practice (experience). If cycle time is 10 min at a non-progressive station, the operator experiences about 45 units/shift. If the cycle time is 1 min at a line station, the operator experiences 450 units/shift. This beneficial effect of experience is counteracted to some extent by the balance delay time as the line operates at the speed of the slowest operator.

Skill requirements and, thus, training costs are higher for non-progressive. Each person needs to know the entire job, not just a small part; this will require more training. The more knowledge required, the more training required. However, at least some of this training may be through craft and apprentice training. With lines, unskilled workers with brief training (and specialized tools and procedures) are able to produce excellent quality; with non-progressive, the same quality requires skilled workers. (This assumes someone [perhaps an engineer?] is able to design the job and communicate the procedures to the unskilled workers.) The skilled workers may not be available; if available, they may require higher pay. Skilled workers may have more job opportunities elsewhere and, thus, have higher turnover, or they may like their job so much that turnover becomes low.

Equipment capital cost will be higher for non-progressive since equipment will be duplicated at each station. The smaller number of units/day at each station discourages special-purpose equipment (which tends to be more productive).

In-process inventory will be higher for non-progressive, as each component will be stocked at many stations instead of just one. Buffers between line stations often hold a few minutes' output while non-progressive buffers often are much larger. The finished goods inventory usually is higher for the line, due to lack of scheduling flexibility. (A typical annual inventory cost is 25% to 30% of inventory value; $1,000 of inventory costs .25 (1,000) = $250/year or 250/365 = $.68/day.)

Supervision is more difficult for non-progressive, because individual motivation, training, and performance problems are more obvious. However, multi-skilled workers may be able to take over some supervisory duties and thereby cut supervisory costs. There will be more "paperwork" as lines have predetermined ("automatic") routing and scheduling. Lines have line pressure, instead of supervisory pressure, on output quantity. Lines are affected more by "shocks" (absenteeism, machine breakdown, schedule change).

3.3 **Summary** Even though flow lines have many disadvantages, they are common for three reasons:

1. Some of the advantages of flow lines, such as lower labor cost and lower capital cost, are emphasized by decision makers. Note that the decision makers work for management, so they may ignore factors such as workers' job satisfaction.

2. Labor cost and capital cost are quite visible, whereas scheduling flexibility, cumulative trauma, and material handling cost are lost in the overhead figures.

3. Many of the disadvantages of flow lines can be overcome by proper system design. See Guideline 5.

4 BALANCE FLOW LINES

4.1 Standard Balancing Technique

The first question is whether you wish to balance the line. As is pointed out in the discussion of buffer design section (Guideline 6 of this chapter), it is feasible, and often desirable, to use an unbalanced line.

The line balance problem has three givens: (1) a table of work elements with their associated times (see Table 12.1), (2) a **precedence diagram** showing the element precedence relationships (see Figure 12.2), and (3) required units/minute from the line. To be determined are (1) the number of stations, (2) the number of workers at each station, and (3) the elements to be done at each station. The purpose of **balancing flow lines** is to minimize total idle time.

First, what is the total number to be made, and in how long a time? For example, 20,000 units could be made in 1,000 h at the rate of 20/h, 500 h at 40/h, 250 h at 80/h, or in many other combinations. Continuous production is only one of the many alternatives. Hansen and Taylor (1982), for example, discuss the conditions under which a periodic shutdown is best. Assume we wish to make the 20,000 units in 1,000 h at the rate of 20/h. Since we are dealing with a balanced line, each station will take 1,000 h/20,000 = .05 h/unit; **cycle time** = .05 h.

Second, guess an approximate number of stations by dividing total work time by cycle time: for example, .1818 h/.05 h/station = 3.63 stations. Then use four stations with one operator at each.

Third, make a trial solution as in Table 12.2 and Figure 12.3. Identify each station with a cross-

Precedence diagram showing the sequence required for assembly. The lines between the circles are not drawn to scale; that is, elements 4 and 9 both must be completed before 6, but 9 could be done before or after 4. Precedence must be observed; thus elements 3, 4, and 9 could not be assigned to one station and elements 8 and 6 to another. However, 8, 9, and 10 could be done at one station.

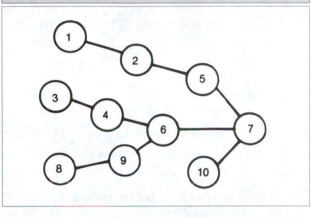

hatched area. Remember not to violate precedence. For example, elements 1 and 5 cannot be done at one station and element 2 at another. Then calculate the idle percentage **(balance-delay percentage):** .0182/(4 × .05) = 9.1% in our case.

As an example of flexible thinking, consider Table 12.3. Here stations 1 and 2 are combined into one superstation; the elemental time now totals .0950. Since there are two operators, the time available is 1.000 and the idle time is .0050 at the station and .0025 for each of the operators. So far, there is no improvement over the solution of Table 12.2. However, note that there is *idle time at each station.* Therefore, the amount can be reduced at all stations until there is zero idle time. Thus, the line cycle time can be reduced to .0475.

Table 12.3 shows that the new idle time is .0083 h. Expressed in percentage terms, the idle time now is .0083/(4 × .0475) = 4.4% instead of the 9.1% of Table 12.2.

With larger lines, the problem's complexity grows rapidly, and grouping the elements into zones (which either prevents or requires certain elements to be done at the same station) is one attempt at simplification. Another source of complexity is the change in product volume; that is, 20/h in May, 24/h in June, 26/h in July, and so forth.

Another complication is that actual lines often are multiple-product lines. First we assemble a four-door Pontiac, then a two-door Buick with a V4 engine, then a Buick SUV with a V6 but no air conditioning, and so

Elements and work times for assembly-line balancing problem. Each element time is assumed constant. In practice, each element time is a distribution.

ELEMENT	WORK TIME/ UNIT, H
1	.0333
2	.0167
3	.0117
4	.0167
5	.0250
6	.0167
7	.0200
8	.0067
9	.0333
10	.0017
	.1818

TABLE	12.2				

Trial solution for assembly-line balance problem.

STATION	ELEMENT	ELEMENT TIME, H/UNIT	STATION ELEMENT TIME, H/UNIT	STATION IDLE TIME, H/UNIT	LINE IDLE TIME, H/UNIT
1	1	.0333			
	2	.0167	.0500	0	0
2	8	.0067			
	9	.0333	.0400	.0100	.0100
3	3	.0117			
	4	.0167			
	6	.0167	.0451	.0049	.0149
4	5	.0250			
	7	.0200			
	10	.0017	.0467	.0033	.0182

Idle percent = .0182/(4 × .05) = 9.1%

on. In addition, there are mix changes (e.g., in March we produce 90% with air conditioning and in April 95%).

The problem complexity and the need for repeated solutions have led to efforts to use computer programs. However, Ghosh and Gagnon (1989), in their extensive survey of the literature, report that very few firms (about 5%) actually used computer programs for line balancing. Part of the problem is that user-friendly programs were not available. Another problem is that computers act on input as immutable facts.

4.2 Modifications to Standard Technique
If the computer solution gives some idle time at each station, the cycle time can be decreased until the time at one station (the bottleneck station) is zero. Here are some useful modifications.

First, consider **element sharing.** That is, operators/station need not equal 1.0. One possibility is more than one operator/station. Some examples are 2 operators/station (operators/station = 2), 3 operators/2 stations (operators/station = 1.5), and 4 operators/3 stations (operators/station = 1.33). This permits a cycle time that is less than an element time. For example, with 2 operators/station, each would do every other unit. (Often, combining 2 single stations with 1 operator each into one "super" station with 2 operators dramatically improves the balance.) Super stations also can be formed by combining subassembly stations with assembly stations.

You also can have fewer than 1 operator/station by having operators walk between stations or having work done off-line (i.e., use buffers). Also, it is possible in some situations to have operators from 2 adjacent stations share one or two elements. Station D does elements 16 and 17 on one-half or one-third of the units, and Station E does elements 16 and 17 on the remaining units. Elements shared do not have to be adjacent stations if precedence requirements are not violated.

Second, remember that cycle times are not fixed. At the start, we assume a cycle time of .05 h (i.e., the line runs 1,000 h or 1,000/8 = 125 days). It may be more efficient to have a cycle time of .048 h (i.e., the line runs 20,000 × .048 = 960 h = 960/8 = 120 days). In addition to this balance cost, consider setup cost and inventory carrying cost. That is, what is the best combination of balance costs, setup costs, and inventory costs? The computer programs can do a quick check on many different alternatives.

FIGURE	12.3

Graphic solution of Table 12.2.

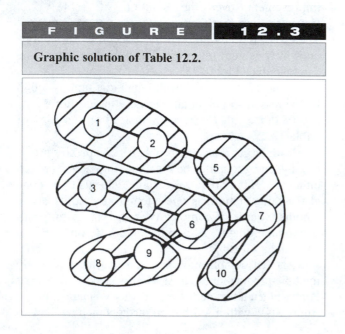

		T A B L E 1 2 . 3				

Trial solution for assembly-line balance problem with two operators at one station and cycle time of .0475 h.

STATION	NO. OF OPERATORS	ELEMENT	ELEMENT TIME (H)	WORK TIME (H)	IDLE TIME (H)	CUMULATIVE IDLE TIME (H)
1	2	1	.0333			
		2	.0167			
		3	.0167			
		4	.0167			
		6	.0166	.0950	.0000	.0000
2	1	8	.0067			
		9	.0333	.0400	.0075	.0075
3	1	5	.0250			
		7	.0200			
		10	.0017	.0467	.0008	.0083

Idle percent = $.0083/(4 \times .0475)$ = 4.4%

Third, remember that elements often can be redefined. One possibility is to take former elements 16, 17, and 18 and eliminate element 17 by splitting it between elements 16 and 18. Or elements 16 and 17 might be combined and then split into 16a and 17a so that although the total time is the same, the relative allocation to 16 and 17 changes. Still another possibility is to split an element even further.

For example, element 9 might be "pick up screwdriver, drive 20 screws, release screwdriver," with a time of .0167 h. For balancing purposes, it may be desirable to have element 9a be "pick up screwdriver, drive 15 screws, release screwdriver" with a time of .0125 h, and element 9b be "pick up screwdriver, drive 5 screws, release screwdriver" with a time of .0075 h. You have added extra work to the tasks (an extra pickup and release of the screwdriver) but may be able to cut the time of the bottleneck station and thus the time. Be careful about this technique since, when conditions change, the reason for the extra work may be forgotten and the unnecessary work retained without reason.

Fourth, interchange elements from the assembly task and the subassembly tasks. For example, a nameplate might be added at a subassembly station instead of the assembly station. An adjustment might be done on the assembly instead of the subassembly.

For more on line balancing, see Hanna and Konz (2004).

5 MINIMIZE MATERIAL HANDLING COST

Material handling does not add value—just cost. Reduce the cost by analysis of its components. Cost of material handling can be broken down as follows:

- Material handling cost/yr = Capital cost + Operating cost
- Operating cost = (Number of trips/yr) (cost/trip)
- Cost/trip = Fixed cost/trip + (Variable cost/distance) (Distance/trip)

5.1 Capital Cost of Systems   The **capital costs** of material handling (return on investment and depreciation) do not vary appreciably with the amount of material moved. For example, you may purchase an electric fork truck for $20,000 and a recharging station for $3,000. Then $23,000 invested at 10% returns $2,300. This cost occurs whether you use the truck one h/month or 100 h/month; whether your downtime is 10% or 90%. In addition, depreciation depends more on age of equipment than usage. For example, resale value of the fork truck after 2 years might be $5,000 if you used the truck 1 h/day and $4,000 if you used it 8 h/day. A used conveyor probably will sell for the same amount regardless of use.

Thus, if utilization is poor, the lowest total cost might be obtained for a system with high operating cost but low capital cost. If utilization is high, the high capital cost alternative may be best.

Eliminating peak loads by scheduling may eliminate the need for some equipment. For example, schedule shipments for 5 days a week, not just Thursday and Friday; receive material from vendors 5 days/week. Move by priority—not just first come, first served.

5.2 Number of Trips/Year   The ultimate would be to make number of trips equal zero, eliminating not only operating cost but also capital cost. Question the need for the trip; it may not really be required. A

repair or maintenance call might be eliminated by using higher quality maintenance (e.g., use a component that requires service once every 120 days instead of once every 60 days). A sales call might be eliminated by using a letter or electronic communication. The opposite of **transportation** is **communication.**

Reduce the number of trips by scheduling and combining trips. For example, a trip from San Francisco to New York with a stop in Chicago is less expensive than two trips, one to Chicago and one to New York. The tradeoff is among reduced travel cost, increased scheduling problems, and capacity/trip. The same type of tradeoff must be made in other problems. Should the server bring you a cup of coffee or a carafe of coffee? Should the clerk take each item to the duplicating machine or accumulate a batch before going? Should the money be deposited in the bank once a week, once a day, or once an hour? Should the operator send material from the machine to the next station once/min, once/h, or once/day? Should the pallet hold 50 units and move once/day or hold 25 and move twice/day? A sales call might be eliminated by using a letter or parcel (transport of object instead of person); if the "object" is information, consider electronic communication.

5.3 Fixed Cost/Trip

Fixed cost/trip has two components: (1) information transfer (mainly paperwork) and (2) start and stop.

Information transfer is a material handling cost that often is overlooked. Reduce these costs by using *line* production. In a job shop, even if the many paperwork forms are completed correctly, costs are substantial. It is not just the cost of filling out the forms; it is the cost of transporting the forms, filing the forms, transferring information from one form to another, and so on. Mistakes occur. Products can get misplaced, workers can run out of supplies, trips can be made to the wrong place. One of the major advantages of line assembly is the standardization of routing and scheduling—thereby reducing information transfer costs. Computer and electronic sensor technology, however, can reduce information transfer cost, so single-product assembly lines no longer are always desirable. For example, electronic sensors can "read" a box number as it moves along a conveyor and send the information to a "brain," which then consults its "memory," decides to send this box to station 14, and moves its "arm" to put the box in station 14.

Start and stop (pick up and put down; load and unload; pack and unpack) is a substantial cost that does not vary with the distance moved. A large part of the cost of flying a commercial airplane is the takeoff and landing cost, just as a large portion of a fork truck's cost and time is spent picking up and putting down the load. If load time = 1.0 min, travel time =

.01 min/m, and unload time = 2.0 min, a 50 m trip costs 3.5 min and a 100 m trip costs 4.0 min. Twice as far doesn't cost twice as much (see Figure 9.2).

Much transportation (and communication) is **distance insensitive** (i.e., price varies little with distance). Over the last 100 years technology has increased this death of distance. Water transport, especially, is insensitive to distance. Goods can be moved from Japan to New York for not much more cost than from Boston to New York. Land transport has been speeded by improved highways, and air transport by improved airplanes. Improved electronics—both wired and wireless—speed communication of words and data. These increases in insensitivity affect plant design and location because products now come from a specialized factory in Dusseldorf or Milan or Chicago rather than a number of local plants, each with a variety of products with low production volumes. Increased mobility of workers (due to the automobile) and of products (due to trucks instead of railroads) permits decentralization of places of employment and, thus, decentralization of cities.

Within a factory, fork trucks and tractor-trailer trains have increased distance insensitivity. Formerly, factories were built vertically to minimize product movement distance. Offices (paperwork factories) are still in the early stage of development (multistory buildings with workstations—desks—close together). But even in offices, communication is replacing transportation. For example, people fax material to other people in the same building rather than carry it a few feet.

5.4 Variable Cost/Distance

Costs/distance are a function of energy consumed and labor cost. Energy consumption does not make much difference in many cases since it is a small portion of the total cost. Electric fork trucks do tend to be cheaper to operate than diesel trucks, which are cheaper than gasoline trucks, which are cheaper than liquid petroleum (propane) trucks. Low resistance to motion also helps; so trains use less energy than trucks and ships are cheapest of all per km-ton.

Care must be taken that low energy costs are not overcome by high labor costs. Move more product/labor hour—the ultimate is infinite volume or zero labor hours. Large oil tankers use much less labor/barrel of oil transported than small tankers, as do large trucks versus small trucks—more volume for the same labor. For distances within a plant of over 150 m, tractor-trailer trains may be more economical than fork trucks. If the route is standardized (and perhaps with fewer than 20 destinations), the train need not have a driver because sensors and computers can replace a driver in some applications—the same volume with less labor.

5.5 Distance/Trip   Reduce distances by efficient layout and arrangement. Trade off short trips for local supply versus decreased inventories for central supply. For example, fewer micrometers are needed with a tool crib than if everyone is issued one, but distance moved to get the "mike" becomes 100 m, not 2 m. Micrometers have low capital costs, whereas fork trucks have high capital cost. Thus, giving each department its own fork truck reduces distance traveled, but the extra capital cost can be very high. Sharing may work; that is, department A "owns" it in the morning and B in the afternoon.

All other things being equal, a short trip costs less than a long trip; however, a long trip on a bus may be cheaper than a short trip in a taxi. Figure 12.4 shows a bus route around an area. A **bus** goes around the area on a standardized route. Material going from B to A must first go to C and D before reaching A.

Why use a bus instead of a **taxi** system (point-to-point service)? *First,* cost of movement tends to be relatively insensitive to distance due to high pick-up and put-down costs in relation to movement costs (see Figure 9.2). *Second,* if distance moved is important, usually total distance moved by the *carrier* (distance/loop × number of trips around loop) is what is important rather than distance moved by the objects. *Third,* time for the physical movement of products tends to be relatively small in relation to the time in storage at each end of the move, and thus not very important. Overhead conveyors often wind for long distances around the ceiling to act as work-in-progress storage. In the international oil trade, tankers often leave port without a specified destination. Their cargo is sold when they near Europe.

Jenkins and Rickards (2001) describe how workers sorted 100 different product cases to pallets. Ergonomic problems included frequent back, leg, and upper body injuries. Although the working area was 100 ft long, the incoming conveyor was only 12 ft long. In addition, there was no systematic location of the pallets. The conveyor was extended to 100 ft and the pallets were located systematically. The savings were $492,000/yr with a payback of 4 days: a good example of how improved ergonomics usually leads to good economics.

Emphasize minimizing total material handling cost—in itself a subset of the goal of reducing manufacturing cost—rather than minimizing distance/trip, variable cost/distance, and so forth.

6 DECOUPLE TASKS

This guideline is adapted from Hanna and Konz (2004). See Box 12.1.

6.1 Introduction   Figure 12.5 shows three types of **flow lines,** distinguished by the presence of operations and/or transportations. In one extreme, the **operation-only line,** a single component goes through a series of operations (item is processed or changed at stations); no additional components are added. Examples are an engine block being machined on several machines, a steel rolling mill, a rotary index table with several "heads," and university class enrollment (visit various tables to sign up or pay for various activities).

In the other extreme, the **order-picking line,** items are accumulated together without any operation at the station. There are transportations but no operations. Examples are order picking in a warehouse and a customer obtaining food in a cafeteria.

The most common flow line, the **assembly line,** has both operations performed and items added at the station. There are both operations and transportations. Examples are product assembly (autos, TVs, clothing), packaging lines, chemical processing lines, and filling lines. A reverse version is the disassembly line, often used in food processing. Example disassembly lines are slaughter operations and grain mills.

F I G U R E   12.4

Bus service (such as from a power and free conveyor or an automatically guided vehicle) follows a standardized route while taxi service (such as from a lift truck) goes directly to the desired location. Bus service tends to be cheaper than taxis, but it may take an hour or two for the delivery instead of the minutes of the taxi.

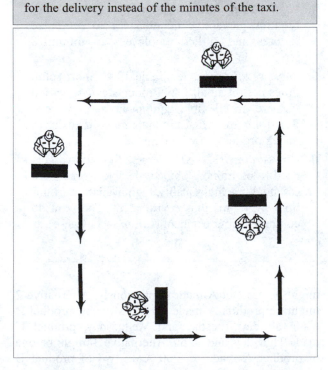

BOX 12.1   *Just-in-Time*

A technique called **just-in-time** currently is popular in management circles. Unfortunately, some managers have become enthusiasts of this technique without understanding why the Japanese found it so useful.

The simplistic view is to reduce work-in-process inventories to very small amounts to reduce inventory costs. In effect, this means small buffers. However, inventory cost reduction is not the reason for using just-in-time.

What is the cost of inventory—that is, buffers?

A rule of thumb is that annual inventory carrying cost is about 30% of the product price. (The 30% is primarily the cost of capital, although there is some cost for the building, heat, lights, etc.) Thus, a product costing $100 will cost .30 ($100) = $30 to store for 1 year. For simplicity, assume a factory works 250 days/year. This means it costs about 30%/250 production days = .125% of the product cost to store an item for 1 production day or (assuming an 8-h shift) .125%/8 = .0156%/production hour. A $100 buffer then would have an inventory cost of $100 $\times$ .125% = $.125 = 12.5 cents/production day or 1.57 cents/production hour. Unless there are truly enormous inventories between stations, therefore, there is little inventory savings available.

Why do the Japanese advocate use of just-in-time? Because it forces management to solve problems. Consider the flow of inventory through a facility as a river upon which you are using a boat. When the river level is reduced (inventory is reduced), **rocks in the river** (problems) appear that were hidden by the large inventory. Lowering the river forces the management to solve the problems (scheduling, quality, etc.), which formerly could be concealed by large inventories. After the problems are solved, the river is lowered further and more problems are solved. The solution of these hidden problems is the justification for just-in-time, not minor reductions in inventory costs. In theory, managers should have solved the problems without "holding their feet to the fire," but just-in-time seems a practical technique to get their attention and make them do what they should have done anyway.

Experience has shown that the just-in-time tactic (also referred to as **lean production**) leads to six strategies to remove the rocks:

1. *Little product variety.* Little variety implies a focused factory with a limited number of products. However, group technology can permit greater product variety.

2. *Produce only what the consumer wants and only when it is wanted.* Perfect scheduling often is implemented through "pull" scheduling (build-to-replenish) instead of the conventional "push" scheduling (build-to-forecast). It requires close coordination with vendors (often through a retailer's computer point-of-sale information being transferred directly to the vendor's computer); expediting no longer is feasible. Because stable production is "quiet," a sudden defect ("noise") is easily detectable.

   The operator has to be presented not just with data, but also with information (information = data + meaning). For example, all scrap containers might be painted red; parts might be supplied to a workstation in a standardized container that contains a known number of parts (thus, it gives information on the time until stockout).

3. *High quality.* Strategies often use statistical process control and employee involvement, such as Quality Circles, to reduce errors. Make processes foolproof (*poka-yoke* in Japanese). Reducing errors tends to lead to consistent production times. Consider vendors as well as internal operations.

4. *High equipment availability.* Availability requires preventive maintenance to minimize failures and skilled employees to minimize repair time.

5. *Short setup times.* See Table 12.4. Short setup times permit small lots. Products can be varied if there are flexible equipment and workers. Small lots of varied products make it easier to match production with demand.

6. *Cross-trained skilled workers.* Skilled workers need to be trained. Skilled, flexible workers are essential in a high-quality, high-availability, multiple-lot, no-margins environment. They can do continuous improvement (*kaizen* in Japanese).

Flow lines do not have to make a single product continuously. Figure 12.6 shows three alternatives: (1) the single product made continuously, (2) multiple products made sequentially in batches, and (3) multiple products made simultaneously. Alternative 1 might be product A made continuously. Alternative 2 might be product A made all day Monday, product B made all day Tuesday and Wednesday, product C made Thursday, and so on. Alternative 3 might be one of product A made at 8:00 A.M., two of product B

T A B L E	1 2 . 4

Steps to single-minute setup (adapted from Cochran and Swinehart, 1991).

1. **Separate internal setup actions from external setup actions.**
   - Internal setup = setup while machine is stopped.
   - External setup = setup while machine is operational. After videotaping setups, classify and analyze data.
2. **Convert internal setup actions into external setup actions.** Don't interrupt internal setup actions for external setup actions. Make fixture setup, tool setup, and gauge acquisition external. Have common tool packets at the machine.
3. **Eliminate adjustment.** Adjustment consumes as much as 50% of setup time (time from completion of last good part A to acceptance of first good part B). Use quick change tooling, such as sine key location of fixtures, angle plates, and other work-holding devices, to establish predetermined locations on the worktable. Use part probes to minimize tool cutting position errors.
4. **Achieve single-minute setup.**

made at 8:07 and 8:14, one of product C made at 8:17, one of product A made at 8:21, and so on.

Table 12.5 shows that there also are alternatives for conveyor movement, location of the work, and operator posture.

Another decision is what should be assembled in sub-assemblies versus what should be assembled on the line. In general, experience shows that it is best to minimize the components added at final assembly—have a "short main line." That is, add a complete seat to a car as one unit; don't build the seat on the main line.

Box 12.2 discusses coffee and meal breaks.

The **elements** (work) of the task are divided among the line's stations. If the amount of work is equal at each station, it is a **balanced line;** if not equal, it is an unbalanced line. Depending upon the type of line, one or more elements can be done at each station. An additional possibility is the same element's being done at more than one station. A well-designed line will have:

- minimum idle time at the stations
- high quality (enough time at each station for operators to complete assigned work)

F I G U R E	1 2 . 5

Flow lines can be operation-only, order-picking, assembly, or disassembly lines.

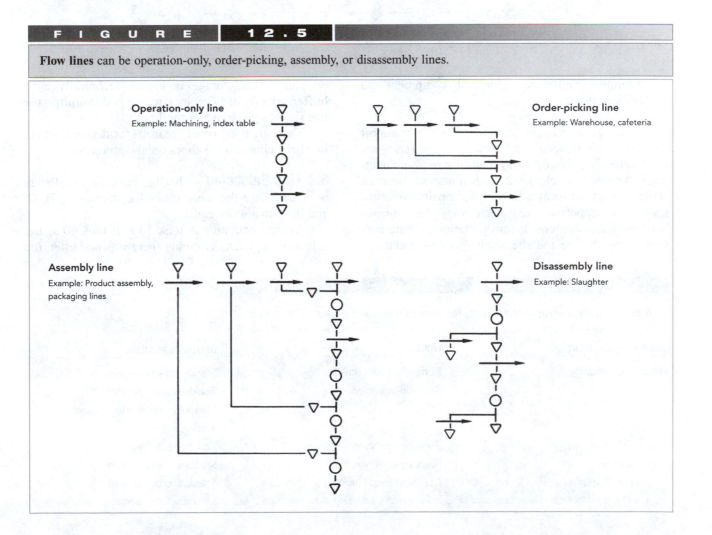

Operation-only line
Example: Machining, index table

Order-picking line
Example: Warehouse, cafeteria

Assembly line
Example: Product assembly, packaging lines

Disassembly line
Example: Slaughter

Flow lines can make a single product continuously, multiple products sequentially in batches, or multiple products simultaneously.

- minimum capital cost (for both equipment and work in process)

Although it may be obvious, (1) the transport between stations need not be by conveyor (carts are one alternative, either pushed manually or as automatically guided vehicles), (2) the transport between stations need not be at a fixed speed or time interval, and, very important, (3) there may be storages between the operations or transportations. There may be a storage before and after each operation and trans-

portation. This storage is known technically as a **buffer,** a bank, or float. Its purpose is **decoupling** the line (isolating stations of the line).

There are two primary reasons for decoupling: (1) line balancing and (2) shocks and disturbances.

6.2 Line Balancing The line balancing challenge occurs because the mean times for stations A, B, C, and so forth are not equal.

Assume operation A took 50 s, B took 40 s, and C took 60 s. Then, assuming there was no buffer, the

Alternatives for conveyor movement, location of work, and posture of operator.

CONVEYOR MOVEMENT	WORK	OPERATOR POSTURE
Moves continuously	Removed from conveyor	Stands/sits in one spot
	Stays on conveyor	Stands/sits in one spot
		Stands/sits on moving system
		Walks
Starts/stops on timer	Stays on conveyor	Stands/sits in one spot
Starts/stops at	Stays on conveyor	Stands/sits in one spot
operator discretion	Removed from conveyor	Stands/sits in one spot

12.2 | *Breaks for Lines*

How are coffee and meal breaks scheduled? A simple alternative is everyone stops at the same time. This tends to give peak loads to the toilets and food service. Some time is available for maintenance.

When you don't want to stop the line with product on the line, give the break to parts of the line in sequence. One example is slaughter lines, where people take their breaks in sequence as the last animal goes down the line. Another example is furniture lines, where there is a varnish-drying oven on the line so the line can't stop with units in the oven. People return to the line in sequence. In addi-

tion to reducing peak loads for toilets and food service, the line is available for quick maintenance.

With both of these alternatives, the line output is zero while the line stops. Another alternative is "tag relief." The line is staffed with extra people who float along the line, replacing people in sequence. This maximizes line output and minimizes peak loads on toilets and food service. However, labor inefficiency occurs as less-practiced people replace experienced people, making it difficult to utilize them fully. In addition, maintenance is difficult.

line would have to index at the speed of the slowest station—called the **bottleneck station,** which is station C. At stations A and B there would be idle time, called **balance-delay time,** the difference between the **cycle time** (time/unit of the line) and the work time at a station. Thus, without buffers, the line speed must be set considering the speed of the slowest station.

Figure 12.7 shows another aspect of the problem of mean times—the variation in the ability of human operators. Typically, performance among operators varies about two to one. The best can produce twice what the worst can. Assuming symmetry and putting the average operator at 100%, the range is from about 67% to 133%. If the line is set at the speed of the average operator, 50% can work faster and 50% cannot keep up. (There is a temptation for those who cannot

keep up to reduce safety and quality.) Thus, the speed at a station (assuming the typical balanced line where work content is equal at each station) cannot be set at the speed of an average (e.g., 1.0) operator; instead it is set at the speed of a slow operator.

Referring to Figure 12.7, if a slow operator is defined as a 90% operator (i.e., 90% of the operators can do the job in the mean cycle time), this is 1.28σ below the mean. Considering the range of performance from 2/3 to 4/3 as 6σ, then $(4/3 - 2/3)/6 = 1/9$. Then $1.28(1/9) = .142$, and $1.0 - 0.142 = .858$ for the station speed. That is, if the station could be set for an average operator instead of a slow operator, then it could be 17% faster (as $[1.0 - .858]/.858 = 1.17$). Therefore, without buffers, the line speed must be set considering both the speed of the slowest station and the mean time of the slow operator on the slow station.

But there is a third problem: Cycle times vary.

6.3 Shocks and Disturbances
Shocks and disturbances make the cycle times vary. Figure 12.8 points out the problem of distribution of operation times. Assume operation C has a mean of 60 s and $\sigma = 4$ s. To include 95% of the times, then station C, and thus the line, would operate at a cycle time of 65.1 s.

The variability of cycle times can occur for many reasons. *First,* consider a station with both an infinite supply of incoming components and perfect removal of the completed unit. There may be a temporary shift in the mean because the operator normally doing operation C is absent and a substitute is doing the job. If the temporary worker took 66 s instead of 60 s, each station on the entire line also would take 66 s, if there were no buffer. Or the time of the regular operator may vary for normal reasons—tools becoming dull, short breakdowns of the machine, operator's stopping to light a cigarette or sneeze, talking to the supervisor, or

F I G U R E	1 2 . 7

Variability in cycle times increases the inefficiency of flow lines. If the pace of individual decoupled workstations and stations arranged in a flow line are the same, the flow line would have to be 17% slower to accommodate the slow operators (slow is defined as a pace 90% of operators can do).

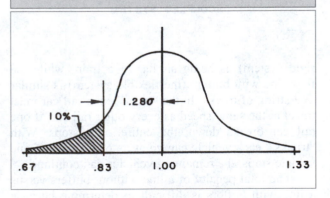

Distribution of times of a specific operator points out that only 50% of the times are average or less. If a paced line is set so that 95% of the cycles are completed before the line indexes, then the cycle time must be slower than average time. If average time = 60 s and σ = 2 s, then the line cycle time (based on this station and assuming normality) would be 60 + 1.64(2) = 63.3 s.

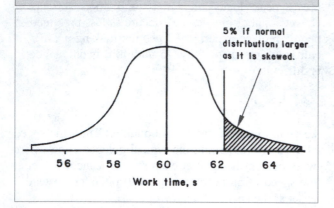

Typical cycle time distributions for unpaced work. Skilled workers have a lower variance and more skew as well as a lower mean. Unpaced time distributions are similar to skilled time distributions; paced time distributions are similar to unskilled time distributions.

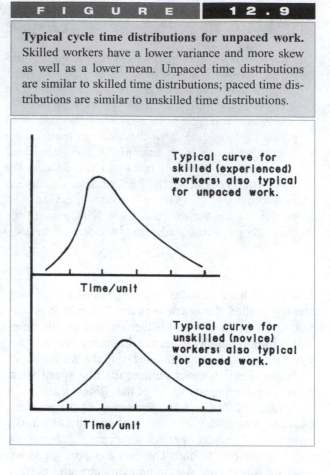

dropping a part. (If the operator is a machine or robot, cycle times still can vary. For example, a machine may fail if the incoming part arrives upside down.)

Figure 12.9 shows typical cycle time distributions for unpaced work (i.e., with sufficient buffers) and paced work (usually work without buffers). The distributions for unpaced work usually are positively skewed (a few long times with a lower absolute minimum time). Paced work has a higher mean time (i.e., pace is slower) and the curve is more symmetrical.

Second, consider the station as part of a line. The station's time can vary because of inadequate supply from the preceding station—**station starvation**—or because the following station is not yet ready to accept a unit—**station blockage.** In addition, there is the problem of what to do with a defective unit (called scrap if it can't be fixed, rework if it can be fixed). After a unit is identified as good, scrap, or rework, the scrap units have to be moved to a temporary storage before disposal. Rework units have to be moved and stored at the rework area. There are two possible locations for rework: by the operator at the workstation or by a rework operator off-line. In general, a rework operator at a rework station works well; the operator does not need to staff the rework station 100% of the time.

Thus, without buffers, the line speed must be set considering: (1) the speed of the slowest station, (2) the mean speed of the slowest operator on the slowest station, and (3) the slowest cycle time of the slowest operator on the slowest station.

Buffers give the flow line flexibility or tolerance. Figure 12.10 shows the flow line without buffers (the

Flow lines without buffers can be symbolized as a train, with initial storage (S) followed by operations (O), that is, S-O-O-O. Flow lines with buffers can be symbolized as trucks, that is, S-O, S-O, S-O.

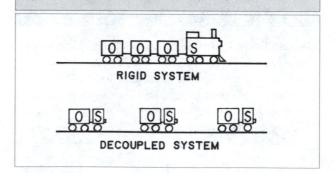

rigid system) as being similar to a train, while the flow line with buffers (the flexible system) is similar to a string of trucks. In the "train," each rail car must travel at the same speed as every other rail car; if one rail car breaks down, the entire train stops. With "trucks," each vehicle can go at its own speed; if one vehicle stops, the remaining vehicles can continue.

The total penalty of a line without buffers versus a line with buffers is difficult to determine because most lines have some buffers. See Box 12.1. However, a U. S. machine-paced auto assembly line (i.e., a line with few or no buffers) usually has a balance-delay time of 8% to 15%. U. S. auto companies also allow an extra relief of 22 min/480 min shift (about 5%) for a machine-paced line (total of 46 min per shift). Thus, U. S. auto companies have a built-in inefficiency of 13% to 20%, ignoring the problem of slowing down the line to the speed of the slowest station.

Toyota has demonstrated that auto lines can be built with buffers. It has a buffer of 3 cars approximately every 10 stations. Each worker has a button that can stop the line if there is a problem such as bad quality. In U. S. auto plants there are no buffers and only a few people are authorized to stop the line (since if the line stops, everybody stops), so they rarely stop the line. For other industries, Kilbridge (1961) gave 5% to 10% as a typical balance-delay percent. Figure 12.11 shows that balance-delay percent usually declines for longer cycle times.

Buxey (1978) reported on a number of lines in Scotland. In case 1 there were 20 stations with a cycle time of 15 s; items/station (i.e., buffer) were 1.5; the balance loss was 20%; and there was an additional loss because cycle time was determined by adding 20% to the time of the work at the most difficult station. Approximately 3% of the items were not completed when they finished the line, and had to be finished at a repair station. In case 2 there were 13 stations with a cycle time of 10 s; items/station were 2; balance loss was 4%. In case 3 there were 15 stations with a cycle time of 1 h; items/station were 2. The balance loss was 6%, but in addition there was a utility operator, resulting in an additional cost of 1/15 = 6.7%.

These figures point out that although the fixed-pace line is a manager, it is an inefficient manager.

6.4 Buffer Design
Although the following emphasizes buffers for *product,* also consider buffers for *supplies/services.* Increasing the buffers for supplies allows operators to focus on production operations

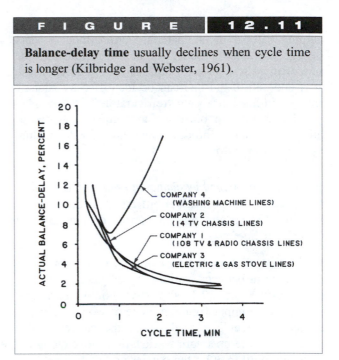

FIGURE 12.11

Balance-delay time usually declines when cycle time is longer (Kilbridge and Webster, 1961).

Source: Reprinted by permission of Kilbridge and Webster, from M. Kilbridge and L. Webster, *Management Science,* Vol. 2, No. 1, 1961. Copyright © 1961, The Institute of Management Sciences.

and decrease potential conflicts between supply and production activities. How about bin size for screws? How long do packaging supplies last before being replenished? Perhaps a larger bin, magazine, or roll can be used. What is the interval between maintenance actions? Can the lubricant reservoir be made larger? Can a longer-lasting lubricant be used? Can the storage area for rejected parts be made larger?

Can the supply/maintenance/inspection activity be made easier (thus increasing the number of parts that can be processed/min) and thus reduce interference between supply/maintenance/inspection time and production time?

Figure 12.12 is a schematic of a workstation. The total workstation is composed of an operator, a machine,

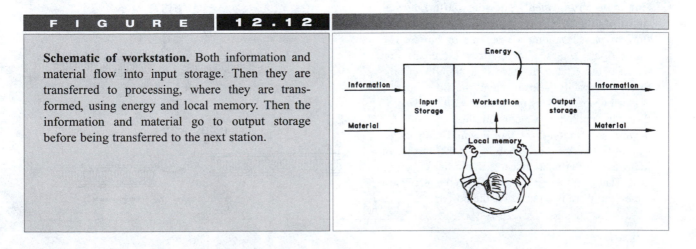

FIGURE 12.12

Schematic of workstation. Both information and material flow into input storage. Then they are transferred to processing, where they are transformed, using energy and local memory. Then the information and material go to output storage before being transferred to the next station.

energy and information input, energy and information output, material input, material output, input product storage, and output product storage. Buffers increase the size of input storage and output storage. Buffers at the start and end of the line can be identified as "stores," whereas in-line buffers are "refrigerators."

There are two buffering techniques: (1) decoupling by changing product flow, and (2) decoupling by moving operators.

6.4.1 Decoupling by changing product flow

There are three subcategories: (1) buffers at or between the stations, (2) buffers due to carrier design, and (3) buffers off-line.

Buffers at or between stations. One possibility for a buffer at or between stations is a physical barrier on a conveyor. Figure 12.13 shows two common arrangements. In the upper figure, a piece of wood, a pipe, or a piece of steel is placed across the conveyor. The pieces from the upstream workstation move along the conveyor until they hit the barrier and stop. The operator lifts them across the barrier, works on them, and puts them back on the conveyor downstream of the dam. Rotary tables (lower figure) can be used to increase the size of the reservoir upstream of the dam. Parts stay on the rotary table and go round and round until they are picked up.

Buffer capacity can be increased by increasing the time the item is available to the operator or increasing the space within the reach of the operator. Increase time by having the operator face upstream. Arm motions are easier forward than backward, and when the object can be seen, timing can be better. If the object must approach from the operator's rear, use a rear-view mirror so the operator need not turn around. Increase space within reach with a rotary table, as in Figure 12.13. A fixed-pace conveyor

with items fixed to the conveyor tends to be a poor design. For a moving assembly, where access time is minimized, the components can be stored on a second conveyor positioned above the assembly conveyor or behind the operator and moving at the speed of the assembly conveyor. Figure 12.14 shows two techniques of putting more items within the operator's reach.

The buffer can be designed for line balancing purposes as well as for shocks and disturbances—that is, the line can be unbalanced. Figure 12.15 shows a schematic pair of stations.

First we will discuss buffer input rate equal to buffer output rate. For example, assume that line output is 10/h or 80/shift of 8 h, and that station A produces 20/h for 4 h and station B produces 10/h for 8 h. During the morning, A sends 10/h to B and puts 10/h into the bank. After 4 h, the bank has 40 units. Then B is fed from the bank at the rate of 10/h while operator A works elsewhere.

Suppose the buffer input rate is not equal to output rate. Assume, for example, that A has a rate of 20/h, B has a rate of 15/h, and desired line rate is 15/h. Then operate B at a rate of 15/h for 8 h. A produces 20/h but for only 6 h. During the 6 h, A sends 15/h to B and puts 5/h into the buffer. At the end of 6 h, the buffer holds 30 units. For the last 2 h of the shift, feed B from the buffer while A works elsewhere. Or, assume A has a rate of 20/h, B a rate of 15/h, and the desired line rate is 20/h. Then operate A for 8 h at 20/h and have B work 8(20/15) = 10.7 h/day. (It may be easier in some cases to have a partial shift or Saturday work than to work 2.7 hours of overtime each day.)

If a machine must be fed at a constant rate, it is more efficient for operators to load a magazine at their own speed and the machine to work from the magazine than for a machine to feed the machine

F I G U R E   12.13

Common arrangements showing buffers at stations. A physical barrier on a conveyor can dam the flow of parts, creating a reservoir or buffer. The lower figure shows a larger reservoir created by using a rotary table. If there is a "flood" and the reservoir capacity is insufficient, the flow must be stopped upstream. This is called *station blocking*. If there are not enough items in the reservoir, the downstream station must shut down. This is called *station starvation*. The variability of the number of items in a buffer is an index of the buffer effectiveness. That is, if there is no variance in the number in the buffer, there is no need for the buffer!

FIGURE 12.14

Put more items in reach. Increase storage space at a
station by using the cube of the space or by making a U
in the line to take advantage of the operator's ability to
turn. Close spacing of items on a conveyor belt and
slow belt speed is preferable to wide spacing with high
speed (since more items are within reach), even though
average rate of arrival is the same.

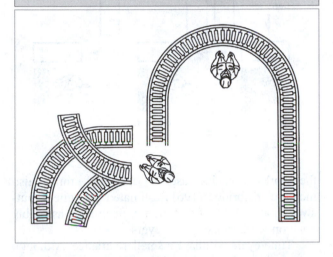

FIGURE 12.15

Use buffers to balance lines and to absorb shocks.
Assume the first station produces 60 units/h for 4 h—
putting 30/h on the line and 30/h into the buffer
(curved portion). Then the first station shuts down. For
the second 4 h of the shift, the second station is fed
from the buffer.

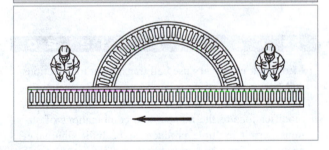

FIGURE 12.16

**Pallets on tracks improve the output buffer by
decoupling.** Pallets decouple the operator from the
material handlers. When the operator completes a pallet, it is pushed into the removal position, a new pallet
is put into position, and work is resumed. Without the
track, the operator must stop work when the pallet is
full until the material handler moves the pallet. This
tends to result in overstaffing of material handlers.

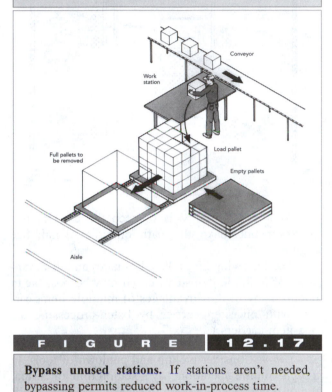

FIGURE 12.17

Bypass unused stations. If stations aren't needed,
bypassing permits reduced work-in-process time.

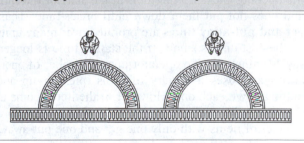

directly. This applies even if the machine cycle time
from the magazine is no faster than the mean operator
feed time (Corlett, 1982). See also Figure 12.16.

The concept so far has been to maximize time a
unit is available to a station. Some items may not have
to stop at each station; then a technique is needed that
bypasses unwanted stations. Figure 12.17 shows the
general concept. Figure 12.18 shows this idea applied
to cafeterias, where the product is the human customers and the stations are the salads, desserts,
drinks, and so forth.

Buffers due to carrier design. Items often are
moved between workstations by carriers. The **carrier**
can be a pan, box, pallet, index table, hook, or cart. If
the carrier can be removed from the line, the effect
might be that of a buffer. Transport between stations
can be with wheeled carts pushed by hand. Heavy
items (such as with tractor assembly or mounting jet
engines to aircraft) can be pushed if they are on air-
film pallets. If power is desired, it can be from
overhead (power and free conveyor) or below (a towline). See Figure 12.19.

Scramble-system cafeterias assume customers will stop at only a fraction of the available service areas. Since the goal is to minimize the customer's waiting, the system permits customers to skip stations at which no service is desired.

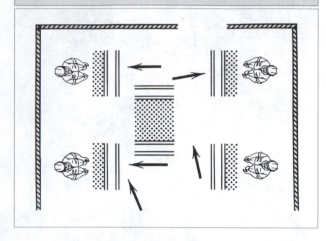

Remove a carrier from the line's path to aid buffer creation. The carrier can be completely mobile (e.g., hand cart, air pallet) or normally connected to a power source but able to be disconnected (power and free conveyor, towline).

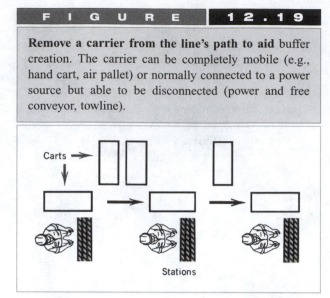

the workstation increase, so the "do" times also increase. Kilbridge (1961) estimated get time + put-away time as 13% of do time for electronics assembly done on worker-paced conveyors.

Time/cycle will have a smaller variance. Although a carrier with 4 units probably will have approximately 4 times the mean do time of carriers with 1 unit, the variance of the longer cycle time probably will be less than the variance of the 4 short times, because long- and short-unit processing times may cancel each other in the multiple-item cycle time.

Multiple items/carrier encourage use of both hands since 2 units can be worked on at the same time. When using multiple items/carrier, make N an even number.

Another possibility is to keep the carrier on a conveyor but make the path omnidirectional. See Figure 12.20.

The following gives the advantages and disadvantages of multiple items/carrier. (It may be possible to obtain many of the advantages of multiple items/carrier with one item/carrier by batch-processing the one-item carriers.)

1. *Labor.* Consider pickup and putdown of tools. In a high-volume operation, say a station time of .1 min, the operator picks up the tools at the start of the shift and does not put them down until break time. Thus, **get and put-away times** are prorated over many units so the cost/unit is small. If the station time is longer, say 1.0 min, then the operator does a number of operations and uses a variety of tools, picking up and putting down each one. However, if the items come in a carrier with multiple items, the operator can do a number of items with only one get and one put-away.

$$TTIME = (GTIME + PATIME)/N$$

where

$TTIME$ = Transport time/unit

$GTIME$ = Get time/unit

$PATIME$ = Put-away time/unit

N = Number of units

Assume that $GTIME + PATIME = X$. Then, for $N = 1$, $TTIME = X$; for $N = 2$, $TTIME = .5X$; for $N = 4$, $TTIME = .25X$; for $N = 8$, $TTIME = .125X$. The point of diminishing returns comes fairly rapidly. In addition, as N increases, the reach and move distances in

Multipath conveyors use ball transfers at intersections and horizontal gravity roller conveyors for accumulators. Take-away is by powered rollers. Quick modifications to the number and combinations of stations permit multiple products to be built simultaneously. It is a cart system but with conveyors.

Multiple items/carrier may restrict access to individual units on the carrier. For humans, this may just mean more time. For robots and machines, however, the restricted access may make the operation not feasible or the device very expensive.

2. *Material handling.* Multiple units/carrier give more units/foot of the line. For a specified distance, multiple units/carrier give more buffer. For a specified buffer size, the buffer will fit into a shorter distance for multiple units/carrier.

Multiple units/carrier require heavier carriers. The carrier will be harder to push, pull, and lift—although fewer carriers will be moved. Motors rather than muscles may be required for the heavier carriers.

Disposal of rejected units is more difficult for multiple units/carrier. If the defective unit remains on the carrier, take care that additional work is not done on it; be sure it does not get included with good units. The defect also fills up buffer space. If the defect is removed from the carrier, empty space moves down the line. In addition, a carrier and means of transport must be provided to move the rejects to the rework station or the scrap pile.

3. *Equipment costs.* Carrier cost/unit usually is less when there are multiple units/carrier. The cost/carrier is higher but fewer carriers are required. For example, 1 carrier holding 8 units might cost $200 while 1 carrier holding 1 unit might cost $40.

Automatic processing of units is more difficult with multiple items/carrier. One possibility is to use duplicate heads on one machine so that all units on the carrier are done simultaneously; another possibility is to do the units in sequence by indexing either the carrier or the head. However, unless this station is the bottleneck station, the extra heads or indexing equipment may be just extra capital expense, since one head may have sufficient capacity. If a robot is used, it may have to be a more expensive robot.

Buffers off-line. On-line buffers (or those in-line) can handle minor disturbances. Major shocks (e.g., machine breakdowns, employee absenteeism, learners) and line-balancing problems may benefit from **off-line buffers.** Off-line buffers can be remote either in time or in space.

Additional time to compensate for a disturbance can be obtained by overtime work, partial shifts, and working holidays on the existing equipment. For example, assume the buffer size between stations = 1 h. Then, for any shock of less than 1 h (e.g., short machine breakdown, small difference in production between a learner and an experienced worker), fill up the buffer again by having the worker work extra time at the end of the shift.

Additional space for an off-line buffer can be made several ways. Figure 12.21 shows an off-line

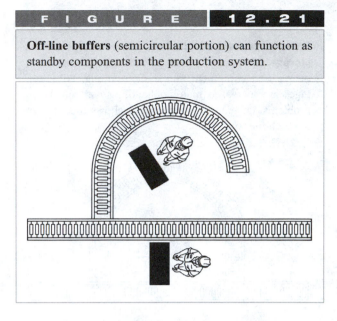

Off-line buffers (semicircular portion) can function as standby components in the production system.

buffer, a semicircular conveyor. In this situation the buffer acts as a standby circuit. A standby circuit analysis considers the device (in this case, the conveyor with units on it), the device that detects circuit failure (the operator), the switch that activates the standby system (the operator), and the reliability of the standby device (how good the units on the semicircular conveyor are). Naturally the off-line buffer does not have to be conveyorized. It simply may be items stored on a cart or pallet, either close to the workstation or perhaps several hundred feet away.

Off-line buffers can include processing as well as storage. See Figure 12.22. For example, assume station B was able to produce only 15 units/h when the line rate was 20 units/h. Then a duplicate of station B could be built (5 or 500 ft from the line) and operated the number of hours necessary to obtain the extra units. This technique is most useful when the capital cost of an additional workstation is relatively low. If the line is "one-sided," the buffer station can be built opposite the primary station (A station). This "B" station would have flow from right to left (assuming "A" station flows left to right). Having a B station for each A station gives a great deal of flexibility to line output rate. The extra workstation can be used for training purposes, or to use idle time of a worker on another job with a large machine-time component, or to use idle time of a worker whose primary job does not require 8 h/day. Another possibility is for workers being rehabilitated; they could work for (say) 2 h/day for the first week, 4 h/day for the second week, 6 h/day for the third week, and so on.

So far we have decoupled by moving the product. There is another alternative (often overlooked): move the operator.

FIGURE   12.22

Standby systems can include processing as well as storage. The main advantages are better utilization of people and equipment and easier training. Disadvantages are increased material handling and scheduling problems. (A gate in the conveyor allows the operator to reach the workstation.)

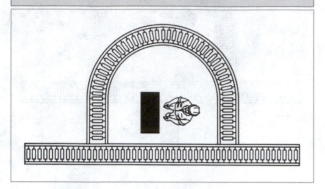

6.4.2 Decoupling by moving operators
There are four subcategories: (1) utility operator, (2) help your neighbor, (3) *n* operators float among *n* stations, and (4) *n* operators float among more than *n* stations.

Utility operator. Figure 12.23 shows the utility operator approach. In this concept, most of the operators work at specific workstations. However, one operator is a **utility operator,** or relief operator. The utility operator's assignment is to help the individual operators if they have trouble for a few minutes, if they want to go to the toilet, and so forth. In the U. S. auto industry, for example, a common situation is 1 relief worker for every 6 stations; that is, 7 people work at 6 stations with 1 always being off. The line

FIGURE   12.23

Utility operator approach. Relief operators move from station to station while the station operators all stay at their own stations. The utility operator must know all the jobs and so frequently becomes the trainer. In many cases, the utility operator is given minor management responsibility and is called a group leader or working supervisor.

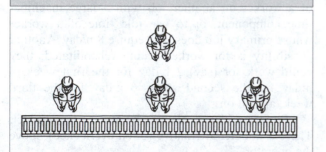

doesn't stop for breaks. (However, if capacity is greater than demand, it may be worthwhile to eliminate the "tag relief" system and stop the line during breaks, saving money. Chrysler has used this strategy.) In other industries, the utility operator does not have formal times assigned to relieve specific operators but just helps out when and where needed.

The duties of this operator vary widely; additional work is needed when there is no line worker taking a break. In these situations, the utility operator often is called a group leader (working supervisor); responsibilities include training new employees and making minor decisions (if the supervisor is absent) in addition to working at the various stations. Minor maintenance work or product rework are other duties.

Help your neighbor. Figure 12.24 shows the **help-your-neighbor** approach. Each operator, by management directive, is "your brother's keeper." That is, you help your neighbor not because you are a good person but because it is part of your job responsibility. If management does not formally require operators to help each other, those helping may feel that they are "suckers." If a fellow worker gets behind, this is not a reason for everyone else to take a break until the person catches up. One approach is to divide the work at a station into thirds. The middle third is the sole responsibility of the station operator, the first third is entitled to help from the upstream operator, and the last third is entitled to help from the downstream operator.

***n* operators float among *n* workstations.** Figure 12.25 shows the *n* operators float among *n* workstations approach. Stations are not given specific times/unit; instead, the operators are just told the total time for the entire unit. For example, instead of saying that each of the 5 stations has 1.0 min of work/unit, the operators are told there is a total of 5 min of work. It is the operators' decision as to which operator does what job at what rate. The operators move upstream and downstream as they desire, and the operators decide when to switch jobs. This type of line management tends to be efficient since

FIGURE   12.24

Help your neighbor. Shared responsibility extends both directions from each operator.

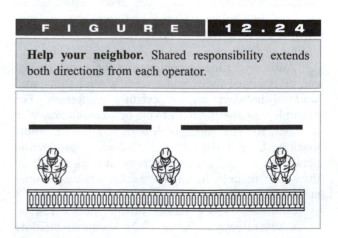

F I G U R E   12.25

Full-float design. *n* operators float among *n* stations is the full-float design.

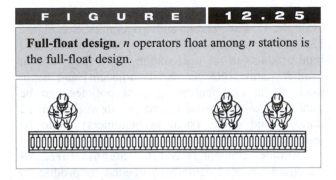

F I G U R E   12.26

Paired stations of semiautomatic machines are a version of *n* operators among more than *n* stations. The two stations for an operator can be identical (see 1A and 1B) or different (see 2 and 3). The machine can either run automatically while the operator loads/unloads the other station, or can load/unload automatically while the operator processes. Thus operator utilization is high while machine utilization is low. Naturally there need not be a conveyor since material handling could be by cart or hand.

it minimizes buffer problems (if a buffer = 0, the operator moves to another station); group pressure to produce is high; the line runs at the average speed of the group (rather than the speed of the slowest member); everyone tends to be able to do every job (so absences and illness are less of a problem); and, since the line need not be balanced, there is no balance-delay time.

***n* operators float among more than *n* stations.** Figures 12.26 and 12.27 show two examples of the approach in which *n* operators float over more than *n* stations. Supervisors assign operators to the station as a whole instead of to individual workstations. Operators move from station to station as the need arises. Thus, the station need not be balanced. The rationale of **more places than people** is the minimization of the total cost of the system.

In the United States, labor costs tend to be higher than capital costs. Labor costs of $10/h become, after 20% fringe costs, costs of $12/h. At 1,800 h/year, this

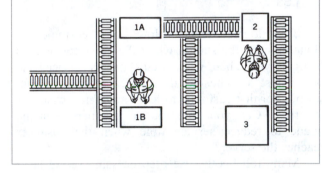

means that minimum labor cost for a single shift is $21,600/yr. For a double shift, minimum cost is $43,200/yr. But many factory workers cost $15 or $20/h or even more.

But a workstation may be just a bench, a chair, a few bins, and some power handtools—costing a total of perhaps $5,000. Assuming that it lasts 3 years and

F I G U R E   12.27

One-worker line using a U shape to cut worker walking. Since the final test was done upon completion of each unit, the worker got quick feedback on quality, so quality problems were reduced drastically (Gargano and Stewart, 1975). The wheeled carts hold a complete period's (day or week, depending on the unit) supply of parts. The next two periods' supply is on the second and third shelves, which helps keep an inventory count and pinpoint supply problems.

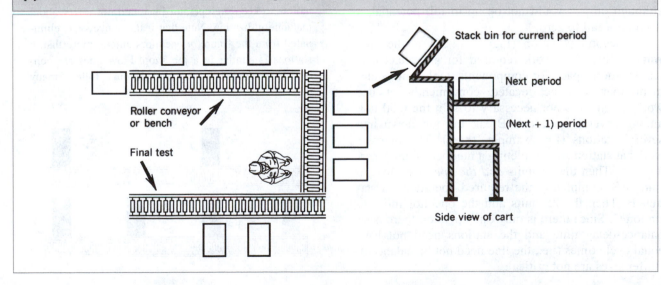

has a scrap value of $2,000, annual cost is only (5000 − 2000)/3 = $1,000/yr. Thus, it is far more important to keep the expensive labor busy than the cheap workstation busy.

Another example of "more places than people" is a queue-server such as a drive-in or a cafeteria checkout. Two alternatives (where C = Customer and S = Server) are:

```
C        C        C
C        C        C
C        C  [S]   C
[S]
```

The double queue allows one customer to "load/unload" the station while the other customer is being served. Then, when a customer is serviced, the server just switches to the next customer, without waiting for that customer to leave and a new customer to arrive. Can you "preprocess" the person in the queue to reduce service time when the customer reaches the server?

Many toll booths use preprocessing (a tag hung on the car deducts toll fees automatically as the vehicle is driven past the toll booth). Airlines can use customer identity cards to reduce processing time at airports. Disney has a "Fast Pass" to reduce queue waiting time. You insert your pass into a reader and it prints out a pass assigning a time window during which the guest can return and enter an express queue, with little or no wait. The next time you visit a Disney facility, notice how queues are handled.

Figure 12.26 shows the **paired station** approach. Two stations are built (if they are identical, it is called double tooling); the operator goes back and forth between the two. This approach is quite useful when the operator has a large idle time due to machine time. This also makes the line more reliable, because if one machine fails, the other still can work, and although output would not be up to full potential, it would not fall to zero.

A second variation (Figure 12.27) is the **one-worker line.** The work required for a product may require more space for components, tools, and equipment than can be located conveniently at one workstation. It is not necessary to split the total task among several operators. Break the job down into several stations (for example, three). The operator works at station A, completing a number of units, perhaps 25. Then the 25 units *and the operator* move to station B, completing the required operations at station B. Then the 25 units and the operator move to station C. Since there is only one operator, there is no balance-delay time and the stations need not have equal cycle times (i.e., the line need not be balanced). Buffer sizes are not critical.

Another version is a single-product line with, for example, 12 workstations and 4 operators. See Figure 12.28. The workers work at a specific station and send products to the next station. Then they walk to another station (not necessarily adjacent) and begin work again. Different assignment policies can be used. For example, some operators can work at all 12 stations, and others (such as beginners) might be restricted to just a few.

Another concept is **cellular manufacture.** All the machines and equipment needed to produce a product are grouped in a cell. For example, three operators might run 10 machines. Operators switch among machines as needed. The goal is maximum use of the expensive cost component, human labor. Note that since the operators are surrounded by machines, they may be exposed to high noise levels. Cellular layout advantages include scheduling flexibility and job rotation (and thus less cumulative trauma). A disadvantage is the need for more skilled employees. See "Non-progressive assembly" in Section 3 of this chapter.

Another version is multiple lines, each set up for a single product (say line A for product A, line B for product B, line C for product C). The workers might work on line A on Monday, line B on Tuesday and Wednesday, line C on Thursday morning, and then line A for the rest of the week.

A furnace manufacturer had 9 lines for assembly of 171 models. Teams of 2 roved from one line to another, doing complete assembly of a given model. Meanwhile the setup operator converted a line for the next batch of another model. Each team specialized in a range of models, and so the members didn't have to

FIGURE   12.28

More places than people is a different way of saying *n* operators among more than *n* workstations. The rationale is to keep the operator busy and not worry about machine utilization. Note that if the conveyor is eliminated from the figure, *n* operators among more than *n* stations is similar to a job shop. Flow lines are concepts; material handling and layouts follow many patterns.

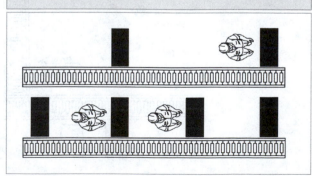

know all 171 models. If there was a shortage of components for any line, workers simply shifted to another line until the supply was sufficient. Production scheduling was flexible. This flexibility is useful when there is insufficient demand for just one product for an entire year. Although equipment is duplicated, setup and put-away costs are minimized; maintenance can be done during normal working hours instead of at premium pay hours.

The "more places than people" concept is very useful for short runs and operators who are learning.

Letting the worker walk requires walking time, which must be added to the work time. The MTM predetermined time system (see Chapter 29) allocates 5.3 TMU/foot (.2 s). Thus, walking 10 ft requires 2 s. If 10 ft were required for every 20 units, add 2/20 = 0.1 s/unit. From a physiological and comfort viewpoint, standing with occasional walking reduces venous pooling in the legs and is less fatiguing than standing without walking.

7 MAKE SEVERAL IDENTICAL ITEMS AT THE SAME TIME

Tasks can be broken into three stages: (1) **get ready,** (2) **do,** and (3) **put away.** Reduce cost/unit by prorating the get-ready and put-away stages over more units. Manufacturing similar parts in sequence (parts families) reduces setup time by minimizing the number of changes necessary. Items may differ only at a later stage: B is blue, C is green, and D is red; or B has 1 hole, C has 2, and D has 3. Decrease lead time and increase lot sizes by making the early operations as item A (unpainted part or part without holes). Then, for item B, pull item A from stock and finish.

7.1 Assembly Example

In the assembly example, the tradeoff is the physical work in doing versus physical work in get ready + put away. The example could apply to driving nuts on a bolt, putting pickles on hamburgers, or marking cans in a store, but the example in Table 12.6 is for soldering.

Trade off prorating the pickup and putdown over more units versus the increased distances moved during the *do* portion of the cycle. (See the comments about multiple items/carrier in Guideline 6.) Distances moved increase because of the larger workstation. In general, it takes less time to move a greater distance than to have additional reaches and grasps during the pickup and additional move-asides and releases during the *put away.* As the size of the workstation increases, there is a tendency to begin moving the product instead of the worker; this mechanized handling and increased worker specialization lead to the assembly line.

7.2 Inspection Example

The inspection example trades off mental work during do versus get ready + put away. In Table 12.6, the inspector must inspect n items for m characteristics (see Figure 12.29). The *get ready* is the mental work of fixing in the mind the quality standard for the characteristic m. The *do* is the sensing of the object, comparing it with the mental standard, making a decision, and executing the decision. The *put away* is the mental transfer of the quality standard from working memory to long-term memory. Examples could be a potato inspector looking for mold, eyes, or cuts (symbolized by circles, squares, and triangles in Figure 12.29); it could be a machine shop inspector inspecting for surface finish, concentricity, and length; or it could be a secretary looking for misspelled words, punctuation mistakes, and tense mistakes in a letter.

One item at a time requires less physical handling of items but considerable mental manipulation of characteristics. One characteristic at a time (less mental work but more physical work) ensures that a characteristic is not omitted, that the mental standard is more consistent, and that there is less halo effect of one characteristic on another characteristic. In the extreme it may cause boredom.

Konz and Osman (1977) had 24 women inspect numbers on slides. For one item at a time, they made 16% errors for defect A and 9% for defect B; for one characteristic at a time, they made 5% for defect A and 7% for defect B. Effectively all the errors were type 2 errors. See Figure 12.30 for an explanation of type 1 and 2 errors. Total inspection time was held constant. Su and Konz (1981) found that, if inspection is easy, there is no difference in accuracy between inspection for one or multiple characteristics at a time but a considerable time penalty for one characteristic at a time. If the inspection is difficult, there is a tradeoff needed, as one characteristic at a time gives fewer errors but an increase in time.

8 COMBINE OPERATIONS AND FUNCTIONS

Do several steps at the same time by using **multifunction** materials and equipment rather than single-function materials and equipment. Material cost/unit will be lower. Labor cost/unit will be reduced. Capital cost/unit generally will be higher. Total cost will be lower since material and labor cost/unit generally are more important than capital cost/unit.

8.1 Multi-Function Materials

Use a compound that waxes at the same time it cleans. Use a water-pump lubricant that also has a rust inhibitor. Although

T A B L E   1 2 . 6

Soldering example. Items can be assembled two ways, the one-item-at-a-time method or the multiple-unit method. Items can be inspected one item or one characteristic at a time. See Figure 12.29.

ONE-ITEM-AT-A-TIME METHOD (ASSEMBLY)	TIME, SEC		MULTIPLE-UNIT METHOD	TIME, SEC
Get soldering iron	3		Get soldering iron	3
			Solder diode on unit 1	5
Solder diode on unit 1		5	Move iron to unit 2	1
Put iron away	2		Solder diode on unit 2	5
			Move iron to unit 3	1
Additional work		X	Solder diode on unit 3	5
			Put iron away	2
Get soldering iron	3			
Solder diode on unit 2		5	Additional work	3X
Put iron away	2			
Additional work		X		
Get soldering iron	3			
Solder diode to unit 3		5		
Put iron away	2			
Additional work	X	X		
Soldering time/unit = 15/3 + 15/3			Soldering time/unit = 5/3 + 17/3	
= 5 + 5 = 10			= 1.7 + 5.7	
			= 7.4	

ONE-ITEM-AT-A-TIME METHOD (INSPECTION)	ONE-CHARACTERISTIC-AT-A-TIME METHOD
Recall standards for circles	Recall standard for circles
Inspect for circles on unit 1	Inspect for circles on unit 1
Dispose of standard for circles	Aside unit 1
	Get unit 2
Recall standard for triangles	Inspect for circles on unit 2
Inspect for triangles on unit 1	Aside unit 2
Dispose of standard for triangles	Get unit 3
	Inspect for circles on unit 3
Recall standard for squares	Aside unit 3
Inspect for squares on unit 1	Dispose of standard for circles
Dispose of standard for squares	Recall standard for squares
Etc.	Etc.

the basic chemicals will cost the same whether they are bought together or separately, the manufacturing and distribution costs will be reduced since one container is used instead of two, material handling will be less for one container than two, and stocking expense on the store shelf will be lower for one container. Labor cost will be lower and quality may be better since, if the two compounds were bought separately, one might not be used. Henry Ford had supplies delivered in special wooden boxes; the boxes became part of the Model T floor.

Paperwork can fill multiple functions. For example, on your monthly utility bill, the computer prints the address as well as the name so that the invoice can be used with a window envelope. The invoice also serves as a change-of-address form, which saves the user from writing a letter and using a stamp; the company saves by reducing processing time; and errors are reduced because the users do not have to transmit their names or account numbers since they are on the invoice.

Another example of multiple function paperwork is a magnetically coded identification card that acts also as a key, or as a meal ticket. A parking permit may have two possible expiration dates. If it expires at the end of the shorter date, cut off a corner; if it expires at the end of the longer date, don't cut off the

Two inspection strategies can be used. One item at a time (upper figure) is faster, but one characteristic at a time (lower figure) probably gives better quality.

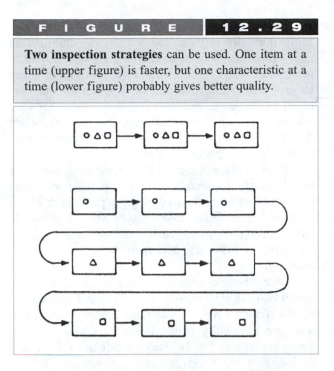

Type 1 and 2 errors. Inspection devices sort good and bad items into two categories. However, they are not perfect. Rejecting good material as bad is called a **type 1** risk, α risk, or producer's risk. Accepting bad material as good is called a **type 2** risk, β risk, or consumer's risk. Remember which is which by remembering that 1 comes before 2 and α comes before β; that is, 1 and α are on the left, and 2 and β are on the right.

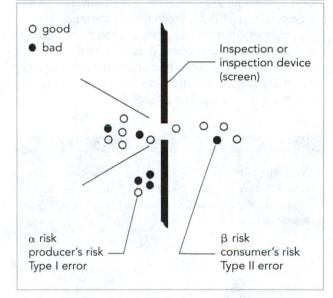

corner. Thus, the shape of the permit identifies the expiration date. A farmer can use a fertilizer that adds nitrogen and trace compounds and can plant two crops (each with a different growth time) at the same time.

8.2 Multi-Function Tools

A multi-function tool is used to combine operations. Farmers can fertilize at the same time they plow. In the home, one compressor can cool both a refrigerator and a freezer. In the factory, a special-purpose drill can drill and countersink at one stroke; a special-purpose drill press can drill several holes at one stroke just as a multiple die can punch several holes at one stroke; a lathe tool can form as well as cut off; a fork truck can lift and move. In the office, a ruler can be used as a straightedge as well as a measuring device.

9 VARY ENVIRONMENTAL STIMULATION INVERSELY WITH TASK STIMULATION

Tasks are divided into low and high stimulation.

9.1 Low-Stimulation Tasks

See Chapter 21 for more on this topic. Many industrial tasks are quite automatic for the operator and require little conscious attention. Some even require little physical movement. Some examples of this minimum of mental attention and minimum of physical movement are inspecting items on a moving conveyor, monitoring an automatic pilot in an airplane, watching a chemical process indicator board, and monitoring a radar screen. If the

person is seated rather than walking, if the environmental temperature, humidity, lighting, noise, and air velocity all are controlled at a constant level, the brain has minimum **task stimulation.** Performance (measured, for example, as percent of defective units noticed) declines as the brain "goes to sleep" for periods of 1 to 20 s—even longer in some cases! (See the vigilance literature for more on this topic.) Operators strongly dislike this type of work situation—solitary confinement is the most feared of punishments. Variety is not the spice of life; it is the very essence.

Cure by adding stimulation to either the task or the environment.

9.1.1 *Add physical movement to the task*

For example, have the night security guard walk around as well as monitor a TV screen. Eliminate automatic equipment and replace it with something requiring operator movement and attention. Have inspectors dispose of rejects as well as indicate that they are rejects. Machine-paced tasks result in very poor quality if the products can pass the station while the operator is "asleep." If machine pacing must be used (and usually it need not be), the operator should be required to make a conscious act to pass an item rather than make a conscious act to reject an item.

9.1.2 *Add stimulation to the environment* The easiest **environmental stimulation** solution is to let operators talk to each other. There is little reason not to arrange workstations so that workers with low-stimulation tasks are permitted to talk. Figure 12.31 shows seven schematic arrangements in order of our judgment of their stimulation (socialization) value. More stimulation occurs when people are face to face—they are close, there are no barriers, and noise is less. Reducing noise and encouraging visual and auditory contact also improves communication, which is especially useful for feedback on work quality.

Another common example of external stimulation is the use of background music, which should be stimulating but not too stimulating (no vocals, played only a fraction of the time, neither "soft strings" nor "big brass"). It should be a "soft fog."

F I G U R E	1 2 . 3 1

Vary the stimulation by adjusting orientation in relation to other people, by changing distance, and by using barriers such as equipment between stations. The lowest stimulation situation is 7.

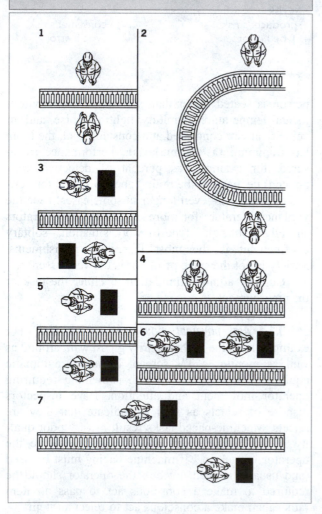

Windows (see Box 23.2) also furnish stimulation. Light normally is furnished by electric illumination and ventilation by fans, so keep the windows small to minimize energy losses. The upper portions of many large windows are covered with venetian blinds, curtains, or shades to reduce glare, indicating that they are too large for their actual function. The important design feature is to have a view of the horizon with perhaps a 20° view of the ground.

Paint walls a variety of appropriate colors, not just "industrial green." In large open office areas (e.g., holding more than 10 people), paint each of the four walls a different color; use artwork. Color-code stock racks, bins, pipes, chairs, and tables to establish "ownership" (territory) and identify function as well as add variety.

When people cannot see each other, increase visual contact with mirrors or even closed-circuit TV. Audio contact with two-way radios helps keep people who are physically isolated (such as guards) from being socially isolated. Truckers can use CB radios. Police, fork truck drivers, and salespeople can use two-way radios and cell phones.

It may be possible to increase socialization during time not at the workstation (e.g., on breaks, while getting/disposing supplies, during contacts with maintenance or supervision). Is there a pleasant eating/break area with opportunities for conversation? See Box 12.3.

In general, the stimulation should not be expected to improve productivity over what a fresh person could do but just to reduce the decrement in performance.

9.2 High-Stimulation Tasks Many of the non-routine tasks that require concentration are office tasks. Over half of the U. S. working population works in an office. However, even engineering design, calculations, and detailed inspection rarely require complete freedom from environmental stimulation. Konz (1964) demonstrated that background music had no effect on output or errors for a repetitive clerical task (mark sensing numbers), output or errors of hand addition of numbers, or output on a creative mental task (anagrams). Workers may occasionally need freedom from high-information-content noise (conversation or vocal music); so it may be best to have two workstations—their usual one and one for concentration (a "think tank"). It could be created by just closing a door or by using an entirely separate enclosed area. Auditory privacy can be obtained by physical enclosure but also by masking the high-information-content noise with low-information- content noise such as air ventilation noise or background music.

Evaluations of "office landscape" arrangements have indicated that auditory privacy, although necessary, is not sufficient. Visual privacy is needed also.

12.3   *Break/Rest Area Design to Improve Socialization*

The area should have good aesthetics. Consider windows with a view, carpet on the floor, good noise control (at least enough to permit easy conversation), artwork on the walls, indirect lighting, warm-white instead of cool-white fluorescent lamps, uneven ceiling fixture spacing (giving more uneven illumination), wood chairs and tables (instead of plastic), upholstered chairs, glass plates and tumblers (instead of plastic), and artificial flowers on the tables (changed periodically).

The tables should be a mixture of sizes and shapes. Circular tables accommodate both even- and odd-number groups and encourage eye contact and conversation. Long rectangular tables discourage eye contact and conversation. Tables should be the pedestal type and should be easily movable. Chairs should be easily moved.

Have a bulletin board for personal notices.

In addition to vending machines, consider a sink with water, a microwave, a coffee pot, and a refrigerator.

The important thing about visual privacy seems to be to obscure the face. To that end, use a barrier from .6 to 1.6 m above the floor. In general, orient chairs at workstations so the workers' eyes do not meet the eyes of passersby.

Many employees are perfectly willing to be distracted and will talk at length about sports, sex, politics, or the weather. If work standards are vague (as in most offices), and if conversation interferes with their work or the work of others, discourage excess conversation with desk or machine orientation (side by side rather than face to face, not facing open doors) or with head-high barriers.

Review Questions

1. How does labor specialization affect quantity of output, quality of output, and unit cost/h?
2. Assuming a job has N elements, what is the difference between progressive and non-progressive assembly?
3. What is balance-delay time?
4. Discuss how the slowest operator slows down a balanced line.
5. What is the difference between scrap and rework?
6. Assuming the arrival rate is the same, why are close spacing and a slow conveyor belt speed preferable to wide spacing and a high belt speed?
7. Briefly describe the group technology concept.
8. Using numbers, discuss the cost of labor and the cost of a workstation.
9. Using a sketch, discuss a double queue for a single server.
10. Discuss design of a break area to improve socialization.
11. Discuss the rationale of just-in-time.
12. What is the rationale of making several identical items at the same time? Discuss in relation to making hamburgers, citing *get ready, do,* and *put away.*

References

Black, J. Cellular manufacturing systems reduce setup time, make small lot production economical. *Industrial Engineering,* Vol. 15, 11, 36–48, Nov. 1983.

Buxey, G. Incompletion costs versus labor efficiency on the fixed-item moving belt flow. *Int. J. of Production Research,* Vol. 16, No. 3, 233–47, 1978.

Cochran, D. and Swinehart, K. The total source error of adjustment model: A methodology for the elimination of setup and process adjustment. *Int. J. of Production Research,* Vol. 29, 7, 1423–35, 1991.

Corlett, N. Design of handtools, machines, and workplaces. In *Handbook of Industrial Engineering,* Salvendy, G. (ed.). New York: Wiley & Sons, 1982.

Gargano, H. and Stewart, F. Material handling system is key to efficient assembly operation. *Material Handling Engineering,* Vol. 30, No. 4, 53–55, April, 1975.

Ghosh, S. and Gagnon, R. A comprehensive literature review and analysis of the design, balancing and scheduling of assembly systems. *Int. J. of Production Research,* Vol. 27, No. 4, 637–70, 1989.

Hanna, S. and Konz, S. *Facility Design: Manufacturing Engineering,* 3rd ed. Scottsdale, AZ: Holcomb Hathaway, 2004.

Hansen, D. and Taylor, S. Optimal production strategies for identical production lines with minimum operable production rates. *IIE Transactions,* Vol. 14, No. 4, 288–95, December 1982.

Jenkins, S. and Rickards, J. The economics of ergonomics: Three workplace design case studies. In *Applied Ergonomics,* Alexander, D. and Rabourn, R. (eds.), 239–43. London: Taylor and Francis, 2001.

Kilbridge, M. Non-productive work as a factor in the economic division of labor. *J. of Industrial Engineering,* Vol. 12, No. 3, 155–59, 1961.

Kilbridge, M. and Webster, L. The balance delay problem. *Management Science,* Vol. 2, No. 1, 69–84, 1961.

Konz, S. The effect of background music on productivity of four tasks. Ph.D. dissertation, Urbana: University of Illinois, 1964.

Konz, S. and Osman, K. Team efficiencies of a paced visual inspection task. *J. of Human Ergology* (Japan), Vol. 6, 111–19, 1977.

Krumwiede, D., Konz, S., and Hinnen, P. Standing comfort on floor mats. *Occupational Ergonomics,* Vol. 1, 2, 135–43, 1998.

Oxenburgh, M. *Increasing Productivity and Profit through Health and Safety.* Chicago: CCH, 1991.

Su, J. and Konz, S. Evaluation of three methods for inspection of multiple defects/item. *Proceedings of 25th Annual Meeting of the Human Factors Society,* Rochester, NY, 1981.

WORKSTATION DESIGN

13

Overview

This chapter gives 14 guidelines concerning the physical design of the workstation. The emphasis is on repetitive work.

Key Concepts

acceleration/deceleration

area of vision

bit

coefficient of friction

damaging wrist motions

dominant hand/eye

eye focus/eye travel

Fitts' law

gravity as a fixture

heel strike

human power

line of sight

movement angles

normal work area

optimum work height

physiological cost versus
    organizational cost

Power Zone

seating posture
    variability

slip

static load

stepping-on-air

three-contact rule

trip

weight penalty

WORKSTATION DESIGN

1 Avoid Static Loads and Fixed Work Postures

2 Reduce Musculoskeletal Disorders

3 Set the Work Height at 50 mm Below the Elbow

4 Furnish Every Employee with an Adjustable Chair

5 Use the Feet as Well as the Hands

6 Use Gravity; Don't Oppose It

7 Conserve Momentum

8 Use Two-Hand Motions Rather Than One-Hand Motions

9 Use Parallel Motions for Eye Control of Two-Hand Motions

10 Use Rowing Motions for Two-Hand Motions

11 Pivot Motions About the Elbow

12 Use the Preferred Hand

13 Keep Arm Motions in the Normal Work Area

14 Let the Small Person Reach; Let the Large Person Fit

Ergonomic design should consider four aspects:

1. Product/equipment
2. Job aids
3. User selection
4. Training of user.

The sections on ergonomic guidelines and work environments consider many aspects of design of the product and workstation.

Job aids include workstation aids (e.g., chairs, footsupports, positioners, balancers), material-handling aids, handtools, controls and displays, lighting aids (e.g., task lights, glare shields), climate aids (e.g., fans, heaters), and protective clothing aids (e.g., gloves, aprons, glasses). Selection of workers is less popular now as a result of discrimination charges. However, this has put a greater burden on training.

▮▮ AVOID STATIC LOADS AND FIXED WORK POSTURES

In the following discussion, the cardiovascular effects of static loading from posture will be discussed. The biomechanical effects of torques about the spine (from the body and from objects) are discussed in Chapter 15.

Static (isometric) **load** (from low variability in postures and movements) is bad for the blood supply of a specific muscle as well as the total body.

Static loading is divided into (1) standing, (2) falls, (3) sitting, (4) head/neck, and (5) hand/arm.

Figure 13.1 shows how static (isometric) work (muscle does not move) increases both systolic and diastolic blood pressure, while rhythmic (isotonic) work does not change diastolic pressure much and only slightly increases systolic pressure. In addition, metabolic wastes tend to accumulate in the muscles during isometric work due to the minimum blood flow. When a job has a static load, consider increasing the recovery time. See Box 21.4.

1.1 Standing   Four aspects of standing are anatomy, physiology, shoes, and floors. Anatomy and physiology are discussed in Chapter 4.

1.1.1 *Shoes*   Opila et al. (1988) found that the line of gravity is forward of the spine (even L4–5), meaning that the body normally has a forward bending moment, counterbalanced by ligament forces and back muscle forces. If the heel is too high (as in cowboy boots, women's high heels), the center of gravity is moved forward, causing a variety of biomechanical stresses while standing or walking (Lee et al., 2001).

The general goal is to have the hips parallel to the floor (i.e., to stand with weight equally on both feet). However, unequal leg lengths or uneven shoe wear may

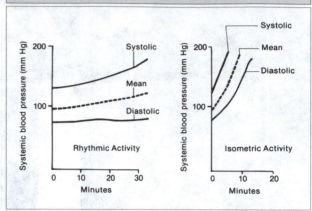

FIGURE 13.1

Static (isometric) loads increase both systolic and diastolic blood pressure. During rhythmic activity, diastolic blood pressure increases very little and systolic increases slightly.

be a problem. A difference of as little as 6 mm in leg length can cause considerable stress on the back. Shoe heels may wear unequally, presenting another problem. Many people wear down a corner of the heel when walking. Then they are standing not on a flat surface but on a curved surface. A solution is to have a shoemaker build up the heel with heel plates. Figure 13.2 shows how a bar rail can be used to vary the work posture. Use bar rails along conveyor lines as well as individual workstations. The rail should have a nonsharp surface for the foot and allow either foot to be used. A small platform

FIGURE 13.2

Bar footrests can provide comfort to industrial workers as well as tavern customers (Rodgers, 1984).

Reprinted with permission of S. Rodgers.

(see Figure 13.17) is another alternative. The changed height of the foot rotates the thigh bone forward, enabling the hip on that side to be fixed; it also flattens the lumbar curve and relaxes the iliopsoas muscle. When a leg is on the rail/footrest, the large back muscles on that side of the body are relaxed and receive a flow of blood (bringing nutrients and removing waste products).

For most tasks, ankle support is not needed. Higher sides (e.g., boots) often are used in sports activities and walking over uneven terrain; the high sides also can protect the leg from vegetation and bites. Athletic shoes divide into (1) running shoes (designed for forward motion) or (2) court shoes (designed for quick side-to-side motion).

A good shoe will mold itself to the foot, giving support over a relatively large area and thus minimizing pressure on the foot. Wooden shoes (Dutch shoes), once broken in, give good area support. In modern shoes a cushioned inner sole does the same job more quickly.

The outer sole of the shoe also should be cushioned. This can be done by material (e.g., crepe) or by form (e.g., ripple soles), or a combination of material and form. In many jobs, resistance to slipping is important. In this case, consider deck shoes—that is, shoes with no arch. They increase contact area (more "rubber on the road") and have high **coefficient of friction** (see Figures 13.3 and 13.4) materials. See Table 15.4 for shoe and floor coefficients of friction. Rubber-soled boots give excellent grip on clean surfaces but poor grip on greasy or muddy surfaces. To reduce slipping, use deck shoes (i.e., no heel) with a tread design with many braking edges that act in all directions. Small flexible cleats with draining canals facilitate movement of liquid from under the sole.

When shoes are used for standing work, they should be slightly oversized—1/2 to 1 size too large, as the feet will swell during the day. Thus, those shoes should be purchased after work, not on weekends or before work. A Buckingham palace guard commented, "Stood on parade four to five hours at a time. The trick is to keep the weight off your heels. That's why guards' boots bulge in front—lots of room to wiggle your toes." It is the rare person whose feet are both the same size. See Figure 13.5. How much do yours differ? Shoes with more holes for laces have more adjustability for foot size difference—that is, shoes with four lacing holes adjust better than shoes with three lacing holes.

1.1.2 Floors Hard floors cause standing fatigue in the feet, legs, and back. Metal gratings are the worst of all, since they have no resilience and also have minimum surface area, thus acting as knives. A conventional ladder (with a rung or 3-inch step) is another example of a minimum surface area; if a ladder is used for standing (e.g., in an orchard) instead of just for moving between levels, the step should be 12 inches deep so it supports the entire foot. Concrete is fatiguing; plastic or cork tile is slightly better; wood is better; and carpet is best of all.

F I G U R E	13 . 3

Heel strike is when most slips occur (Chaffin et al., 1992). The vertical foot force is normal force; the horizontal foot force is foot shear force. Since the two vertical forces are equal (i.e., the floor is stiff enough to hold the person's weight and inertia), the key is the relation of the horizontal forces. If the foot's shear force is less than the friction force, the foot will not slip.

The slipping coefficient of friction *(SCOF)* required to stop the foot from slipping is horizontal shear force/normal force.

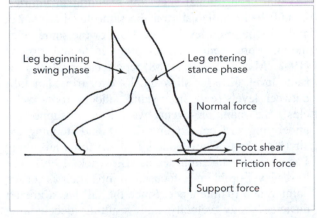

F I G U R E	13 . 4

The slipping coefficient of friction (SCOF), required for walking without slipping, is shown with the solid line. The dashed line shows a microslip and recovery during a step.

FIGURE **13.5**

Comparison of left and right feet. Left feet, on the average, are the same size as right feet (Rys and Konz, 1989). However, for a specific individual, there can be considerable variability between the left and right feet.

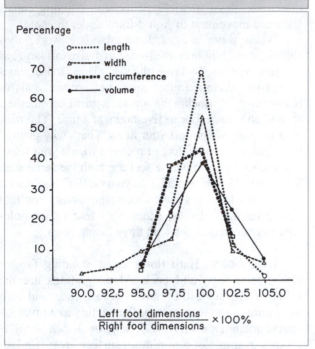

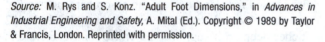

Source: M. Rys and S. Konz. "Adult Foot Dimensions," in *Advances in Industrial Engineering and Safety*, A. Mital (Ed.). Copyright © 1989 by Taylor & Francis, London. Reprinted with permission.

If the entire floor is not carpeted, individuals can modify their own work area by covering a local area with a mat, a rug, or a wooden platform (a favorite of machine-shop operators). Some people even use pieces of cardboard.

Rys and Konz (1988) demonstrated that carpet reduced standing heart rate by 5% (vs. standing on concrete). When selecting a mat, look for the following features: It should compress 3%–7% under adult weight (Krumwiede and Konz, 1998) and should have beveled edges to reduce tripping. The underside of the mat should be constructed so the mat does not move on the floor; an alternative is to attach the mat to the floor with duct tape, which also tends to "bevel" the edge. The size of the mat depends on how much movement the person makes—24 inches deep by 36 inches wide is a common size. In some industries, mats must be cleaned and sanitized periodically. If this is a problem, an alternative is viscoelastic material poured into a floor insert. Since the top of the surface is level with the floor, there is no tripping hazard and sanitizing materials can be used without problem.

Although carpet has higher capital cost than tile, carpet should have lower maintenance cost. A solid-color carpet shows spots and stains more than a multi-color (sculptured) carpet. Covering an unheated concrete floor with carpet will give about a 1% savings in heating cost. Cold floors with high thermal conductivity (metal, concrete) cool the feet, increasing vasoconstriction and restricting blood flow to the feet.

A light-colored floor surface (painted concrete, light-color carpet) increases reflected light, improving lighting distribution and thus improving visual acuity.

1.2 Falls This section is divided into problem, causes of falls, and solutions for falls.

1.2.1 *Problem* Courtney et al. (2001) provide the following statistics to indicate the magnitude of the slip, trip, and fall problem:

- Slips and falls are the second largest source of unintentional injury deaths.
- Slips and falls are the leading reason for unintentional emergency department visits (21% of visits or about 550,000/year).
- Slips and falls have an annual direct cost/capita of occupational injuries of $50–400 (depending on the industry).

Occupational exposures result in about 1,500 deaths/yr, and 300,000 injuries (Leamon, 1992; Leamon and Murphy, 1995). In industrial fatalities, falls account for about 12%, which is greater than the total for electrical current, fires, burns, drowning, and poisons. Of workers injured in falls from heights, about 20% die (Eisma, 1990).

The risk of a fall varies very much with occupation. Construction workers, cleaning personnel, transportation workers, and restaurant serving personnel have higher risks (Chaffin et al., 1992). The fatality rate increases greatly with age; the male fatality rate at age 25 is 4.4, while at age 75 it is 211 (Grongvist, 1999).

Andersson and Lagerloff (1983) analyzed 121,000 occupational accidents resulting in injuries; 20,600 had a fall. Falls on the same level were 2/3, and falls between levels were 1/3. For the same level, the main pre-events were slipping (55%) and tripping (19%). Manning et al. (1988) reported, for falls on the same level, 62% for slips and 17% for trips. For falls between levels (e.g., from stairs, ladders, roofs, vehicles), the main pre-events were loss of support of underlying surface, slipping (28%), and stepping-on-air (8%). Falls from ladders and scaffolds are about 1% of total accidental deaths (Bloswick, 1999). The lower-level problem is focused in jobs such as roofer, painter, and maintenance. Since the fall has a greater distance, body velocity and resulting deceleration become greater.

Falls that occur when a person is carrying something are especially dangerous. The object carried decreases stability as a function of the torque above the ankle (weight $\times$ object height above ankle). Other problems are that the arms cannot be used for balance (to prevent a fall), to grab a railing, or to break the fall.

Not all underfoot accidents result in falls, and not all falls result in a lost-time injury. Some falls result in no lost time, some result in sprains and strains, some in broken bones, and some in death. In addition, falls often are not recorded by accident-recording procedures. Thus, the accident reports tend to drastically underestimate the number of falls.

1.2.2 *Causes of falls* Falls can occur from slips (unexpected horizontal foot movement), trips (restriction of foot movement), and stepping-on-air (unexpected vertical foot movement). In addition, people can fall as a result of alcohol or drug use, fainting, and so on.

Slips. Slips occur primarily during foot pushoff and heel strike.

During *pushoff,* the person falls forward (less common and less dangerous); in addition, during pushoff, most of the weight has already been transferred to the other foot.

During **heel strike,** the person falls backward. The critical time is .05 to .10 s after heel strike. See Figures 13.3 and 13.4. Leamon (1992) defined a *microslip* as a slip less than 2 cm, a *slip* as 8–10 cm, and a *slide* as uncontrolled movement of the heel. Microslips occur very often, and normally are not perceived by the person. A slip usually is perceived, and the person typically jerks the upper body, moves the arms, etc. A slide involves loss of control and usually a fall.

Slips also can occur when the "ground" slopes (front to back or side to side). Examples are ramps and ladder rungs. Slips also can occur, with stationary feet, during pushing and pulling, but there does not tend to be a fall and injury.

During a slip, a lubricant (water, oil, grease, dust, ice, snow) usually is present, either on the surface or on the shoe heel. See Table 15.4 for some coefficients of friction. In the special outdoors circumstances of snow and ice, slipping can be common; in Finland, slipping outdoors is 10 times more common in winter (Grongvist and Hirvonen, 1995). The most danger occurs when the ice is "wet" (i.e., close to the freezing point), as the water is a lubricant.

Table 13.1 summarizes how to reduce slips.

Trips. Trips occur during foot swing. As the foot swings forward, it hits an obstacle and the person falls forward; the problem is lack of leg movement. Usually there is a visual problem. Outdoor trips often occur from uneven surfaces (e.g., walkways, parking lots) that the person expects to be even. Indoor trips tend to be from obstacles on the floor.

Stepping-on-air. Unexpected vertical movement can occur on steps when the distance between stairs is unequal; when there is a hole in the ground; or when there is no ground (e.g., "cliff," edge of scaffold, unexpected step, step on spiral stairs, unexpected curb or ramp). **Stepping-on-air** often occurs with "single steps" (small changes in elevation such as curbs or one-step changes in floor level). Steps descending from large trucks and off-road vehicles often present problems. On steps, the fall usually occurs when descending; the fall can be for a considerable distance.

In some cases, the surface is there initially but breaks or moves (e.g., step breaks, floor mat slides, a chair used as a stepstool moves, ladder feet move). Often, stepping-on-air has a visual cause.

1.2.3 *Solutions for falls* The goals are to: (1) prevent the fall, and (2) reduce the consequence of the fall.

Prevent the fall. We will consider roofs, ladders, scaffolds, steps, vehicle steps, ramps, and horizontal surfaces.

Roofs present many problems; for some solutions, see U. S. Dept. of Labor (1999a, 1999b).

Ladders, when fixed, should have a slant from horizontal between 75° to 90° (ANSI, 1992). There should be a 30.5 cm distance between rungs, 40.6 cm between side rails, a 17.8 cm toe clearance behind the rung, and a minimum 1.9 cm rung diameter. Side rails should be uniform and allow a power grip along the ladder length. MIL-STD 1472F (1999) recommends that portable ladders should be at angles of 75°–85°, stair ladders at 50°–60°, stairs at 30°–35°, and ramps at 7°–15°. Figure 13.6 gives the recommended dimensions for stair ladders (slope 50°–75°) and fixed ladders. Fixed ladders (generally 90°) should have a cage if they are more than 20 ft in height. MIL-STD 1472B and OSHA .25–27 have more details. The ideal angle for a portable ladder is about 75°—a greater angle increases the danger of the ladder falling backward and a smaller angle increases the danger of the base slipping. On portable ladders, the majority of injuries occur when the person reaches too far to the side, causing the ladder to move (Faergemann and Larsen, 2001). Possible ladder modifications are a wider distance between rails at the base, outriggers at the ladder base, and a high-friction surface on the ladder where it contacts the vertical surface.

Bloswick (1999) has an extensive analysis of ladder and stair biomechanics.

Scaffolds and work platforms should have a waist-high (107 cm) guardrail, as well as a 10 cm high toeboard (reduces slips over the edge as well as reducing falling objects). (See U. S. Dept. of Labor, 1999a.) The top of the guardrail should discourage sitting.

T A B L E	1 3 . 1

Minimization of slips and slip effects.

1. Eliminate the lubricant.
   A. Avoid presence/spilling of lubricant.
   B. Quickly clean up lubricant. Note that the lubricant (water, mud) could be on the shoe. "Lubricants" also can be solid objects such as coins, paper clips, hairpins, screws, and metal chips.
   C. Don't add lubricants during cleaning (e.g., don't use an oil mop to clean a waxed floor).
   D. Improve drainage of rain/snow on exterior walks and stairs.

2. Choose good flooring.
   A. Carpet is best (high-friction, low effect of lubricants)
   B. For hard surfaces, stainless steel and ceramic are worst as they are the smoothest. Grooved or porous floors reduce lubricant problems but are hard to clean.
   C. Use mats and duckboards (elevated slatted flooring) for local areas where wet floors are common. For example, building entrances often are wet because of water and snow tracked in. Machines using oil or coolant can be a problem. Mats should have beveled edges to reduce tripping, and holes to encourage drainage.

3. Choose good shoes. The heel is critical.
   A. Bevel the rear of the heel (reduce the contact angle during heel strike to 0 from 10°–15°).
   B. Penetrate (squeeze out) the lubricant. This can be done when the tread or high surface roughness (the minute peaks, known as asperites) of footwear and floor make contact (Chang et al., 2001).
   C. Have soft material to increase contact area and, thus, grip. Slip resistance of shoes increases after about 5 km of walking, so tests on new shoes underestimate the slip resistance (Leclercq, Tisserand, and Saulnier, 1995).

4. Realize a slip may occur (be alert).
   A. Walk carefully (short, slow steps).
   B. Keep the body's center of gravity within the stride.
   C. Reduce heel angle at heel strike (i.e., shuffle).

5. If there is a slip, eliminate the fall (e.g., use handrails).

6. If there is a fall, decrease consequences of the fall.
   A. Less distance to fall.
   B. Lower impact force/pressure (use soft surfaces such as carpet; minimize sharp objects).

F I G U R E	1 3 . 6

Stair ladders and ladder recommendations (Rodgers, 1983; Woodson, 1981).

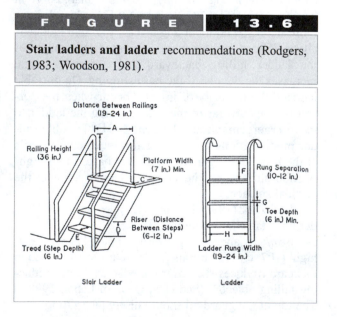

Safe steps: (1) have easily visible steps, (2) have consistent tread and riser dimensions (no more than .375 inch [9.5 mm] variation between risers or between runs within a stairway [Uniform Building Code, 1997]), (3) provide high-friction treads, and (4) provide handrails that are both within reach and graspable. The handrail should extend at least 12 in beyond the final riser. See Figure 13.7.

Note that not everyone's vision is perfect. Examples include, among many others, people not wearing their glasses, vision of the elderly, and steps being out-of-focus for people with bifocals when descending. Illumination solutions consider both quantity of light and quality of light.

Quantity of light typically is increased with fixed sources (e.g., ceiling lights, street lights). But lamps fail, and the resulting lack of light is especially critical for stairs. One solution is to have two lamps

Prevent falls into the lower level by putting a barrier above the railing at the foot of the stairs. The photo is from the reconstructed Globe Theatre in London.

illuminate critical areas; another is to have a window on the stairwell (which will help during the day). If you don't wish to leave the light on continuously, use a motion sensor so the person doesn't have to find and actuate the light switch. Another problem is glare from too much reflected light. Solutions include installing non-reflecting surfaces and shielding both natural and artificial illumination.

Quality of light also is important. Ideally the light gives moderate shadows (shadows aid depth perception). Improve depth perception by using multiple sources and considering the orientation/direction of the light. Camouflage is concerned with obliterating contrast; we are concerned with anticamouflage. Contrast is especially important on steps.

Attention must be drawn to steps—especially if the step is camouflaged so there is an "ambush." Do not distract attention from stairs by a "view" as a person begins the descent. Call attention to steps by changing the color of the floor (e.g., red carpet on stairs vs. green carpet on approaches), having a handrail (especially for "one-step" stairs), changing wall color on stair walls (e.g., paint changes color and descends at the stair angle), and avoiding patterns that confuse depth perception (e.g., narrow strips with strong contrast).

For stairs, the key to friction is the nosing rather than the tread. A simple solution is to carpet the stairs. Outdoor stairs often are lubricated by rain and snow. These stairs should have a wash (slope of less than 1:60) to permit water to drain. Perhaps a roof is feasible—even if it doesn't give 100% protection. Prevent water (from the ground or a building) from draining onto stairs.

Handrails on stairs should permit a power grip (11–13 cm circumference), have a clearance from the wall of about 3.8 cm, and be 89–97 cm above the stair (Hanna and Konz, 2004). A handrail must be within reach distance; at a minimum, there should be a handrail on the right side descending. Templer (1992) and NFPA (1994) give detailed information on stair design. Carrying objects on stairs (1) reduces ability to see the step and (2) reduces ability to grasp the handrail.

For *vehicle steps,* avoid: steps too small for both feet, lowest step too far from pavement (if the lowest step is flexibly mounted to reduce rough terrain impacts, use old conveyor belt rubber rather than cables for the suspension, as belts give less sway when the driver steps on the step), and excessive reaches (due to placement of either steps or handrails). For mounting/dismounting vehicles, use the **three-contact rule** (at each phase of mounting/dismounting, at least three limbs should maintain contact with steps or handles at the same time). Miller et al. (1991) noted the predominant foot movement is vertical rather than horizontal and the contact point is the ball of the foot rather than the heel. Can the step have drain holes?

For shoe sole friction, oil-resistant rubber is always best; the slip resistance of crepe drops greatly when it is covered with water or diesel oil (crepe then becomes even worse than leather). Sometimes the person wears the wrong type of shoe because of vanity. For example, truck drivers like to wear boots. But slippery leather soles and heels lead to slipping when truck steps are lubricated by rain or fuel.

Ramps for people should have an angle of 5°–15° walking down a ramp results in about 15 times more falls than walking up a ramp (Redfern et al., 2001). For vehicles, maximum angles are 3° for a power-operated handtruck, 7° for a powered platform truck, 10° for an electric fork truck, and 15° for a gasoline fork truck (Hanna and Konz, 2004). If handtrucks are pushed up the ramp, there should be a landing at least every 3 m in elevation. Ramps should have handrails and, if used by vehicles, heavy curbs. Have a non-skid surface in the center of each lane. If a vehicle ramp is exposed to rain or snow, have a 60 cm strip of abrasive metal plate in the track for each wheel; attach it to the concrete with countersunk holes and flat-head expansion screws.

For *horizontal surfaces,* reduce slips by having good friction (carpet instead of tile, roughened concrete instead of smooth concrete, abrasive strips on concrete, avoiding low friction waxes on tile). Minimize lubricants such as rain and snow. (Lubricants rarely are a problem on carpets but are a big problem on hard surfaces.) For example, have carpets at building entrances so people don't track rain or snow onto slick surfaces and make them even more slippery. When it is raining, some stores with hard-tile floors give people a plastic bag so they can "sheath" their umbrellas and avoid water dropping on the floor. Avoid using oil-treated mops to remove dust. Remove any lubricants quickly. Reduce trips by making floors level (filling holes and removing objects on the floor). For stepping-on-air, see the points above concerning single-step stair visibility.

If people know the surface is slippery, they can change how they walk. A short stride reduces foot velocity, gives a smaller foot shear force at the heel/ground interface, and keeps the body's center of gravity between the feet. Leaning forward helps keep the center of gravity between the feet and, if you fall, it will be forward instead of backward. When walking down a ramp, people over age 35 decrease both stride length and steps/min (Sun et al., 1996).

Reduce consequence of fall. One possibility (akin to auto seat belts) is to interrupt the fall. For example, for workers on a scaffold or roof, use a full-body harness attached to an anchorage point. Another choice is safety nets. Handrails permit the person to prevent the fall.

Another possibility (akin to auto airbags and dashboards) is to soften the impact. Carpet can reduce peak body deceleration on the hip by 20% over hard surfaces (Maki and Fernie, 1990). In addition, carpets have high coefficients of friction and, thus, few slips occur. Stair landings reduce the distance of a fall. To minimize impact injuries, stairs, handrails, and balustrading should be free of hostile elements such as projecting features, sharp edges, and corners. A fall down some stairs is comparable to falling into a hole with jagged rocks at the bottom.

1.3 Sitting

At first thought, getting tired of sitting seems surprising. However, remember that students get "twitchy" whenever the lecture approaches 60 min. What if you had to sit continuously for 120 min as many workers do? Sitting will be discussed in more detail in Section 4. The foot swelling during stationary seated deskwork can be overcome by modest leg activity (such as rolling the chair about the workstation) (Winkel and Jorgensen, 1986).

1.4 Head Weight

The head weighs about 7.3% of body weight, so if you weigh 90 kg, your head weighs about .073 (90) = 6.6 kg. In common terms, this is the same as a bowling ball.

The neck supports this "bowling ball." The stress depends upon the position of the head's center of gravity relative to the spine. Expect more problems (tired neck syndrome) when (1) the neck is long and thin, and/or (2) the head is tilted forward or tilted back excessively. The head position usually is determined by the visual requirements of the task.

1.4.1 *Forward tilt* In general, keep the **line of sight** (see Figure 18.11) below the horizontal. This not only reduces neck fatigue but also tends to reduce direct glare from ceiling lighting. Chaffin (1973), using electromyography and subjective pain measurements, recommended a maximum forward inclination of 30°. Kroemer and Hill (1986) suggest a forward head tilt when seated at a VDT of 10°–15°; thus, the center of the screen should be about even with the upper torso. See Box 13.1 and Section 6.1 in Chapter 18 for more information.

The head position may be relatively independent of what the hands are doing. An example is driving. In driving, the seat is semi-reclined; thus, the eye can look horizontally while the head is centered over the spine.

The head may be tilted forward so an object is closer to the eyes. Two work subdivisions are (1) where the hand position is independent (e.g., VDT work, inspection) and (2) where the hands work on the object (e.g., fine assembly). VDT operators have less neck tension when the source document is on a holder (i.e., perpendicular to the line of sight and closer) than when the source document is flat on the table (i.e., not perpendicular to the line of sight and farther) (Hamilton, 1986). If the hands are raised to work on objects close to the eyes (by elevating or tilting the work), consider forearm supports on the chair. See Section 2.5.1 in Chapter 23 for some more solutions.

1.4.2 *Backward tilt* Occasionally, people tilt their heads backward, again causing sore necks as the muscles that support a backward tilt are weak. Bifocal lenses may cause this backward tilt as people attempt to use the bottom of the bifocals. A solution is to use single-vision glasses with a short focal length (work glasses) at the workplace. Another possibility is to raise or lower the work or the chair.

1.4.3 *Sideward tilt* Some people cradle a telephone between their neck and shoulder; avoid this by using a head-mounted microphone or a speaker phone.

1.5 Hands/Arms Holding a tool or workpiece causes a static load. Holding not only causes fatigue in the hand/arm but also restricts productivity (since the person can only work with the one remaining arm). Thus using the hand to hold something is a "flag" for possible improvement.

If you weigh 90 kg, one of your hands weighs about .0065 (90) = .6 kg, a hand plus a forearm about .0227 (90) = 2 kg, and an entire arm about 4.4 kg. If you hold a 25-g feather, you also are holding 4,400 g of bone and muscle. Complete elimination of the 25-g feather doesn't reduce the load much. Thus, avoid work where the upper arm is not vertical, that is, where the hands are above heart level (the upper arm is moved forward) or upper arm is abducted (upper arm angled from the side). See Figure 13.8. Working with elevated hands also may make the head tilt back, causing neck pain and possible vertigo.

(Position of the arm also substantially affects the flow of blood, as well as arm and hand temperature. To minimize the flow of blood and drop arm temperature about 1°C, hold your hand above your head. To maximize the flow of blood from the warm central torso, hold your arm straight down or lie down and put your arm at your side.)

Weight of the arms can be supported by a worksurface or chair arms. Many worksurfaces have sharp edges, making padding desirable. Figure 13.18 shows one commercially available design. Supporting the arms also reduces tremor and thus permits more accurate work with the hands. The work area should not have sharp edges, corners, bolt heads, or other impediments to snag any body area (e.g., hands, hips, thighs). In addition, if the worker reaches into a cardboard box, protect the forearm with a long-sleeve shirt or a sock (with the toe cut off) worn the forearm.

One reason the arms are elevated is that the work requires close visual attention and thus is elevated to move it closer to the eyes. An alternative is to magnify the object, which allows "friendly" positions for both the head and the hands. A 4X (multiplying size by 400%) lens mounted on a stand (or post-mounted with a swivel arm) with accompanying light will allow a field of view of approximately 25 × 75 mm with severe restrictions on the depth of field. A 2X lens (multiplying size by 200%) will have a field of view of approximately 100 × 500 mm and a reasonable depth of view. Both approaches tend to keep the head in a relatively fixed location. Obtain more freedom for the head by wearing eyeglasses with magnification lenses (e.g., 1.5X) or by taking a digital photo with a magnification lens and then having the operator view the screen.

2 REDUCE MUSCULOSKELETAL DISORDERS

This guideline is covered in detail in Chapter 14. Table 13.2 summarizes the guidelines for hand–arm positions and movement given in Chapters 13 and 14.

T A B L E	1 3 . 2

Guidelines for hand–arm position and movement.

TEXT PAGE	GUIDELINE
	Height
202	Set the work height at 50 mm below the elbow.
	Joint Movement
241	Don't bend your wrist.
242	Don't lift your elbow.
252	Don't reach behind your back.
	Hand Motions
213	Use the feet as well as the hands.
214	Use gravity, don't oppose it.
214	Conserve momentum.
216	Use two-hand motions.
217	Use parallel motions for eye control.
218	Use rowing motions.
218	Pivot motions about the elbow.
219	Use the preferred hand.
220	Keep arm motions in the normal work area.
221	Let the small person reach; let the large person fit.

F I G U R E	1 3 . 8

Minimize arm abduction by keeping the upper arm vertically downward. The elbows can be raised either by carrying something too wide or by having the hands too high (say at heart level).

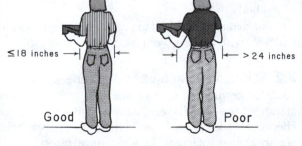

3 SET THE WORK HEIGHT AT 50 MM BELOW THE ELBOW

3.1 Optimum Height   There are no "cliffs" in ergonomics; that is, a single inch is unlikely to make a major change. If an article gives a recommendation to a tenth or hundredth of an inch, it is too precise. For comments on the location of controls, see Chapter 17.

3.1.1 *Manipulative work*   The **optimum work height** for manipulative hand–arm work (50 mm below the elbow; slightly below heart level) is based on both productivity (i.e., cost to the organization paying the employee) and physiological cost (i.e., cost to the individual to achieve a specified output).

Barnes (1940) stated that the hand should be "allowed to work 1 to 3 inches lower than the elbow, the average height of the work surface." Although Barnes did not cite any evidence for his recommendation, all the following studies tend to confirm his judgment. The key points are as follows:

- Work height is defined in terms of *elbow height* rather than a fixed height from the floor. Since individual heights vary, any fixed-height design must be wrong.

- Optimum height is slightly *below* the elbow. Some research indicates it is farther below than other research, but the consensus is below.

- Optimum height from the elbow is the *same* for both sitting and standing. This means work height from the floor will differ for sitting and standing, unless the chair height is adjusted.

- Work height is not table height. Most items (e.g., mechanical assemblies, keyboards, hamburgers on a grill) have a thickness that is typically 25 to 50 mm. Thus, if the optimum height for the hands is 50 mm below the elbow and the object being worked on is 50 mm thick, the table should be 100 mm below the elbow.

Konz (1967) surveyed the literature. There is a relatively flat performance response around the optimum. That is, although the optimum performance seems to be about 50 mm below the elbow, output does not decrease more than a couple of percent within a range from 125 mm below to 25 mm above the elbow; beyond this the penalty is greater.

Wiker et al. (1989) reported, from a laboratory study, increases in time of less than 8% when the hand was kept below the shoulder but increases of over 20% when above the shoulder. In industrial work, the penalties of nonoptimal positions should be even greater due to fatigue.

Physiological cost vs. organizational cost (i.e., cost to the worker rather than gain to the organiza-tion) also has been used as a criterion for many years; the effect of physiological cost now is known as cumulative trauma.

Within the range of knee to chest, there seems to be a greater penalty for working above the optimum than below. This may be related to upper arm abduc-tion when working above the optimum. As pointed out in Section 1.5 of this chapter, it is good policy to keep the hands below the heart level. However, if the operator is seated and needs to reach below the knee (e.g., to get supplies), this involves considerable twist-ing and bending, which is bad for the back. Consider storing such items some distance away so the operator must rise from the chair to obtain the supplies.

For precision work, there is a conflict between an elbow height location for arm comfort vs. a higher height for good vision. See Chapter 23, especially Section 2.5, for improvements to vision. If the arms are raised, consider supporting the arms. Work height for precision work typically would be 100–150 mm above the elbow.

This section can be summarized by the **Power Zone** concept (Hilgen, 2001). This is the area within which people can work with maximum efficiency; it ranges from mid-thigh to the chest (the center of the baseball strike zone). Elbow height is in the heart of the Power Zone. Rather than give workers too much detail, just have them move low-level or overhead-level work to the Power Zone. For example, don't work on items on the floor; work on a cart or table. A landscaper, using a standard length fertilizer injector gun, has to bend forward. The solution is to have guns with long barrels for tall workers and guns with shorter barrels for shorter workers.

3.1.2 *Non-manipulative work*   There is little information concerning the optimum work height when a downward force is required, such as a polish-ing or sanding operation; a lower height permits use of body weight on tools and the work. It probably is with the lower arm at about a 45° angle—a distance below the elbow of about 150 to 200 mm. Magnusson and Ortengren (1987) reported that butchers preferred a table height 17 to 22 cm below the elbow with a 5–10° tilt; they recommend varying the height during the day, because different heights stress different parts of the body.

For manual handling, the optimum height is at the knuckle, with the arm vertical.

3.2 Solution Techniques   See Boxes 13.1 and 13.2 for comments on two specific types of work-stations—the VDT workstation and the grocery checkout workstation. In general, the three approaches are to change machine height, adjust elbow height, and adjust work height on the machine.

BOX   **13.1**   *VDT Workstations*

VDTs have become pervasive. Although the physical problems of VDTs have been greatly reduced, the "new frontier" is the psychosocial problems resulting from lack of autonomy, lack of variety, and high pressure.

VDT stands for *video display terminal,* but another meaning is *very demanding task.* It is demanding physically due to the sedentary, minimum-activity posture for most of the body combined with highly repetitive motions by the fingers. It is demanding mentally due to the constant attention required. It is demanding visually due to the poor-quality character reproduction on screens.

VDT tasks include:

- data entry (document-intensive because the operator routinely enters data from documents)
- data acquisition (screen-intensive because information from a form is matched with information from the screen)
- word processing (document- and screen-intensive because attention is focused on both places)
- interactive (screen user such as travel agent, CAD/CAM user, programmer, Web searcher)

VDT job organization Traditionally, the office worker (white collar) was treated differently (better) than blue collar workers. However, as the office has begun to have production aspects, individualized consideration is disappearing. VDT operators will likely have fewer complaints if they are treated as individuals rather than "faceless production workers." However, remember that VDT stands for very demanding task, and one reason for that is the high number of repetitions of keystrokes.

Assume a person keys words at the rate of 70 words/minute. Assuming that a typical word (including spaces and punctuation) has 7 strokes, then 70 words/min $\times$ 7 strokes/word = 490 strokes/min. It would take about 22 years to reach 1 billion strokes.

We would be impressed with any machine that operated over 1 billion cycles. We need to reduce the stress on the "human machine." Stress can be reduced in two primary ways: reduce exposure, and increase worker ability to endure the stress. See Chapter 14, especially Section 1.4.2, and Box 21.4.

VDT lighting See the discussion on VDT lighting and glasses for VDTs in Chapter 23.

VDT furniture The workstation has three key items: the screen, the keyboard, and the document holder. The user has two key items: the eyes and the hands. How should these five items be arranged?

Start with a seated person; this provides a location for the eyes and hands. However, since size varies, (1) the hand location in relation to the floor will not be the same for everyone, (2) the eye location in relation to the floor will not be the same for everyone, and (3) the relation between the eyes and hands will not be the same for everyone. The above obvious statements are given because they lead to a key guideline: *Workstation furniture must be adjustable.*

Next locate the primary visual element ahead of the eye; this is the screen for screen-intensive work and the document for document-intensive work.

There remains the vertical location of this primary element. Visually based studies tend to recommend lower locations while biomechanical studies tend to recommend higher ones. Noting that real people rarely "sit tall" and to encourage variation in posture, Ankrum and Nemeth (1995) recommend that the *top* of the monitor be at least 15° below horizontal eye level. Sommerich et al. (1998) and Psihogios et al. (1998) recommend users be provided with the flexibility to place the VDT *center* in locations of their own choosing but within a viewing angle envelope of 0° to −17°. The vertical location of the screen is more critical for people using contact lenses. A "high" monitor position allows the eyes to be open wider, causing less blinking and therefore allowing the eyes to dry out faster. Use lens re-wetting drops.

The screen (document) should be perpendicular to the line of sight (Brand and Judd, 1993). The distance from the eyes depends on the size and quality of the displayed material. Akbari and Konz (1991) evaluated distances of 50, 65, 80, and 100 cm; 65 was best and 100 was the worst. Considering the many tradeoffs, the consensus seems to be 20 to 30 inches (500–750 mm) from the eyes. This is the "dark focus" distance (the distance at which the focus mechanism has minimum effort). Avoid distances of less than 20 inches (Jaschinski-Kruza, 1990).

Next locate the documents (screen). To minimize the need for visual accommodation, both the document and screen should be the same distance from the eyes. Since the head can move side to side easily (especially if the chair swivels), side by side is a common arrangement. If the document is used more, place the document ahead and the display at

(continued)

BOX 13.1 *VDT Workstations, continued*

its right or left (operator's choice). If the display is used more, place the display straight ahead and the document on the operator's preferred-hand side, to avoid cross-body reaches when the operator is changing or marking the document. For additional screen location comments, see Section 4.1 in Chapter 23.

In practice, adjustable VDT furniture usually involves an adjustable chair and document holder. In some cases, the keyboard and worksurface also are adjustable. *It is essential that the operator be trained in (1) the proper adjustments and (2) how to make the adjustments on the specific equipment being used.* After a group training session, the ergonomist should make a checkup visit at each workstation, followed by a periodic checkup visit (say at a 3-month interval).

Locate the keyboard in relation to both the eyes and the hands. On a typewriter, the operator memorized the positions of the 50 keys. On a computer keyboard, many function keys were added so the resulting keyboard has over 100 keys; therefore, vision has become more important. However, the location versus the hands is more important than location versus the eyes. The forearm should be approximately horizontal with the hands at or slightly above elbow height. The keyboard should be directly ahead of the person so no twisting is needed.

A wrist rest elevates the wrist and thereby decreases the vertical extension movement of the wrist; vertical extension/flexion movements present a large risk for CTS (Hedge and Powers, 1995). To minimize wrist extension, Hedge et al. (1996) recommend placing a conventional keyboard on a downward-sloping surface that tilts the base of the keyboard away from the user. The key tops, relative to the hand, are at a 0° or slightly negative angle. See their website (www.cornell.edu/research/articles/cie/iri/hedge/) for an impressive visualization of the experimental results.

The wrist support should be gently contoured and padded so there are no pressure points on the wrist. Aaras et al. (1997) reported stress was lower on the trapezius and lower back when the forearm was supported on the table. Since this requires a "deep" table (as the edge of the keyboard closest to the operator is, say, over 6 inches from the edge and the monitor then is quite far from the eyes), a more practical arm support might be on the chair rather than the table. Computer users reported that an articulating forearm support improved comfort and reduced Rate of Perceived Exertion (although there was no change in heart rate) (Garcia et al., 1997).

Locate the mouse so the forearm is horizontal and the hand is even with the keyboard. Since hand sizes vary, consider a custom mouse for the individual. As well as different sizes, mice also are available in left- and right-hand versions. There are also Y connections so two mice can be plugged in simultaneously. Although most people are not very ambidextrous, mousing with either hand is a skill that can be acquired to reduce cumulative trauma. Another possibility is a right-hand mouse for the first shift and a left-hand mouse (or different size mouse) for the second shift. Figure 13.9 shows an ergonomic keyboard.

Finally, the workstation should have some space for work-in-process storage of documents, supplies (disks, pens), and personal items (family pictures, purse). For VDTs used by engineers and executives, the input and output are less standardized, and so additional space is needed to hold drawings, reports, documents, and other material for interactive work with the computer.

To repeat, the key consideration is adjustability of the furniture.

FIGURE 13.9

Ergonomic keyboards reduce radial/ulnar wrist deviation on keyboards by having a V-shaped gap in the middle of the keys.

Reduce flexion and especially extension by locating the keyboard vs. the elbow. There are even specialized "tenting" keyboards to reduce pronation/supination. (See Figure 5.2 for descriptions of radial/ulnar, flexion/extension, and pronation/supination.)

BOX   **13.2**   *Supermarket Checkout Workstations*   Lehman et al., 2001

Perhaps the first question is whether the checker sits or stands. Checkstands in North America, Asia, and Australia typically use standing, but in Europe and South America, they use sitting. Musculoskeletal disorders are reported for both sitting and standing stations.

The literature generally recommends a front-facing design (i.e., the equipment is directly in front of the checker). Its advantage is that it minimizes twisting and shares the load between the left and right hands/arms/shoulders.

A handheld scanner permits scanning heavy items without lifting them. An American guideline is Food Marketing Institute (1996).

Based on an experiment's results, Lehman et al. (2001) reported that standing had lower EMG than sitting. A problem with seated scanning was higher shoulder abduction since the work was performed above elbow height. Performance was about 18% faster when using a bi-optic scanner (scanners in both horizontal and vertical windows, thus being able to read barcodes on 4 or 5 sides of a product, reducing the need to reorient the barcode toward the scanner) than a single vertical-window scanner.

3.2.1 *Change machine height*   If a variety of people use the machine, adjust the height to the average height of the workforce. Don't just use the height that comes from the vendor.

However, many machines and people are one-on-one. That is, one person is the sole machine operator for a long time period—1, 2, or even 5 years. Figure 15.22 shows how conveyor heights can be adjusted depending on whether loading or unloading is performed. The workstation could be adjusted to individual worker heights. Many conveyors (as well as tables) have a pin-and-hole system on the legs; adjustment is simple. Many lightweight machines are mounted on a worksurface (computer keyboard, sewing machine); certainly spending 30 min to adjust the bench height would be a small price to pay for freedom from back and shoulder pain.

Another alternative is a multiple-level table. A common example is a desk with a lower platform for the keyboard. Figure 13.10 shows a multiple-level table. In one welding shop visited, welding tables were built with surfaces 500, 700, and 1,000 mm above the floor; when welders had thick pieces, they used the 500 and 700 mm surfaces. A variety of surfaces also permitted the worker to shift surfaces (even for the same item) to get a variety of postures. Some workstations are multi-level. In these cases, keep the levels close to the elbow. In the meatpacking industry, previously the take-away conveyor on the cutting line was elevated above the conveyor bringing the product. The worker had to throw waste product above her shoulder. The disposal conveyors were lowered so the disposal now is chest high and, in some cases, even below the work conveyor.

Many worktables now have adjustable heights, either cranked by the operator (for occasional

changes) or motor-driven (for frequent changes). See Figure 15.15.

Of course, assembly need not be done on a table. For example, there are "assembly stands." A typical design has a floor-mounted pole with a horizontal fixture to hold the assembly. The pole can be adjusted

FIGURE   13.10

Multiple-level tables permit easy work height adjustment. In the top view, parts with the same thickness can be processed by different people using different portions of the table. In the lower view, the same person can process parts with different thicknesses using different portions of the table.

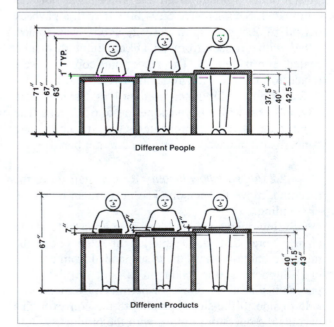

Different People

Different Products

vertically to fit not only the worker but also the stage of assembly. The horizontal fixture usually can be rotated so the assembly can be worked on from various orientations.

Wick and DeWeese (1993) describe modifying a packing workstation by adjusting the height of the workstation, putting a tilt on the workstation table, and putting the supplies in better positions. **Damaging wrist motions** (force to the wrist or fingers while the wrist is not in neutral position) were reduced from 3,000/h to 1,400, high-force pinch grips (≥ 8 lbs) from 4/cycle to 0/cycle, and extreme motions of the shoulder, neck, and back from 44/cycle to 0/cycle; in addition, cycle time was reduced 12%.

A person unloading a pallet transported on a lift truck can leave the pallet on the truck forks while unloading and occasionally stop unloading to raise the pallet and thus reduce bending. One firm had approximately 20 packaging stations in which operators placed product into cardboard boxes. The operators rotated to the next station every hour so they would use a variety of muscles and a variety of postures during the day. Since the operators varied in height, the company had a packing stand designed and built that was variable in height (10 heights) and could be changed in height within 10 seconds. It even had an adjustable tilt surface so the box could be tilted toward the operator at varying degrees to facilitate loading product into the box.

Jenkins and Rickards (2001) present two interesting case studies triggered by ergonomic problems of the back. In case 1, the product was obtained from a floor-level bin, lifted to a conveyor, and packaged. The bin was moved to worksurface height so the excessive time for bending and reaching was reduced. The product spillage from the floor-level bin was eliminated. Savings were $294,000/yr with a payback period of 2.5 weeks. In case 2, a box was folded, filled with product from an ankle-height dispenser, sealed, and palletized. The feeder and conveyor were raised to elbow height, reducing cycle time by 12%. A feeder guide eliminated product loss. Savings were $37,500/year with a payback period of 6.5 weeks. The point here is that improvements due to ergonomic concerns often have very large economic benefits.

3.2.2 *Adjust elbow height*

Rather than move the machine, move the person. The person can be sitting or standing.

Sitting operators should have an adjustable-height chair. Note that adjustable-height chairs can be mounted underneath products suspended from conveyors. Supporting the chair in a slot in the floor perpendicular to the conveyor permits movement from side to side. If the slot is parallel to the conveyor, this permits the operator to move with the product.

Standing operators also can have their work height adjusted. For a stationary workstation with fixed height of the work above the floor, fix the work height for a tall operator. Then short workers stand on a wooden platform (say 36 inches wide $\times$ 72 inches long); maintenance can build platforms both 3 and 6 inches high. Then when the worker height changes (say for an evening shift), a platform is moved into position or moved away. If the desired adjustment is just a couple of inches, consider using one or two additional floor mats.

For products moving along a conveyor, the conveyor can rise/fall at a slope (permitting operators to move along the line to find the work location most appropriate to their height). An alternative is a level conveyor but a ramp parallel to the conveyor upon which the operator stands; the ramp can be alongside the line or underneath the product (such as the pits under some auto assemblies). A variation is to put two or three platforms on the ramp so the feet are level (the operator picks the platform to work on). (If using platforms, make sure the platform is large enough to permit some movement of the feet and to minimize the risk of falling.)

In agricultural labor, it often is necessary to work at or below the level of the feet; examples are planting vegetables and picking from low-growing plants such as strawberries. Vos (1973) divides such jobs into stationary jobs and jobs requiring movement (as along a row of beans).

For stationary work, sitting is best, squatting is almost as good, and bending and kneeling are poor. If bending or kneeling is necessary, supporting the body with one hand on the knee or ground will decrease net energy required by 25% to 55% over no arm support. If a tool is used, it should be usable by either hand so the support hand can be alternated.

For movement, squatting always requires less energy than sitting on a 175 mm stool attached to a belt around the waist; picking performance was 6% to 7% higher with squatting also. Although bending required 1 kcal/min more than squatting when movement was 2 m/min, its curve "crossed over" at 4 m/min forward speed; at 10 m/min, bending required 1 kcal/min less than squatting. Since bending causes local overload of the back muscles, bending should be used with caution.

3.2.3 *Adjust work height on machine*

Figure 13.10 shows how work height can be adjusted with a multiple-level table. When the worker works both sitting and standing, set the work height for the sitting situation; when he stands, have a spacer under the work. A spacer under the work also allows for adjustment between short and tall workers and thick and thin work. Alternatively, set the table height for a standing worker and provide a high chair with a footrest for sitting. Barbers raise the height of children's heads by having them sit on a board across the chair's arms. Items also may have to be lowered. If container walls make the arms lift too high, lower the walls. For example, tip component boxes on their side, tip them on a 45° angle (on a support), or cut out the side of the box with a cardboard knife (see Figure 15.26). In packaging operations, can the container for the finished product be recessed into the table so the packaged items can be put aside with a slide motion instead of a lifting motion? This not only saves time but also reduces cumulative trauma.

Perhaps a container has deep sides so it can hold lots of product. Consider a short-sided box filled more often. Also consider the orientation of the item in the container. Orienting the item vertically instead of horizontally may decrease the number of very deep reaches and moves. In sacking groceries, have the bag on its side to reduce high reaches. Another alternative, of course, is to have a lower shelf built into the checkout stand so the bag can remain upright.

If the part/assembly is held in a fixture, design the fixture to permit both vertical and horizontal adjustment. For example, cars are now assembled in rollover frames that allow the operator to work on the car while it is tilted at various angles. Usually the part does not move in the fixture. However, in some cases, work on the part is easier if the part can move. In these cases, design the fixture to permit this movement. For example, consider the problem of back stress of Figure 13.11 and a solution in Figure 13.12.

For more comments on tilted worksurfaces, see joint deviation in Section 3.2.1 of Chapter 14.

FIGURE 13.11

Back stress. This Japanese inspector of the drum suffered from back stress. What can be done to reduce the stress?

FIGURE 13.12

Change the orientation from vertical to horizontal. After doing this, it was realized that rollers permitted easy turning of the drum; thus the inspector did not have to walk around the drum. This, in turn, permitted consistent lighting for the inspection.

4 FURNISH EVERY EMPLOYEE WITH AN ADJUSTABLE CHAIR

When sitting, a person's knees and legs protrude from the front of the chair. Thus, the worksurface should have space underneath (thigh clearance) for the legs.

4.1 Justification/Selection Think of the chair as a tool. Sitting reduces physiological load compared to standing. For example, dentists who work seated with the patient horizontal have fewer backaches. Table 4.3 shows the results from one of the many studies in the literature showing the benefits of sitting. Although standing does permit greater reach distances and application of force, supervisors, without good reasons, often require lower-status employees to stand. For more on chairs, see Rodgers (1984), Eastman Kodak (1983), Chaffin et al. (1999), and Corlett et al. (1986).

The cost of an adjustable chair is very low. Chair cost is entirely a capital cost since operating cost and maintenance costs are zero. Assuming a cost of \$200/chair, a life of 11 years, and a one-shift operation of 1,800 h/year, the cost/hour is \$200/(11 × 1800) = 1 cent/h. (Often the real comparison is between a chair without good ergonomics and one with ergonomic features, and the incremental cost of the good chair is \$100 or less—that is, .5 cent/hour.)

The cost of labor (wages plus fringes) of the person sitting in the chair will vary with the job. Typically this will be at least \$10/h, with \$15 or \$20 fairly common. Assuming a cost of $10/h, a .1% change in productivity equals 1 cent/h. The improved productivity is likely to occur from the person working more minutes rather than more output/min. That is, a secretary who does not have to get up to relieve a sore back will not key more words/min of working but will work more minutes. In a 480-min workday, .1% is .5 min or 30 s.

The question becomes whether a person will work 30 s more per day with a good chair than a poor chair. Naturally the breakeven time becomes lower if the chair cost is less than 1 cent/h or the wage cost is over $10/h.

When selecting specific chairs for a specific job, a committee (say ergonomics, purchasing, facilities) should narrow the possible chairs to 3 to 5 chairs; don't forget maintenance and spare parts considerations. Then, however, the *users* should try the alternatives in their specific jobs before purchasing. After all, they, not you, will be using the chairs. Some people advocate a 5-min trial, some a 30-min trial, and some an all-day trial for each alternative. Then the alternatives should be lined up side-by-side before the final decision is made.

Assume that there are three chairs in the "finals." Users will test the three in turn. First they should adjust the chair to their preference. (Note that the initial setting biases the selected value. For example, the selected seat height will be lower when the initial setting is low than when the initial setting is high [Helander and Little, 1993].)

Then they should sit and work in the chair for at least 2 hours and vote on their body part discomfort (see Fig. 9.19) every 30 minutes. In addition, they should evaluate the chair on a chair feature checklist. See Figure 13.13 for an example checklist.

Finally, select one of the chairs, using the discomfort votes, checklist evaluation, price, and any other information as input. Since not all people may like the same chair, a decision will have to be made whether to standardize on one chair or let employees select their own. Although it is obvious, it should be noted that not all tasks done in chairs are the same, and different chairs will be selected for different situations.

One of the primary factors in selecting a chair is the importance of easy adjustability. The chair should have adjustable seat height, back height, back in-out location, and back tension. It may have even more adjustments, but those are the basics. If several people share the chair, easy adjustment is important. Even if only one person uses the chair, the user may wish to vary its adjustments during the shift so as to vary the posture. So, easy adjustment still is important. People will have to be trained on the importance of adjustments, how to make them, and which settings to use.

Caution: In Asia, many people sit on the floor or on a mat and do not use a chair. The legs can be crossed in front of the body (lotus position), one leg can be horizontal and one in a vertical "A shape," or both in a vertical A shape (squatting). The key point is that these postures give low eye and hand positions rather than the heights Westerners are accustomed to.

4.2 Chair Design

Chair components are divided into seats, backrests, armrests, and legs/pedestal. See Figure 13.14 and Table 13.3.

4.2.1 *Seats* This section is divided into seat construction and seat dimensions.

Seat construction. When sitting, the weight is not supported by the entire buttocks but by two small areas called the ischial tuberosities (sitting bones). The blood vessels in the tissue overlying the tuberosities (and the tissue on the heels in the feet) are

---

FIGURE 13.13

Chair evaluation form (Drury and Coury, 1982).

	Too high	Correct	Too low
Seat height from floor			

	Too long	Correct	Too short
Seat length			

	Too wide	Correct	Too narrow
Seat width			

	Too high	Correct	Too low
Slope of seat			

	Too shaped	Correct	Too flat
Seat shape			

	Too high	Correct	Too low
Position of backrest			

	Too shaped	Correct	Too flat
Molded chair back			

	Too high	Correct	Too low
Curvature of back support			

	Too high	Correct	Too low
Clearance of feet and calves under chair			

Source: Adapted from *Applied Ergonomics*, Vol. 13, Drury and Coury, "A Methodology for Chair Evaluation," pp. 195–202, © 1982, with permission from Elsevier Science.

I G U R E   **1 3 . 1 4**

Industrial chairs. Because they must be used for sitting 8 h/day, industrial chairs can have features selected for specific jobs. Models A, B, and C show different seat height ranges. Model A shows rug casters, B shows normal casters, and C has no casters. Model A has no footrest, while B has a footrest that moves with the seat and C has a footrest that doesn't move. There are a variety of mechanisms to adjust the height of the seat and the location (vertical and horizontal) of the backrest.

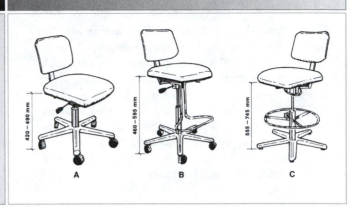

arranged in a special manner to reduce the effects of pressure. Figure 13.15 shows the compression force for normal sitting and for sitting cross-legged. The amount of load depends also on the sitting posture, because when sitting upright the center of mass of the body is directly above the tuberosities and the feet support about 25% of body weight. Leaning forward shifts more load to the feet and leaning backward reduces the load support of the feet (Chaffin and Andersson, 1991).

A well-designed chair is not contoured (form fitting), because contouring forces the body into one standardized position—keeping the pressure on the same area. A well-designed chair thus permits micropostural changes. (When driving long distances, periodically make a small adjustment in the power seat tilt and height.)

Cushioning is desirable because it reduces pressure by increasing support area. The upholstery should give way about 25 mm. If it gives way too much, the

T A B L E   **1 3 . 3**

Recommended dimensions for office chairs (Chaffin et al., 1999). Dimensions are in cm, angles in degrees.

FEATURE	BRITISH STD. (BS 3079 & 3893)	EUROPEAN (CEN)	DIFFERENT ET AL.	DANERO & ZELNIK	GRAND-JEAN	GERMAN STD. (DIN)	SWEDISH STD. (SS)
Seat							
Height	43–51	39–54	35–52	36–51	38–53	42–54	39–51
Width (breadth)	41	40	41	43–48	40–45	40–45	42
Length (depth)	36–47	38–47	33–41	39–41	38–42	38–42	38–43
Slope angle	0–5	0–5	0–5	0–5	4–6	0–4	0–4
Backrest							
Top height	33				48–50	32	
Bottom height	20						
Center height		17–26	23–25	19–25	30	17–23	17–22
Height		10	15–23	10–20		22	22
Width (breadth)	30–36	36–40	33	25	32–36	36–40	36–40
Horizontal radius	31–46	40 min	31–46		40–50	40–70	40–60
Vertical radius	convex					70–140	convex
Backrest-seat angle	95–105		35–100	95–105			
Armrest							
Length	22	20	15–21			20–28	20
Width (breadth)	4	4	6–9				4
Height	16–23	21–25	18–25	20–25		21–25	21–25
Interarm rest	47–56	46–50	48–56	46–51		48–50	46

F I G U R E   13.15

Sitting cross-legged increases pressure upon the ischial tuberosities. Padding the seat reduces the pressure. Avoid "bucket" seats (form fitting) as they don't permit micropostural changes and thus changing of the pressure point.

Wu et al. (1998) reported that mean distance between tuberosities is about 110 mm; dynamic (i.e. in vehicles) ischium pressure peaks around 4 to 5 Hz (resonant frequency of seated human); dynamic pressure is approximately 1.5 (static pressure).

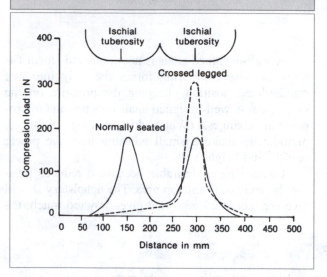

body is not firmly supported and must be supported by the muscles. Some lunch counters encourage rapid eating (thus maximizing seats available) by using small-diameter, hard stools with no backrests.

A curved front edge (waterfall front) is desirable to maximize the surface area contacting the underside of the thigh. Avoid upholstery beading in this area.

The material of the seat (and backrest) should be fabric since it breathes and reduces sliding of the body (better coefficient of friction). In some applications a stain-repellent finish may be desired. Avoid plastic since it causes perspiration problems (body heat can't dissipate, especially if the sitter is wearing synthetic-material clothing such as nylon or acetate underpants, panty hose, or slips), and probably has a shorter life due to rips.

The typical chair seat has a backward slope of 1°–5°, which encourages use of the backrest. However, some people advocate having the seat slope forward (Mandal, 1982; Congleton et al., 1986; Bendix and Bloch, 1986). They cite evidence that the relaxed, minimum-strain position between the back and thigh is about 135°—a sleeping angle; the load on the lower spine is proportional to the distance between the line of gravity and the weight of the structures above the L4 disc.

There are several ways of supporting the body on a forward tilt seat so it doesn't slide forward. The

chair can have a "saddle horn," the arms can rest on a tilted table, the support can come from the knees (see Figure 13.16), or the support can come from the feet. Seats with a forward slope have a high coefficient of friction (i.e., cloth, not plastic or leather). At the present time, the vast majority of chairs still have a backward slope; therefore, an option permitting the user to select the desired slope should be good.

Seat dimensions. See Table 13.3 for recommended dimensions.

The most critical dimension is the height. Measure it from the work height, not the floor. As pointed out in Section 3, the work should be slightly below elbow height for manipulative work, although keyboard work possibly should be slightly higher. The distance between the top of the work and the top of the seat allows room for three things: the work, the work-surface, and the thighs. Burandt and Grandjean (1963) recommend this distance be 275 ± 25 mm.

Since the 95% thigh thickness for both U. S. males and females is 175 mm, it is important when purchasing worksurfaces to make them thin so there is maximum space for the thighs and the work. Thus, do not have a drawer between the thighs and the work. These thigh clearance dimensions have been considered in *table* dimensions (as well as chair adjustments). The underside of office tables should be 65 cm from the floor according to the German and European standards and 63 according to the Swedish standard (Chaffin et al., 1999).

In addition, since the knees occupy the space ahead of the chair, the machine must not have any panel projecting downward from the work, thus preventing the knees from occupying the space. (This is

F I G U R E   13.16

Thigh–back angle. A thigh–back angle of 135° can be achieved with various designs: "kneelers," a saddle chair, or a sit–stand stool.

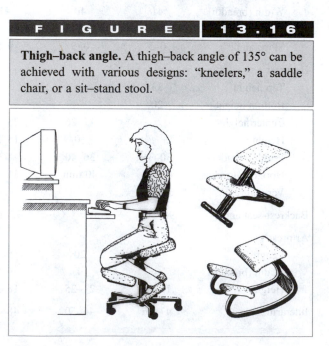

emphasized because some machine designers don't seem to realize where the knees go when you sit down and insist on designing machines that cannot be operated from a seated position.)

Once the upper portion of the body is satisfied, turn your attention to the lower portion—the distance from the seat to the floor. If the feet are not flat on the floor, they should be supported by an adjustable footrest (see Figure 13.17), a footrest on the chair pedestal, or a footrail on the workstation.

Since the operator dimensions and work thicknesses vary, seat height should be adjustable. A common problem is that the seat cannot be lowered far enough to permit sufficient thigh clearance or to permit short workers to put their feet on the floor. (This latter problem can be solved with a footrest.)

For seat width, the wider the better. Wide seats (benches) not only accommodate more of the population but also permit more varied postures. If armrests are used, they should be farther apart than the seat.

For seat depth, the most common problem is a seat that is too deep. The user either must sit forward (and lose the backrest support) or sit back (and have the legs dangle in the air). When you sit back, there should be 2 to 4 finger widths space between the chair edge and the back of the knees so the seat doesn't cut off circulation to the lower legs. Although the ANSI/HFS Standard 100 gives a recommended seat depth for office chairs of 38–43 cm, Goonetilleke and Feizhou (2001) report that is too long for shorter people; they found 31–33 cm was better for the South China region population.

4.2.2 *Backrests*

The prime function of the backrest is to take a load off the back—to rest the back. This works only if there is contact between the back and the backrest. The ideal backrest is adjustable both horizontally and vertically. In the best design, the backrest has a spring action so that the backrest "tracks" with the back and thus moves in and out as the back moves in and out. It should be relatively small if there is arm movement and elbow impact is to be avoided.

The shape should be concave to give area support to the back, especially in the lumbar region. It should be stiffly upholstered and covered with fabric, not a nonpermeable material. See Table 13.3 for recommended dimensions. Note that seats without good backrests (e.g., most automobile seats, nonadjustable chairs) can be retrofitted with a small pillow placed between the back and the backrest.

4.2.3 *Armrests*

Armrests support the arms and thus take some load off the ischial tuberosities. However, they do restrict movement and may prevent a chair being brought close to a workstation. A possible solution is to use short armrests that support the elbows but do not restrict placing the chair next to the worksurface. A chair with only one arm may be an alternative.

A common design error in lounge furniture is to have armrests (sides) that are far too high. Check armrest height by looking at shoulder posture. If the shoulders slump, the armrest is too low; if the shoulders hunch up, the armrest is too high. If the posture is relatively fixed (precise assembly), consider support pads on the table. See Figure 13.18. For keying work,

---

FIGURE 13.17

Footrests should be flat and adjustable. Flat is better than round due to reduced pressure on the foot. This specific model has a 3/4 inch vertical adjustment (other models adjust up to 8 inches); the angle adjusts up to 30°. (Photo courtesy of AliMed, Inc.)

FIGURE 13.18

Arm supports prevent sharp edges of furniture from creating pressure points on the forearms. Various models give 2–5 inches of support. For operators working along a conveyor, use pressure pads to reduce pressure points on the thighs. (Photo courtesy of AliMed, Inc.)

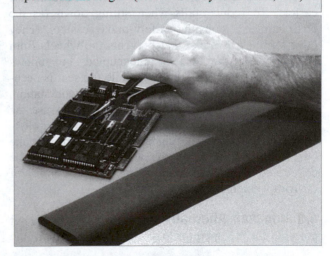

consider wrist supports. A pad is placed at the front edge of the keyboard, and the wrists rest on it while not keying (for example, while proofreading or waiting for the computer to complete a search). Note that if repetitive keying is done while the arms are supported on armrests, the elbows are held farther from the body than if there are no armrests. This, in turn, increases the radial and ulnar deviation at the wrist.

4.2.4 *Legs/pedestal*

In most circumstances the seat should swivel. (An exception is when operating a pedal.) If the task requires turning the torso and the operator is locked into position by a chair seat that does not swivel, there is twisting in the torso. In addition, a swivel seat permits micro adjustments in posture, may permit easier entrance and exit from the chair, and increases the operator's range of reach.

If the chair has a pedestal with 4 or 5 horizontal supports, the horizontal supports should be designed to minimize tipping. Minimize the tip angle (the angle from the vertical at which the unloaded chair will tip completely). Generally, this requires 5 legs, each 72° apart (rather than 4 legs 90° apart). The feet should be set in a circle at least as big as the seat itself. Chaffin et al. (1999) recommend a minimum radius of 300 mm to prevent the chair from tipping over and a maximum radius of 350 mm to prevent the worker from tripping over the chair base.

Design the seat so users can tuck their legs under the seat. This will shorten the hamstrings (reducing their pull), making it easier on the back. Experience this yourself by sitting on a table with your legs fully extended in front of you (90° trunk–thigh angle). You will feel the hamstring pull and resulting back stress. Then rotate your body 90° and let your legs hang over the table side. The hamstring pull disappears and back stress decreases.

For non-workstation chair applications such as in restaurants, physician's offices, and other "guest" applications, use chairs without casters. In workstations where the seated worker moves around, use casters. To reduce falls when sitting down (as the chair moves), consider safety-brake casters. They have an internal brake that prevents the wheels from rolling when the seat is unoccupied, but allows smooth, effortless chair rolling while the seat is occupied. If the chair is not moved around the workstation, don't use casters; they force the operator to use leg muscles to keep the chair from moving. Another alternative is to mount the chair on rails to permit the operator to move along the workstation yet not be concerned with chair stability or precise control of chair movements.

4.3 Nonchair Alternatives

In some jobs, it is not possible for the operator to sit on a chair 100% of the time. In that case, permit the operator to sit for a smaller percent of the time. For example, some firms have pull-down benches mounted along the walls. During rest breaks, the operators can sit instead of stand. Or assume a service counter operator (e.g., bank teller, airline service agent) stands while serving the customer. If you can't get management to consider a seated workstation, suggest pull-out seats for use when there are no customers.

Another alternative is a sit–stand stool where the person's legs are almost vertical. The post office uses such a stool for people manually sorting letters to bins. The adjustable height (65–85 cm) seat should tilt forward 15°–30°. These slopes were useful in upholstery work even when they could be used only 15% of the time. Michel and Helander (1994) found that sit-stand stools were more comfortable than chairs for people with herniated discs, while conventional chairs were more comfortable for those with healthy discs.

Chester et al. (2001) compared sitting, standing, and sit/stand for 90 min. Standing was less comfortable than sit/stand (which supports about 2/3 of body weight). Standing especially caused lower leg and foot discomfort. For the sit/stand chair, Chester et al. (2002) reported a 90° footrest–calf angle was better than no footrest (120° footrest–calf angle) or a 105° footrest-calf angle.

Sit–stand seats can be supported from the floor (generally with a single "leg"), from the front of the workbench, or from overhead (generally on a rail so the person can move the seat along the rail while working). In any case, prevent sliding of the seat backward. Another alternative used for keying operations is the Balens kneeler (see Figure 13.16). Kneelers generally fatigue the knees, but they can be used for short periods (e.g., 30 min) several times per day.

4.4 Seating Posture Variability

Evidence has shown that even with an "optimum" chair design, people still have back pain—if they sit in one posture all day. Physiologically, this seems to be connected with nutrition of the intervertebral disc. The disc is avascular and depends upon diffusion for its nutrition. Diffusion takes place when there are alternations of pressure on the disc (Grieco, 1986; Bendix, 1986). Prolonged sitting also causes discomfort in the buttocks (due to surface pressure) and increases foot volume. Van Dieen et al. (2001), while investigating dynamic chairs, reported that all of the chairs tested increased back stature; this was interpreted as a positive effect as it reflects an influx of fluids and nutrients into the avascular disc.

Sitting posture variability can be accomplished in a number of ways. One way is to walk. A worker can walk to the office door to welcome a visitor and then sit in a different chair from the normal work chair. (If the different chair is not behind a desk, the relationship with the visitor becomes less formal.) The worker can walk to the printer or walk to another part of the office to get the mail. Thus, to encourage walking, you may wish to remove visitor chairs from offices and require the use of adjacent conference rooms.

Another way is to stand occasionally—such as when using the phone. The phone should be on a surface so that writing notes is possible; a footrest is desirable.

Grieco (1986) recommends a "physiological pause" of 15 min for every 75 min of seated work. From an economic viewpoint, this need not be idle time but just different work. Design the job so people do not sit continuously. Possible techniques are to have the word processor operator get the mail and sort it; the inspector or operator get a supply of parts (instead of having them furnished by a material handler); a receptionist/secretary stand when dealing with a customer but sit when keying; or the secretary run the copy machine as well as key. Movement also gives the eyes a chance to rest.

Sitting behavior is influenced by the task, the chair, and the training of the person doing the sitting. Rather than focusing solely on the chair, encourage posture variability by focusing on the task and education. Education of the person doing the sitting can focus on disc nutrition and backache problems and how they can be reduced by activity—both on and off the job.

5 USE THE FEET AS WELL AS THE HANDS

The foot moves more slowly than the hand and, due to the construction of the ankle versus the wrist and the weight of the leg vs. the arm, it is not as dexterous.

For power generated from muscles, **human power** (in contrast to power from machines), the 2 legs have approximately 3 times the power of the 2 arms; the arms are slightly more efficient per kg of muscle, but the legs have much more muscle. With 2 arms a man can generate about 1/25 hp; with 2 legs about 1/10 hp; that's why you power a bicycle with your legs, not your arms. The 1/10 hp estimate is based on a long-term human work rate of 5 kcal/min and 20% efficiency, yielding a 1 kcal/min work output. (1 hp = 746 W = 10.7 kcal/ min.)

Don't use pedals for standing work, as the body would be supported unevenly. In addition, weight on the entire leg or even the entire body must be moved. Although the muscles can compensate for the unnec-

essary strain, the resulting unnecessary energy expenditure, pain, and fatigue are a reflection on the engineer's competence. In addition, since the operator is off balance, reaction time in an emergency is increased. (However, proving there is an exception to every rule, Halpern and Dawson (1997) reported that they developed a pedal with a pivot point in the center that could support the leg while standing; the pedal was actuated by a shift in body weight.)

Pedals can be used for power and control.

5.1 Power Power generation can be continuous (bicycle) or discrete (nonpowered automobile brake pedal).

Continuous power usually is generated with both limbs with a rotary pedal arrangement so each limb can rest for 50% of the cycle although output is continuous. Ancient Greek ships (e.g., 500 B.C.) maximized power by using a sliding seat (which allowed the legs to produce more power). The technique was forgotten but rediscovered in the 1870s (Hale, 1996). Bicycle pedaling (at 20% to 25% efficiency for an experienced cyclist) is first in efficiency among traveling animals and machines. For more on human power generation, see Whitt and Wilson (1982) and Brooks et al. (1986).

Discrete power usually is applied by one leg since application time usually is less than 10 s and thus fatigue is not a problem. There does not seem to be any power advantage to using the right or left foot. Force using both feet is about 10% higher than that using a single foot, but since people will not always use both feet, the designer should not design for use of both feet.

Force capability depends on a number of factors, but individual capability and pedal location are important. See the discussion in Chapter 17.

5.2 Control An example application of a foot pedal for continuous control is the auto accelerator. Examples of discrete (on–off) applications are a pedal-controlled punch press and an automobile foot switch for high–low beam. See Chapter 17.

In most industrial situations, the time it takes a person to move a foot to a control is not important because the movement can be done at the operator's leisure or can be done simultaneously with some other motion. However, in vehicles, control time is important. Time to move the foot from an accelerator pedal to a brake pedal is about .55 s; if the pedal acts as a rocker switch and your foot is already on the pedal, it takes about .28 s to move the foot from a toe-depressed position to a heel-depressed position (Konz et al., 1971).

Using a conventional brake pedal with your foot resting on the brake, you can save about .27 s (about 1 car length at 60 mph) over moving your foot from the accelerator. However, with present pedal designs, poising the left foot on the brake pedal is tiring, so you should use left-foot braking only in heavy traffic. All the above times include signal-detection time (time to detect a red light), decision time (time to decide to push the pedal), and effector time (time for the nerve impulse to travel to the foot and the foot to act).

USE GRAVITY; DON'T OPPOSE IT

Consider the weight of the body and weight of the work.

6.1 Body   Holding 25 g of feathers also requires holding 4,500 g of arm. Therefore, make movements horizontal or downward—avoid lifting.

In certain circumstances, the weight of the human body can be used to increase the force on a lever or pedal. From a conservation of energy viewpoint, this is just a substitution of potential energy for kinetic energy with no net gain. The key practical point, however, is that the kinetic energy can be applied over a period of time and the potential energy can be released all at once. An example is a wheel with a ratchet and a release.

6.2 Work   Gravity can be used to move material to the work. Examples are paint from a paintbrush, a welding bead from a welding rod, and solder on a solder joint. Gravity also can be used to hold components before assembly, called **gravity as a fixture.** For example, contrast driving a screw into the ceiling with doing it horizontally or vertically downward.

Use gravity in the feeding and disposal of components. Vibratory feeders (see Figure 13.19) use gravity to orient components mechanically before they are fed into machines. Since orienting parts can be done by machine at low cost, less care is needed for part orientation during disposal from the previous operation.

Defective parts fall back into the central reservoir, which eventually fills up with rejects. Thus, consider using two feeders in sequence. The first feeder is an "inspector" and sorts good from bad parts (e.g., screws without heads, without slots). The second feeder is loaded with good parts from the first feeder; it feeds the production machine.

An additional advantage of the vibratory feeder is that the inexpensive orientation of parts for feeding permits parts ejected from the *preceding* operation to fall in a random orientation. If the component is fragile, cushion the fall of the ejected part with a chute. (A chute also permits horizontal transportation at zero labor cost.) For greater distances, use gravity wheel conveyors. For maximum use of the floor space while still using gravity, use spiral conveyors and chutes.

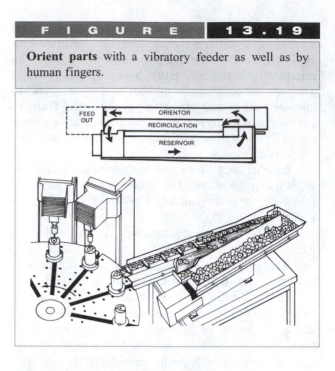

FIGURE   13.19

Orient parts with a vibratory feeder as well as by human fingers.

CONSERVE MOMENTUM

The goal of conserving momentum is to avoid unnecessary **acceleration** (increase in speed) and **deceleration** (decrease in speed) since they take both time and energy. For example, in the MTM-1 predetermined time system, an 18-in type B reach takes 17.2 TMU but only 10.5 TMU if the hand is in motion at the start or end of the reach.

7.1 Stirring and Polishing Motions   There are a number of operations in which the arm is in relatively continuous motion. An ancient example was the conversion of grain to flour with a mortar and pestle. This pounding, with its acceleration and deceleration of the hand, was replaced by grinding in a circular motion. Eventually water power replaced muscles for this job, and now the millstone is powered by mechanical power.

Figure 13.20 shows how this same principle applies to hand-polishing operations, whether they are with a rag (in a factory or on your car) or performed with pressure applied by the end of a pole or hose (broom, mop, vacuum cleaner). Writing vs. printing is another example. In a kitchen, stirring soup represents the same principle. (If there is insufficient mixing of product with circular stirring in a circular container, use a rectangular container to furnish the turbulence rather than using a zigzag motion.) Bicycle pedals are another example of the principle of circular motion.

7.2 Disposal Motions   Acceleration/deceleration can be minimized in disposal motions. In sports, an important principle is to "follow through" to impart

Avoid sharp decelerations in vacuum sweeper, mop, and hand polishing operations (Barnes, 1940).

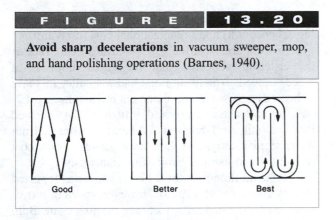

| Good | Better | Best |

maximum velocity and to minimize deviations from the desired path. Abrupt deceleration gives poor performance. Figure 13.21 shows how abrupt deceleration can be avoided when loading/unloading a punch press. Reduce precise disposal of completed units; instead, toss them aside. If the unit might be damaged by abrupt deceleration, cushion its fall with a resilient surface or by using chutes. If the part must be oriented for the following operation, orient the part with a vibratory feeder.

In addition to reducing the strain on the body, there are considerable time benefits. For example, using MTM technology (see Chapter 29), an 18-inch move to toss aside a part is an M18E and an RL1—a total of .63 s. A precise placement would require an M18B, a P1SE, and an RL1—a total of .89 s. This is

an increase of 42%. In addition, the precise placement usually requires eye control, so other motions cannot be done simultaneously.

7.3 Grasping Motions   Grasping motions can affect acceleration/deceleration. Figure 13.22 shows how the sharp edge of a bin can be modified with a rolled edge. If there is a rolled edge the operator does not need to slow down to prevent injury. Figure 13.23 shows how the thickness of the tabletop can affect the speed of grasping small objects (such as coins) from a flat surface. With a thick tabletop, the hand must come to a stop for a precise grasp. A thin tabletop permits the fingers to slide the object to the edge and then get a good grasp. A thin table with a small front lip improves the ease of the grasp even more.

Eliminate grasping by sliding the item to a hole for a drop disposal. Demonstrate the time benefit by sliding 25 pennies to a hole vs. picking up 25 pennies and putting them in a cup. The table lip also reduces the chance of objects rolling off the table and gives a more favorable hand orientation. (Note the counter design at McDonald's.)

7.4 Transport Motions   It requires extra effort and extra time to transport weight in the hand—a **weight penalty.** Figure 13.24 shows the recommendations given by three predetermined time systems, as well as some experimental data. The amount of extra time is

Avoid sharp deceleration by placing bins so the operator can grasp or dispose "on the fly." The top sketch shows the right hand inserting the part and automatic disposal. The lower sketch shows the right hand inserting and the left hand removing the part.

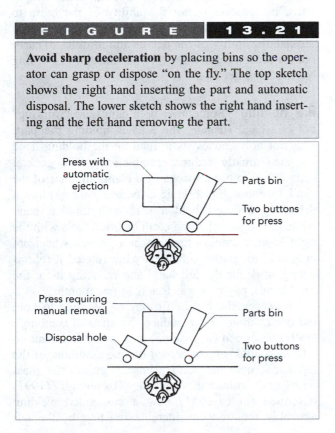

Avoid knife edges on bins by using a rolled edge.

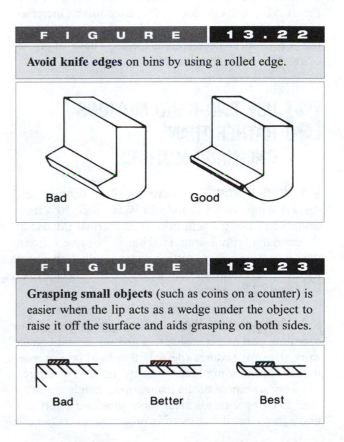

Grasping small objects (such as coins on a counter) is easier when the lip acts as a wedge under the object to raise it off the surface and aids grasping on both sides.

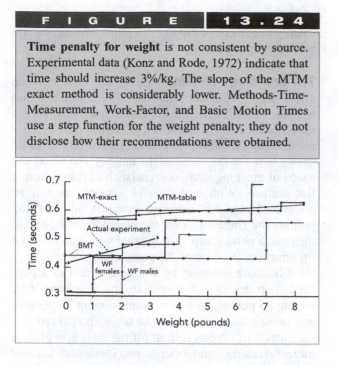

Time penalty for weight is not consistent by source. Experimental data (Konz and Rode, 1972) indicate that time should increase 3%/kg. The slope of the MTM exact method is considerably lower. Methods-Time-Measurement, Work-Factor, and Basic Motion Times use a step function for the weight penalty; they do not disclose how their recommendations were obtained.

indicated by the slope of the lines; the intercept indicates varying definitions of a normal pace.

Our study was concerned with only the *control* effects of the additional weight; fatigue effects are additional. The increase in time per move is 3%/kg. The increase in physiological cost (as measured by the integrated output of the three axes of a force platform) was 6%/kg. Since the time/move increased 3%/kg, this is an increase of about 6 − 3 = 3%/kg in the acceleration–deceleration forces. These values are compatible with Ayoub's (1966).

8 USE TWO-HAND MOTIONS RATHER THAN ONE-HAND MOTIONS

8.1 Human Power Andrews (1967) demonstrated that cranking, for loads up to 25 W, required 10% fewer watts when using 1 arm instead of 2 arms. Beyond 25 W, cranking with 2 arms is about 25% more efficient than with 1 arm. For exerting a static pull, 1-arm work required 42% more watts at a 5 kg load, 18% at a 10 kg load, and 127% more at a 15 kg load.

8.2 Manipulative Work Use jigs (guides tool or operating part of a machine to a precise location on the work item) or fixtures (devices that hold one or more items for processing). Don't use the hand as a fixture.

For movement of the hand/arm, 2 hands are better than 1. Using 2 hands takes more time and effort than using just 1 hand, but more is produced so cost/unit is

lower. The reduced cost is both individual cost (physiological cost/unit) and organizational cost (time/unit).

Nichols and Amrine (1959), using heart rate as the criterion, reported that for equal amounts of pieces moved, 1-hand motions had a smaller increase in heart rate than nonsimultaneous but symmetrical 2-hand motions. Salvendy and Pilitsis (1974) showed that kcal/min of 1-hand and 2-hand motions did not differ significantly, and thus, on a per-unit basis, cost was less when using 2 hands simultaneously.

Reduced time/unit for 2 hands vs. 1 was reported first by Barnes et al. (1940). However, speed of movement is confounded with accuracy of movement. Both speed and accuracy can be combined into one index, bits/second. See Box 13.3.

Konz et al. (1969) had subjects move a stylus at 7 angles and 2 distances with one or two hands. Using just the preferred hand gave 61% of the bits/s of two-hand motions (21.2 bits/s), and the non-preferred hand gave 55%. The body can produce about 8–9 bits/s more with 2 hands than 1 hand. The maximum effect of the visual field (difference in angle) was about 3 bits/s. These values are compatible with Langolf et al. (1976), who reported fingers could process 38 bits/s, wrists 23, and arms only 10.

It seems the bottleneck in the output of the brain–eye–muscle system is neither the brain (command system) nor the eyes (tracking subsystem) but, rather, the muscles and nerves (effector and feedback subsystem). The limiting factor in hand–arm manipulative movements is not the ability of the brain to command or ability of the eyes to supervise but, instead, the ability of the nerves and muscles to carry out the orders. Remember this, as "the spirit is willing but the flesh is weak."

8.3 Holding Sometimes both hands are "working" but one hand (usually the left) is holding the part. This not only causes static load on the holding hand but also greatly reduces productivity. The general approach is to use a mechanical clamp in place of the hand. Oxenburgh (1991) described (in case 43) how a deburring operator held a part with the left hand while moving a polishing cloth or small tools with the right hand; clamping the part in a potter's wheel not only held the part mechanically but rotated it (eliminating work for the left hand and reducing it for the right hand); payback was less than one month.

However, the hand still may be required to hold the object; then try to reduce the stress. Oxenburgh (1991) described (in case 45) how, in cutting meat on a table, a hook supplemented the meat holding of the left hand; now the hand primarily guides the meat with only minimal exertion. Oxenburgh (1991) described (in case 51) how a suspended welding assembly required considerable twisting by the left

13.3 | *Information Content of Motions*

Shannon (1948) defined information in terms of a signal-to-noise ratio transmitted from a transmitter over a channel to a receiver. Since the ratio was logarithmic and log to the base 2 ($\log_2$) customarily has been used, the unit of information commonly has been called a **bit,** short for *bi*nary digi*t.* Fitts (1954) and Fitts and Peterson (1964) developed this concept into a formula for hand–arm movements. Fitts' concept was that any movement was limited by the amount of information to be processed. Fitts used distance of the move as the signal and width of the target as noise. **Fitts' law** is

$$ I = \log_2 \frac{D}{W/2} $$

where

I = Information/move, bits

D = Distance of the move

W = Width (in movement direction) of target

In summary, a bigger target (the D) and less accuracy (the $W/2$) take less time. You can quantify the effect with the formulas or by using the MTM tables in Chapter 29.

The validity of this formula has been confirmed by others, especially in a series of elegant investigations by Hoffman (1991a, 1991b); Hoffman (1991a) showed it applied also to foot motions.

Fitts' law can be solved to determine movement time:

$$ MT = a + b\,I $$

where MT = Movement time, ms

a = constant

b = constant

Fitts' law for arm motions is only applicable for visually controlled motions—that is, when $ID > 3$. When $ID < 3$, the motion is ballistic and just amplitude (but not target width) is important. Hoffman (1991a) gives the following:

$$ HMT = 56.6 + 4.43\,A^{.5} $$
$$ ID < 3 \text{ bits (ballistic)} $$
$$ -56.9 + 59.2\,ID $$
$$ 3 < ID < 6 \text{ bits (visually controlled)} $$
$$ FMT = 107.5 + 6.5\,A^{.5} $$
$$ ID < 3 \text{ bits (ballistic)} $$
$$ = -57.7 + 115\,ID - 34.6 \log_2 (W) $$
$$ 3 < ID < 6 \text{ bits (visually controlled)} $$

where HMT = Hand movement (discrete, not reciprocal) time, ms

FMT = Foot movement (discrete, not reciprocal) time, ms

A = Movement amplitude, m

ID = Index of difficulty, bits

W = Target width, mm

The foot takes about 1.7 times as long as the hand for ballistic movements and 2 times as long for visually controlled movements.

---

hand holding the assembly while the right hand triggered the spotwelder. A circular grip permitted a more friendly posture; a ball grip (as on some auto steering wheels) also would work.

Another alternative is a "backstop" against which the object being worked on can be held. This replaces holding (with weak finger muscles) with pushing (with stronger arm and shoulder muscles).

USE PARALLEL MOTIONS FOR EYE CONTROL OF TWO-HAND MOTIONS

Gilbreth (1911) first stated:

When work is done with two hands simultaneously, it can be quickest and with least mental effort, particularly if the work is done by both

hands in a similar manner, that is to say, when one hand makes the same motions to the right as the other does to the left.

Barnes (1940) was more concise:

Motions of the arms should be made in opposite and symmetrical directions, and should be made simultaneously.

However, Barnes also stated:

Eye fixations should be as few and as close together as possible.

Which principle has precedence? Figure 13.25 poses the dilemma.

The conclusion, using both time/unit and physiological cost/unit, is to minimize the degree of spread rather than worry about the symmetry of the motions (Konz, 1983; Raouf and Tsuchiya, 1986). The problem with spread is the cost of eye control. See Figure 13.26.

Parallel vs. symmetrical motions. When is each best?

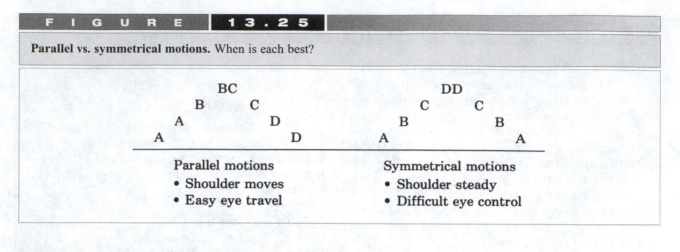

Parallel motions
- Shoulder moves
- Easy eye travel

Symmetrical motions
- Shoulder steady
- Difficult eye control

Proper location of the disposal chute reduces eye control as well as conserving momentum.

The various predetermined time systems enable us to estimate the cost of eye control. The two eye activities are a change in viewing distance—**eye focus**—and a change in line of sight—**eye travel.** The normal **area of vision** is a circle with a 100 mm (4 inch) diameter at a viewing distance of 400 mm (16 inches).

Eye focus is allocated .0044 minutes by MTM. The version of MTM used by General Motors gives .0020 min for eye focus, .0030 for eye reaction, and .0030 for eye interpretation.

Eye travel is .009 *(W/D)* in the MTM system, where W is the distance between the points and D is the perpendicular distance to the line of travel. General Motors gives a flat .0050. In Work-Factor, it is called eye shift. For a shift of 0° to 5°, time = .0004, which increases to .0015 for a 40° shift; beyond 40° it is called a head or body turn. White et al. (1962) give .0012 min for a 10° shift, .0015 min for a 20° shift, and .0020 min for a 40° shift.

USE ROWING MOTIONS FOR TWO-HAND MOTIONS

When moving both hands, should the hands move in a rowing motion or an alternating motion?

Nichols and Armine (1959) reported that alternating motions had heart rates 1.5 beats/min higher than when the same motions were performed in a rowing manner. Konz, Jeans, and Rathore (1969) reported that force platform output (i.e., work cost) was 10% greater when alternating motions were used in place of rowing motions. In both of these studies, the work output was controlled to be the same for alternating and rowing motions.

For both types of motions, the hands move in a relatively flat plane with considerable acceleration and deceleration at each end of the stroke. Alternation, however, has more movement of the shoulder and twisting of the torso. See also Section 9.

Note that for human generation of power (bicycle, winch), the handles or pedals are arranged so that the arms or legs alternate strokes while the path is circular to conserve momentum. Harrison (1970) demonstrated that maximum power output came from a device in which both pedals were at the same angular position on both sides of the hub instead of the 180° out of phase used for bicycles. A large flywheel was used to return the pedals for the power stroke. In addition, a "forced" motion, in which kinetic energy of the limbs was fed back into the mechanical system, had greater power output than a "free" motion, in which the kinetic energy was absorbed by the limbs.

PIVOT MOTIONS ABOUT THE ELBOW

The question is: For horizontal movements at a height, does direction of movement affect (1) movement speed, (2) movement accuracy, and (3) movement physiological cost?

Yes. Yes. Yes.

Figure 13.27 shows the effect of various **movement angles** on motion time. The least time is with a pivot about the elbow (i.e., movement of only the forearm), and maximum time is a pivot about the

Effects of movement angles on motion time. Pivoting about the elbow takes less time than cross-body movements (Konz, Jeans, and Rathore, 1969; Konz and Rode, 1972). Output at 90° (straight ahead, with 0° as 3 o'clock) is defined as 100%.

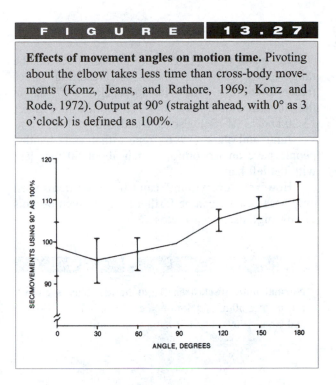

Effect of various angles on accuracy. Preferred hand is more accurate. In addition, maximum accuracy for a hand is better for cross-body movements than pivoting about the elbow (Konz, Jeans, and Rathore, 1969; Konz and Rode, 1972). 0° = 3 o'clock.

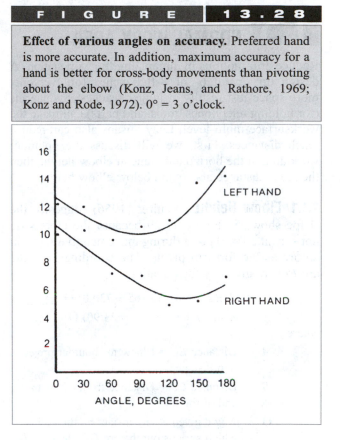

shoulder (movement of both the forearm and upper arm). As a rule of thumb, use standard time for movements pivoted about the elbow (say 30°–60° for the right hand, 150°–180° for the left), give 5% additional time for straight-ahead moves (say 60°–120° for either hand), and give 15% additional time for cross-body moves (over 120° for the right hand, below 60° for the left).

Figure 13.28 shows the effect of various angles on accuracy. The somewhat surprising conclusion is that cross-body movements (i.e., pivoted only on the shoulder) are more accurate than movements pivoted about the elbow.

Physiological cost of movements at various angles has been studied by a number of people, including Konz and Rode (1972). Physiological cost is lower for movements pivoted about the elbow. (Moving the total arm and hand requires moving 4.9% of body weight; moving just the forearm and hand requires moving 2.3% of body weight.) Thus, although cross-body movements are more accurate, they require more effort by the person and, as Figure 13.27 shows, they take about 15% more time. Avoid them. Encourage elbow pivoting motions by putting bins ahead of the shoulder—not straight ahead of the nose.

USE THE PREFERRED HAND

The **dominant hand** (preferred hand) is about 10% faster for reach-type motions; it also is more accurate (Konz, Jeans, and Rathore, 1969). The

preferred hand, because it is used more, gets more practice. The good news is that it is farther down the learning curve and thus faster; the bad news is that it is more exposed to cumulative trauma. The preferred hand is 5% to 10% stronger (Dickson et al., 1972; Kroemer, 1974). About 10% of the population uses the left hand as the preferred hand.

In addition to a dominant hand, you have a **dominant eye** (your "shooting" eye). You can check which eye is the dominant one by holding out your arm. Align an object with your thumb. Close one eye. If the object moved, you closed your dominant eye. Fisher (1974) studied 300 people; 88% used the right hand as the writing hand (the writing hand is the best single indicator of which side of a person is dominant), in 60% the right eye was the dominant eye, and in 54% the right eye was the more acute eye. There was a nonsignificant relationship between the writing hand and eye dominance and acuity but a significant relationship between dominant eye and most acute eye.

In general, work should come into a workstation from the operator's preferred side and leave from the nonpreferred side. The reason is that reach and grasp are more difficult motions than dispose and release. Avoid transfer grasps. However, obtaining the new item on the same side as the disposal eliminates a body turn.

13 KEEP ARM MOTIONS IN THE NORMAL WORK AREA

Reduce arm motions by organizing the workstation. A design tip: Avoid 6- or 8-ft benches for everyone; more space just results in longer reaches. Swingarms (for holding telephones, tools, and parts) can make the worksurface multi-level. Lazy Susans also can reduce reach distances. First, we will discuss the optimum work area in the horizontal plane at elbow height, then the reach distance above and below elbow height.

13.1 Elbow Height Squires (1956) suggested the shape shown in Figure 13.29 because the elbows do not stay at a fixed point during movement but move in an arc as the forearm pivots. The coordinates of the arc PQ are given by the equation:

$$x = A \cos \Theta + B \cos (65 + 73/90) \Theta$$
$$y = A \sin \Theta + B \sin (65 + 73/90) \Theta$$

where

A = Distance EC = Elbow to shoulder projection distance

B = Distance CP = Distance from elbow to end of thumb

Θ = Angle given at any instant by the radius which sweeps out the arc DC, degrees; D = Point at which $\Theta = 0$;

C = Point at which $\Theta = 90$.

Konz and Goel (1969) determined values for the range of the U. S. population. The resulting values (reach to end of thumb with no "back assist") depict the **normal work area** and are plotted in Figures 13.30 and 13.31. See also Das and Grady (1983).

Jung and Park (1996) report that right-handed people have an isocomfort reach about 50 mm less with the left hand.

However, "everything" can't be close; items used only occasionally can be farther away. Remember this as "for high use, keep it close."

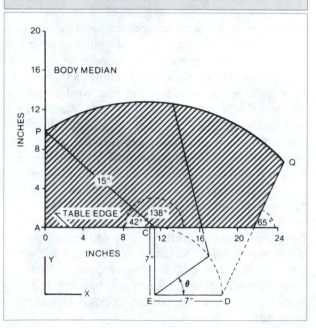

FIGURE 13.29

"Windshield wiper" pattern. This is shown for the right hand (Squires, 1956). *CD* is the projection of the right elbow during movement of the hand from point P to Q.

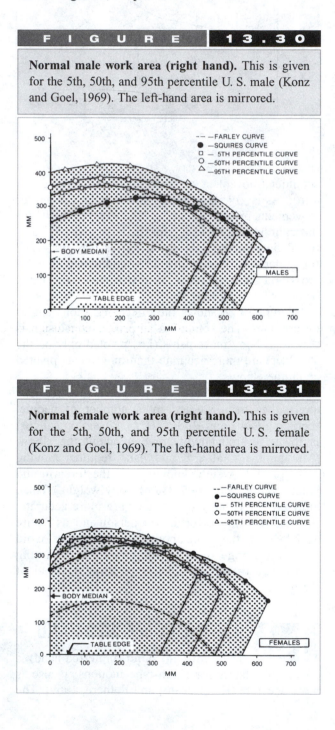

FIGURE 13.30

Normal male work area (right hand). This is given for the 5th, 50th, and 95th percentile U. S. male (Konz and Goel, 1969). The left-hand area is mirrored.

FIGURE 13.31

Normal female work area (right hand). This is given for the 5th, 50th, and 95th percentile U. S. female (Konz and Goel, 1969). The left-hand area is mirrored.

13.2 Reach at All Heights　Figure 13.32 is a general guide for average U. S. workers (males and females combined). It assumes reach distances are the same for sitting as for standing. Sengupta and Das (2000), however, report that, on average, maximum reach for females was 13% less than for males. They also reported that standing reach distance was about 5 cm greater than for sitting—probably due to a change in the spinal curve and increased scope for upper body mobility. Note that Figure 13.32 shows horizontal reach distance, while standing decreases quickly for heights below the waist.

For the effect of horizontal angle, remember the arm pivots on the shoulder, not the nose, so it is easier to reach ahead of the shoulder than ahead of the nose. For angles outside the shoulder, the reach distance for the hand on that side decreases rapidly since the elbow pivots (see Figure 13.29). O'Sullivan and Gallwey (2002) report that the shoulder is especially sensitive to small changes in workplace layout. Therefore, rather than use the same assembly station for the tall and the small, lower the worksurface (or raise the seat) for the tall and move the bins inward for the small.

Just because it is possible to reach these distances does not mean it is desirable. Closer is better. See Figure 15.24 and Section 6.9 in Chapter 15.

In some larger assemblies (such as aircraft, automobiles), components may restrict access to other components. It may be desirable to install a component, then remove it temporarily to permit access, and then reinstall it. Nagamachi and Matsubara (1994) described the "doorless assembly system" used by Mazda, Ford, Honda, and Toyota (among others). The doors are first assembled to the vehicle frame, painted with the frame, removed while the remainder of the interior is assembled, and then remounted.

Reach distance into bins that are loaded from the rear can be decreased by having the bin bottom slant toward the operator. Have the entire front of the bin open (although a strip across the top may be needed for rigidity).

Allow enough space for standing workers' feet. A space 150 mm × 150 mm × 500 mm wide (6 in. × 6 in. × 20 in.) is sufficient. See Figure 13.35. If there is rotating machinery near the toe, a guard gap 150 mm above the floor probably will be sufficiently small (Bottoms and Butterworth, 1990).

14 LET THE SMALL PERSON REACH; LET THE LARGE PERSON FIT

As was pointed out in Chapter 5, the designer designs to include a certain proportion of the population rather than for the population mean. If the designer selects a chair to fit under a table but uses the 50th percentile thigh dimension, 50% of the people will not fit under the table.

Therefore, design to permit most of the user population to use the design. An alternative statement is "Exclude few." Another statement is "Design for the tall; accommodate the small."

14.1 User Population　The problem in selecting a specific population has become more difficult for the engineer. Some points to consider:

- Jobs now must be designed for both sexes.
- Multiperson use of equipment and workstations is becoming more common with greater shift work and more part-time workers. That is, people of different dimensions will be using the equipment—either within the same shift (e.g., 10 different people use the photocopy machine) or over multiple shifts (e.g., 3 different police officers use the same vehicle over a 24-hour period). Thus, easy equipment adjustability becomes important.
- Civilian industrial population data are not the same as military population data. Military populations heavily emphasize youth and physical fitness and are primarily male. General popula-

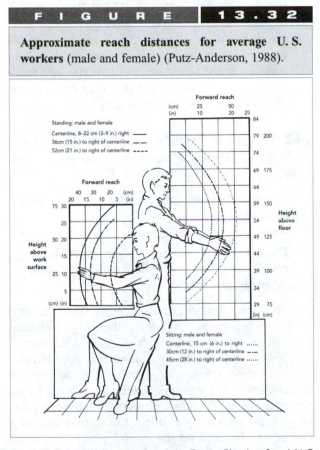

FIGURE 13.32

Approximate reach distances for average U. S. workers (male and female) (Putz-Anderson, 1988).

Source: V. Putz-Anderson, (ed.). *Cumulative Trauma Disorders.* Copyright © 1988 by Taylor and Francis, London. Reprinted with permission.

FIGURE   **13.33**

Good and poor design features. Five desirable design features are shown in the good layout (Rodgers, 1984). Can you find them? First, the operator has a 90° turn to the pallet instead of a 180° turn to the pallet. Second, there is a shorter reach to the cartons since the long axis of the pallet is parallel to the shoulders instead of perpendicular. Third, there is a shorter horizontal reach to the conveyor. Fourth, there is less vertical reach down to the pallet. Finally, there is storage under the work table.

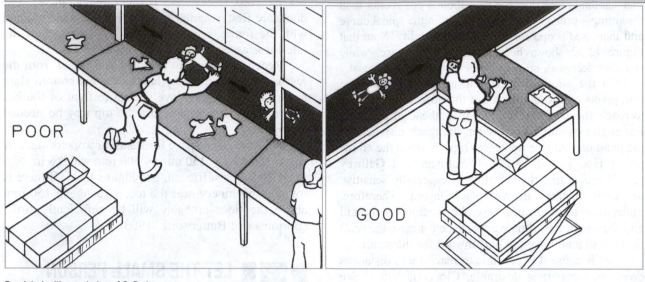

Reprinted with permission of S. Rodgers.

FIGURE   **13.34**

Four ways of reducing strain from forward reaches (Rodgers, 1984). (a) Reaching for a control behind a barrier can be reduced by putting a long handle on the control. (b) A hook can help a worker obtain cartons when order picking from the second-level rack. (c) An extension to a tool. (d) A cutout in the table moves the man closer to the conveyor. If you don't want to cut a semicircle in the table, don't have a table at all between the operator and the conveyor; just have a table to the left and right of the operator.

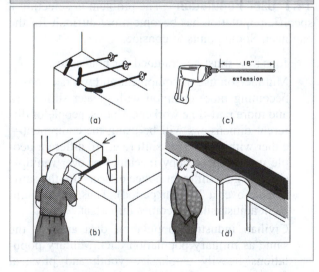

Reprinted with permission of S. Rodgers.

tion data for adults include retired people as well as those who have never worked.

■ International populations may have to be considered. Many countries have "guest workers." In addition, many firms are multinational with facilities in many countries and thus may use the same workstation in multiple countries.

14.2 Percent to Exclude   As indicated in Figure 13.36, people can be excluded from the job in three ways:

1. Exclude the lower percentiles (e.g., short people or weak people).
2. Exclude the upper percentiles (e.g., tall people).
3. Exclude both lower and upper percentiles (e.g., people with low and high intelligence from an assembly-line job).

The proportion to exclude depends upon the seriousness of being designed out and the cost of including more people. In some cases, a design can accommodate both the tall and the small at no cost. For example, when selecting the height of hooks for hanging the operator's personal protection clothing, place the hooks conveniently for the small person; the tall person has no problem with a lower hook. Consider design of a tote box to be used on the assembly line. We might design the box to hold a weight that 90% of the population could lift. In other words, 10% would be

FIGURE 13.35

Allowing room (150 × 150 × 500 mm) for the feet (DeLaura and Konz, 1990). Even better would be to also allow room for the knees (say 100 mm) by indenting the lower portion of the support.

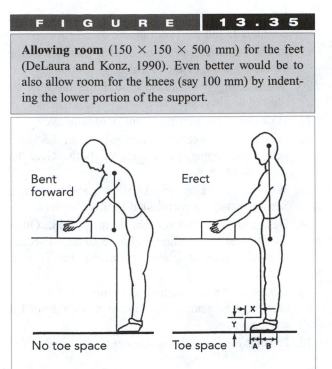

FIGURE 13.36

Excluding people from jobs can be done in three ways. Excluding 10% can mean excluding the upper percentile, some from each end, or the lower percentile.

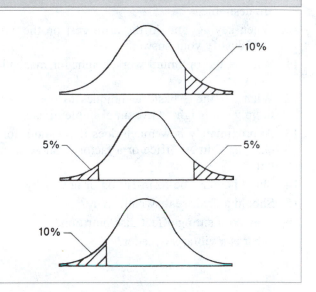

excluded. This might give, for example, a total load of 20 kg. If you would like to exclude fewer, then the load would drop, perhaps to 18 kg. In this case, excluding fewer gives a continuing lower productivity—a tradeoff of including more people and making the movement easier for everyone vs. the cost of requiring more movements. Or consider the design of a door height. A height of 80 inches would require that only a small percent of people duck their heads. However, increasing the height to 86 inches would include effectively 100% of the population. There would be no continuing cost and perhaps a small additional initial cost. However, the cost to the person of ducking the head is small also. As a rule of thumb, the UAW-Ford design guide excludes 5% of women for reach, 5% of men for clearance, and 0% of men and women for safety.

Exclusion can be for dimensions other than size, such as language, strength, vision, and so forth. In general, exclusion has become less acceptable. To include many (exclude few), the three basic alternatives are: (1) one size fits all, (2) multiple sizes, and (3) adjustability.

For *one size fits all* (tall door or big bed), there is an advantage of design and manufacturing simplicity, with perhaps a slight increase in material cost. Rather than having the machine/device adjust to the person, the person adjusts to the machine/device.

Multiple sizes (clothing) present more manufacturing and inventory problems. However, the machine/device adjusts to the person.

Adjustability presents more challenges to the designer, and the product is more complex. Adjustability allows the person to adjust the environment. Adjustable chairs are a well-known example. We also expect to be able to adjust our ambient environment (sound, light, temperature). For workstation furniture, excessive reach distances tend to occur for women; insufficient leg and knee space tend to occur for men. Design so a small person (such as the gymnast Tara Lipinksi or the actors Danny DeVito and Sally Fields) can reach and a large person (such as Arnold Schwartzenegger or Michael Jordan) can fit.

The most practical design technique is to make the machine adjustable.

Review Questions

1. Give four reasons why falls when a person is carrying something are especially dangerous.
2. What is the difference in foot movement between a slip, a trip, and stepping-on-air?
3. Give the characteristics of good floor mats.
4. Give three techniques for reducing falls on one-step stairs.
5. For walking with slip-resistant shoes, is the sole or heel more important?
6. What is arm abduction?

7. If a person keys 70 words/min, how many key-strokes is this in a working lifetime? Give assumptions.

8. Why is dark focus distance important?

9. Discuss whether you think easy-adjusting chairs are desirable.

10. When keying, should the arms rest on the wrist rest? Justify your answer.

11. What is the optimum work height for manipulative work?

12. What are the 3 basic techniques to obtain optimum work height? Give an example of each.

13. Approximately how much does it cost/hour for a chair used in an office or a factory? Show calculations.

14. Should a chair be form-fitting or not? Why?

15. Should a chair seat swivel? Why?

16. How does sitting affect disc nutrition?

17. What is a vibratory feeder?

18. What has McDonald's done to the lips of its counters to aid the order taker?

19. Is the bottleneck in manipulative motions in the brain, the eyes, or the muscles?

20. When using two hands, should the motions be rowing or alternating?

21. How can you determine your dominant eye?

22. People can be excluded from jobs from the lower percentile, upper percentile, or both. Give an example of each.

23. Why are Danny DeVito and Arnold Schwartzenegger mentioned in this chapter?

24. Design a supermarket checkout station. Other alternatives are airline ticket counter, discount store checkout, drug store checkout. Justify your design.

25. Design a check-in station at an airport. The operator must be seated. The operator should not lift any baggage.

26. Discuss the Power Zone concept.

References

Aaras, A., Fostervold, K., Ro, O., Thoresen, M., and Larsen, S. Postural load during VDU work: A comparison between various work postures. *Ergonomics,* Vol. 40, No. 11, 1255–68, 1997.

Akbari, M. and Konz, S. Viewing distance for VDT work. In *Designing for Everyone,* Y. Queinnec and F. Danniellou (eds.), 680–82. London: Taylor and Francis, 1991.

Andersson, R. and Lagerloff, E. Accident data in the new Swedish information system on occupational injuries. *Ergonomics,* Vol. 26, No. 1, 33–42, 1983.

Andrews, R. The relative energistic efficiencies of one-armed and two-armed work. *Human Factors,* Vol. 9, No. 6, 573–80, 1967.

Ankrum, D. and Nemeth, K. Posture, comfort and monitor placement. *Ergonomics in Design,* 7–9, April 1995.

Ayoub, M. Effect of weight and distance travelled on body members' acceleration and velocity for three-dimensional moves. *International J. of Production Research,* Vol. 5, No. 11, 3–21, 1966.

Barnes, R. *Motion and Time Study,* 2d ed. New York: Wiley & Sons, 1940.

Barnes, R., Mundel, M., and MacKenzie, J. Studies on one- and two-handed work. Bulletin 21, *Studies in Engineering.* Iowa City: University of Iowa, March 1940.

Bendix, T. Chair and table adjustments for seated work. In *The Ergonomics of Working Postures,* Corlett, N., Wilson, J., and Manenica, I. (eds.). London: Taylor and Francis, 1986.

Bendix, T. and Bloch, I. How should a seated workplace with a tiltable chair be adjusted? *Applied Ergonomics,* Vol. 17, No. 2, 127–35, 1986.

Bloswick, D. Climbing biomechanics. Chapter 18 in *Biomechanics in Ergonomics,* S. Kumar (ed.). London: Taylor and Francis, 1999.

Bottoms, D. and Butterworth, D. Foot reach under guard rails on agriculture machinery. *Applied Ergonomics,* Vol. 21, No. 3, 179–86, 1990.

Brand, J. and Judd, K. Angle of hard copy and text-editing performance. *Human Factors,* Vol. 35, No. 1, 57–69, 1993.

Brooks, A., Abbott, A., and Wilson, D. Human-powered watercraft. *Scientific American,* Vol. 256, No. 12, 120–30, December 1986.

Burandt, U. and Grandjean, E. Sitting habits of office employees. *Ergonomics,* Vol. 6, No. 2, 217–28, 1963.

Chaffin, D. Localized muscle fatigue—Definition and measurement. *J. Occupational Medicine,* Vol. 15, No. 4, 346–54, 1973.

Chaffin, D. and Andersson, G. *Occupational Biomechanics,* 2d ed., New York: Wiley, 1991.

Chaffin, D., Anderson, G., and Martin, B. *Occupational Biomechanics,* 3rd ed. New York: Wiley, 1999.

Chaffin, D., Woldstad, J., and Trujillo, A. Floor/shoe slip resistance measurement. *American Industrial Hygiene Association J.,* Vol. 53, No. 5, 283–89, 1992.

Chang, W-R., Kim, I-J., Manning, D., and Bunterngchit, Y. The role of surface roughness in the measurement of slipperiness. *Ergonomics,* Vol. 44, 13, 1200–16, 2001.

Chester, M., Rys, M., and Konz, S. Leg swelling, comfort, and fatigue when sitting, standing, and sit/standing. In *Advances in Occupational Ergonomics and Safety,* Bittner, A. et al. (eds.). IOS Press, 2001.

Chester, M., Rys, M., and Konz, S. Leg swelling, comfort, and fatigue when sit/standing using a 0°, 15° and 30°

footrest. *Int. J. of Industrial Ergonomics,* Vol. 29, 289–96, 2002.

Congleton, J., Ayoub, M., and Smith, J. The design and evaluation of the neutral posture chair for surgeons. *Human Factors,* Vol. 17, No. 2, 127–35, 1986.

Corlett, N., Wilson, J., and Manenica, I. (eds.). *The Ergonomics of Working Postures.* London: Taylor and Francis, 1986.

Courtney, T., Sorock, G., Manning, D., Collins, J., and Holbein-Jenny, M. Occupational slip, trip, and fall-related injuries—Can the contribution of slipperiness be isolated. *Ergonomics,* Vol. 44, 13, 1118–37, 2001.

Das, B. and Grady, R. The normal working area in the horizontal plane: A comparative analysis between Farley's and Squires' concepts. *Ergonomics,* Vol. 26, No. 5, 449–59, 1983.

DeLaura, D. and Konz, S. Toe space. In *Advances in Industrial Ergonomics and Safety II,* B. Das (ed.). London: Taylor and Francis, 1990.

Dickson, A., Petrie, A., Nichole, F., and Calnan, J. A device for measuring the force of the digits of the hand. *Biomedical Engineering,* 270–73, July 1972.

Drury, C. and Coury, B. A methodology for chair evaluations. *Applied Ergonomics,* Vol. 13, 195–202, 1982.

Eastman Kodak Co. *Ergonomic Design for People at Work.* Belmont, CA: Lifetime Learning, 1983.

Eisma, T. Rules changes, worker training help simplify fall prevention. *Occupational Health and Safety,* 52–55, March 1990.

Faergemann, C. and Larsen, L. The mechanism and severity of nonoccupational ladder fall injuries. *J. of Safety Research,* Vol. 32, 333–43, 2001.

Fisher, G. Handedness, eye dominance and visual acuity. *Ergonomics News Letter,* 2, August 1974.

Fitts, P. The information capacity of the human motor system in controlling the tolerance of the movement. *J. of Experimental Psychology,* Vol. 47, No. 6, 381–91, 1954.

Fitts, P. and Peterson, J. Information capacity of discrete motor responses. *J. of Experimental Psychology,* Vol. 67, 103, 1964.

Food Marketing Institute. *Final Report of the Food Marketing Institute Ergonomics Task Force.* Washington, DC: Author, 1996.

Garcia, D., Fernandez, J., and Agarwal, R. Implementation of arm supports as an aid to computer work in the office. *Advances in Occupational Ergonomics and Safety II,* B. Das and W. Karwowski (eds.). Louisville, KY: IOS Press, 429–32, 1997.

Gilbreth, F. *Motion Study.* New York: D. van Nostrand, 1911.

Goonetilleke, R. and Feizhou, S. A methodology to determine optimum seat depth. *Int. J. of Ind. Ergonomics,* Vol. 27, 207–17, 2001.

Grieco, A. Sitting posture: An old problem and a new one. *Ergonomics,* Vol. 29, No. 3, 345–62, 1986.

Grongvist, R. and Hirvonen, M. Slipperiness of footwear and mechanisms of walking friction on icy surfaces. *Int. J. of Industrial Ergonomics,* Vol. 16, 191–200, 1995.

Grongvist, R. Slips and falls. Chapter 19 in *Biomechanics in Ergonomics,* Kumar, S. (ed.). London: Taylor and Francis, 1999.

Hale, J. The lost technology of ancient Greek rowing. *Scientific American,* Vol. 274, No. 5, 82–85, May 1996.

Halpern, C. and Dawson, K. Design and implementation of a participatory ergonomics program for machine sewing tasks. *Int. J. of Industrial Ergonomics,* Vol. 20, 429–40, 1997.

Hamilton, N. A mathematical model for the reduction of neck tension. *Proceedings of the Human Factors Ergonomics Society,* 1063–67, 1986.

Hanna, S. and Konz, S. *Facility Design: Manufacturing Engineering,* 3rd ed. Scottsdale, AZ: Holcomb Hathaway, 2004.

Harrison, J. Maximizing human power output by suitable selection of motion cycle and load. *Human Factors,* Vol. 12, No. 3, 315–29, 1970.

Heath, L. *The Grey Goose Wing.* Greenwich, CT: New York Graphic Society, 1971.

Hedge, A. and Powers, J. Wrist postures while keyboarding: effects of a negative slope keyboard system and full motion forearm supports. *Ergonomics,* Vol. 38, No. 3, 508–17, 1995.

Hedge, A., McCrobie, D., Morimoto, S., Rodriguez, S., and Land, B. Toward pain-free computing. *Ergonomics in Design,* Vol. 4, No. 1, 4–10, 1996.

Helander, M. Safety hazards and motivation for safe work in the construction industry. *Int. J. of Industrial Ergonomics,* Vol. 8, 205–23, 1991.

Helander, M. and Little, S. Preferred settings in chair adjustments. *Proceedings of the Human Factors and Ergonomics Society,* 448–52, 1993.

Hilgen, T. The power zone. In *Applied Ergonomics,* Alexander, D. and Rabourn, R. (eds.), 251–58, London: Taylor and Francis, 2001.

Hoffman, E. A comparison of hand and foot movement times. *Ergonomics,* Vol. 34, No. 4, 397–406, 1991a.

Hoffman, E. Capture of moving targets: A modification of Fitts' law. *Ergonomics,* Vol. 34, No. 2, 211–20, 1991b.

Jaschinski-Kruza, W. On the preferred viewing distance to screen and document. *Ergonomics,* Vol. 33, No. 8, 1055–63, 1990.

Jenkins, S. and Rickards, J. The economics of ergonomics: Three workplace design case studies. In *Applied Ergonomics,* Alexander, D. and Rabourn, R. (eds.), 239–43, London: Taylor and Francis, 2001.

Jung, E. and Park, S. Comfortable work area of seated operators. *Japanese Journal of Ergonomics,* Vol. 32, No. 6, 275–78, 1996.

Konz, S. Design of workstations. *J. of Industrial Engineering,* Vol. 18, 413–23, July 1967.

Konz, S. *Work Design: Industrial Ergonomics,* 2d ed. Columbus, OH: Publishing Horizons, 1983.

Konz, S. and Goel, S. The shape of the normal work area in the horizontal plane. *AIIE Transactions,* Vol. 1, No. 4, 70–74, December 1969.

Konz, S., Jeans, C., and Rathore, R. Arm motions in the horizontal plane. *American Inst. of Industrial Engineers Transactions,* Vol. 1, No. 4, 359–70, December 1969.

Konz, S. and Rode, V. The control effect of small weights on hand–arm movements in the horizontal plane. *AIIE Transactions,* Vol. 2, 228–33, September 1972.

Konz, S., Wadhera, N., Sathaye, S., and Chawla, S. Human factors considerations for a combined brake–accelerator pedal. *Ergonomics,* Vol. 14, No. 2, 279–92, 1971.

Kroemer, K. Horizontal push and pull forces. *Applied Ergonomics,* Vol. 5, No. 2, 94–102, 1974.

Kroemer, K. and Hill, S. Preferred line of sight angle. *Ergonomics,* Vol. 29, No. 9, 1129–34, 1986.

Krumwiede, D., Konz, S., and Hinner, P. Floor mat comfort. In *Advances in Occupational Ergonomics and Safety,* S. Kumar (ed.). IOS Press, 159–62, 1998.

Langolf, G., Chaffin, D., and Foulke, J. An investigation of Fitts' law using a wide range of movement amplitudes. *J. of Motor Behavior,* Vol. 8, No. 2, 118–28, 1976.

Leamon, T. The reduction of slip and fall injuries: Part I—Guidelines for the practitioner and Part II—The scientific basis (knowledge base) for the guide. *Int. J. of Industrial Ergonomics,* Vol. 10, 23–34, 1992.

Leamon, T. and Murphy, P. Occupational slips and falls: more than a trivial problem. *Ergonomics,* Vol. 38, No. 3, 487–98, 1995.

Leclercq, S., Tisserand, M., and Saulnier, H. Assessment of slipping resistance of footwear and floor surfaces. *Ergonomics,* Vol. 38, No. 2, 209–18, 1995.

Lee, C-M, Jeong, E-H, and Freivalds, A. Biomechanical effects of wearing high-heeled shoes. *Int. J. of Ind. Ergonomics,* Vol. 28, 321–26, 2001.

Lehman, K., Psihogios, J., and Meulenbroek, R. Effects of sitting versus standing and scanner type on cashiers. *Ergonomics,* Vol. 44, 7, 719–38, 2001.

Magnusson, M. and Ortengren, R. Investigation of optimal table height and surface angle in meatcutting. *Applied Ergonomics,* Vol. 18, No. 2, 146–52, 1987.

Maki, B. and Fernie, G. Impact attenuation of floor coverings in simulated falling accidents. *Applied Ergonomics,* Vol. 21, No. 2, 107–14, 1990.

Mandal, A. The correct height of school furniture. *Human Factors,* Vol. 24, 257–69, 1982.

Manning, D., Ayers, I., Jones, C., Bruce, M., and Cohen, K. The incidence of underfoot accidents during 1985 in a working population of 10,000 Merseyside people. *J. of Occupational Accidents,* Vol. 10, 121–30, 1988.

Michel, D. and Helander, M. Effect of two types of chairs on stature change and comfort for individuals with healthy and herniated discs. *Ergonomics,* Vol. 37, No. 7, 1231–44, 1994.

MIL-STD 1472F. *Dept. of Defense Design Criteria Standard,* AMSAM-RD-SE-TD-ST. Redstone Arsenal, AL: U.S. Army Aviation and Missile Command, 1999.

Miller, J., Lehto, M., and Rhoades, T. Prediction of slip resistance in climbing systems. *Int. J. of Industrial Ergonomics,* Vol. 7, 287–301, 1991.

Nagamachi, N. and Matsubara, Y. The ergonomic implications of a doorless system in an automobile assembly line. *Ergonomics,* Vol. 37, No. 4, 611–22, 1994.

NFPA. *NFPA Life Safety Code 1994,* NFPA, 1 Batterymarch Park, Quincy, MA 02269.

Nichols, D. and Amrine, H. A physiological appraisal of selected principles of motion economy. *J. of Industrial Engineering,* Vol. 10, 373–8, September 1959.

Nicholson, A. and David, G. Slipping, tripping and falling accidents to delivery drivers. *Ergonomics,* Vol. 28, No. 7, 977–91, 1985.

Nijboer, I. and Dul, J. Introduction of standing aids in the furniture industry. *Musculoskeletal Disorders at Work,* P. Buckle (ed.). London: Taylor and Francis, 1987.

Opila, K., Wagner, S., Schiowitz, S., and Chen, J. Postural alignment in barefoot and high-heeled stance. *Spine,* Vol. 13, No. 5, 542–47, 1988.

O'Sullivan, L. and Gallwey, T. Effects of gender and reach distance on risks of musculoskeletal injuries in an assembly task. *Int. J. of Industrial Ergonomics,* Vol. 29, 61–71, 2002.

Oxenburgh, M. *Increasing Productivity and Profit through Health and Safety.* Chicago: CCH, 1991.

Psihogios, J., Sommerich, C., Mirka, G., and Moon, S. The effects of VDT location on user posture and comfort: a field study. *Proceedings of Human Factors and Ergonomics Society,* 871–75, 1998.

Putz-Anderson, V. (ed.). *Cumulative Trauma Disorders.* London: Taylor and Francis, 1988.

Raouf, A. and Tsuchiya, K. A study of simultaneous hand motions on a horizontal plane for unequal task difficulty and unequal angles. In *Trends in Ergonomics III,* Karwowski, W. (ed.). Amsterdam: Elsevier, 1986.

Redfern, M., Cham, R., Gielo-Perczak, K., Grongvist, R., Hirvonen, M., Lanshammar, H., Marpet, M., Pai, C., and Powers, C. Biomechanics of slips. *Ergonomics,* Vol. 44, 13, 1138–66, 2001.

Rodgers, S. (ed.). *Ergonomic Design for People at Work.* Belmont, CA: Lifetime Learning, 1983.

Rodgers, S. *Working with Backache.* Fairport, NY: Perinton Press, 1984.

Rys, M. and Konz, S. Standing work: Carpet vs concrete. *Proceedings of the Human Factors Society,* 522–26, 1988.

Rys, M. and Konz, S. Adult foot dimensions. In *Advances in Industrial Ergonomics and Safety I,* Mital, A. (ed.). London: Taylor and Francis, 1989.

Salvendy, G. and Pilitsis, J. Improvement in physiological performance as a function of practice. *International J. of Production Research,* Vol. 12, No. 4, 519–31, 1974.

Sengupta, A. and Das, B. Maximum reach envelope for the seated and standing male and female for industrial workstation design. *Ergonomics,* Vol. 43, 9, 1390–1404, 2000.

Shannon, C. A mathematical theory of communication. *Bell System Technical J.,* Vol. 27, 379–423 and 623–55, 1948.

Shephard, R. *Alive Man.* Springfield, IL: C. T. Thomas, 1972.

Sommerich, C., Joines, S., and Psihogios, J. Effects of VDT viewing angle on user biomechanics, comfort and preference. *Proceedings of Human Factors and Ergonomics Society,* 861–65, 1998.

Squires, P. *The Shape of the Normal Work Area.* Report 275, Navy Department, Bureau of Medicine and Surgery, Medical Research Laboratory, New London, CT, 1956.

Sun, J., Walters, W., Svensson, N., and Lloyd, D. The influence of surface slope on human gait characteristics: A study of urban pedestrians walking on an inclined surface. *Ergonomics,* Vol. 39, No. 4, 677–92, 1996.

Templer, J. *The Staircase: Studies of Hazards, Falls and Safer Design.* Cambridge, MA: MIT Press, 1992.

Uniform Building Code, 1997. Section 1006. Whittier, CA: Int. Conf. of Building Officials.

U. S. Dept. of Labor. 29 Code of Federal Regulations, Part 1926, *Safety and Health for Construction,* Subpart M. Washington, DC: U. S. Government Printing Office, 1999a.

U. S. Dept. of Labor. 29 Code of Federal Regulations, Part 1910, *Occupational Standards, Walking-Working Surfaces.* Washington, DC: U. S. Government Printing Office, 1999b.

van Dieen, J., Looze, M., and Hermans, V. Effects of dynamic office chairs on trunk kinematics, trunk extensor EMG, and spinal shrinkage. *Ergonomics,* Vol. 44, 7, 739–50, 2001.

Vos, H. Physical workload in different body postures while working near to or below ground level. *Ergonomics,* Vol. 16, No. 6, 817–28, 1973.

White, C., Eason, R., and Bartlett, N. Latency and duration of eye movements in the horizontal plane. *J. of the Optical Society of America,* Vol. 52, No. 2, 210–13, 1962.

Whitt, F. and Wilson, D. *Bicycling Science.* Cambridge, MA: MIT Press, 1982.

Wick, J. and DeWeese, R. Validation of ergonomics improvements to a shipping workstation. *Proceedings of the Human Factors and Ergonomics Society,* 808–11, 1993.

Wiker, S., Langolf, G., and Chaffin, D. Arm posture and human movement capability. *Human Factors,* Vol. 31, No. 4, 421–41, 1989.

Winkel, J. and Jorgensen, K. Evaluation of foot swelling and lower-limb temperature in relation to leg activity during long-term seated office work. *Ergonomics,* Vol. 29, No. 2, 313–28, 1986.

Woodson, W. *Human Factors Design Handbook.* New York: McGraw-Hill, 1981.

Wu, X., Rakheja, S., and Boileau, P. Study of human-seat interface pressure distribution under vertical vibration. *Int. J. of Industrial Ergonomics,* Vol. 21, 433–49, 1998.

Websites

AliMed (ergonomic equipment), www.alimed.com

Healthy Computing (information on VDTs), www.pc.ibm.com/healthycomputing

North Coast Medical (ergonomic equipment), www.blvd.com/northcoa.htm

Office Ergonomic Assessments Online, www.ergodoc.com

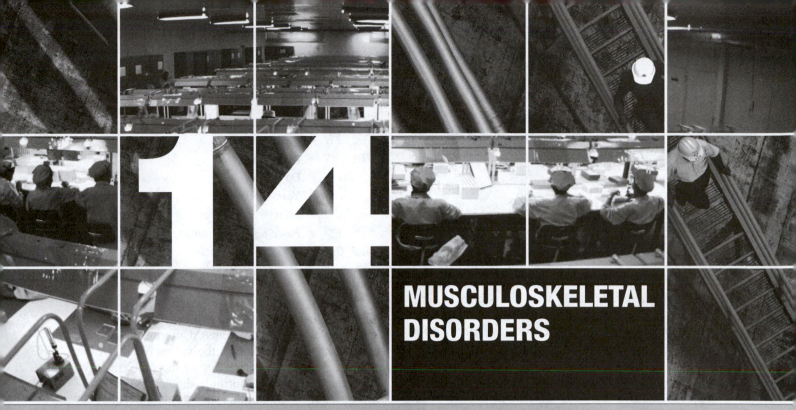

14

MUSCULOSKELETAL DISORDERS

Overview

Musculoskeletal disorders (cumulative trauma) affects the muscles, joints, and ligaments over a period of months and years. The three major areas affected are the hand/wrist, the shoulder/neck/elbow, and the lower back. Reduce these problems with engineering and administrative approaches.

Key Concepts

administrative solutions

automation

carpal tunnel syndrome (CTS)

cross-trained

cumulative trauma disorders (CTD)

damaging wrist motion

duration: short, moderate, long

force

industrial athletes

job enlargement

job rotation

joint deviation

mechanization

musculoskeletal disorder (MSD)

neutral position

one-sided work

pain/impairment/disability/ compensation

prevention (primary, secondary, tertiary)

psychosocial problems

recovery/work ratio

repair

repetitive

risk factors

safety

sit–stand workstation

30 s rule

toxicology

work glasses

working rest

work-related musculoskeletal disorders (WRMD)

During the ages from 18 to 64 years, more people are disabled from musculoskeletal problems than any other category of disorder (Putz-Anderson, 1988). The rate has been rising; musculoskeletal disorders were 21% of work-related illnesses in 1982 and 56% in 1990 (Rigdon, 1992).

GENERAL COMMENTS

1.1 Problem Safety concerns are for short-term (a time frame of seconds) effects of physical agents on the body. An example is cutting off a finger in a punch press. See Chapter 20, Safety. **Toxicology** generally deals with long-term (a time frame of years, or decades) effects of chemicals on body organs. An example is exposure to acetone for 10 years, causing damage to the central nervous system. See Chapter 26, Toxicology. **Musculoskeletal disorders,** the topic of this chapter, concern intermediate-term (months, years) effects of body activity upon the nerves, muscles, joints, and ligaments. An example is back pain due to lifting.

These local overloads have been called many things: repetitive strain, occupational overuse syndrome, and, most commonly, **cumulative trauma disorders (CTD).** The latest names are **musculoskeletal disorders (MSD)** and **work-related musculoskeletal disorders (WRMD);** in this book, we will use musculoskeletal disorders. Whatever the name, the goal is to rid work of strain and pain.

The cumulative trauma gradually wears away at the body. Symptoms appear sooner for people with a weak body and later for people with a strong body, but, with enough trauma, even the strong eventually fail. Thus, although it is good to have a strong body, the emphasis in this chapter is on reducing the trauma. The discussion deals with the ergonomic approach of making the job fit the person instead of the selection approach of making the person fit the job. The ergonomic approach benefits everyone—although the need will not be as evident for those with a strong body.

To reduce musculoskeletal disorders, the standard approach is: (1) a written program, (2) employee (staff and operators) involvement and training, (3) medical management, and (4) program evaluation.

1.2 Risk Factors Musculoskeletal disorders are a function of many risk factors, both occupational and nonoccupational.

1.2.1 *Risk factor formula* The primary occupational factors are:

$$MSD = A\ (RD)^a\ B\ (JD)^b\ C\ (FO)^c$$

where *MSD* = Average risk of a musculoskeletal disorder for a specific part of the body

RD	=	Repetition/duration of joint use factor
	=	$D\ (FH)^d\ E\ (HOURS)^e\ F\ (DAYS)^f\ G\ (YEARS)^g$
FH	=	Frequency/hour
HOURS	=	Hours/day
DAYS	=	Days/year
YEARS	=	Years/work lifetime
JD	=	Joint deviation factor
FO	=	Force resisted by muscle factor
A, B, C, D, E, F, G	=	Constants
a, b, c, d, e, f, g	=	Exponents

Naturally the constants and exponents would be different for different problems (e.g., wrist problems, neck problems, back problems). Unfortunately, at the present time, no one knows the values of any of the constants or exponents for *any* of the problems! We don't know whether the formula should be multiplicative or additive. In addition, the formula assumes no interactions. Yet interactions are known to exist. For example, it is known that force at extreme deviations is worse for the body than force at the neutral position.

Regarding interaction between force and repetition, Silverstein et al. (1986) reported that highly repetitive jobs had a 2.8 odds ratio of injury compared to low-repetition jobs. If the job was highly repetitive and required high force, the odds ratio jumped to 30. In addition, the formula would give average values for a population, not values for specific individuals.

Thus, at present, engineers should reduce the various risk factors (e.g., reduce force from 4 kg to 2 kg) while realizing that an exact prediction of the reduction of risk is not available. (Use of tobacco and cancer is an analogous situation. We are not able to predict the probability of lung cancer for a 22-year-old female, Jane Doe, who smokes 12 cigarettes/day of brand X. There is little doubt, however, that Jane should reduce the number of cigarettes she smokes.)

The three main occupational **risk factors** are repetition/duration, joint deviation, and force. Vibration also is an important risk factor. See Table 14.1. Wick and McKinnis (1998) give the following guidelines:

- Damaging wrist motions (DWM) (the wrist deviates from the neutral position with some force to the hands or fingers) 1,000/h maximum; 2,000 maximum/8-h shift
- Force
  - Pinch grip maximum of 8 lbs (3.6 kg)
  - Power grip maximum of 25 lbs (11.3 kg)
  - Push maximum of 24 lbs (11 kg)
  - Pull maximum of 18 lbs (8.2 kg)
  - Static force exertion maximum of 60 s
  - L5/S1 disc compressive force maximum of 250 kg

■ Extreme position of 0/cycle (body joint such as wrist, elbow, shoulder, neck, or back goes to the maximum range of motion for that joint)

■ Mechanical stress of 0/cycle. Prolonged mechanical stress occurs when a body segment is subjected to external pressure for long periods. Abrupt mechanical stress results from sudden contact with an object; examples are workplace and part edges and corners.

In their Finnish study, Ketola et al. (2001) used the following risk factors for upper extremities:

1. Repetitive use of hand
   ■ Use of hand, wrist, or finger with cycle duration of ≤30 s.
   ■ Similar hand or wrist motion patterns present for >50% of the cycle time.

2. Use of hand force
   ■ Lifts, carries, pushes, or pulls objects ≥4.5 kg with one hand.
   ■ Uses a tool or part ≥2.5 kg with one hand for >1/3 of the cycle time.

3. Use of pinch grip for holding
   ■ The distance between the thumb and finger tip is <5 cm for >1/3 of cycle time.

4. Non-neutral wrist posture
   ■ Flexion, extension, radial, or ulnar deviation of the wrist is >20° for >1/3 of time.

5. Elevation of upper arm
   ■ Angle between upper arm and trunk is ≥90° for >1/3 of cycle time.

6. Local mechanical pressure
   ■ A hard or sharp object, tool, or part of the workstation imposes local pressure on the fingers, palm, forearm, or elbow.

1.2.2 *Repetition/duration* Motions will be defined as a body part changing direction. Thus, one hammer blow would be two motions (down and back); lifting a box from the floor would be two motions (down and up). A repeated sequence of motions is a cycle. In general, a job is considered **repetitive** if the basic (fundamental) cycle time is less than 30 s. This is called the **30 s rule.** A total cycle may take longer. For example, total cycle time to pack a box with product may take 60 s. But if this requires placing 20 items in the box in 10 fundamental cycles of 4 s + 20 s to obtain and dispose of the box, this is a repetitive task. The 30 s rule deals primarily with hand/wrist motions. Back or shoulder movements (i.e., more stressful movements) might be repetitive with a several minute interval.

However, if the task is only done for 15 minutes/shift, there is relatively little risk of MSD because the total duration is short. **Short duration** will

T A B L E   1 4 . 1

Epidemiological evidence of a causal relationship between physical work factors and musculoskeletal disorders (Bernard, 1997).

BODY PART/ RISK FACTOR	STRONG EVIDENCE	EVIDENCE	INSUFFICIENT EVIDENCE
Neck/shoulder			
Posture	x		
Repetition		x	
Force		x	
Vibration			x
Shoulder			
Posture		x	
Repetition		x	
Force			x
Vibration			x
Elbow			
Posture			x
Repetition			x
Force		x	
Combination	x		
Hand/wrist: Carpal tunnel syndrome			
Posture			x
Repetition		x	
Force		x	
Vibration		x	
Combination	x		
Hand/wrist: Tendinitis			
Posture		x	
Repetition		x	
Force		x	
Combination	x		
Hand/wrist: Hand-arm vibration syndrome			
Vibration	x		
Back			
Lifting/forceful movement	x		
Whole body vibration	x		
Awkward posture		x	
Heavy physical work		x	
Static work posture			x

be defined as < 1 h/day, **moderate** as 1 to 2 h, and **long** as > 2 h. Thus, repetition really concerns the number of repetitions per shift. But, since some people work part-time and some work 12-h shifts, and the 5-day week is not a standard, using repetitions/week is more realistic.

There is another complication though: The body is (to some extent) self-repairing. (**Repair** is used in the broad sense of furnishing fuel and oxygen and removing waste as well as repair of the cells themselves.) The more time the body has to repair itself, the better. In addition, some repair can take place even within a motion (but not with static loading). For example, if the hand is moved into and out of a bin, the muscles for moving out can rest while the muscles for moving in are used, and vice-versa. A complication of repair is that the body may not return to the original state but, rather, to a more proficient state (training).

If the work rate is not high, the repair can be done concurrently with the work (see Box 21.4) and the work can be done continuously all day.

During working rest, a joint can be repaired while it is idle and other parts of the body are working. For example, the left wrist joint can be repaired while the person uses the right wrist. The fingers can rest from keying while the brain is making a decision. In addition, most jobs have microbreaks of 1–30 s due to the actions of other operators or the machine. In machine-paced work, the operator has less control over when the microbreak occurs and, thus, less control over when rest/recovery occurs. In addition, the joint can be repaired during nonworking rest (e.g., lunch breaks, coffee breaks, sleeping at home).

Note that repair and recovery is faster for muscles than for tendons, ligaments, and nerves. since muscle blood flow is higher. For an equivalent strain to a muscle and a tendon, the muscle (assuming no rein-jury) might heal in 10 days, while tendon healing might require months.

Duration over the months and years may be a problem if the daily repair is not sufficient to return to normal; the trauma then would start from a higher baseline. The repair process slows down with age; older people heal more slowly than younger people.

There is also great individual variation in physical condition. Strong bodies usually can repair themselves better than weak bodies. Hence, many firms try to encourage strong bodies through wellness programs.

Repetitions have less harmful effects if the joint (muscles, tendons, ligaments) is trained. Athletes go through preseason conditioning drills. Workers should be considered **industrial athletes** and also should have conditioning for the muscles used at work (called work hardening). This can consist of warm-up exercises before work. People who have lost conditioning (due to vacation, layoff, injury) need to take precautions before going full speed.

The above discussion assumes the body is moving and the general thrust is to reduce the extent and frequency of movement. However, MSD also can occur when the body moves too little. Static loading minimizes nutrient and waste exchange in the muscles, eventually causing pain. Thus, MSD can come from too much or too little activity. The human body is meant for movement—but not too much!

1.2.3 *Joint deviation*   Ideally, the joint should operate at the **neutral position**—zero **joint deviation.** Since different joints have different ranges of motion, express the deviation in relative terms (percent of max-imum deviation) as well as in absolute terms (degrees). Posture affects joint deviation, which then affects the internal force required to counteract the external force.

It is well known, and easily demonstrated, that the body is stronger in some postures than others. For example, you can hold a small box of books at waist level against the body for quite a while; holding even one book in an arm held outstretched parallel to the floor soon becomes painful. Thus, one goal is to min-imize torque about the joints (see Table 14.2).

1.2.4 *Force*   Ideally, the internal force on the joint should be low. The observed **force** on the joint typically is an external force multiplied by some lever arm (i.e., we are really talking about a torque). Reduce not only the magnitude of the external force and its lever arm but also the length of time the force is applied. Figure 14.1 gives a model of how repetition and force combine.

Torque exertion capability varies little with nor-mal postures, but extreme postures (e.g., lying on the stomach, leaning sideways from a ladder) cause large differences in capabilities (Mital and Channaveeraiah, 1988).

1.2.5 *Vibration*   Vibration is a risk factor due to interference with blood flow as well as mechanical trauma to the body. Handtool vibration also increases grip forces. See Box 16.3.

1.2.6 *Other occupational risk factors*   Exposure to cold temperatures is a risk factor for MSD because it causes vasoconstriction, thereby reducing blood flow. Reduced blood flow means a reduced supply of nutri-ents and a slower repair process. See Chapter 25. Cold normally is associated with outdoor environments but also can occur from airflow from pneumatic tools.

1.2.7 *Nonoccupational risk factors*   Nonoccupa-tional risk factors can be from trauma outside of work, such as sewing, musical instrument keying, sports (e.g., tennis elbow, golfer's elbow, lifting weights, bowling), or from a nonperfect body. The lack of perfection can be anatomical (e.g., weak back muscles) or physiologi-cal (diabetes, insufficient hormones, use of oral

TABLE 14.2

Ranking of stressfulness of non-neutral postures (Genaidy et al., 1995; Baluyut et al., 1995). 1 = neutrality.

JOINT	JOINT RANKING	RELATIVE MOVEMENT RANKING	POSTURAL MOVEMENT
Shoulder	7	1	Neutral
		5	Elevation, light (16°–45°)
		7	Elevation, severe (>45°)
		7	Extension
		7	Adduction
Wrist	3	1	Neutral
		2	Flexion, moderate (16°–45°)
		2	Radial deviation
		2	Ulnar deviation
		3	Extension, moderate (16°–45°)
		5	Flexion, severe (>45°)
		6	Extension, severe (>45°)
Elbow	3	1	Neutral
		3	Flexion
		3	Extension
		3	Pronation
		6	Supination
Lower Back	3	1	Neutral
		2	Rotation
		3	Flexion (>15°)
		3	Extension
		5	Lateral bending
Neck	2	1	Neutral
		2	Flexion (>45°)
		2	Extension
		2	Rotation
		3	Lateral bending

Source: A. Genaidy, H. Barkawi, and D. Christensen. "Ranking of Static Non-Neutral Postures Around the Joints of the Upper Extremity and Spine." *Ergonomics,* Vol. 38, No. 9, 1851–58. Copyright © 1995 by Taylor & Francis, London. Used by permission. www.tandf.co.uk/journals

contraceptives). The body also can be nonperfect due to an injury. See Atcheson et al. (1998) and Table 14.3.

Psychosocial factors (such as the mental strain of responsibilities at home and work) may result in muscle tension that causes neck and shoulder problems (Bjorksten et al., 2001).

Avoid non-work activities similar to the job. If the job has intensive hand work, avoid playing musical instruments. If the job (such as microscope work) requires

FIGURE 14.1

General dose/response curve. The incidence of a given cumulative trauma disorder shows a low (but not zero) response at low exposure and a high (but not 100%) response at high exposure (Armstrong and Martin, 1997). Tissues are viscoelastic (deformation depends on time and force). As force decreases, the curve shifts to the right.

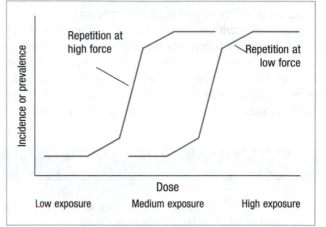

Source: "Adverse Effects of Repetitive Loading and Segmental Vibration" (chapter 12) in *Musculoskeletal Disorders in the Workplace.* M. Nordin, G. Andersson, and M. Pope, eds. Copyright © 1997 by Mosby, St. Louis. Used by permission.

TABLE 14.3

Personal factors of body mass and avocational exercise level in carpal tunnel syndrome (CTS) (*Synergist,* 1995).

PERSONAL FACTOR	PERCENT OF HANDS WITH		
	WRIST NERVE DYSFUNCTION	PROBABLE* CTS	DEFINITE** CTS
Body Mass Category			
Slender	12	19	8
Medium	25	26	15
Overweight	38	35	25
Obese	55	45	37
Morbidly obese	58	57	45
Avocational Exercise Level			
Vigorous	27	24	6
Moderate	29	25	16
Light	45	46	31
Minimal	41	38	28

* Symptoms only

** Symptoms accompanied by nerve dysfunction

Source: From *Synergist,* April 1995. Copyright © 1995 American Industrial Hygiene Association, Fairfax, VA. Used by permission.

concentration and attention, recreation could include rhythmic activities (swimming, walking, dancing).

1.3 Solutions
Solutions occur at three levels: (1) **Primary prevention** (prevent MSD from occurring), (2) **secondary prevention** (arrest MSD while still in the early asymptomatic stage), and (3) **tertiary prevention** (minimize consequences of MSD once symptoms have occurred). Problem jobs can be identified through four approaches: (1) records and statistics from the medical department/safety department, (2) operator discomfort, (3) interviews with operators, and (4) expert opinion.

The ergonomic solutions that follow are divided into engineering and administrative. Administrative procedures should be considered temporary measures, to be superseded by permanent engineering solutions. Medical treatment after the injury is covered briefly.

Some of the solutions involve equipment such as adjustable workstations, wristrests, footrests, supports, handtools, and so forth. Two of the many vendors are AliMed (1-800-225-2610) and North Coast Medical (1-800-821-9319).

1.3.1 *Engineering solutions* First, analyze the job (see Boxes 14.1, 14.2, and 14.3); use a general checklist such as Table 8.3 and a videotape (see Box 14.3). Also see checklists on the ERGO CD. Another possibility is doing a body discomfort analysis (see Figure 9.19).

Gibson and Alexander (1997) recommend working on the high-risk jobs first, as the cost savings will convince management of the benefits of ergonomics. Later you can work on the medium- and low-risk jobs without as detailed a level of justification. High-risk jobs are identified by ergonomic risk

---

BOX **14.1** *Caution Zone Jobs* (Communique, April 2000)

The State of Washington requires employers with "caution zone" jobs to analyze them and provide employee education, employee participation, and hazard reduction:

- "Caution zone" jobs may not be hazardous, but may require further evaluation.
- This rule does not prohibit "caution zone" jobs.
- Employers who have made a reasonable determination that they do not have "caution zone" jobs are not covered by this rule.

A "caution zone" job is a job or task where an employee's typical work includes any of the physical risk factors listed below.

1. *Awkward postures:*
   - Working with the hand(s) above the head or the elbow(s) above the shoulder for over 2 h total/workday.
   - Working with the neck, back, or wrist(s) bent more than 30° for over 2 h total/workday.
   - Squatting for 2 h total/workday or kneeling for 2 h total/workday.

2. *High hand force:*
   - Pinching an object weighing over 2 lb (.9 kg)/hand for over 2 h total/workday.
   - Gripping an object weighing over 6 lb (2.7 kg)/hand for over 2 h total/workday.

3. *Highly repetitive motion:*
   - Repeating the same motion with the neck, shoulders, elbows, wrists, or hands (except

for keying) with little or no variation every few seconds for over 2 h total/workday.
   - Performing intensive keying for over 4 h total/workday.

4. *Repeated impact:*
   - Using the hand or knee as a hammer more than 10 times/h for over 2 h total/workday.

5. *Heavy, frequent or awkward lifting:*
   - Lifting objects over 75 lb (34 kg) once/workday or over 55 lb (25 kg) more than 10 times/workday.
   - Lifting objects over 10 lb (4.5 kg) if done more than twice/min for over 2 h total/workday.
   - Lifting objects over 25 lb (11 kg) above the shoulders, below the knees, or at arm's length for more than 25 times/workday.

6. *Moderate to high vibration:*
   - Using handtools that typically have high vibration levels (examples include impact wrenches, carpet strippers, chain saws) and percussive tools (examples include jack hammers, scalers, riveting and chipping hammers) for over 30 min total/workday.
   - Using grinders, sanders, jig saws, or other handtools that typically have moderate vibration levels for over 2 h total/workday. Employers may assume that handtools vibrating less than 2.5 m/s^2 8-h equivalent are not covered.

For more information, see www.Lni.gov.wa/wisha.

BOX   **14.2**   *Reducing Ergonomics Risks*   (Wick et al., 1996)

Hewlett-Packard in San Diego had a goal of reducing OSHA-recordable injuries by 50%. From a Pareto analysis, production had 58% of the division injuries; of production injuries, 87% were on the upper extremities. Thus, they focused on upper extremity injuries in production.

An Injury-Reduction Strategy team was formed. It had a manufacturing section manager, three production managers, an industrial engineer, an ergonomist, a safety professional, and an occupational health nurse. Its mission was to develop an ergonomics training program for engineers, to develop an ergonomics review process for new products, to conduct an ergonomics assessment of the existing manufacturing system, and to implement solutions to existing ergonomics problems.

Among the tools used were analysis of risk factors for shoulders, elbows/arms, neck, and back for each job. Risk factors were:

> 1,000/h damaging wrist motions (a wrist deviation with some force to the hands or fingers)

> 3.6 kg pinch grip force

> 11.3 kg power grip force

> 11 kg push force

> 8.2 kg pull force

> 60 s of static exertion

> 250 kg of L5/S1 disc compressive force

Any extreme position

Any mechanical stress

First, prototype solutions were developed considering all the stations on the line; example solutions would be training, generic tools, and parts layouts. For example, the parts traveled on a pallet, and it was possible to adjust the height at each workstation. The product also was relocated on the pallet to reduce reach distance. These two improvements removed 47% of the risk factors on the line!

These changes, plus others, were documented in an "Ergonomic Change Notice" (ECN) posted at the workstation. The ECN included the ergonomics problem, the workplace causes, the proposed solutions, and process notes. An action item list tracked progress.

At the end of 1 year, the OSHA injury rate had fallen 33%.

---

factors (e.g., heavy lifting, high hand/arm forces, awkward postures), medical response (lost or restricted workdays within previous 2 years), or indicator of excessive job demands (a subjective high rating of turnover).

Useful supplementary information is:

- Minutes/month the job is performed/shift. Is there job rotation?
- Measurements of work surface heights, chair heights, reaches.
- Weight of objects (including handles) pushed, pulled, or carried.
- Handtool information (manufacturer and model, vibration problems).
- Personal protective equipment (e.g., gloves).

The first possible solution is **automation**—that is, eliminate the person. If there is no person, there is no possible injury. In general, automate "4D" tasks (dangerous, difficult, dirty, disappointing). Food operations often are considered difficult to automate due to biological diversity. However, Purdue Farms automated the evisceration of chickens by using a robotic claw; the diversity of chicken sizes was controlled by only using chickens that were 49 days old.

Robots are especially useful for repetitive "pick-and-place" operations (loading, unloading of machines). A robot can place product in a box; a special robot (called a palletizer) can place cartons on a pallet. Barcoding and scanners can eliminate keying. Crane & Co. had an "ergonomic" problem. The solution was to replace arm motions with a machine feeder; this not only reduced arm repetitions from 5,000/day to 0 but also increased output from 5,000/day to 15,000 (MacLeod and Morris, 1996). Charleston Forge replaced pneumatic wire brushing of steel with an enclosed shot blaster.

A second possibility is to reduce the number of cycles or reduce the difficulty of a cycle. Two approaches are mechanization and job enlargement.

In automation, the system provides both movement and control; people only do maintenance. In **mechanization,** the system provides movement force, but people provide control—the system does part of the job, but the operator is still present. For example, on a packaging operation, a label might have to be applied to each box. The present method might be to use a pinch grip to peel a label off a sticky-back tape. A mechanized method might use a machine to peel the label off the tape and present it to the operator—eliminating the pinch grips of peeling the label. Two

BOX   **14.3**   *Videotaping Jobs*

Videotaping jobs is useful for methods analysis and training. Some shooting tips:

- Have spare batteries and a battery charger. Note that a charger may take 8 h to recharge a battery.

- Good practice is to videotape multiple operators doing the same job (if this is possible). This invites comparisons of methods. Write the name of the job and operator on a sheet of paper and video the sheet at the beginning of each job. Operators usually will have small variations in technique; these can be detected on tape but are difficult to detect by direct observation. For example, how are items oriented? Is the wrist deviation the same? Is the sequence of steps modified?

- Plan the location of camera and subject ahead of time. Use a tripod. Multiple views are best. Consider some combination of a front view, a side view, a back view, floor level views, "stepladder" views (i.e., a partial plan view), overall views, and closeup views orthogonal to the front or side (parallax has been considered). Begin the scene with a full view (far shot, wide-angle view) and then zoom in as desired.

- Take lots of cycles for your stock tape. Each scene should have several cycles. You can always edit, but it is expensive to go back and shoot more tape.

- If the view is orthogonal to the front or side, the projected view can be frozen and angles determined on the screen, using a protractor. These angles then can be used as input to computer models.

- For analysis of time, there are three alternatives:
  1. Put a digital clock in the scene.
  2. Use a camera-VCR system with a "time-code" feature. This will allow you to quickly locate any time on the tape. A timecode that includes seconds is better than one with just minutes as it is easier to located desired activities.
  3. Count the number of frames (VHS has 30 frames/s [.033 s/frame]).

- If later there might be a question of when the tape was made, a camera feature that continuously displays the date on the screen is desirable.

- Videotapes can be used for analysis of non-industrial events. For example, Xiao and Mackenzie (1997) reported on the analysis of more than 100 videotapes of trauma patient resuscitation. The goal was improved decision making. They found it important to have various participants retrospectively comment on the tape to explain what was happening.

- Use audio as a notepad while filming, identifying what you are shooting and what seems interesting. If the tape is used later for a management presentation or training, you can dub in a voice reading a script.

- Have both an engineer and the operator analyze the stock tape. The VCR should have a freeze-frame and a single-frame advance. The operator can point out to the engineer why some things are done, perhaps with audio dubbing. The tape also is a way to show the operator some problems and how other operators do the task.

- For a "training" or "management presentation" videotape, you will need a script. Divide a column of paper into two columns; one column will be audio and one visual. In the audio column, enter the words to be read onto the tape. In the visual column, enter the tape counter reading (start and stop) of the stock videotape. You also will use text shots created in the studio (title page, points you want to emphasize, conclusions, and so on), studio shots of you, and shots of 35 mm photos. Then the video technician will use the script to blend into a finished product the reading of the script, the text shots, shots of you, the 35 mm shots, and the clips from the stock tape. Perhaps you can even have music!

- Keep completed tapes in an archive (rather than taping over previously filmed tapes); often it is useful to refer to old tapes.

other examples of mechanization to reduce manual motions are feeding parts into machines from magazines or vibratory feeders and removing parts from machines with part ejectors.

Power-operated handtools can replace manual handtools. For example, Holloman Air Force Base replaced conventional scissors with spring-loaded models and, in some cases, with electric scissors.

Repetitive inspection may be mechanized. For example, if an inspector must turn over a part so both sides are seen, the turning operation may be mechanized. A checkout clerk could use a barcode scanner instead of keying information.

Job enlargement (the opposite of job simplification) increases the total job content for each person. The same motions are done, but by a larger number of people. If the job takes 4 min instead of 2 min, the repetitive motions per person are reduced.

A third engineering approach is to minimize joint deviation from the neutral position. See examples in Sections 2, 3, and 4.

A fourth engineering approach is to minimize force duration and amount. See examples in Sections 2, 3, and 4.

1.3.2 *Administrative solutions* Administrative

solutions seek to reduce exposure and increase workers' ability to endure stress. Examples of reducing exposure are job rotation and part-time workers. Examples of increasing ability to endure the stress are exercise, stress reduction, and supports.

Job rotation. In **job rotation,** people rotate jobs periodically within the shift. The concept is of **working rest**—the specific part of the body rests but the person is still working. The rotation can be to alternate between two jobs or to rotate among three or more jobs. The concept works best when the alternate tasks differ from one another. For example, a person picking boxes off a conveyor could rotate with a person doing paperwork. A person using a right-handed workstation could rotate to a left-handed workstation (this method assumes that not all workstations emphasize the use of one hand). A person keying could exchange with a person answering phone inquiries. Less satisfactory would be a shift from packing large bags of snack foods to small bags of snack foods or shifting from keying reports to keying forms. As a practical matter, too, it is difficult to rotate jobs between different supervisors.

In addition to the stress-reduction benefits, job rotation has some managerial advantages in that people are **cross-trained** (able to do more than one job), which allows more flexible scheduling, and there is a perceived fairness because everyone shares good and bad jobs.

Job rotation requires broad job descriptions rather than narrow ones—for example, "office worker" rather than "secretary 2" and "word processing operator," and "operator" rather than "assembly operator" and "packing operator."

During rest, recovery from fatigue declines exponentially. Therefore, frequent short breaks are better than occasional long breaks. The rotation should be within the day rather than between days. Rotation every hour is better than rotation every 4 hours.

Part-time workers. When there is no other job to rotate to, several people can be hired part-time. Hire Mary to key for 4 h in the morning and Sam to key for 4 h in the afternoon. Package sorting often is done by large numbers of people working at the same time for only 2 to 3 h/day. The assumption is that the part-time people are not stressed during off-work hours (from another job or hobby).

Advantages of part-time workers, in addition to reducing cumulative trauma, are lower cost/hour (wage and fringes), better fit to fluctuating demand (a 25% increase in time requires each person to work 5 h/day vs. 10 h/day for a full-time worker), and (possibly) higher-quality workers. (It may be difficult to hire full-time high-quality people for repetitive low-paying jobs.) Disadvantages of part-time workers are less time on the job (and thus less learning), possible moonlighting for other employers (and thus being tired when working for you), and a high fixed cost per employee of hiring and training.

Exercise. In general, exercise can improve cardiovascular fitness (endurance), flexibility, and strength; for MSD prevention, the emphasis should be on flexibility and strength. Exercises should be tailored to the specific set of muscles, tendons, and ligaments that are stressed. Some exercises strengthen weak muscles, and other exercises stretch tight muscles and ligaments. Strengthening (work hardening) is needed for people new to a specific task and for people returning to work (e.g., after vacations, injuries).

Stress can be caused by static loads as well as dynamic loads. Exercises can be designed to improve the body for dynamic activity, to counteract the effect of static loading, and to reduce tension. If the work loads the muscles statically, the exercise should move them. If the work loads the muscles dynamically, relax and stretch them.

Stress reduction. Social factors, both on and off the job, can cause stress. On-the-job stressors include workload, deadlines, and interpersonal relationships. Off-the-job stressors include domestic problems and financial problems. Stresses also can be due to personality (e.g., perfectionists, self-pushers, workaholics). Stresses can either aggravate localized MSDs, such as carpal tunnel, or cause diffuse muscle conditions (Wigley et al., 1992). Example diffuse symptoms are pain, weakness, numbness and tingling, and tissue swelling.

Some specific methods of treatment are relaxation (learning to let go), rest (especially microbreaks and working rest, in addition to rest at home), postural modification, exercises (warm-up before work, dynamic exercises to counteract static loads), and medication to minimize sleep disturbances.

Supports. An appealing idea is to support the body. Four commercially available possibilities are wrist braces, elbow braces, back braces (back belts, lifting belts), and lower arm supports. The wrist, elbow, and back braces are worn on the body; the lower arm support holds the lower arm and is suspended from above or attached to the chair with a swiveling mechanism.

These supports are an MSD type of personal protective equipment. However, unlike safety types of personal protective equipment (e.g., hard hats, safety shoes), these supports may have an effect on the underlying anatomy. In general, it seems the anatomy is made weaker because the support was used. When deciding whether to use these supports, therefore, consider not only what happens when they are worn but also what happens when they are no longer worn.

The wrist splint is used to keep the wrist from bending. This is relatively noncontroversial off the job (especially at night). However, wearing the splint during work may not allow the muscles to recover as quickly. In addition, the splint may actually cause injury because the person moves against the resistance of the splint.

Back belts are popular, but the limited scientific evidence tends to be against their use (Rys and Konz, 1995). Relatively few experimental studies have been done, most of which have focused on lifting, ignoring pushing/pulling, carrying, and standing. Most studies have been done only on healthy male university students, using the belt for an hour or two. In addition, there are a wide variety of belt designs; intuitively some should be better and some worse. Some theory would be helpful, as the designs seem to lack an underlying principle.

Lumbar or back belts are popular as a low-cost, temporary alternative to implementing permanent engineering changes. Until the researchers come up with more information, our recommendation is to avoid lumbar back belts.

Arm support did not provide worthwhile benefits during welding or light assembly (Jarvholm et al., 1991). Feng et al. (1997), however, found benefits for forearm supports in simulated tasks. A horizontal moveable arm support was suitable for work at table height, and a spring-loaded arm support (which tracked the arm) had advantages during work above table height. Poonawala and Fernandez (1998) studied arm supports attached to the chair and to the table, as well as counterbalanced arm slings for light bench assembly. All three reduced physiological costs versus no supports; the armrest attached to the table had some slight benefits over the other two types of supports.

1.3.3 *Medical/rehabilitation* Once a person has an MSD, medical personnel such as occupational therapists, physical therapists, and physicians enter the battle. They can provide specific recommendations for treatment, which can include physical therapy, medication, and surgery. Physical treatments include ice (to reduce inflammation), heat (to increase blood flow), exercise, massage, and splints.

Medication (drugs, chemicals) can be used to reduce swelling, promote healing, and so on.

Surgery (see Figure 14.2) is a last resort. For example, for carpal tunnel syndrome (CTS), the liga-ment roofing the carpal tunnel is cut. Unfortunately, the surgery does not always prevent the problem from recurring. Zehel (1997) reported that seven different studies gave a range of 27% to 98% for "excellent results"; in Maine, 25% of Worker Compensation cases were still off work 18 months after surgery for CTS. Naturally, surgery can't help if the nerve has been permanently damaged.

At the start of physical and medication treatments, the worker usually is still on the job. Because the worker has "reported to medical," the MSD problem enters the "paperwork system." This should be a notification to the ergonomist that there is a problem. (Although use of the medical record system is a signal of an ergonomics problem, even better is an "early warning system" in which employees can contact an ergonomist through their supervisor before the problem becomes serious enough to cause medical problems.) Thus, the ergonomist can work on the physical or organizational or training aspects of the problem while the medical personnel work on the person. Just treating the individual medically while leaving the task/environment unchanged tends to be ineffective.

F I G U R E **14.2**

Surgery is a last resort for CTS. "Carpal tunnel release" (severing the transverse carpal ligament) is successful for "almost all" people with medical causes of CTS, but is less successful for occupational causes. The surgery can be one incision (as shown) or several small incisions (using an endoscope camera).

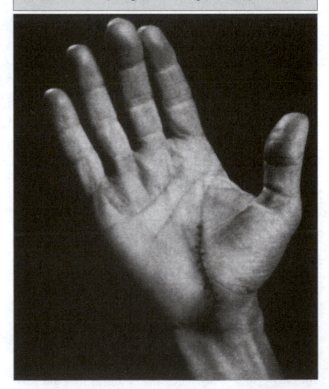

If the injured worker can rehabilitate while working, the firm does not have to pay Worker Compensation premiums. Thus, the choice may be some output at work versus no output while recovering at home.

A physician may specify "light duty" (restricted duty/alternate duty) work. But what is the definition of "light"? It is better if the physician is more specific—for example, restricting lifting, restricting prolonged standing, restricting wrist activity. In addition, for what duration will the person be in light duty? It might be 30 years! Thus, firms may wish to specify that light-duty jobs are temporary, not permanent.

A return-to-work policy does not have to include light-duty work. Some alternatives are modified work schedules and assistance from other workers.

If the rehabilitation activities fail or only partially succeed, consider adapting the workplace for the disability. Ideally, modify the employee's own job (people think they "own" jobs and tend to be most satisfied with retaining their job). Second choice would be a job within the same workgroup.

2 HAND/WRIST

2.1 Problem

The problems occur in the tendon (e.g., tendinitis), the nerve (e.g., carpal tunnel syndrome), or the neurovascular system (e.g., thoracic outlet syndrome or vibration syndrome).

There is a specific problem with the hand and wrist. See Box 14.4 and Figure 4.14. The hand is small and flexible because the muscles that power it are in the bulky forearm. (An exception is the thenar muscle, which powers the thumb.) The fingers are moved by tendons leading from the fingers through the wrist (*carpal* in Latin) tunnel to the muscles. These tendons (think of them as wires inside a sheath) can fray on the bones; the result is called tenosynovitis.

The median nerve also goes through the carpal tunnel. If the median nerve (think of it as a cotton rope)

| BOX | **14.4** | *Assumptions for Work-Related CTS* |

1. The carpal tunnel (see Figure 4.14) is a tightly constrained space. Therefore, an increase in the content inside the tunnel, or pressure from outside, will raise intra-tunnel pressure.

2. If the pressure increase is sufficient, it will cause local venous congestion within the vascular plexus of the nerve, as well as ischemia in arterioles nourishing the nerve, leading to endoneurinal edema. In this initial stage of CTS, the patient feels numbness, tingling, and pain.

3. The edema increases the effect of the initial compression, creating a vicious circle. Fibroblasts within the nerve tissue lead to scarring.

4. Thus, any disease (local or systemic) that increases intra-tunnel pressure can cause CTS.

5. Under normal conditions, when manual work is performed, synovial lubrication of the tendon sheaths is adequate for smooth gliding of the tendons. There is "reasonable and comfortable" usage.

6. In some work situations, workers are not able to stay within the reasonable and comfortable range, so the tendons become strained and tendon lubrication becomes inadequate.

7. Bending of the wrist reduces carpal tunnel size, increasing pressure.

8. Inadequate lubrication leads to increased friction and inflammation.

9. If the stress is reduced at this time, inflammation will subside and normal lubrication will be restored.

10. If the stress is not reduced in time, the inflammation may progress to swelling of the structures. (Tendons need a much longer time to restore normal lubrication than muscles to recover from fatigue; it also takes time for inflammation to subside.)

11. The swelling further increases pressure, and the cycle continues.

12. Initially, various treatments to restore local circulation will give temporary relief. Examples are shaking the hand, administering non-steroidal medication or local steroid injection, or a wrist splint worn at night.

13. Continued stress, however, may lead to chronic tenosynovitis and permanent damage to the median nerve.

14. Carpal tunnel release surgery can be done, but its effectiveness depends on the degree of damage to the median nerve and its recovery potential.

Source: S. Tanaka and J. McGlothlin, "A Conceptual Quantitative Model for Prevention of Work-Related Carpal Tunnel Syndrome (CTS)," *Int. J. of Industrial Ergonomics,* Vol. 11, pp. 181–93. Copyright © 1993 by Elsevier Science, Amsterdam, Netherlands. Reprinted with permission.

is pinched at the carpal tunnel, the result is a compression neuropathy called **carpal tunnel syndrome (CTS).** The size and shape of the cone-shaped carpal tunnel does not differ between people with and without CTS (Pierre-Jerome et al., 1997). (Note that the median nerve can be pinched at a number of locations in the arm and shoulder; thus not all pinched median nerves are CTS.) Pinching the median nerve causes numbness in the thumb and index finger. CTS tends to cause pain in the evening rather than during work.

The compressed nerve can be detected with different tests. Nonclinical tests are Phalen's test and Tinel's test. Phalen's test (wrist-flexion test) has the patient flex the wrist; if numbness or tingling occurs within 60 s, CTS is indicated. In Tinel's test (percussion test), the examiner lightly taps over the median nerve; CTS is indicated if tingling results. Another common clinical test is nerve conduction (a pinched nerve conducts more slowly; conduction latencies are longer). Johnson and Evans (1993) show that nerve conduction tests have large variances both among and within individuals and strongly question the criterion of 4.3 ms as indicating carpal tunnel syndrome. Another clinical test is vibrometry, based on the fact that fingers using a pinched median nerve are less sensitive to vibration (Neese and Konz, 1993; Hong et al., 1995).

When CTS occurs in both wrists it is called bilateral.

2.2 Risk Factors
Tanaka and McGlothlin (1993) proposed the following risk model for CTS, which shows the complexity of the problem:

$$EL = k\ (a)F\ (b)\ R\ e^{cD}$$

where:

EL = Exposure limit

k, a, b, c = Constants and coefficients

e = Base of natural logarithm (2.71 . . .)

F = Force (internal) exerted by the finger–hand–wrist–arm complex

R = Repetition, cycles/min

D = Deviations of the wrist/max deviation, $0 < D < 4$.

= Flexion dev/Max flexion (External dev/Max external (Ulnar dev/Max ulnar dev + Radial dev/Max radial dev

Vibration is considered through the greater force required to hold a vibrating tool. At present, a time factor (duration of exposure and rest/work relationship) is not included in the model. Psychosocial factors (stress) also are not included.

In a study of 100 people doing word processing, Matias et al. (1998) used a log regression analysis to predict risk factors for CTS. The primary risk factor

was keying hours/shift with an important secondary factor of wrist deviation.

In some situations, the hand is used as a hammer (e.g., in auto trim assembly). Potvin et al. (2000) studied people using the base of the bare palm. Using a psychophysical approach, they recommend peak force limits are 259 N (58 lb) at 2 impacts/min and 181 N (41 lb) at 8 impacts/min.

2.3 Solutions
Naturally, not all CTS cases are occupationally related (see Table 14.3). Some are related to an imperfect body (e.g., diabetes) or nonoccupational trauma (e.g., piano playing). In addition, it should be recognized that mental stress (both on and off the job) increases general tension and thus may increase the effects of musculoskeletal disorders. Finally, a few malingerers may report symptoms to reap financial rewards (this is called "compensation neuroses").

Solutions are divided into engineering and administrative.

2.3.1 *Engineering solutions*
The three engineering solution approaches are repetition/duration, joint deviation, and force.

Repetition/duration. Repetitions influence CTS more than force does (Armstrong et al., 1985). A possible solution, therefore, is to reduce lifetime use of the joint. For example, use a foot-operated control instead

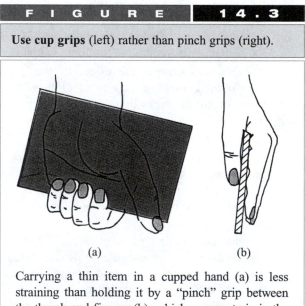

F I G U R E   1 4 . 3

Use cup grips (left) rather than pinch grips (right).

(a)   (b)

Carrying a thin item in a cupped hand (a) is less straining than holding it by a "pinch" grip between the thumb and fingers (b), which causes strain in the hand.

Source: F. Tayyari and J. Emanuel, "Carpal Tunnel Syndrome: An Ergonomics Approach to Its Prevention," *Int. J. of Industrial Ergonomics*, Vol. 11, pp. 173–79. Copyright © 1993 by Elsevier Science, Amsterdam, Netherlands. Reprinted with permission.

of a hand-operated control. Use a telephone (voice) instead of e-mail (keying). Split a 5,000-repetition/day job into 2,500 for the left wrist and 2,500 for the right wrist instead of 5,000 on one wrist. For triggering, reduce trigger-holding duration by using handtools where triggers need not be held continuously.

Joint deviation. When calculating the number of wrist motions/shift, consider breaking them down into flexion, extension, radial deviation, and ulnar deviation. For flexion/extension and isometric movements, any deviation from neutral (0°) decreases both grip force and wrist torque, with a larger decrement than extension. However, for isokinetic movements (i.e., with movement), the optimum position is about 15° toward flexion (Jung and Hallbeck, 2002). Schoenmarklin and Marras (1991) reported that wrist CTDs are predicted better by wrist velocity and acceleration than by wrist angle. Schoenmarklin and Marras (1993) give data on the dynamic capabilities of the wrist.

Guideline: Don't bend your wrist.

Rather than directly emphasizing wrist velocity and acceleration, it is probably easier to minimize wrist deviation by keeping the wrist in the neutral (hand-shake) position. By minimizing deviations, you should decrease velocities and accelerations. Minimize deviations by changing the job or changing the tool.

Changing the job may simply require a change in worker posture. Standing tends to permit longer reaches than sitting. Perhaps the person's chair is too high or too low, thus resulting in an awkward wrist orientation. The work orientation may be adjusted by tilting the entire worksurface or by tilting a fixture or bin on the surface. The fixture need not be fixed in orientation; some commercially available fixtures allow the operator to adjust the workpiece (and thus wrist/elbow/shoulder angles) during the task. A ratchet tool gives more friendly upper-arm angles.

For example, well-designed keyboards are adjustable in angle so the person can change them. Note that if a keyboard operator uses a chair with armrests and rests the elbows on the armrests while keying, this may put the wrists in a more deviated position (radial on left hand, ulnar on right).

Changing the job may require a change in product design. For example, should a screw be slot, Phillips, or hex? How would these different types affect operator hand, elbow, shoulder, and neck orientations? Keying information can be replaced by scanning barcodes. Scanning barcodes, in addition to reducing stress on the hand/wrist, is faster and reduces error rates.

Changing the handtool angle is another possibility. The concept is to bend the tool, not the wrist.

Note that one perfect angle is unlikely. Much more likely is one best angle for each posture and direction of movement. For example, Fogelman et al. (1993) reported, for poultry deboning, that a −30° blade in a dagger grip was best for a table cut and a +30° blade held normally was best for a hanging cut. Jegerlehner (1991) reported that John Deere reduced wrist deviations on the spindle lever of a tapper by using a ball handle on the ends of the levers.

Force. Force influences CTS. Reduce the force duration and amount.

Marras (1992) says that high velocity and, in particular, acceleration increase cumulative trauma. Wick (1994) defined a **damaging wrist motion (DWM)** as a bent wrist involving a force. (See Section 1.3.1 of this chapter.) In addition, all pinch grips >8 lbs are considered dangerous. Figure 14.3 shows gripping thin objects with a cup grip rather than a pinch grip.

Can force be eliminated? Is a robot desirable? If a person performs the action, can a clamp, vice, or fixture replace the hand? Freeing the hand for other uses may increase productivity as well as reduce stress.

Can force be reduced? For assembly, can component tolerances be modified so less force is required for assembly? Can torx screws replace Phillips screws to reduce the pushing force on the screw with the tool? Can component design be modified (e.g., use of a taper)? Can lubricants be used? Can the "shaft" be cooled (shrinking it) and the "bearing" heated (expanding it)? Can previous processes be modified so less trimming is needed?

For handtools, can a larger diameter grip replace a smaller diameter grip so less force is required to prevent tool movement in the hand? Can the grip have a better coefficient of friction? Can the grip shape be changed? For example, a screwdriver with a ball-shape handle will exert less pressure on the roof of the carpal tunnel. Or two similar tools for a task might be suspended from a balancer, one with a pistol grip and one with an inline grip; depending on the orientation required, the operator would use the appropriate tool. If hand knives are used, give each user two sharp knives so when one is dull, the user can switch to the sharp knife while the dull one is being sharpened. Perhaps the resistance to the knife can be reduced. Two examples from meatpacking are better control of frozen temperatures (to prevent cutting frozen meat) and tumbling hams in large tumblers (so they are softer and thus easier to cut).

Vibrating tools require more grip force than non-vibrating tools of the same size and weight (Armstrong et al., 1987); therefore, you should reduce vibration. Perhaps the handtool should not be held! In one meatpacking plant, the worker originally held a power knife and cut the meat; in the revised method, the power knife was mounted in a fixture and the meat held in both hands and pulled through the knife. This not only reduced hand vibration but also allowed both hands instead of one to exert the force. When gripping a torque-controlled power screwdriver, when the screw reaches a preset torque, the screwdriver automatically shuts off. An inertia is absorbed in the operator's hand. The movement is wrist extension for a right-hand operator and wrist flexion for a left-hand operator. Figure 16.26 shows how a device (a torque-arm attachment) can partly absorb this inertia (peak force is about 30% less, while gripping time is cut from 1.7 s to .6 s.) (Neelam, 1994). As with any change, benefits should be explained to the operators, and they should try out the new equipment. See Chapter 16 for more comments on handtools.

Gloves decrease gripping force on an object; if you wish to exert the same amount of control of an object with and without gloves, you will have to exert more force with the gloves.

Note that decreased hand force requirements tend to increase accuracy of movement and thus quality.

2.3.2 Administrative solutions See Section 1.3.2.

3 SHOULDER/NECK/ELBOW

3.1 Problem Here the musculoskeletal disorder problem seems to be primarily in the shoulder and the neck, although the elbow is occasionally involved. Musculoskeletal disorder of the neck and shoulder also is called occupational cerviobrachial disorder (OCD) and upper limb disorder (ULD). Pain in the shoulder region ranks second only to low-back and neck pain in clinical frequency (Sommerich et al., 1993). Disorders can be related to

1. tendons
   - rotator cuff tendinitis
   - calcific tendinitis
   - bicipital tendinitis
   - tendon tear
   - bursitis
2. muscular shoulder pain
3. nerve-related disorder (suprascapular nerve)
4. neurovascular disorder (thoracic outlet syndrome)

Job titles associated with low risk of shoulder/neck musculoskeletal disorder are VDT operator, assembly operator (some jobs), and cash register operator; medium-risk job titles are garment worker, assembly operator (some), and packer; high-risk titles are welder and letter carrier (Winkel and Westgaard, 1992). Note that when the hands work above the shoulders, there is stress (1) in the shoulder muscles (to support the arms) and (2) in the neck (C7–T1 level) to support the backward tilt of the head.

Hagberg and Wegman (1987) reported that work at shoulder height (versus work below the shoulder) increased the risk of rotator cuff tendinitis by 1100%.

3.2 Solutions See Box 14.5 for a procedure to prioritize upper-arm musculoskeletal disorders investigations. (See also Tables 14.8 and 14.9. Solutions are divided into engineering and administrative, later in this chapter.)

3.2.1 Engineering solutions Decrease repetition/duration, joint deviation, and force.

Repetition/duration. The first guideline (as with the hand and wrist) is to reduce the lifetime use of the joints.

To protect the shoulder, can manual material handling be eliminated (e.g., with a machine)? Can a clamp replace static holding?

A key design concept is to minimize **one-sided work.** That is, design the job so that both hands do the work rather than just the right or left hand. Avoiding one-sided work applies to assembly work as well as manual material handling. For example, some checkout stations can be "left-handed" and some "right-handed"; workers could rotate. On two-person sheet-handling jobs on presses, the workers should alternate sides periodically.

Repeated movement of the neck is rare. If there is repeated neck movement from side to side, consider using a swivel chair seat.

Frequent use of the elbow means frequent movement of the lower arm, which requires considerable energy. The primary problems, however, occur when frequent use is accompanied by extreme deviations or considerable force—as in throwing (lateral epicondylitis or tennis elbow) or rotating the forearm while the wrist is bent (medial epicondylitis or golfer's elbow).

Joint deviation. Joint deviation is especially critical when it is combined with high repetition. Reduce reaches from (say) 8 to 6 inches; reduce turns from (say) 60° to 47° and then try to go to 38°; reduce hand position during lifts from (say) 3 inches above the elbow to .5 inch. Reduce joint deviation from the neutral position. People have considerable variability in their techniques of doing any task. Therefore, when studying people in various jobs, don't assume everyone uses the same motions and has the same joint deviations. To protect the shoulder and neck, keep the upper arm vertical downward, not horizontal or even elevated (Viikari-Juntura, 1997).

Guideline: Don't lift your elbow.

The work can be moved or the shoulder can be moved. For example, the work height can be reduced. The point here is to ask why the hands are elevated. Figure 17.13 shows how controls can be placed at a

14.5   *Rapid Upper Limb Assessment (RULA)*

RULA (McAtamney and Corlett, 1993) uses an additive model emphasizing posture to determine priorities for action.

Hignett and McAtamney (2000) developed a different RULA (called REBA) for handling patients, such as in health care. Rani Leuder developed a "Revised RULA for Computers" (http://humanics-es.com/etc.htm). See the ERGO disc for RULA and REBA calculations.

Stage 1 (Observe job; score for posture, repetition, and force)

Step 1: Determine posture score (Figure 14.4) for Group A:
- upper arm
- wrist
- lower arm
- wrist twist

Step 2: Determine posture score (Figure 14.5) for Group B:
- neck
- legs
- trunk

Step 3: Determine frequency score (Table 14.4) for
- Group A
- Group B

Step 4: Determine the force (load) score (Table 14.5) for
- Group A
- Group B

Stage 2 (Calculate risk index)

Step 5: Determine the posture index (Table 14.6) for Group A. Enter into appropriate box in form (Figure 14.6).

Step 6: Determine the posture index (Table 14.7) for Group B. Enter into appropriate box in form (Figure 14.6).

Step 7: Enter repetition and force scores into appropriate boxes for Group A and Group B.

Step 8: Calculate total score for Group A and Group B. Enter into appropriate boxes.

Step 9: Calculate grand score, using Figure 14.7.

Step 10: Take action.

Action

LEVEL	SCORE	COMMENT
1	1–2	Posture is acceptable if not maintained or repeated for long periods.
2	3–4	Further investigation is needed; changes may be required.
3	5–6	Investigation and changes are required soon.
4	7	Investigation and changes are required immediately.

Source: Reprinted from *Applied Ergonomics,* Vol. 24, L. McAtamney and E. N. Corlett, "RULA: A Survey Method for the Investigation of Work-Related Upper Limb Disorders," pp. 91–99, © 1993, with permission from Elsevier Science.

more convenient height. Try to place the hand position so the elbows are below the shoulders (tucked in) rather than abducted (moved away from the body centerline). Figure 13.8 shows how carrying a narrower load will permit the elbows to be tucked closer to the body. The work height also can be increased. An example is placing a spacer under the work. If people work with different size objects, consider adjustable height work surfaces.

The height of the shoulder (relative to the work) can be increased if the work is too high. For example, a van was originally spray-painted by workers standing on the floor—requiring them to reach upward. The job was modified by having the workers stand on a platform, thus painting horizontally and downward. This had the additional benefit of less paint settling back onto the painters' faces. Bjoring and Hagg (2000) studied manual spray-painting. As upper-arm abduction over 30° greatly reduces blood flow to the supraspinatus muscle and tendon in the shoulder, they recommended powered, adjustable-height worksurfaces to reduce shoulder abduction. (To reduce triggering force, they recommended greasing the trigger mechanism inside the gun and decreasing the spring pressure on the fluid needle.)

Arm elevation can also be reduced by using tools with long handles; examples include handle extenders on paint rollers for upper wall and ceiling work and long handles on tree-pruning saws and clippers.

Sometimes the work is elevated toward eye level to improve vision of the task. However, this requires elevation of the arms, which causes potential shoulder problems. One alternative is to support the arms, either with a solid armrest (typically mounted on a chair) or a sling under the forearm. Vendors can furnish armrests that move horizontally while still furnishing support versus gravity; they give some freedom of movement of the hand/arm.

F I G U R E   14.4

Posture scores for Group A. Upper arm, lower arm, wrist, and wrist twist are illustrated (McAtamney and Corlett, 1993).

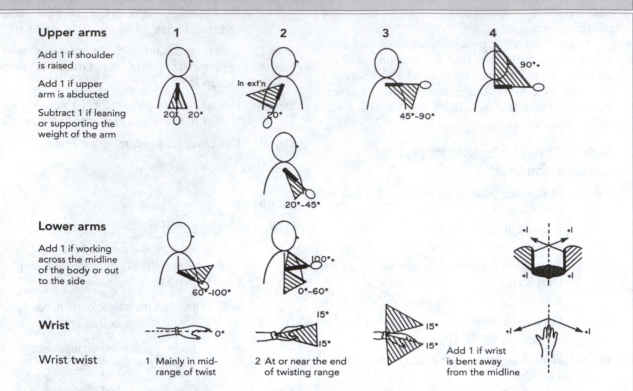

Source: Reprinted from *Applied Ergonomics,* Vol. 24, L. McAtamney and E. N. Corlett, "RULA: A Survey Method for the Investigation of Work-Related Upper Limb Disorders," pp. 91–99, © 1993, with permission from Elsevier Science.

F I G U R E   14.5

Posture scores for Group B. Neck, trunk, and legs are illustrated (McAtamney and Corlett, 1993).

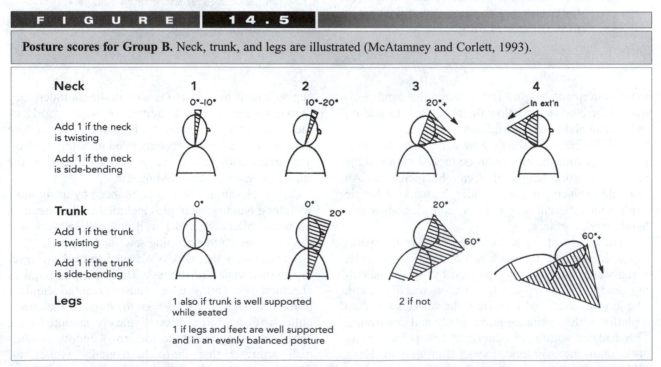

Source: Reprinted from *Applied Ergonomics,* Vol. 24, L. McAtamney and E. N. Corlett, "RULA: A Survey Method for the Investigation of Work-Related Upper Limb Disorders," pp. 91–99, © 1993, with permission from Elsevier Science.

T A B L E	**14.4**
Frequency scores for RULA (McAtamney and Corlett, 1993).	

SCORE	SITUATION
0	Moderate posture, not static, not highly repetitive
1	Static posture, held longer than 1 min *or* highly repetitive posture repeated more than 4 times/min

Source: Reprinted from *Applied Ergonomics,* Vol. 24, L. McAtamney and E. N. Corlett, "RULA: A Survey Method for the Investigation of Work-Related Upper Limb Disorders," pp. 91–99, (1993, with permission from Elsevier Science.

T A B L E	**14.5**
Force (load) scores for RULA (McAtamney and Corlett, 1993).	

SCORE	SITUATION
0	No resistance *or* Less than 2 kg intermittent force or load
1	2–10 kg intermittent force or load
2	2–10 kg static load *or* 2–10 kg repeated force or load
3	≥ 10 kg static load ≥ 10 kg repeated force or load
4	Shock or forces with a rapid buildup

Source: Reprinted from *Applied Ergonomics,* Vol. 24, L. McAtamney and E. N. Corlett, "RULA: A Survey Method for the Investigation of Work-Related Upper Limb Disorders," pp. 91–99, © 1993, with permission from Elsevier Science.

T A B L E	**14.6**
Group A (upper arm, lower arm, wrist, wrist twist) index (McAtamney and Corlett, 1993).	

| | | WRIST POSTURE SCORE | | | | | | | |
| | | **1** | | **2** | | **3** | | **4** | |
Upper Arm	Lower Arm	W. Twist 1	2	W. Twist 1	2	W. Twist 1	2	W. Twist 1	2
1	1	1	2	2	2	2	3	3	3
	2	2	2	2	2	3	3	3	3
	3	2	3	3	3	3	3	4	4
2	1	2	3	3	3	3	4	4	4
	2	3	3	3	3	3	4	4	4
	3	3	4	4	4	4	4	5	5
3	1	3	3	4	4	4	4	5	5
	2	3	4	4	4	4	4	5	5
	3	4	4	4	4	4	5	5	5
4	1	4	4	4	4	4	5	5	5
	2	4	4	4	4	4	5	5	5
	3	4	4	4	5	5	5	6	6
5	1	5	5	5	5	5	6	6	7
	2	5	6	6	6	6	7	7	7
	3	6	6	6	7	7	7	7	8
6	1	7	7	7	7	7	8	8	9
	2	8	8	8	8	8	9	9	9
	3	9	9	9	9	9	9	9	9

Source: Reprinted from *Applied Ergonomics,* Vol. 24, L. McAtamney and E. N. Corlett, "RULA: A Survey Method for the Investigation of Work-Related Upper Limb Disorders," pp. 91–99, © 1993, with permission from Elsevier Science.

Another alternative is to keep the arms low (upper arm vertical) but reduce the visual problem. See Section 1.5, Hands/Arms, in Chapter 13, and 2.5, Task Requirements, in Chapter 23. Figure 13.18 shows a pad to reduce trauma on the underside of the forearm from table edges.

A variation of moving the shoulder or the work is to use a **sit–stand workstation.** Sometimes the person sits and sometimes the person stands.

One possibility is to have part of the job done sitting and part standing. For example, inspection and recordkeeping work can be done sitting, whereas assembly is done standing. Another possibility is to have adjustable-height worksurfaces and chairs so the same task can be done sitting or standing, at the person's option. Note that standing postures may be better than sitting postures. For example, reach is better with standing due to better movement of the hips; in addition, the feet can move. Occasional standing also uses different body muscles than continuous sitting.

Even if the relative height of shoulder and product cannot be changed, can the orientation of the work be changed? There are two possibilities: (1) rotating the work, and (2) tilting the work.

Rotating the work is aided by having low friction on worksurfaces (tables, shelves, carts, conveyors). Roller balls are a common technique.

Tilting the work toward the worker not only improves shoulder, neck, and wrist orientations, but it also brings the work closer to the eyes. For reading (e.g., displays), the tilt tends to be about 45°. For the insertion or removal of items from a restrained container or assembly, consider 30°–40°. If the items are not restrained, a lower tilt (say, 15°) can be used.

For information on the neck, see Figure 14.8. The neutral position is facing forward and slightly downward (10°–15°). Neck flexion of over 20° is a risk

Scoring form for RULA (McAtamney and Corlett, 1993).

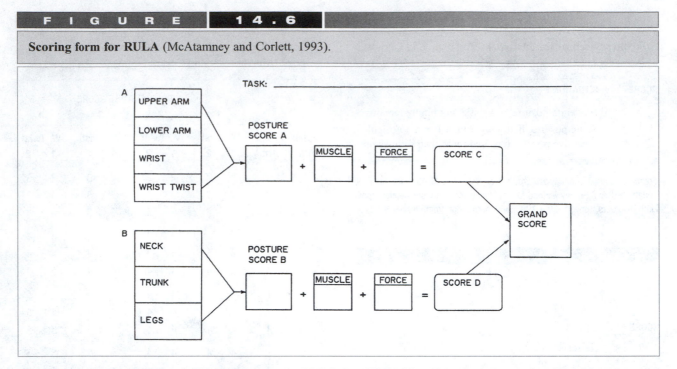

Source: Reprinted from *Applied Ergonomics,* Vol. 24, L. McAtamney and E. N. Corlett, "RULA: A Survey Method for the Investigation of Work-Related Upper Limb Disorders," pp. 91–99, © 1993, with permission from Elsevier Science.

factor for neck disorders in electronic assembly (Kilbom et al., 1986). Can the worksurface be tilted?

People who use the telephone by cradling it between their head and shoulder should expect a sore neck. The recommended solution is a headset (typical cost is <$100). A second solution is a speaker phone, which may require a private office due to the noise. The poorest solution (although better than nothing) is a handset cradle. For VDT work, screens and docu-ments should be located so the gaze is down and ahead rather than horizontal and to the side. (See Chapter 18, Section 6.1.) Bifocals cause people to hold the head in unnatural postures when working at VDTs; therefore, workers should use single-vision glasses **(work glasses).**

To reduce strain on the elbow, keep both the upper and lower arm pointed downward if weight (of the arm or an object) must be supported. If the angle

Group B (neck, trunk, legs) index (McAtamney and Corlett, 1993).

	TRUNK POSTURE SCORE											
	1		**2**		**3**		**4**		**5**		**6**	
Neck Posture Score	Legs		Legs		Legs		Legs		Legs		Legs	
	1	2	1	2	1	2	1	2	1	2	1	2
1	1	3	2	3	3	4	5	5	6	6	7	7
2	2	3	2	3	4	5	5	5	6	7	7	7
3	3	3	3	4	4	5	5	6	6	7	7	8
4	5	5	5	6	6	7	7	7	7	7	8	8
5	7	7	7	7	7	8	8	8	8	8	8	8
6	8	8	8	8	8	8	8	9	9	9	9	9

Source: Reprinted from *Applied Ergonomics,* Vol. 24, L. McAtamney and E. N. Corlett, "RULA: A Survey Method for the Investigation of Work-Related Upper Limb Disorders," pp. 91–99, © 1993, with permission from Elsevier Science.

Grand score index for RULA (McAtamney and Corlett, 1993).

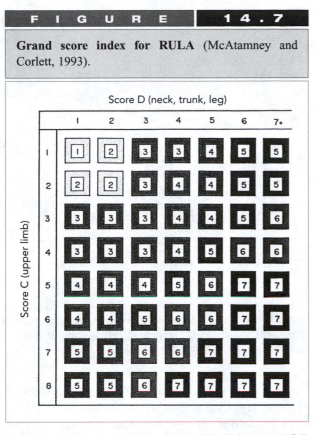

Score D (neck, trunk, leg)

Score C (upper limb)

Source: Reprinted from *Applied Ergonomics*, Vol. 24, L. McAtamney and E. N. Corlett, "RULA: A Survey Method for the Investigation of Work-Related Upper Limb Disorders," pp. 91–99, © 1993, with permission from Elsevier Science.

between the upper and lower arm is approximately 90° (as with keying or bench assembly), then the forearm and hand weight must be supported by muscles, causing fatigue. Typical solutions are arm pads or occasional rest breaks.

A chisel hammer is a heavy portable tool with a horizontal thrust used in construction; thus, a balancer is not feasible. Oxenburgh (1991) reported that a telescoping pole was used to support the tool from below; the 15% increase in productivity paid for the pole within 1 month.

Force.   Reduce the magnitude and duration of the force. (See Chapter 15 for comments on manual handling.)

To protect the shoulder, reduce the static load of tools, hoses, or product with balancers. Consider reducing tool weight (remember Taylor's experiments with shovels, described in Chapter 2). Make battery-powered tools lighter by having the battery remote from the tool—say, on the belt. Overhead welding is often a problem. If a tool action is horizontal, the ideal suspension is above the tool center of gravity with the thrust axis at elbow height.

For work at shoulder height, can the opposite hand support the body? Can hands be alternated? Can the body be turned to allow better use of the muscles?

Engineering (E) and administrative (A) controls to reduce risk of shoulder musculoskeletal disorders (adapted from Sommerich et al., 1993).

1. REPETITION

   Do not design tasks at either end of the repetition continuum (highly repetitive or static postures).
   - (E) Design sequential tasks, not short-cycle repetitive ones.
   - (A) Rotate tasks, especially if highly repetitive or static.
   - (E or A) Reduce speed of highly repetitive movements (less than 1 s/cycle).
   - (A) Minimize use of incentive pay plans for tasks with high-speed arm movements.
   - (A) Train workers to relax nonessential muscles.

2. POSTURE

   Minimize shoulder flexion and abduction.
   - (E) Keep work close to the body and about elbow height.
   - (E) If the arms must be abducted or flexed, minimize the time.
   - (E) Tool grip (inline or pistol) depends on posture. See Figure 16.19.
   - (E) Have adjustable chairs and worksurfaces. Have sit/stand options.

3. FORCE

   Minimize hand-held weight.
   - (E) Suspend tools.
   - (E) Hold parts with fixtures, not hands.
   - (E) Use mechanical aids for lifting and moving.
   - (E) Keep static load ≤ 20% of maximum strength.

   Minimize forceful or heavy work.
   - (E) Minimize direct load-bearing activities (time and weight).
   - (A) Consider job rotation, provided alternate job reduces shoulder loading.
   - (E) Use power tools instead of hand-powered tools. Maintain tools.
   - (E) Ensure parts can be assembled easily.

4. REST

   Provide rest breaks.
   - (E) Design breaks into the work. Breaks at the individual's option are best.
   - (A) If piece-rate incentives are used, require people to take their breaks.
   - (A) Teach people about advantages of micro and mini-breaks. Encourage use of breaks.

Source: C. Sommerich, J. McGlothlin, and W. Marras, "Occupational Risk Factors Associated with Soft Tissue Disorders of the Shoulder: A Review of Recent Investigations of the Literature," *Ergonomics*, Vol. 36, No. 6, pp. 697–717. Copyright © 1993 by Taylor and Francis, London. Reprinted with permission. www.tandf.co.uk/journals

TABLE	14.9

Sample checklist for upper extremity cumulative trauma disorders (Lifshitz and Armstrong, 1986). A "no" indicates a risk factor. Checklist was tested only in an automobile final assembly plant.

NO	YES	RISK FACTORS
		Physical Stress
☐	☐	1. Can the job be done without hand/wrist contact with sharp edges?
☐	☐	2. Is the tool operating without vibration?
☐	☐	3. Are the worker's hands exposed to temperatures > 70° F (21° C)?
☐	☐	4. Can the job be done without using gloves?
		Force
☐	☐	1. Does the job require exerting less than 10 lbs (4.5 kg) of force?
☐	☐	2. Can the job be done without using a finger pinch grip?
		Posture
☐	☐	1. Can the job be done without wrist flexion or extension?
☐	☐	2. Can the tool be used without wrist flexion or extension?
☐	☐	3. Can the job be done without deviating the wrist from side to side?
☐	☐	4. Can the tool be used without deviating the wrist from side to side?
☐	☐	5. Can the worker be seated while performing the job?
☐	☐	6. Can the job be done without a clothes-wringing motion?
		Workstation Hardware
☐	☐	1. Can the worksurface orientation be adjusted?
☐	☐	2. Can the worksurface height be adjusted?
☐	☐	3. Can the tool location be adjusted?
		Repetitiveness
☐	☐	1. Is the cycle time longer than 30 s?
		Tool Design
☐	☐	1. Are the thumb and finger slightly overlapped in a closed grip?
☐	☐	2. Is the tool handle span between 2 and 2.75 inches (5 and 7 cm)?
☐	☐	3. Is the tool handle made from material other than metal?
☐	☐	4. Is the tool weight below 9 lbs (4 kg)? Note exceptions to the rule.
☐	☐	5. Is the tool suspended?

Source: Adaptation of Table 1 in "A Design Checklist for Control and Prediction of Cumulative Trauma Disorder in Hand Intensive Manual Jobs" by Yair Lifshitz and Thomas J. Armstrong, in *Proceedings of the Human Factors Society 30th Annual Meeting,* 1986. Thomas J. Armstrong, Dept. of Environmental and Industrial Health, University of Michigan, 1205 Beal Ave., Ann Arbor, MI 48109-2117; 734/763-3742, fax 734/764-3415; tja@umich.edu. Copyright © 1986 by the Human Factors and Ergonomics Society. All rights reserved.

FIGURE	14.8

Neck postures (Hidalgo et al., 1992). For flexion, neutral is $-15° \leq \alpha \leq 15°$; moderate is $15° \leq \alpha \leq 45°$; severe is $\geq 45°$. For extension, neutral is $\beta \leq 15°$; moderate is $\geq 15°$. For rotation, neutral is $\gamma < 15°$. See also Table 14.10.

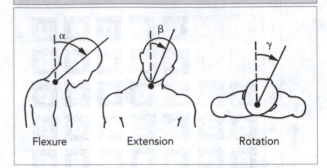

Source: J. Hidalgo, A. Genaidy, R. Huston, and J. Arantes, "Occupational Biomechanics of the Neck: A Review and Recommendations." *J. of Human Ergology,* Vol. 21, pp. 165–81. Copyright © 1992 by Center for Academic Publications, Tokyo. Reprinted with permission.

Can feet or torso be repositioned to reduce stretching? Welders have many shoulder problems because they hold a relatively heavy object in a precise location (i.e., static load). Consider a balancer for the welding equipment. If a guard must be lifted, can it be counterbalanced?

When push or pull movement is needed, push or pull below the shoulder and above the hip, because in this range the muscles are strongest. When cutting with a knife, have the cutting edge down. Cutting away from or toward the body has twice the strength of cross-body motions.

Valves require a torque to open and close. Therefore, determine whether the moment arm can be increased so the force is less; don't ignore valve maintenance to reduce required torque.

Note that even if the hand is empty, an arm is about 4.9% of body weight. Consider supporting this weight. For example, can the arm rest on a support when using a VDT mouse?

Shoulder symptoms probably will differ for static and dynamic work (Torner et al., 1991).

Reduce dynamic loads by using the guidelines in Chapter 15, Manual Handling. Can motors instead of muscles furnish the power? Can two surfaces be the same height so sliding replaces lifting? Can a short section of gravity roller conveyor bridge the gap between the workstation and a powered takeaway conveyor—thus permitting sliding instead of lifting? Sometimes force requirements can be reduced by maintenance, such as sharpening equipment (drills, knives) and properly lubricating equipment (handtools, valves) or product (to reduce sticking).

TABLE			14.10	

Posture checklist (Keyserling et al., 1992) for neck, trunk, and legs. A zero indicates insignificant risk. An X indicates a potential risk. An asterisk indicates a significant risk.

	PERCENT TIME POSTURE USED IN JOB		
Job Studied	Never	<1/3	>1/3
Neck			
1. Mild forward bending (>20°)	0	0	X
2. Severe forward bending (>45°)	0	X	*
3. Backward bending (>20°)	0	X	*
4. Twisting or lateral bending (>20°)	0	X	*
Trunk			
5. Mild forward bending (>20°)	0	X	*
6. Severe forward bending (>45°)	0	*	*
7. Backward bending (>20°)	0	X	*
8. Twisting or lateral bending (>20°)	0	X	*
General body/legs			
9. Standing stationary (no walking or leaning)	0	0	X
10. Standing, using footpedal	0	X	*
11. Knees bent or squatting	0	X	*
12. Kneeling	0	X	*
13. Lying on back or side	0	X	*

Total X = _____   Total * = _____

Comments:

Source: M. Keyserling, M. Brouwer, and B. A. Silverstein, "A Checklist for Evaluating Ergonomic Risk Factors Resulting from Awkward Postures of the Legs, Trunk, and Neck." *Int. J. Industrial Ergonomics,* Vol. 9, pp. 283–301. Copyright © 1992 by Elsevier Science, Amsterdam, Netherlands. Reprinted with permission.

For the neck, the load typically is static (e.g., microscope or VDT work). Waersted and Bjorklund (1991) pointed out that mental effort increases muscle tension, adding to the biomechanical force requirements. Helander et al. (1991) gave suggestions for improving microscope work.

3.2.2 *Administrative solutions*   See Section 1.3.2.

4 BACK

4.1 Problem   Musculoskeletal disorders of the back occur primarily from manual material handling, although some problems arise from body movement without a load. Back problems also can occur from lack of movement, such as from sitting.

Khalil (1991) gave some statistics:

- On any given day, 6,500,000 people in the United States are in bed with back pain.
- 75,000,000 Americans have back pain problems.
- In industrialized societies, 80% of working adults will develop back pain during their career.
- In the United States, only colds cause more physician visits than back pain. An estimated 50% of all chiropractor visits are due to low-back symptoms.

In 1988, estimated total compensable cost of low-back disorders in the United States was $15.3 billion. In 1988, 35% of all Liberty Mutual workers compensation claim costs were for low-back disorders. About 1/3 of the costs were for medical treatment and 2/3 for lost wages. The cost distribution is quite skewed, with 25% of the cases accounting for 95% of the costs: average cost/claim = $7,400, while median cost = $360 (Snook, 1991). (*Statistical note:* For the median, the sum of the deviations of individual values from the median equals zero. For the mean, the sum of the deviations squared is a minimum; the exponent of 2 emphasizes "outliers.")

Snook (1991) pointed out a hierarchy of low-back problems:

1. low-back **pain**
2. low-back **impairment** (reduced ability to perform various musculoskeletal activities)—experienced by about 11% of U. S. working population
3. low-back **disability** (time lost from the job or assignment to restricted duty)—experienced by about 2% of workers each year
4. low-back **compensation** (reimbursement for medical costs and lost wages)—about .75 claims presented each year/100 workers with approximately a 10–1 range from the best to worst industry

4.2 Risk Factors   Khalil (1991) gave risk factors for low-back pain (LBP):

- individual physical factors (e.g., weight, physique, age, gender, flexibility)
- psychological factors (e.g., depression, anxiety, job dissatisfaction)
- task demand factors (e.g., posture, speed, repetition, twisting, prolonged sitting or standing)
- environmental factors (e.g., workplace design, slippery floors, distractions, bulky containers)

For another review of risk factors, see Pope et al. (1991).

The following is a concise summary of Garg and Moore's (1992) review in which 19 risk factors are divided into personal and job categories.

4.2.1 *Personal* Eleven personal factors are discussed briefly in the following.

Age. Incidence is maximal between ages 35 and 55, but the exact form of the risk is not fully understood.

Gender. The incidence of low-back pain is equal among males and females. However, women (versus males performing similar work) performing physically heavy jobs have a higher incidence of low-back pain and have a larger percent of expensive back-injury claims. However, about 75%–80% of back injury claims are filed by males.

Body size. Body dimensions (stature, weight, build), in general, do not have a strong correlation with low-back pain. However, taller people seem to have more low-back pain.

Physical fitness and training. Although the importance of physical fitness and training is generally accepted, there is little epidemiological evidence supporting its benefit to low-back injuries. However, regular exercise with large-muscle groups (e.g., jogging, swimming, cycling) may have considerable benefit and is unlikely to do harm.

Lumbar mobility. There is no evidence that reduced spinal mobility is a risk factor for low-back pain.

Strength. Although mean isometric trunk muscle strength is higher for normal healthy people than for people with low-back pain, there is considerable overlap between those with and without back pain.

Medical history. A previous history of back or sciatic pain is one of the most reliable predictive factors for subsequent work-related back problems. A person with a history of repeated low-back pain should not be given a job requiring heavy lifting.

Years of employment. Although inexperience would seem a likely risk factor, epidemiological evidence is lacking.

Smoking. Although many studies have found smoking a risk factor, some have not.

Psychosocial. Patients with chronic and disabling low-back pain often have significant **psychosocial problems.** (Psychosocial problems include hysteria, anxiety, emotional instability, depression, job dissatisfaction, family problems, relatives with disabilities, and alcoholism.) It is not clear which comes first, the back disorder or the psychological problems. After successful back rehabilitation, most psychosocial problems tend to dissipate. Johansson et al. (1993) emphasize the need for analysis of the psychosocial variables as well as the physical (ergonomic) workload.

Structural abnormalities. Most abnormalities, at least as a single factor, do not seem to predispose to low-back pain. However, there are studies showing evidence for and against low-back pain for most abnormalities, so the evidence is mixed.

4.2.2 *Job risk factors* The following lists eight job-related risk factors.

Heavy physical work. The consensus is that low-back pain and disc degeneration are more prevalent in heavy physical jobs.

Lifting. Low-back pain is clearly related to lifting. See Chapter 15, Manual Handling, for a discussion of the risk factors in lifting.

Bending, stretching, and reaching. When lifting is combined with torques about the spine, risk of low-back pain increases.

Twisting. Twisting when lifting increases risk of low-back pain.

Pushing and pulling. Pushing and pulling increase risk of low-back pain.

Prolonged sitting and standing. Static load (lack of movement) increases risk of low-back pain.

Accidents. Acute (sudden) events as well as MSD trauma can cause low-back pain.

Whole-body vibration. Examples of whole-body vibration are: on-road vehicles (trucks, buses), off-road vehicles (tractors, dozers), rail vehicles, aircraft (helicopters, fixed-wing aircraft), sea vehicles (hovercraft, ships), and even parts of buildings (near generators, pumps, heavy machinery, ventilation systems).

4.3 Solutions Solutions depend upon the three basic problems (1) underuse of the back, (2) whole-body vibration, and (3) overuse of the back.

4.3.1 *Underuse of the back* When people sit for prolonged periods, the intervertebral disc is not properly nourished. The disc receives its nutrition by diffusion, which occurs when there are alterations of pressure (i.e., from movement). The solution is to avoid prolonged sitting. In addition, people in sedentary jobs should be encouraged to be active in their nonwork activities.

4.3.2 *Whole-body vibration* Truck drivers combine static sitting with whole-body vibration (Wikstrom et al., 1994). Even worse is driving with prolonged head rotation; for example, driving an industrial truck in a sideways sitting position

(Wikstrom, 1993). Truck drivers who load and unload their vehicles have more musculoskeletal complaints than drivers who just drive (van der Beck et al., 1993). Drivers of tractors and heavy equipment are at considerable risk (Wilder et al., 2002).

Work = Kinetic energy = $1/2\ mv^2 = 1/2\ m\ (a^2\ t^2)$

where

m = mass
v = velocity
 = at
a = acceleration
t = time

Thus the work on the spine is a function of the square of the vibration's acceleration and time. If acceleration or time is reduced 10%, work on the spine is reduced to $(.9)^2$ or 81%. Thus, the general goal is to reduce vibration acceleration and exposure time.

Impedence of the human body increases with frequency up to a first peak around 5 Hz—probably due to the spine. There is an additional peak between 10 and 14 Hz, representing a bending vibration of the upper torso (Wilder et al., 2002).

Ebe and Griffin (2000), using Steven's psychophysical law, show that seat discomfort is a function of both static and dynamic factors:

$$D = -50.3 + 2.68\ S^{1.18} + 1.01\ V^{929}$$

where D = Discomfort score (0 $<D<$300)

S = Seat stiffness at load of 490 N (110 lb), N/m^2

V = Vibration magnitude, VDV, m/s$^{1.75}$ (see British Standard 6841)

The latest ISO standard on vibration (ISO 2631-1.2, 1997) uses the overall Root-Mean-Square value to evaluate exposure. It also has a factor for "jolts and jars." It has three zones: a likely risk zone, an intermediate caution zone, and a lower acceptable zone.

Possible specific solutions include reducing the vibration transmitted to the driver (better vehicle suspension, better seat design, seat cushions; see Figure 14.9), good posture, and variability in posture (so the same muscles and ligaments are not continuously loaded), such as through occasional standing or walking.

Some lifestyle changes are reduced tobacco and alcohol consumption. Prolonged bed rest can actually inhibit healing in the back. The general recommendation now is a moderate level of activity rather than inactivity. For additional comments, see Section 4.4 in Chapter 13.

ISO 6897 (1984) considers the special case of human response to low-frequency (.063–1 Hz) horizontal vibration in buildings and offshore fixed structures.

F I G U R E   14.9

Seat schematics. Which of the three seat schematics will give the least vibration to subway train drivers? Seat A is best; seats B and C are cantilevered and so have extra vibration (Ozkaya et al., 1996). Pope et al. (1989) reported that relatively thin and hard viscoelastic seat cushions were best for vibration reduction.

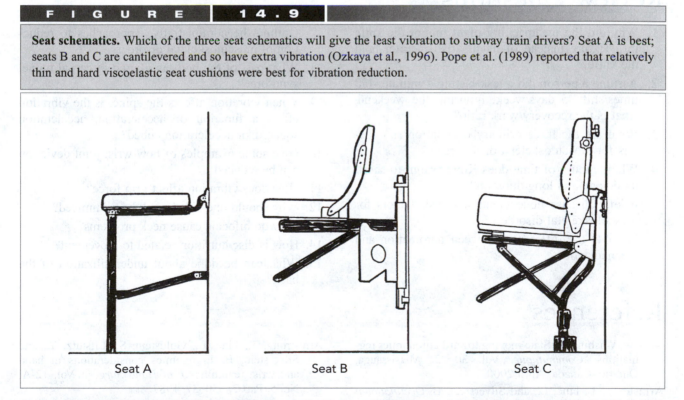

Seat A   Seat B   Seat C

Source: N. Ozkaya, D. Goldsheyder, and B. Willems. "Effect of Operator Seat Design on Vibration Exposure." *Am. Ind. Hygiene Assoc. J.,* Vol. 57, 837–42, 1996. Copyright © 1996 by the American Industrial Hygiene Association, Fairfax, VA. Used by Permission.

4.3.3 *Overuse of the back* While underuse of the back tends to lead to disc problems, overuse tends to lead to muscle and ligament problems. The examination of the occupational risk factors in Section 4.2.2 shows that manual handling is the primary problem. For more on manual handling, see Chapter 15.

Twisting (such as when reaching for a part behind you) also is a problem. Demonstrate this by moving your extended horizontal arm slowly from straight ahead to the side and then to the rear. Just after you pass "3 o'clock" you will begin to feel the strain. This strain occurs sooner when sitting than standing because sitting tends to lock your torso in place. Design workstation supply and disposal areas so operators don't have to twist to get supplies or dispose of completed units. This may even require placing items a little farther away so that the operators must get off their chairs or move their feet (rather than just twist). A swiveling chair tends to be better than a nonswiveling chair for assembling while seated.

Guideline: Don't reach behind your back.

5 LEG

5.1 Problem
Most jobs have a relatively low incidence of musculoskeletal disorders in the lower leg. The exception is the knee—if the worker spends a lot of time kneeling (e.g., carpet and tile workers). The workers are putting approximately 89% of their body weight on a small surface area with minimal fatty tissue. The result is bursitis of the knee (Kuorinka and Forcier, 1995).

Carpetlayers use a device actuated by the knee to stretch carpets. Carpetlayers represent .06% of the workforce but submit 6% of the knee-injury claims. Normalizing the data by using bodyweight (BW), impact forces on the knee are 1.3 BW for walking, 3 BW for running, and 4 BW when using the knee-kicker (Village et al., 1993).

Standing work while being vibrated (e.g., fishing) may cause a bent-knees stance (Torner et al., 1990). This leads to prepatellar bursitis.

5.2 Solutions
The primary solution is to reduce the time on the knees. Provide maintenance workers with a wheeled cart so they can maintain parts on the cart instead of on the floor. Or, use a handtool with a long handle (e.g., a dustpan with a 36-inch handle) versus a short handle (3 inches). A secondary, personal-protective-equipment approach is pads on the knee (very portable) or floor (more comfortable) to reduce the pressure by exerting the force over a larger area.

Review Questions

1. Why did the meatpacking plant mount the knife in a fixture instead of having the operator hold the knife?

2. Assume a person did a task lasting 1 minute, 450 times/shift, 5 days/week. Ignoring the weekend, what is the recovery/work ratio?

3. What are the three primary occupation risk factors for musculoskeletal disorders?

4. What amount of time does Konz assign to short, moderate, and long duration?

5. Briefly discuss nonoccupational risk factors for musculoskeletal disorders.

6. What is the difference between automation and mechanization?

7. Outline the administrative approaches to reduction of musculoskeletal disorders.

8. What part of the body is injured in carpal tunnel syndrome?

9. When vibration affects the spine, is the vibration effect a function of acceleration, acceleration squared, or acceleration cubed?

10. Give some examples of how wrist joint deviation can be reduced.

11. How does vibration affect grip force?

12. Why should one-sided work be minimized?

13. How do bifocals cause neck problems?

14. How is disc nutrition related to movement?

15. What can be done about underutilization of the back?

References

———, Washington State moving toward ergonomics regulations. *Communique,* Vol. 30, 2. Mississauga, Ontario, Canada, April 2000.

Armstrong, T., Fine, L., and Silverstein, B. *Occupational Risk Factors: Final Contract Report to NIOSH,* No. 22-82-2507, Cincinnati, 1985.

Armstrong, T., Fine, L., Goldstein, S., Lifshitz, Y., and Silverstein, B. Ergonomics considerations in hand and wrist tendinitis. *J. of Hand Surgery,* Vol. 12-A, No. 5, Part 2, 830–37, 1987.

Armstrong, T. and Martin, B. Adversive effects of repetitive loading and segmental vibration. Chapter 12 in

Musculoskeletal Disorders in the Workplace, M. Nordin, G. Andersson and M. Pope (eds.). St. Louis: Mosby, 1997.

Atcheson, S., Ward, J., and Lowe, W. Concurrent medical disease in work-related carpal tunnel syndrome. *Archives of Internal Medicine,* Vol. 158, 14, 1506–12, July 27, 1998.

Baluyut, R., Genaidy, A., Davis, L., Shell, R., and Simmons, R. Use of visual perception in estimating static postural stresses: Magnitudes and sources of errors. *Ergonomics,* Vol. 38, No. 9, 1841–50, 1995.

Bernard, B. Musculoskeletal disorders and workplace factors: A critical review of the epidemiologic evidence. Cincinnati: NIOSH, 1997.

Bjoring, G. and Haag, G. Musculoskeletal exposure of manual spray painting in the woodworking industry—An ergonomic study on painters. *Int. J. of Industrial Ergonomics,* Vol. 26, 603–14, 2000.

Bjorksten, M., Boquist, B., Talback, M., and Edling, E. Reported neck and shoulder problems in female industrial workers: The importance of factors at work and at home. *Int. J. of Industrial Ergonomics,* Vol. 27, 159–70, 2001.

Ebe, K. and Griffin, M. Quantitative prediction of overall seat discomfort. *Ergonomics,* Vol. 43, 6, 791–806, 2000.

Feng, Y., Grooten, W., Wretenberg, P., and Arborelius, U. Effects of arm support on shoulder and arm muscle activity during sedentary work. *Ergonomics,* Vol. 40, No. 8, 834–48, 1997.

Fogelman, M., Freivalds, A., and Goldberg, J. An ergonomic evaluation of knives for two poultry cutting tasks. *Int. J. of Industrial Ergonomics,* Vol. 11, 257–65, 1993.

Garg, A. Occupational biomechanics and low-back pain. In *Ergonomics: Low Back Pain, Carpal Tunnel Syndrome, and Upper Extremity Disorders in the Workplace,* Moore, J. and Garg, A. (eds.). Philadelphia: Hanley and Belfus, 1992.

Garg, A. and Moore, J. Epidemiology of low-back pain in industry. In *Ergonomics: Low Back Pain, Carpal Tunnel Syndrome, and Upper Extremity Disorders in the Workplace,* Moore, J. and Garg, A. (eds.). Philadelphia: Hanley and Belfus, 1992.

Genaidy, A., Barkawi, H., and Christensen, D. Ranking of static non-neutral postures around the joints of the upper extremity and spine. *Ergonomics,* Vol. 38, No. 9, 1851–58, 1995.

Gibson, J. and Alexander, D. A filtering approach to ergonomics surveillance. *Proceedings of the Human Factors and Ergonomics Society,* 722–24, 1997.

Griffin, M. *Handbook of Human Vibration.* San Diego: Academic Press, 1990.

Hagberg, M. and Wegman, D. Prevalence rates and odds ratio of shoulder-neck disease in different occupational groups. *British J. Industrial Medicine,* Vol. 44, 602–10, 1987.

Helander, M., Grossmith, E., and Prabhu, P. Planning and implementation of microscope work. *Applied Ergonomics,* Vol. 22, No. 1, 36–42, 1991.

Hidalgo, J., Genaidy, A., Huston, R., and Arantes, J. Occupational biomechanics of the neck: A review and recommendations. *J. of Human Ergology,* Vol. 21, 165–81, 1992.

Hong, C., Xiang-chun, Z., Yongkui, M., and Jian-xin, W. Equal vibrotactile sense thresholds of the fingers and its diagnostic significance for hand-arm vibration syndrome. *Am. Ind. Hygiene Association J.,* Vol. 56, No. 1, 11–15, 1995.

ISO. Guide to the evaluation of the responses of occupants of fixed structures especially buildings and off-shore structures. Int. Org. for Standardization, 6897, 1984.

Jarvholm, U., Palmerud, G., Kadefors, R., and Herbets, P. The effect of arm support on supraspinatus muscle load during simulated assembly work and welding. *Ergonomics,* Vol. 34, No. 1, 57–66, 1991.

Jegerlehner, J. Ergonomic analyses of problem jobs using computer spreadsheets. In *Advances in Industrial Ergonomics and Safety III,* Karwowski, W. and Yates, J. (eds.). London: Taylor and Francis, 865–71, 1991.

Johansson, J., Kadefors, R., Rubenowitz, S., Klingenstierna, U., Lindstrom, I., Erngstrom, T., and Johansson, M. Musculoskeletal symptoms, ergonomic aspects and psychosocial factors in two different truck assembly concepts. *Int. J. of Industrial Ergonomics,* Vol. 12, 35–48, 1993.

Johnson, S. and Evans, B. Tracking median nerve conduction as a method of early detection of carpal tunnel syndrome. *Proceedings of the Human Factors and Ergonomics Society,* 759–63, 1993.

Jung, M-C and Hallbeck, M. The effect of wrist position, angular velocity, and exertion direction on simultaneous maximal grip force and wrist torque under isokinetic conditions. *Int. J. of Ind. Ergonomics,* Vol. 29, 133–43, 2002.

Kao, H. Differential effects of writing instruments on handwriting performance. *Acta Psychologia Taiwanica,* Vol. 21, 9–13, 1979.

Ketola, R., Toivonen, R., and Vikari-Juntura, E. Interobserver repeatability and validity of an observation method to assess physical loads imposed on the upper extremities. *Ergonomics,* Vol. 44, 2, 119–31, 2001.

Keyserling, M., Brouwer, M., and Silverstein, B. A checklist for evaluating ergonomic risk factors resulting from awkward postures of the legs, trunk, and neck. *Int. J. of Industrial Ergonomics,* Vol. 9, 283–301, 1992.

Khalil, T. Ergonomic issues in low back pain: Origin and magnitude of the problem. *Proceedings of the Human Factors Society,* 820–24, 1991.

Kilbom, A., Persson, J., and Jonsson, B. Risk factors for work-related disorders of the neck and shoulders—With special emphasis on working postures and movements. In *The Ergonomics of Working Postures,* Corlett, N., Wilson, J., and Manenica, I. (eds.). London: Taylor and Francis, 1986.

Krag, M., Cohen, M., Haugh, L., and Pope, M. Body height change during upright and recumbent posture. *Spine,* Vol. 15, No. 3, 202–7, 1990.

Kroemer, K. Avoiding cumulative trauma disorders in shops and offices. *Am. Industrial Hygiene Association J.,* Vol. 53, No. 9, 596–604, 1992.

Kuorinka, I. and Forcier, L. (eds.). *Work Related Musculoskeletal Disorders,* 109–14. London: Taylor and Francis, 1995.

Lifshitz, S. and Armstrong, T. A design checklist for control and prediction of cumulative trauma disorders in hand intensive manual jobs. *Proceedings of the Human Factors Society,* 837–41, 1986.

MacLeod, D. and Morris, A. Ergonomics cost benefits case study in a paper manufacturing company. *Proceedings of HFES,* 698–701, 1996.

Marras, W. Toward an understanding of dynamic variables in ergonomics. In *Ergonomics: Low Back Pain, Carpal Tunnel Syndrome and Upper Extremity Disorders in the Workplace,* Moore, J. and Garg, A. (eds.). Philadelphia: Hanley and Belfus, 1992.

Marras, W. and Sommerich, C. A three-dimensional motion model of loads on the lumbar spine: II. Model validation. *Human Factors,* Vol. 33, No. 2, 139–49, 1991.

Matias, A., Salvendy, G., and Kuczek, T. Predictive models of carpal tunnel syndrome causation among VDT operators. *Ergonomics,* Vol. 41, No. 2, 213–26, 1998.

McAtamney, L. and Corlett, E. N. RULA: A survey method for the investigation of work-related upper limb disorders. *Applied Ergonomics,* Vol. 24, No. 3, 91–99, 1993.

Mital, A. and Channaveeraiah, C. Peak volitional torques for wrenches and screwdrivers. *Int. J. of Industrial Ergonomics,* Vol. 3, 41–64, 1988.

Neelam, S. Using torque arms to reduce CTDs. *Ergonomics in Design,* 25–28, Oct. 1994.

Neese, R. and Konz, S. Vibrometry of industrial workers: A case study. *Int. J. Industrial Ergonomics,* Vol. 11, No. 4, 341–45, 1993.

Nussbaum, M., Chaffin, D., Stump, B., Baker, G., and Foulke, J. Motion times, hand forces, and trunk kinematics when using material handling manipulators in short-distance transfers of moderate mass objects. *Applied Ergonomics,* Vol. 31, 227–37, 2000.

Oxenburgh, M. *Increasing Productivity and Profit Through Health and Safety.* Chicago: CCH International, 76, 1991.

Ozkaya, N., Goldsheyder, D., and Willems, B. Effect of operator seat design on vibration exposure. *Am. Ind. Hygiene Assoc. J.,* Vol. 57, 837–42, 1996.

Pierre-Jerome, C., Bekkelund, S., Mellgren, S., and Nordstrom, R. Quantitative MRI and electrophysiology of preoperative carpal tunnel syndrome in a female population. *Ergonomics,* Vol. 40, No. 6, 642–49, 1997.

Poonawala, M. and Fernandez, J. Effect of using arm supports as an aid to light assembly work. In *Advances in Occupational Ergonomics and Safety,* S. Kumar (ed.). Amsterdam: IOS Press, 479–82, 1998.

Pope, M., Broman, H., and Hansson, T. The dynamic response of a subject seated on various cushions. *Ergonomics,* Vol. 32, No. 10, 1155–66, 1989.

Pope, M., Frymoyer, J., Andersson, G., et al. *Occupational Back Pain: Assessment, Treatment and Prevention.* St. Louis: Mosby Year Book, 1991.

Potvin, J., Chiang, J., Mckean, C., and Stephens, A. A psychophysical study to determine acceptable limits for repetitive hand impact severity during automotive trim installation. *Int. J. of Ind. Ergonomics,* Vol. 26, 625–37, 2000.

Putz-Anderson, V. (ed.). *Cumulative Trauma Disorders.* London: Taylor and Francis, 1988.

Rigdon, J. The wrist watch. *Wall Street Journal,* September 28, 1992.

Rodgers, S. A functional job analysis technique. *Occupational Medicine: State of the Art Reviews,* Vol. 7, No. 4. Philadelphia: Hanley & Belfus, Oct.–Dec. 1992.

Rys, M. and Konz, S. Lifting belts: A review. *Int. J. Occupational Safety and Ergonomics,* Vol. 1, No. 3, 294–303, 1995.

Schoenmarklin, R. and Marras, W. Quantification of wrist motion and cumulative trauma disorders in industry. *Proceedings of the Human Factors Society,* 838–42, 1991.

Schoenmarklin, R. and Marras, W. Dynamic capabilities of the wrist joint in industrial workers. *Int. J. of Industrial Ergonomics,* Vol. 11, 207–24, 1993.

Silverstein, B., Fine, L., and Armstrong, T. Hand–wrist cumulative trauma disorders in industry. *British J. Industrial Medicine,* Vol. 43, 779–84, 1986.

Snook, S. Low back disorders in industry. *Proceedings of the Human Factors Society,* 830–33, 1991.

Sommerich, C., McGlothlin, J., and Marras, W. Occupational risk factors associated with soft tissue disorders of the shoulder: A review of recent investigations of the literature. *Ergonomics,* Vol. 36, No. 6, 697–717, 1993.

Synergist (Newsletter of American Industrial Hygiene Association, 2700 Prosperity Ave., Fairfax VA 22031), April 1995.

Tanaka, S. and McGlothlin, J. A conceptual quantitative model for prevention of work-related carpal tunnel syndrome (CTS). *Int. J. of Industrial Ergonomics,* Vol. 11, 181–93, 1993.

Tayyari, F. and Emanuel, J. Carpal tunnel syndrome: An ergonomics approach to its prevention. *Int. J. of Industrial Ergonomics,* Vol. 11, 173–79, 1993.

Torner, M., Zetterberg, C., Hansson, T., and Lindell, V. Musculoskeletal symptoms and signs and isometric strength among fishermen. *Ergonomics,* Vol. 33, 1155–70, 1990.

Torner, M., Zetterberg, C., Anden, U., Hansson, T., and Lindell, V. Workload and musculoskeletal problems: A comparison between welders and office clerks (with reference also to fishermen). *Ergonomics,* Vol. 34, No. 9, 1179–96, 1991.

van der Beck, A., Frings-Dresen, M., van Dijk, F., Kemper, H., and Meijman, T. Loading and unloading by lorry drivers and musculoskeletal complaints. *Int. J. of Industrial Ergonomics,* Vol. 12, 13–23, 1993.

Viikari-Juntura, E. The scientific basis for making guidelines and standards to prevent work-related musculoskeletal disorders. *Ergonomics,* Vol. 40, No. 10, 1097–1117, 1997.

Village, J., Morrison, J., and Layland, A. Biomechanical comparison of carpet-stretching devices. *Ergonomics,* Vol. 36, No. 8, 899–909, 1993.

Waersted, M. and Bjorklund, R. Shoulder muscle tension introduced by two VDT-based tasks of different complexity. *Ergonomics,* Vol. 34, No. 2, 137–50, 1991.

Waersted, M. and Westgaard, R. Working hours as a risk factor in the development of musculoskeletal complaints. *Ergonomics,* Vol. 34, No. 3, 265–76, 1991.

Wick, J. Force and frequency: How much is too much? In *Advances in Industrial Ergonomics and Safety VI,* F. Aghazadeh (ed.). London: Taylor and Francis, 521–25, 1994.

Wick, J., Bockman, M., Herring, C., and Beeunas, M. An approach to ergonomics risk assessment and abatement in manufacturing. In *Advances in Occupational Ergonomics and Safety I (Vol. 2),* A. Mital, H. Krueger, S. Kumar, M. Menozzi, and J. Fernandez, (eds.). Cincinnati: Int. Society for Occupational Ergonomics and Safety, 991–96, 1996.

Wick, J. and McKinnis, M. A structured ergonomics design review process. In *Advances in Occupational Ergonomics and Safety,* S. Kumar (ed.). Amsterdam: IOS Press, 143–46, 1998.

Wigley, R., Turner, W., Blake, B., Darby, F., McInnes, R., and Harding, P. *Occupational Overuse Syndrome: Treatment and Rehabilitation.* Wellington, New Zealand: Department of Labor, 1992.

Wikstrom, B. Effects from twisted postures and whole-body vibration during driving. *Int. J. of Industrial Ergonomics,* Vol. 12, 61–75, 1993.

Wikstrom, Bengt-Olav, Kjellberg, A., and Landstrom, U. Health effects of long-term occupational exposure to whole-body vibration: A review. *Int. J. of Industrial Ergonomics,* Vol. 14, 273–92, 1994.

Wilder, D., Wasserman, D., and Wasserman, J. Occupational vibration exposure. In *Physical and Biological Hazards of the Workplace,* Wald, P. and Stave, G. (eds.), 79–104. New York: Wiley, 2002.

Winkel, J. and Westgaard, R. Occupational and individual risk factors for shoulder–neck complaints: Part I—Guidelines for the practitioner. *Int. J. of Industrial Ergonomics,* Vol. 10, 79–83, 1992a.

Winkel, J. and Westgaard, R. Occupational and individual risk factors for shoulder–neck complaints: Part II—The scientific basis (literature review) for the guide. *Int. J. of Industrial Ergonomics,* Vol. 10, 85–104, 1992b.

Xiao, and Mackenzie, C. Uncertainty in trauma patient resuscitation. *Proc. of Human Factors and Ergonomic Society,* 168–71, 1997.

Zehel, D. Psychosocial & treatment factors implicating carpal tunnel syndrome outcomes. In *Advances in Occupational Ergonomics and Safety II,* B. Das and W. Karwowski (eds.). Louisville, KY: IOS Press and Ohmsha, 395–98, 1997.

Websites

Agriculture Ergonomics Research Center, www.engr.ucdavis.edu/~ergo/papers/
Papers on agricultural ergonomics from University of California, Davis.

ErgoWeb, www.ergoweb.com/Pub/Info/ewhome.shtml
Strength is inclusion of links to ergonomic standards and guidelines and the professional organizations in ergonomics.

Computer Related Repetitive Strain Injury (RSI), www.engr.unl.edu/ee/eeshop/rsi.html
Gives links and comprehensive resource list on RSI.

NIOSH, www.cdc.gov/niosh/ergoweb.html
More than 40 links.

OSHA, www.osha.gov
Has safety and musculoskeletal disorder statistics.

Typing Injury, www.cs.princeton.edu/~dwallach/tifaq/
Gives "frequently asked questions" on therapeutics, equipment, software, and injury mechanisms on RSI.

15 MANUAL HANDLING

Overview

Manual handling is a major safety problem. Force limits are given for pushing and pulling. Carrying recommendations are given for both distance and local movement. After explaining NIOSH guidelines, principles of manual handling are discussed. If you can't make the job perfect, make it better.

Key Concepts

acute/chronic	job severity index	origin/destination	spinal torque
angle of asymmetry	lifting duration	physiological approach	static load
balancers	lifting frequency	psychophysical approach	tipping aids
bend the knees	lifting index	recommended weight limit	turntables
biomechanical approach	load constant	(RWL)	vertical location
horizontal location	manipulators	recovery time	vertical travel distance
J hook	one-hand lift	scissors lift	workstation positioners

257

The problem of manual handling (MH) is demonstrated by some example statistics. MH is associated with:

- 27% of all industrial injuries
- 670,000 injuries/yr in the United States
- 60% of all money spent on industrial injuries
- 93,000,000 workdays/yr on industrial injuries

Dempsey and Hashemi (1997a) analyzed more than 200,000 manual material-handling claims. The cost distribution was very skewed (skewness = 13), with the average cost of a claim 16 times higher than the median cost. Of low-back claims, 10% are responsible for 86% of the cost. The low-back area represented 29% of the claims but 41% of the cost; upper arm was 8% of the claims and 11% of the cost, knee was 3% of the claims and 5% of the costs.

Injuries generally are to the skeletomuscular system—muscles, ligaments, and especially the back. The trauma may be **acute** (results from a one-time event) but most is **chronic** (results from cumulative events over a time period). That is, it is cumulative strain or repetitive trauma. However, a specific event may have been the last straw on a previously weakened system and thus give the appearance that the problem is acute rather than chronic. Managements may like to think of MH injuries as acute (and therefore an "act of God" and beyond their control) rather than chronic (and therefore subject to change). OSHA classifies all back problems as injuries (instantaneous) even though most are cumulative.

■■ BACKGROUND

1.1 Criteria   Various groups have given recommendations for the amount a person can push, pull, carry, and lift. Their criteria are grouped into three categories: biomechanical, physiological, and psychophysical.

1.1.1 *Biomechanical*   The **biomechanical approach** emphasizes the forces and torques of MH and their effect on the parts of the body. In general, the back is the weak link—especially the low back, with its L4–L5 disc and L5–S1 disc. See Figure 4.1. The emphasis is on measuring external forces and torques due to the task, measuring body dimensions and strengths, and then computing the effect on the back. A key problem of the biomechanical approach is that the permitted load does not vary with frequency; the answer is the same whether the lift is 1, 60, or 300/hour.

Another biomechanical approach (*Force Limits,* 1980) emphasizes intra-abdominal pressure. (Intra-abdominal pressure is obtained by having a person swallow a pressure transducer, which then radios the pressure while the person does lifting.)

1.1.2 *Physiological*   The **physiological approach** emphasizes the energy requirements of the task and the effects on the cardiovascular system. Energy requirements have little impact on occasional lifting but can become important for repetitive lifting—for example, once/min. For MH tasks at frequencies greater than 4 times/min, the physiological criterion defines the task limits (Shoaf et al., 1997). In general, the goal is to limit metabolic rate to less than 5 kcal/min.

1.1.3 *Psychophysical*   The **psychophysical approach** has people actually do various MH tasks under controlled conditions. Based on the amount of MH that the sample of workers does for the sample of time, predictions are made as to what the population of workers will do in real jobs. A virtue of the psychophysical approach is that it combines the biomechanical and the physiological stresses.

1.2 MH Variables   The many variables in MH are divided into three broad categories: individual variables, technique variables, and task variables. The general thrust is to (1) increase the strength of the worker, (2) decrease the stress due to technique and task, or (3) increase strength *and* decrease stress.

1.2.1 *Individual*   Selection variables include gender, age, back muscle strength, arm strength, and intra-abdominal pressure. Although there is no doubt that it is safer to have a strong person do MH than a weak person, there are many questions when it comes to selecting individuals. In addition, our society tends to discourage excluding people from jobs. The question becomes not, "Who has the strongest back?" but, "What can be done so a small person can do the job?"

1.2.2 *Technique*   Training variables include body posture, hand orientation, foot position, accelerations, and lifting training. Although there is no doubt that a trained, knowledgeable person will be less likely than a novice to be injured during MH, there are many problems when it comes to specific techniques. The primary challenge is that people are not machines and they forget, make mistakes, fail to learn, and so on.

1.2.3 *Task*   Ergonomic variables include object, weight, ease of handling, initial and final height of object moved, angle of rotation, lift symmetry, clothing, and thermal environment. A strong advantage of modifying the task to improve MH is that it is a permanent change as opposed to the temporary changes of personal selection and training. Although selection and training will not be ignored, this chapter will focus on ergonomics, that is, on job design.

2 PUSHING AND PULLING

Pushing and pulling is better than lifting and lowering. Thus, use carts, not only in production areas but also in support areas such as food service, trash, custodial, and maintenance. After giving recommended force limits, some task modifications will be given.

2.1 Force Limits An excellent overview of push and pull forces is given by Imrahn (1999); the following borrows heavily from his article. Five major factors affect push/pull strengths.

2.1.1 *Handles* In the chain of force transmission, a poor hand/handle interface is a weak link. A handle is necessary for pulling, but pushing may just use a flat surface.

2.1.2 *One hand vs two hands* Although two hands are better than one, depending on the conditions, the ratio of one-hand to two-hand-strength varies from 64% to 104%. The ratios are well above 50% because (1) push/pull comes from the trunk as well as the arms, and (2) one-hand exertions permit greater postural freedom (and thus better use of the body's weight and center of gravity). The ratio is higher when arm strength is more important.

The arms and shoulders (rather than the back) tend to be limiting when the activity is repetitive (thus causing local muscle fatigue) or when the posture is poor. In general, arm strength is greatest at .5 (reach distance), drops some at .75 (reach distance), and is lowest at 1.0 (reach distance). Pushing/pulling above the shoulder or below the hip also is poor.

2.1.3 *Body posture* The three most common postures are standing, sitting, and kneeling.

For standing, foot and hand placement is critical. For pushing, lean toward the load with the rear foot positioned behind the body's center of mass. For pulling, lean away from the load with the front foot ahead of the body's center of mass. See Table 15.1 for initial force for two-hand pushing, Table 15.2 for two-hand pulling, and Table 15.3 for one-hand pushing and pulling. Sustained forces (required to keep an object

T A B L E   1 5 . 1

Recommended maximum initial TWO-HANDED PUSHING forces (kg) given for male (female) industrial workers at 2.1-m pushing distance (Mital et al., 1993). Mital et al. also have initial and sustained forces for other distances and frequencies. Values in parentheses are for females.

Handle Height (cm)	Population %	PULLING FREQUENCY				
		10/min	5/min	1/min	1/5 min	1/8 h
144(135)	90	20(14)	22(15)	25(17)	26(20)	31(22)
	75	26(17)	29(18)	32(21)	34(24)	41(27)
	50	32(20)	36(22)	40(25)	42(29)	51(32)
	25	38(24)	43(25)	47(29)	50(33)	61(37)
	10	44(26)	49(28)	55(33)	58(38)	70(41)
95(89)	90	21(14)	24(15)	26(17)	28(20)	34(22)
	75	28(17)	31(18)	34(21)	36(24)	44(27)
	50	34(20)	38(22)	43(25)	45(29)	54(32)
	25	41(24)	46(25)	51(29)	54(33)	65(37)
	10	47(26)	53(28)	59(33)	62(38)	75(41)
64(57)	90	19(11)	22(12)	24(14)	25(16)	31(18)
	75	25(14)	28(15)	31(17)	33(19)	40(21)
	50	31(16)	35(17)	39(20)	41(23)	50(25)
	25	38(19)	42(20)	46(23)	49(27)	59(30)
	10	43(21)	48(23)	53(26)	57(30)	68(33)

Source: A. Mital, A. Nicholson, and M. M. Ayoub, *A Guide to Manual Materials Handling.* Copyright © 1993 by Taylor and Francis, London. Reprinted with permission.

TABLE	15.2

Recommended maximum initial TWO-HANDED PULLING forces (kg) given for male (female) industrial workers at 2.1-m pulling distance (Mital et al., 1993). Mital et al. also have initial and sustained forces for other distances and frequencies. Values in parentheses are for females.

Handle Height (cm)	Population %	PULLING FREQUENCY				
		10/min	5/min	1/min	1/5 min	1/8 h
144(135)	90	14(13)	16(16)	18(17)	19(19)	23(22)
	75	17(16)	19(19)	22(20)	23(23)	28(26)
	50	20(19)	23(22)	26(24)	28(28)	33(31)
	25	24(21)	27(25)	31(28)	32(32)	39(35)
	10	26(24)	30(28)	34(31)	36(36)	44(39)
95(89)	90	19(14)	22(16)	25(18)	27(21)	32(23)
	75	23(16)	27(19)	31(21)	32(25)	39(27)
	50	28(19)	32(23)	36(25)	39(29)	47(32)
	25	33(22)	37(26)	42(29)	45(33)	54(37)
	10	37(25)	42(29)	48(32)	51(37)	61(41)
64(57)	90	22(15)	25(17)	28(19)	30(22)	36(24)
	75	27(17)	30(20)	34(22)	37(26)	44(28)
	50	32(20)	36(24)	41(26)	44(30)	53(33)
	25	37(23)	42(27)	48(30)	51(35)	61(38)
	10	42(26)	48(31)	54(34)	57(39)	69(43)

Source: A. Mital, A. Nicholson, and M. M. Ayoub, *A Guide to Manual Materials Handling.* Copyright © 1993 by Taylor and Francis, London. Reprinted with permission.

TABLE	15.3

Maximum force (kg) for ONE-HAND PUSH AND PULL while standing (Mital et al., 1993).

Condition	GENDER	
	Male	Female
Push: one time	16	11
Push: repeated	11	7.5
Pull: one time	15	10
Pull: repeated	10	7

Source: A. Mital, A. Nicholson, and M. M. Ayoub, *A Guide to Manual Materials Handling.* Copyright © 1993 by Taylor and Francis, London. Reprinted with permission.

moving) generally are lower than initial forces (required to get a stationary object moving). The lack of a solid support because of a slippery floor decreases force capability. See Table 15.4 for some coefficients of friction of floors and shoes. When moving patients in hospitals from gurney to gurney, some hospitals reduce friction under the draw sheets by putting garbage bags under the sheets. Another option is a plastic slide board.

Friction depends upon a number of factors, including (1) static (starting the load moving) vs kinetic (keeping the load moving) (kinetic is lower than static, so it takes less force to keep a load moving once it has started), (2) material pairs (static coefficient is .5 for oak on oak, .6 for wood on brick, and .2 to .6 for wood on metal; kinetic coefficient is .7 to .9 for mild steel on mild steel, .8 to 1.2 for aluminum on aluminum, and .5 to .6 for aluminum on mild steel), and (3) sliding vs rolling (ball transfers as on a conveyor have kinetic friction of .03 to .15, so pushing a 50 lb container on balls would require a push force of 1.5 to 7.5 lbs. All of the above assume no lubricant. Chang et. al. (2001) give .67 as the static coefficient for shoes on ice at −40°C, but .01 as the dynamic coefficient at −1°C (when there is a thin film of water).

MTM (see Chapter 29) does not have a time value for pushing and pulling. Resnick and Chaffin (1995) report that people pushed loads for 1.5 m at only .2 to 1.1 m/s.

Pulling a load in a rickshaw is at least six times more efficient than carrying the load on the head

T A B L E	1 5 . 4				

Coefficients of friction of floors and shoes, developed from Kroemer (1974).

COEFFICIENT OF FRICTION	FLOORS	FLOOR CLEAN	FLOOR SOILED	SHOES: SOLES
1.0	Soft rubber pad	.8	.6	Rubber-cork
.8	End grain wood	.75	.55	U.S. Army–U.S. Air Force standard
.7	Concrete, rough finish	.7	.5	Rubber-crepe
.65	Working decorative, dry	.6	.4	Neoprene
.5	Working decorative, soiled	.5	.3	Leather
.4	Steel			
				SHOES: HEELS
		.7	.5	Neoprene
		.65	.45	Nylon

(Datta et al., 1978). The rickshaw studied could have been improved by better tires, bearings, and light metals, but that would have increased its capital cost.

Sitting is difficult to compare directly to standing because of the large differences in body geometry. However, Mital and Faard (1990) found that isokinetic pulls while sitting unrestrained were 73% of the standing values.

Kneeling versus standing gives (for some situations) about the same strengths as standing, but generalization is difficult.

See Table 15.5 for general recommendations for horizontal pushing/pulling for standing, sitting, and kneeling. Snook and Ciriello (1991) have detailed push and pull recommendations.

2.1.4 Application height For standing, the best height for pushing is at waist level (between the elbow and hip) and for pulling, it is at thigh level (between the hip and knee).

2.1.5 Direction Generally, people push/pull perpendicular to the shoulders, but, in some cases, they pull parallel to the shoulders or vertically. For perpendicular to the shoulders, Kodak (1986) recommends 50–60% of the values in Table 15.5. For vertical, see Table 15.6.

T A B L E	1 5 . 5			

Upper force limits for horizontal pushing and pulling perpendicular to shoulders (Eastman Kodak, 1986). The recommendations permit a large majority of workers to do the job.

POSTURE	LOCATION	MAXIMUM FORCE, KG	EXAMPLE ACTIVITIES
Standing: whole body involved	Between waist and shoulder	23.0	Truck and cart handling Moving equipment on wheels or casters Sliding rolls on shafts
Standing: primarily arm and shoulder muscles, arms	Between waist and shoulder	11.2	Leaning over an obstacle to move an object Pushing an object at or above shoulder height
Kneeling	Between waist and shoulder	19.2	Removing or replacing a component from equipment (as in maintenance work) Handling in confined areas (as in tunnels or large conduits)
Seated	Between chest and shoulder	13.3	Operating a vertical lever (as in floor shift on heavy equip. Moving trays or product on and off conveyors

T A B L E	1 5 . 6

Upper force limits for vertical pushing and pulling while standing (Eastman Kodak, 1986). The recommendations permit a large majority of workers to do the job. For seated downward pulls, use 85% of table values.

ACTION	LOCATION	MAXIMUM FORCE, KG	EXAMPLE ACTIVITIES
Pull down	Above head	55.1	Hook grip (safety shower handle, manual control)
		20.4	Power grip with less than 5-cm grip diameter (operating a chain hoist)
Pull down	Shoulder level	32.1	Hook grip, activating a control
			Threading operations (as in paper mfg. and stringing cable)
Pull up	25 cm above floor	32.1	Lifting an object with one hand
	Elbow height	15.1	Raising a lid or access port, cover, palm up
	Shoulder height	7.7	
Push down	Elbow height	29.3	Wrapping, packing, sealing cases
Push up (boosting)	Shoulder height	20.6	Raising a corner or end of an object (pipe, beam)
			Lifting an object to a high shelf

2.1.6 *Push/pull summary:*

- Two hands usually are better than one.
- Force capability goes down as it is exerted more often.
- Initial force capability is higher than sustained capability.
- Pushing capability is higher than pulling.
- Push at waist level; pull at thigh level.

2.2 Task Modifications
Use a force gauge to measure the force required to move all wheeled equipment. Enter this force in a maintenance database, and require the maintenance department to periodically check the forces. Replace defective wheels, bearings, and casters; lubricate the good ones. Two-wheel handcarts have a blade that is slid under the box bottom; periodically sharpen this blade.

The push/pull bar on carts should be vertical, not horizontal, as this allows its use by people of different heights. In addition, the wrist orientation is better for a vertical bar. For braking, rotate the vertical bar rather than having a fixed brake location. The two bars should extend from 90 to 120 cm from the floor with a grip space of >7 cm. The two wheels on the handgrip side should swivel; avoid using four swivel wheels as this increases the need to steer.

Generally, it is better to push loads than pull them. However, there may be an obstruction (e.g., elevator gap); then, pulling is better because it tends to lift the cart upward while pushing tends to push the cart downward into the obstruction.

Avoid muscle-powered pushing and pulling for ramps, long distances, and high-frequency moves. As a preventive measure, take the wheels off heavy carts. This will require the worker to use mechanical equipment instead of manual pushing/pulling.

Figure 15.1 shows the effect of posture when pushing. Figure 15.2 shows the beneficial effect of drum

F I G U R E	1 5 . 1

Pushing with the back (lower figure) gave a peak abdominal pressure 50% lower (Ridd, 1983) than pushing with the arms (upper figure). Note the knees are bent and one foot is forward.

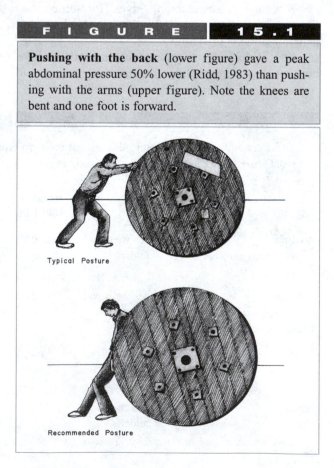

Typical Posture

Recommended Posture

F I G U R E   1 5 . 2

Drum carts. (Eastman Kodak, 1986). (a) shows a two-wheel cart; it should have a latch over the top rim during movement. (b) and (c) show a four-wheel cart, useful for heavier drums. In (b), the foot can be used to help tip the drum. Note that the hand positions are different in (b) and (c). There also is another handle, forward of the main handles, which is useful when tilting and maneuvering the drum for scales and pallets.

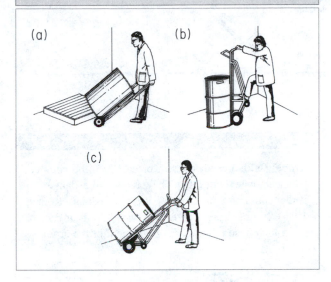

carts (mechanical aids). Of course, some aids are better than others. Figure 15.3 shows that, even without mechanical aids, momentum can help. Figure 15.4 shows some solutions to handling of rolls. Figure 15.5 shows the benefits of large wheels. Therefore, buy carts

with large wheels, and then clean and maintain the floor. If a two wheeled cart must be pulled over curbs or steps (as in retail delivery of beverages), large wheels are better. In addition, remove door sills. If the gap between door and floor must be sealed, use a flap on the door.

For horizontal transfer in and out of a machine, reduce force by replacing frictional contact (e.g., pallets on rails, boxes on polished metal tables) with rolling contact (rollers, wheels). For input or output from a workstation, put the ball transfer tables and wheel conveyors on a slight incline to reduce the pushing and pulling forces.

3 HOLDING

In contrast to most manual handling (a dynamic activity), holding gives a **static load.** Holding involves (1) a load from the body weight, and (2) a load from an object weight.

3.1 Problem   Assume you wish to determine the effect of working on an object on a conveyor that is either .5 m from the spine centerline or .6 m from the spine centerline. Further assume a person weighs 80 kg. Then the torso would weigh .507 (80) = 40.6 kg, the head would weigh .073 (80) = 5.8 kg, and the arms would weigh .098 (80) = 7.8 kg.

The additional torque on the body from an object .1 m farther away would be .1 (40.6 + 5.8 + 7.8) = 5.4 kg-m. The problem is worse if, instead of an empty hand, the hand holds an object. Unfortunately, because of spine biomechanics, the lever arm in the spine that resists this torque is relatively short and the counteract-

F I G U R E   1 5 . 3

Chiming a drum (rotating a tipped drum). With skill, drum momentum can be used with little effort to move it onto a pallet (Eastman Kodak, 1986). A straight push, however, as shown on the right, requires considerable effort. A drum cart is another alternative.

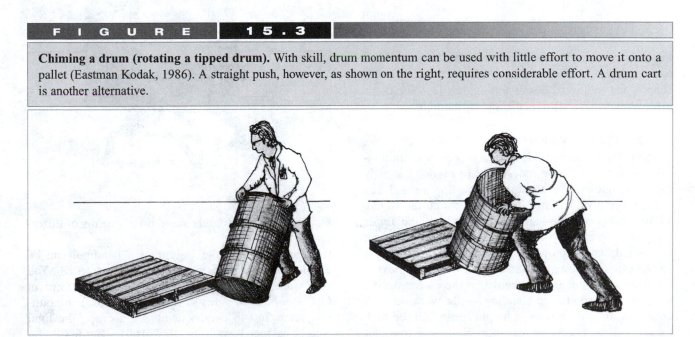

Reprinted courtesy of Eastman Kodak.

FIGURE 15.4

Problems with rolls. The lower figure shows a ramp block for setting a roll on a machine or roll stand. The roll is pushed along the floor to gain momentum to easily climb the incline.

An air shaft (the upper figure) reduces problems of handling heavy center bars and roll shafts. The air shaft is hollow with internal rubber tubes that expand (as opposed to protruding lugs, leaves, or buttons) to grip rolls or cores. Besides being lighter in weight than solid shafts, they are easier to insert and move. (Sketch courtesy of Liberty Mutual Insurance.) Shafts should be stored on a wheeled, A-frame shaft cart.

FIGURE 15.5

Pushing force depends on the ratio of a wheel radius to the height of an obstruction. A small radius gives a small lever arm, so small wheels can get hung up on bumps, objects on the floor, and holes. (Courtesy of Liberty Mutual.)

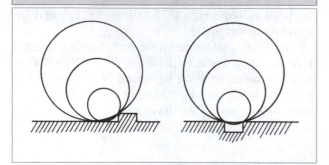

FIGURE 15.6

Tipping aids permit a drum or carboy to be counterbalanced when pouring. They reduce the danger of spills and operator muscle stress (Eastman Kodak, 1986). If a pump is used to empty the drum or carboy, use a long hose to minimize movement of the drum.

ing force is considerably greater; in practice, this leads to low back pain. See Guidelines 6.7 and 6.9 later in this chapter for additional discussion. Figure 13.1 shows the cardiovascular effects of static and dynamic loads.

3.2 Solutions Reduce the torque and reduce the duration of the torque. Figure 8.3 shows how automobile workstations were redesigned to reduce the body torque. Figure 15.6 shows how a tipping aid can reduce strain of holding a drum or container. Figure 15.14 shows a "one-hand lift," in which the upper body is supported by one hand. In a snack food plant, an angled bar (a "plow") was placed on the conveyor so boxes came down the side of the conveyor next to the operator instead of the center of the conveyor. If a number of workers are standing while working on a conveyor, the differences in height mean that the back torque will be excessive for some. Raise the conveyor height to the height appropriate for the tallest worker

and let the short workers stand on platforms of different heights.

Torque due to the weight of a handtool can be eliminated with a balancer; see Figure 15.18. You may want to balance the weight of the hand/forearm (2.7% of body weight) as well as the tool. For example, for a 160 lb person using a 2 lb tool, the total weight balanced would be .027 (160) + 2 = 6.3 lb. So have the balancer pull up with 6.5 lbs.

Figure 21.2 shows the typical exponential trade-off between load and time. The key point is that high loads can be endured for only a relatively short time.

4 CARRYING

As anyone who has carried a suitcase through an airport knows, pulling or pushing is better than carrying. Carrying indicates poor job design; replace with pulling or pushing (e.g., wheels on suitcases, carts, conveyors, hoists). Long-distance carrying usually is on the back/shoulders; short-distance carrying is in the hands.

4.1 Back and Shoulders (Long Distance)

Table 15.7 shows the cost of carrying heavy weights long distances; carrying objects in the hand (an asymmetric loading of small-muscle groups) is the worst—approximately 50% more energy is required than for a load on the back. Figure 15.7 shows how to carry a serving tray. Transporting loads for longer distances (over 10 m) normally should be done with mechanical aids. These mechanical aids can be mechanically powered (lift trucks, conveyors) or human-powered (carts). A good motto is "Everything on wheels." Even within the local area, aids (chutes, jib cranes, carts, wheel conveyors) should be used for repetitive carrying. Use the human only as a last resort.

Students often carry bookbags; 10% of body weight is a recommended maximum (especially for children); be sure the load is supported by both shoulders. A convenient locker can reduce the load carried. Trained soldiers can carry a maximum of 33% of body weight due to their training and because the knapsack frame supports the load.

The key guidelines are the following:

1. *Minimize the moment arm of the load relative to the spine.*
2. *Carry large loads occasionally rather than light loads often.* However, this minimization of energy cost increases stress on the back and thus may lead to back pain.

Balogun et al. (1986) showed that a frontal yoke was worse than a transverse yoke because the trunk was bent to the side of the body on which the yoke was placed.

Telephone and cable technicians often carry ladders from their truck to a jobsite (perhaps on slopes, with overhead obstacles, and so forth). Some possible improvements are: (1) have a short and a long ladder (the long, heavy ladder often is not needed), (2) have a shoulder pad to protect the shoulder from the ladder rail, and (3) have the upper rail on the shoulder and the arm through the rungs. This gives the lowest physiological cost and best visibility and control of the ladder (Imbeau et al., 1998).

TABLE 15.7

Comparison of seven modes of carrying on a horizontal plane (Datta and Ramanathan, 1971). The 50-kg Indian males carried 30-kg weights 1 km.

Carrying Method	Energy, kcal/min	Incremental Heart Beats/Min	Comments
Double pack 15 kg in two packs across shoulder—one in front and one in back	337	50	Load must be divided in two. Special harness. May not be suitable for repeated short trips without quick release harness.
Head Basket on head	348	64	Requires training. Body movement restricted. Very suitable for repeated short distance carrying. Arms free.
Rucksack High pack across the shoulder	368	62	Not good for repeated short-distance carrying.
Sherpa Load in a gunny sack supported on back by a strap across forehead	387	57	Requires practice. Arms can carry stick for hill climbing.
Rice bag Load in a gunny sack supported on back by holding two corners of sack with hands or hooks	414	60	No advantage over rucksack. Rather unsafe.
Yoke 15 kg is suspended by 3 ropes on each end of a bamboo strip across shoulder. Strip held with one or two hands	434	66	Uncomfortable without practice. Contorted posture.
Hands Two canvas bags with padded handles; 15 kg in each hand	486	81	Least efficient and most fatiguing. Even worse with only one hand.

FIGURE 15.7

Serving trays stress the wrist. Reduce this stress by supporting one end on the shoulder; a towel makes a good pad. Note that the forearm is parallel to the axis of the hand to reduce twisting of the wrist under load. By wrapping the fingers around the tray edge, the forearm muscles instead of the finger muscles support the load. The right hand remains free to pick up small items, open doors, carry a tray stand, and so forth. If there is enough room between tables, replace the tray with a cart.

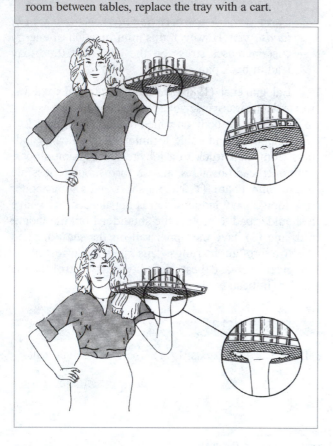

TABLE 15.8

Recommended weight of carry (kg) for one-handed infrequent carrying (Mital et al., 1993). Reduce weight by 30% if carrying is performed frequently.

CARRYING DISTANCE, M	POPULATION PERCENTILE	MALES	FEMALES
30.5	90	6.5	5.5
	75	8.5	7.0
	50	11.0	8.0
	25	13.5	9.0
	10	15.5	10.5
61.0	90	6.0	5.5
	75	8.0	6.5
	50	10.0	7.5
	25	12.0	8.5
	10	14.0	9.5
91.5	90	6.0	5.0
	75	7.5	6.5
	50	9.0	7.0
	25	10.5	8.0
	10	12.0	9.0

Source: A. Mital, A. Nicholson, and M. M. Ayoub, *A Guide to Manual Materials Handling.* Copyright © 1993 by Taylor and Francis, London. Reprinted with permission.

In addition to the transport cost, also consider the problems of loading and unloading. Teamwork is one possibility. A loads B, who carries to C, who unloads B; periodically A, B, and C switch jobs. The Korean A-frame has legs and the porter uses a walking stick. To rest, the porter squats, slips the frame off, and props it with the stick.

4.2 Hand Carrying (Short Distance)   See Table 15.8. Mital et al. (1993) also have tables for two-handed carrying. Hand carrying is more difficult to mechanize than long-distance carrying. However, consider the use of balancers, manipulators, and even robots to minimize humans moving product around a workstation. Consider a short section of a roller conveyor (perhaps portable); trucks often are loaded/unloaded using an extendable belt conveyor. Short-distance transport often is associated with twisting

and bending, which stress the back, while the load stresses the muscles of the arms and shoulders. Laursen et al. (2000) reported that asymmetrical carrying (e.g., carrying 10 kg in one hand versus 5 kg in each hand) increased metabolic rate 10%.

Continuous carrying primarily is limited by the cardiovascular system, although there may be local muscle fatigue problems. Figure 15.8 shows an example of a simple carrying aid. Figure 15.9 shows recommended tray handholds. Figure 15.10 shows maximum weight to be carried in the hands.

For short distances (.5 to 2 m), reduce the large metabolic cost of lifting an object from the floor by raising the initial location; see Figure 15.11.

Burton (1986) pointed out that shopping bags with handles were not as desirable as bags without handles. Those without handles tended to be clutched to the body and thus closer to the body's center of gravity. They also tended to be placed on a table rather than the floor, reducing the stress of picking them up. Morrissey and Liou (1988) found that handles on boxes led to a significantly lower weight carried (8% less); boxes without handles tended to be clutched close to the body, allowing the forearms, upper arms, and body to support the box, not just the

F I G U R E   1 5 . 8

J hooks reduce sheet-carrying problems (Rodgers, 1984). For large sheets, the J hook with a large grip contact area reduces finger strain caused by sharp edges of the sheet (if no hook is used). In addition, because the right hand can be placed in a comfortable position, the posture (and thus back stress) is better; walking and maneuvering with the sheet is easier than without the hook.

Reprinted with permission of S. Rodgers.

F I G U R E   1 5 . 9

Tray handholds ranked from (a) to (h) (Eastman Kodak, 1986). The contoured gripping block (a) is superior to the straight gripping block (b) because it provides more grip security and stability when the weight is handled in high lifts; both permit an oblique (semipower) grip. Grips (c) and (d) permit a hook grip and work well for lifts below chest height; they present problems for lifts above shoulder height. Avoid grips (e), (f), (g), and (h) as they put pressure on a localized part of the hand or only permit use of a lateral pinch grip. On all the designs, avoid sharp edges.

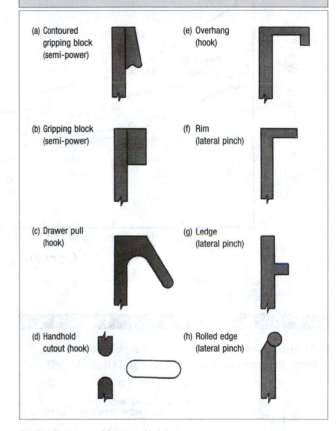

(a) Contoured gripping block (semi-power)

(b) Gripping block (semi-power)

(c) Drawer pull (hook)

(d) Handhold cutout (hook)

(e) Overhang (hook)

(f) Rim (lateral pinch)

(g) Ledge (lateral pinch)

(h) Rolled edge (lateral pinch)

Reprinted courtesy of Eastman Kodak.

wrists and forearms as is required with handles. Figure 15.12 points out that people may strain their backs simply to avoid soiling their clothes. A related problem is carrying tall loads. Because the load hits the legs, the person tends to hold the object away from the body, causing more torque on the back.

Mital and Ilango (1983) demonstrated that carrying containers with liquids instead of lead shot resulted in a 12% reduction of load carried. The movement of the liquid caused the decrease.

Don't forget maintenance and "non-production" activities. Oxenburgh (1991) described (in case 35) how a pallet maker was strained by carrying pallets he had just made from his workstation to a storage location. A hoist on a monorail was installed; there was a 30% improvement in productivity and a 4-month payback.

Carrying objects up and down stairs and ladders is especially dangerous as (1) the hands are occupied holding the object and thus not free to grasp a handrail if there is a slip and (2) the object may impair vision. Therefore move loads between levels with hoists, platforms, and elevators, not manually on stairs. If the object must be carried on the stair/ladder, keep the hands free (e.g., use toolbelt, backpack).

5 LIFTING

5.1 Revised NIOSH Lifting Guidelines

In 1993 the National Institute of Occupational Safety and Health (NIOSH) revised its lifting guidelines (Waters et al., 1993, 1994). The basic concept is to have a load constant of 51 lb (23 kg). This is the maximum that can be lifted or lowered. The **load constant** is multiplied by various factors (all equal to or less than one) to obtain the **recommended weight limit (RWL).** Then, a lifting index is calculated:

$$LI = LW/RWL$$

where: LI = Lifting index

Maximum weight to be carried for four types of grips (Eastman Kodak, 1986). (A) is for one hand holding a compact load close to the side (e.g., carrying a briefcase). (B) is for two hands with the arms straight and the object rested against the lower abdomen during the carry. (C) is for two hands with the elbows bent and the object rested against the upper abdomen; the biceps in the arms are used to maintain elbow flexion. (D) is for one hand holding a bulky object at least 25 cm from the side to prevent it from banging against the legs during the carry. This statically loads the shoulder.

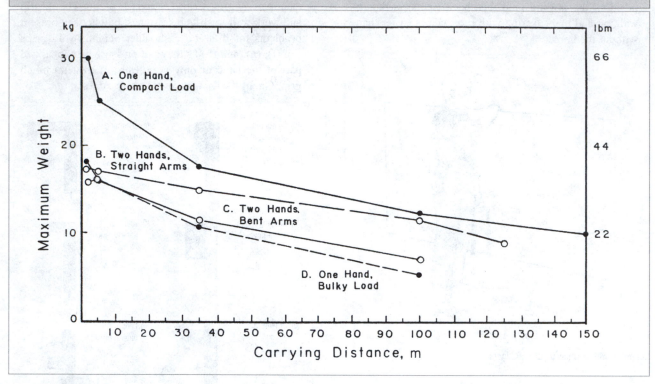

Minimize metabolic load by not picking up the object from the ground (Mueller, Vetter, and Blumel, 1958).

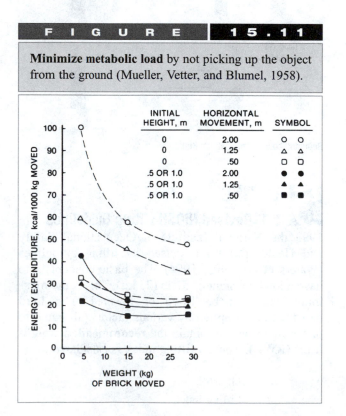

LW = Load weight

RWL = Recommended weight limit

If $LI \leq 1.0$, the task is acceptable. If $LI > 1$, the task is not acceptable.

Karwowski et al. (1994) say the compressive force on L5–S1 is:

At lift origin $CF = (LI + 1.418)/(.001\ 384)$

At lift destination $CF = (LI + .871)/(.001\ 703)$

where: CF = Compressive force on L5–S1, kN

LI = Lifting index

The NIOSH biomechanical criterion is a 350 kg (3.4 kN) compressive force on L5–S1. The physiological (metabolic) criterion is 9.5 kcal/min (max aerobic capacity of 50% female, age 40), multiplied by 70% (due to arm work) and by 50% (for 1 h), or 40% (for 2 h), or 33% (for 8 h). The NIOSH psychophysical criterion is based on the 75% female (99% male) for a 34-cm wide box, 76-cm vertical displacement, and lifting frequency of 4 lifts/min.

5.1.1 *Basic formula* The NIOSH formula is:

F I G U R E   15.12

Protecting your clothes can protect your back (since the load is held close to the body).

dirty object

POOR

dirty object

Apron

GOOD

$$RWL = LC \times HM \times VM \times DM \times FM \times AM \times CM$$

where

RWL = Recommended weight limit, lb

LC = Load constant = 51 lbs

HM = Horizontal multiplier, proportion

VM = Vertical multiplier, proportion

DM = Distance multiplier, proportion

FM = Frequency multiplier, proportion

AM = Asymmetry multiplier, proportion

CM = Coupling multiplier, proportion

For metric units, $LC = 23$ kg. Enter distances in cm.

The NIOSH formula **does not apply** if any of the following occur:

- lifting/lowering in which the feet move more than one or two steps
- lifting/lowering with one hand
- lifting/lowering for over 8 h
- lifting/lowering while seated or kneeling
- lifting/lowering in a constrained or restricted workspace
- lifting/lowering hot, cold, or contaminated objects
- lifting/lowering with unpredicted conditions (unexpected heavy loads, slips, falls)
- lifting/lowering of an unstable load (center of gravity varies significantly during the lift)
- lifting/lowering while carrying, pushing, or pulling
- lifting/lowering with wheelbarrows or shovels
- lifting that is high speed (speed of about 30 inches/second—a lift from floor to table height in < 1 s)
- unreasonable foot/floor interface (< .4 coefficient of friction between the sole and the floor)

- unfavorable environment (temperature significantly outside 66–79°F (19–26°C) range; relative humidity outside 35–50% range)

Although engineers like the implied precision of the NIOSH calculations, they should remember the many assumptions and realize that the specific numbers are not as accurate as they seem. That is, a lifting index of .51 may really be plus or minus 10% or even 20%. The primary purpose of the NIOSH guidelines, however, is to *rank* alternatives, not give absolute risks. That is, is method A better than method B? Assume method A had .51 and method B had .75. The critical information is that A is better than B; the change in the lifting index of .24 is useful information but not as precise as it seems.

The required input information depends on whether significant control over the object is needed (1) only at the origin of the movement, or (2) at both origin and destination. Control at destination (precise placement) is implied by (a) a regrasp near the destination, (b) a momentary hold near destination, or (c) a need to carefully position or guide the load near the destination.

If control of the object is needed only at the origin, you need:

- initial horizontal location of the hands from the ankle midpoint
- initial vertical location of the hands
- initial angle of asymmetry of object center
- vertical travel distance between the lift origin and destination
- frequency of lifts per minute
- lifting duration (h) and recovery time (h)
- hand–container coupling classification.

If control is needed at both **origin** and **destination,** you need in addition:

- final horizontal location of the hands
- final vertical location of the hands
- final angle of asymmetry of object center.

5.1.2 *Formulas for multipliers*

Horizontal multiplier.

$$HM = BIL/H$$

where

HM = Horizontal multiplier, proportion

BIL = Body interference limit = 10 for inches

  = 25 for cm

H = Horizontal distance from the large knuckle at the end of the third finger to the ankle midpoint (midpoint of inner ankle bones); this gives the object's **horizontal location.** The maximum value of H (functional reach limit) = 25 inches (63 cm). In good design, the load center of gravity is centered below the handles.

If H is measured, it is measured from the projection of the hand midpoint (i.e., load center) to the midpoint of a line connecting the ankles. Note that the feet should not be aligned if a turn is involved.

If H is not measured, estimate H from:

Vertical location of hands from the floor

< 10 inches $H = 10 + W/2$

≥ 10 inches $H = 8 + W/2$

where W = Width of the container in the plane perpendicular to the shoulders

The value of HM declines as the hands move farther from the spine. If $H \leq BIL$, then the value of $HM = 1.0$.

However, Potvin and Bent (1997) reported that BIL is not really a constant; boxes are held with approximately a 10-inch (25 cm) gap at floor and shoulder height and at 7 inches (18 cm) at knuckle height; in addition, the distance decreased as the box got wider. Their resulting equation is:

$$H \text{ (cm)} = 29.3 + .3\,W + .1\,|\,V - 75\,|\quad r^2 = .97$$

Vertical multiplier.

$$VM = 1 - VC\,|\,V - KH\,|$$

where

VM = Vertical multiplier, proportion

VC = Vertical constant = .0075 for inches

= .003 for cm

V = Initial vertical height of knuckles—this gives the object's **vertical location.** Note that this usually is several inches above the container bottom. The maximum value of V (vertical reach limit) is 70 inches (175 cm).

KH = Knuckle height (optimum height) of typical lifter (assumed stature height of 66 inches (165 cm))

= 30 inches (75 cm). When $V \leq 30$ inches, the lifting is considered as whole body; when $V > 30$ inches, the lift is considered upper body.

The value of VM declines from 1.0 for any height departing from optimum knuckle height of 30 inches. The concept is a 22.5% penalty for lifts from the floor or shoulder (60 inch; 150 cm).

Distance multiplier.

$$DM = .82 + DC/D$$

where

DM = Distance multiplier, proportion

.82 = Multiplier at maximum hand height of 70 inches (175 cm)

DC = Distance constant = 1.8 for inches

= 4.5 for cm

D = Distance moved vertically (absolute value)—the **vertical travel distance,** inches or cm

If $D \leq 10$ inches (25 cm), the value of $DM = 1.0$. Maximum $D = 70 - V$ (for inches) and $175 - V$ (for cm).

Asymmetry multiplier.

$$AM = 1 - .0032\,A$$

where

AM = Asymmetry multiplier, proportion

A = Angular deviation (also called **angle of symmetry**) (degrees) of the midpoint of the two hands (container center) from straight ahead (neutral body posture; sagittal plane). A can range from 0 to 135°; ignore direction as clockwise movement is considered equivalent to counterclockwise movement. The concept is a 30% penalty for a 90° angle.

Frequency multiplier. See Table 15.9. **Lifting frequency** can range from less than 1 in 5 minutes (.2 lifts/min) to 15 lifts/min. It is the mean number of lifts in a 15-minute period. If lifting is not continuous, count the number of lifts in 15 minutes and divide by 15. Any frequency less than .2 lifts/min is set equal to .2 lifts/min. The frequency multiplier varies depending on **lifting duration**/session and whether the initial vertical location of the hands is above or below typical knuckle height (30 inches or 75 cm).

Lifting duration/session in hours has three categories:

- short = .001 h to ≤ 1 h with recovery time of at least 1.2 (duration)
- moderate = > 1 h but ≤ 2 h with recovery time of at least .3 (duration)
- long = > 2 h but ≤ 8 h

During **recovery time,** the person is resting or has light work (such as sitting, standing, walking, monitoring). If a person does not meet the recovery criterion, omit the recovery time and add the work times together.

Coupling multiplier. See Table 15.10 and Figure 15.13. The coupling multiplier depends on the height (i.e., whether V is ≥ 30 inches) of the initial and final hand–container coupling and whether the coupling is good, fair, or poor. Table 15.11 defines optimal container design, handle design, and handhold cutout design. The following is an example problem and solution.

T A B L E	1 5 . 9

Frequency multiplier (FM).

	≤ 1 HRS		> 1 BUT ≤ 2 HRS		> 2 BUT ≤ 8 HRS	
FREQUENCY Lift/Min	**V < 75 cm** (30 in)	**V ≥ 75 cm** (30 in)	**V < 75 cm** (30 in)	**V ≥ 75 cm** (30 in)	**V < 75 cm** (30 in)	**V ≥ 75 cm** (30 in)
≤0.2	1.00	1.00	.95	.95	.85	.85
0.5	.97	.97	.92	.92	.81	.81
1	.94	.94	.88	.88	.75	.75
2	.91	.91	.84	.84	.65	.65
3	.88	.88	.79	.79	.55	.55
4	.84	.84	.72	.72	.45	.45
5	.80	.80	.60	.60	.35	.35
6	.75	.75	.50	.50	.27	.27
7	.70	.70	.42	.42	.22	.22
8	.60	.60	.35	.35	.18	.18
9	.52	.52	.30	.30	.00	.15
10	.45	.45	.26	.26	.00	.13
11	.41	.41	.00	.23	.00	.00
12	.37	.37	.00	.21	.00	.00
13	.00	.34	.00	.00	.00	.00
14	.00	.31	.00	.00	.00	.00
15	.00	.28	.00	.00	.00	.00
>15	.00	.00	.00	.00	.00	.00

T A B L E	1 5 . 1 0

Coupling multiplier (cm).

COUPLINGS	V < 75 CM (30 IN)	V ≥ 75 CM (30 IN)
Good	1.00	1.00
Fair	0.95	1.00
Poor	0.90	0.90

Example problem with solution. Assume a container with a weight of 15 lb was lifted and control was needed at both origin and destination. (Waters et al., 1994, has 10 detailed examples.)

Load weight = 15 lb

Initial horizontal location = 12 in.

Initial vertical location = 33 in.

Final horizontal location = 12 in.

Final vertical location = 22 in.

Initial angle of asymmetry = 5°

Final angle of asymmetry = 6°

Lift frequency = .5 lifts/min

F I G U R E	1 5 . 1 3

Decision tree for hand/object coupling condition (Waters et al., 1994).

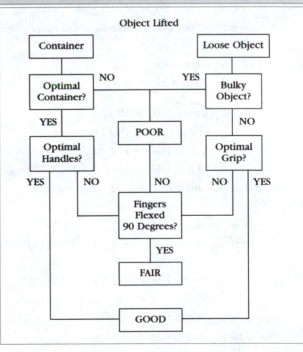

T A B L E   1 5 . 1 1

Hand-to-CONTAINER coupling classification and definitions of optimal container, handle, and cut-out.

1. good   optimal container design with optimal handles or optimal handhold cut-outs
           loose parts or irregular objects with comfortable grip (hand can easily be wrapped around object)
2. fair   optimal container design with nonoptimal handles or nonoptimal handhold cut-outs
           loose parts with no handles or handhold cut-outs
           irregular objects with a grip in which fingers can be flexed about 90°
3. poor   nonoptimal design containers with no handles or handhold cut-outs
           loose parts or irregular objects that are bulky or hard to handle

	OPTIMAL	NONOPTIMAL
CONTAINER design		
Frontal length	≤ 40 cm (16 in)	Nonoptimal is failure to meet
Height	≤ 30 cm (12 in)	one or more optimal conditions
Surface	smooth, nonslip	
Edge	nonsharp	
Center of mass	symmetric	
Load	stable	
Gloves required	no	
HANDLE design		
Diameter	1.9 to 3.8 cm (0.75 to 1.5 in)	
Length	≥ 11.5 cm (4.5 in)	
Clearance	≥ 5 cm (2 in)	
Shape	cylindrical	
Surface	smooth, nonslip	
HANDHOLD CUT-OUT design		
Height	≥ 3.8 cm (1.5 in)	
Length	≥ 11.5 cm (4.5 in)	
Clearance	≥ 5 cm (2 in)	
Container thickness	≥ 1.1 cm (.43 in)	
Shape	semi-oval	
Surface	smooth, nonslip	

Lift duration/session = 3 h
Recovery time = 6 h

Then initial HM = 10/12 = .83
Final HM = 10/12 = .83
Initial VM = $1 - .0075\,|33 - 30| = .98$
Final VM = $1 - .0075\,|22 - 30| = .94$
Vertical distance multiplier = DM = .82 + 1.8/11
    = .98
Frequency multiplier = FM = .81
Initial asymmetry multiplier = AM = 1 − .0032 (5)
    = .98
Final asymmetry multiplier = AM = 1 − .0032 (6)
    = .98
Initial coupling multiplier = CM = 1.0
Final coupling multiplier = CM = .95

Thus RWL at lift origin = $51 \times .83 \times .98 \times .98$
    $\times .81 \times .98 \times 1.0$
    = 32.6 lb
RWL at destination = $51 \times .83 \times .94 \times .98$
    $\times .81 \times .98 \times .95$
    = 29.7 lb

The 29.7 lb at the destination is limiting since it is lower than the 32.6 at the origin.

The lifting index *(LW/RWL)* = 15/29.7 = .51. Since the lifting index should be less than 1.0, the situation is satisfactory.

If the situation is not satisfactory, see Table 15.12 for suggestions and then rerun the analysis.

The above describes analysis of a single task. The Guideline also has a "multi-task" procedure. This is for the situation in which several tasks are done. An exam-

T A B L E	1 5 . 1 2

Ergonomic design suggestions (Waters et al., 1994).

SITUATION	SUGGESTION
$HM < 1$	Bring load closer to body (remove horizontal barriers, reduce object size). Avoid lifts near the floor; if unavoidable, object should fit easily between the legs.
$VM < 1$	Raise (lower) the origin (destination) of lift. Avoid lifting near the floor or above the shoulders.
$DM < 1$	Reduce vertical distance between origin and destination.
$AM < 1$	Reduce twisting by reducing distance between origin and destination; an alternative is to *increase* the distance so the worker must step rather than twist the body.
$FM < 1$	Reduce frequency rate. Reduce duration. Provide longer recovery periods (working rest of light work).
$CM < 1$	Improve containers, handles, cutouts, and handholds for irregular objects.
RWL at destination $> RWL$ at origin	Eliminate need for control at destination Change job or container.

ple would be alternately placing a box on a conveyor on the left and on the right; another example would be lifting the first, second, and third row of boxes off a pallet. The multi-task procedure is:

1. Compute two versions of the recommended weight limit: frequency-independent *(FIRWL)* and single-task *(STRWL)*.
2. Compute two versions of the **lifting index:** frequency-independent *(FILI)* and single-task *(STLI)*.
3. Compute the composite lifting index *(CLI)*.

1. Recommended weight limit
   A. Frequency-independent *RWL (FIRWL)*. For each task, compute *RWL* but set the frequency multiplier to 1.
   B. Single-task *RWL (STRWL)*. For each task, multiply *FIRWL* by its appropriate frequency multiplier. (Each *STRWL* is calculated as if each task were the only task being performed.)

2. Lifting index
   A. For each task, compute the frequency-independent lifting index *(FILI)*. The formula is:

$$FILI = L/FIRWL$$
where
$FILI$ = Frequency-independent lifting index

L = Load of the task
$FIRWL$ = Frequency-independent RWL

B. For each task, compute the single-task lifting index *(STLI)*. The formula is:

$$STLI = L/STRWL$$
where
$STLI$ = Single-task lifting index
L = Load for that task. If the load varies, use the average of the various loads as this best represents the metabolic demand.
$STRWL$ = Single-task recommended weight limit

3. Composite lifting index
   A. Renumber the tasks in order of the *STLI* value (i.e., greatest physical stress first).
   B. Compute composite lifting index *(CLI)*. The formula is:

$$CLI = STLI_1 + ILI$$
where
CLI = Composite lifting index
$STLI_1$ = Largest (first) single-task RWL
ILI = Sum of incremental lifting indices
$= FILI_2 (1/FM_{1,2} - 1/FM_1)$
$+ FILI_3 (1/FM_{1,2,3} - 1/FM_{1,2}) \ldots$
$+ FILI_n (1/FM_{1,2,3\ldots n} - 1/FM_{1,2\ldots n-1})$

The subscripts are for the new task numbers. The *FM* values are from the frequency table.

Example Problem with Solution. Assume an operator moved three types of boxes from a 36-inch high conveyor to three pallets; the 10-lb boxes were moved 4/min (task 1), the 20-lb boxes were moved 2/min (task 2), and the 30-lb boxes were moved 1/min (task 3). The job is done for less than 1 h/day.

1. Recommended weight limit
   A. Assume the *FIRWL* (i.e., using a frequency multiplier of 1) for the three tasks was 15, 20, and 20 lbs.
   B. From Table 15.9, the appropriate multipliers are .84, .91, and .94. Then the single-task *RWL (STRWL)* is $(15)(.84) = 12.6$, $(20)(.91) = 18.2$, and $(20)(.94) = 18.8$ lbs.

2. Lifting index
   A. Compute *FILI*. For the three tasks, *FILI* is $10/15 = .67$, $20/20 = 1$, and $30/20 = 1.5$.
   B. Compute *STLI*. The average weight for tasks 1, 2, and 3 are 10, 20, and 30 lbs, so the *STLI*s are $10/12.6 = .8$, $20/18.2 = 1.1$, and $30/18.8 = 1.6$.

3. Composite lifting index

A. Renumbering the tasks in order of stress (i.e., *STLI* value), the 30-lb weight task is numbered 1, the 20-lb task is numbered 2, and the 10-lb task is numbered 3.

B. Compute *CLI*. From the new task 1, the initial lifting index is 1.6.

Then add the *FILI* value from task 2, adjusted by the combined frequencies of tasks 1 and 2. The frequency of task 1 is 1/min so the *FM* value is .94. The combined frequencies of tasks 1 and 2 are 3 lifts/min so the *FM* value is .88. The additional *FILI* is 1.0 (1/.88 − 1/.94) = 1.0 (1.136 − 1.064) = .07.

Then add the *FILI* value from task 3, adjusted by the combined frequencies of tasks 1, 2, and 3. The combined frequencies of tasks 1, 2, and 3 are 7 lifts/min so the *FM* value is .70. The additional *FILI* is .67 (1/.70 − 1/.88) = .67 (1.429 − 1.136) = .20.

The total *CLI* is 1.6 + .07 + .20 = 1.9.

5.2 Force Limits   The formula used (Mital et al., 1993) is:

$$FL = A\ (F)\ (DIST)$$

where

FL = Force limit, kg

A = Age factor

= 1.0 for males < 40 years

= .915 for males 41–50 years

= .782 for males 51–60 years

F = Frequency factor

= 1.0 for frequencies <1/min

= .7 for frequencies ≥ 1/min

$DIST$ = Distance factor

= $50.15 + .332\ V − .0066\ V^2 − .000\ 087\ 7\ V^3 − .647\ H − .003\ 72\ VH + .000\ 073\ 5\ V^2H$

V = Vertical distance of the load from the shoulder, cm

H = Horizontal distance of the load from the shoulder, cm

Freivalds (1987) has an interesting comparison of the Force Limits Guideline and the 1981 NIOSH Guideline:

- Only males were considered by Force Limits, versus males and females for NIOSH.

- Age is an adjustment for Force Limits but not for NIOSH.

- Frequency has only two categories for Force Limits but varies continuously for NIOSH; NIOSH also varies the factor depending on lifting duration.

- Force Limits is based on a maximum abdominal pressure of 90 mm Hg for the fifth percentile weight and fifth percentile height male. Kumar (1997), however, proves that "intra-abdominal pressure is not an active spine load-relieving mechanism." NIOSH used three criteria: (1) compressive force on the L5–S1 disc (350 kg for Action Limit and 650 kg for Maximum Permissible Limit), (2) metabolic rate (3.5 kcal/min for AL and 5.0 kcal/min for MPL), and (3) psychometric votes.

- The two guidelines do not agree very well—with the Force Limits guideline, on average, permitting a load of 1.8 times the NIOSH load.

5.3 MH Guide   Mital et al. (1993) have a 114-page booklet with detailed recommendations. For example, Mital's Table 4.2 gives 720 recommended weights of lift for male industrial workers for two-handed symmetrical lifting for 8 h. It has 4 variables:

1. box size (75, 49, and 34 cm)

2. frequency of lift (1/8 h, 1/30 min, 1/5 min, 1/min, 4/min, 8/min, 12/min, and 16/min)

3. lifts (floor to 80 cm, floor to 132 cm, floor to 183 cm, 80 to 132 cm, 80 to 183 cm, and 132 to 183 cm)

4. population percentile (90, 75, 50, 25, 10).

There also are modifying values for work duration (1, 4, 8, 12 h); limited headroom (full upright, 95% upright, 90% upright, 85% upright, and 80% upright); asymmetrical lifting (30°–60°, 60°–90°, and above 90°); load asymmetry (sidewise shift in frontal plane of 0, 10, 20, 30 cm); coupling (comfortable handles, poor handles, no handles); load clearance at destination (unlimited to 30 mm, 15 mm, 3 mm); and heat stress (up to 27°C WBGT (Wet Bulb Globe Temperature), 32°C). Their values are based on a maximum load of 27.2 kg.

5.4 Biomechanical Software   In addition to evaluating a design alternative with the NIOSH Guidelines (section 5.1), Force Limits (section 5.2), or MH Guide (section 5.3), various biomechanical software programs are available. Perhaps the most popular are the "2D Static Strength Prediction Program" and "3D Static Strength Prediction Program" developed at the Center for Ergonomics, University of Michigan. The 2D version assumes all lifts occur directly in front of the operator in the sagittal plane. The 3D version permits non–sagittal plane symmetric lifting. In addition to evaluating alternatives, the programs produce graphics and reports for management and for training. Andres et al. (1995), for example, described investigating various order-picking alternatives at L. L. Bean. One approach they evaluated was having

shorter operators pick from the lower 4 shelves and taller operators pick from the top 4 shelves.

6 GUIDELINES FOR MANUAL HANDLING

The NIOSH guidelines, the Force Limits, and the MH Guide follow the approach of recommending maximum weights for specific situations. This section, however, will follow a different approach and give design guidelines without any specific numerical recommendations.

Table 15.13 summarizes the excellent work of Ayoub et al. (1987).

Table 15.14 gives 10 guidelines for occasional lifting. They are discussed in more detail below. They are divided into three groups: (1) select individual, (2) teach technique, and (3) design the job.

6.1 Select Strong People Based on Tests
A number of studies (Liles, 1986; Ayoub et al., 1987; Herrin et al., 1986) have shown the importance of the **job severity index**:

$$JSI = f(WEIGHT/CAPACITY)$$

where

JSI = Job severity index

$WEIGHT$ = Weight lifted or moved

$CAPACITY$ = Capacity of worker for that specific task

One approach is to select people with large capacities. Capacity is primarily a function of fat-free body weight. Females may have a fat-free weight as much as 25 kg below males as they tend to have both a lower weight and higher percent fat. Selection, however, should be made on tests rather than gender alone.

X-rays of the back are not recommended as a screening device due to their poor predictive ability (Rowe, 1985; Deyo, 1998; Chaffin et al., 1999); in addition, they give a radiation exposure to the sex organs of over 1,000 times that associated with a chest X-ray. If employees are going to be eliminated from lifting jobs, use a multiple-criteria screen including variables such as fat-free weight, isometric strengths of specific muscle groups, previous back injuries, and uneven leg length. For example, a large belly adds a constant stress to the back muscles. Uneven leg length puts an unbalanced load on the back.

Ayoub et al. (1987) recommend weight, shoulder height, arm strength, back strength, abdominal depth, and dynamic endurance. Jackson et al. (1997) reported that lifting capability was equally well predicted by fat-free weight and by the sum of four isometric tests (arm, torso, shoulder, and leg). The goal is to use only people who have a capacity at least 150% of requirements.

Note that the job severity index forces analysis not only of the worker capacity but also of the task

TABLE 15.13

Manual handling guidelines; adapted from Ayoub et al. (1987).

GUIDELINE	EXAMPLES
1. Eliminate heavy MH	Use mechanical aids (hoists, lift tables, conveyors). Provide best work height (change height of work or height of worker).
2. Decrease stress	Reduce object weight (split load between two workers or containers, reduce container size, reduce container (tare) weight). Change type of MH (lower instead of lift, push not pull, pull not carry). Reduce distances (both horizontal and vertical) in reaching for object and in transporting it. Avoid twisting (both standing and seated work). Make object easier to handle (handles, balanced containers, reasonable width) Increase recovery time (lower frequency, job rotation).

TABLE 15.14

Guidelines for occasional lifting.

GUIDELINE

Select Individual

1. Select strong people based on tests.

Teach Technique

2. Bend the knees.
3. Don't slip or jerk.
4. Don't twist during the move.

Design the Job

5. Use machines.
6. Move small weights often.
7. Get a good grip.
8. Put a compact load in a convenient container.
9. Keep the load close to the body.
10. Work at knuckle height.

requirements. Naturally it is desirable to reduce the task requirements. This gives two benefits: (1) It permits a larger proportion of the population to do the job, and (2) it reduces the stress on everyone doing the job. The following guidelines (as well as the NIOSH guideline) focus on reducing task requirements.

6.2 Bend the Knees

Brown (1975) says, "The straight back, bent knees technique has been enthusiastically promoted for 40 years with no decrease in back injuries... which raises a question as to the benefit of lifting procedures advocated." Perhaps it's because no one uses the bent knees technique. One possible reason there has been a lack of worker acceptance of squat lifting is that when you **bend the knees,** you lower the torso and thus require more energy. Garg et al. (1983) compared squat lifting (upper and lower leg have 70°–90° angle, back angle versus floor is about 20°–30°) versus free-style lifting (upper and lower leg have about a 135° angle, back angle versus floor is about –10°). They found that, with free-style lifting, subjects tended initially to pull the load toward themselves as they lifted and then lift vertically, thus decreasing the strain of the straight vertical lift used in squat lifting.

Squat lifting also rotates the pelvis back, causing higher spinal moments. Burgess-Limerick et al. (1995) report that bending the knees gives better interjoint coordination between the knee and hip and reduces muscular effort (hamstrings, quadriceps, erector spinae). For bulky loads, use a straddle stance (feet not aligned) so the load can be kept closer to the spine.

Figure 15.14 shows the **one-hand lift.** During the stoop lift of items out of the container, the worker is

FIGURE 15.14

One-hand lifts have the worker support the back (by grasping the box) while the other hand grasps (Lovested, 1980).

trained to support the back muscles by holding one side of the container with the hand that is not grasping the object. However, don't use training as a substitute for design.

6.3 Don't Slip or Jerk

The problem with slipping is a sudden unexpected load on the back. Reduce slipping by having a high coefficient of friction between the shoe and the floor. See Section 1 of Chapter 13. In summary, this involves workers having shoes with high coefficient of friction soles and large contact areas.

Data gathered on a force platform (e.g., Konz and Bhasin, 1974) indicate that peak forces and torques during a lift are "spiked." The peak force often occurs during the initial lowering of the body before the object is even grasped! The accelerations and decelerations during the lifting and lowering should be fast enough so the body gets the benefits of momentum but not so fast as to cause injury. Professional weightlifters use "clean and jerk" movements but these movements are highly practiced in precisely standardized situations, not industrial lifts. Patterson et al. (1987) demonstrated that, when lifters know the weight of the object being lifted, they have less strain on their bodies because they use different movement patterns. They believe teaching the worker to recognize the type of load to be lifted is important. Marras et al. (1986) also pointed out that additional strain occurs because of unexpected loads. When you check in at British Airways, for all luggage over 25 kg, the clerk adds an orange tag to the luggage with a "Heavy" indicator and the weight.

6.4 Don't Twist During the Move

Although spine biomechanics are complex during symmetrical two-handed lifting (as in NIOSH 1981 guidelines), they are even more complex when twisting is involved. These values are being quantified (Marras, 2000), but much work needs to be done.

Twisting while bent over (such as when taking parts off the floor) probably is especially bad. A general recommendation is to tell the workers to move their feet instead of twisting, but this is difficult to get people to follow.

Figure 15.15 shows how to reduce lifting and lowering by having the two surfaces at the same height; this also reduces bending and twisting.

In general, the strategies of personnel selection (Guideline 6.1) and training (6.2, 6.3, and 6.4) have not been very fruitful in reducing back problems. This recalls the analogy of the open manhole. The selection approach is to choose people who can walk around the open hole. The training approach is to train the people to walk around the open hole. The engineering approach is to put a cover on the hole. The engineering

Workstation positioners reduce lifting, bending, and twisting. Marras et al. (2000) showed that the use of lift tables reduced both sagittal flexion and the velocity of lateral trunk movements; that is, they reduce the time spent in non-neutral postures. (a) shows a scissors lift. (b) shows a bin on an adjustable-height cart—useful for temporary workstations such as stocking of shelves. (c) shows self-leveling trucks. The self-leveling can be through springs (similar to cafeteria tray dispensers) or a motor triggered by an electric eye ("Level Eye"). Level Eyes can be retrofitted to existing lifts. Note that all three positioners have wheels.

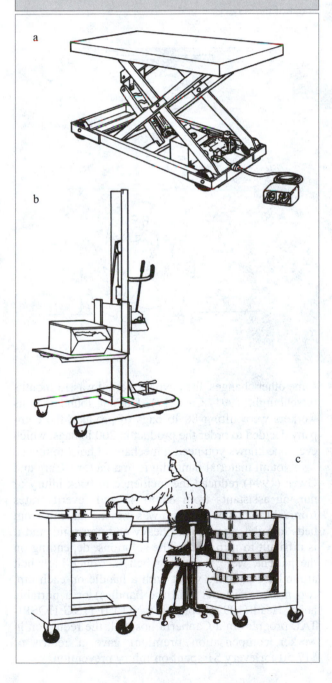

approach is recommended because it solves the problem permanently. The selection and training approaches do not guarantee a solution and require continual repeating as the employees either forget or change jobs.

6.5 Use Machines   Although this guideline concerns *manual* handling, first consider using machines to *eliminate* the manual handling. The discussion will first cover handling between workstations (transport), then handling at the workstation (hold, load/unload).

Conveyors and lift trucks are common machines to reduce transport stress. Use portable and telescoping conveyors when unloading trucks. Be sure the conveyor (or at least a spur) goes right to the workstation and doesn't stop 10 ft away. Conveyor gates (for people) can be hinged vertically (drawbridges), be hinged horizontally, or slide; floor-mounted conveyors are another option. Flexible (snake) conveyors demonstrate that conveyors don't have to be linear. For roller conveyors, consider sloping them to reduce pushing force. A chute is another option for between-station transfers.

Lift trucks can have a wide variety of attachments (forks, rams, rotators, clamps, push–pull, etc.). Can carrying be replaced by a cart? Figure 15.16 shows that mail carriers in England use carts instead of shoulder bags. More hand-powered carts are shown in Figures 15.2 and 15.15.

Handling at the workstation also can be improved. Figure 15.17 shows how the effect of gravity was

Carts for moving mail are used in England, rather than the shoulder bag used in the United States. The precut pieces of twine are looped around the frame for easy access.

FIGURE 15.17

Use of lever arms. Simple lever arms can drastically reduce strain on people moving items between levels. Fishermen can lift loads out of the unstable boat and also weigh them.

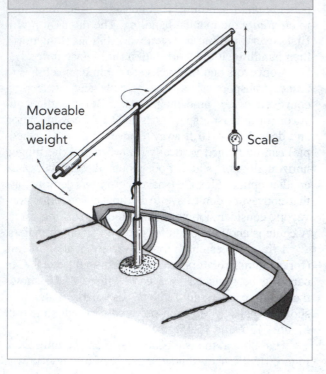

Moveable balance weight

Scale

FIGURE 15.18

Balancers reduce tool weight from pounds to ounces. Note that the balancer is suspended from a jib crane to minimize horizontal forces as the tool is moved about the workplace. Ulin et al. (1993) showed that an increased weight tool increased the torque at the elbow and shoulder, decreasing the comfort of the neck and back as well as the arm.

When the tool is released, it will rise a few inches and will be in a consistent, convenient location for the next use. Suspension tends to give easier access to tools than "holsters" do.

If the tool is suspended separately from the power cord, have a low-tension reel to keep the power cord out of the way.

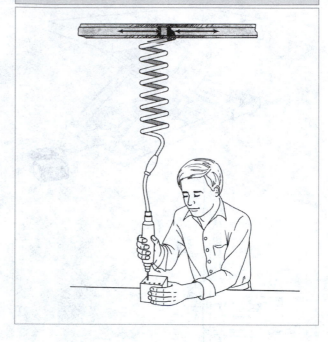

reduced by using a lever arm. Car hoods and trunk lids are supported, when lifted, by spring-loaded cylinders. **Balancers** (see Figure 15.18) and **manipulators** (see Figure 15.19) reduce the effect of gravity. Although manipulators reduce the effect of gravity, thereby significantly reducing force, accelerating, moving, and decelerating the mass of the arm horizontally increases the movement time over a manual transfer (Nussbaum et al., 2000). In some cases, robots (manipulators with "brains") are appropriate. Lever arms (such as pry bars, ramps, and screws) are machines. Figure 15.6 showed how a tipping aid reduced the holding load. Figure 15.20 shows how moving the fulcrum of a ladder support on a truck improved the lever arm and thus reduced the job stress.

Design the workstation to permit sliding transfer rather than lifting by eliminating lips and different machine heights. Reduce vertical transfer differences with scissors lifts and workstation positioners (see Figure 15.15). Reduce the horizontal transfer force of sliding with turntables (see Figure 15.21), ball-transfers, air tables, and low-friction surfaces.

Perhaps the load itself can be reduced. An industrial cafeteria in Sweden more than halved the weight the restaurant staff handled by having 400 g porcelain plates replaced with 157 g plastic plates; including

some other changes, the payback period was 13 months (Oxenburgh, 1991, Case 17). DuPont found that its workers were lifting 80 lb bags of product; the company decided to order the product in 200 lb bags, which everyone knows you need a mechanical hoist to move.

Not all material handling is in a factory. Garg and Owen (1994) reduced the incidence of back injury of nursing assistants from 83 to 43 and severity rates from 634 to 0. The problem was moving patients from beds to toilets; people are heavy and non-rigid, and it is difficult to grip them. The solutions, depending on the patient, were a walking belt (a 6-inch-high belt around the patient's waist with a handle on each hip; two nurse assistants held the handles) or a portable hoist. Head (1997) reported a NO LIFTING HOSPITAL program in a Canberra hospital; the reduction in worker compensation premium gave a return of $17.50 for every $1 spent on injury prevention.

FIGURE 15.19

Manipulators (balancers with arms) can support tools or can be used to move product around the workstation.

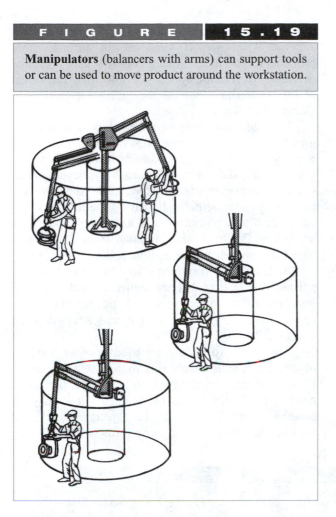

FIGURE 15.20

Positioning the fulcrum can help (Kantowitz and Sorkin, 1983). The original fulcrum was at the right, so when raising the left end of the ladder the entire weight had to be lifted above the head. When potential female employees couldn't do the job, the task was analyzed and the fulcrum moved (lower figure). Now the weight of the right portion of the ladder counterbalances the portion being raised. This helped not only the new female workers but also the existing male workers.

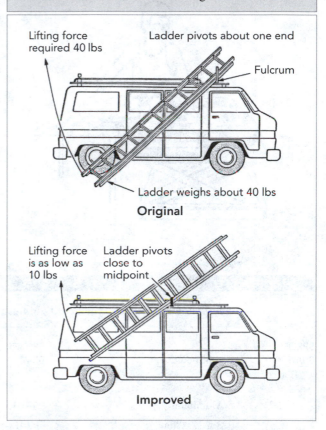

Source: B. Kantowitz and R. Sorkin, *Human Factors.* Copyright (c) 1983 by John Wiley & Sons. Reprinted by permission of John Wiley & Sons.

6.6 Move Small Weights Often

From a viewpoint of reducing strain on the musculoskeletal system, small is beautiful. That is, small weights are better than big weights. What this means in practice is that weights must be reduced or loads moved more frequently.

The total weight to be moved is the weight of the product plus the weight of the container. Can a steel container be replaced with a plastic or fiberboard container? Can a light wood such as pine replace the heavier fiberboard? See Table 15.15 for specific gravities.

For example, assume 1,000 recycled flat cardboard boxes (each weighing .6 kg) need to be moved from a truck to a pallet. The knocked-down boxes can be tied in bundles of 25 at the supermarket or in bundles of 20. If there are 25 in a bundle, 40 bundles of 15 kg have to be moved. If there are 20 in a bundle, 50 bundles of 12 kg have to be moved. In general, keep loads (including container weight) less than 15 kg—especially if the load is awkward. A load below 10 kg has relatively little strain, and the number of moves rises quite rapidly.

Sometimes the object moved has a resistance in addition to its weight. Cardboard cases of product often are held together with glue, making it difficult to separate them easily; see if your vendors can reduce the amount of the glue. Oxenburgh (1991) described (in case 38) how a 5/8-inch thick sheet of plywood held in a vertical slot had to be lifted. The binding in the slot was greatly reduced by using a 1/2-inch thick sheet; in addition, the weight was reduced 20% and the sheet was 20% cheaper.

Pay close attention to the container size that vendors use when shipping to you. Get purchasing department personnel away from their desks and out to the receiving dock! Reducing strain on your receiving personnel also may reduce strain on vendors' shipping personnel.

Note that vendors may be exceeding package weight or size specifications in their deliveries.

F I G U R E   15.21

Turntables can reduce stress when loading/unloading. The turntable is rotated after a few items are moved. The turntable can be mounted on the floor and a pallet placed on the turntable. If the turntable surface is rollers or ball casters or an air table, rotation can be manual. If the turntable is mounted on a **scissors lift** (as shown), horizontal transfer can replace lifting/lowering.

Refuse to accept shipments that do not meet specifications. Also, see if vendors can furnish more products to you in cases weighing less than 50 lbs or over 200 lbs (obviously too heavy to lift). The threat of loss of business should convince most vendors to change their ways.

Naturally, one way to reduce a weight is to let gravity do the work. Lower loads rather than lift loads. See Figure 15.22. Move downhill whether from a conveyor to a pallet or a pallet to a conveyor. When loading a conveyor from a pallet, adjust the conveyor to be low; raise the pallet by having the lift truck driver place it on a platform (such as an empty pallet) or a platform. When loading a pallet from a conveyor, have the conveyor higher and the pallet on the floor.

Another way to reduce a weight is to lift with a partner rather than lift the entire weight yourself. For best lifting efficiency, both people should be approximately the same height and strength (Lee and Lee, 2001).

Any time two people are used to move a single object, alarm bells should ring in the engineer's mind. If the job can be changed so only one person is needed, productivity can be doubled. Or it may be possible to lift one end of the object, move it, and then lift the other end and move it (as with furniture).

T A B L E   15.15

Specific gravity of various materials. The density of fresh water (at 4°C) is 1.0 g/cubic cm (62.43 lbs/cubic foot).

SPECIFIC GRAVITY	SUBSTANCE	SPECIFIC GRAVITY	SUBSTANCE
.79	Acetone	13.60	Mercury
2.7	Aluminum	.7–1.15	Paper
8.3	Brass, yellow	1.3–1.4	Polyester (PET)
1.4–2.2	Brick	0.9–1.0	Polypropylene
.69	Cardboard	0.95	Polypropylene (PE)
2.7–3.0	Concrete, set	1.05	Polystyrene (PS)
.66–.69	Gasoline	7.83	Steel, mild
2.4–2.8	Glass, common	.87	Turpentine
1.1–1.25	Nylon	1.00	Water, fresh
.92	Ice	1.02	Water, sea
7.2	Iron, cast	.66	Wood, ash
7.7	Iron, wrought	0.11–0.15	Wood, balsa
.82	Kerosene	.62	Wood, chipboard
0.90	Human body, fat	0.79	Wood, oak
1.03	Human body, typical female	0.58	Wood, fiberboard
1.06	Human body, typical male		(med. density)
1.10	Human body (0 fat)	0.40	Wood, pine

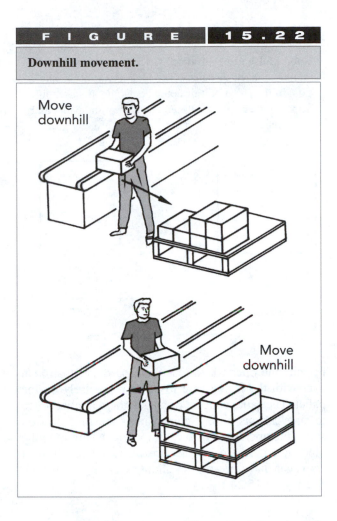

FIGURE 15.22

Downhill movement.

Move
downhill

Move
downhill

There are a variety of simple techniques to orient and reorient items on conveyors. Some are just a protruding bar or an angled piece of metal. If you see a person twisting to orient an item on a conveyor, ask why the orientation isn't done by a device.

When sliding a carton or item into or from a workstation from a wheel or roller conveyor, make the movement downhill. For example, when loading a carton, have the conveyor at a small angle immediately after the assembly area to minimize the force required to slide the packed carton.

6.7 Get a Good Grip Cardboard boxes with gripping holes are poor because (1) the hand can't rotate as the object is lifted from the knee to above the waist and (2) the cardboard surface area is small and tends to put too much pressure on the hands.

For bags, Smith (1981) reported that people were willing to lift 10% less for a 70%-full bag than a 90%-full bag; they were willing to lift 10% more when the bag had handles on both ends. Of course most objects don't have handles.

Course and Drury (1982) reported that the best grip for boxes without handles was an opposition handhold—one hand on the upper-outer corner and the other on the opposite lower-inner corner. Although it causes a higher load on the lower hand than both hands on the bottom, it gives more stability.

6.8 Put a Compact Load in a Convenient Container
Within a job design the key concept is to keep the load close to the spine. Consider the **spinal torque**:

$$SPINET = OBJWT (OBMARM)$$

where

$SPINET$ = Spinal torque that body exerts in reaction, kg-m

$OBJWT$ = Object weight, kg

$OBMARM$ = Moment arm of the object, m

= $DISTO + DISTCG$

$DISTO$ = Distance between spine and object (closest portion), m

= .2. However, Damon et al. (1966) say mean male waist depth is .20 to .25 m so .3 might be a better value. See Figure 15.12. Note the effect of a protruding belly.

$DISTCG$ = Distance from closest portion of the object to its center of gravity = $L/2$, m

For example, if $L = .2$, the $DISTCG = .1$ and $SPINET = .3$ $OBJWT$. Thus, because of the bulk, it is more difficult to lift 25 kg of feathers than 25 kg of iron. Konz and Coetzee (1977) reported that increasing a box's volume (up to a 30-cm cube) did not bother men but strongly bothered women. Getting a good grip may require stacking items so there is more access on the side; i.e., access is not just from the front.

Assume the internal lever arm in the back is .05 m. Then, an external torque of 2 kg-m requires an internal force by the muscles of 2 kg-m/.05 m = 40 kg.

6.9 Keep the Load Close to the Body The farther away, the less it should weigh. The equation below is a follow up to the $SPINET$ equation in Section 6.8. Actually the equation should include an additional term for the body in addition to the term for the load. That is,

$$SPINET = OBJWT (OBMARM) + UBWT (BMARM)$$

where

$UBWT$ = Upper body weight, kg. See Table 5.2.

$BMARM$ = Upper body moment arm, m

For example, a 70-kg person has a head of .073 (70) = 5.1 kg, two arms and hands of .098 (70) = 6.9 kg, and a torso of .51 (70) = 35.7 kg. The key problem is not during the carrying of the load but, rather, reaching for and disposing of the load.

Let's assume, during a .3-m reach, the center of gravity of the head is .15 m forward, the arms are .2

m forward, and the torso is .1 m forward. Then the head torque is .76 kg-m, the arm torque is 1.38 kg-m, and the torso torque is 3.57 kg-m—a total of 5.71 kg-m, even with a zero torque from the object! If an object is only .1 m closer (by reducing reach distance), then .05 (5.1) + .1 (6.9) + 0 = .94 kg-m instead of 5.7 kg-m. However the situation is even worse than this simplified example because F = ma. The previous calculations ignored acceleration, so the real force and, thus, the real torque will be higher.

Reduce reach distance by (1) moving the object closer to the person and/or (2) moving the person closer to the object.

For moving the object closer, an example is a plow on a conveyor that directs objects to the side of the conveyor (rather than having objects travel down the conveyor center). Another conveyor example is using two conveyors—one above the other. The lower level conveyor could furnish product, while the upper level conveyor is for scrap/waste (i.e., the operator sorts/disassembles). Another alternative is that the two conveyors furnish different products and the operator merges/assembles the items.

Another simple technique is to use a work table of the appropriate size. If a task only requires a 2 ft × 2 ft worksurface, don't use a 6- or 8-ft long bench as everything just gets spread out unnecessarily. Swing arms and Lazy Susans can reduce reach distances for tools, parts, instructions, and telephones.

For moving the person, reduce barriers between the person and the object. One common problem is not allowing room for the feet (standing person) or legs (sitting person).

Although the previous paragraphs emphasized horizontal reach distance, if the conveyor is too low (excessive vertical distance), the torque again will be excessive. Modifying the vertical distance implies adjusting conveyor height or operator height. Conveyor height is easy to modify for a single operator but is more complex if multiple stations use the conveyor. Conveyors, however, can be different heights at different workstations if the conveyor sections are connected by slanting sections (powered if uphill). Adjust operator height with a platform; normally it is a simple wooden structure, but it could be motorized to move up and down.

Another way to keep the load close to the body centerline is to consider the foot position when turning with the load. Rather than having both feet aligned, have the foot opposite the direction of turn ahead and the foot on the side of the turn to the rear (Konz and Bhasin, 1974).

Orient pallets and bins to reduce reach distance. See Figure 15.23.

When loading a pallet with cases, consider use of a wooden backboard on two sides of the pallet. This

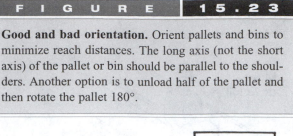

Good and bad orientation. Orient pallets and bins to minimize reach distances. The long axis (not the short axis) of the pallet or bin should be parallel to the shoulders. Another option is to unload half of the pallet and then rotate the pallet 180°.

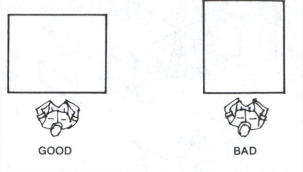

permits the operator to toss the case rather than lean over with the heavy case to place it precisely on the pallet. The same concept of a backboard applies when tossing cartons onto a conveyor; if the rails are too short, the operator has to exert too much care. (On the other hand, where cartons are being picked from a conveyor, have no rails so sliding can replace lifting. See Figure 15.24.)

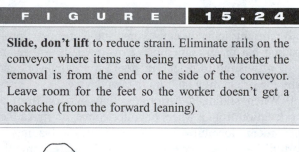

Slide, don't lift to reduce strain. Eliminate rails on the conveyor where items are being removed, whether the removal is from the end or the side of the conveyor. Leave room for the feet so the worker doesn't get a backache (from the forward leaning).

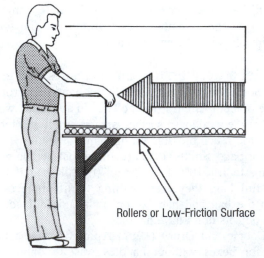

Rollers or Low-Friction Surface

Poulsen and Jorgensen (1971) gave the following formula concerning back pain from working stooped (that is, with no external load):

$$MISBCK = .4 \, (WT) \, (\sin \alpha \, / \, LTSLPR)$$

where

$MISBCK$ = Maximum isometric back muscle strength needed to avoid back pain while working standing stooped at angle α, kg

WT = Body weight, kg

α = Acute angle between the back and the line of gravity, degrees

$LTSLPR$ = Maximum long-term static load proportion of the maximum isometric strength. A value of 10% to 15% is commonly used.

Thus, if a worker bent over at an angle of 20° and $LTSLPR$ = .15, then $MISBCK$ = .4 WT (.342)/.15 = .91 WT. This individual would have back pain unless the individual's back strength were at least 91% of the individual's body weight. The solution generally is to raise the height of the object being worked on.

The discussion has assumed that distance is the only variable that can be changed. But it also is possible to reduce lumbrosacral joint torque by using lifting aids such as hoists, balancers, and manipulators, discussed earlier in this chapter.

6.10 Work at Knuckle Height

Of course, the first thought should be to avoid lifting altogether. Drag it, pull it, push it, but don't lift it. Wheeled luggage and trash containers are examples. Three people can easily push an automobile on a level road, but they certainly can't lift it! If a lift is necessary, however, the work behind the NIOSH guideline emphasizes the desirability of material handling at knuckle height. On the other side of the coin, don't put a load on the floor or work above your shoulder.

6.10.1 *Knuckle height*

For example, when loading cartons into a semitrailer from a conveyor, have the conveyor height adjustable. When loading cartons into a semitrailer from a pallet, leave the pallet on the lift truck's forks. Periodically adjust fork height. If you don't want to tie up the lift truck, have the pallet placed on a wheeled lift table.

At supermarket checkouts, the clerk normally picks up and scans items and sets the items aside for later packing. However, for heavy items (such as packs of soda, dog food), avoid lifting by leaving the item in the basket and using a hand-held supplementary scanner or keying the code manually. An alternative strategy is to lift the item out of the cart, scan, and immediately replace it in the cart (so the weight isn't handled twice).

6.10.2 *Don't put a load on the floor*

There is a large penalty for lifting from the floor. "Shift it; don't lift it." (In addition to the stress of lifting a load from the floor, there is the stress of putting it on the floor.) Avoid this penalty by not putting an object on the floor in the first place. Figure 15.25 shows how laundry workers reduced their strain by having drop-delivered items fall onto a pallet instead of the floor. The Union Pacific has a shop that repairs rail cars. Formerly 90 lb car couplers were stored on the ground next to the cars; now, to reduce lifting stress, they are stored on a hip-high table.

When order-picking from racks in a warehouse, to minimize picking stress, store the heavy items between the knee and the shoulder; only light (and non-breakable) items should be above the shoulder. If the box is stored low, open the box top; if it is stored high, open the box side.

Lovested (1980) reported that many problems are associated with workers obtaining parts by reaching into deep wood, cardboard, and wire containers placed on the floor. Some solutions included using boxes in which one-half of one side could be folded down, cutting away the side of cardboard boxes, placing boxes on their sides (on a table or stand), using shorter boxes (19 in. high versus former 33 in. high), and placing a short box on a platform (Figure 15.26). The

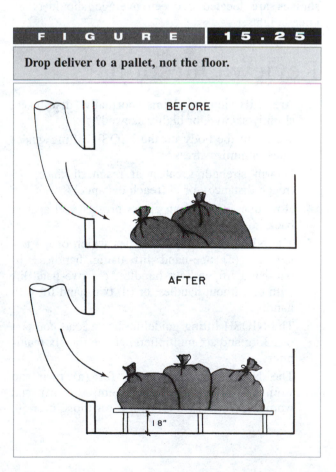

F I G U R E   1 5 . 2 5

Drop deliver to a pallet, not the floor.

BEFORE

AFTER

18"

Post Office uses a large plastic bin with a 12" × 18" cutout on two sides; the cutout is covered with a web held with a bungee cord. The bin fits on a separate wheeled base so the bin can be wheeled or removed from the base and stacked.

Another alternative is to put a short box (or box with flap or cut side) on a scissors lift; if the scissors lift has a turntable, both bending and reaching are reduced.

A final alternative is to suspend a flat sheet (wood or plastic) in the bin with four springs hooked to the corners of the bin. The sheet will rise or fall depending on the weight on the sheet, thus reducing rounded backs. The stress on the back also can be reduced by picking up multiple items with each reach, thereby reducing the number of times the operator has to bend over.

6.10.3 *Don't lift above the shoulder* The final location of the load is as important as the initial location. High lifting is bad from two viewpoints: (1) Muscular strength is relatively poor above the shoulder because the relatively small shoulder and arm muscle groups take over for the leg and back muscles. (2) It is dangerous to remove an object from a high shelf because the object may be dropped and damaged (also possibly damaging you!). Optimally, shelves are located between average shoulder and knee heights.

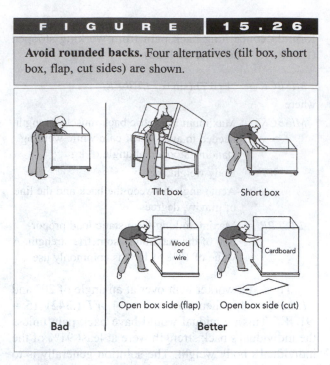

F I G U R E   15.26

Avoid rounded backs. Four alternatives (tilt box, short box, flap, cut sides) are shown.

If you have to stand on tiptoe, the stress, of course, is even worse on the arms and legs. In addition it stresses the feet and legs. Tiptoe standing (i.e., overreaching) decreases maximum weight of lift 10% to 15% over reaching as high as possible with the feet flat (Mital and Aghazadeh, 1987).

Review Questions

1. Are MH injury claims normally distributed, slightly skewed, or highly skewed?

2. Where in the body do the NIOSH lifting guidelines minimize stress?

3. Is arm strength greatest at reach distance, .75 (reach distance), or .5 (reach distance)?

4. How does wearing an apron protect you against back injury?

5. The NIOSH guideline assumes which of the following? (a) one-hand lift using handles, (b) one-hand lift without handles, (c) two-hand lift with or without handles, or (d) two-hand lift with handles.

6. The NIOSH lifting guideline has a load constant of 23 kg and six multipliers. Name the six multipliers.

7. The NIOSH guidelines are for (a) men and women, with no age adjustment, (b) men and women, with a 10% reduction for those over 50,

(c) men only, with no age adjustment, or (d) men, with a 10% reduction for those over age 50.

8. Is fat-free body weight or X-ray a better screen for selecting material handlers?

9. Briefly discuss the job severity index.

10. Discuss the open manhole analogy. Which approach is best?

11. How should a 40 × 48 × 9-inch pallet be oriented to minimize strain when loading or unloading boxes from the pallet?

12. What is the concept of the one-hand lift?

13. What could be carried with a J hook?

14. Why would you use a "plow" on a conveyor?

15. *"The farther away
    The less it should weigh."*

    Express this in an equation of spinal torque, considering object and body weight.

References

Andersson, G. and Chaffin, D. A biomechanical evaluation of five lifting techniques. *Applied Ergonomics,* Vol. 17, 2–8, 1986.

Andres, R., Wood, D., Laurie, N., Herrick, D., and Rooney, T. Ergonomic analysis of order picking at L. L. Bean. In *Advances in Industrial Ergonomics and Safety VII,* Bittner, A. and Champney, P. (eds.). London: Taylor and Francis, 397–402, 1995.

Ayoub, M. M., Selan, J., and Jiang, B. Manual material handling. In *Handbook of Human Factors,* Salvendy, G. (ed.), Chapter 7.2. New York: Wiley & Sons, 1987.

Balogun, J., Robertson, R., Goss, F., Edwards, M., Cox, R., and Metz, K. Metabolic and perceptual responses while carrying external loads on the head and by yoke. *Ergonomics,* Vol. 29, No. 12, 1623–35, 1986.

Brown, J. Factors contributing to the development of low back pain in industrial workers. *American Industrial Hygiene Association J.,* Vol. 36, No. 1, 26–31, 1975.

Burgess-Limerick, R., Abernethy, B., Neal, R., and Kippers, V. Self-selected manual lifting technique: Functional consequences of the interjoint coordination. *Human Factors,* Vol. 37, 395–411, 1995.

Burton, A. Spinal strain from shopping bags with and without handles. *Applied Ergonomics,* Vol. 17, No. 1, 19–23, 1986.

Chaffin, D., Andersson, G., and Martin, B. *Occupational Biomechanics,* 3rd ed. New York: Wiley, 1999.

Chang, W-R., Gronqvist, R., Leclercq, S., Myung, R., Makkonen, L., Standberg, L., Brungraber, R., Mattke, U., and Thorpe, S. The role of friction in the measurement of slipperiness. *Ergonomics,* Vol. 44, 13, 1217–32, 2001.

Course, B. and Drury, C. Optimum handle positions in a box holding task. *Ergonomics,* Vol. 25, 645–62, 1982.

Damon, A., Stoudt, H., and McFarland, R. *The Human Body in Equipment Design,* 226–27. Cambridge, MA: Harvard University Press, 1966.

Datta, S., Chatterjee, B., and Roy, B. The energy cost of rickshaw pulling. *Ergonomics,* Vol. 21, No. 11, 879–86, 1978.

Datta, S. and Ramanathan, N. Ergonomic comparison of seven modes of carrying loads on the horizontal plane. *Ergonomics,* Vol. 14, No. 2, 269–78, 1971.

Dempsey, P. and Hashemi, L. Analysis of worker's compensation claims associated with manual materials handling. *Ergonomics,* Vol. 42, 183–95, 1999.

Deyo, R. Low back pain. *Scientific American,* Vol. 279, No. 2, 48–53, August 1998.

Eastman Kodak Ergonomics Group, Rodgers, S. (ed.). *Ergonomic Design for People at Work: Vol. 2.* New York: Van Nostrand-Reinhold, 1986.

Freivalds, A. Comparison of United States (NIOSH Lifting Guidelines) and European (ECSC Force Limits) recommendations for manual work limits. *AIHA Journal,* Vol. 48, No. 8, 698–702, 1987.

Garg, A., Sharma, D., Chaffin, D., and Schmidler, J. Biomechanical stresses as related to motion trajectory of lifting. *Human Factors,* Vol. 25, No. 5, 527–39, 1983.

Garg, A. and Owen, B. Prevention of back injuries in healthcare workers. *Int. J. of Industrial Ergonomics,* Vol. 14, 315–31, 1994.

Head, M. Measuring the effects of training and workplace change. *Ergonomics Australia,* 17–21, Oct. 1997.

Herrin, G., Jaraidi, M., and Anderson, C. Prediction of overexertion injuries using biomechanical and psychophysical models. *American Industrial Hygiene Association J.,* Vol. 47, No. 6, 322–30, 1986.

Imbeau, D., Desjardins, L., Montpetit, Y., Riel, P., and Allan, J. Comparison of four methods for carrying a fiberglass extension ladder. *Int. J. of Industrial Ergonomics,* Vol. 22, 161–75, 1998.

Imrhan, S. Push-pull force limits. Chapter 23 in *The Occupational Ergonomics Handbook,* W. Karwowski and W. Marras (eds.). Boca Raton, FL: CRC Press, 1999.

Jackson, A., Borg, G., Zhang, J., Laughery, K., and Chen, J. Role of physical work capacity and load weight in psychophysical lift ratings. *Int. J. of Industrial Ergonomics,* Vol. 20, 181–90, 1997.

Kantowitz, B. and Sorkin, R. *Human Factors.* New York: Wiley & Sons, 642–43, 1983.

Karwowski, W., Caldwell, M., and Gaddie, P. Relationship between NIOSH (1991) lifting index, compressive and shear forces on the lumbosacral joint, and low back injury rate based on industrial field study. *Proc. of Human Factors and Ergonomics Society,* 654–57, 1994.

Konz, S. and Bhasin, R. Foot position during lifting. *American Industrial Hygiene Association J.,* Vol. 35, No. 12, 785–92, 1974.

Konz, S. and Coetzee, K. Prediction of lifting difficulty from individual and task variables. *Proceedings of the 4th Int. Congress on Production Research.* Tokyo, 1977.

Kroemer, K. Horizontal push and pull forces. *Applied Ergonomics,* Vol. 5, No. 2, 94–102, 1974.

Kumar, S. Arm strength at different reach distances. In *Trends in Ergonomics/Human Factors IV,* Asfour, S. (ed.). Amsterdam: Elsevier, 1987.

Kumar, S. The effect of sustained spinal load on intra-abdominal pressure and EMG characteristics of trunk muscles. *Ergonomics,* Vol. 40, No. 12, 1312–34, 1997.

Laursen, B., Ekner, D., Simonsen, E., Voigt, M., and Sjogaard, G. Kinetics and energetics during uphill and downhill carrying of different weights. *Applied Ergonomics,* Vol. 31, 159–66, 2000.

Lee, K. and Lee, J. A study of efficiency of two-man lifting work. *Int. J. of Ind. Ergonomics,* Vol. 28, 197–202, 2001.

Liles, D. The application of the job severity index to job design for the control of manual materials-handling injury. *Ergonomics,* Vol. 29, No. 1, 65–76, 1986.

Lovested, G. Reducing warehouse material handling strains. *Proceedings of 24th Annual Meeting of the Human Factors Society,* 653–54, 1980.

Marras, W. Occupational low-back disorder causation and control. *Ergonomics,* Vol. 43, 7, 880–902, 2000.

Marras, W., Allread, W., Burr, D., and Fathallah, F. Prospective validation of a low-back disorder risk model and assessment of ergonomic interventions associated with manual materials handling tasks. *Ergonomics,* Vol. 43, 11, 1866–86, 2000.

Marras, W., Lavender, S., and Rangarajulu, S. The effects of expectation on trunk loading. *Proceedings of the Human Factors Society,* 91–95, 1986.

Mital, A. and Aghazadeh, F. Psychophysical lifting capabilities for overreach heights. *Ergonomics,* Vol. 30, No. 6, 901–09, 1987.

Mital, A. and Ilango, M. Load characteristics and manual carrying capabilities. *Proceedings of the Human Factors Society,* 274–78, 1983.

Mital, A., Nicholson, A., and Ayoub, M. M. *A Guide to Manual Materials Handling.* London: Taylor and Francis, 1993.

Morrissey, S. and Liou, Y-H. Maximum acceptable weights in load carriage. *Ergonomics,* Vol. 31, No. 2, 217–26, 1988.

Mueller, E., Vetter, K., and Blumel, E. Transport by muscle power over short distances. *Ergonomics,* Vol. 1, 222–25, 1958.

Nussbaum, M., Chaffin, D., Stump, B., Baker, G., and Foulke, J. Motion times, hand forces, and trunk kinematics when using material handling manipulators. *Applied Ergonomics,* Vol. 31, 227–37, 2000.

Oxenburgh, M. *Increasing Productivity and Profit Through Health & Safety,* Chicago: CCH International, 1991.

Patterson, P., Congleton, J., Koppa, R., and Huchinson, R. The effects of load knowledge on stresses at the lower back during lifting. *Ergonomics,* Vol. 30, No. 3, 539–49, 1987.

Potvin, J. and Bent, L. NIOSH equation horizontal distances associated with the Liberty Mutual (Snook) lifting table box widths. *Ergonomics,* Vol. 40, No. 6, 650–65, 1997.

Poulsen, E. and Jorgensen, K. Back muscle strength, lifting and stooped working postures. *Applied Ergonomics,* Vol. 2, No. 3, 133–37, 1971.

Resnick, M. and Chaffin, D. An ergonomic evaluation of handle height and load in maximal and submaximal cart pushing. *Applied Ergonomics,* Vol. 26, 3, 173–78, 1995.

Ridd, J. A practical methodology for the investigation of materials handling problems. In *Ergonomics of Workstation Design,* Kvalseth, T. (ed.). London: Butterworths, 1983.

Rodgers, S. *Working with Backache.* Fairport, NY: Perinton Press, 1984.

Rowe, M. *Orthopaedic Problems at Work.* Fairport, NY: Perinton Press, 1985.

Shoaf, C., Genaidy, A., Karwowski, W., Waters, T., and Christensen, D. Comprehensive manual handling limits for lowering, pushing, pulling and carrying activities. *Ergonomics,* Vol. 40, No. 11, 1183–1200, 1997.

Smith, J. A manual material handling study of bag lifting. Paper at annual meeting of American Industrial Hygiene Association, Portland, Oregon, 1981.

Snook, S. and Ciriello, V. The design of manual handling tasks: Revised tables of maximum acceptable weights and forces. *Ergonomics,* Vol. 34, No. 9, 1197–1213, 1991.

Tichauer, E. Ergonomic aspects of biomechanics. In *The Industrial Environment—Its Evaluation and Control,* Chapter 32. Washington, DC: Supt. of Documents, 1973.

Ulin, S., Armstrong, T., Snook, S., and Keyserling, M. Examination of the effect of tool mass and work postures on perceived exertion for a screw driving task. *Int. J. of Ind. Ergonomics,* Vol. 12, 105–15, 1993.

Warwick, D., Novak, G., Schultz, A., and Berkson, M. Maximum voluntary strengths of male adults in some lifting, pushing and pulling activities. *Ergonomics,* Vol. 23, No. 1, 49–54, 1980.

Waters, T., Putz-Anderson, V., Garg, A., and Fine, L. Revised NIOSH equation for the design and evaluation of manual lifting tasks. *Ergonomics,* Vol. 36, No. 7, 749–76, 1993.

Waters, T., Putz-Anderson, V., and Garg, A. *Applications Manual for the Revised NIOSH Lifting Equation* (NIOSH Publ. No. PB94-176930). Washington, DC: Dept. of Health and Human Services, 1994.

Winters, J. and Chapanis, A. Thumb push forces exertable by free-standing subjects. *Ergonomics,* Vol. 29, No. 7, 893–902, 1986.

Websites

Information from Britain's Royal College of General Practitioners, Clinical guidelines; low back pain, www.rcgp.org.uk/backpain/index.htm

HANDTOOLS

16

HANDTOOLS

1 Use Special-Purpose Tools

2 Design Tools to Be Used by Either Hand

3 Power with Motors More Than with Muscles

4 Use the Proper Grip

5 Make the Grip the Proper Thickness, Shape, and Length

6 Make the Grip Surface Smooth, Compressible, and Nonconductive

7 Consider the Angles of the Forearm, Grip, and Tool

8 Use the Appropriate Muscle Group

Overview

Engineers can select from a wide variety of handtools. The eight guidelines will help you in your selection. Guideline 1 emphasizes the desirability of specialized tools, Guideline 2 using tools with both hands, and Guideline 3 powering with motors. Guidelines 4, 5, and 6 focus on the grip. Guideline 7 emphasizes the angles involved and the reduction of musculoskeletal disorders. Guideline 8 focuses on the use of the proper muscle group.

Key Concepts

attenuation	get ready/do/put away	precision grip
bearing surface	grip strength	pulp pinch
benefits/costs	hard joints/soft joints	resonates
capital/maintenance/utility cost	in-line grip	semipower grip
chuck pinch	lateral pinch	special-purpose tool
conductivity	normally open	triggering
dominant hand	pistol grip	vibration syndrome
	power grip	wedge shape

287

Handtools extend the capability of the hand. This chapter will help you to select from the many designs available. See Chapter 17 for a related topic, controls—the interface between the body and non-portable machines.

Selecting a handtool has two dimensions: (1) *what* the tool can do, and (2) *how* the tool is used (e.g., grip, posture, force). This chapter focuses on how the tool is used—ergonomics. Purchasing departments may focus only on what the tool can do. For best results, have multiple inputs (e.g., engineers, maintenance, purchasing, and, especially, the operators); this will tend not only to get better-quality decisions but also achieve more acceptance of the decision. See Box 16.1.

USE SPECIAL-PURPOSE TOOLS

Return on investment in handtools usually is high due to high output with use of the tool versus the low cost of the tool.

1.1 Benefits   Tools extend the capability of the hand. The capability can be more grip strength (pliers), impact strength (hammer), torque (wrench), speed (drill rpm), reach (fly swatter), protection (gloves), or even functions that cannot be done with a bare hand (saw, soldering iron). Use of tools is one of the key things that differentiates humans from animals.

One question is how specialized the tool should be. Should a general-purpose tool (knife, hammer, screwdriver) be used, or a special-purpose tool (fishing knife, butter knife, razor blade; claw hammer, ball-peen hammer, shoemaker's hammer; a nail gun instead of a hammer; a tool on each side of a large machine; both a pistol-grip and in-line grip tool at the same station so the operator can use the one appropriate for the posture).

Think of a job as composed of three elements: (1) **get ready,** (2) **do,** and (3) **put away.** A general-purpose

tool may save on the get-ready and put-away tasks since one tool does it all and there is less search-and-select time. The general-purpose tool may be extended into a multifunction tool. For example, a claw hammer combines a hammer and a nail claw; a pliers combines a gripper and a wire cutter; a pencil combines writing and erasing. Two tools in one eliminates reach, grasp, move, and lowers labor costs; get-ready and put-away costs are lower. An extreme example of a multifunction tool is a camping shovel, which also is a hammer, saw, ax, bottle opener, and wrench!

Often the multifunction and general-purpose tools don't really do any specific job very well. Thus, for most industrial tasks (tasks that are repeated tens, hundreds, or thousands of times/week), a **special-purpose tool** is best. This special-purpose tool (e.g., a knife to cut open cardboard boxes or an air-powered nutrunner) can be selected for the exact characteristics necessary for the specific job. Some users, whose jobs vary more, will have an "arsenal of weapons." For example, a mechanic would consider it foolish to try to do the day's work with only one or two tools.

1.2 Costs   Handtool costs are divided into capital cost, maintenance cost, and utility cost.

Capital cost of handtools tends to be low. Common nonpowered handtools (scissors, knives, pliers, wrenches) may be less than $10. Generally, all cost less than $100. Powered handtools cost from $10 to $1,000, depending on the tool and whether it is sold on the consumer market as well as the industrial market.

For maintainability and reliability reasons, consider having duplicate handtools. For example, in meatpacking, have two sharp knives/worker so when one becomes dull, the other can be used while the first is sharpened. Have a backup battery for battery-operated tools.

Maintenance costs of nonpowered handtools tend to be trivial. Maintenance costs of powered handtools

---

| BOX | **16.1** | *Handtool Selection* | (adapted from Feeney et al., 1997) |

Select handtools by taking the following steps:

1. **Do a job analysis.** Make a *detailed* analysis of the tasks the operator is to perform with the tool or tools. Consider task sequences, use of more automatic tools, workstation layout, and the like.

2. **Identify tool-use issues.** Example issues are:
   - operating forces
   - repetitions per minute and per shift

   - postures (joints in hand, wrist, elbow, shoulder)

3. **Select the right tool.** Select a number of candidate tools from different manufacturers. Have users evaluate the candidate tools; use under production conditions for some time. Finally, make the selection, considering all factors, not just initial capital cost.

depend upon the tool, of course, but $100/year would be considered high for most powered handtools.

Utility cost is zero for nonpowered tools. For powered tools, it depends upon the power source, energy used per minute, and the duty cycle (% of time the tool is used). A small air motor (such as used on an air-powered screwdriver) uses 12–35 cubic ft/min of air when operating. A typical duty cycle is 20%–25%, so 5 cfm or 300 cu ft/h is a reasonable value. Compressed air costs (capital + operating + maintenance) about 25–30 cents/1,000 cu ft of free air ingested by the compressor. Cost would be 8–9 cents/h. A 1/4 hp electric motor uses .746 (1/4) = .197 kWh; at $.07/kWh, this is about 1 cent/h. Clearly, utility costs for both air and electric motors are low.

1.3 Benefits/Costs

Analysis of **benefits/costs** is easiest to understand if it is put on a benefit/use and cost/use basis. The engineer must estimate how often the handtool will be used. This, in turn, requires two estimates: (1) years of tool use, and (2) usage/year. Years of tool use probably will be determined by how long the application lasts rather than the physical life of the tool. Two to five years is a reasonable estimate in most situations. For use/year, estimate usage/day or usage/week and multiply by the number of days or weeks used. A production worker might use a tool once a minute or 450 times/day × 190 days/yr = 85,000 times/yr. A maintainer might use a tool 5 times/day but only part of the year (say 100 days) or 500 times/yr.

Thus, a common nonpowered handtool might be used by a maintainer 500 times/yr × a 5-year life = 2,500 uses/life. A powered handtool might be used by a production worker 85,000 times/yr × 3 years = 250,000 times. (A power handtool should last 250,000 to 500,000 cycles.)

In summary, costs of the nonpowered handtool might be $20 for capital cost, $0 for maintenance, and $0 for utility cost—a total of $20 or $20/2,500 = $.008/use. Cost of the air-powered handtool might be $500 for capital cost, $100/year × 3 years = $300 for maintenance, and 190 days × 7.5 h/day × 50% duty cycle × $.30/h × 3 years = $640 for utility cost—a total of $1,440/250,000 = $.006/use.

The benefits depend on how much the proposed tool improves the capability and quality, reduces time, and so forth. See Figure 7.1 for a form showing some things to consider. For the nonpowered handtool, assume it saved $.01/use for quality and 2 s/use for time. If labor cost is $14.20/h, this is $14.20/3,600 s/h = $.004/s × 2 s/use = $.008/use: total savings of $.018/use. For the powered handtool, assume $.005/use for reduced downtime, $.001/use for improved quality, and 2 s/use. Using labor cost of $14.20/h, this is $.004/s × 2 s/use = $.008/use; total savings = $.014/use.

The above is a brief example making two points. *First,* whether a tool is expensive depends upon a detailed analysis, not just upon initial capital cost. *Second,* benefits include savings beyond just labor savings. The above estimates show how tool benefits far exceed tool costs and why a smart worker has special-purpose tools.

2 DESIGN TOOLS TO BE USED BY EITHER HAND

In most circumstances the tool should be in the user's preferred hand. The preferred hand or the **dominant hand** is the right hand for about 90% of the population; the percent seems constant across cultures and for both sexes.

Table 16.1 shows that the nonpreferred hand tends to have 94% of the grip strength of the preferred hand. See also Figure 16.1. Table 16.2 shows, in Study 2, that individual fingers on the nondominant hand are weaker than the corresponding fingers on the dominant hand.

Dexterity without handtools was measured by Kellor et al. (1971). The nonpreferred hand rate was 96% on a 9-hole pegboard task and 93% on a 50-hole pegboard task. Konz and Warraich (1985) reported that the nonpreferred hand rate was 84% for threading

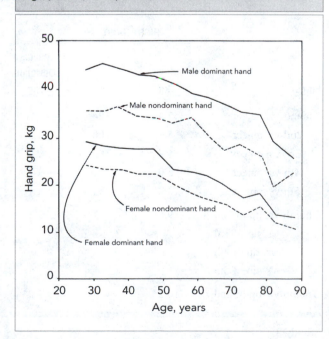

FIGURE 16.1

Handgrip strength for dominant and nondominant hands. Handgrip strength is less for the nondominant hand, is less for females than males, and declines with age (Shock, 1962).

				T A B L E		1 6 . 1		

Maximal static **grip strength** (hand squeeze), kg, from various studies.

HAND	GENDER	5TH PERCENTILE	STANDARD DEVIATION	GROUP
R	M	48.2	9.14	Army personnel
R	M	47.8	8.18	Air Force air crewmen
Pref.	M	44.6	7.64	Air Force rated officers
Pref.	M	41.8	6.87	Industrial personnel
R	M	41.4	8.23	Truck and bus drivers
R	M	40.6	9.64	Rubber industry
R	M	33.6	9.55	University men
R	M	19.1	5.46	University men, force for 1 min
L	M	45.0	9.55	Army personnel
L	M	44.6	7.64	Air Force rated officers
L	M	43.6	7.27	Air Force air crewmen
L	M	41.8	7.00	Industrial personnel
L	M	39.1	7.46	Truck and bus drivers
L	M	39.1	10.09	Rubber industry
L	M	29.5	8.18	University men
L	M	17.7	4.54	University men, force for 1 min
(R + L)/2	F	26.4	4.00	Navy personnel
Pref.	F	25.9	4.68	Industrial workers

				T A B L E		1 6 . 2		

Maximal static finger force for adult males. Study 1 had $N = 100$ (Hertzberg, 1973). Study 2 had $N = 20$ (Dickson et al., 1972). Study 3 had $N = 15$ (Hertzberg, 1973). (See also Table 16.9.)

	RIGHT HAND				DOMINANT HAND		NONDOMINANT HAND	
Finger	Mean, kg	%	Standard Deviation, kg	Standard Deviation/ Mean, %	Mean, kg	%	Mean, kg	%
Thumb vs. object	7.3	124	1.7	23				
2nd vs. object	5.9	100	1.3	22	4.6	100	4.4	96
3rd vs. object	6.4	108	2.0	31	4.3	93	3.9	85
4th vs. object	5.0	85	1.7	34	2.9	63	2.8	61
5th vs. object	3.2	51	1.1	37	2.4	52	2.4	52
Thumb vs. tip of 2nd	9.6*		2.3*	24*	7.5	163	6.9	150
vs. tip of 3rd					8.8	191	8.4	183
vs. tip of 4th					6.4	139	7.8	170
vs. tip of 5th					5.0	109	4.8	104
Thumb vs. tip of 2nd	10.5*		2.2*	21*				

*Study 3

a nut on a bolt. An, Askew, and Chao (1986) reported that the nonpreferred rate for manipulating objects was 87%. Hoffman (1997) found no difference between the preferred and nonpreferred hand for ballistic (non-visually controlled) movements but increasing differences as the difficulty increased.

When handtools are used, performance of the nonpreferred hand declines more. Konz and Warraich (1985) had 40 subjects do four tasks with each hand: drilling with an electric drill, hand sawing, hammering a nail, and cutting a pattern with scissors. Kaster et al. (1987) had 15 subjects do five tasks: nut assembly on a bolt, hand sawing, hammering a nail, cutting a pattern with scissors, and drawing a line. Table 16.3 summarizes the time effect for these novices. In addition, errors (accuracy) are much worse with the nonpreferred hand.

In summary: (1) left-handed operators should be as proficient as right-handed operators (assuming the workstations can be "mirrored" and tools can be used with either hand) and (2) the penalty of the nonpreferred hand is minimal for simple movements/tasks and increases with movement/task difficulty.

Box 16.2 describes gloves.

A tool usable in either hand has two benefits. The first is for the 10% of the population left out. In sports, where emphasis is on maximum performance, both left- and right-hand products usually are available. The same emphasis on performance is desirable for industry.

The second benefit is that the nonpreferred hand can be used when the preferred hand is otherwise engaged or is resting. Figure 16.2 shows a foodscoop that can be used only by the right hand. Figure 16.3 shows an alternative version that can be used by both hands. A common design solution is to put a control at the tool centerline so it is accessible from either side. Certain tools (e.g., a scissors) are peculiarly right-handed in design and require a different action when used in the left hand. Rather than force a left-handed person to use a right-handed scissors, buy a left-handed scissors. The goal is to emancipate the left hand.

T A B L E	16.3

Time decrement for novices when using nonpreferred hand. Practice may change the ratios.

DECREMENT, %	HANDTOOL	SKILL AND MOVEMENT
5–10	No	Simple hand/arm movements
10–20	No	Complex hand/arm movements
25	Yes	Minimum skill (saw, hammer)
50	Yes	Moderate skill (scissors)

F I G U R E	16.2

Right-hand tools. Left-handers have difficulty with right-hand only tools. In addition, right-handed users can't shift the tool to the left hand and continue working while resting the right hand. Note how all the load from the 1.2 kg spring must be overcome by a single digit, the thumb.

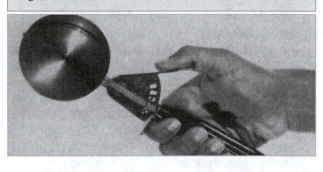

F I G U R E	16.3

Foodscoop. Either hand can use this tool. In addition, note how the force of the spring is overcome by the muscles of the entire hand, not just the thumb.

3 POWER WITH MOTORS MORE THAN WITH MUSCLES

First of all, mechanical energy (motors) is 10 to 1,000 times cheaper than human energy for the following reasons:

- People run 24 h/day × 365 days = 8,760 h/yr while machines run only when in use (say 1,800 h if a 100% duty cycle; only 450 h if 25% duty cycle).
- The worker energy cost to the firm is covered by wages. Wages must cover not only food for the worker, but also food for the worker's family. Wages also cover other goods such as housing, entertainment, and transportation.
- People are relatively inefficient as a power source. Bicycle pedaling, the most efficient method of human-generated power, is only 20% to 25% efficient.

BOX   **16.2**   *Gloves*

Gloves commonly protect the hand against abrasion and impact as well as chemicals (see Chapter 26 on dermatitis), heat (flame, sparks), and cold. Meatcutters wear special chainmail gloves to protect against knife cuts. Rubber gloves can protect a surgery patient against infection; rubber gloves (inside protective leather gloves) protect from electricity; and gloves can be used to reduce vibration. Goel and Rim (1987) reported vibration reductions of 24% for leather gloves and 45% for Sorbothane-padded gloves. (An alternative approach would be to pad the handle on the hand not holding the knife.)

Of course, not all gloves cover the hand the same. Technically, a glove has a separate division for the thumb and each finger. Mittens cover the entire hand with a separate thumb division (giving greater thermal protection with a loss of dexterity). Individual fingers can be guarded with finger guards (cots) and thimbles. Hand pads protect the palm against cuts, abrasions, and hot objects. Partial gloves (covering the hand and the first phalange of the finger) permit dexterity while still protecting against the cold. Fransson-Hall and Kilbom (1993) and Muralidhar and Bishu (2000) report that certain areas of the hand (e.g., thumb tip and base of the palm) are more sensitive to mechanical trauma; one solution is extra glove padding in these areas. See Figure 16.20. In some extremely cold environments, electrically heated gloves are an option. A sock (with the toe cut off) can be placed on the forearm to protect it against abrasion of cardboard boxes when packaging.

Protective work gloves have three wrist styles: (1) knitwrist (a knit cloth fitting snugly about the wrist, keeping loose material from entering; this snugness makes them dangerous near moving machinery as they can pull the hand into pinch points), (2) safety cuff (wide, stiff cuff at the wrist, permitting easy putting on and taking off), and (3) gauntlet (protects some or all of the forearm, depending on its length).

Gloves probably decrease manual dexterity (versus bare hands), although receivers in football wear gloves with high coefficients of friction to improve their pass-catching ability; golfers and baseball hitters also wear gloves. Plumber et al. (1985) reported that assembly time with handtools increased 15 to 37% with gloves. Tsaousidis and Freivalds (1988) estimate 15%. Bradley (1969) reported that times to actuate toggle switches, levers, knobs, and pushbuttons increased 2% to 13% with gloves; the increase tended to be less than .1 s, and so the percent increase may have little practical significance.

Gloves also decrease grip force. Depending on the glove, Cochran et al. (1986) estimated a decrease of 7%–17% and McMullin and Hallbeck (1991) estimated 11%–21%. The decrease in grip force with gloves (versus barehanded) is an estimate of the percent reduction in maximum holding time at any force (Cochran et al., 1987). Mital et al. (1994) reported that gloves increased the torque exerted on screwdrivers and wrenches even though muscle activity did not differ significantly between wearing and not wearing gloves. Gloves add to hand thickness. The amount depends upon the glove, but 5 mm (latex gloves) to 20 mm (heavy gloves) is a reasonable assumption.

Gloves for chemical protection must not be permeable to that specific chemical. Chemicals can penetrate the gloves (1) if the material degrades (change in physical property), (2) through penetration on a non-molecular level (seams, holes, and even pores of materials such as leather), and (3) through permeation (chemical penetration on a molecular level).

In addition, chemical protection gloves should have long sleeves (gauntlets) with a turn-back cuff to reduce chemicals dripping into the glove. Rinse gloves before removal; between wearings, wash and air-dry gloves. A cotton liner may reduce skin irritation due to sweat.

Multiple latex gloves (double gloving) often are used to reduce the risk of exposure to contaminated body fluids. Double gloving with latex gloves does not affect manipulative performance, but may increase manipulative effort.

As pointed out in Guideline 1, a small air motor, such as used on an air-powered screwdriver or nutrunner, costs about $.08–.09/h for utilities. A 1/4 hp electric motor costs about $.01/h. These certainly are a very small percentage of labor costs.

The second reason to replace human muscles with motors is to extend capability. A motor can exert a torque all day—it doesn't get tired! In addition, motors can exert forces and speeds beyond human capabilities. Try to imagine rotating a drill at 3,600 rpm by hand! The development of battery-operated power tools permits more safety (no danger from electrical shorts) as well as improved convenience (no power cord, no need to be near an outlet). Balancers (see Figure 15.18) reduce the use of muscles to support the weight of the tool.

If a nonpowered handtool is used, be sure to have plenty of mechanical advantage. Don't design just for a strong male.

A third reason to use motors is to permit a larger percent of the workforce to do a job; large forces and torques of manual tools might prevent some workers from doing a job. Motors also reduce cumulative trauma and injuries for the entire workforce.

Motors potentially have a vibration problem; see Box 16.3. Motors powered by air may have a cold exhaust; use attachments to direct the exhaust away from the person.

BOX   16.3   *Hand–Arm Vibration*

Tingling, blanching, and numbness of the fingers of normally healthy people is called Raynaud's disease. Occupationally induced cases were called vibration white finger (VWF), but more recently, as it was realized that nerves and tendons were affected as well as the blood vessels, the recommended term is **vibration syndrome** (VS).

Threshold Limit Values are published by a nongovernmental agency (ACGIH, 2001), but there is no governmental regulation as of 2003.

It is relatively difficult to estimate the amount of time a person is exposed to vibration. One possibility is occurrence sampling. Teschke et al. (1990) used a noise dosimeter to divide chainsaw use into saw off, idling, and cutting.

Engineering procedures to minimize VS are the following:

- Use a process with zero operator vibration. For example, to remove burrs, use deburring machines instead of hand-held grinders.

- Use a process with low operator vibration. For example, to cut meat, can the power knife be mounted and the operator guide the meat (instead of holding the knife)? At Ford, most power tools use a rotary air motor with gearing; impact wrenches are banned.

- Purchase equipment with lower levels of vibration. Some design possibilities are increasing the effective mass, reducing the excitation forces (e.g., balancing), and attenuation (Lindqvist, 1986). Deadblow hammers have heads filled with shot to absorb shock. Composite hammer handles may transmit less vibration than wood handles.

- Avoid resonance. Elastic structures vibrate freely at their natural frequency. Vibration applied close to this frequency **resonates** (is amplified); at other frequencies, the body reduces the input intensity, called **attenuation.** In general, frequencies in the 20–200 Hz range seem especially dangerous (Armstrong and Martin, 1997). Lower frequencies (<50 Hz) cause a greater load on the elbow and shoulders; frequencies over 100 Hz put more load on the hand and fingers (Kihlberg, 1995).

- Purchase equipment with vibration-isolated handles. See Lindqvist (1986) and Andersson (1990) for design techniques to reduce hand–tool vibration. For example, baseball bats and hammer handles use woods with good vibration characteristics.

- Furnish vibration-isolated gloves to reduce grip force and protect the hand from cold. If a glove is to be considered "antivibration," it should comply with the ISO 10819–1996 standard.

Work practices to reduce the effect of VS include the following:

- Maintain equipment. Keep chisels and cutters sharp, rebalance rotating equipment (especially hand-held grinders), replace tool shock absorbers, and maintain internal tool workings such as pneumatic cylinder stops.

- Consider a pad under an impact surface when using an impact tool (e.g., a hammer). A pad will reduce the rate of deceleration.

- Minimize handgrip force and push force on the tool, consistent with safe working (Toppila et al., 1997). For example, can the tool be supported with a balancer so it is guided with a loose grip instead of being held tightly? Can a hard, slippery handle be covered with tape (*a la* a baseball bat) to reduce grip force?

- Rest the tool on a support or workplace as much as possible. For example, can a steady rest or balancer be used?

- Avoid continuous vibration (have 10 min of nonvibration/h). For example, select tools that can be used with either hand.

- Keep the body and hands warm and dry (to prevent vasoconstriction). Gloves should cover the fingers, not just the palm, as vibration syndrome begins at the fingertips. Avoid drafts from exhausts of air-powered tools.

- Avoid smoking (nicotine and carbon monoxide adversely affect the finger arterial system).

For additional information, see Wilder et. al, 2002. For comments on whole-body vibration (especially for vehicle drivers), see Section 4.3.2 in Chapter 14.

For comments on nonpowered tools for working with dirt, see Box 16.4.

4 USE THE PROPER GRIP

Three types of grips are discussed: (1) the power grip, (2) semi-power grips, and (3) precision grips.

4.1 Power Grip Figure 16.4 shows a **power grip.** Typically the tool handle is perpendicular to the forearm axis. The direction of force, however, may be (1) parallel to the forearm (typically the wrist is fixed and the elbow moves), (2) at an angle to the forearm, or (3) applied as a torque about the forearm.

4.1.1 *Parallel to forearm* The muscles can apply force along the forearm axis, as with an electric iron, a saw, and a Y-handle shovel. The muscles also can resist force along the forearm axis, as with an electric drill, a suitcase handle, a pistol (the power grip sometimes is called a pistol grip). Typically, the tool handle is approximately perpendicular to the forearm axis—an angle of 80° is common. (It is not 90° because the carpal bones in the palm are shorter on the little finger side.) The two moment arms are caused by (1) tool action force and (2) tool weight. Mital and Kilbom (1992) recommended keeping the weight of the tool supported by the user at about 1.1 kg but no more than 2.3 kg.

See Figure 16.5. Note that if a balancer is suspended from a single point (such as a hoist), vertical force, but not horizontal force, is compensated. Better is to put the balancer on an articulated arm or a jib crane so both vertical and horizontal forces are compensated.

Tool support also can come from below the tool. Deere formerly had workers tighten wheel nuts on

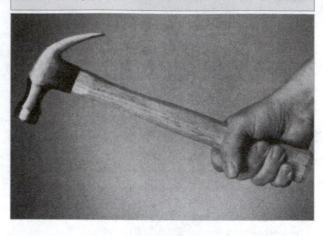

Power grips are for power. The four fingers reach around the handle and are "locked" by the thumb over the first finger.

tractors one at a time while kneeling and holding a power driver. Now they sit, using a supported tool that tightens two nuts (opposite ends of nut circle diameter) at a time; the $2,500 device paid for itself in less than 6 months.

If tool action force is high and tool weight is low (a light tool, a suspended tool, or a tool sliding along a surface), put the handle grip at the rear of the tool. If tool weight is high, place the tool handle under the tool center of gravity (tool balance point) to minimize unnecessary torques (i.e., a "nose-heavy" tool, giving a static load), as well as to permit sighting along the tool to improve accuracy.

In England, aircraft refueling required holding a 17 kg hose above the head and coupling it to the plane; it

---

In agriculture and construction, dirt is moved using human-powered tools.

For shovels, Freivalds and Kim (1990) and Freivalds (1996) summarize the literature. Using a criterion of minimization of energy of shoveling sand at 18 scoops/min, the optimum shovel had a ratio of $B/W = .07$, where B = blade size (m²), and W = shovel weight (kg).

A shovel is used for digging as well as scooping and throwing. Van der Grinten (1987) reported that shovels with a relatively large curvature were good for scooping and throwing but not for digging. Degani et al. (1993) had some success with a two-shaft, two-handle shovel. For shoveling snow, lubricate the blade with cooking spray. Some shov-

els have angled blades or wheels so the snow is plowed rather than lifted.

For hoes, Nag and Pradham (1992) recommended that Indian agricultural workers use a 2-kg hoe with a blade–handle angle of 65°–70°, blade length of 25–30 cm, blade width of 22–24 cm, handle length of 70–75 cm, and handle diameter of 3–4 cm.

In a comparison of weeding devices, Tewari, Datta, and Murthy (1991) reported that a spade and a three-tine hoe had approximately equal work hours/land area, but a khurpi took 2.4 times as long.

For rakes, Kumar and Cheng (1990) reported that a straight rake handle reduced spinal load over a variety of experimental nonstraight handles.

F I G U R E   1 6 . 5

Original and improved tool weight. Tool weight was reduced for Volkswagen workers (Echard, Smolenski, and Zamiska, 1987). In the improved method, the 5-lb gun and hose were replaced by a lightweight wand, the hose and gun were suspended from an overhead trolley, and the hose between the suspension point and the operator was attached to a belt around the operator's waist. Another technique to reduce fighting the hose is to use swivel couplings.

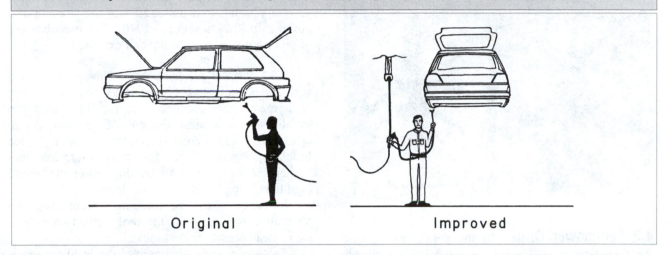

Original   Improved

From *Ergonomic Interventions to Prevent Musculoskeletal Injuries in Industry,* by M. Echard et al., pp. 122–123. Copyright © 1987 by Lewis Publishers, Inc., Chelesa, MI. Used with permission.

was a two-person operation. The back strain was reduced by using a two-step platform (taller workers stood on the lower step, shorter workers on the upper step) so the coupling was done at head height, not at arm's reach. The union agreed to make the revised job a one-person job after the new approach was shown to be safe (a pressure transducer pill was swallowed, and it radioed abdominal pressure during the task).

4.1.2 *Angle to forearm*   The muscles can apply force at an angle to the forearm (hammer, hand ax, ice pick, chisel, reverse grip pliers, and pizza cutter). See Figure 16.6. The tool force angle varies from tool to tool. The tool may be above the hand (hammer) or below (ice pick, pizza cutter); the wrist may be flexed (hammer, fishing rod, tennis racquet) or locked (ice pick, pliers, power screwdriver). When the tool is above the hand, the wrist is in "high gear"—the top of the hand moves more than the bottom. When the tool is below the hand, the wrist is in "low gear"—movement at the extremity is reduced but power at the wrist is increased.

Although for minimum stress the tool shaft angle should be perpendicular to the forearm, the angle of the worksurface may result in a deviated wrist. A simple solution is a tilted worksurface.

4.1.3 *Torque about forearm axis*   Figure 16.7 shows a power grip on a triaxial Allen wrench. An extension of the forearm axis projects through the fingers. A corkscrew is another example.

A common problem for torque on controls is insufficient bearing surface and lever arm. In Europe, most doors are opened by handles (i.e., good lever arms), but in the United States architects rely on squeezing the fingers tightly on a polished sphere, a doorknob.

F I G U R E   1 6 . 6

Pizza cutter. Power grip with tool below the hand and with wrist locked is shown. The guard not only protects against injury but permits the four fingers' muscles to be relaxed.

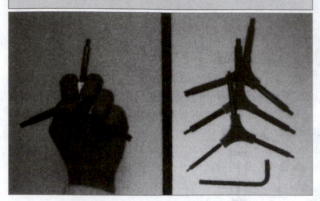

F I G U R E   1 6 . 7

Power grip on triaxial Allen wrench. Tool axis is aligned with forearm. The triaxial Allen wrench has three different sizes on each wrench; the wrench is color-coded for size.

4.2 Semipower Grips

In the **semipower grips,** the four fingers still act as a group but the thumb position changes. The two variations are the oblique grip and the hook grip.

In the *oblique grip,* the thumb is aligned along the tool axis to improve precision but with a loss of power. Strength is about 2/3 of the power grip. Patkin (1969) mentions pointing along a surgeon's needle-holder with the thumb. Holding a golf club is a more common example.

In another version, the *hook grip,* the four fingers still wrap around the tool shaft but the thumb is relaxed (passive) and not used. Figure 16.8 shows how Gilbreth improved bricklaying by substituting a hook grip for a pinch grip. One application is carry-

F I G U R E   1 6 . 8

Use hook grips for bricks. A century ago, Gilbreth recommended using a hook grip (lower) in place of a pinch grip (upper) to hold a brick in place. Still other hook grips are horizontal pulling of a tray or control and downward pulling on a hook or strap.

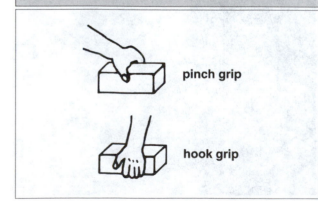

pinch grip

hook grip

ing a light load (e.g., briefcase); another is lifting a box without handles. Of course, resistance to the object being pulled from the hand is not as good as the power grip since the thumb is not acting as a lock.

4.3 Precision Grips

The **precision grip,** used for precise aim, has only about 20% of the strength of a power grip (Swanson et al., 1970). The two divisions of precision grip are internal and external.

4.3.1 *Internal precision grip*

This grip is used with a tableknife (see Figure 16.9), toothbrush, and blade razor. Three characteristics are: (1) a pinch grip by the thumb against the first finger (or thumb against first and second fingers), (2) support by the little finger and side of the hand (to reduce tool tremor), and (3) the shaft passing under the thumb (and thus being "internal" to the hand).

In many cases, the forearm is supported. An alternative is support of the tool (artists have been using steady rests for centuries).

The arm muscles that control the hand are sensitive to tremor following "overexertion." Patkin (1969), an Australian surgeon, recommended that surgeons not carry a suitcase for 24 h before an operation. Hudgens et al. (1988) reported individual differences; least steady were women on oral contraceptives, men were intermediate, and most steady were normally cycling women. Davis and Konz (1995) reported that after 1 min of pushups, hand steadiness did not return to basal within 6 h.

If tool rotation is required (e.g., small screwdriver), the tool shaft tends to be perpendicular to the work and the end of the tool shaft tends to bore a hole into the palm of the hand. Reduce this problem by (1) using a shaft so long that it extends beyond the palm, (2) reducing palm penetration pressure by using a tool end with a larger **bearing surface** (such as a spherical surface), or (3) reducing penetration pressure by reducing the force required along the tool axis.

F I G U R E   1 6 . 9

Internal precision grip. Three characteristics are: (1) a pinch grip, (2) support by the little finger or side of the hand, and (3) shaft being "internal" to hand.

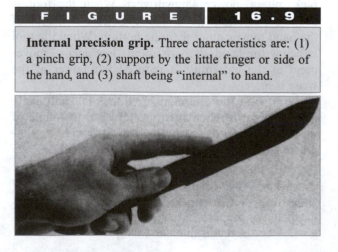

F I G U R E   16.10

External precision grip. Three characteristics are: (1) a pinch grip, (2) support by the side of the second finger or skin at the thumb base, and (3) shaft being "external" to hand.

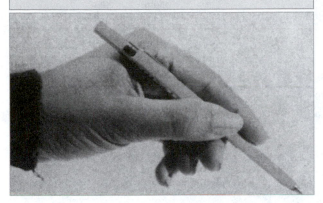

4.3.2 *External precision grip* This grip is used with a pencil or pen (see Figure 16.10), a spoon, or chopsticks. Three characteristics are (1) a pinch grip by the thumb against the first finger (or thumb against first and second fingers), (2) support on the side of the second finger or the skin at the base of the thumb, and (3) the shaft passing over the thumb and thus being "external" to the hand. The tool shaft usually is at an angle to the work surface.

5 MAKE THE GRIP THE PROPER THICKNESS, SHAPE, AND LENGTH

Every tool has two ends—one working on the material, the other on the hand.

Figure 16.11 and Table 16.4 give key dimensions of small and large bare adult hands. Since female hands tend to be smaller than male hands, handtools designed for men tend to be too large for women.

5.1 Grip Diameter: Power Grip   Ayoub and Lo-Presti (1971) used electromyography on 40, 50, and 85 mm dia.; if force at 40 mm is 100%, then force at 50 was 95% and at 85 was 70%. Making recommendations for container handles, Rigby (1973) gave 6 mm as the minimum for weights of less than 7 kg, 13 mm for weights of 7 to 9 kg, and 19 mm for weights over 9 kg. Greenburg and Chaffin (1977, pp. 51 and 77) recommended that power grip handles be between 50 and 85 mm, with the goal toward the 50. Rodgers (1986) recommended 38 mm. Johnson (1988) said the best grip for a power screwdriver is about 50 mm. Shih and Wang (1997) used subjective weight of a container as a criterion for handles of 25, 32, 38, 44, 51, and 57 mm dia.; they recommended 51 mm. Hall (1997) recommended cylinders between 30 to 40 mm.

If the grip can be customized to an individual, Grant et al. (1992) recommended a diameter 10 mm less

F I G U R E   16.11

Hand dimensions of Table 16.4 (Pheasant, 1996). Gloves increase the dimensions. Hands differ not only in size, but also in strength and dexterity. For male adults, the length of the last phalange of the little finger and the width of the thumb approximate 1 inch. This is known as a "rule of thumb!"

T A B L E	1 6 . 4

Hand dimensions (mm) of British adults (Pheasant, 1996); see Figure 16.11. Dimensions of Americans should be similar.

	MEN				WOMEN			
Dimension	5th %ile	50th %ile	95th %ile	SD	5th %ile	50th %ile	95th %ile	SD
1. Hand length	173	189	205	10	159	174	189	9
2. Palm length	98	107	116	6	89	97	105	5
3. Thumb length	44	51	58	4	40	47	53	4
4. Index finger length	64	72	79	5	60	67	74	4
5. Middle finger length	76	83	90	5	69	77	84	5
6. Ring finger length	65	72	80	4	59	66	73	4
7. Little finger length	48	55	63	4	43	50	57	4
8. Thumb breadth (IPJ)[a]	20	23	26	2	17	19	21	2
9. Thumb thickness (IPJ)	19	22	24	2	15	18	20	2
10. Index finger breadth (PIPJ)[b]	19	21	23	1	16	18	20	1
11. Index finger thickness (PIPJ)	17	19	21	1	14	16	18	1
12. Hand breadth (metacarpal)	78	87	95	5	69	76	83	4
13. Hand breadth (across thumb)	97	105	114	5	84	92	99	5
14. Hand breadth (minimum)[c]	71	81	91	6	63	71	79	5
15. Hand thickness (metacarpal)	27	33	38	3	24	28	33	3
16. Hand thickness (including thumb)	44	51	58	4	40	45	50	3
17. Maximum grip diameter[d]	45	52	59	4	43	48	53	3
18. Maximum spread	178	206	234	17	165	190	215	15
19. Maximum functional spread[e]	122	142	162	12	109	127	145	11
20. Minimum square access[f]	56	66	76	6	50	58	67	5

[a] IPJ is the interphalangeal joint, i.e., the articulations between the two segments of the thumb;

[b] PIPJ is the proximal interphalangeal joint, i.e., the finger articulation nearest to the hand;

[c] as for dimension 12, except that the palm is contracted to make it as narrow as possible;

[d] measured by sliding the hand down a graduated cone until the thumb and middle fingers only just touch;

[e] measured by gripping a flat wooden wedge with the tip end segments of the thumb and ring fingers;

[f] the side of the smallest equal aperture through which the hand will pass.

than inside grip diameter. The powered knives used in meat cutting now come with quick change handles; the handle shaft remains constant but four different outer-diameter handles fit on the same inner-diameter shaft.

In summary, a power grip between 30 and 50 mm probably will be satisfactory. A better choice, though, is 35 to 45 mm.

If handle diameter is too small, there is too much pressure on the fingers (Hall, 1997). (Workers often use tape to increase handle diameter.)

If the handle is too large, the fingers don't overlap, there is no locking with the thumb, and strain increases sharply.

Note that if the tool "head" (such as a screwdriver tip) becomes smaller, the hand doesn't shrink. Therefore, the handle should not shrink!

On double-handed tools (see Figure 16.12), the span should be 50 to 63 mm (Rodgers, 1986). Greenburg and Chaffin (1977) recommended a minimum initial span of about 50 mm (if tool force is low during closure) and a maximum of 100 mm (due to maximum hand size).

5.2 Grip Diameter: Precision Grip   Nonpowered screwdrivers have a tradeoff; maximum torque is associated with screwdrivers that require the maximum time to drive a screw and minimum torque is associated with minimum time (Magill and Konz, 1986; Gainer and Konz, 1987).

For pens, avoid diameters less than 6 mm as they cut into the hand. Kao (1974) reported that boys had better handwriting with pens of 13 mm dia than with

F I G U R E   16.12

Double-handed tool. Maximum grip strength is achieved when the opening is about 75 mm (Greenburg and Chaffin, 1977). The 50 males and 50 females were electronics manufacturing employees in the United States. Fransson and Winkel (1991) reported that the optimum was 50–60 mm for females and 55–65 for males.

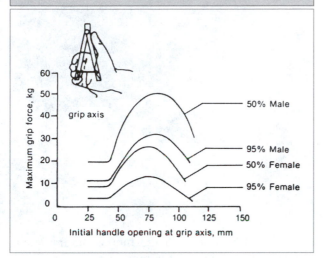

10 or 6 mm. Konz and Oetemo (1988) reported that pen diameters of 9.5 and 12.7 mm were preferred over 6.3 mm.

In a study with a smooth grip, a grip with grooves parallel to the pen axis, and a grip with concentric circular grooves, the grip with concentric grooves had the lowest EMG of the flexor pollicis brevis and lowest pen-point pressure (Udo et al., 1995). Udo et al. (2000) compared a conventional cylindrical 8.3 mm diameter pen with the ergonomic pen shown in Figure 16.13. The ergonomic pen had a significantly lower

F I G U R E   16.13

Ergonomic pen. Features include: (1) a large grip diameter (14 mm), (2) a compliant rubber grip to permit micro- motions as well as increase friction, and (3) a wedge shape grip to restrict forward motion of the fingers. A design by Hiroshi Udo, a Japanese physician, has sold more than 60,000,000 copies. In addition, there are many "knockoff" copies.

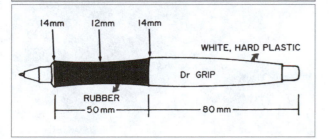

EMG for the flexor pollicis brevis as well as lower pain scores for thumb, forefinger, middle finger, forearm, and shoulder.

5.3 Shape: Section Perpendicular to Grip Axis

For most situations, you want the tool to remain captive in your hands; that is, it does not rotate. Rotation is prevented by a countertorque in the hand. Since a torque is a force times a moment arm, improve the moment arm and thus reduce the required force. Improve the moment arm by (1) making it longer, or (2) improving its bearing surface to minimize slippage.

Patkin (1969) showed how a thumb conoid reduced accidental twisting on a surgeon's forceps. Tremor was reduced by using the thumb to rotate the tool while the forearm was supported. Pointing with the thumb aided movement precision and, since the thumb can move up and down, it could open the jaws. A thumb conoid is better than a thumb ring since (1) it fits multiple thumb diameters, (2) it has greater bearing surface, and (3) it has a wider range of up-and-down movement (since the thumb tip, not knuckle, moves). Figure 16.14 shows how a bayonet forceps was modified to resist turning in the hand.

The second strategy is to improve the bearing surface. A tool with a circular cross-section tends to permit slippage. A rectangular cross-section gives a good bearing surface (in addition, a rectangular cross-section tool does not roll when placed on a table). A noncircular cross-section also allows tactile orientation of the tool. For example, workers in a cellophane plant file a flat area on the bottom of their knife handles. The flat area permits them to orient the knife without looking at it.

A third strategy is to improve the coefficient of friction of the handle. Gainer and Konz (1987) found that screwdriver handles with a soft rubber surface were preferred over those with hard plastic.

F I G U R E   16.14

Accidental twisting of the surgeon's forceps (a) was reduced by adding the vertical bearing surface on (b) (Miller et al., 1971).

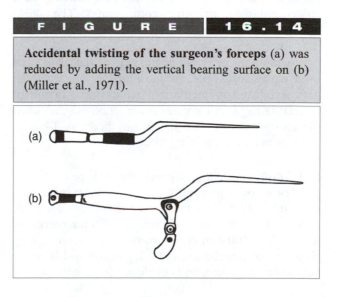

If rotation of the tool is neither good nor bad, a circular cross-section is more forgiving on the hand since there are no sharp edges. (Economics, not ergonomics, is the reason 80% of wooden pencils are hexagonal, as 9 hexagonal pencils can be cut from a slat that yields only 8 round ones.)

Sometimes the tool should rotate within the hand. Make the cross-section within the pinch grasp circular to permit rotation by simple finger–thumb movements rather than the complex regrasps or forearm movements needed for rectangular cross-sections. Support the forearm to reduce tool tremor (if the forearm is not required to move during tool rotation).

5.4 Shape: Section Along Tool Grip Axis
The grip shape can be constant over the grip length, or it can vary. A change in cross-section (1) reduces movement of the tool forward and backward in the hand, (2) permits greater force to be exerted along the tool axis due to the better bearing surface, and (3) can act as a shield if placed at the front.

Many handles have a **wedge shape,** which reduces forward movement of the hand. Since digit 3 is about 25 mm longer than the thumb or digit 5, the diameter at digit 3 can be about 25/3.14 = 8 mm larger. Avoid finger grooves or indentations between the front and rear of the grip since hand width (metacarpal breadth) varies about 18 mm in the population; thus the ridges between the valleys fit no one except the tool designer and become pressure points for other users.

Figure 16.15 shows a guard on the front of a grip. Injury from movement can come from the tool itself (knives, soldering irons) or simple impact of the hand on any unyielding or sharp surface. Greater force can be exerted along the tool axis since the strong muscles of the forearm are not limited by the grip strength of the fingers on the handle. A front shield also can act as a shield against heat or materials (stirring soup, solder splashes, irritating compounds). The shield also permits holding the tool farther forward, which may improve accuracy.

A pommel (a shield at the rear of the grip, often used with swords) prevents loss of the tool when the grip is relaxed momentarily, but its most important benefit is to permit greater force to be exerted when the tool is being pulled toward the body. A T-handle permits maximum pulling force.

5.5 Length
Length depends on the type of grip.

For a power grip, all four fingers must make contact. Table 16.4 gives 69 mm hand breadth for a 5th percentile woman and 95 mm for a 95th percentile male. Thus, 100 mm is a reasonable minimum dimension for the population, but 125 mm would be more comfortable. If the grip is enclosed (e.g., handsaw) or

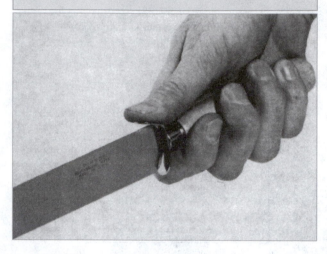

F I G U R E   16.15

Grip guard. Guards between the grip and the knife can improve thrust capability as well as reduce accidents. A grip guard should be 16 mm high (Mital and Kilbom, 1992).

a glove will be worn, use 125 mm as the minimum. For an oblique grip, use 125 mm.

For an external precision grip, the tool shaft must be long enough to be supported at the base of the first finger or thumb. Golf pencils don't comply. Use 100 mm as a minimum for external precision grips.

For an internal precision grip, the tool must extend past the tender palm but not so far as to hit the wrist. The pliers shown in Figure 16.16 demonstrate this principle. Screwdrivers usually are designed to be held in an internal precision grip or oblique grip. However, the user tries to exert force parallel to the

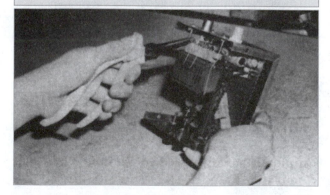

F I G U R E   16.16

Improved pliers. Bend the tool, not the wrist. In addition, they prevent slippage in the hand and don't dig a hole in the palm since the handle end extends beyond the palm. A spring opens the tool. Because most assembly workers are female, the tool was designed for female hand sizes.

tool axis and uses the palm of the hand for the pushing force rather than squeezing the fingers. The result is pressure on the palm, causing pain. Use a large-diameter spherical surface at the handle end and give a good gripping surface on the tool handle to minimize the palm pressure.

6 MAKE THE GRIP SURFACE SMOOTH, COMPRESSIBLE, AND NONCONDUCTIVE

Smooth and compressible concerns pressure points on the hand. Nonconductivity relates to electricity and temperature problems.

6.1 Smooth   Reduce pressure points by minimizing protrusions from the grip surface and sharp edges. A knife works by exerting a force over a very small area; sharp edges on a grip act as knives to the hand. Keep edge radii over 2 mm; females are more sensitive to sharpness than males (Konz, Aye and Fu, 1996). Since considerable force may be needed on wrenches and prybars, consider round rather than sharp edges; see Figure 16.17. Grind away sharp edges (forging lines, casting parting lines, sharp radii); an alternative is to cover them with tape or dip the grip into plastic. Smoothness also tends to aid sanitation. Avenor had problems with cutting the wires on bales of recycled paper; one of the solutions was to pad the cutter handles.

A poor grip leaves its mark—on the hand.

6.2 Compressible   Once the grip is smooth, consider making it compressible because a compressible grip minimizes pressure on the hand by increasing contact area, reducing slippage (due to high coefficient of friction), and reducing vibration transmission to the hand. Resistance to absorption of sweat, oil, and blood (meat cutting) improves sanitation. Bacteria count can be reduced by periodically placing the grip in a germicide.

Rubber, compressible plastic, and wood are superior to hard plastics and metals. Be cautious of very soft grip materials, as they may embed chips or splinters. Sport examples of compressible grips are tennis racquets, golf clubs, and baseball bats with tape. Figures 16.16 and 16.18 show handtools with a compressible grip. The grip in Figure 16.18 uses not only a compressible material (rubber), but also geometry (many small "fingers"). Barr Bros. (Redding, CA) has developed a T-handle meat hook; the handle is not only compressible, but it is also customized to the individual (the handle is heated with a heat gun, then grabbed by the individual's soapy hand to form the handle to the hand).

Sharp radii on tools (as on left) can cut into the hand.

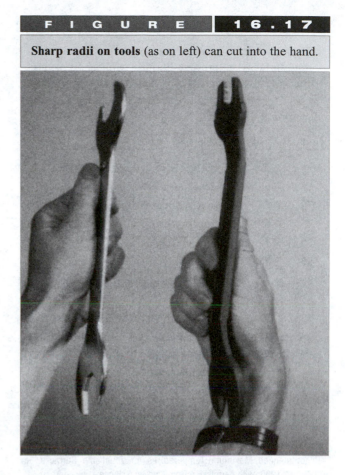

Compressible rubber grip on screwdriver. This makes it easier on the palm.

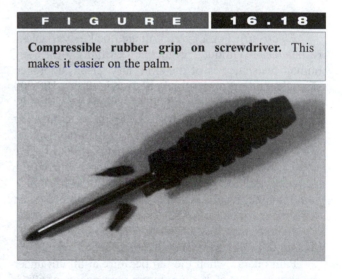

6.3 Nonconductive   Grips should not conduct electricity or temperature. Materials with good electrical **conductivity** tend to be good conductors of temperature. Thus, wood or rubber conducts less than plastic, which is better than metal. Note that metal rivits in a wood or plastic handle conduct even if the rest of the handle has low conductivity. Although high temperatures generally are the problem, cold surfaces may be a problem in outdoor construction.

T A B L E		16.5
Recommended maximum temperatures (°C) for touchable surfaces to prevent burning with short contact times (accidental contact) (Siekman, 1990).		

DURATION, S

1	3–4	Material
65	60	Water
65	60	Metals, uncoated, smooth surface
70	65	Metals, uncoated, rough surface
75	65	Metals, coated with 50 µm thick varnish
80	70	Concrete, ceramics, marble
80	75	Ceramics, glazed (tiles)
85	70	Metals, coated with 100 µm thick varnish
85	75	Porcelain
85	75	Polyamid 11–12 plastic with glass fiber
—	85	Teflon, Plexiglas
95	85	Pertinax (smooth surface); Duroplast with fiber inlay
115	95	Wood (For very dry and very light woods, values may be up to 140 and 120.)

Source: Reprinted from *Applied Ergonomics,* Vol. 21, H. Siekman, "Recommended Maximum Temperatures for Touchable Surfaces," pp. 69–73, © 1990, with permission from Elsevier Science.

T A B L E		16.6
Recommended maximum temperatures (°C) for touchable surfaces to prevent burning with long contact times (Siekman, 1990).		

TEMPERATURE, °C	MATERIAL
Duration: Up to 1 min	
50	Water, metals (coated and uncoated), and other materials with high conductivity
55	Ceramics, concrete, glass, polyamid 11–12
60	Duroplast, Pertinax, Plexiglas, Teflon, wood
Duration: Up to 10 min	
48	All materials
Duration: Up to 8 h	
43	All materials

Source: Reprinted from *Applied Ergonomics,* Vol. 21, H. Siekman, "Recommended Maximum Temperatures for Touchable Surfaces," pp. 69–73, © 1990, with permission from Elsevier Science.

Electricity. For a given voltage, the key variable is resistance. Without protective clothing, the key human resistance is of the skin. Dry, clean, unbroken skin, depending on its thickness, varies from 100,000 to 600,000 ohms; wet or broken, it may be only 500 ohms. A dry finger with 400,000 ohms contacting 120 volts gives 120/400,000 = .3 milliamps. Contact of a wet finger with 15,000 ohms would give 120/15,000 = 8 milliamps. Thus, for safety, keep the skin dry and dirty (dirt can double the skin ohms). Don't increase conductivity with metal objects such as watches, rings, or keys.

Temperature: heat. The two key variables are (1) contact duration and (2) contact surface material.

Pain occurs when the temperature at 80 um under the skin reaches 50°C; maximum pain occurs at 60°C; cell death through protein denaturalization occurs at 70°C. Table 16.5 gives the recommended maximum surface temperatures for short contact periods—for accidental contact. Table 16.6 gives maximum temperatures for long contact periods—for intentional contact. Comfort is maximized at object temperatures of 33–35°C (skin temperature).

Low conductivity materials (wood, rubber) are good for two reasons: (1) they release heat to the hand more slowly, so they can be held for a longer time before injury occurs (you can let go before you are burned), and (2) they gain heat more slowly, so they are less likely to reach a high temperature. With wood, the lower the density and moisture content and the rougher the surface, the higher the burn threshold. Table 16.5 shows the benefits of coating metals with varnish.

Temperature: cold. The same concepts for heat apply to cold. Table 16.7 gives recommendations for cold. Extremely cold pain sensation occurs at finger temperatures of 7°C and freezing finger temperatures of 0°C. A key difference from heat is that there seems to be a strong gender effect—females are much more sensitive to cold surfaces than males (Geng et al., 2001).

An air-powered tool can become cold due to compressed air expansion; a plastic sleeve will reduce thermal transfer as well as dampen vibration.

7 CONSIDER THE ANGLES OF THE FOREARM, GRIP, AND TOOL

Here the division is (1) angles, and (2) clearance.

7.1 Angle   The goal is to keep the wrist in the neutral (handshake) position. When the wrist is not in the neutral position, not only is grasp strength less (Putz-Anderson, 1988; McMullin and Hallbeck, 1991), but risk of cumulative trauma also increases. Achieve wrist neutrality by changing the job or changing the tool. Figure 16.19 shows how the best tool angle

T A B L E		1 6 . 7

Contact time for skin temperature to reach 7°C and 0°C while touching cold metallic surfaces (Geng et al., 2001).

			Time(s) to reach	
MATERIAL	$T_{surface}$, °C	GENDER	7°C	0°C
Aluminum	+2	F	15	
		M	66	
	−4	F	6	60
		M	15	87
	−10	F	4	30
		M	2	15
	−15	F	2	12
		M	3	21
Steel	+2	F	45	
		M	117	
	−4	F	8	86
		M	35	198
	−10	F	9	47
		M	13	103
	−15	F	5	20
		M	9	49

varies with the posture. Although power tools tend to have a **pistol grip** (tool axis parallel to forearm) or **inline grip** (tool axis perpendicular to forearm), there are other possibilities. Figure 16.20 shows a right-angle nutrunner. **Hard joints** are formed when two solid objects (e.g., pulley to a crankshaft) are brought together. The torque increases (ramps up) quickly, and the joint is completed in perhaps .5 s. **Soft joints** involve two objects having elastic properties. The torque increases more slowly and the joint is completed in perhaps 2 s (Radwin et al., 1989).

7.1.1 *Changing the job* Changing the job may simply require a change in worker posture. Standing tends to permit longer reaches than sitting. If the person is sitting, perhaps the chair is too high or too low for that specific person, resulting in an awkward wrist orientation.

Consider holding the part, not the tool. Oxenburgh (1991) describes (in Case 54) how a hand-trimmer operation (14,000 cuts/shift) was modified by using an air-powered gate cutter, mounted on a bench. The operator held the part, not the tool, and just inserted it into the cutter's mouth.

The work orientation can be changed also by tilting the entire worksurface, tilting a fixture on the

F I G U R E		1 6 . 1 9

Tool location affects the best tool grip. Optimum tool angle depends on posture. Ulin et al. (1993) say repetitive screwdriving should not be done on horizontal surfaces above the elbow; if elevated work must be done on horizontal surfaces, avoid pistol-grip tools. At midthigh and lower, use pistol-grip tools.

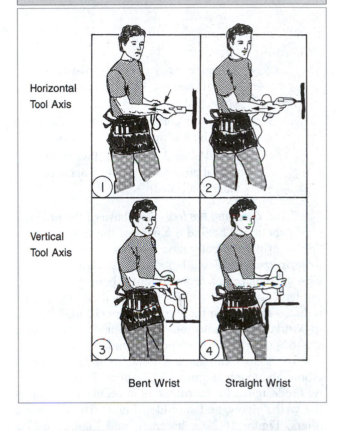

Horizontal Tool Axis

Vertical Tool Axis

Bent Wrist   Straight Wrist

F I G U R E		1 6 . 2 0

Right-angle grip on nutrunner. Right-angle nutrunners are popular for securing fasteners with high (> 20 Nm) torque.

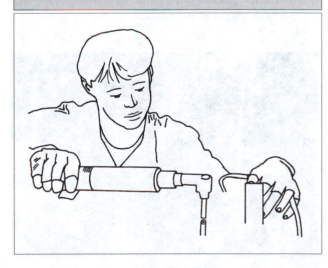

surface, or tilting the work itself. Examples of tilting the entire worksurface are some keyboards that have adjustable angles.

Terrell and Purswell (1976) quantified the effect of awkward wrist postures on grip strength; the maximum pronation/supination effect is 12%, flexion/extension effect is 25%, and radial/ulnar effect is 15%:

$$GS = 95.7 + 4.3 \, PS + 3.8 \, FE - 25.2 \, FE)^2 - 16.8 \, (RU)^2$$

where

GS = Grip strength, %

PS = Pronation/supination (0 if wrist is in a neutral position; 1 if pronated or supinated)

FE = Flexion/extension (0 if wrist is in a neutral position; 1 if fully flexed or extended)

RU = Radial/ulnar deviation (0 if wrist is in a neutral position; 1 if fully radially or ulnarly deviated)

7.1.2 *Changing the tool* The base of the little finger is about 10° behind the base of the first finger, so "pistol grips" typically have about a 10° angle. A pistol-grip poultry-deboning knife designed by Ian Chong replaced a conventional boning knife; its implementation at one firm resulted in greatly reduced cumulative trauma disorders ($500,000 saved in Worker Compensation costs over 5 years) and a 2%–6% increase in line speed (Hendrick, 1997).

Tools also can have a bend to reduce wrist or elbow abduction. Figure 16.21 shows how a scissors was redesigned for hairdressers to reduce deviation of the wrist, elbow, and shoulder. Figure 16.16 shows a pliers, Figure 16.22 a hammer, and Figure 16.23 a soldering iron.

When the tool "line of action" is perpendicular to the chest, consider having a tool with handles for each hand so both hands, not just one, can control the tool. Wrist, elbow, and shoulder posture should be improved.

7.2 Clearance Sufficient clearance minimizes burns and pinch points.

7.2.1 *Burns* Increase the distance of the hand from the hot surface to reduce accidental contact and to reduce the effect of radiated heat. See Figure 16.24. A shield permits the actual distance to remain close while increasing protection. However, if the grip is designed so the hand is trapped in the grip, contact time may be increased. Wet clothing from the spill of

F I G U R E   **16.22**

Hammer handles with a small bend (5°–10°) are preferred over a handle with no bend. Schoenmarklin and Marras (1989a, 1989b) reported hammers with a 20°–40° bend could be beneficial.

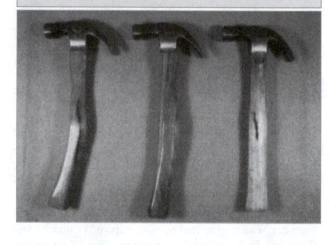

F I G U R E   **16.21**

Bending the scissors grip makes the fingers parallel to the blades instead of perpendicular. (Photo courtesy of M. Rys.)

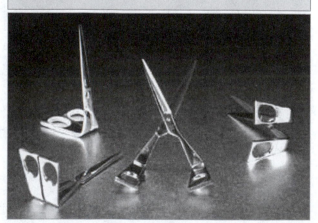

F I G U R E   **16.23**

Bend the tool, not the wrist is illustrated with this soldering iron. Note the wrist support to reduce tremor. Also note how the shield permits the operator to hold the iron closer to the tip (since heat and splashes are not a problem), thus giving improved accuracy.

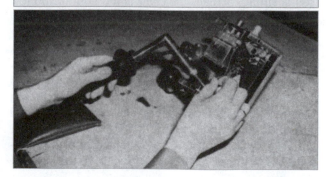

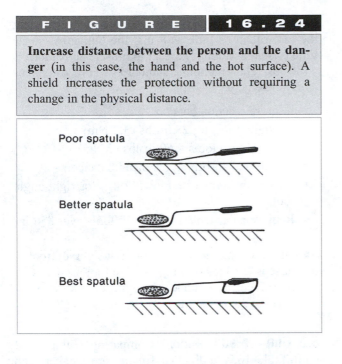

Increase distance between the person and the danger (in this case, the hand and the hot surface). A shield increases the protection without requiring a change in the physical distance.

Poor spatula

Better spatula

Best spatula

a hot liquid presents a hazard because it clings to the skin and therefore increases contact time.

Heat gain also can be reduced by handle shape. For example, a narrow neck between a handle and the remainder of the tool reduces conductive heat transfer. Consider this when you buy heat-generating tools such as soldering irons. It also applies to coffee cups!

7.2.2 *Pinches* Repetitive-use tools are the real problem in pinches. That is, 1 pinch/100 uses is tolerable in a tool used 10 times per year (say in the home). But if the tool is used 100 times/h, that is 8 pinches/day. Greenburg and Chaffin (1977, p. 124) recommended that double-handle tools (especially those with locking handles and toggle clamps) have an opening of at least 25 mm in their fully closed position.

Pliers present a specific problem as the operator may insert the first finger into the pinch point in order to open the pliers. For solutions, see Sections 8.1 and 8.2.

8 USE THE APPROPRIATE MUSCLE GROUP

8.1 Muscle Direction Muscles generally are paired. One moves the hand out, and one moves the hand in; one rotates it clockwise, and the other rotates it counterclockwise. Generally the strengths and ranges of motion are not the same in both directions. For example, the muscles that close the hand are much stronger than those that open the hand. Thus, when using pliers, grass clippers, or scissors, closing the hand is not a problem, but opening it is relatively tiring. A good idea is to use some type of spring to

open these tools so the tool is **normally open.** Table 16.8 gives the recommended maximum torques for power versus pinch grips as well as for various directions. Flexion is stronger than extension; using 15 repetitions/min and the population mean, for a power grip, 1.30/1.03 = 126%; for a pinch grip, 0.95/0.74 = 128%. Power grips are stronger than pinch grips; 1.30/.95 = 137% and 1.03/0.74 = 139%.

Giving the muscle something to push against helps. For example, loops on the outside of scissors handles allow the muscles to push against something when opening the scissors. However, the tops and sides of fingers are thin (not padded), and so are injured by repetitive pressure. On conventional pliers without a spring, the fingers have to shift position to open them.

8.2 Muscle Size Normally, bigger is better, but the moment arm also has to be considered. For example, operators often try to open pliers by putting the first finger into the pinch point. Not only does this lead to pinches but there is a very short lever arm. If a

Maximum acceptable torques (Nm) for various percentages of the female population (adapted from Ciriello et al., 2001).

		REPETITION RATE		
Grip	Population	15/min	20/min	25/min
Power Grip	75	0.61	0.62	0.57
Flexion	50	1.30	1.10	1.13
	25	1.99	1.58	1.69
	75	0.59	0.50	0.41
Extension	50	1.03	0.84	0.72
	25	1.47	1.18	1.03
	75	0.59	0.53	0.47
Ulnar deviation	50	1.14	1.03	0.94
	25	1.69	1.53	1.41
	75	2.40	2.07	1.32
Handgrip*	50	4.63	4.15	3.42
	25	6.86	6.23	5.52
Pinch Grip	75	0.47	0.51	0.41
Flexion	50	0.95	0.96	0.83
	25	1.43	1.41	1.25
	75	0.38	0.37	0.38
Extension	50	0.74	0.67	0.68
	25	1.10	0.97	0.98

*Similar to a pliers' task.

spring is not used to open the tool, use the little finger (although it is weak) to open the pliers since it is at the end of a relatively long moment arm of the tool.

A cylindrical power tool (such as the one shown in Figure 16.25) usually is held in a power grip. Movement of the tool in the hand is prevented by squeezing the fingers. Replace the load on the small muscles of the fingers by using a bearing surface under the little finger. See Figure 16.25. In addition, cover the cold hard metal with rubber or plastic (Johnson, 1988). A push-to-start power screwdriver reduces stress on the trigger finger since the force occurs on the forearm muscles. Another advantage of push-to-start (versus a finger-operated trigger) is that the fingers do not have to be as precisely located on the tool—especially useful if the tool is used intermittently.

A conventional screwdriver is rotated by finger motions. In a human-powered mechanical screwdriver, the bit is rotated by a linear motion of the forearm—a better way.

Figure 16.26 shows a reaction bar absorbing the torque when a screw or nut finishes its torquing. The duration of torque exposure depends on how the tool

is shut off. On shut-off tools, a mechanism can shut the tool off in as little as 8 ms; the human response time (visual or auditory signal to muscle activation) is >150 ms. The ergonomic standard at Ford (Stephens and VanBergeijk, 1998) is:

- Require reaction bars on
  - straight tools > 28 in-lbs (3.2 Nm)
  - pistol grip tools > 60 in-lbs (7 Nm)
- Use torque-absorbing overhead balancers
- Maximum force of 60 lbs (27 kg) for right-angle tools
- Require an articulating arm for tools over 850 in-lbs (100 Nm)
- Use articulating arms only if weight of tool + hose is > 10 lbs (4.5 kg) and the tool used is < 25 in. (63 cm) (i.e., knuckle height) or > 45 in. (114 cm) (i.e., shoulder height).

8.3 One versus Many Comparing Table 16.2 with Table 16.9, individual fingers are weaker than the fingers in combination. Very roughly, the strength of an individual finger is 10% of the strength of the hand as a unit. If only one finger is to be used, the thumb is the strongest. The little finger has about 50% of the thumb's strength.

FIGURE 16.25

Use the large muscles of the forearm (instead of the little muscles of the fingers) to resist the tool thrust force by having a bearing surface under the little finger. The specific design shown also allows the forearm to absorb the tool torque. Simple circular bearing surface accessories are available as add-ons for most tool diameters.

Designed for reduction of fatigue in drilling or screwdriving applications. Flange is easily attached to the lower diameter of the tool. It makes the tool easier to handle while reducing muscle tension in the operator's arm. Since the heel of the hand exerts downward pressure, the fingers need not be tightly clenched.

Flanges are furnished in three different mounting diameters to fit 0000, 000, and 0-Series straight tool. Order 41364 with proper dash number.

Flange Assembly	Used On
41364.1	0000 Series Straight Tools
41364.2	000 Series Straight Tools
41364.3	0 Series Straight Tools

FIGURE 16.26

Reaction bars use large muscles of the forearm instead of the small muscles of the fingers gripped around a tool shaft to absorb torque. Another version of this concept is a torque tube.

T A B L E	16.9						
Normal hand strength in newtons (An et al., 1986) (1 *N* = .22 lb or .1 kg). See also Table 16.2.							

					RADIAL DEVIATION		ULNAR DEVIATION	
	Grasp	Tip Pinch	Pulp Pinch	Key Pinch	Thumb	Index	Thumb	Index
Male	400	65	61	109	43	43	75	42
Female	228	45	43	76	25	31	43	28

For gripping spheres or cylinder ends from above, Kinoshita et al. (1996) reported that, although the contribution of individual fingers varied with object weight and diameter, the thumb contribution was always over 38%. The ring and little fingers were 18%–23%, and the index finger was <11%. They concluded that (1) the ring and little fingers make large contributions so the more fingers used, the better, and (2) the optimum cylinder diameter was 7.5 cm (3 inches) (5 cm was too small and 10 cm was too large).

For finger pull strengths, Imrhan and Sundararajan (1992) reported a **pulp pinch** grip (index finger opposes thumb) had a relative strength of 100%, a **chuck pinch** grip (index and middle oppose thumb) had a relative strength of 150%, and a **lateral pinch** grip (side of index finger buttressed by other 3 fingers opposes thumb) had a relative strength of 240%. Klein and Fernandez (1997) found that the maximum acceptable frequency for lateral pinches was exponentially affected by angle, force, and duration; the limits are 2/3 of maximum wrist flexion, 50% of maximum voluntary contraction, and 7 s duration.

For a five-finger static pinch (e.g., squeezing a pliers handle), the mean contributions of the index, middle, ring, and small fingers were 33%, 33%, 17%, and 15%, respectively. For a five-finger static lifting task, the mean contributions of the index, middle, ring, and small fingers were 35%, 26%, 20%, and 19%, respectively. For both situations, the percentages changed as force levels changed (Radwin et al., 1992).

Moving part of the tool independently while the tool is kept steady in the hand is called **triggering**. Triggers often are actuated by a single finger. Trigger strips usually are preferred to trigger buttons. See Figure 16.27. If a single finger must be used, the thumb is preferable (for repetitive motions) over the first finger. If the thumb opposes the other fingers (as with tweezers), move the thumb so it is aligned with the middle finger; then the ring and little finger can support the middle finger.

When it is important to avoid accidental activation (and tool steadiness is not important and the trigger is not used frequently), consider a thumb slide.

F I G U R E	16.27

Trigger strips are better than trigger buttons because multiple fingers are stronger than one; multiple fingers reduce muscle fatigue and permit more force to be exerted. A minimum length strip would be about 5 cm.

Note that a tool can be actuated (triggered) without a trigger! For example, the tool can be actuated by a timer, by a "push to start" (moving the entire tool with the forearm), by a foot control, or even by movement of the product (e.g., mount the tool in a fixed position and move the hand-held product to the tool, which is actuated by a photocell; an example is a checkout scanner in a supermarket). Vacuum triggers can be used. The hollowed-out tool is put under vacuum. There is a hole on the side of the tool, and when the finger is placed over the hole, the vacuum is sealed and the tool starts. Finger force is minimal.

8.4 Rotate Inward With the hand in the neutral (handshake) position (thumb at "11 o'clock"), the right hand and arm can rotate about 70° clockwise about the forearm axis (pronation) and about 150° counterclockwise (supination). Table 16.10 gives the time needed to rotate the hand about the forearm; no distinction is made for direction.

8.5 Muscle Time Reduce the amount of time the muscle is used. For example, there are clamping tools

TABLE	16.10

Time for the hand to rotate about the forearm.

ANGLE ROTATED, DEGREES	METHODS TIME MEASUREMENT, MIN
45	.0021
90	.0032
135	.0044
180	.0056

such as locking pliers—once clamped, the muscle no longer needs to exert force. Trigger actuation can be separated from continuous trigger holding. There are locking triggers on power tools. For example, a sander may have a trigger, but it also has a button to keep the sander on without the need to hold the trigger. Triggers, once actuated, also can remain actuated with a timing circuit. On–off also can be controlled with discrete controls such as rocker switches and thumb slides.

Another possibility is to support a grasp with a strap across the back of the hand—a common example is the strap used with small camcorders. When a tool or part has to be inserted into a precise location, reduce the positioning time by using guides or funnels to the location.

Review Questions

1. How do the three elements of jobs affect the decision to use a general-purpose or special-purpose tool?
2. Calculate the cost/use for a specific handtool. Show calculations and assumptions.
3. The preferred hand is the right hand for approximately what percent of the population?
4. What percent performance would you expect for the nonpreferred hand (using the preferred as 100%) for bench assembly work without tools? What percent for use of a manual screwdriver?
5. What are the two reasons a tool should be usable with either hand?
6. Give an example of a tool using: (1) power grip with force parallel to the forearm, (2) power grip with perpendicular angle to the forearm, (3) torque about the forearm, (4) an oblique grip, (5) a hook grip, (6) an internal precision grip, and (7) an external precision grip.

7. What is the advantage of putting a balancer on an articulating arm?
8. Discuss three characteristics of an "ergonomic" pen.
9. Give three ways to actuate a tool (in addition to a trigger).
10. What is a pommel?
11. Give two reasons why wood is a good material for a handle.
12. Why does a bent wrist cause problems?
13. Are the hand-opening or hand-closing muscles stronger? Why?
14. From the neutral position, can the hand rotate more in pronation or supination?
15. What is the difference between a glove and a mitten? When should a mitten be used in place of a glove?

References

ACGIH. *2001 TLVs and BEIs threshold limit values for chemical substances and physical agents and biological exposure indices.* Cincinnati, OH: American Conference of Governmental Industrial Hygienists, 122–29, 2001.

An, K., Askew, L., and Chao, E. Biomechanics and functional assessment of upper extremities. In *Trends in Ergonomics/Human Factors III,* Karwowski, W. (ed.). Amsterdam: Elsevier, 1986.

Andersson, E. R. Design and testing of a vibration attenuating handle. *Int. J. of Ind. Ergonomics,* Vol. 6, 119–25, 1990.

Armstrong, T. and Martin, B. Adverse effects of repetitive loading and segmental vibration. Chapter 12 in *Musculoskeletal Disorders in the Workplace.* St. Louis: Mosby, 1997.

Ayoub, M. and Lo-Presti, P. The determination of an optimum size cylindrical handle by use of electromyography. *Ergonomics,* Vol. 14, No. 4, 509–18, 1971.

Bradley, J. Effect of gloves on control operation time. *Human Factors,* Vol. 11, No. 1, 13–20, 1969.

Ciriello, V., Snook, S., Webster, B., and Dempsey, P. Psychophysical study of six hand movements. *Ergonomics,* Vol. 44, 10, 922–36, 2001.

Cochran, D., Albin, T., Bishu, R., and Riley, M. An analysis of grasp force degradation with commercially available gloves. *Proceedings of the Human Factors Society,* 852–55, 1986.

Cochran, D., Bishu, R., and Riley, M. The effects of gloves on holding time. *Proceedings of the Human Factors Society,* 894–97, 1987.

Corlett, E. and Clark, T. *The Ergonomics of Workspaces and Machines.* London: Taylor and Francis, 1995.

Davis, R. and Konz, S. Effects of muscular exertion on hand steadiness. In *Advances in Ind. Ergonomics and Safety VII,* Bittner, A. and Champney, P. (eds.). London: Taylor and Francis, 1995.

Degani, A., Asfour, S., Waly, S., and Koshy, J. A study of two shovel designs. *Applied Ergonomics,* Vol. 24, No. 5, 306–12, 1993.

Dickson, A., Petrie, A., Nicolle, F., and Calnan, J. A device for measuring the force of the digits of the hand. *Biomedical Engineering,* 270–73, July 1972.

Eastman Kodak. *Ergonomic Design for People at Work,* Vol. 1. New York: Van Nostrand Reinhold, 1983.

Echard, M., Smolenski, S., and Zamiska, M. Ergonomic considerations: Engineering controls at Volkswagen of America. In *Ergonomic Interventions to Prevent Musculoskeletal Injuries in Industry.* Chelsea, MI: Lewis Publishers, 117–31, 1987.

Feeney, R., Bobjer, O., and Jansson, C. Selecting handtools—Guidelines for the prevention of upper limb disorders. In *Advances in Occupational Ergonomics and Safety II,* B. Das and W. Karwowski (eds.). Louisville, KY: IOS Press and Ohmsha, 211–14, 1997.

Fransson, C. and Winkel, J. Hand strength: The influence of grip span and grip type. *Ergonomics,* Vol. 34, No. 7, 881–92, 1991.

Fransson-Hall, C. and Kilbom, A. Sensitivity of the hand to surface pressure. *Applied Ergonomics,* Vol. 24, 181–89, 1993.

Freivalds, A. Tool evaluation and design. Chapter 13 in *Occupational Ergonomics: Theory and Applications,* A. Bhattacharya and J. McGlothlin (eds.). New York: Dekker, 1996.

Freivalds, A. and Kim, Y. Blade size and weight effects in shovel design. *Applied Ergonomics,* Vol. 21, No. 1, 39–42, 1990.

Gainer, G. and Konz, S. An evaluation of six screwdriver handles. *Proceedings of IX Int. Conf. on Production Research.* Amsterdam: Elsevier, 1987.

Garrett, J. The adult human hand: Some anthropometric and biomechanical considerations. *Human Factors,* Vol. 13, No. 2, 117–31, 1971.

Goel, V. and Rim, K. Role of gloves in reducing vibrations: An analysis for pneumatic chipping hammer. *American Industrial Hygiene Association J.,* Vol. 48, No. 1, 9–14, 1987.

Grant, K., Habes, D., and Steward, L. An analysis of handle designs for reducing manual effort: The influence of grip diameter. *Int. J. of Industrial Ergonomics,* Vol. 10, 199–206, 1992.

Greenburg, L. and Chaffin, D. *Workers and Their Tools.* Midland, MI: Pendall Publishing, 1977.

Hall, C. External pressure at the hand during object handling and work with tools. *Int. J. of Industrial Ergonomics,* Vol. 20, 191–206, 1997.

Helander, M. *A Guide to the Ergonomics of Manufacturing.* London: Taylor and Francis, 1995.

Hendrick, H. Good ergonomics is good economics. *Proceedings of the Human Factors and Ergonomic Society.* Santa Monica, CA: HFES, 1–10, 1996.

Hendrick, H. The economics of ergonomics. In *Advances in Occupational Ergonomics and Safety II,* B. Das and W. Karwowski (eds.). Cincinnati: IOS Press and Ohmsha, 3–8, 1997.

Hertzberg, H. Engineering anthropometry, Chapter 11 in *Human Engineering Guide to Equipment Design,* H. Van Cott and R. Kincaid (eds.). Supt. of Documents, 1973.

Hoffman, E. Movement time of right- and left-handers using their preferred and non-preferred hands. *Int. J. of Industrial Ergonomics,* Vol. 19, 49–57, 1997.

Hudgens, G., Fatkin, L., Billingsley, P., and Muzurczak. Hand steadiness: Effects of sex, menstrual phase, oral contraceptives, practice, and handgun weight. *Human Factors,* Vol. 30, No. 1, 51–60, 1988.

Imrhan, S. and Sundararajan, K. An investigation of finger pull strengths. *Ergonomics,* Vol. 35, No. 3, 289–99, 1992.

International Organization for Standardization (ISO). *Method for the Measurement and Evaluation of the Vibration Transmissibility of Gloves at the Palm of the Hand (ISO 10819-1996).* Geneva, Switzerland: ISO, 1996.

Johnson, S. Evaluation of powered screwdriver design characteristics. *Human Factors,* Vol. 30, No. 1, 61–69, 1988.

Kao, H. Human factors design of writing instruments for children: The effect of pen size variations. *Proceedings of 19th Annual Meeting of the Human Factors Society,* 1974.

Kaster, E., Katagihara, A., and Konz, S. Performance of preferred versus non-preferred hand and arm. *Proceedings of IX Int. Conf. on Production Research.* Cincinnati, OH, 431–36, 1987.

Kellor, M., Kondrasuk, R., Iverson, I., Frost, J., Silberberg, N., and Hoglund, M. *Hand Strengths and Dexterity Tests,* Manual 721. Minneapolis: Sister Kenny Institute, 1971.

Kihlberg, S. Biodynamic response of the hand-arm system to vibration from an impact hammer and a grinder. *Int. J. of Industrial Ergonomics,* 16, 1–8, 1995.

Kinoshita, H., Murase, T., and Bandou, T. Grip posture and forces during holding cylindrical objects with circular grips. *Ergonomics,* Vol. 39, No. 9, 1163–76, 1996.

Klein, M. and Fernandez, J. The effects of posture, duration and force on pinching frequency. *Int. J. of Ind. Ergonomics,* Vol. 20, 267–75, 1997.

Konz, S., Aye, D., and Fu, Y. Sharpness of lid edges. *Proc. of Human Factors and Ergonomics Society,* 390–93, 1996.

Konz, S. and Oetemo, I. Comfort of various size and shape pens. *Proceedings of South East Asian Ergonomics Society Conference,* Denpasar, Bali, 1988.

Konz, S. and Warraich, M. Performance differences between the preferred and non-preferred hand when using various tools. *Ergonomics International* 451–53. (Proc. of 8th Int. Congress of IEA, Southampton). London: Taylor and Francis, 1985.

Kumar, S. and Cheng, C. Spinal stresses in simulated raking with various rake handles. *Ergonomics,* Vol. 33, No. 1, 1–11, 1990.

Lindqvist, B. *Ergonomic Tools in Our Time.* Stockholm: Atlas Copco, 1986.

Magill, R. and Konz, S. An evaluation of seven industrial screwdrivers. In *Trends in Ergonomics/Human Factors III,* Karwowski, W. (ed.). Amsterdam: Elsevier, 1986.

McMullin, D. and Hallbeck, M. Maximal power grasp force as a function of wrist position, age and glove type. *Proceedings of the Human Factors Society,* 733–37, 1991.

Miller, M., Ransohoff, J., and Tichauer, E. Ergonomic evaluation of a redesigned surgical instrument. *Applied Ergonomics,* Vol. 2, No. 4, 194–97, 1971.

Mital, A. and Kilbom, A. Design, selection, and use of hand tools to alleviate trauma of the upper extremities: Part I—Guidelines for the practitioner. *Int. J. of Industrial Ergonomics,* Vol. 10, 1–2, 7–21, 1992a.

Mital, A. and Kilbom, A. Design, selection and use of hand tools to alleviate trauma of the upper extremities: Part I—Guidelines for the practitioner and Part II—The scientific basis (knowledge base) for the guide. *Int. J. of Industrial Ergonomics,* Vol. 10, 1–5 and 7–21, 1992b.

Mital, A., Kuo, T., and Faard, H. A quantitative evaluation of gloves used with non-powered hand tools in routine maintenance tasks. *Ergonomics,* Vol. 37, No. 2, 333–43, 1994.

Muralidhar, A. and Bishu, R. Safety performance of gloves using the pressure tolerance of the hand. *Ergonomics,* Vol. 43, 5, 561–72, 2000.

Nag, P. and Pradham, C. Ergonomics in the hoeing operation. *Int. J. of Ind. Ergonomics,* Vol. 10, 341–50, 1992.

Oxenburgh, M. *Increasing Productivity and Profit Through Health and Safety.* Chicago: CCH International, 1991.

Patkin, M. Ergonomic design of a needleholder. *Medical J. of Australia,* Vol. 2, 490–93, September 6, 1969.

Pheasant, S. *Bodyspace,* 2nd ed. London: Taylor and Francis, 1996.

Plumber, R., Stobbe, T., Ronk, R., Myers, W., Kim, H., and Jaraiedi, M. Manual dexterity evaluation of gloves used in handling hazardous materials. *Proceedings of the Human Factors Society,* 819–23, 1985.

Putz-Anderson, V. *Cumulative Trauma Disorder—A Manual for Musculo-Skeletal Disease of the Upper Limbs.* London: Taylor and Francis, 1988.

Radwin, R., Oh, S., Jensen, T., and Webster, J. External finger forces in submaximal five-finger static pinch prehension. *Ergonomics,* Vol. 35, No. 3, 275–88, 1992.

Radwin, R., VanBergeijk, E., and Armstrong, T. Muscle response to pneumatic hand tool torque reaction forces. *Ergonomics,* Vol. 32, No. 6, 655–73, 1989.

Rigby, L. Why do people drop things? *Quality Progress,* 16–19, September 1973.

Rodgers, S. (ed.). *Ergonomic Design for People at Work,* Vol. 2. New York: Van Nostrand, 1986.

Schoenmarklin, R. and Marras, W. Effects of handle angle and work orientation: I. Wrist motion and hammering performance. *Human Factors,* Vol. 31, No. 4, 397–411, 1989a.

Schoenmarklin, R. and Marras, W. Effects of handle angle and work orientation: II. Muscle fatigue and subjective ratings of body discomfort. *Human Factors,* Vol. 31, No. 4, 413–20, 1989b.

Shih, R., Vasarhelyi, P. Dubrowski, A., and Carnahan, H. The effects of latex gloves on the kinetics of grasping. *Int. J. of Ind. Ergonomics,* Vol. 28, 265–73, 2001.

Shih, Y-C, and Wang, M-J. Psychophysical evaluation of diameter and angle of container handles. *Int. J. of Industrial Ergonomics,* Vol. 19, 437–44, 1997.

Shock, N. The physiology of aging. *Scientific American,* Vol. 206, 100–10, January 1962.

Siekman, H. Recommended maximum temperatures for touchable surfaces. *Applied Ergonomics,* Vol. 21, No. 1, 69–73, 1990.

Stephens, A. and VanBergeijk, E. Ergonomic issues and guidelines for the selection of hand-held power tools. In *Advances in Occupational Ergonomics and Safety,* S. Kumar (ed.). Amsterdam: IOS Press, 424–27, 1998.

Swanson, A., Matev, I., and Groot, G. The strength of the hand. *Bulletin of Prosthetics Research,* 145–63, Fall 1970.

Terrell, R. and Purswell, J. The influence of forearm and wrist orientation on static grip strength as a design criterion for hand tools. *Proc. Human Factors Society,* Santa Monica, CA, 28–32, 1976.

Teschke, K., Brubaker, R., and Morrison, B. Using noise exposure histories to quantify duration of vibration exposure in tree fallers. *Am. Ind. Hygiene Association J.,* Vol. 51, No. 9, 485–93, 1990.

Tewari, V., Datta, R., and Murthy, A. Evaluation of three manually operated weeding devices. *Applied Ergonomics,* Vol. 22, No. 2, 111–16, 1991.

Toppila, E., Starck, J., and Pyykko, I. Transmission of vibration from handle to hand; effect of biodynamic factors. In *Advances in Occupational Ergonomics,* B. Das and W. Karwowski (eds.). Louisville, KY: IOS Press and Ohmsha, 507–10, 1997.

Tsaousidis, N. and Freivalds, A. Effects of gloves on maximum force and the rate of force development in pinch, wrist flexion and grip. *Int. J. of Industrial Ergonomics,* Vol. 21, 353–60, 1988.

Udo, H., Bheema, R., and Konz, S. Pen grip versus grip electromyograms and pen point pressure. *J. of Science of Labour,* Vol. 71, 1–9, 1995.

Udo, H., Otani, T., Udo, A., and Yoshinaga, F. An electromyographic study of two different types of ballpoint pens. *Industrial Health,* Vol. 38, 47–56, 2000.

Ulin, S., Armstrong, T., Snook, S., and Franzblau, A. Effect of tool shape and work location on perceived exertion for work on horizontal surfaces. *Am. Ind. Hygiene Association J.,* Vol. 7, 383–91, 1993.

van der Grinten, M. Shovel design and back load in digging trenches. In *Musculoskeletal Disorders at Work,* Buckle, P. (ed.). London: Taylor and Francis, 1987.

Wilder, D., Wasserman, D., and Wasserman, J. Occupational vibration exposure. In *Physical and Biological Hazards of the Workplace,* 2nd ed., Wald, P. and Stave, G. (eds.). New York: Wiley, 79–104, 2002.

CONTROLS

1 Select the Proper Type of Control

2 Select the Proper Control Characteristics

3 Prevent Unintended Activation

4 Prevent Incorrect Identification

5 Make Accomplishments Equal Intentions

6 Properly Locate and Arrange the Controls

Overview

This chapter presents six control guidelines. Detailed information and examples accompany each guideline.

Key Concepts

color stereotypes

control/response ratio

discrete/continuous

exclusion percent

human–machine system

interlocks

lockout/tagout

manipulative controls

open/closed loop

population stereotypes

reaction time

shape coding

unintended activation

zero mechanical state

311

SELECT THE PROPER TYPE OF CONTROL

1.1 Control Systems Figure 17.1 shows a **human–machine system.** People impose their will on the machine through controls; the machine communicates to the people through displays. The entire system exists in a physical environment with temperature, noise, illumination, chemicals, and so forth. Example controls are levers, wheels, pedals, cranks, switches, buttons, and knobs. Surrounding the physical environment is a social and organizational environment. A control is a tool attached to a machine, so Chapter 16 can provide additional comments.

Figure 17.1 shows the human as an operator of the machine. Using an automobile example, the human uses a manual transmission to shift the gears of the machine. But it is also possible for the human to function as a supervisor of the machine, giving only general orders and having the machine use a servomechanism to carry out the details. Automobile examples are cruise control and automatic transmission. Camera examples are automatic light adjustments, focusing, and film advancing. With microprocessors, considerable ability to carry out orders can be built into the machine.

Systems can be divided into two general types: open loop and closed loop. In an **open-loop** system, there is a desired input or setting of the device but there is no feedback of what the device is doing to affect the desired input. In a **closed-loop** system, feedback affects the desired input. Consider turning a valve to let water flow. In an open-loop system, the valve is turned and it is assumed that the water flows. In a closed-loop system, the flow of the water is "fed back" to influence the valve opening. For example, if no water flows, an alarm may sound and an operator fixes the system. If the flow is too small or too large, the feedback element adjusts the input (valve position). Another control example is a traffic light. A light controlled by a timer is open-loop. A light controlled by magnetic sensors in the pavement that detect the presence of a vehicle is closed-loop. In many systems, a human is the feedback element.

Before designing a control, get information on what specifically is to be controlled, the control task requirements (e.g., precision, force), the operator's information needs, the workplace restrictions, and consequences of accidental operation.

1.2 Types of Controls *First,* decide whether the command to the machine will be **discrete** or **continuous.** For example, discrete automobile controls are the ignition (on–off), headlight (low–high), gear shift (1st, 2nd, drive, park, reverse). Continuous automobile controls are the radio volume, steering wheel, and accelerator.

Second, decide what part of the body will implement the mental command. In most cases it is the hand–arm; occasionally it is the foot. Rare applications include voice (box shifting on conveyor lanes), eye focus point (helicopter guns), and body temperature (elevator call buttons). (Some elevator call buttons are actuated by temperature rather than pressure. Check this by pushing a button with a pencil to see if it responds.) This text focuses on hand–arm controls.

Third, decide on the mechanical interface between the human body and the machine interior. This depends both upon body biomechanics and upon the machine mechanism. In some cases, it is better to use a linear control motion and in some cases a rotary control motion is better. For example, if the human motion is to cause a gear or screw to turn, it is easier mechanically to rotate a crank or knob than to make a linear control motion. Both linear and rotary motions can be in the *X, Y,* or *Z* axis.

Table 17.1 shows example applications for discrete controls; Table 17.2 shows example applications for continuous controls.

When selecting the type of control, consider the amount of human power required. Some controls transmit human force to the machine while others just are switches. Using automotive examples, are the brakes conventional or power? Is the window moved by a crank or a motor? If the power is furnished by muscles, consider controls with mechanical advantage—that is, a lever arm. The longer the lever arm, the less muscle

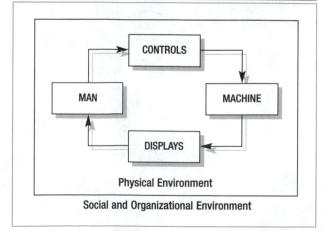

FIGURE   17.1

Human–machine system. Information flows from human to machine through controls. Information flows from machine to human through displays. Displays include instruments, labels, and accompanying printed instructions and warnings. The boundary between the human and the machine is the "user interface."

TABLE 17.1

Discrete control selection guide (Hutchinson, 1981).

CONTROL REQUIREMENT	LINEAR OR ROTARY	TYPE	EXAMPLES
■ Select two discrete settings or states: stop–start on–off insert momentary signal set state	L	Manual pushbutton	Keyboards, vending machines Elevator floor buttons Doorbell, horn (auto) Cruise control (auto)
	L	Rocker switch	Hard-copy word processor
	L	Toggle switch	Wall lights
	L	Foot-actuated button	Headlight dimmer (older auto)
	L	Slide switch	Flashlight
	L	Pull cord	Houselamps, ceiling fans
	L	Push/pull switch	Headlights-on/off (auto)
	R	Key-operated switch	Ignition (auto)
	R	Knob (volume/on combo)	Radio
■ Two settings—larger force	L	Detent lever	Landing gear (aircraft)
	L	T-handle or stirrup	Hand brake (auto)
■ Select three or more settings	L	Groups of legend switches or back-lighted pushbuttons	Car radio Keyboards, TV channels, dialing
	L	Lever	Wiper/washer (auto), temperature control, mode selection, seat position, steering wheel position
	L	Lever with detent	Throttle (aircraft), gear shift (auto)
	R	Circular dial (poor)	Rotary-dial telephone
	R	Rotary selectors	Microwave timer

TABLE 17.2

Continuous control selection guide (Hutchinson, 1981).

CONTROL REQUIREMENT	LINEAR OR ROTARY	TYPE	EXAMPLES
■ Precise adjustment small range, little force	R	Knob	Volume controls
	L	Continuous lever	Joystick (aircraft)
	R	Continuous thumbwheel	Air vent vanes (auto)
■ Rapid adjustment large range, small force	R	Spinner on multirotational knob	Music box windup
	R	Small crank	Manual windows (auto)
	R	Toggle or bat-handle	Slew command marker (USAF aircraft)
■ Gross adjustment large force, small range	R	Hand wheels	Steering wheels (auto) Valves
	L	Translatory pedal	Brake (auto) Accelerator (auto)
	L	Reciprocating pedal	Brake (auto)
	R	Rotary pedal	Bicycle
	L	Continuous lever	Lawnmower throttle
large force, large range	R	Large crank	Artillery
■ Multiple continuous positioning	L	Joystick	Attitude (aircraft)
	L	Wheel/yoke and joystick combo	Attitude (aircraft)
	L	Pantograph	Remote manipulator

force is needed. When considerable force is needed, consider two-handed controls such as wheels. For maximum force, replace the arm with the leg and use pedals.

When selecting the control type, consider errors. For example, the error rate/1,000,000 characters is about 30,000 for a keyboard, 900 for an optical character recognition wand, and .3 for a barcode and hand-held wand (Allais, 1982). Table 17.3 shows control recommendations using criteria of speed of operation, accuracy, mounting space, operation in an array, and ease of check reading.

The control also may have special features. Pushbuttons, for example, may be alternate action (push on, push off), momentary contact (doorbell), touch-sensitive (calculator keys), interlocking (when button A is depressed, button C is released), connected to a display (light when depressed), and so forth.

▌2▌ SELECT THE PROPER CONTROL CHARACTERISTICS

Once the proper type is selected, specify the control size and shape, amount of control movement, and actuation force.

2.1 Force
The amount of force (torque) that can be exerted on a control depends on people variables and control variables.

2.1.1 People variables
People variables include the muscles used, the user population, and the percentile of the population designed for.

Larger muscle groups can exert more force. The general sequence from weaker to stronger is finger, combination of fingers, arm, both arms, foot, both feet. See Table 16.1 for grip strength, Table 16.2 and Table 16.9 for finger strengths, and Table 4.2 for arm strengths. Summarizing: (1) The leg is approximately 3 times stronger than the arm; (2) direction is important, with arm forces at the nonoptimum angles being 50% to 80% of the force at the optimum angle; (3) the nonpreferred arm averages 60% to 150% of the strength of the preferred arm (depending upon the angle and the direction); (4) there seems to be no appreciable difference between the strength of the left and right legs; (5) all force recommendations assume that the fingers/hand/arm/leg have sufficient clearance to operate.

Figure 17.2 shows how pedal force varies between populations and within populations.

In general, do not design for the mean of a population, as that results in 50% of the population not being able to do the task. The percent of the population to exclude—the **exclusion percent**—is a design decision that depends upon the cost of excluding weak people and the benefits of including weak people. In addition, just because most people can exert 7 N-m of torque on a particular control is not a reason

---

TABLE 17.3

Characteristics of common controls (Eastman Kodak, 1983).

CONTROL	SUITABILITY WHERE SPEED OF OPERATION IS REQUIRED	SUITABILITY WHERE ACCURACY OF OPERATION IS REQUIRED	SPACE REQUIRED TO MOUNT CONTROL	EASE OF OPERATION IN ARRAY OF LIKE CONTROLS	EASE OF CHECK READING IN ARRAY OF LIKE CONTROLS
Toggle switch (on–off)	Good	Good	Small	Good	Good
Rocker switch	Good	Good	Small	Good	Fair[1]
Pushbutton	Good	Unsuitable	Small	Good	Poor
Legend switch	Good	Good	Small	Good	Good
Rotary selector switch (discrete steps)	Good	Good	Medium	Poor	Good
Knob	Unsuitable	Fair	Small-Medium	Poor	Good
Crank	Fair	Poor	Medium-Large	Poor	Poor[2]
Hand wheel	Poor	Good	Large	Poor	Poor
Lever	Good	Poor (Horizontal) Fair (Vertical)	Medium-Large	Good	Good
Foot pedal	Good	Poor	Large	Poor	Poor

[1]Except where control lights up for "on."

[2]Assumes control makes more than one revolution.

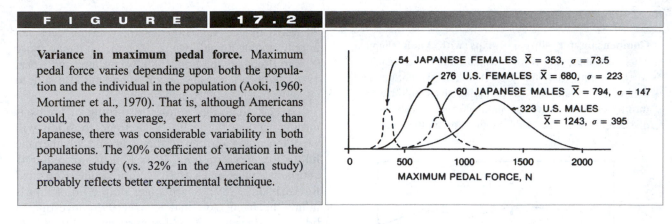

F I G U R E   1 7 . 2

Variance in maximum pedal force. Maximum pedal force varies depending upon both the population and the individual in the population (Aoki, 1960; Mortimer et al., 1970). That is, although Americans could, on the average, exert more force than Japanese, there was considerable variability in both populations. The 20% coefficient of variation in the Japanese study (vs. 32% in the American study) probably reflects better experimental technique.

54 JAPANESE FEMALES $\bar{X} = 353$, $\sigma = 73.5$
276 U.S. FEMALES $\bar{X} = 680$, $\sigma = 223$
60 JAPANESE MALES $\bar{X} = 794$, $\sigma = 147$
323 U.S. MALES $\bar{X} = 1243$, $\sigma = 395$

MAXIMUM PEDAL FORCE, N

---

to use 7 N-m in your design—less is better. Thus the percent to exclude should be quite small, perhaps 1 in 1,000 or less.

Assuming the normal distribution, to exclude 1% use 2.33σ. To exclude .1% use 3.09σ. To exclude .01% use 3.84σ.

Thus, if the population mean could exert 10 N-m torque on a knob and the standard deviation is 1 N-m, then a $10 - 3.09 (1) = 6.9$ N-m knob would exclude .1% of this population, assuming the normal distribution is valid. However, human finger–arm strength measurements tend to have a positive skew, so the normal distribution estimates lower values than the actual values. The above exclusion estimates, therefore, tend to predict more exclusions than would really occur.

Consider that someone from a weaker population may use the control and that many controls are used repetitively. In addition, the control may not be in a good position but may be at knee height, around a corner of a panel, or behind some apparatus; it may be covered with grease; the operator may wear slippery or bulky gloves, and so on. Therefore, strive to reduce the force required to actuate the control.

2.1.2 *Control variables*

The force required to actuate the control depends upon the control's purpose and design. Assume, for example, that the designer has a leadscrew to be rotated and decides to use a knob. First, information is needed on how much torque is needed to rotate the leadscrew. If it is large, consider redesigning the mechanical system or using power assist. Consider a muscle-powered system only if the force is well within human capability.

2.2 Keys and Pushbuttons

A special type of pushbutton (a key) is used for data entry. Keys generally should not be round. A concave top helps center the finger; a "pimple" on a frequently used key allows a user to locate a key by touch. Because of the repetitive action and multiple fingers, displacement should be consistent between keys. Key interlocks prevent simultaneous activation of two keys by preventing triggering until 75% of displacement has occurred. They improve speed and decrease errors. (Reportedly when Samuel Soule in 1867 devised the QWERTY key layout [named after the top left row of letters on the keyboard] that is used today, his intent was to make it awkward so a fast typist couldn't jam the levers and gears!) Feed back (tactile, auditory, or visual) the key activation to the operator.

Numerical keys can be calculator format (1-2-3 on the bottom row), phone format (1-2-3 on the top), or keyboard format (1–10 in a single row). If space is limited, reduce the number of keys by having a key do multiple functions, with the function selected with a shift key; examples are calculator and computer keyboards. Membrane keypads require tactile and/or kinesthetic feedback. Rectangular or square buttons are easier to label than round ones. Different-shaped buttons can indicate different functions. On hand-tools, triggers (i.e., multifinger operation) are better than buttons. Avoid large pushbuttons (palm buttons) in repetitive operations because the constant blow on the palm of the hand from the hard surface may cause trauma. See Section 2.2 in Chapter 14.

2.3 Knobs

With circular knobs, you depend upon hand friction along the circumference; with the other shapes, you have a bearing surface. Figure 17.3 shows how knob shape can compensate for a slippery grip. Figure 17.4 shows that even circular knobs can have a bearing surface. For a 35 mm (1.4 inch) dia or length, maximum torque should be 7 N-m (Eastman Kodak, 1983). An oval doorknob (vs. a round doorknob) is a good compromise of a bearing surface and esthetics. With both types, eliminate sharp edges and small radii, which can exert high pressure on the hand.

For the circular design, if the rotation axis is parallel to the base of the fingers (i.e., forearm rotation), increasing diameter increases the torque up to a diameter equal to the hand grip span (fingers and palm just touch). This is about 50 mm (Replogle, 1983). If the axis is perpendicular to the palm/forearm, torque increases with

Compensate for slippery grips with knob shape. Minimize the number of sides of knobs—especially when gripping friction is poor (Kohl, 1983). For torque applications, clamping screws and knobs should have a turning circle diameter of about 90 mm; a rubber- or plastic-coated surface reduces abrasion on the fingers.

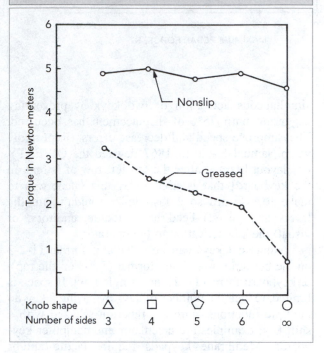

Poor (top) and better (bottom) knobs.

diameter up to about 50% of hand length, which is about 90 mm (Imrahan and Loo, 1986); knurling does not improve torque capability up to 90 mm, but it may above 90 mm (Imrahan and Loo, 1986; Nagashima and Konz, 1986). With a lever, any length is possible. Be sure to allow sufficient hand–arm clearance.

A task somewhat similar to turning of knobs is turning jar and bottle lids. The finger position will vary depending on the lid diameter and whether the lid also requires pushing. If pushing is not required, knurls permit as much as 70% more torque (Konz and Ravishankar, 1989). Sharp edges on the lid or knurls injure the hand. Aye and Konz (1995) investigated lids with edges having radii of curvatures of 0, .8, 1.6, 2.4, and 3.2 mm for lids with diameters of 32, 70, and 82 mm. For the 32 mm lid, all radii caused discomfort. For the larger lids, a curvature over 2 mm gave relatively little discomfort. If lids are opened often, use a V-shaped gripper (to fit all sizes). The gripper can be hand-held or permanently mounted.

2.4 Cranks For one-hand controls, Table 17.4 and Figure 17.5 give design recommendations for cranks. (Also see Table 29.3.) Since the grip normally does not move within the hand, a high coefficient of friction is good; however, the grip should rotate on the crank to allow good hand–wrist orientation throughout the rotation. Another grip option is a 50-mm diameter sphere, because a sphere does not limit hand position as much as a cylinder. When power output is measured, there is less than a 5% advantage for a vertical axis of turning (vs. horizontal) and clockwise rotation (vs. counterclockwise); there is approximately a 20% advantage for a 100-mm radius over a 300-mm radius (Raouf, Imanishi, and Morooka, 1986).

2.5 Hand Wheels Two common applications are for valves in process industries and for vehicle control.

2.5.1 Valve control An advantage of hand wheels is that two hands can be used, permitting greater torque. Two forces are involved: (1) the cracking force to unlock the valve (ending when the wheel begins to move) and (2) turning force. The cracking force tends to be higher than the turning force, but the turning force may be required for multiple minutes (Amell and Kumar, 2001). Be sure the valve stem is properly lubricated.

The amount of torque is:

$$\text{Torque (N-m)} = (\text{Tangential force, N})(\text{Radius, m})$$

Reduce the tangential force required by the operator by increasing the radius. The operator's force also depends upon the operator's posture relative to the hand wheel, which in turn depends on the hand wheel's ori-

T A B L E		1 7 . 4
Crank design recommendations for Figure 17.5 (*Human Engineering Design Data Digest,* 1984).		

VARIABLE	MINIMUM	PREFERRED	MAXIMUM
Light Loads (Wrist and finger movements; less than 22 N)			
Handle length (L), mm	25	38	75
Handle diam. (D), mm	10	13	16
Turning radius (R), mm			
Rate below 100 rpm	38	75	125
Rate over 100 rpm	13	65	115
Heavy Loads (Arm movement; over 22 N)			
Handle length (L), mm	75	95	
Handle diam. (D), mm	25	25	38
Turning radius (R), mm			
Rate below 100 rpm	190		510
Rate over 100 rpm	125		230

T A B L E		1 7 . 5
Design values for vertical hand wheels (adapted from Amell and Kumar, 2001).		

WHEEL DIAMETER, CM		
96–122 CM ABOVE FLOOR	<96 OR >122 CM ABOVE FLOOR	OPERATOR TORQUE, N-M
15.2	25.4	2.2–4.4
25.4	40.6	4.4–6.6
25.4	40.6	6.6–9.9
40.6	40.6	>9.9

F I G U R E		1 7 . 5
Crank dimensions for Table 17.4.		

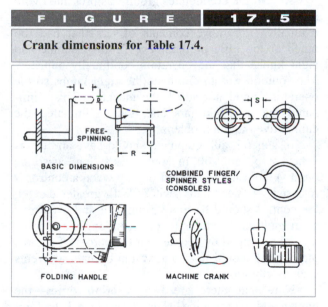

entation (vertical or horizontal) and location versus the body (between hip and shoulder versus below hip or above shoulder). Table 17.5 gives recommended heights for vertically oriented hand wheels. For a horizontally oriented hand wheel, place it 1250–1400 mm above the floor (ideally, chest height for the shortest operator and waist height for the tallest operator).

The rim diameter should be 20–50 mm. However, McMulkin and Woldstad (1995) report that the grip shape has a major influence on the force exerted. On the standard circular wheel with a 28 mm diameter grip, torque was 95 N-m (100%). A 43 mm grip diameter gave 132 N-m (139%). Mounting 65 mm spherical knobs on the rim gave 147 N-m (155%), while making the rim a zig-zag gave 191 N-m (201%). Operators often grip the spokes (even with a lower lever arm) due to the poor grip surface of the rim.

For precision with the hand wheel, the key is the dial or display being set; the better the size/legibility of the display, the better the precision.

2.5.2 *Vehicle control* Vehicle steering wheels should have a wheel diameter of 350–400 mm for power steering and 450–510 mm for nonpower steering. Grip diameter should be 20–32 mm. For power steering, the preferred orientation is 30°; for nonpower steering, preferred orientation is 45° (*Human Eng. Design Data Digest,* 1984). Many vehicles permit wheel-angle adjustment by the operator.

2.6 Foot/Leg Controls   For still greater force, use the leg. Use of the leg also frees the hand. For foot switches, see Table 17.6 and Figure 17.6; for foot pedals, see Table 17.7, Figure 17.7, and Figure 17.8.

Bullinger et al. (1991) discuss design variables of foot controls. Also see Section 5 of Chapter 13 and Section 6 of this chapter. Note that the contact surface of a pedal usually will be a shoe sole, so slipping may be a problem. In addition, pedals, being on the floor, may have dirt or other debris on them, further reducing friction.

For continuous control (such as with an auto accelerator), it is better to bend the ankle by depressing the toe rather than depressing the heel or moving the entire foot and leg. The foot of a 70-kg person weighs 1 kg versus the 4.1 kg of the leg + calf or the 11.3 kg of the entire leg. Moving just the toe permits the heel to rest on a support and reduces the amount of weight supported by muscles. The range of movement at the ankle should be between 80° and 115° (Nowak, 1972).

TABLE   17.6

Foot-operated switch design recommendations for Figure 17.6 (*Human Engineering Design Data Digest*, 1984; Eastman Kodak, 1983).

Variable	HUMAN ENGINEERING DIGEST		EASTMAN KODAK		
	Min	Max	Min	Preferred	Max
Diameter, mm	13		12	50–80	
Displacement, mm					
Normal operation	13	65			
Heavy boot	25	65			
Ankle flexion only	25	65	12		65
Total leg movement	25	100	25		180
Resistance, N					
Foot doesn't rest on control	18	90	15		75
Foot rests on control	45	90			

FIGURE   17.6

Foot switch dimensions for Table 17.6.

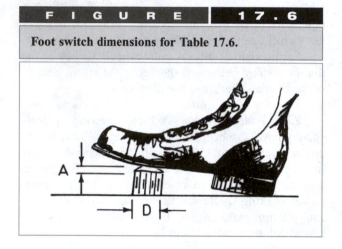

On–off controls (such as faucets and clamping fixtures) can be actuated by lateral motion of the knee, as well as by the vertical motion of the foot. The knee should move less than 75 mm to 100 mm (3–4 inches); force requirements should be light. The advantage compared to the foot is that the weight of the foot need not be lifted. Hospitals use knee switches to actuate faucets to improve germ control on the hands.

Use large-force controls only for occasional or emergency use.

3 PREVENT UNINTENDED ACTIVATION

The more severe the consequences of **unintended activation** (activating a control unintentionally), the greater should be the precautions taken. However, if a protective measure makes it difficult to use the control in normal circumstances, operators will be tempted to bypass the guard. Therefore, judgment must be used. A management policy should be established on who can adjust various process controls. That is, can operators change the settings on their own or is management approval required?

At 3M, the ergonomics group was presented with a "cumulative trauma problem" as operators had to manually fill/remove contents of jars that had too much or too little product. The filling machine had eight knobs that the operators continually adjusted. The solution was to eliminate the eight knobs so the operators could not adjust the machine. This eliminated the misfilled jars and, thus, eliminated the cumulative trauma problem.

In general, all equipment should have an "emergency stop" control. In some cases (e.g., gasoline pumps) they should turn off or stop when a control is released—a "deadman" switch. With greater danger, the control should be more prominent and even may be at multiple locations (e.g., cord along machine so it can be stopped by people near the cord). Of course, the control should not be activated by natural events such as vibration.

Note that there are two **reaction times**—the human and the machine. Thus, it may take 1.0 s for a person to decide to stop a car and depress the pedal. Then the car may take 4.5 s to stop.

Human reaction time can be further divided into sensing, making a decision, and carrying out the decision. Sensing depends upon which sense (e.g., eye, ear) is used, the strength of the signal (relative to its background), and whether the operator is paying attention to a potential signal. Making the decision depends on the complexity of the decision (number of alternatives, knowledge of consequences of decision, amount of practice). Carrying out the decision

T A B L E	1 7 . 7				

Pedal design recommendations for Figure 17.7 (*Human Engineering Design Data Digest,* 1984; Eastman Kodak, 1983). The ankle should stay in the range from the neutral position to 20° up and 30° down.

| Variable | HUMAN ENGINEERING DIGEST | | | EASTMAN KODAK | |
	Min	Preferred	Max	Min	Max
Height (H), mm	25			80*	
Width (W), mm	75			90	
Separation (S), mm					
One foot random	100	150			
One foot sequential	50	100			
Displacement (D), mm					
Normal operation	13		65		
Heavy boots	25		65		
Ankle flexion only	25		65	12	65
Total leg movement	25		180	25	180
Resistance, N					
Foot doesn't rest on pedal	18		90	15	90
Foot does rest on pedal	45		90	15	90
Ankle flexion only			45		
Total leg movement	45		800		

*250 mm if used constantly.

depends upon the body member used, the distance and accuracy necessary for the move, and the amount of practice. Laboratory studies of reaction time (where the "signal" occurs many times/h) may not be relevant to occupational environments where the signal may occur less than once/week. Reaction time increases with age, especially over age 60.

F I G U R E	1 7 . 7

Pedal dimensions for Table 17.7.

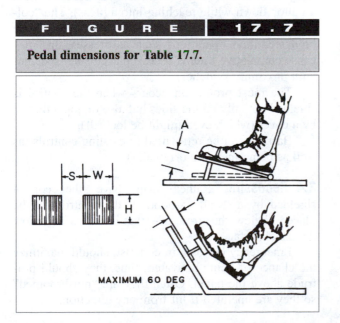

MAXIMUM 60 DEG

Sivak and Flannagan (1993) recommend reducing sensing time by using a brake light filament that is continuously preheated at a 2-volt level (i.e., below the visible). Then when such a lamp is activated, it reaches full brightness in 50 ms instead of the 250 ms required for the nonpreheated lamp; sensing reaction time (and total reaction time) is reduced by about 115 ms (10 ft at 60 mph).

The high center-mounted brake light is an ergonomic success story. The National Highway

F I G U R E	1 7 . 8

Pedal design alternatives. Pedal strokes/minute vary with pedal design. Barnes et al. (1942) reported 187 strokes/min for design 1, 178 for 2, 176 for 3, 140 for 4, and 171 for 5. Trumbo and Schneider (1963) reported the time to depress the pedal through 15° of arc was 346 ms for 1, 395 for 2, 350 for 3, 370 for 4, and 355 for 5. Using either criterion, design 1 is best.

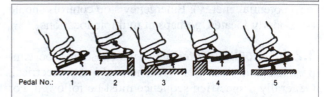

Pedal No.:   1   2   3   4   5

Traffic Safety Administration, based on 6,500,000 crashes, reported that brake lights reduced rear-impact crashes by 4.3%; this prevents 92,000 crashes/yr and 58,000 injuries/year. The $655,000,000 saving in property damage is equivalent to $3.18 for every dollar of cost for these lights.

Have the control indicate (by position, light, sound, touch, etc.) when it has been activated. Then, if it is activated accidentally, the person may be able to reverse the control. If someone else activates an inconspicuous control a casual user of the device may not recognize the device has been activated (as when your hotel alarm clock rings at 5 A.M.). Rocker switch activation is difficult to detect unless connected to a light.

Seven methods of reducing accidental activation follow. Often these methods are combined.

3.1 Key or Special Tool Activation (Locks)

Locks prevent activation by unauthorized people, as opposed to accidental activation. Generally, locks should not be used for emergency controls since the key or tool may not be available. Designing a device (such as a thermostat) to be actuated with an Allen wrench or a Bristol wrench makes it difficult for a casual user to use the control. Maintenance also can be controlled if covers, modules, and so forth have Bristol heads and other nonstandard fasteners. Locks function by (1) what you have (e.g., a key), (2) what you know (e.g., a number), and (3) who you are (e.g., a photograph, fingerprints). More secure locks use methods 1 plus 2 (e.g., key plus number) or method 3.

A related control problem is an authorized person turning on a machine when it should remain off (e.g., during equipment maintenance). A **lockout/tagout** system in which the maintainer has the only key is the best solution. A visual lock is a tag attached to controls during maintenance, indicating that the control should not be activated. If the system is maintained by a crew, each individual should attach a personal lock. Each lock should be accompanied by a tag that contains the employee's name, date, and purpose of the lockout.

Remember that electrical lockout is not sufficient because there may be energy stored in hydraulic lines, compressed air, or springs, or there may be potential energy of the suspended parts. Unfortunately, people have a stereotype that power = electricity and they tend to forget about hydraulic energy, compressed air energy, spring energy, and suspended-parts energy. The machine should be in a **zero mechanical state** (have zero potential energy). Emergency stop controls should be properly located, perhaps at multiple locations.

3.2 Interlocks

Interlocks, which should be tamper-resistant, can be mechanical or electrical. Generally a specified sequence must be followed. For example, a car transmission must be in neutral or park before the ignition will work. Some controls are sequential in two directions. The first direction move releases the control; the second permits operation. A detent is a slot with short perpendicular slots for a lever. Toggle switches and rotary handles can be designed so they require a pull motion before the linear or rotary motion; container caps for dangerous products commonly require turn and pull or depress and turn.

A parameter (e.g., temperature, light, time, flow) may have to be within specifications before the control will operate. Controls may be dual (require both hands or multiple people to be operated).

Enabling controls are another option. Control A must be activated before control B or C can be activated. An example is a button release on an auto transmission lever. If the enabling switch is remote or hidden, it can serve as a lock.

3.3 Barriers or Covers

Controls can be accidentally activated from hand movement while operating an adjacent control. It is even possible to activate controls by hitting them while walking by or by falling against them. The key is to avoid accidental activation while minimizing difficulty of normal operation.

Some protection is provided by a barrier on one side of a control. A guardrail on the front of the panel reduces the danger from falls but may interfere with normal operation. Some protection from hand movement is obtained by a non-sharp strip barrier between adjacent controls (e.g., pushbuttons, toggle switches).

A barrier offers more protection when it is on all sides of a button. For example, if the button is in a "collar," there is less chance of accidental activation; it also reduces deliberate activation by a part of the body other than a finger (e.g., using an elbow to hold a button down while reaching into a press). The "collar," however, may require awkward wrist postures; on high repetition operations such as presses, this may cause cumulative trauma. GM replaced such switches with proximity switches.

The most protection occurs when the control is shielded not only on the sides but also on top—that is, by a cover (which even might be locked!).

Barriers can be retrofitted to existing controls (as well as being installed originally).

3.4 Recessing

Rather than have the control shielded by a "wall" around it, the control can be placed "below the ground"—that is, recessed below the panel surface.

Emergency buttons, in contrast, should maximize the chance of being activated; thus, they should protrude above the panel. Often they are "mushroomed" so they are operated if hit from any direction.

3.5 Spacing   Reserve space for both the controls and their labels. Clearance between controls must be sufficient so the worker does not operate one control when reaching for another. See Table 17.8 and Figure 17.9. If controls may be added later, reserve space for them. Spacing and painted lines can be used to group and differentiate controls. Try to keep spacing consistent within a panel; that is, don't put three related pushbuttons 50 mm apart in one part of the panel and 100 mm apart in another.

Generally the problem is insufficient distance between controls—especially controls used without vision (e.g., pedals). Occasionally the control is too far from its label or associated display. Miniature switches and buttons are available, but don't forget that sizes of human fingers haven't shrunk, too.

3.6 Resistance   The control should offer sufficient resistance in its designed line of travel so that light touches do not activate the control. However, keep the force reasonable, especially at the limits of reach.

3.7 Direction   The line of travel can be selected (in some situations) to minimize accidental activation. For example, a lever might move up–down so that, if a person walking by the control brushes it, the contact force might be normal to the activation direction. Snagging on clothing also may be a problem.

4 PREVENT INCORRECT IDENTIFICATION

Six methods of reducing control identification errors are labeling, color, shape, size, mode of operation, and location. Often these methods are combined.

4.1 Labeling   Labels should be:

1. Legible
   - Have good contrast (in both bright and dim environments).
   - Have sufficiently large characters.
2. Located properly

T A B L E	17.8	

Recommended minimums edge-to-edge spacing (mm) between various types of hand controls shown in Figure 17.9 (Kinkade and Anderson, 1984). Greater spacing is better—especially if gloves are worn or labeling is used.

	NUMBERED TYPE										
Type of Control	1	2	3	4	5	6	7	8	9	10	11
1. Key-operated controls	25	13	38	25	19	19	13	19	19	125	50
2. Pushbuttons (not in an array)	13	13	50	50	13	13	13	13	13	150	75
3. Pushbutton arrays*	38	50	50	50	38	38	38	50	50	150	75
4. Legend switches or legend switch arrays†	25	50	50	50	38	38	38	50	50	150	50
5. Slide switches or rocker switches	19	13	38	38	13	19	13	13	13	125	50
6. Toggle switches‡	19	13	38	38	19	19	13	13	13	150	75
7. Thumbwheels or thumbwheel arrays	13	13	38	38	13	13	13	19	19	125	50
8. Rotary selector switches	19	13	50	50	13	19	19	25	25	125	50
9. Continuous rotary controls	19	13	50	50	13	19	19	25	25	125	50
10. J-handles (large)	125	150	150	150	125	150	125	125	125	75	125
11. J-handles (small)	50	75	75	75	50	75	50	50	50	125	25

* Pushbuttons within an array, 19 mm center-to-center.

† Legend switches within an array, no minimum distances, but should be separated by a barrier that is at least 3 mm wide, 5 mm high, with rounded edges. Legend switches manufactured as elements of a module or modular array may be mounted as closely as engineering considerations permit.

‡ Toggle switches arrayed in a horizontal line, 19 mm center-to-center.

Minimum separable distances (mm) for Table 17.8.

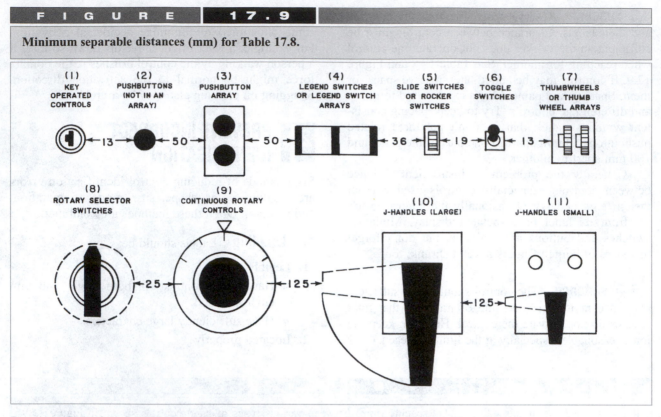

From *Human Factors Guide for Nuclear Power Plant Control Room Development*, by R. Kincaide & S. Anderson. Used with permission.

- Be sure it is unambiguous which label is for which control.
- Place the label above the control so the label is readable when a hand is on the control (hands obscure labels below the control).

3. Understandable

- Avoid labels with *almost* identical words.
- Use consistent wording for similar labels.
- Avoid abbreviations—a *C* on a faucet stands for cold in English but hot in Spanish (*caliente*) and French (*chaud*).
- Be brief and precise (e.g., "pump on–off," not "pump control"; "hold for 2 s," not "spring-loaded").
- If possible, use words with icons. Note the "DANGER OF DEATH" accompanying the icon in Figure 18.9.

4.2 Color   About 8% of males (but .4% of females) have color-perception problems. Color identification requires standard white illumination. Only a relatively few colors (eight or fewer) should be used. Red, orange, green, yellow, white, and blue are good. **Color stereotypes** have special connotations—for example, red for stop, halt, danger, off; yellow for caution, marginal situation; green for OK, safe, go, on. Color stereotypes are not constant across cultures.

4.3 Shape   Colors cannot be identified in the dark! Knobs have been studied extensively for differentiation by shape—**shape coding.** Up to nine different shapes can be used. Excluding shapes with special meanings (e.g., swastika, cross, crescent, airplane), a tactually discriminable set of shapes is: circle, star, ellipse, square (Eastman Kodak, 1983). Tactual shape coding, which depends on a bare or lightly gloved hand, is not as fast as color coding, but controls can be used without vision. Shapes also can be a visual signal. Thus, keep shapes consistent for the same type of control. For example, all stop buttons could be round.

A tactile signal may help. For example, some keyboards have a "pimple" on the F and J keys, which allows the operator to identify the home keys by feel. On the Kodak slide projector remote control, the forward button is smooth but the reverse button has a ridge on it so you can identify each button by feel.

4.4 Size   Only a few sizes (2 to 3) can be differentiated. A large size gives a mechanical advantage. Larger sizes are needed for cold environments (unheated areas and outside) because gloves may be used.

4.5 Mode of Operation   Controls can have distinctive ways of operation—push/pull versus rotate versus slide. However, only when the operator tries to actuate the control by turning and it won't turn does the operator know the wrong control mode was used. Thus, use mode of operation as a backup for other identification methods.

4.6 Location   Both individual controls and groups of controls can be identified by location.

5 MAKE ACCOMPLISHMENTS EQUAL INTENTIONS

Be sure that the operation accomplishes what the operator intended. For example, for critical computer commands, such as delete file, the computer should be programmed to require verification of the command. In effect, this is a version of an interlock or enabling switch, requiring critical actions to be two-stage instead of one-stage. Figure 17.10 shows a badly designed control and a suggested alternative.

Complex sequences of actions (such as computer or microprocessor inputs) have to be user-friendly. There is a possibility that the designer has designed so many options into the controls (or one control with multiple functions) that a novice user is not able to use the device. VCR controls drive many to tears. The clocks on some Dodge autos were so complicated to adjust that people brought them into the dealer to adjust for daylight savings time! You may be familiar with other examples of poorly designed controls. The key is to field-test a control design before going into production.

More care and testing are needed if the action has multiple steps (as with computer commands). Novices will need more help (well-thought-out and field-tested documents, as well as displays giving feedback of the results of actions) than will experienced operators. The detail of the "prompt" should be adjustable by the user so the novice can have lots of detail and the experienced user can hit just the highlights. A good computer program also will check input data for validity. For example, all social security numbers entered must have 9 digits, all ZIP codes have 5 (or 9) digits, all part numbers have the proper number of letters and numbers in the specified locations, part numbers entered must be numbers in use, and so forth.

Another challenge is posed by **population stereotypes** (habit patterns). The engineer's habit patterns should not be considered to be the user's habit pattern. Table 17.9 gives common habit patterns in the United States. The designer cannot depend upon the control user following the habit pattern, but if the control violates the operator's expectation, there is more chance for error. The U. S. expectation is strong for power switches to be up = on and down = off, but stereotypes for left–right and front–back are mixed. Thus, the power switch should be on the front of the machine and up = on. If it must be on the side, put it on the right side.

Unfortunately, stereotypes are often country-specific. For example, in England flipping a light switch up turns the light off. In most of the world, elevator doors have a safety pressure strip running vertically on the door edges. In Brazil, however, a light beam at

FIGURE	17.10

Five improvements to the poor design control/display (on the left): (1) improving the knob shape so its direction is obvious, (2) replacing the abstract thermometer symbol with the word TEMPERATURE (although automobiles must follow international symbol coding, other manufacturers should give customers in each country the courtesy of their own language), (3) moving the TEMPERATURE legend to above the control so the hand won't obscure it, (4) putting the heat levels on a semicircle instead of the ambiguous lines (do you point the knob at the line or the number?), and (5) replacing the Roman numerals with Arabic numerals.

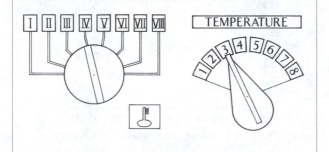

TABLE	17.9

Conventional control movements in United States (*Human Engineering Design Data Digest*, 1984).

FUNCTION	CONTROL ACTION
On	Up, right, forward, clockwise, pull
Off	Down, left, rearward, counterclockwise, push
Increase	Up, right, forward, clockwise
Decrease	Down, left, rearward, counterclockwise
Raise	Up
Lower	Down
Right	Right, clockwise
Left	Left, counterclockwise
Retract	Up, rearward, pull
Extend	Down, forward, push

knee level senses the presence of an obstacle. A person from North America injured his hand in Rio de Janeiro when he put it between the elevator doors at chest level. In Japan, taxi drivers open the rear doors remotely; Japanese tourists in other countries often stand at taxis waiting for the door to open.

Displays also have habit patterns that also may differ by population. For example, in Mexico, using the left blinker light on your car does not indicate that you want to turn left; it indicates to cars behind you that they can pass *you* on the left! In Mexico, the hot water faucet is labeled *C,* which is logical since *C* stands for *caliente* (hot). In China, the color for funerals is white.

Labeling may help. For example, have two numbers on a thumbwheel to show the operator which direction is increase or decrease.

For continuous controls, consider the **control/ response ratio** (the distance the control moves/the distance the display indicator moves). Two basic movements are gross adjustment to the vicinity of the target and precision adjustment to the exact target. See Sanders and McCormick (1993) for a more extensive discussion.

A control does not exist in isolation. Controls have to be compatible with other controls and with displays. Control positions often act as displays; therefore, have good color contrast between the control and the panel.

6 PROPERLY LOCATE AND ARRANGE THE CONTROLS

6.1 Location   Location depends primarily on whether the control will be used by the hands or the feet.

6.1.1 *Foot controls*   Avoid foot controls for standing operators because these are tiring. In addition, if used with hand motions, there are safety problems (e.g., in presses) as the hand and foot motions are coordinated. Foot controls can be for continuous power (e.g., bicycle) or discrete power (brake pedal).

For continuous power, the seat-to-pedal distance should be adjusted so the leg is fully extended at the bottom of the stroke. The crank length should be approximately 20% of leg length, that is, 10% of stature height (Gross and Bennett, 1974). The pedal should be in line with the axis of the lower leg so the force is exerted by the leg muscles rather than the ankle muscles.

Discrete power usually is furnished by one leg since application time is usually less than 10 s and, thus, fatigue is not a problem. There does not seem to be any power advantage to using the right or left foot (Mortimer et al., 1970; Von Buseck, 1965). Adjusting Von Buseck's data for learning, force using both feet is 106% to 118% greater than using a single foot, but

people will not always use both feet and the designer should not depend upon use of both feet.

In general, maximal force can be exerted if there is a straight line between the pedal and back support (Rees and Graham, 1952). That is, if the pedal is 250 mm below the seat, the back support should be 250 mm above the seat. Aoki (1960) reported maximal pedal force when the calf–thigh angle was 110° and the thigh–back angle was 73°. Hugh-Jones (1947) reported maximum at a knee angle of 160°. Figure 17.11 shows the mean results of 155 males each exerting force at 26 different positions. The mean efficiency index is defined as "force at a specific position for an individual/force at the individual's best position."

Note that maximum force capability may not be as important as comfort. Figure 17.12 shows the preferred seat reference point (intersection of the planes of the seat and back) relative to the accelerator (Martin and Johnson, 1952).

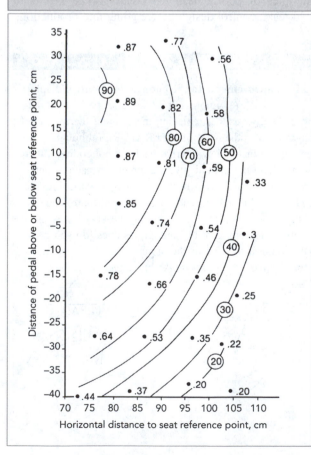

| F I G U R E | 17.11 |

Pedal forces in relation to distance from pedal. Pedal force decreases as distance from the pedal increases (Martin and Johnson, 1952). Note the maximum force is when the foot is above the seat reference point (SRP, the intersection of the planes of the seat and the seat back).

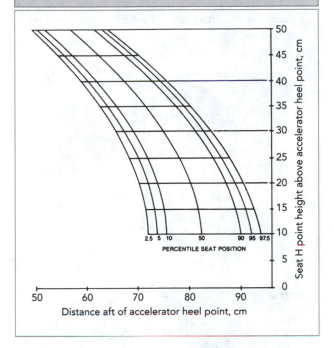

FIGURE   17.12

Preferred seat heights in relation to accelerator pedal. Preferred seat height above the accelerator pedal rises as you move closer to the pedal. The values are for the U.S. driving population in 1973 (Roe, 1975).

If the pedal will be used repeatedly, muscle fatigue will become a problem. Four design solutions are:

1. a wide pedal so either foot can be used at the operator's option
2. a pedal for each foot
3. lateral movement of the chair
4. a wide chair (a bench) upon which the operator can change position from time to time.

In most industrial applications, the time required to move the foot from one location to another is not critical as the movement can be done at the operator's leisure or can be done simultaneously with some other motion. However, in some situations (such as auto braking) minimum reaction time is important. If your foot is already on the control, you can save about .25 s over moving your foot to the control. But if one foot is poised over the brake and the other is on the accelerator, you are in a "straight jacket" and this position restriction is tiring. Within the distance of 5 to 13 cm of movement, foot reaction time is approximately the same. Some separation of controls (e.g., brake and accelerator) is necessary or both controls might be actuated. On the other hand, if the separation is too great, the brake might be missed! Thus, multiple criteria have to be considered.

6.1.2 *Hand controls*   Hand controls are divided into keyboards, manipulative controls, and force controls.

Keyboards.   Keyboards have two special characteristics: They are used repetitively, and they are used (generally) with both hands. It is assumed that the keyboard location is independent of the location of a display for the eyes; however, some devices do have both the keyboard and a display in the same housing and the choice becomes whether to locate the display for the eyes or the keyboard for the hands.

The approximate location of the keyboard should be at elbow height. Since elbow height varies with sitting and standing and with individuals, a keyboard location should not be specified from the floor. Desks often are designed so a large proportion of the population can sit with the feet on the floor and not have the upper portion of the thigh touch the underside of the desk. This tends to result in a relatively high keyboard. The solution is a chair that can be raised to position the elbow properly so that it is even with the bottom row of the keyboard. In turn, however, this often requires a footrest. Having no footrest will result in uncomfortable legs (since the feet dangle without support). The alternative is to keep the feet on the floor, but now the keyboard will be too high and the neck and shoulders will hurt.

If you study the keyboard hand position in detail, as Kroemer (1990) and Nakeseko et al. (1985) did, you will find that hand position is important. The minimum stress position for the hand is the handshake position. However, when operating most keyboards, the hands must rotate so the palm is approximately horizontal, with the knuckles above the wrist. In addition, the elbow tends to be lifted outward and forward (which is bad). Both Kroemer and Nakeseko et al. recommended splitting the keyboards and orienting them to minimize deviations. When using a conventional nonsplit keyboard, reduce this cumulative trauma (repetitive strain) through job rotation and task variety. A wrist support below the keyboard for use in the pauses between entries is recommended.

Ideally the user can adjust the keyboard orientation on the work surface for all three axes.

Manipulative controls.   **Manipulative controls** (low-force controls such as knobs and switches—see Tables 17.1 and 17.2) should be within reach. Define reach distance as the first percentile of the population, not the design engineer's reach. Define reach to the center of the palm, not the fingertip. Ideally, the operator should not have to change posture when reaching (e.g., kneel or bend over when standing, rise when sitting). If possible, avoid blind reaches (in which the operator cannot see the control due to its location or darkness); if a blind reach is necessary, consider distinctive control shape or location.

A design question is how much attention to pay to lefthanders. Discrete controls (e.g., toggle switches) reflect elementary control tasks and handedness is not relevant. But handedness is relevant to continuous controls (e.g., joysticks). One possibility is to place the control in the center; however, this uses valuable space and compromises the majority of the population. Garonzik (1989) has a design guide for control location that considers handedness.

In the special circumstances when the vehicle seat rotates (such as a timberjack's forest harvesting equipment), the controls and displays must be mounted on the seat. Foot controls are duplicated for the rear-facing position.

Force controls. Force controls, like other manipulative controls, should be within reach to reduce user stress. See Figure 17.13. However, some postures permit greater muscle force and torque on the control due to human biomechanics.

In general, while standing, force capability is better at waist height than knee or shoulder height and is better when the person is braced. At waist height, push is better than pull, and up and down are equal. At shoulder height, push is better than pull, and down is better than up (Collier et al., 1986). For kneeling, pull is better than push, and up is better than down.

For sitting cross-legged, place controls 10 to 25 cm above the floor; for kneeling, place controls 30 to 50 cm above the floor (Conway et al., 1981). For kneeling, exertable force is about 20% less when the arm is fully extended; lateral force exertions toward the sides are quite awkward and are relatively weak (Haselgrave, Tracy, and Corlett, 1987).

Grieve (1984), in studying the effect of height on pull for outboard motor starting, reported great differences for different postures.

6.2 Arrangement
Spacing of controls was discussed in Section 3.5, Spacing. See Table 17.8. See also Section 6.2, Arrange Instrument Displays, in Chapter 18.

If the control action is reported on a display (as it often is), the arrangement of the control with respect to the display must be obvious so the operator knows which control is related to which display.

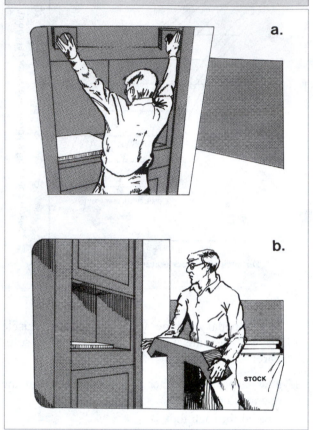

FIGURE 17.13

Avoid overhead positions for press safety controls as shown in (a)—they can result in "frozen shoulder," causing severe pain and functional impairment (Putz-Anderson, 1988); (b) shows a better alternative. In addition, make the buttons "friendly to the hand" by minimizing wrist deviations and contact pressure (large, soft buttons).

From the concepts of Tullis (1983):

- Group related controls and displays together.
- Minimize layout complexity by aligning controls vertically and horizontally instead of randomly.
- Have blank space on the panel. Blank space not only reduces inadvertent operation (Table 17.8) but also provides visual structure. Make spacing between groups of related controls greater than between related controls.

Review Questions

1. Sketch a schematic (see Figure 17.1) of human, machine, controls, displays, and environment.

2. Give an example of a closed-loop system and an open-loop system.

3. For an automobile, give five continuous controls and five discrete controls.

4. Assume you are designing a control for a milling machine. What percentage of the population should be excluded from using the machine because these people are too weak to operate the control? Justify your answer.

5. List the seven methods of reducing accidental activation of controls.

6. Discuss lockout/tagout with emphasis on the concept of "zero mechanical state."

7. What is an enabling control? What is an interlock?

8. Should the control label be above or below the control? Why?

9. List the six methods of preventing incorrect identification of controls.

10. Briefly discuss population stereotypes.

11. Give four design solutions that permit a person to use either foot to operate a pedal.

12. For a standing person, briefly summarize force capability at knee, waist, and shoulder heights.

References

Allais, D. *Bar Code Symbology.* Lynwood, WA: Intermec, 1982.

Amell, T. and Kumar, S. Industrial handwheel actuation and the human operator: A review. *Int. J. of Ind. Ergonomics,* Vol. 28, 291–302, 2001.

Aoki, K. Human factors in braking and fade phenomena for heavy application. *Bulletin of Japan Society Mechanical Engineers,* Vol. 3, No. 12, 587–94, 1960.

Aye, D. and Konz, S. Sharpness of edges. *Proc. of IEA World Congress,* Rio de Janeiro, Brazil, 510–12, 1995.

Barnes, R., Hardaway, H., and Podolsky, O. Which pedal is best? *Factory Management and Maintenance,* Vol. 100, No. 98, January 1942.

Boyles, J., Yearout, R., and Rys, M. The effectiveness of an ergonomic tool design (ETD) scissors. *Int. J. of Industrial Ergonomics,* in print, 2003.

Bullinger, H., Bandera, J., and Muntzinger, W. Design, selection and location of foot controls. *Int. J. of Ind. Ergonomics,* Vol. 8, 303–11, 1991.

Collier, S., Chan, W., Mason, S., and Pethick, A. *Ergonomic Design Handbook for Continuous-Miners* (Report TM/86/11). Edinburgh, Scotland: Institute of Occupational Medicine, 1986.

Conway, E., Helander, M., and Curtin, R. Optimum control heights for sitting cross-legged and kneeling. *Proceedings of the Human Factors Society,* 767–71, 1981.

Eastman Kodak. *Ergonomic Design for People at Work,* Vol. 1. Belmont, CA: Lifetime Learning Publications, 1983.

Garonzik, R. Hand dominance and implications for left-handed operation of controls. *Ergonomics,* Vol. 32, No. 10, 1185–92, 1989.

Grieve, D. The influence of posture on power output generated in single pulling movements. *Applied Ergonomics,* Vol. 15, No. 2, 115–17, June 1984.

Gross, V. and Bennett, C. Bicycle crank length. *Proceedings of the 6th International Ergonomics Meeting,* College Park, MD, 1976; see also Gross, V., Bicycle crank length and load, M. S. thesis, Manhattan: Kansas State University, 1974.

Haselgrave, C., Tracy, M., and Corlett, N. Biomechanical effects of force exertions while kneeling. *Proceedings of the Human Factors Society,* 318–22, 1987.

Hugh-Jones, P. The effect of limb position in seated subjects on their ability to utilize maximum contractile force of the limb muscles. *J. of Physiology,* Vol. 105, 332–44, 1947.

Human Engineering Design Data Digest. Redstone, AL: Human Engineering Laboratory, U. S. Army Missile Command, 1984.

Hutchinson, R. *New Horizons for Human Factors in Design.* New York: McGraw-Hill, 1981.

Imrahan, S. and Loo, C. Torque capabilities of the elderly in opening screw top containers. *Proceedings of the Human Factors Society,* Santa Monica, CA: 1167–71, 1986.

Kinkade, R. and Anderson, J. (eds.). *Human Factors Guide for Nuclear Power Plant Control Room Development.* Palo Alto, CA: EPRI, 1984.

Kohl, G. Effects of shape and size of knobs on maximal hand-turning forces applied by females. *Bell System Technical T.,* Vol. 62, No. 6, 1705–12, July–August 1983.

Konz, S. and Ravishankar, H. Knurls on pop bottle lids. *Proceedings of the Human Factors Society,* 483–85, 1989.

Kroemer, K. Cumulative trauma disorders. *Applied Ergonomics,* Vol. 20, 274–80, 1990.

Martin, W. and Johnson, E. *An optimum range of seat positions as determined by exertion of pressure upon a foot pedal* (AMRL Report 86). Fort Knox, KY:

Army Medical Research Laboratory, June 1952 (AD 21654).

McMulkin, M. and Woldstad, J. Effects of wheel design on the torques applied to large hand wheels. *Int. J. of Ind. Ergonomics,* Vol. 15, 205–13, 1995.

Mortimer, R., Segel, L., Dugoff, H., Campbell, J., Jorgeson, C., and Murphy, R. *Brake Force Requirement Study,* National Highway Safety Bureau Final Report FH-11-6952. Washington, DC, April 1970.

Nagashima, K. and Konz, S. Jar lids: Effect of diameter, gripping material and knurling. *Proceedings of the Human Factors Society,* 672–74, 1986.

Nakeseko, M., Grandjean, E., Hunting, E., and Gierer, R. Studies on ergonomically designed alphanumeric keyboards. *Human Factors,* Vol. 27, No. 2, 175–87, 1985.

Nowak, E. Angular measurements of foot motion for application to the design of foot pedals. *Ergonomics,* Vol. 15, No. 4, 407–15, 1972.

Putz-Anderson, V. (ed.). *Cumulative Trauma Disorders.* London: Taylor and Francis, 1988.

Raouf, A., Imanishi, H., and Morooka, K. Investigations pertaining to continuous and intermittent cranking motion. *Int. J. of Industrial Ergonomics,* Vol. 1, 29–36, 1986.

Rees, J. and Graham, N. The effect of backrest position on the push which can be exerted on an isometric foot-pedal. *J. of Anatomy,* Vol. 86, 310–19, 1952.

Replogle, J. Hand torque strength with cylindrical handles. *Proceedings of the Human Factors Society,* 412–16, 1983.

Roe, R. Describing the driver's workspaces eye, head, knee and seat positions. Society of Automotive Engineers (paper 730 356), February 1975.

Sanders, M. and McCormick, E. *Human Factors in Engineering and Design,* 7th ed. New York: McGraw-Hill, 1993.

Sivak, M. and Flannagan, M. Fast-rise brake lamp as a collision-prevention device. *Ergonomics,* Vol. 36, No. 4, 391–95, 1993.

Trumbo, D. and Schneider, M. Operation time as a function of foot pedal design. *J. of Engineering Psychology,* Vol. 2, No. 4, 139–43, 1963.

Tullis, T. The formatting of alphanumeric displays: A review and analysis. *Human Factors,* Vol. 25, No. 6, 657–82, 1983.

Von Buseck, C. Excerpts from maximal brake pedal forces produced by male and female drivers, (Research Report EM-18). Warren, MI: GM, January 1965.

18 DISPLAYS

DISPLAYS

1 Select Legible Characters

2 Arrange Characters and Symbols

3 Decide Among Menus, Tables, Formulas, Graphs, Symbolic Messages, and Maps

4 Project Your Message

5 Select the Instrument Display

6 Locate/Arrange the Display

Overview

Passive displays are alphanumeric characters and their arrangements. Active displays are instruments. Specific recommendations are given to improve legibility and reduce errors.

Key Concepts

analog/digital

codes

conversion line

discrete/continuous/
    representational

divided bar graph

dot charts

dot pitch

doughnut chart

explicit/implicit

fonts

formulas

graphs

icons

justified

line of sight

menus

outside-in/inside-out

picas

pictographs

pie chart

pixels

points

portrait versus
    landscape

reverse image

serifs

significant digits

slide/transparency

stroke width

time series

visual angle

The failure of a display to communicate can be at two levels. *First,* and perhaps most obvious, is legibility or detectability. The letters on the display may be too small or the contrast too poor. *Second* is the problem of understanding. For example, what is the meaning of the word *subsequent* or *prior?* What is the meaning of a pointer pointing to a value of 220? Although this chapter focuses on solving the first-level (legibility) problems, the designer should not forget level-two (understanding) problems.

There are six guidelines. The first four deal with alphanumeric characters and their arrangements; the last two deal with instruments.

■■ SELECT LEGIBLE CHARACTERS

1.1 Font   Handwritten characters tend to be less legible than printed characters due to the wide variation in individual concepts of what various letter shapes should be and poor execution of the ideal concept. Tables 18.1 and 18.2 give recommended handwriting styles for capital letters and numbers. Commas and peri-

ods can be confused easily, as can the capital letters D and O and the numbers 6 and 0 and 4 and 9.

For print, there is relatively little difference in legibility for most reasonable type styles, or **fonts.** Readers not only find extreme styles less legible, but they also consider them less attractive. See Figure 18.1. Roman fonts have **serifs** (little flourishes and embellishments); sans serif fonts (*sans,* French, without) are without serifs. In this book's tables, the word TABLE and the column headings are sans serif. The **stroke width** (thickness of lines within a letter) is almost constant in sans serif, varies some in Roman, and varies considerably in modern fonts. The spacing between characters also varies with fonts. New Times and Times Roman (which have serifs) are popular, but America On Line uses Arial (a sans serif font) as their default. Avoid using Roman numerals. This applies everywhere—chapter numbers in books, volume and table numbers, dates. Perry (1952) reported that Roman numerals took 50% to 100% more time to read and produced from 3 to 30 times as many errors.

T A B L E	1 8 . 1

Handwriting character recommendations, guide for understanding the nuances of each character, and the rationale for selection (Association for Computing Machinery, 1969).

LETTER	GUIDE	LETTER	GUIDE
A	Use of squared top not supported by sufficient evidence of confusion.	N	Parallel legs.
B	Overhang top and bottom is used to reduce possibility of confusion with numeral 8 or 13. Distinct center division required to avoid similarity to letter D.	O	Loop added at top to distinguish from number zero. The use of a slash was too confusing.
C	No evidence of confusion; there is some similarity to left parenthesis if curve is not deep enough.	P	Overhang at top added for consistency with letters B, D, and R.
D	Overhang top and bottom is used to reduce possibility of confusion with numeral zero. This convention is similar to that for letter B.	Q	No special convention.
		R	Overhang at top added for consistency with letters B, D, and P.
E	Rounded left side is to be avoided to reduce confusion with ampersand.	S	Serif added at top only for ease of preparation and to distinguish from numeral 5 and special character dollar sign.
F	Similar to letter E above.	T	No special convention.
G	Strong, emphasized serif reduces possibility of confusion with letter C or numerals 6 and 10.	U	This flat-bottom convention adopted to distinguish from letter V and lowercase letter u.
H	Parallel sides.	V	This pointed-bottom convention distinguishes letter V from letter U.
I	Use serifs on top and bottom.	W	Center division extends to top of letter. Rounded bottom should be avoided.
J	Top serif reduces confusion with letter U.	X	No special convention.
K	Slanting legs are joined at center.	Y	Vertical leg bisects angle formed by top legs to avoid confusion with numeral 4.
L	No special convention.		
M	Legs spread at bottom; center division extends to bottom of letter. Rounded tops should be avoided.	Z	Use horizontal bar to distinguish from number 2.

TABLE 18.2

Handwriting numbers recommendation, guide for understanding of the nuances of each number, and the rationale for selection (Association for Computing Machinery, 1969).

NUMBER	GUIDE
0	Closed circle with no added identifying characteristic
1	Single vertical bar, no added identifying characteristic
2	No loop at bottom
3	Curved lines, no straight top line
4	Open top to reduce confusion with 9
5	Vertical and top lines joined at right angles
6	Loop closed at bottom to avoid confusion with zero or lower case b
7	Crossbar used in Europe considered confusing with letter A, and does not have support in United States
8	Made with two circles adjoining vertically to avoid confusion with special characters ampersand and dollar sign
9	Straight leg from common usage

FIGURE 18.1

Legible fonts are easier to read than non-legible fonts and readers find them more attractive (Faulkner, 1972).

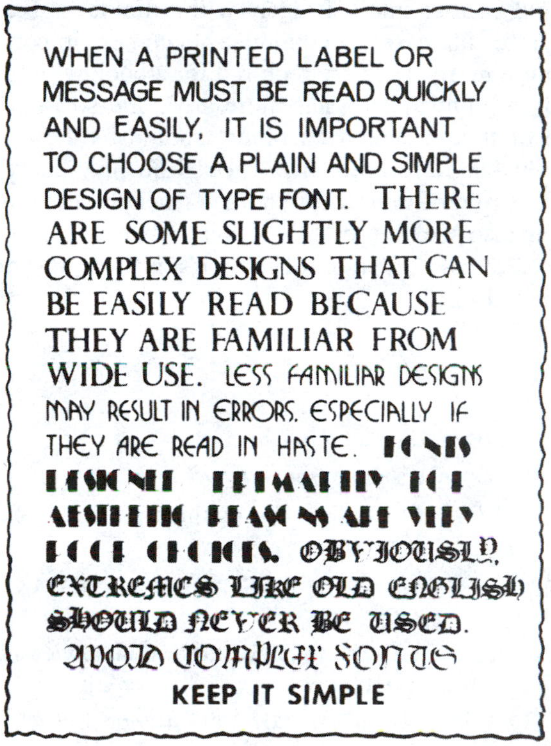
WHEN A PRINTED LABEL OR MESSAGE MUST BE READ QUICKLY AND EASILY, IT IS IMPORTANT TO CHOOSE A PLAIN AND SIMPLE DESIGN OF TYPE FONT.
THERE ARE SOME SLIGHTLY MORE COMPLEX DESIGNS THAT CAN BE EASILY READ BECAUSE THEY ARE FAMILIAR FROM WIDE USE.
LESS FAMILIAR DESIGNS MAY RESULT IN ERRORS, ESPECIALLY IF THEY ARE READ IN HASTE.
OBVIOUSLY, EXTREMES LIKE OLD ENGLISH SHOULD NEVER BE USED.
KEEP IT SIMPLE

Characters printed on signs often must be read under difficult conditions. The optimum stroke width is 12% to 18% of the height when it is black on white and 8% to 10% for white on black and transilluminated characters (Konz and Mohan, 1972).

Garvey et al. (1998) reported, for highway signs (using recognition of words rather than of characters), that mixed-case signs were better than all-capital-letter signs. They also found irradiation at night (blurring of letters due to high-brightness sign materials). They redesigned the font to increase the open spaces in the letters; the new font (for highway-sized signs at 55 mph) can be read 160 ft (49 m) farther away—an advantage of 2 s.

For computer screens, type style is more critical (Shurtleff, 1980). Reading speed is about 25% slower on VDTs than print, primarily due to the poor contrast and sharpness of characters on screens (Dillon, 1992).

VDT screen quality is defined by **pixels** (the smallest element of a display screen that can be independently assigned color and intensity) and **dot pitch** (the distance between two phosphor dots of the same color on the screen). Legibility increases with more pixels and lower dot pitch. To avoid flicker, use a noninterlaced monitor in which the lines on the screen are painted every cycle; on interlaced monitors they are painted every other pass.

To equal the resolution of printed matter requires a screen resolution of at least 150 pixels/inch (double the resolution of most screens today). In addition, screens are designed for watching, not reading. Most printed materials are taller than wide (**portrait** orientation); screens are wider than tall (**landscape** orientation). TV pictures are 4 units wide × 3 units high—a ratio of 1.33. Movies, which are "widescreen," are 16 units × 9 units—a ratio of 1.78.

Dot matrix displays conventionally are 5 × 7, 7 × 9, 9 × 11, or 9 × 14 dots. (Avoid 5 × 7 displays.) For 9 × 14, the 9 is composed of 7 horizontal character dots × 1 left spacer dot × 1 right spacer dot. The 14 is composed of 9 vertical character dots × 2 top leading dots × 2 descender dots × 1 bottom leading dot. Stroke width for 7 × 9 is 1/9 = 11%, for 9 × 11 is 1/11 = 9%, and for 9 × 14 is 1/14 = 7%. Raster-written displays (i.e., lines, not dots) are better (Chang and Konz, 1993), probably because they more closely duplicate "curves and slants" of printed characters. In addition, because they fill more space, square dots are better than oblique or round dots (Helander, 1987).

1.2 Size   The optimum size of a character depends upon a number of environmental factors.

The minimum visible size (character height) depends upon the distance of the character from the eye. However, just because someone with perfect eyes can read a character does not mean the character should be that small. Bigger (within limits) is better. As size increases, economics becomes important because more pages are required for a book with large print, a highway sign has more area, and so forth. A rule of thumb is that an object should be 2.5 times larger than threshold size. The following equation gives a rule of thumb for character height versus distance; also see Figure 18.2. *K* is in radians. *K1* is from Kinkade and Anderson (1984); *K2* is from Eastman Kodak (1983).

$$CH = K(D)$$

where

CH =   Character height

D =   Distance from eye

$K1$ =   .004 radians for minimum character height at ≥300 lux

=   .006 for preferred character height at ≥300 lux

$K2$ =   .001 700 to .005 500 for routine viewing at ≥100 lux

=   .003 500 to .007 300 for critical viewing at ≥100 lux

Eastman Kodak (1983) recommends, for low-light situations (such as darkrooms), multiplying *K2* by 1.5 and using white characters.

Size also can be expressed in terms of **visual angle** to eliminate the effect of distance. (See Figure 18.2 and Section 1.1.2 of Chapter 23.) For characters on VDT screens, Grandjean (1987) recommends 16–25 min of arc. The American National Standard (1988) and ISO 9241–3 recommend 20–22 min of arc. Chang and Konz (1993) confirmed these values but showed severe penalties for characters less than 15 min of arc. For characters viewed from less than 1 m, use values at the upper end of the range (Smith, 1979; Sherr, 1979; Winkler and Konz, 1980).

For very short messages, such as control labels, signs, figure legends, words on projected transparencies, and the like, use all capitals since, for the same type size, capital letters are about 30% larger than lower case letters. Capital letters also can be used to EMPHASIZE a word on a monochromatic display. For longer messages (i.e., text), use a mixture of capital and lowercase letters as the characters should be far above threshold size and the mixture gives structure to the text to improve readability. Table 18.3 shows how mixed case is more legible than all uppercase.

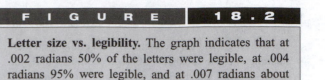

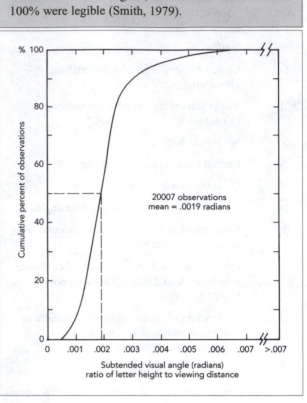

Letter size vs. legibility. The graph indicates that at .002 radians 50% of the letters were legible, at .004 radians 95% were legible, and at .007 radians about 100% were legible (Smith, 1979).

2 ARRANGE CHARACTERS AND SYMBOLS

2.1 Text   Printers measure type height in **points** (where 1 point is 1/72 inch = .353 mm) and type width in **picas** (where 1 pica = 1/6 inch = 4.233 mm). (This is the height of the metal slug on which type used to be set; use 1 point = .01 inch for the character height.) Computer printers allow changing the pitch (characters/linear inch). This book is set in 10.5 point Times Roman type with 12 points leading (space between lines), with columns 19 picas (228 points) wide.

Figure 18.3 gives changes in reading speed for 10-point type. The easiest reading is with text in columns (magazines, newspapers) rather than across the entire page. An additional advantage is that some figures and tables can be set one column wide (see Table 18.4) so they don't use the entire page width. Table 18.4 compares the optimum for each type size.

T A B L E	1 8 . 3

Old and improved CRT designs. Directory assistants at Ameritech saved .6 s/call using the mixed-case addresses and a change from san serif to a serif font (Hendrick, 1996); because of the large numbers of calls, this saving was $2,900,000/yr.

OLD CRT DESIGN

MAIL BOX RENTALS 931 ROSELLE RD SCHAUMBURG 60193 . . . . 708 893-5705

MAIL BOXES ETC

    836 ARLINGTON HEIGHTS RD ELK GROVE VILLAGE 600 . . . . 708 956-1112

    1749 W GOLF RD MOUNT PROSPECT 60056 . . . . 708 640-7788

    318 HALF DAY RD BUFFALO GROVE 60069 . . . . 708 913-0335

    830 W MAIN LAKE ZURICH 60047 . . . . 708 540-8550

MAIL BOXES ETC 126 E WING ARLINGTON HEIGHTS GREATER

    CHICAGOLAND TOLL-FREE 800 300-3229

IMPROVED CRT DESIGN

Mail Box Rentals 931 Roselle Rd SCHAUMBURG 60193 . . . . 708 893-5705

Mail Boxes Etc

    836 Arlington Heights Rd ELK GROVE VILLAGE 600 . . . . 708 956-1112

    1749 W Golf Rd MOUNT PROSPECT 60056 . . . . 708 640-7788

    318 Half Day Rd BUFFALO GROVE 60069 . . . . 708 913-0335

    830 W Main LAKE ZURICH 60047 . . . . 708 540-8550

Mail Boxes Etc 126 E Wing ARLINGTON HEIGHTS GREATER

    CHICAGOLAND TOLL-FREE 800 300-3229

Tinker (1963) recommends 11-point type, as readers prefer it and it gives greater flexibility in line width and leading. Tinker also says that, although readers generally prefer some leading, they prefer a 10-point type set solid (minimum spacing) over an 8-point type with 2 points leading.

F I G U R E	1 8 . 3

Changes in reading speed for 10-point type. Reading speed for 10-point type is best at 19 pica width (228 points) and 2-point leading (Tinker, 1963).

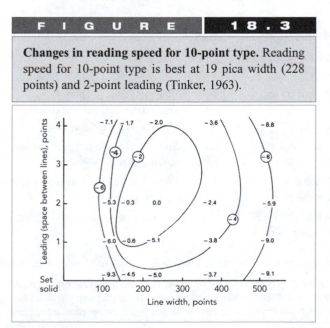

Put a space between a number and the units—for example, 1.5 mm, not 1.5mm.

For characters on VDTs, typical center-to-center distance of characters is 2.8 mm horizontally and 5.6 mm vertically (15.9 points including spacing) (Tullis, 1983). Kruk and Mutter (1984) reported that readability of text on VDT screens was 11% better if the lines were double-spaced instead of single-spaced. Trollip and Sales (1986) reported that reading speed was 11% greater if the right edge of the VDT text was uneven—not **justified.** Gould and Grischkowsky (1986) reported best reading performance when the line width of text subtended about 20°; there was little difference within the range of 16° and 36°.

Long lines of text form a pattern of stripes, which causes reading problems (Wilkins and Nimmo-Smith, 1987). This pattern can be broken up by using relatively short paragraphs and short line length (as in newspapers or magazines); short lines also help the eye return to the beginning of the following line. Typed material typically should be double-spaced, although 1 1/2-line spacing can be used. Reserve single spacing for short items (summaries, footnotes, references, table headings), provided no difficulty arises due to sub- or superscripts.

Reports, articles, and textbooks should have organized headings to aid the reader. Three levels are

T A B L E	1 8 . 4

Comparison of optimum line length for type size. For each type size a "near optimum" line length was used; the type was Granjon with 2-point leading (504 subjects) (Tinker, 1963).

TYPE SIZE, POINTS	LINE LENGTH, PICA	LINE LENGTH, POINTS	READING SPEED, PERCENT
12	24	288	100.0
11	22	264	99.0
9	18	216	98.7
10	20	240	97.3
8	16	192	95.6
6	14	168	94.0

typical. Identify the level with case and position. For example, 1st level is upper case and left-justified; 2nd level is upper and lower case and left-justified; 3rd level is lower case and indented. If possible, make all the headings boldface (rather than some boldface and some italic) (Gilreath, 1994). Organization also can be shown by making the level 1 heading a larger size.

For manuals, people like a good table of contents, labeled tabs, and distinctive headings. They also appreciate color to highlight types of information, and they like lots of figures and examples (Angiolillo and Roberts, 1991).

2.2 Codes Part numbers, telephone numbers, voucher numbers, charge numbers, e-mail addresses, and so forth are **codes**. The goal is to make it difficult to generate an error and easy to detect an error. To minimize errors in coded transmission:

■ *Automate the code transfer.* Examples of automated transfer are barcodes, magnetic ink bank identifiers on checks, and other machine-readable devices. Other examples of automation are using the reply function for e-mail (avoids entering an address), using address books for e-mail (just click on a name instead of entering a code), memory dialing on the phone (1 number instead of 7 to 10), and using stick-on labels for mail. Automated transfer tends to be error-free as well as fast.

■ *Make codes checkable.* Codes transferred by computer can be made self-checking by adding check digits to the code and by having the computer check its memory to see if the transferred number is in its memory. When a person gives you a number by voice, reflect it back in a revised format. For example, if the person gives you the phone number 532-5606 as 5-3-2-5-6-0-6, reflect it back as 5-32-56-06. Table 18.5 shows some additional checks that can be done either with computer software or manually. Since people often make reversal (transposition) errors (e.g., entering ei instead of ie), design the system so reversal errors are not accepted or at least are challenged. Spell checkers are an example.

T A B L E	1 8 . 5

Error opportunities in coding (Eastman Kodak, 1983; Caplan, 1975). The key is to add structure to the code.

ERROR TYPE	PREVENTIVE FEATURE IN CODE DESIGN	REASON
Omission or addition of characters to code	Use uniform length and composition	Omission or addition will result in code immediately recognized as nonexistent.
Substitution between numbers and letters	Use consistent location for numbers and letters	Substitution will result in code immediately recognized as nonexistent
Transposition of letters	Use a familiar acronym or pronounceable word (instead of random letters) that is visually and audibly distinct	It will be remembered as one element rather than individual elements, as random letters are remembered
Transposition of numbers	Introduce a rule for the relationship between adjacent numbers in the string	Transposition will yield a code with a pair of digits out of order
Illegibility	Use consistent number and letter locations. Control handwriting by providing an individual box for each character	Poor handwriting more easily deciphered

Source: Adapted from Table 1 from "Guidelines for Reducing Human Errors in the Use of Coded Information" by Stanley H. Caplan in *Proceedings of the 19th Annual Meeting,* 1975. Stanley H. Caplan, 27 Woodmount Rd., Rochester, NY 14620-3357; 716/271-0696; wood27@netacc.net. Adapted with permission from *Proceedings of the 19th Annual Meeting,* 1975. Copyright © 1975 by the Human Factors and Ergonomics Society. All rights reserved. Also reprinted with permission from Eastman Kodak Company.

■ *Use short codes.* With manual transfer, the human error rate increases exponentially if the code has more than 5 or 6 symbols (Konz et al., 1968; Stanhagen and Carlson, 1970); 5 numbers or 4 letters will have an error rate of about 5%, and 4 numbers about 2% (Caplan, 1975). Note that 1 letter gives 26 possible characters while 1 number gives 10 possible characters.

Thus, using mixtures of numbers and letters gives 36 possible choices. However, if using a mixed code, reduce errors by eliminating 1 and L and O and 0, so you really are down to 32 choices. If L and O are retained (as in people's names), don't use 1 and 0. If both L and 1 are retained, make the letter L, not 1. If both 0 and O are retained, make the letter o, not O.

Break long codes into shorter segments of 2 or 3. For example use 399-29-7456, not 399297456; use 660 50 009, not 66050009. If the product code is 2562 and style is 0148, present the information as 2 separated numbers instead of 25620148. Color can supplement digits. For example, for a visual display, one code category should be black digits on white and another category could be red digits on white.

When using voice transmission, speak slowly and pause after every 2 or 3 symbols, avoid using similar sounding characters (8 and H; E, D, C, and B), and use distinctive words such as *echo* in place of the letter E (see Table 24.6).

■ *Make the code more meaningful.* Keep a code all upper case (ABCD) or lower case (abcd) but not a mixture (Abcd). Placing key information in a prominent position in the code (i.e., first or last) is beneficial. If the user can chunk the information, errors are fewer. For example, the telephone number has a 3-digit exchange segment followed by a 4-digit random number. Be careful about including the letters O and L, as they can be confused with the numbers 0 and 1. However, letters can make codes meaningful. When using letters, keep them together rather than spreading them over all positions. RL J2042 on a Kansas license plate means the car is from Riley County and the owner's last name starts with J, K, or L, so the license expires in July. Pronounceable or meaningful letter groups (PAR) are better than random (FXT) groups. Good examples are the mnemonics for hotel phone numbers (1-800-HOLI-DAY and 1-800-2-RAMADA), the Texas Instruments service number (1-800-TI-CARES), and the Army recruiting number (1-800-USA-ARMY). Some single-letter mnemonic codes are: M = male, F = female, U = unknown; U = up, D = down; L = left, R = right; M = married, S = single, D = divorced, W = widowed; Y = yes, N = no; H = husband, W = wife, J = joint; H = hourly, S = salaried.

For computer passwords, the goal is to make them easy for you to enter and difficult for everyone else to copy. Have separate passwords for separate activities. Passwords should be a combination of letters, numbers, and symbols; use both upper and lower case; use fewer than 9 characters to reduce keying errors. An example is:

4Jly&&**

As a warehouse example, consider showing the three dimensions of a storage location. First identify the rack with a letter (2 letters if there are more than 26 racks). Then identify the position in the rack with a number (i.e., a contrast to the letter). Start at one wall and keep numbers aligned for all racks—possibly skipping numbers in some racks if necessary. Finally, identify the vertical dimension with a letter (a contrast to the number)—A is on the floor. Thus, a code M62C means rack M, 62 spaces from one wall, and the third level up.

Designing codes for word processor files is another example of the desire to code several dimensions in a single code. An outline for course 625 might be 625OUT. L12SEP could indicate a letter sent on September 12th (note how the letter–number contrast is better in L12SEP than LSEP12). On the other hand, the computer probably sorts in sequence, so the LSEP12 code would have all September letters together and then be sorted by date within September.

2.3 Abbreviations
Words can be abbreviated to speed data or command entry (i.e., reduce number of keystrokes); this is encoding. Conversely, if abbreviations are used to reduce display space, the operator must translate the abbreviation back into a word; this is decoding. Abbreviations should not include periods. (To avoid confusion, you may choose not to abbreviate inch.) Abbreviations should be used with caution; when in doubt, spell it out.

Some research results (Ehrenreich, 1985) follow:

■ For encoding, results are better when rules are followed than when people can "freewheel." The most popular rules are truncation (TRANSFER becomes TRA) and vowel deletion (TRANSFER becomes TRN). Truncation seems to give abbreviations as well or better than other rules. Encoding performance can be improved by using a simple rule and teaching that rule to the user. For example, when looking up your flight reservation, the gate agent just enters the first 3 letters of your last name.

■ For decoding, there are no consistent differences among techniques.

■ Rules best for encoding are not necessarily best for decoding.

Our personal decoding preference is vowel deletion for, as any "Wheel of Fortune" fan knows, it is easier to guess vowels than consonants. Note that a computer can be programmed to accept multiple abbreviations for the same command. For example, for DELETE the computer could accept DELETE, DEL, DTE, or even DE. However, the computer should be consistent in its display of the abbreviation; for example, always display DEL. Note also that just because you key an abbreviation into the computer doesn't mean it can't be programmed to print out the full word.

3 DECIDE AMONG MENUS, TABLES, FORMULAS, GRAPHS, SYMBOLIC MESSAGES, AND MAPS

3.1 Menus   Lists of options are called **menus.** The information may be computerized and the menu presented in a hierarchical structure (after selecting baseball, you have a list of teams; after selecting the Royals, you have a list of players). In general, menus should be deep, not shallow. That is, each level of a menu might have 10 options instead of 3 options. Avoid multiple-page menus because users get lost. With many options (such as on websites), consider multiple paths. For example, at a book site, you could get to *Work Design: Occupational Ergonomics* by Konz, S. and Johnson, S. by keying the book title or an author's name and initial. Provide shortcuts for experienced users. Options may be highlighted to reduce search time in a number of ways: underlining, boldface, reverse video, color, and blinking.

1. Minimize frame density. Less than 25% of all the possible character spaces in a frame should be filled. To keep the display uncluttered, this may require strict attention to ensure that only relevant information is displayed.
2. Have ample blank space between items. Blank space provides structure to the user. Text should be double-spaced. Groups of items should be separated by 3 to 5 rows or columns of blank space.
3. Group related items together.
4. Minimize complexity of layout. If working with a paperwork form, the form and the screen should have the same format. Words and alphanumeric data should be left-justified; numeric data should be aligned on the decimal point. Alphabetical lists are better than random lists, but alphabetical within categories is better yet. Another possibility (for a short list) is the common options listed under rule 1.

3.2 Tables   Although the distinction is not always clear, tables are divided into travel information tables and data tables.

Travel information tables present travel information. These tables are sometimes near elevators, in plane/train/bus terminals, or other public areas. The best format (Verhoef, 1993) is to structure the table so the user enters the table with known information (such as destination, sequence of alphabet) to determine the unknown (flight gate, departure time, floor of building), rather than the converse. Butler et al. (1993) reported that a series of signs is better than "you are here" maps (which tend to require too much memory and interpretation of directions).

The goal of a data table is to make patterns; exceptions should be obvious at a glance, at least if you know what they are. Eight guidelines for good table design follow.

3.2.1 *Round data to two significant digits*   Final zeros don't count. When rounded to two **significant digits,** 5311 becomes 5300 and .0511 becomes .051. The reason is that a difference of less than 1% (the third digit) rarely is important and the surplus digits make it difficult to compare the data. This rounding rule may make totals of columns and rows not exactly equal to their components. Note also that rounding is well accepted on graphs and that the basic data (in the computer, an equation, or your detailed records) need not be rounded—just the data that you present to others.

3.2.2 *Use explicit tables*   **Explicit** tables give all the information directly; **implicit** tables, however, require the user to make calculations. Table 18.6 is an explicit table of the normal distribution. In the implicit form, only the upper half of the table is printed; the reader is assumed to know that the distribution is symmetrical and to be able to "mirror" calculations. Table 18.7 shows explicit and implicit tables for converting C to F. In this implicit table, you must make additions; in other implicit forms, you interpolate.

Although implicit tables save space, they cause more errors and take more time, especially for novice users (Wright and Fox, 1970, 1972).

3.2.3 *Avoid matrix tables*   Matrix tables on a diagonal, such as Table 18.8, are bad. Use an explicit linear table, such as the telephone book or Table 18.9. Note that the table can be "folded" (have multiple columns) to save space. If a matrix table is used, present the information vertically and horizontally, as in Table 18.10.

3.2.4 *Make the primary comparison down the columns*   The eye can make comparisons more easily when reading down a column than across a row (Wright and Fox, 1970; Ehrenberg, 1977). For values, use decimals rather than fractions. Align values along a common decimal point. Within a column, put the large number on top because it is easier to do mental

T A B L E	1 8 . 6

An explicit table of the normal distribution. In an implicit table, to save paper, the table would use the mean as the reference point instead of negative infinity; it would give 5% for 1.96 (since ± 1.96 z excludes 5% in total—2.5% on the low end and 2.5% on the high end).

NUMBER OF STANDARD DEVIATIONS, Z	CUMULATIVE AREA FROM NEGATIVE INFINITY	AREA FROM MEAN $+z$
−3.84	.000 1	
−3.09	.001	
−3.0	.001 300	
−2.33	.01	
−2.0	.022 800	
−1.96	.025	
−1.64	.05	
−1.28	.10	
−1.00	.159	
−0.80	.212	
−0.60	.274	
−0.40	.345	
−0.20	.421	
0	.5	0
+0.20	.579	.1585
+0.40	.655	.3108
+0.60	.726	.4915
+0.80	.788	.5763
+1.00	.841	.6827
+1.28	.90	.80
+1.64	.95	.90
+1.96	.975	.95
+2.0	.977 200	.9545
+2.33	.99	.98
+3.0	.998 700	.9973
+3.09	.999	
+3.84	.999 9	

In the conventional table, you enter from the left (text) and scan to the right (for numbers); see Table 18.9. If you use the conventional entry on the left approach, lead the eye with lines (see Table 18.10) or dots.

But the columns can be reversed (see Table 27.10) so you first read the right-hand column (for text) and then scan to the left (for the numbers). The variation in the length of the numbers usually is small compared to the variation in the length of the text entries; see Table 14.2 for an example. Thus there is less difficulty with row alignment.

However, Allen et al. (1991) demonstrated that the conventional table arrangement, with dots (leaders) connecting the text with the numbers, took 10% less time than the numbers-on-the-left approach.

3.2.6 *Facilitate comparisons* Arrange the sequence of rows and columns. A logical grouping (categories) is better than an alphabetic sequence (McDonald, Stone, and Liebelt, 1983). The mean value in the columns can increase or decrease as you go to the right in the table, without any substantial effect on performance. People generally start in the left column. In general, the lower the usage of a column, the farther to the right it should be.

3.2.7 *Reduce column selection errors* Tinker (1963) reported better legibility for columns separated by a pica of space than by a vertical line (a rule); legibility was equal for columns separated by a pica and by a pica plus the rule. Columns also can be distinguished by printing them in different type fonts or darkness. Set off "related pairs" (e.g., observed versus theoretical; last year's data versus this year's) by close spacing between the related-pair columns (see Table 18.7).

3.2.8 *Include averages for rows and columns* The average gives a frame of reference and allows the reader to make easy comparisons between rows and between columns (i.e., the "main effects"). The average also facilitates comparisons of individual values versus the row or column mean.

subtraction between rows if the large number is on top. Put the units in the column heading, not in the table itself.

3.2.5 *Reduce row alignment errors* One technique is to divide rows into groups. (Generally, rows should be single-spaced.) Groups of 5 are better than groups of 10, which are better than no groups at all (Tinker, 1963). Grouping can be with spaces or light lines. Logical grouping, if possible, is good. Another technique is to reduce the horizontal distance between columns.

3.3 Formulas

Formulas permit exact calculations while **graphs** give approximate values and show relationships. Formulas can also be used for multiple input variables. In addition, formulas (and tables) can show many independent variables in relation to the criterion (Y is a function of A, B, C, D, and E), whereas it is difficult to show more than two variables in relation to the criterion on a graph. Formerly, hand calculations presented a problem in using formulas, but the widespread use of calculators and computers has eliminated this problem.

TABLE				18.7			

Examples of implicit and explicit tables. The less desirable implicit table saves space but requires the user to make calculations.

IMPLICIT FORMAT				EXPLICIT FORMAT			
Degrees, C	Degrees, F	Degrees, C	Degrees, F	Degrees, C	Degrees, F	Degrees, C	Degrees, F
0	32.0	1	1.8	0	32.0		
10	50.0	2	3.6	1	33.8	11	51.8
20	68.0	3	5.4	2	35.6	12	53.6
30	86.0	4	7.2	3	37.4	13	55.4
40	104.0	5	9.0	4	39.2	14	57.2
50	122.0	6	10.8	5	41.0	15	59.0
		7	12.6	6	42.8	16	60.8
		8	14.4	7	44.6	17	62.6
		9	16.2	8	46.4	18	64.4
		10	18.0	9	48.2	19	66.2
				10	50.0	20	68.0

To reduce computational errors, present the formula in units that the user will enter; the answer also should be in the desired units. For example, if the user will enter cm and wants the answer in TMU, use the first equation below, not the second. Reduce decimal point errors by presenting numbers in groups of 3 with an intervening space and following zeros. Decide how many significant digits are needed. The last equation probably has sufficient accuracy for most applications.

$$R - A = 3.488 + 1.225\ 740\ (DCM)$$
$$R - A = 3.488 + .482\ 574\ (DI)$$

TABLE				18.8			

Matrix table with diagonals. If a matrix table must be used, present the information horizontally and vertically as Table 18.10.

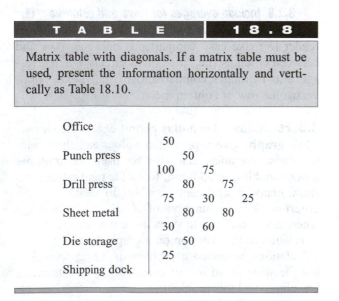

$$R - A = 3.5 + .5\ (DI)$$
where
$R - A$ = Time for R - A reach, TMU
DI = Distance, inches
DCM = Distance, cm

3.4 Graphs

The section is divided into graphs versus tables and types of graphs.

3.4.1 Graphs versus tables Use graphs to compare complex relationships; graphs are not good for determining exact relationships. Statistical graphics should help people reason about numbers; they should encourage comparisons. Graphs have an advantage over tables only when (1) the displayed data have inherent structure, and (2) the structure is relevant to the task. Use graphs to compare trends and relationships; tables are best for exact values. Design graphs to make your points about trends, relationships, and comparisons. Meyer (2000) says that exact values are reported most accurately and fastest with tables—then with bar graphs, then with line graphs.

Simple things belong in the text or in tables. Tables almost always outperform graphs for small (fewer than 20) sets of numbers.

Graphs (and tables) should be "stand-alone," as they may be duplicated and distributed separately from the report.

- Each graph or table should have a title.
- Each graph should have all axes, including units, labeled.

T A B L E	1 8 . 9

Linear explicit table. This type of table has advantages of the fewest errors in the least time, but it requires more space than matrix tables. "Fold" (have multiple columns) as shown, to save space.

Office to		Sheet Metal to	
Punch press	50	Office	75
Drill press	50	Punch press	80
Sheet metal	75	Drill press	75
Die storage	70	Die storage	30
Shipping dock	25	Shipping dock	80
Punch Press to		**Die Storage to**	
Office	50	Office	70
Drill press	100	Punch press	30
Sheet metal	80	Drill press	80
Die storage	30	Sheet metal	30
Shipping dock	50	Shipping dock	25
Drill Press to		**Shipping Dock to**	
Office	50	Office	25
Punch press	100	Punch press	50
Sheet metal	75	Drill press	60
Die storage	80	Sheet metal	80
Shipping dock	60	Die storage	25

- Tables should include units for each data column.
- Graphs and tables should appear close to the text rather than be placed in an appendix at the rear of the report.

Figure 18.4 shows the relationships of time versus distance for MTM reaches; they also are given in Table 29.1. The table is superior to the graph, as the numerical values can be obtained more easily and more accurately from the table and the graphical relationship is quite simple.

3.4.2 *Types of graphs* Figure 18.5 shows a **conversion line.** This is a poor device, as it does not have

T A B L E	1 8 . 1 0

Matrix tables are difficult for the general public to use without error, even when they do not contain diagonals. Use linear explicit tables such as Table 18.9 if possible even though they do use more space.

	1	2	3	4	5	6
1. Office	—	50	50	75	70	25
2. Punch press	50	—	100	80	30	50
3. Drill press	50	100	—	75	80	60
4. Sheet metal	75	80	75	—	30	80
5. Die storage	70	30	80	30	—	25
6. Shipping dock	25	50	60	80	25	—

Graphs show general relationships well; however, it is difficult to determine accurate values.

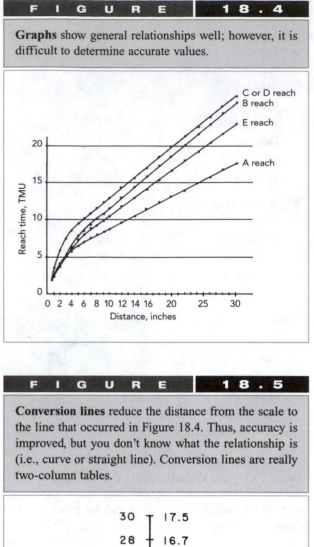

the advantage of a graph (showing a relationship) or of a table (easily providing exact numbers).

Certain types of graphs are better. The most common graph is a **time series** (see Figure 3.2); sometimes a "picture in a picture" is used in which "recent" data is displayed in the upper corner of the long-term graph. The relational graph (e.g., Figure 4.26) also is excellent. Cleveland and McGill (1985) recommend dot charts (see Figure 18.6) over divided bar graphs. Figure 18.7 shows some techniques of indicating data variability. Line charts have an advantage over vertical bar graphs (where the data point is the end of a column from the axis) in that the line chart emphasizes a key feature, the slope, without the distractions (clutter) of the vertical lines of the bars. However, line charts require a continuous axis. Scales on the axes either are continuous (time, temperature, weight) or discrete (cities, people, experimental conditions). You can connect the data points (i.e., have a line) for continuous axes (see Figure 18.4) but not for discrete axes (see Figure 18.6). Lines also are better for comparison of multiple data sets. If a bar chart

F I G U R E   1 8 . 5

Conversion lines reduce the distance from the scale to the line that occurred in Figure 18.4. Thus, accuracy is improved, but you don't know what the relationship is (i.e., curve or straight line). Conversion lines are really two-column tables.

F I G U R E   1 8 . 6

Divided bar graphs (upper figure) **versus dot charts.** Dot charts communicate better because they minimize the need to judge length and position (Cleveland and McGill, 1985).

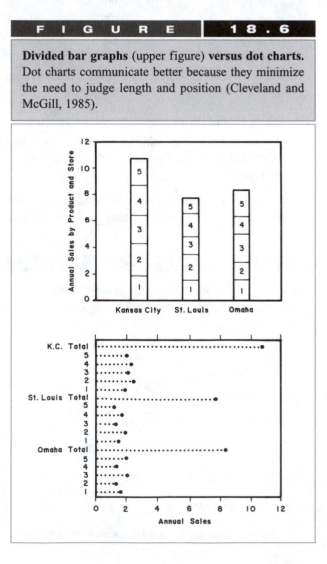

F I G U R E   1 8 . 7

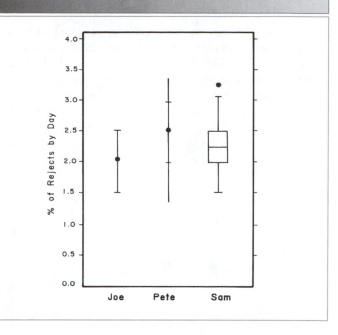

Three techniques to show data variability. Joe's data show mean and + and − 1 standard deviation (i.e., 68% confidence if data is normally distributed). However, a high confidence (such as 95%) usually is more useful. Pete's data show the mean, the inner bars at 1σ and the ends of the line at 2σ; these are 68% and 95% confidence if the data are normally distributed. Sam's data are shown as a "Tukey plot." The horizontal line is the 50th percentile of the data; the lower and upper box edges are the 25th and 75th percentile. The ends of the lines are "adjacent values." The box length is t and adjacent values are 1.5 t from the mean. Individual outliers beyond the adjacent values are shown as small circles. If the data are distributed normally, the 50% is the mean, the 25% and 75% are − and + $.675\sigma$, and the adjacent values (.4% and 99.6%) are − and + 2.67σ.

must be used, make the bars horizontal as they are much easier to label than vertical bars.

A table is almost always better than a **pie chart,** a circular chart divided into segments illustrating relative magnitudes or frequencies (which has low data density and a failure to order numbers along a visual dimension). If a pie chart is used, give the percentages in numbers on the figure. A variation on the pie chart is the **doughnut chart,** in which the sample size is displayed in the circular center section (doughnut hole). Another pie chart alternative is the double pie chart; the outer pie can be compared to the inner pie—for example, sales by division this year versus last year or cumulative trauma by division versus carpal tunnel syndrome by division.

Do not make the graph lie by using area or volume of an object (a pictograph) to represent a change in a one-dimensional value. For example, if you want to represent the height of people at different ages, don't use figures of people as the figure will increase both the height and width (i.e., area); showing a cube (such as an isometric sketch of barrels of oil of varying height to show change in oil price versus time) is even more deceiving.

Another common technique of distorting data is to start the vertical axis at a nonzero value. For example, if sales increased from $5,400,000 to $6,000,000, starting the axis at $5,000,000 is deceptive. Be careful with the semi-log graph (log of quantity on the Y axis and time on the X axis), as it is deceiving to most viewers (Taylor and Taylor, 1986). However, it does have the advantage that a constant percent change is a straight line.

For good graphs, do the following:

■ Make graphs about 50% wider than tall (Tufte, 1983), as the X axis normally is the axis to emphasize and labeling is easier than if the Y axis is longer than the X axis. (Transparency graphs, however, will fit the projection area better if they are taller than they are wide.)

■ Make scales on axes in units of 5 or even units of 2. That is, use 5, 10, 15 or 50, 100, 150 or 20, 40, 60. Avoid 1, 3, 5, 7 or 10, 30, 50. Worst of all are computerized scales where the decision to have the graph use as much of the page as possible results in scales such as 1.31, 2.62, 3.93, and the like. Under no circumstances should you change the scale interval within the scale. If you see years 1960, 1970, 1980, 1985 plotted at equal intervals or defects 1, 2, 3, 4, 5, 10 plotted at equal intervals, you know the graph is lying to you. Start each axis at zero or show a "break" symbol. Don't forget to give the units of each axis. If the scales are chosen so the data have a slope over 30°, it tends to be interpreted as being significant; a slope of 5°–10° tends to be interpreted as nonsignificant.

■ Show scale subdivisions with tick marks—especially for nonequal interval scales (log scales, probability scales). A "light" grid is helpful.

■ Don't use hatching, as it gives a "moire vibration" (Tufte, 1983). Instead, replace it with screens of varying density and shades of gray. In general, make the lower areas darkest and the top areas lightest. See Figure 18.8.

■ Use only a few curves (4 is maximum) on a single graph. Make curves distinctive by using color;

F I G U R E   1 8 . 8

Three ways of showing data. Time series should not be given as bar charts. Use a dot chart (Figure 18.6) or lines (right part of this figure). In addition, dividing the bar makes it difficult to compare components. If you insist on a bar chart, make the bars wider than the spaces between the bars, have shading go from dark on bottom (or left) to light on top (right), and make the lettering horizontal. Give the value at the end of the bar. Numbers inside columns or bars (middle figure) permit a more compact figure. Columns or bars with numbers permit omitting the scale. Best is a time series with the individual components and total displayed. Be sure that the line is much darker than the grid. Label each line rather than using keys; here the coding of products is made redundant through use of symbols and line characteristics. Note also that the legends are within instead of outside the figure. The reproduced size must consider the figure and legends; so inside labeling allows a larger reproduced size. Be sure to make the numbers large enough.

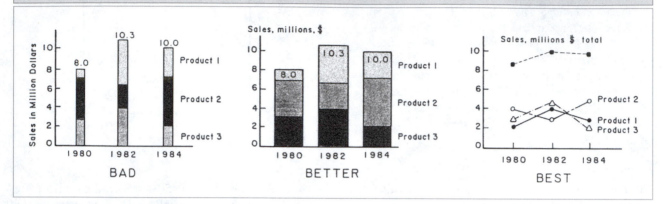

thin vs. thick lines, solid vs. dashed lines, or another method. Redundancy is good; for example, connect open circles with a dashed line and solid circles with a solid line. Color printing used to be very expensive, so the emphasis was on black and white reproduction. Now, however, color printers are common. Red, blue, and green contrast well with each other and with white paper. Contrasting symbols, such as circles versus triangles, is a last resort; if you do use them, make the symbols big and bold.

■ Indicate data points with open circles, squares, and triangles. Worst are dots, crosses, and Xs.

■ Use brief labels rather than keys (Milroy and Poulton, 1978).

■ Make labels and legends sufficiently large. Graphs often are reduced; therefore use all capital letters rather than caps and lower case, because capital letters are about 30% larger.

3.5 Symbolic Messages Symbolic messages can be language-free, can be read more quickly than the group of words they replace, can conserve space, and can be read at greater distances than text signs. Symbolic messages do not always meet all four of these ideals, however. The primary problem is errors in understanding what the symbol means, especially by novices.

Displays can be "real items," not just representations of items. For example, communications between

ships used to be through flags. A restaurant menu can be a display to the server (that you have not yet ordered).

Use color to identify categories. For example, this year's car plate could be green and next year's red. Different sections of a resort or airport terminal could have blue, red, and orange signs. Different services could be identified by color (e.g., food by green, toilets by yellow, information by orange, etc.). Parking areas could be color coded—red for floor or lot A, green for floor or lot B, and so forth.

There has been considerable use of symbolic interfaces—**icons**—on computers to replace text. For example, a traffic light with the green light on replaces "GO." Benbasat and Todd (1993) reviewed the literature on icons and demonstrated experimentally that icon representation has no advantage over text-based representation of actions and objects. Huang et al. (2002) describe factors for icon design.

Considerable research has been done on symbolic messages in the field of transportation. Examples are on vehicle controls and displays, directions at transportation terminals, and highway signs.

The symbolic messages can be geometric shapes and colors (octagonal red stop sign, shield-shaped blue interstate highway sign), diagrams (left exit from interstate highway), or pictorial silhouettes, also called **pictographs** (school crossing showing people walking, deer warning, male and female symbols on toilet doors, baggage doors at airport). As Figure 18.9 shows, in practice, words often accompany the symbols in the messages.

FIGURE 18.9

Pictographs in theory do not need the accompanying words, but real signs often retain the words. Wogalter and Sojourner (1997) demonstrated that these short verbal labels substantially improved comprehension, even if the label was removed later.

For highway use, the fact that symbolic signs can be recognized at 1 to 4 times the distance of text signs is important (Paniati, 1988); the average was 2.8 times as far. The wide range indicates that the legibility of some symbolic signs can be improved. Kline and Fuchs (1993) modified symbolic signs after studying them in a "low pass filter" and found recognition distance could be increased about 50% over the standard symbolic signs.

Arrows can indicate direction. An arrow has both a head and a shaft. Both should be present and distinguishable, and the head has to be distinct from the shaft.

Before using a symbolic message, decide if the benefits are worth the cost. Bruyas et al. (1998) point out some problems in pictograph design. Use words instead of symbols if (1) readers are novices to the message, (2) readers all use the same language, (3) space is plentiful, and (4) reading time (distance) is not critical. Field-test the proposed symbols with actual users before deciding to use the symbols. If the symbols will be used internationally, test in multiple countries.

3.6 Maps   Maps can show data distributions and relationships among locations. An example of data distribution is sales/state or region.

For relationships among locations, most maps are scaled with a dimension of distance. However, the dimension could be time (e.g., walking time from the present sport). Maps can be not-to-scale; examples are the London underground network and Figures 9.25 and 12.2.

4 PROJECT YOUR MESSAGE

Presentations to groups often include projected images. Examples are movies, videos, computer-projected slides, 35-mm slides, transparencies, and opaque projectors.

For legible displays and accurate viewing, the screen's vertical height should be 1/6 of the maximum viewing distance as measured from the far side of the display to the farthest off-axis viewer. For relatively unobstructed and comfortable viewing, the bottom of the projection should be about eye height when seated (assumed to be 48 inches above the finished floor). The screen should extend upward a distance equal to 1/6 of the maximum viewing distance. Add at least 6 inches for trim above the screen (Hanna and Konz, 2004).

$$MCH = 54 + MVD/6$$

where

MCH = Maximum ceiling height, inches

MVD = Maximum viewing distance, inches

Note that maximum viewing distance may be less than room length. Table 32.5 summarizes information on effective overhead and slide presentations.

The first decision is what medium to use. Movies and videos have the advantage of movement; they tend to require longer lead times to produce and are relatively expensive. Opaque projection and handwritten transparencies are "quick and dirty"; they tell the audience you didn't take time to prepare. The usual choice is between **slides** and **transparencies.** The slide is the high-visual-quality alternative.

4.1 Slides   The choice is 35 mm slides or computer-projected images.

4.1.1 *35 mm slides*   A 35 mm slide is normally in color, but the object presented (i.e., text) may be black and white. Then the basic decision is whether to emphasize legibility (black on white) or esthetics (colored text and/or background). Color also permits you to emphasize and organize portions of the image. For example, the heading could be one color and the subpoints another color; the advantages could be in green and the disadvantages in red. Multicolor text can be done relatively easily with various computer graphics packages.

A slide of black type or print on white paper can be made more esthetic by covering the developed film with an overlay; the result is black print with a yellow, blue, red, or green background. The overlays reduce the brightness of both the text and the background and thus reduce contrast and legibility. In my opinion, only yellow overlays are worth considering, since the pink, green, and blue overlays reduce legibility too much.

Some film will color the text red, green, blue, or another color while leaving the background white. This reduces contrast (compared to black text) but not as much as an overlay.

You may use a **reverse image**—light letters on a dark background. Although reversed images may give better legibility in a darkened room, the white letters on the film also can be "painted"; the result is yellow, green, orange (or whatever color) letters on black. Painting allows different colors on different parts of the slide. An overlay can be used that makes all the text one color with a black background.

You may use a solid color overlay (e.g., yellow) while making the background another color. An example result is yellow letters on a red background.

Reduced contrast (and, thus, reduced legibility) is more critical if the room is more brightly lighted, the audience is farther away, or the screen quality is poorer (e.g., if a back projection screen is used).

The next problem is size of individual projected characters, which will depend upon the distance of the audience from the screen. Text should be double-spaced. Graphs and tables that are satisfactory in print should be reformatted and simplified and lines emphasized for slides.

4.1.2 *Computer-projected images*

In the 1990s, computer programs (such as Microsoft's PowerPoint) for generating slides became available. They permit the slide to have a wide variety of backgrounds, font sizes, formats, colors, and so on. Graphics can be added. "Dynamic" slides can build line by line, transitions can fade, and audio and video can be added. The slides can be presented three ways. One is to present the material on conventional 35 mm slides using a slide projector. A second technique, for large group presentations, is to connect the computer to a special projector. However, these projectors are not always available. If you use such a projector, use larger fonts and excellent contrast on your slides. The third technique, the most common, is to present the material to a small group using a laptop computer.

4.2 Transparencies (Overheads)

The most common transparency is black text on clear film, giving a black image on a white screen. The background can be colored, leaving the text black, or the text can be colored (leaving the background white) either by the film or by special colored pens. Dark blue text on a white background gives a good appearance with little loss in legibility (Konz et al., 1988). Multicolor graphs can be made with computer graphics; color transparencies can be made from color photographs.

Because the projected image from a transparency is lower quality than from a slide, even more attention must be paid to character size. As a general rule, use characters larger than 18 points (printer type usually is 10 points). Use all upper case letters with a simple font such as sans serif (Verschelden and Konz, 1988). Be sure the transparency is readable from the farthest viewer position in the room you will use. Simplify graphs and tables. Note that the

projected shape is taller than it is wide. Computer printouts and detailed tables can be used by giving each audience member a printed copy and using a transparency as a map to show the audience information of interest in the handout.

4.3 Video

You may be on "candid camera," with videoconferencing, distance education, desktop video, or telemedicine. Table 18.11 gives some tips to help you appear your best on camera.

The room with the camera needs some design features:

- *Sound.* In general, use one omni-direction microphone for every two to three conferees. A lavaliere microphone may be more suitable for a person moving around. A voice-activated mixer limits the number of live mikes, thereby reducing room echo. Deaden sound reflections with acoustic treatments, including ducts and doors. Eliminate windows (noise and glare problems).

- *Lighting.* Use even, non-glare lighting with a high color rendering index.

- *Decor.* The walls should be non-distracting; use a pastel paint. Consider a sign on one wall to identify the conference site. Desks require modesty panels. Conceal electrical cords.

T A B L E	**1 8 . 1 1**

Tips for videocamera appearances.

CLOTHING

- The eye is drawn to the brightest part of the screen; your face should be the brightest part of your image. Thus, your clothes should be darker than your face.
- The camera does not show extreme contrast well. Medium pastels work well for most people. Avoid white. Don't have a black tie on a light-colored shirt or a light tie on a dark shirt.
- Avoid busy prints and small stripes and checks; solid colors are best.
- The camera doesn't reproduce highly-saturated colors well—especially red and orange. Use gray, brown, beige, and blue. Consider the set as background: you don't want to blend into the walls.
- Don't wear glittery jewelry or silk ties or scarves; they may have distracting bright reflections.

YOU

- Men: Shave within a few hours before going on camera.
- Women: Use makeup sparingly; avoid eye shadow.
- Style hair to keep it out of the eyes and allow the face to be seen from many angles.

■ *Communication.* Consider installing a phone (voice and fax), a computer outlet, and overhead and slide projectors in the room.

■ *Etiquette/procedure.* Have a detailed agenda. Start and stop on time. Number handouts; have people read handouts before the meeting. Speak in turn into the mike; avoid side conversations; don't handle paper near the mikes.

5 SELECT THE INSTRUMENT DISPLAY

Instrument displays are divided into four categories: discrete, continuous, representational, and video.

(1) **Discrete** (also called qualitative) displays indicate a status among a finite choice of options, such as go/slow/stop or on/off; (2) **continuous** (also called quantitative) displays indicate a point on a scale, as with a clock; (3) **representational** (also called pictorial) displays show a diagram or picture of the system being measured; and (4) video. Carefully analyze the operator's specific task before selecting a specific instrument among or within the four categories. For a short checklist, see sections G and I of Table 8.2.

With increasing computerization, the operator often becomes more of a supervisor than an active operator, so warning messages have become more common. Warning signals can fail with false signals, missing signals, and multiple signals (Bliss and Gilson, 1998). False signals can be minimized at the cost of missing dangerous situations. But if there are too many false alarms, the operator tends to ignore them (the "cry wolf" phenomenon). Missing signals may be the result of the operator turning off the alarm because of too many false alarms. Multiple alarms can be attributable to the tendency to signal "everything" (at one loss-of-coolant incident at a nuclear reactor, more than 800 annunciators changed status within the first 2 minutes); information about everything may be information about nothing.

Emergency messages should (1) be both visual and aural, (2) be within the primary field of view, and (3) give guidance information rather than status information (i.e., "Turn off pump 3 due to overheating" rather than "Pump 3 is overheating.") Table 18.12 gives a checklist for visual alerts.

Lighting problems with instruments are often due to too much light (i.e., from the sun) rather than too little. This veiling luminance (glare) tends to desaturate colors, decreasing any color-coding effect, as well as decreasing legibility. Computer-generated displays, with their low contrast, tend to "wash out." Careful shielding and nonreflective glass covers help.

TABLE 18.12

Visual alerts on VDTs (Cardosi and Murphy, 1995).

■ The design effectively directs the user's attention by means of alerting, coding, and emphasizing techniques.

■ High-alerts and other critical information are located within the central display area (the central 15° of the area where the user normally looks, given the normal viewing position).

■ Alerts have a low incidence of false alarms.

■ For a time-critical warning system (such as a conflict detection or resolution advisory), the user response time that is assumed by the algorithm has been measured.

■ The same color-coding strategy is applied to every display used by the same controller.

■ For status:
  ■ red is used only for warning/danger.
  ■ yellow is used to indicate caution.
  ■ green is used to indicate normal/ready.

■ Highlighting and blinking are used sparingly.

■ Information that the user must read and understand quickly (such as alarms and critical error messages), never blinks or flashes rapidly (> 3 Hz).

■ If blinking is used:
  ■ the user can cancel it.
  ■ no more than two levels of blinking are used.
  ■ information that is blinking has an "on" period at least as long as the "off" period.
  ■ the blink rate is between 2 and 3 Hz.

5.1 Discrete Discrete status (motor is running or not running, power is on or off, system status is go or no go) often is indicated by indicator or warning lights. Traffic lights (red = stop, yellow = caution, green = go) are an example of multiple discrete levels with color coding. Table 18.13 summarizes some indicator and warning light recommendations.

A control position also can act as a display. It is better if the meaning of the position is confirmed by a legend. On automobiles, a legend confirms the position of the automatic transmission lever but no legend confirms the position of manual door locks (you must not only know that up = unlocked and down = locked but also must be able to visually recognize which state the control is in).

5.2 Continuous Continuous scales are divided into two versions: analog and digital.

5.2.1 *Analog* The **analog** instrument typically has a pointer and a scale. In some designs, the scale is omitted (e.g., a clock with hands on a blank background). In other designs, the scale is omitted but the background is

Indicator and warning light recommendations (Eastman Kodak, 1983; Hutchinson, 1981; Sanders and McCormick, 1993).

- Label the light so people know what it is indicating.

- Indicator and warning lights have to be detectable. First of all, they must be close to the operator's line of sight (say 30°)—certainly not behind the operator or in another room. For remote warnings, use an auditory warning plus indicator lights. Second, they need to be reasonably bright—especially in sunlight or well-lighted areas. Third, consider reducing background clutter to improve detectability; one example is a solid black panel around traffic lights.

- Use steady state for continuous, ongoing conditions; use flashing for warnings requiring immediate attention. For nonemergency warnings, a tradeoff has to be made between alerting the user and the annoyance of a flashing light.

- Flash rate (if used) should be approximately 4/s (range 2–10/s) with approximately 50% on and 50% off time. If the flashing light is connected to a time (e.g., self-timer on a camera), an increase in the flash rate can indicate when the period is ending.

- Warning lights generally should be red (because of population stereotype) or possibly yellow. A different color can be used to differentiate types of warning (blue lights for police cars, red lights for ambulances).

- Warnings should be indicated by a light coming on (a "quiet dark" display), not the light going off. Either a bulb-test capability or 2 bulb assemblies should be used.

color-coded (e.g., background for automobile oil pressure is green, yellow, or red). This is an attempt to communicate meaning instead of a mere number. The pointer does give more information than discrete "idiot lights," but the skilled specialist likes to have numbers as well as just a colored background. The goal is to maximize legibility of the pointer and the scale.

Generally, there should be only one pointer per instrument. (In spite of generations of experience with clocks, two pointers often lead to confusion.)

Good pointers (Sanders and McCormick, 1993) have:

- a point (about 20° tip angle), not a "fancy" tip
- a tip that doesn't overlap the scale but doesn't meet it either (maximum gap of 2 mm)
- the pointer close to scale surface to avoid parallax
- good color contrast versus scale, preferably same color as lettering
- the pointer extending one direction from center (for circular scale)
- the pointer moving off scale if the meter fails.

The scale should be legible:

- Scale numbers should progress by 1s, 2s, or 5s. If decimals are needed, omit the zero before the decimal point.
- Numbers should be large enough.
- Numbers should increase clockwise, left to right, bottom to top.
- The 0 should be at a logical position. For round dials with a continuous scale, put 0 at 9 or 12 o'clock. If the scale has a gap, put the 0 at 6, 7, or 12 o'clock.

- Numbers should be oriented vertically. (For a moving circular scale and fixed pointer, align the numbers radially so they are vertical when opposite the pointer.)
- If a window is used, two numbers should appear in the window to indicate movement direction.

The pointer and scale arrangement can be a fixed scale and moving pointer (in both circular and linear versions) or a moving scale and fixed pointer (also in both circular and linear versions). See Table 18.15.

5.2.2 Digital The **digital** instrument gives the numerical value directly. Examples are digital clocks, digital speedometers, digital radio frequencies, digital television channels, and digital odometer mileage. Figure 18.10 shows a digital caliper. For digital counters, numbers should:

- be large enough
- have a character height-to-width ratio of 1:1 (due to distortion of curved drum surface)
- have no more than one digit appear in a window at a time (In addition, numbers should change by snap action, not continuous movement.)
- not be shielded from view or shadowed by the sides of the instrument
- have spacing (commas, decimal point, or space every 3 numbers) if more than 4 numbers are to be read
- advance (on manual counters) about 50 counts for one revolution of the control knob.

Andre and Segal (1996) discussed the problem of easily and accurately setting clocks on products. The first point is that a "Set clock" button is needed.

TABLE 18.14

Comparison of three types of mechanical displays (*Human Engineering Design Data Digest,* 1984).

USE	FIXED SCALE MOVING POINTER	MOVING SCALE FIXED POINTER	COUNTER
Continuous information	*Fair:* May be difficult to read when pointer is in motion.	*Fair:* May be difficult to read when scale is in motion.	*Good:* Minimum time and error for exact numerical value.
Discrete information	*Good:* Easy to locate pointer; numbers and scale need not be read; position change is easily detected.	*Poor:* Hard to judge direction and amount of deviation without reading numbers and scale.	*Poor:* Numbers must be read; position changes are hard to detect.
Setting	*Good:* Simple, direct relation of pointer motion to setting knob; position change aids monitoring.	*Fair:* Possible ambiguous relation of motion to setting knob; no pointer position change to aid monitoring; not readable during rapid setting.	*Good:* Most accurate monitoring of numerical settings; relation of display to setting knob not as direct as moving pointer; not readable during rapid setting.
Tracking	*Good:* Pointer position is easily controlled and monitored; simplest relation to manual control motion.	*Fair:* No position change to aid monitoring; ambiguous relation to control motion.	*Poor:* No gross changes to aid monitoring.
General	Largest exposed and lighted panel area; scale length is limited unless multiple pointers are used.	Only small section of scale need be exposed and lighted; use of tape allows long scale.	Least space and light. Scale length is limited only by number of counter drums.

FIGURE 18.10

Digital displays permit the user to obtain the number directly (here a diameter of .7495 inches) instead of converting analog information. The left button on the caliper switches the reading between mm and inches. The right button sets the distance to 0 (say from .750) so the reading would show deviation from the nominal—that is, it acts as a gauge.

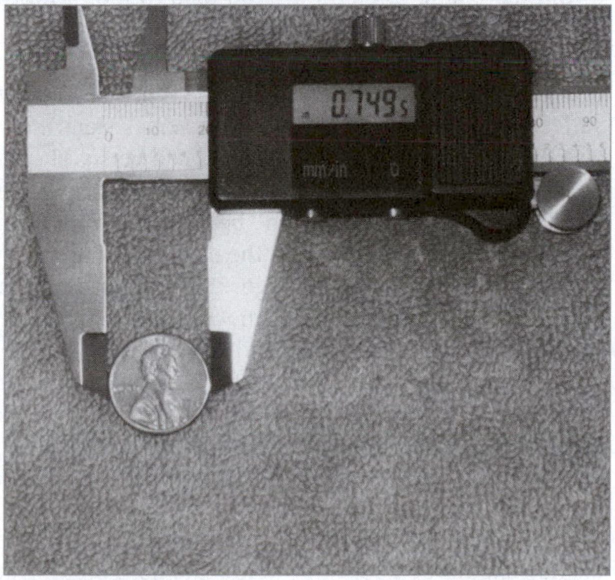

Second, the user must be able to change the time easily. Third, select A.M. or P.M. (if differentiated).

5.3 Representational These pictorial displays (graphic panels) mimic the status of a system. One example is the light display on auto control panels showing which doors are not closed. Chemical process plants, railroad switchyards, factory conveyor networks, and HVAC systems also often have a series of lights indicating the status of various components of a system. Pilots can be given information concerning the angle of the wings versus the ground. Pictorial views usually are **outside-in** (i.e., view from outside the system), although **inside-out** (pilot's eye view) is used occasionally.

5.4 Video Monitors can combine many types of displays, including text. Screens typically are identified as VGA (resolution of 640 × 480), SVGA (resolution of 800 × 600), or XGA (resolution of 1024 × 768). Tables 18.12 and 18.15 give some guidelines. Also see Box 13.1.

6 LOCATE/ARRANGE THE DISPLAY

6.1 Location Since visual displays are visual, locate them where they can be seen easily. Although that sounds obvious, there are many examples of displays that are "around the corner," too high,

T A B L E	1 8 . 1 5

VDT screen design guidelines (Liu, 1997, adapted from Smith and Mosier, 1986; Tullis, 1988; and Murch, 1987).

SCREEN DESIGN (FROM TULLIS)

- Use familiar data formats.
- Arrange related items as groups.
- Present information in a proper sequence.
- Use tabular formats with column headings.
- Avoid unnecessary details.
- Use concise wording.
- Make appropriate use of abbreviations.
- Use highlighting to attract user attention to certain elements.

DATA DISPLAY (FROM SMITH AND MOSIER)

- Display data in directly usable forms.
- Maintain consistent format from one display to another.
- Use short, simple sentences.
- Use affirmative rather than negative statements.
- Left-justify columns of alphabetic data to allow rapid scanning.
- Label each page to show its relation to other pages.
- Provide an information header or title for every display.
- When blink-coding is used, the blink rate should be 2 to 5 Hz.

SCREEN COLOR (FROM MURCH)

- Do not overuse colors.
- Use similar colors to convey similar messages.
- Not all colors are equally discernible.
- For color-weak viewers, avoid single-color distinctions.
- Avoid pure blue for text, thin lines, and small shapes.
- Avoid red and green in the periphery of large-scale displays.
- Use a common background color to group related elements.
- Use brightness and saturation to draw viewer attention.

Source: Y. Liu. "Software User Interface Design," 1689–1724. In *Handbook of Human Factors and Ergonomics,* 2nd ed., G. Salvendy (ed.). Copyright © 1992 by John Wiley & Sons. Reprinted by permission of John Wiley & Sons, Inc.

too low, and so forth. As a small example, the architect for an office building put the room numbers above the office doors; since people rarely look at the ceiling, visitors had difficulty finding specific offices.

Hendrick (1996) reported that the center-high-mounted brake lamp on vehicles (versus depending only on the lower lamps) avoids 126,000 crashes/yr at a property savings of $910,000,000/yr; medical savings are in addition!

F I G U R E	1 8 . 1 1

Three head landmarks are the ear canal (meatus), the corner at which the eyelids meet (canthus), and the lower rim of the eye socket (orbis) (Kroemer, 1993). The ear–eye line passes through the ear canal and the eyelid corner. The Frankfurt line passes through the ear canal and the lower rim of the socket; it is about 11° below the ear–eye line. Using the ear–eye line as a reference, the line of sight (LOS), projected into the sagittal plane, gives the angle LOSEE.

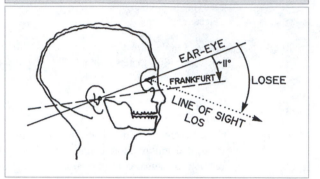

Source: Erratum figure for "Locating the Computer Screen: How High, How Far?" by K. H. E. Kroemer. *Ergonomics in Design,* 40, Jan. 1994. Karl Kroemer, ISE Dept., Virginia Tech, 551 Whittemore Hall, Blacksburg, VA 24061; 540/231-5677, fax 540/231-3322; karlk@vt.edu. Reprinted with permission from *Ergonomics in Design,* 1994. Copyright © 1994 by the Human Factors and Ergonomics Society. All rights reserved.

Another aspect of vision is the lighting. Some common visual display problems are: too much light (direct, reflected glare), too little light, and locating displays where people with bifocals can't read them. See Chapter 23.

A good location for name badges at meetings is centered just below the chin. The badge is hung around the neck with a string to avoid the need to clip or pin the badge to clothing. You tend to look toward the face when looking at the badge.

For computer monitor location, consider (1) the eye height and (2) the head orientation. Eye height varies—primarily due to posture (sit versus stand), but also due to stature (adult versus child, tall versus short).

The next challenge is the head orientation. The orientation of the eye can be specified as the Frankfurt Plane (line between the earhole and the bottom of the eye socket). See Figure 18.11 and Heuer et al. (1991). The Frankfurt Plane coincides with the horizontal when the head is held straight up.

Kroemer and Hill (1986) and Hill and Kroemer (1986) studied the preferred **line of sight;** 90% of all their data were within a 20° cone about the line of sight.

Hill and Kroemer (1986) reported the preferred angle was about 30° below the Frankfurt Plane. Thus, if you believe the head will be held straight up, the display should be about 30° below the horizontal. But they also found a typical seated operator has a forward head tilt of 10–15°. This would place the line of sight at 40–45° below the horizontal.

Naturally, as the number of displays increases, not every display can be at the optimum location.

6.2 Arrangement   For an excellent detailed discussion of panel design, see Kinkade and Anderson (1984). The panel of instruments may include some controls. The goal is to organize the items on the panel to aid operator performance. Therefore, the first requirement is to determine what the operator is required to do. Consistency is important in tying items together or separating them and in establishing visual patterns. Hence, there should be an overall plan for the panel as well as all panels in the facility.

An early decision is the grouping logic. For example, assume the facility has 3 packaging lines, each with 6 different machines, and each machine has a number of displays of motor status, process temperature, and so forth. Communicate the display logic to the user by panel color, lines on the panel, shape of the instruments, etc. For example, if the display is grouped by the three packaging lines, line 1 displays might have a brown panel background, line 2 displays have grey, and line 3 displays have blue. Or, all line 1 displays are grouped and surrounded by a line. Or, all temperature displays are 3 inches in diameter, all motor status displays are indicator lights, etc. There is no general rule for which logic is best, but some logical format must be decided upon and implemented consistently.

Computer programs allow the designer to simulate the grouping of displays on a panel (Metz et al., 1987; Palmiter and Elkerton, 1987). Consider "link analysis" of the displays (see Section 2 of Chapter 9). The displays are the areas to arrange.

Palmiter and Elkerton's program uses four criteria for panel layouts:

1. Overall density—the ratio of the free space (space in the panel not occupied by controls or displays) to occupied space.

2. Local density—how close the controls or displays are to each other. The general goal is to group related items closely and then separate them by blank space or lines.

3. Layout complexity—the irregularity of control and display arrangement. If the upper left edges of controls or displays are in horizontal or vertical lines, complexity is low.

4. Display grouping—the number of displays and display groups. The goal is to group like-functioned entities.

Some instrument displays are in "control rooms" in which a seated operator monitors the displays (often with the aid of a computer). Two guidelines are:

1. *Avoid extreme postures.* To reduce neck problems, consider placing displays so the gaze is relatively low. For backs, use chairs with easy adjustments. For wrists, consider a joystick rather than a mouse.

2. *Vary posture.* Perhaps the best way is to encourage getting out of the chair. Example techniques are to place the phone so the person must stand to answer it and to require the operator to move to other locations in the room (e.g., to do other tasks such as go to the reception desk or get material from a printer).

Review Questions

1. Give the two levels at which a display can fail to communicate.

2. What is the recommended handwriting form for the capital letters U and V? For the numbers 4 and 9?

3. What is the optimum stroke width for black on white? For white on black?

4. What are two ways of improving readability of text on a VDT screen by changing the format?

5. Approximately how much higher are capital letters than lower case letters?

6. Give some examples of how a telephone number can be presented so as to reduce errors.

7. How can you reduce confusion with the numbers 0 and 1?

8. Assume you have 5,000 bin locations in your stockroom. Describe your recommended coding system, giving at least two example bin codes.

9. For the command COMPRESS, give a 3-digit abbreviation using the truncation rule and the vowel deletion rule.

10. Design a system for frequent-flyer numbers. Justify your design.

11. Should data in tables be rounded to 2 significant digits? Why?

12. Give an example of an implicit and an explicit table. Which is best to minimize errors?

13. When should a graph be used, and when a table?

14. Should lettering on graphs be all capitals or capitals and lower case? Why?

15. Give three different ways to make a figure deceiving.

16. Should graphs be wider than tall or vice-versa?

17. Should lines on graphs be labeled or keyed?

18. When should a word message be used in place of symbols?

19. Give the four categories of instrument displays and an example of each.

20. When should numbers on a scale be aligned radially?

21. Briefly discuss the angle for the preferred line of sight.

References

Allen, R., Bailey, R., McIntyre, G., and Bozza, M. Placement of menu choices. *Proceedings of the Human Factors Society,* 379–82, 1991.

American National Standard for Human Factors Engineering of Visual Display Terminal Workstations. Santa Monica, CA: Human Factors Society, ANSI/HFS 100, 1988.

Andre, A. and Segal, L. A matter of time. *Ergonomics in Design,* Vol. 4, No. 3, 4–6, 1996.

Angiolillo, J. and Roberts, L. What makes a manual look easy to use? *Proceedings of the Human Factors Society,* 222–24, 1991.

Association for Computing Machinery. *Communications of ACM,* Vol. 12, No. 12, 697–98, December 1969.

Benbasat, I. and Todd, P. An experimental investigation of interface design alternatives: Icon versus text and direct manipulation versus menus. *Int. J. Man-Machine Studies,* Vol. 38, 369–402, 1993.

Bliss, J. and Gilson, R. Emergency signal failure: Implications and recommendations. *Ergonomics,* Vol. 41, No. 1, 57–72, 1998.

Bruyas, M-P., Le Breton, B., and Pauzie, A. Ergonomic guidelines for the design of pictorial information. *Int. J. of Industrial Ergonomics,* Vol. 21, 407–13, 1998.

Butler, D., Acquino, A., Hissong, A., and Scott, P. Wayfinding by newcomers in a complex building. *Human Factors,* Vol. 35, No. 1, 159–73, 1993.

Caplan, S. Guidelines for reducing human errors in the use of coded information, *Proceedings of the Human Factors Society,* 154–58, 1975.

Cardosi, K. and Murphy, E. (eds.). *Human Factors Checklist for the Design and Evaluation of Air Traffic Control Systems* (DOT/FAA/RD-95/3.1). Springfield, VT: National Technical Information Service, 1995.

Chang, P. T. and Konz, S. Character size versus viewing distance on VDTs. In *Work with Display Units,* Luczak, H., Cakir, A., and Cakir, G. (eds.). Amsterdam: Elsevier, 1993.

Cleveland, W. and McGill, R. Graphical perception and graphical methods for analyzing scientific data. *Science,* Vol. 229, 828–33, August 30, 1985.

Dillon, A. Reading from paper versus screens: A critical review of the empirical literature. *Ergonomics,* Vol. 35, No. 10, 1297–1326, 1992.

Eastman Kodak. *Ergonomic Design for People at Work,* Vol. 1. Belmont, CA: Lifetime Learning Publications, 1983.

Ehrenberg, A. Rudiments of numeracy. *J. Royal Statistical Society,* Vol. 140, No. 3, 277–97, 1977.

Ehrenreich, S. Computer abbreviations: Evidence and synthesis. *Human Factors,* Vol. 27, No. 2, 143–55, 1985.

Faulkner, T. Keep it simple. *AIIE Ergonomics News,* April 1972.

Garvey, P., Pietrucha, M., and Meeker, D. Clearer road signs ahead. *Ergonomics in Design,* Vol. 6, No. 3, 7–11, July 1998.

Gould, J. and Grischkowsky, N. Does visual angle of a line of characters affect reading speed? *Human Factors,* Vol. 28, No. 2, 165–73, 1986.

Grandjean, E. *Ergonomics in Computerized Offices.* London: Taylor and Francis, 1987.

Hanna, S. and Konz, S. *Facility Design: Manufacturing Engineering,* 3rd ed. Scottsdale, AZ: Holcomb Hathaway, 2004.

Helander, M. Design of visual displays. In *Handbook of Human Factors,* Salvendy, G. (ed.), Chapter 7. New York: Wiley & Sons, 1987.

Hendrick, H. Good ergonomics is good economics. *Proceedings of the Human Factors and Ergonomics Society,* Santa Monica, CA: HFES, 1–10, 1996.

Heuer, H., Bruwer, M., Romer, T., Kroger, H., and Knapp, H. Preferred vertical gaze direction and observation distance. *Ergonomics,* Vol. 34, No. 3, 379–92, 1991.

Hill, S. and Kroemer, K. Preferred declination of the line of sight. *Human Factors,* Vol. 28, No. 2, 127–34, 1986.

Huang, S-M., Shieh, K-K., and Chi, C-F. Factors affecting the design of computer icons. *Int. J. of Industrial Ergonomics,* Vol. 29, 211–18, 2002.

Human Engineering Design Data Digest. Redstone, AL: Human Engineering Laboratory, U. S. Army Missile Command, 1984.

Hutchinson, R. *New Horizons for Human Factors in Design.* New York: McGraw-Hill, 1981.

Kinkade, R. and Anderson, J. *Human Factors Guide for Nuclear Power Plant Control Room Development* (NP-3659). Palo Alto, CA: EPRI, 1984.

Kline, D. and Fuchs, P. The visibility of symbolic highway signs can be increased among drivers of all ages. *Human Factors,* Vol. 35, No. 1, 25–34, 1993.

Konz, S., Braun, E., Jachindra, K., and Wichlan, D. Human transmission of numbers and letters. *J. of Industrial Engineering,* Vol. 19, No. 5, 219–24, 1968.

Konz, S., Jackson, R., Knowles, J., and Verschelden, M. Legible and attractive transparencies. *Proceedings of Int. Ergonomics Association 1988.* London: Taylor and Francis, 1988.

Konz, S. and Mohan, R. The effect of illumination level, stroke width and figure ground on legibility of

NAMEL numbers. *Proceedings of the Human Factors Society,* 431–35, 1972.

Kroemer, K. Locating the computer screen: How high, how far. *Ergonomics in Design,* 7–8, October 1993.

Kroemer, K. and Hill, S. Preferred line of sight angle. *Ergonomics,* Vol. 29, No. 9, 1129–34, 1986.

Kruk, R. and Mutter, P. Reading of continuous text on video screens. *Human Factors,* Vol. 26, No. 3, 339–45, 1984.

Liu, Y. Software-user interface design. In *Handbook of Human Factors and Ergonomics,* 2d ed., Salvendy, G. (ed.). New York: Wiley, 1689–1729, 1997.

McDonald, J., Stone, J., and Liebelt, L. Searching for items in menus: The effects of organization and type of target. *Proceedings of the Human Factors Society,* 834–37, 1983.

Metz, S., Richardson, R., and Nasirudden, M. Rapid software for prototyping user interfaces. *Proceedings of the Human Factors Society,* 1000–04, 1987.

Meyer, J. Performance with tables and graphs: Effects of training and a visual search model. *Ergonomics,* Vol. 3, 11, 1840–65, 2000.

Milroy, R. and Poulton, E. Labelling graphs for improved reading speed. *Ergonomics,* Vol. 21, No. 1, 55–61, 1978.

Murch, G. Color graphics: Blessing or ballyhoo? In *Readings in Human-Computer Interaction: A Multidisciplinary Approach,* Baecker R. and Buxton W. (eds.). San Mateo, CA: Morgan Kaufmann, 333–41, 1987.

Palmiter, S. and Elkerton, J. Evaluation metrics and a tool for control panel design. *Proceedings of the Human Factors Society,* 1123–27, 1987.

Paniati, J. Legibility and comprehension of traffic sign symbols. *Proceedings of the Human Factors Society,* 568–72, 1988.

Perry, D. Speed and accuracy of reading: Arabic and Roman numerals. *J. of Applied Psychology,* Vol. 36, 346–47, October 1952.

Sanders, M. and McCormick, E. *Human Factors in Engineering and Design,* 7th ed. New York: McGraw-Hill, 1993.

Sherr, S. *Electronic Displays.* New York: Wiley-Interscience, 1979.

Shurtleff, D. *How to Make Displays Legible.* La Mirada, CA: Human Factors Design, 1980.

Smith, S. Letter size and legibility. *Human Factors,* Vol. 21, No. 6, 661–70, 1979.

Smith, S. and Mosier, J. *Guidelines for designing user interface software* (Report ESD TR 86 278). Bedford, MA: Mitre Corp., 1986.

Stanhagen, J. and Carlson, J. Identifying and controlling coding errors in information systems. *Ergonomics,* Vol. 22, No. 4, 441–52, 1970.

Taylor, B. and Taylor, W. Graphs that result in erroneous conclusions. *Proceedings of Int. Industrial Eng. Conference,* 470–76, 1986.

Tinker, M. *Legibility of Print.* Ames, IA: Iowa State Press, 1963.

Trollip, S. and Sales, G. Readability of computer-generated fill-justified text. *Human Factors,* Vol. 28, No. 2, 159–63, 1986.

Tufte, E. *The Visual Display of Quantitative Information.* Cheshire, CT: Graphics Press, 1983.

Tullis, T. The formatting of alphanumeric displays: A review and analysis. *Human Factors,* Vol. 25, No. 6, 657–82, 1983.

Tullis, T. Screen design. In *Handbook of Human-Computer Interaction,* Helander M. (ed.). Amsterdam: Elsevier, 377–411, 1988.

Verhoef, L. A new conceptual structure for travel information. *Applied Ergonomics,* Vol. 24, No. 4, 263–69, 1993.

Verschelden, M. and Konz, S. Absolute and relative ratings of type fonts and styles. *Proceedings of Ergonomics Society 1988.* London: Taylor and Francis, 1988.

Wilkins, A. and Nimmo-Smith, M. The clarity and comfort of printed text. *Ergonomics,* Vol. 30, No. 12, 1705–20, 1987.

Winkler, R. and Konz, S. Readability of electronics displays. *Proceedings of SID,* Vol. 21, No. 4, 309–13, 1980.

Wogalter, M. and Sojourner, R. Comprehension and retention of safety pictorials. *Ergonomics,* Vol. 40, No. 5, 531–42, 1997.

Wright, P. and Fox, K. Presenting information in tables. *Applied Ergonomics,* Vol. 1, 234–42, 1970.

Wright, P. and Fox, K. Explicit and implicit tabulation formats. *Ergonomics,* Vol. 15, No. 2, 175–87, 1972.

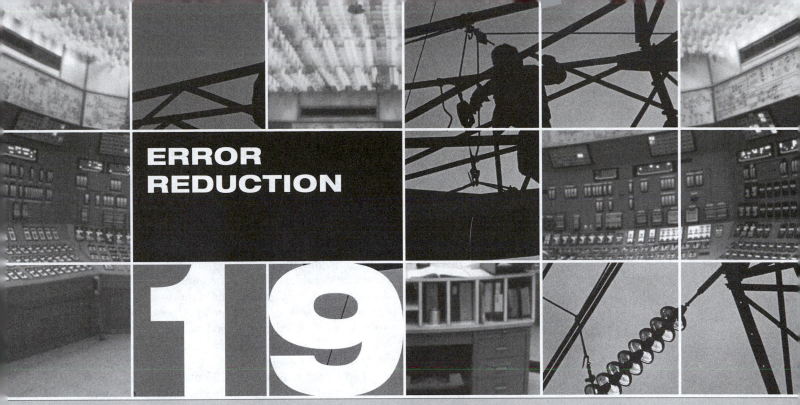

ERROR
REDUCTION

19

Overview

Error reduction is a major goal of ergonomics. This chapter discusses many aspects of errors and error reduction. Ten guidelines for error reduction are given.

Key Concepts

calibration

closed-loop/open-loop
    system

cognitive ergonomics

detectability

ease of recovery

error

error-checking code

error costs

fail-safe

information feedback

inspection

job aid

justifications for
    ergonomics

latent failures

lockout/tagout

maintenance budget

malice

memory aids

mistakes

omission/commission

open and obvious

paired comparison

population
    stereotypes

protocols

receiver operating
    curve

redundancy

signal detection
    theory

signal/noise ratio

slips

social pressure

type 1/type 2

INTRODUCTION

Ergonomics is a design philosophy. Common goals are safety, productivity, and user (operator) satisfaction. Two common **justifications for ergonomics** (leading to these goals) are reduction of physical stress on people and reduction of errors (waste). Error reduction often is called **cognitive ergonomics.**

Reduction of errors, of course, is strongly related to both safety and quality. Perhaps not as obvious is that reduced errors give a strong improvement in productivity. So reduced errors benefit safety, quality, and productivity. The general concept of ergonomics is to reduce stress, typically by reducing job demand.

Stress Index = Job Demand/Worker Capability

Errors are caused by poor design and management of equipment, procedures, and training, among other factors. Errors are therefore not beyond control ("acts of God") but are events that can be reduced. For example, birds striking an aircraft could be considered an "act of God" and therefore impossible to prevent. Two prevention strategies are using collies to drive birds from airports and choosing routes with fewer birds (consult www.ahas.com for routes).

Because error reduction is discussed throughout the book, this chapter consolidates the information.

1.1 Definitions An **error** is defined as an event when "an action other than desired takes place." We will be concerned with quick actions, not actions with long-term results such as selecting a poor handtool that gives musculoskeletal disorders.

The general sequence is: normality—error—accident—minor loss (time, property, person)—major loss—catastrophe. An example of time loss would be the time to pick up a dropped part. An example of property loss would be damage to the dropped part. An example of person loss would be an injured toe from the dropped part. The goal is to maintain normality as much as possible.

Rather than considering accidents as due to unpredictable events and unpreventable events, challenge the adjectives *unpredictable* and *unpreventable* to reduce accidents. In addition to the strategy of reducing errors, consider "breaking the chain" that makes errors turn into accidents, losses, and catastrophes. As discussed in Section 1.1 of Chapter 20, there is considerable similarity between minor and major accidents; thus, a study of minor accidents and even near accidents can be fruitful.

1.2 Costs and Cost Reduction This section considers error costs and error cost reduction.

1.2.1 Costs **Error costs** (the negative results of mistakes) can range from a few seconds of lost time to multiple millions of dollars. The cost of human injury and death is especially difficult to quantify. Other obscure costs are costs of cleanup, fines, loss of market share, and legal costs. Context may turn a trivial error into a costly error; the person committing the error may not even realize there was an error. For example, what if a client's name is misspelled on a report and, because of this, the contract is not renewed? What if a potential vendor is late for a meeting and thus loses the contract because the customer considers the vendor unreliable? The vendor may not even realize an error was made! Or consider the story of a student who lost out on a job offer because he salted his food before tasting it at a lunch interview. (The recruiter took this as a sign of hasty decision making.)

Part of the reason it is difficult to quantify error costs is that errors and their costs often are concealed. People do not want to broadcast to the world (or at least to their supervisors) that they made an error. It is easier to conceal errors (at least in the formal, paperwork, on-the-record system). Errors should not be individualized; experience has shown that the best approach is to assume initially the error is due to "the system."

Even governments conceal errors. For example, in 1970, the government of Iraq purchased about 96,000 tons of seed grain (Casey, 1993). It was treated with alkylmercury fungicide to inhibit spoilage. The grain was dyed red, and each bag displayed a skull and crossbones and a warning (in English) that the grain could not be consumed or fed to animals. But, in 1972, the crops failed in northern Iraq. The government distributed the grain without warnings that it was only for seeding and could not be consumed. About 60,000 Kurds suffered neurological damage; the government imposed a news blackout to the rest of the world.

Our society does not perceive all costs equally. For example, society considers a death in a nuclear power plant as more important than a death in a coal mine. Occupational deaths (especially for large corporations) are considered more important than nonoccupational deaths. The success of certain organizations (e.g., air traffic control, aircraft carriers) indicates that failure does not have to be an option. These organizations tend to have detailed "standard operating procedures" and "excessive" emphasis on communication and training.

1.2.2 Cost reduction Generally, pay more attention to a problem if the error's potential cost ("potential energy") is higher. For example, the potential energy of 100 tons of poisoned grain is greater than 1 ton; an airplane with 500 people has more potential energy than one with 4 people; a procedure used by 1,000 people is more important than one used by 20; and a procedure causing a system to "crash" is more important than one causing a 2 s delay.

In reducing errors, the analyst should be a scientist, not an advocate. The legalistic approach of blaming someone (instead of the engineering approach of solving the problem) does not address the root causes of the incident and, in fact, shields the incident from further scrutiny and treatment (Kirwan, 1992a). Punishment tends to lead to nonreporting of errors.

1.3 Types   There are many ways of categorizing errors. Approximately 90% of accidents are due to human error; approximately 10% are due to "technical faults" (victim was run over because vehicle accelerator stuck) (Salminen and Tallberg, 1996).

Errors can be of **omission** (passive, something not done) or **commission** (active, something done incorrectly). Commission can be further divided into errors of timing, sequence, selection, and magnitude (Proctor and van Zandt, 1993).

Errors can also be **type 1** (also called alpha risk and producer's risk) or **type 2** (also called beta risk and consumer's risk). See Figure 12.30. In type 1, a good item is rejected. In type 2, a bad item is accepted. A false alarm is a type 1 error. A failure of an alarm to function is a type 2 error.

Observed error = system error ± measurement error. The point here is that what is observed can be due to either the system or the measurement of the system.

Errors can be divided into perception, decision, and action. Did the person perceive the situation incorrectly? Was the perception correct but the decision wrong? Was the decision correct but the action incorrect? **Signal detection theory** analyzes perception and decision. See Box 19.1.

The SDT concept is that an inspector's performance is determined not only by the detectability of the target but also by the criterion used by the inspector.

Rasmussen et al. (1987) say behavior is at a skill (S), rule (R), or knowledge (K) level. Skill-based behavior (S) occurs in situations requiring highly practiced and essentially automatic behavior, with only minimal conscious control. The behavior can be inadequate or inappropriate. An example of inadequate behavior would be driving a fork truck along a familiar route and missing a turn. An example of inappropriate behavior would be driving the fork truck too fast.

Rule-based behavior (R) occurs when the person deals with a situation by a stored rule (procedure) of the following form: IF *situation*, THEN *action*. The rules are either memorized or obtained from an aid. R errors can be divided into slips and mistakes. **Slips** are not deliberate, while **mistakes** results from conscious planning (i.e., the intended action is successful, but the outcome is not as anticipated). An example of a slip is misreading Baaken Lane on a map as Baker Lane. An example of a mistake is if Jane got her hair caught in moving machinery while deliberately not wearing a hairnet. Slips represent the failure of correct intentions, while mistakes represent wrong intentions.

Knowledge-based behavior (K) occurs when there are no useful rules to apply. The person must use problem-solving skills and knowledge of system characteristics. A K error is also called a *mistake*. An example would be driving through an area looking for an address not on a map and arriving at the wrong house. In general, for error reduction, eliminate applications of K behavior, then work on the R behavior.

There is relatively little knowledge of why people deliberately violate established rules and procedures. When a deliberate violation (**malice**) occurs, the difficulty of preventing the error increases dramatically. If there is a conflict between a machine and a person, the common assumption is that the machine is wrong and the person is right. However, this can lead to catastrophes such as Three Mile Island and Chernobyl, in which the operators in both cases overrode the system. If your system design permits operator override, communication to the operator and operator training should have high priority.

The following material will emphasize technical approaches to error reduction. However, error reduction is managerial as well as technical. Consider rules and regulations (both governmental and organizational) and managerial approaches such as Total Quality Management and Quality Circles (see Chapter 32). If errors are to be reduced, error reduction has to be an organizational goal.

The first step is to have an experienced designer. The design should incorporate the "state of the art." This book gives many examples of job design. For another example, Nielsen (1999) wrote an excellent book on webpage design.

The second step is a usability review. See Box 19.2.

2 ERROR ANALYSIS TECHNIQUES

Four error analysis techniques (checklists, decision structure tables, fish diagrams, and fault trees) are described in detail elsewhere in this book.

1. *Checklists.* Checklists range from detailed lists of specific questions to lists of general guidelines. See Chapters 8 and 14 for examples.

BOX 19.1 *Signal Detection Theory (SDT)*

Problem

Figure 19.1 shows, for two populations, eye pressure level. The problem is to distinguish (detect) the "signal" from the "noise." The signal is the difference between the two population means—in this case, 31 – 20 = 11. The noise is the variability (variance). To get overall variance, add the two individual variances and take the square root—in this case, 49 + 49 = a variance of 98 and a standard deviation (SD) of 9.9. The resulting **signal/noise** is 11/9.9 = 1.1.

Figure 19.2 shows the effect of making a yes–no decision using a criterion threshold of 20.

Figure 19.3, a **receiver operating curve,** plots, for various criterion threshold values, true positive probability versus false positive probability.

In this example, the "good" distribution is on the left and the "bad" is on the right. Naturally, the positions can be reversed. For example, an inspector may be inspecting shafts for length. Both good and bad shafts have a distribution. The threshold might be 300 mm—that is, any shafts less than 300 mm are bad.

You can simulate the results of various decisions using the Signal Detection program on the ERGO disk.

Solutions

One possibility is to accept the means and standard deviations as unchangeable and just vary the criterion threshold. Figure 19.4 shows the effects of using strict and lenient thresholds.

Ideally, the cost of each type of error (false alarms versus true positives) could be calculated. Then, the threshold could be set to minimize the total cost.

Another possibility is to change either the mean or standard deviation of either or both distributions. That is, change the **detectability** (discriminability) of the signal/noise ratio by either increasing the signal or by decreasing the noise.

Increasing the signal requires moving the two distributions farther apart. For example, assume the eye pressure reading is related to age. Have one pair of curves for those under age 50 and another pair of curves for those over 50. Then, a 35-year-old patient would use the set for younger people. Assume the young healthy curve had a mean of 15 and SD of 7, while the glaucoma curve had a mean of 31 and SD of 7. The distance between the two curves has increased from 11 to 16, while the variance has not changed. The new signal/noise is 16/9.9 = 1.6 versus the former 1.1. For any specific threshold, this greater distance will decrease the false alarms and give a sharper ROC—thus, a larger area under the curve.

FIGURE 19.2

Effect of criterion threshold on correct decision (Sweats et al., 2000). Assume a criterion of 20 was used. It would detect 90% of the glaucoma group (true positives) but miss 10% (false negatives). In the healthy group, 50% of the group (false positives, false alarms) would be identified falsely as having glaucoma and 50% (true negatives) would be correctly rejected as having glaucoma. Figure 19.3 shows the effect of using other threshold values such as 10, 15, 25, etc.

FIGURE 19.1

Population distributions (hypothetical) for healthy eyes (mean = 20, SD = 7) and eyes with glaucoma (mean = 31, SD = 7) (Sweats et al., 2000). Below 10, there are only healthy eyes; above 40, all eyes have glaucoma. But a reading between 10 and 40 could come from either distribution.

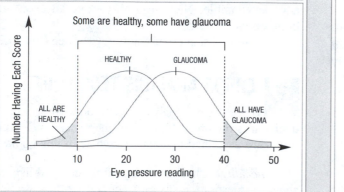

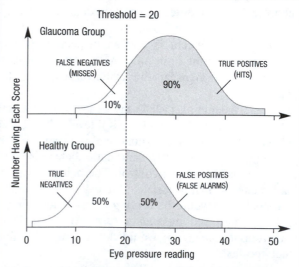

Illustrations based on those by Jennifer Johansen from Better decisions through science (box: Better decision making: step by step), *Scientific American*, October 2000.

BOX | **19.1** | *Signal Detection Theory, continued*

Another possibility is to change the variance. Again, using the age example, assume the young healthy curve had an unchanged mean of 20 but a reduced SD of 5. Then, the combined variance is 25 + 49 = 74 and SD = 8.6. The signal/noise has become 11/8.6 = 1.3 instead of 1.1.

One technique to reduce the variance is to use a more precise instrument—either a better device or a better operator (e.g., better trained). See Figure 30.1 for a discussion of random versus constant error; see Section 4.2 of Chapter 31 for information on limit aids to improve operator inspection.

FIGURE | 19.3

Receiver operating curve (ROC) plots, for various threshold values, a *y* value and an *x* value (Sweats et al., 2000). For the criterion of 20, $y = 90$ while $x = 50$. This gives one value for the curved line. (The curved line is a geometric curve of the form $Y = AX^B$ where $A = 1$; see Fig. 30.5.) The more the curve bends, the higher the amount *(A)* is under the curve. The ROC curve may be improved by using multiple criteria; for example, using patient age as well as eye pressure reading.

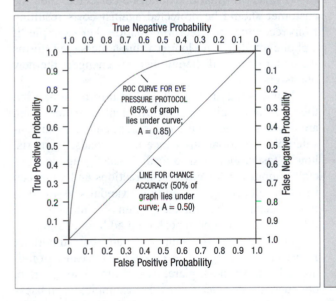

Challenges

This box describes signal detection *theory*. Implementing the theory into practice has proved to be a challenge.

One challenge has been to determine the mean and standard deviations of the two curves. In many industrial situations, both the mean and variability change as raw materials change, cutting tools wear, etc.

Another challenge has been that decision makers such as inspectors are not consistent—Joe's variance differs from Pete's, and Joe's varies from morning to afternoon. Even the threshold may vary from person to person or during the day.

However, to improve decision making, remember there are *three* variables to consider: the signal, the noise, and the criterion threshold. Work on all three.

FIGURE | 19.4

Strict versus lenient threshold (Sweats et al., 2000). Strict thresholds limit false alarms, but miss many affected causes (true positives). Lenient thresholds maximize true positives, but at a cost of many false positives. Ideally, a cost could be determined for each type of error and the total error cost could be minimized.

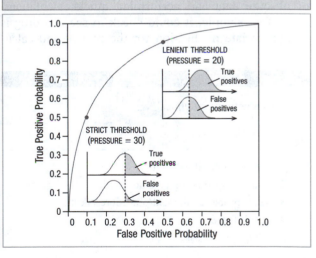

2. *Decision structure tables.* To minimize decision-making errors, use a decision structure table. See the discussion in Chapter 9 and Figures 31.4, 31.6, and 31.7.

3. *Fish diagrams.* You may wish to organize causes and effects of a situation. One approach is to make a list. However, the relationships often can be communicated more clearly in a graphic format than in a tabular format (list). Figures 9.16 and 9.17 show fish

diagrams, which are graphic presentations of a list with subheadings.

4. *Fault trees.* Errors sometimes occur only when a specific chain of events occurs. If the chain can be broken, the error will not occur. The relationships of these events is called a fault tree. See Box 20.3. See Kirwan (1992a, 1992b) for a detailed comparison of six different methods of human error identification.

19.2   *Usability Studies*

"Usability reviews" are a type of design evaluation. The general concept is to evaluate (debug) a product/process before putting it into production. For example, firms may have people try out their product while being observed through one-way mirrors.

A well-known application is beta versions of computer programs. After trying to eliminate all of the bugs in a program, the software firm gives copies of the program to hundreds or even thousands of potential users. They try it out, reporting any problems. These problems are then fixed before the final release of the program. They are not always successful as can be seen by the many numbered versions following the original release.

Another application is the "test market." Before a product has national release, it is released in a few cities or states.

3 ERROR REDUCTION GUIDELINES

Table 19.1 presents 10 general guidelines to reduce errors. The guidelines are organized in three categories: planning, execution, and allowing for error. Guidelines 1 through 5 consider planning.

Guideline 1: Get Enough Information

Getting enough information calls for (1) generating or collecting the relevant information and (2) ensuring that the user receives the information.

Generate Relevant Information

A computer has the capability of storing vast amounts of obscure data and performing quick calculations. Thus, for example, it could check to see if a drug is an appropriate medication for the patient and calculate the appropriate dose for the age and body weight; yet, if the doctor doesn't use a computer, there can be potential errors.

Generating the relevant information may be difficult if the information is subjective. How do you evaluate potential employees so the best one is hired?

Organizations have a responsibility to provide correct information to their "customers" (both internal and external customers). When the customer receives the information, the assumption is made that the information is correct. Unfortunately, this is not always true.

If false information cannot be corrected, then the customer should be protected against costs resulting from receiving incorrect information. For example, if a phone number is no longer valid, a message informs the caller of this; if the number has changed, the new one is given.

Novices require a great deal of information; often the information given is not sufficient. Travelers often are novices in the local environment and so need considerable information concerning roads, airports, hotels, restaurants, and so forth. Road signage is especially important for novices. Directions and signs can be incorrect (changed conditions, vandalism). In addition, because the traveler often is moving, the information has to be repeated on additional signs.

Good visual information can be important. However, there may not be a good view because of failure to look, darkness, glare, lack of time, snow or rain, obstructions, or other factors. For example, when backing up a vehicle, you need to look behind the vehicle. But the field of view is not complete and it is difficult to judge distances. One solution is to park so backing up isn't necessary. If backing up is necessary, however, reduce its difficulty. For example, when backing up a semitrailer, it is easier to see from the driver's side; therefore, design the shipping dock approach so the driver can back up using the left-side mirror.

A warning can alert people to potential danger. For example, in baseball a warning track in the outfield

T A B L E	1 9 . 1
Error reduction guidelines.	

Planning

1. Get enough information.
2. Ensure information is understood.
3. Have proper equipment/procedures/skill.
4. Don't forget.
5. Simplify the task.

Execution

6. Allow enough time.
7. Have sufficient motivation/attention.

Allow for Errors

8. Give immediate feedback on errors.
9. Improve error detectability.
10. Minimize consequences of errors.

alerts the fielder about a potential collision with the wall. A yellow band behind a needle on an instrument warns that the equipment response is in a caution zone. An auditory alarm sounds when a lift truck backs up.

See Box 19.3 for making decisions/actions public.

Ensure Information Reception

Be sure people have and know how to use information sources such as local contact persons, phone directories, information directories, and help services. Sometimes the message (letter, fax, phone, e-mail) is not received at the proper address. Or the person may not check the mailbox (voice mail, e-mail messages). With the increasing variety of communication techniques, you may need to be able to locate people by physical address, phone (fixed and cell) number, fax number, e-mail, or even face-to-face.

Sometimes the information is all there but people don't know how to find it. Just because an expert user, or even a casual user, knows how to obtain the information does not mean the novice knows how to find it. The designer may assume an expert is using a production device, but devices are used by maintenance workers, people on the first day of the job, and other untrained workers, and their errors should be minimized also. Just because a computer has help messages does not mean the user knows how to access them or, if read, understand them. Thus, a

series of prerecorded messages has to be backed up by a resource person who can help the user.

Learning how to use sources is best done through training, although trial (and error!) is a possibility.

Guideline 2: Ensure That Information Is Understood

Many signs, labels, and displays are poorly designed, yielding communication errors. On one of the author's cars, a brake warning light was lit; he assumed it meant the emergency brake was not working, and he ignored it. Actually, it meant the brake fluid level was low. It's not what you know but what you think you know!

Information for use by the general public is more difficult to communicate than information for employees of your firm. The general public is a group of first-time users with diverse characteristics (age, vision, language ability, and so on). Butler et al. (1993) showed that when giving directional information, using a series of signs was more effective than giving a map marked with "you are here" and letting people find their way. Andre and Koonce (1991) reported that "you are here" maps were better when the map top was "track up" rather than north.

Words have to be translated and standardized. When giving instructions, don't say "second floor"

19.3   *Making Decisions/Actions in Public*

Many errors could be eliminated if the decision/action were not private (secret). Most crimes (embezzlement, robbery, burglary) are concealed. Many errors are made by single individuals acting in haste. Thus, one prevention technique is to make decisions/actions visible (public).

On a physical level, this could be to add lighting or put objects/people where they are visible to people. Robbery at ATM machines is reduced by placing the machines at locations with lots of people. Another possibility is recording by surveillance devices (videocameras of an area; computer records of transactions). Alarms (deviations from norm) can be automatically-actuated or actuated only upon human inspection.

One procedural approach is to have a policy in which deviation from policy requires approval (justification) by others. The lower the normal authority level and the more important the decision, the more people (and/or higher the level) needed to give approval. For example, a secretary may be authorized to spend up to $25 without higher

approval, an engineer up to $200, a plant manager up to $5,000, and so on. Slowing the speed of decision making/actions reduces the chance for errors. Some actions (e.g., embezzlement, burglary) may be done with the thought that "I'll be gone before they realize what they're missing."

Another procedural approach is to increase the number of required decision makers. For example, before the engineer can modify a workstation, approval must be obtained from the department manager and the ergonomics committee of the plant. A key point here is that the decision maker is forced to justify the decision to others; this justification requirement makes errors less likely. This is not only due to the input from the people consulted but also better decision making by the person making the proposal since the proposer knows the decision will be scrutinized.

Making actions/decisions more public tends to slow down decision making, but it results in better-quality decisions (fewer errors). The key decision point here is the risk and cost of errors.

when the elevator has only "upper level" and "lower level." Be sure information uses the same words (not synonyms) everywhere. It is obvious that you may not know the meaning of a Spanish word (or a person with a Spanish background know the meaning of an English word). But how about common English words such as *cedar?* Is your definition of the color of cedar the same as someone else's? Even if the surface colors of two items are identical, as pointed out in Section 2.3.2 of Chapter 23, perceived color depends not only on the surface color, but also on the spectrum of the ambient light and the spectral characteristics of the eye.

Avoid double negatives—especially in oral communication when the "noise" is high. Be sure information is specific enough. At a conference, "meet at the conference registration desk" is better than "meet at the registration desk" because some may go to the hotel registration desk.

Rather than assuming that the user has understood the information about a standard procedure, a better approach is to field-test the procedure. For example, for assembly instructions for consumer products, videotape typical customers (with permission) assembling the product. To test the effectiveness of inspection procedures, mark some defective units with paint visible under black light. Then include the defective units with regular production and see if the defects are caught. (This technique is to evaluate procedures, not to blame individuals. No blame or punishment should be given to individuals who do not catch the defects.)

When transmitting information to others, a good technique is to have them repeat the information back to you in their own words to be sure they understood you. For example, an assistant could repeat back to the engineer, "Make three copies, sign your name, and mail." In technical terms, the forward communication (you to them) has been fed back to you—called **information feedback**—in the secondary communication (they to you).

As the number of nodes increases, the need for feedback increases. For example, if you tell person A to tell person B to tell person C, the chance for error increases. As the message complexity increases, the chance for error also increases. If the message is transmitted without a permanent record (e.g., by conversation), the receiver must depend on memory, and the chance for error increases. If the information in the message is unexpected (e.g., it conflicts with standard procedure), the chance for error increases. Critical messages should therefore be written (so a reference is available for reexamination of the message) and require confirmation from the user, not only of the receipt of the message but also of the user's understanding of its meaning.

In summary, put important messages in writing; if an auditory message is used, keep it short, use standard terminology, and have the receiver repeat the message back.

Guideline 3: Have Proper Equipment/Procedures/Skill

This guideline discusses equipment, then procedures, then skill.

Equipment

Four aspects of equipment are design, amount, arrangement, and maintenance.

Design With proper equipment, you can design out the potential error; then procedures and skill are not necessary. Properly designed equipment will tolerate foreseeable use and misuse (both mistakes and malice). Design for illogical misuse and for malice (easy to say, but hard to do). Consider an open manhole. People could be trained to walk carefully when near an open hole (skill). People could learn to avoid open manholes (procedure). But, if you put a cover on the hole (engineering), there no longer is the possible error of falling in! Engineering also has the virtue of being a permanent solution.

An agricultural example is manure pits on pig farms. Vapors from such pits can displace oxygen, so entry can cause death. Design the pit so there is no need to enter it (e.g., for maintenance), and put a cover on the pit so people don't fall in accidentally. (Also add warnings so people don't enter the pit deliberately.)

There are numerous design examples. A pedestal chair with 5 legs is more stable than one with 4 legs. The legs should not extend beyond the chair base or they will present a tripping hazard (see Section 4 in Chapter 13). Equipping an outlet with a ground-fault circuit interrupter minimizes the risk of electrocution. Put surge protectors on electronic equipment such as computers and modems. In sports, baseball players (especially amateurs) often are injured by sliding into bases. A breakaway base increases the margin for error because, if excessive force is applied to the base, it breaks away from its support (instead of being rigid and breaking the ankle). When designing mechanical or electrical connectors, make the connectors of different sizes and shapes so people cannot make the wrong connection. Design parts so they cannot be assembled in the wrong orientation.

Some jet engines have a Kevlar (armor) lining; unfortunately, the Concorde that crashed didn't. Scales typically measure to a constant percent of the total weight; thus, weighing a heavy container plus objects may give an inaccurate weight of the objects.

Sony had this problem when measuring the weight of a sealant after it was added to a TV screen. The solution was to weigh the sealant *before* it was added to the glass, not after.

Occasionally the goal is to make it *difficult* for something to work—"anti-ergonomics." Patkin (1998) gives the example of the "Broad Street pump." In 1854, John Snow was able to demonstrate that cholera cases (averaging 50 deaths/day) were due to contaminated water at the Broad Street pump in London. He had the officials remove the pump handle, and the epidemic was contained. (You can see the handle at the John Snow Pub in London.)

A consumer products example is making prescription drug containers and disposable cigarette lighters difficult for children to use. In industry, you may wish to avoid casual users running or activating equipment. An example of this is **lockout/tagout,** which prevents the equipment from being activated while it is being maintained.

Guards help reduce errors. Be sure the guards are purchased and *remain* installed. (People often remove safety equipment.) If personal protection equipment should be used, be sure it is used. A common personnel policy is discharge for removal of guards or failure to use personal protection equipment. (Generally one warning is made and discharge occurs on the second offense.) If such policies are not enforced, it will be difficult to avoid accidents.

Equipment also can be designed to reduce the skill needed to avoid errors. For example, outside stairs might accumulate snow and ice. Instead of requiring care in walking, design the stairs with a tread of open expanded metal (see Figure 19.5) that minimizes snow/ice accumulation and also provides good friction.

Amount Equipment can be duplicated. For example, you could have an umbrella at the office, in your car, and at home. Then if you forget to bring your umbrella, it is not a problem since an umbrella is already there. You can have duplicate pens or keys.

Duplicate your computer files in case they are destroyed or erased (by accident or virus). Duplication is primarily for low-cost components. For critical situations, however, equipment can be duplicated. Oil tankers have double hulls. The Boeing 747 has a triple redundant control system. Commercial jet aircraft have four engines but can fly on only one.

Even labor can be duplicated (e.g., the copilot). People also can back up equipment. For example, a locksmith can open a door if you lose the key.

Arrangement The arrangement also is important. For example, components in parallel and components with a standby system improve system reliability, whereas components in series decrease system relia-

Expanded metal stairs to reduce slipping. External stairs should have a "wash" (slope) of less than 1:60 to permit water to drain. Expanded metal stairs encourage drainage and thus reduce slipping on snow and ice.

bility. Availability can be improved by improving reliability or maintainability. For more on these topics, see Section 3 in Chapter 11.

Redundancy also is a powerful error-reducing tool. It provides a backup, safeguarding the system.

One use of redundancy is to repeat a procedure—checking the second answer against the first. For example, add a column of figures twice. Have a test for cancer repeated. When doing machining or carpentry work, good practice is to take measurements twice. To fire a missile, two people may both have to enter the same command. A device may transfer information two ways—for example, mechanically and electronically or over two separate paths. A message may be sent both by phone and by mail.

A second possibility for redundancy is to provide information in which some of the information confirms the rest. For example, when making appointments, it is good practice to give both the day and the date (Thursday, February 25). The Thursday and the 25 are an **error-checking code** in that Thursday confirms the 25. When writing a check, you write the amount in words as well as writing the number. Barcodes include a check digit so the sum of the information digits is confirmed by the check digit; if they don't agree, it is a "no read." On a letter, a ZIP code is backed up by the city, state, and street address.

Another redundancy variation is using a two-step procedure for critical actions. For example, to delete a computer file requires depressing two separate keys. To actuate critical controls may require initial actuation of an enabling control, or the control may have to be moved in two directions (e.g., over and then up).

Maintenance   The standard assumption is that the equipment is properly maintained and operates properly. Unfortunately, this is not always true. For example, at the Union Carbide plant at Bhopal, a cloud of escaping methyl isocyanate killed at least 2,500 people and severely injured tens of thousands more (though none of the staff of the chemical plant, who fled in time). The problem began when a maintenance crew, by mistake, added water to the methyl isocyanate, setting off a chemical reaction. The facility had a number of safeguards and emergency procedures, but they could not be implemented because pipe connections were missing, meters didn't work, and other problems. Management had made maintenance a low priority (Casey, 1993). It is clear that an important error reduction technique is to provide a sufficient **maintenance budget,** one that allocates funds both for spare parts and for personnel.

Procedures

The discussion of procedures is divided into computer procedures (software) and human procedures (liveware).

Computer procedures   Software errors are difficult to eradicate. For example, a programmer may not anticipate the "field" use. Failure of some Patriot missiles to intercept Scud missiles during the 1991 Gulf War has been attributed to accumulations of inaccuracies in the computer clock (Littlewood and Strigini, 1992). The designers anticipated that the Patriot system would be turned on and off, but the users just left the computer on.

Part of the problem of software is that response to change is not a "well-behaved" function (small changes in stimuli produce small changes in output). Small changes in a program (changing one bit from a 0 to a 1) can cause a radical response.

Another software problem is that users may accept the computer's solution as "gospel" without realizing the assumptions built into the program (such as that input information is correct or that the programmer has considered all rare events).

Techniques for obtaining error-free software are beyond the scope of this text, but it is obviously an important problem.

Human procedures   Procedures describe the sequence of body motions necessary to accomplish a task. Skill (see the following section) is the eye/brain/hand coordination to do the body motion.

Designers often assume "everyone knows. . . ." In legal terms, it is **open and obvious.** A better approach is to assume "not everyone knows. . . ." The designer should make an explicit list of the things it can be assumed the user actually knows. Doing this will force realization of how little can be put on the list!

Standard procedures, **protocols,** should be developed. Then users should be trained in the protocol. The protocol can be considered a "technology transfer." At Starbucks stores, employees are taught a procedure for hearing and calling orders with a specific sequence (size, flavoring, milk, decaf) with automatic defaults. The person making the drink echoes the order aloud. Not all standard protocols are perfect, however. Figure 9.17 shows how errors were reduced at a Bridgestone plant after it was found the standard protocol gave worse results than a nonstandard protocol.

If people are going to use equipment, ensure that they are trained on that equipment. (It's not what we don't know that hurts us; it's what we think we know but don't!) When designing instruction manuals and operator manuals, have one manual for each model number and language. That is, do not force a person to try to find (to filter) the relevant information from a mass of irrelevant information. In Florida, a surgeon amputated the wrong leg of a patient. The reason was that an incorrect copy of the surgery schedule remained posted at the operating room even though the original had been changed (*Root Cause Network Newsletter,* 1997). Thus, dispose of obsolete information and equipment so people don't use the obsolete information or equipment by mistake.

Training may require a formal procedure of (1) writing down the training procedure and training aids, (2) designating specific people as trainers, and (3) recording that a specific person has been trained by a specific trainer on a specific date. On a larger scale, there may be special training, such as for airline pilots, electricians, nurses, and others. Training can be in vocational schools or in apprentice programs.

For assembly work, time is greater and errors tend to be more frequent if parts are missing and the assembly must be placed aside to be completed later. A good policy is not to start an assembly until all parts are there.

Skill

There are both physical and mental aspects of skill. The "skill" of the machine also can be called machine capability. Consider how much of the necessary skill should be in the machine and how much in the person. Properly selected tools may have the skill in the tool. For example, a proper box knife makes it very difficult to cut one's skin.

An example of skill in the machine is the use of barcodes on medicines and on patient's wrists. The nurse swipes both codes before administering a medicine. The computer checks whether the medicine is proper for that patient (including whether the medicine is appropriate for that diagnosis, dose/kg of body weight, time since last administration, etc.).

Designers normally assume a capable and fully trained operator. However, capability of even a fully trained person can be reduced by fatigue, prescription drugs (e.g., some antihistamines cause drowsiness), and recreational drugs (marijuana, alcohol). (Hahn and Price, 1994, discuss the effects of alcohol on job behavior.) In addition, some employees may not be fully trained. (This lack of full training can be due to management not providing the training or to the inability of the trainee to comprehend the standard training.) In addition, some employees have physical or mental handicaps (and thus require eyeglasses, hearing aids, job aids, and so on).

Oxenburgh (1991) described (in case 50) how assembly workers were fatigued when holding a power tool above their shoulders and, thus, tended to release the trigger of the nutrunner too soon. The problem of the improperly torqued nuts was eliminated by reducing the fatigue (a lighter tool at a lower height).

Knowledge can be memorized or provided by a **job aid,** a source of constantly available information (e.g., assembly drawing). As computers have become lower in cost and capable of storing vast quantities of information, computerized job aids have become more feasible. There remains a problem of how to provide access to the specific information needed.

Training is a lifetime activity; that is, people need not only initial training but also refresher training. Refresher training may be critical because of expectancy. That is, when employees become very familiar with a task, they ignore some safety hazards and need to be reminded of the dangers.

Using the rule of "practice makes perfect" not only reduces errors but also reduces time. A "rookie mistake" is another way of saying that novices make many more errors than "old pros" do. To detect errors, therefore, check the rookies. Consider the technique of green, yellow, and red operators/operations, discussed in Section 3.6 of Chapter 8.

Practice can be dress rehearsals (such as fire drills) or can be in simulators, as for pilots. Nuclear power plant control rooms have emergency operating procedures for management of severe accidents. Practicing for various accident scenarios shows how to avoid the problems. However, in most jobs, practice is obtained by normal work on the job.

Guideline 4: Don't Forget

Two approaches to avoid forgetting are to reduce the need to remember and to use memory aids.

Reduce the Need to Remember

Avoid verbal orders. The reason is that verbal orders leave no reference that can be consulted to refresh the memory. (If you do receive verbal information, create a database by writing it down so you can refer to it later if necessary.)

Make a list. Whenever you have something to do, put it on a list. An advantage of a list (in addition to its being a memory aid) is that it encourages setting priorities (which item is done first). Many electronic and paper organizers work on this concept. Of course, periodically you need to look at the list!

One way to reduce the need to remember is: DO IT NOW, DO IT NOW, DO IT NOW.

There are many well-known techniques to remind an operator that a machine needs maintenance. Some examples are the fuel gauge and warning light in automobiles, a red stripe at the end of a roll of paper, and a sticker on the windshield stating when the oil was last changed.

People often forget where they put something. One solution is to put it in a standard place that is always checked. Keep all handtools on a pegboard with the tool shape in black to remind you what is missing. When you take something out of a file temporarily, write on the paper the name of the file so you know where to put it back, or leave the file folder partially pulled out.

Use Memory Aids

Memory aids are systems or devices to improve memory. People often depend on memory to recall information and, as is well known, memory is not perfect; thus, there is a need to make memory aids such as databases (files, books, notes, computer files, road maps) complete, convenient to use, and accessible. A phone number in the phone book is no help if you don't have the phone book! This explains the development of numerous organizers (both paper and electronic) to give people a method of easy access to information on appointments, addresses, phone numbers, and so forth. Forms aid remembering inasmuch as a blank spot on the form indicates something is missing. In the parking garage at Chicago's O'Hare airport, each floor is decorated with icons of local sports teams (the Bulls floor, the White Sox floor, and so on) and has its own signature song: "You never forget on which floor you parked."

Memory aids can have a downside. Consider a checklist. It minimizes forgetting but also stereotypes behavior (i.e., people ignore items not on the list).

Another memory aid is to reduce the amount to be remembered by remembering a pattern rather than specific items. (We can remember complex patterns in music.) For example, schedule a meeting on the first Friday of each month. Then you have to remember only one day—the first Friday—rather than 12 individual dates. At McDonald's, the orders are filled in a standard sequence. Next time you are at McDonald's, observe and see if you can determine the standard sequence.

A calendar is also a memory aid. Writing appointments on a paper calendar works well, although many electronic alternatives are now available. Will you remember to make the proper entry on the "personal digital assistant"? Making changes and corrections is relatively easy on the electronic versions, and the computer also can print out a daily "to do" list.

Giving appointment cards to people is a tried-and-true technique. They probably will lose the card, but at least they have something written down that they can transfer to their calendar. For best results, however, call before the appointment and remind them!

Guideline 5: Simplify the Task

Two ways to simplify tasks are to reduce the number of steps and improve communication.

Reduce the Number of Steps

An autodialer on the telephone can give one-button dialing in place of multiple-button dialing. It saves time and also reduces errors. Other simplification procedures are auto-logon for computers and macros for word-processing programs. When communicating, minimize the number of nodes in the communication network because each node is a potential source of error. For example, a verbal message is less likely to have errors if it goes through two people than if it goes through four.

Another approach is to reduce opportunities for error. For example, the FAA recommends that, when aircraft inspectors input data to a computer, only reasonable choices are permitted. If an inspector selects Boeing as the aircraft make, only Boeing models appear in the model field. Furthermore, if Mythical Airways owns only Boeing 757 and 767 aircraft, only those models appear on the computer screen as choices. When using the computer program ERGO, which accompanies this book, various values are checked for reasonableness. For example, if you are asked to insert a weight, the computer will not accept an entry of L.

Many retailers now have their local stores' computers communicate directly with various vendors' manufacturing computers. For example, a computer in a Wal-Mart store in Manhattan, Kansas, might communicate with a GE computer in Indiana, reporting that 40 units of product X were sold today. The GE computer then would trigger replacement shipments and adjust manufacturing schedules. Although such direct communication originally was installed to reduce lead time, a significant benefit is the virtual elimination of errors in the "paperwork."

Taken to the extreme, reducing steps is automation—that is, eliminating the person as an operator and using the person only as a supervisor (of the machine). But we automate what we understand. What remains is complex, obscure, low probability, and not well understood. Thus, an argument can be made that the automation should handle the low-probability events since the cost of computer memory is minimal (although the engineering analysis cost of the low-probability events is high).

Improve Communication

A designer may consider a task trivial and wonder why any instruction has to be given. However, novices may not even be able to do the task. Thus, instructions should be field-tested.

Confusion matrices show that people often confuse the characters zero and O (zero/oh) and 1 and l (one/el). For this reason, it is best to use all letter codes or all numeric codes. If a mixed numeric and alphabetic code is used, omit zero, oh, one, and el. Also, do not use both a dash and an underline—or at least distinguish between them.

In written communication, emphasize the important information by bold print, larger print, capitals, use of color, and so forth. (Color is a powerful communicator. For example, use tan containers for medicine for people and green containers for medicine for animals. Use color to identify types of customers or to identify "ownership" of tools and equipment.) Avoid complex words, as they must be "translated." For example, is a flammable or a combustible liquid more dangerous? *Hint:* Flammable liquids have a flashpoint of < 100°F; combustible ones have a flashpoint > 100°F. *Second hint:* Gasoline is flammable; charcoal starter is combustible.

In many situations, the person faces data overload. The temptation is to simplify the task by having a computer filter the information presented. However, the filter may eliminate the relevant information. Consider having the type and level of filters under operator control so that the operator can decide how much information is filtered, and how. Another possibility is changing the filter characteristics if certain types of responses go beyond predetermined limits.

See Boxes 19.1, 19.4, and 19.5 for discussions of inspection.

Guidelines 1 through 5 discussed error reduction through planning. Guidelines 6 and 7 discuss error reduction through execution.

19.4 | *Inspection*

The following borrows extensively from Drury (2001). See also Gallwey (1998a; 1998b).

For inspection of people, the arrival of the inspectors can be scheduled or a surprise. If the inspection is scheduled (the division head will be here next Tuesday morning), everything is in good shape when the visitor arrives. But that is the real purpose of the inspection—to get everything ship-shape. If the inspection is a surprise, housekeeping may be bad, but it is a good way to catch embezzlers and see how procedures really are done.

Inspection (viewing closely and critically) can be done *manually,* often using small tools, or by machines. For inspection by a *fully automatic* machine, a person will be involved in setup and calibration. *Semiautomatic* machines typically will examine an object and present a recommendation to a person for a decision. In all three cases, errors occur.

As acceptable defect rates have gone from parts/hundred to parts/million, it no longer is practical to have inspectors sort bad items from good items (output control); the inspector must inspect the process that produces the product (process control). This, in turn, often means that the operator and the inspector are the same person.

Tables 19.2 and 19.3 describe inspection outcomes. EFN is an index of system performance:

$$EFN = \text{Effective fraction nonconforming (fraction of total input rejected by inspector)}$$

$$= \text{False alarms + hits}$$

$$= (1 - p_1)(1 - DR) + p_2 (DR)$$

$$= (1 - p_1) - DR (1 - p_1 - p_2)$$

where

$$DR = \text{Defect rate probability}$$
$$p_1 = \text{Probability of correct acceptance}$$
$$p_2 = \text{Probability of a hit}$$

There are two basic techniques for repetitive inspection (see Section 7 in Chapter 12). The inspector can inspect all *n* items for characteristic A, then all n items for characteristic B, and so on. Or the inspector can inspect item 1 for characteristics A, B, . . ., then item 2 for each characteristic, and continue with the rest of the items. For minimum errors, use the first method. For example, a teacher should grade all exams for question 1, then all exams for question 2, and so on, because the opposite method (grading all questions of student 1, then all questions of student 2, and so on) is less consistent.

Table 19.4 lists the five basic inspection functions: setup, present, search, decision, and action. Search and decision are the critical functions.

Search. Search time is affected by (among other things) field heterogeneity (number of types of nontargets), target uncertainty (number of types of targets), nontarget density, size differences (between target and nontargets), directed attention (cued or not cued on target location), peripheral position (angular separation from the fixation point), and meridian (angle of the axis of the eye) (Lee, Jung, and Chung, 1992). To maximize search performance, consider task, environment, and personnel factors.

Task

- Know exactly what to search for. Current information on the probability and importance of various types of defects improves performance. Good symptom descriptions aid mechanics and physicians.

- Know where to search. (Tell the inspector where defects are likely to be; for example, experienced radiologists know where to look on X-rays for cancer.)

- Organize the items to be searched (as opposed to using a random pattern). For example, if you have to search a long list, organize the list into logical sections so you can skip areas not of interest. This is the procedure for computer menus.

- The area of sharp vision is relatively small. Koenig et al. (1998) used a visual lobe diameter of 22 mm at 500 mm from the eye (visual angle of 2.5°) for inspecting for the letter X. The area for normal reading is 100 mm at 400 mm from the eye.

- Note that, when inspecting on conveyor belts, inspectors tend to look only in a certain band (especially if they wear bifocals or trifocals); they ignore items straight down and on the far side of the belt. Belt orientation may be a factor also. Eastman Kodak (1983) says inspection on a moving belt is more accurate when the belt is perpendicular to the shoulders and moves toward the operator rather than parallel to the shoulders. However, Suresh and Konz (1991) found the belt should move parallel to the shoulders; they also recommended analyzing the scanning pattern to maximize viewing time, because if the inspection

BOX | **19.4** | *Inspection, continued*

is done under time pressure, the last items inspected may have higher error rates.

■ Make the object conspicuous in relation to its background (improve the contrast).

■ Allow sufficient search time. (However, if the target occurs very rarely, there may be boredom and a vigilance problem.) For example, at airports, operators scan X-ray projections of passenger baggage, but a real weapon may show up only rarely. "Threat-image projection" (TIP) superimposes a dummy weapon on the screen (a false signal) a couple of times/shift to keep the operator alert (as well as assessing operator performance).

Avoid paced inspection as it may not allow sufficient time in some circumstances. Before September 11, 2001, airport security checkpoints ran continually, giving screeners only about 5 s/bag. Since September 11, the machines must stop at each bag, and screeners must push a button to move each bag onward.

■ Consider having machines do the search and then present candidate flaws to inspectors who decide which candidate flaws are faults.

Environment. Design for "inspectability" for both machines and humans by increasing the visual size of the flaw (magnification, special lighting techniques, decreasing background clutter, and so on). Think of this as anticamouflage. See Section 2.5 of Chapter 23. Can a contrasting color dot be placed on each component location for printed circuit boards? This would make a missing component distinctive. In calculating the benefits of "design for inspectability," include not only the benefits to the inspector but also the benefits of a higher quality product (and thus less maintenance and repair cost in the field). Is the lighting adequate? Should ambient lighting be supplemented with portable (task) lights or even personal lights (flashlights)? For more on inspection lighting, see Section 4.2 of Chapter 23. If both sides of an object are inspected, place a mirror behind the object to reduce its manipulation.

Personnel. A number of tests have been developed to identify good inspectors; however, due to legal reasons, it is difficult to implement these tests on industrial workers. The large differences in inspection performance among inspectors (as much as 10 to 1) are due not only to differences in search performance but also to differences in decision making. However, it should not be controversial to have inspectors pass periodic vision exams.

Decision Making. The inspector must compare the flaw to a standard. If the standard is only in the inspector's memory, it can vary (from the firm's standard, from inspector to inspector, or even from day to day for the same inspector). Therefore, use a job aid called a limit aid (see Chapter 31, Section 4) to change an absolute judgment to a more accurate comparative judgment. Note that it is very important to have an unequivocal objective standard. One of the practical problems of inspectors is that they have not received a precise definition of what is defective. For more on an inspector's criterion, see Box 19.1.

Training of inspectors should include (1) what to perceive, (2) feedback on the effectiveness of the search and decision, and (3) a process of learning the job step by step (progressive part training). An inspection manual should include:

■ information on the cause and effects of each defect type

■ conspicuousness and location of defects

■ frequency of occurrence

■ method for inspecting defects

■ a clear representation of the standards

Kleiner and Drury (1993) give a detailed discussion of a specific training program they used for inspectors.

Note that social pressure can affect quality of decisions. Konz and Redding (1965) demonstrated many years ago that social pressure can be used either to enhance or to degrade decision-making accuracy; thus, it is a good idea to encourage procedures that use social pressure to enhance accuracy.

Complex decisions should be analyzed and the procedure presented in decision structure tables (see Chapter 9).

T A B L E		1 9 . 2
Inspection outcomes and Type 1 and 2 errors.		

	INNOCENT	GUILTY
Acquit	OK	2
Convict	1	OK

T A B L E	1 9 . 3

Inspection outcomes (Drury, 2001). Sinclair (1979) gives an extensive tabulation of data values of p_1 (values range from .90 to .99) and of p_2 (values range from .8 to .9).

Inspection Decision	TRUE STATE OF ITEM	
	Conforming	Nonconforming
Accept	Correct accept (p_1)	Miss ($1 - p_2$)
Reject	False alarm ($1 - p_1$)	Hit (p_2)

Source: C. Drury, "Inspection Performance," in *Handbook of Industrial Engineering,* 3d ed., G. Salvendy (ed.). Copyright © 2001 by John Wiley & Sons. Reprinted by permission of John Wiley & Sons, Inc.

T A B L E	1 9 . 4

Inspection functions (Drury, 2001).

TASK	DESCRIPTION
Setup	Make system functional and correctly calibrated
Present	Present items for inspection
Search	Search items to locate possible faults (called flaws)
Decision	Decide whether each flaw exceeds the standard (and is thus a fault)
Action	Take action to accept or reject the item

Source: C. Drury, "Inspection Performance," in *Handbook of Industrial Engineering,* 3d ed., G. Salvendy (ed.). Copyright © 2001 by John Wiley & Sons. Reprinted by permission of John Wiley & Sons, Inc.

Guideline 6: Allow Enough Time

Although vigilance—too much time and too little to do—may be an inspection problem, the typical problem is too little time, resulting in stress and errors.

When people are under stress (fatigue, fear, personal problems, being new on the job), they do not perform as well. (The Yerkes-Dodson law says that performance is an inverted U, with the low performance when the stress is either too low or too high.) One way to reduce the effects of the other stresses is to reduce the time stress. When under time stress, people take chances and shortcuts. This can lead to safety problems and quality problems.

Some people do not plan ahead and allow enough time. If a report is due Wednesday and you don't start until Tuesday night, you don't have any margin for delays, illnesses, and unexpected problems. Another example is driving a fork truck too fast and hitting a rack when turning.

A schedule change may force a reduction in the allowed time. For example, an airplane may be late and the goal becomes reducing turnaround time from 30 minutes to 20 minutes. A production schedule may be changed to allow only 3 days before shipment instead of 5 days. In these cases, additional staff should be assigned to the task or errors will occur due to the time stress. The organization should have the flexibility to shift job assignments, which requires cross-trained employees.

Guideline 7: Have Sufficient Motivation/Attention

Motivation

Don't consider motivation as a replacement for engineering. For example, consider gamblers. Just wanting to win isn't enough—they need skill and

BOX	19.5	*Inspection Workstation*

Benden (1994) described ergonomic improvements of an inspection workstation that used a microscope. Among the improvements were:

- Replacement of inspection through microscopes with a video camera showing the object on a monitor. Microscopes were retained for backup for especially difficult inspections (they give a 3D view).
- Use of a salmon-colored background behind the objects.

- More adjustability in chair, worksurface, and lighting.

Ergonomic problems were reduced. In the year before the change, there were 12 medical cases (5 reported to OSHA); in the year afterward, there were 3 (0 reported to OSHA). In addition, as is also common in "ergonomic" cases, there was a cost reduction (payback of 18 months) due to increased inspection rate (5%) and increased inspection quality (20%).

luck. Equipment operators also depend on skill and luck. To reduce errors, improve their skill and reduce the importance of luck.

Motivation can be positive (helping performance) or negative (hindering performance).

Social pressure can help or hinder the performance of the decision maker (Konz and Redding, 1965). Social pressure often is confounded with rank. Many cases have been reported in which lower rank/status people did not want to challenge higher rank/status people and the higher ranked person's error was not corrected. For example, in 1923, 7 destroyers of the U. S. Navy ran aground in California because their group commander (1) required them to follow his ship at an interval of 13 s in a heavy fog and (2) ignored direction-finding signals and ran his ship (and the following 6 ships) onto the rocks (Casey, 1993). In a similar vein, the wrecking of the tanker *Torrey Canyon* on rocks off West England, spilling 31,000,000 gallons of oil, was due in part to lower ranking personnel not wanting to challenge the captain. Orasanu et al. (1998) show how superiors are willing to challenge subordinates but subordinates are not willing to challenge superiors.

It is easy to recommend that decision makers consult others before making decisions, but this is difficult to implement—especially in hierarchical organizations. And, even if the decision maker consults, will others give their true opinion or just nod their heads and say yes?

People can be motivated by many things, not all of which are obvious. This is demonstrated when people deliberately disregard known rules. The crash of an Airbus 320 at the Mulhouse air show was due in part to "overconfidence of the pilot," who had turned off the automatic flight protection system (Casey, 1993). This accident, Three Mile Island, and Chernobyl are all examples of operators shutting off automatic protection

FIGURE 19.6

Publicly assigning responsibility can improve motivation; this tag came from a pair of shoes. Another firm, Cooper Tire, calls this responsibility policy "The Tire with Two Names." Once a finished tire has been pulled from the press, the employee sticks a label inside with his or her name.

systems. When you are designing a system, will you permit the operator to shut off the safety features?

People and organizations can be motivated if given credit or blame for their actions. See Box 19.6 and Figure 19.6.

Attention

Attention lapses can range from the disastrous to the trivial. The *Herald of Free Enterprise* sank with 188 dead because, in part, the sailor whose job it was to

---

BOX 19.6 *Medical Errors*   (Martinez, 2002)

A group of more than 100 of the largest employers in the U.S. (General Electric, General Motors, IBM, Boeing, etc.), called the Leapfrog Group, spends over $53 billion annually for health care for more than 31,000,000 people. They have started a program to steer their employees to hospitals that promote patient safety.

The initial focus is on hospitals that:

■ computerize doctor's orders (physicians enter medication orders via computers linked to software that spots prescribing errors such as bad drug interactions)

■ employ specialized doctors in intensive-care units (doctors have credentials in critical-care medicine)

■ have extensive experience in certain medical procedures (e.g., coronary-artery bypass surgery is done only at a hospital that performs that surgery at least 500 times/yr)

Leapfrog publishes information about hospitals (including those that decline to inform Leapfrog about their safety initiatives) at www.leapfrog group.org.

close the bow doors was sleeping while on duty. Doctors in training (residents) often are scheduled to work 36-h shifts in a kind of rite of passage; unfortunately, they get tired and make mistakes. Although working very long hours causes errors, in general, people working the night shift do not have any more accidents/hour than people on the day shift. (A study of miners in Minnesota, however, showed higher accident rates for people driving home after working a night shift.)

People may also lack attention due to substance abuse. It is difficult to test people's fitness for duty, especially on a continuous basis. That is, you can give drug tests, which may (or may not) detect whether a person has previously taken drugs. But testing minute-by-minute alertness is difficult. One common technique is to have people work in a group so others can detect sleeping, heart attacks, drunkenness, or other problems. It also is possible to observe workers remotely through closed-circuit TV. The deadman's switch on a locomotive, if not held, stops the train. Some night security guards have to actuate a signal periodically to show they are still OK.

Attention lapses also can occur from distractions. Distractions can be from many causes (e.g., talking, listening to the radio, people-watching, trying to do two things at once). So, for critical decisions and actions, minimize distractions.

Guidelines 8, 9, and 10, explore the concept of allowing for errors.

Guideline 8: Give Immediate Feedback on Errors

Naturally it is necessary that instruments periodically have **calibration.** That is, when a display reads 1,000, is the value *really* 1,000? If the bag is only to contain compound X, does it *really* contain only compound X?

Feedback distinguishes between a **closed-loop** and an **open-loop system.** See Figure 19.7. Early error detection is aided by feedback or information. Control charts feed back the state of the process. Instruments feed back the status of equipment.

The two subdivisions of feedback are error detection and reducing delay.

Error Detection

The error can be detected by people and by machines. The person can be the person doing the action or someone else. (Feedback on manufacturing procedures is called inspection, but feedback on office procedures tends to be called review.) Refer back to Box 19.4 for comments on inspection.

When a machine detects an error, it can display the information and wait for the human to take action through a control, or it can take action (either responding or not responding). If it takes action, it can actuate a display or not actuate a display. Displays can be audio, visual through instruments, or printed. Information also can come from failure to respond. Examples of failing to respond would be a door not opening when the wrong key was used and a computer program not responding when the wrong command was entered. The display also can be multimodal. For example, when a needle on an instrument goes into the red zone, an audio warning may sound (indicating there is a problem on some display).

Systems can correct errors without notifying the operator, but good practice is to notify the operator that an error has been corrected. Because what the machine considers to be an error may not really be an error, the machine may present the error as a *possible error* and await a human decision. An example of this approach is spell-checking programs.

Feedback distinguishes a closed-loop system from an open-loop system.

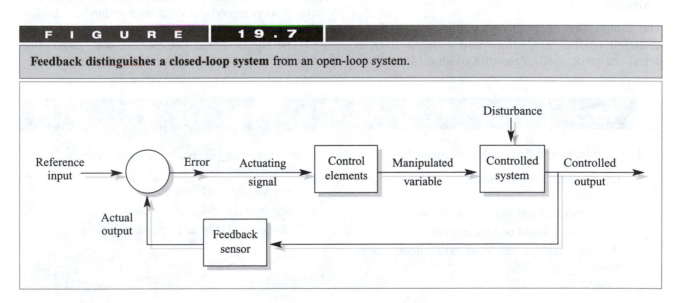

As discussed in Guideline 9, displays of errors are very useful to operators. Note that errors can be displayed to multiple people or locations.

Error messages should be specific and understandable (see Box 19.7). A message of "Error" flashing on the screen is not very useful. Only slightly more useful is "Type 3 error." Better would be "Invalid input—value too high"; better yet would be "Invalid input—value too high. Permissible range is 18 to 65." Do not combine types of errors in the message. For example, it would not be helpful if a fax machine were to give a message "Number busy, please redial" when the other number is busy and also when you dial a phone number instead of a fax number.

Alarms (especially audio alarms) can be too irritating and people will turn them off. In autos, the first seat belt alarm was an audio buzzer. It was so annoying that many people cut the alarm wires. Other alarms can be multilevel. For example, low fuel level in an auto could be signaled first by a steady warning light and then, as fuel gets even lower, by a flashing light and an occasional beep. Some cameras with timers will flash every second during the countdown until the last few seconds, and then the flash rate increases.

An example of the importance of error feedback is "precinct counting" versus "central counting" of votes. In precinct counting, the vote is checked for over-votes (voting for more than one person in a race) and under-votes (no votes in a specific race) before the voter leaves. If an over-vote or under-vote is detected, the voter is asked if he wants to change the ballot. In central counting, the voter leaves after voting and the ballot is counted at a central location with no feedback on errors. In the November 2000 election, Florida precincts with optical-scanning and precinct counters had an average error rate of <1%; it was nearly 6% in optical-scanning central counting precincts.

Reducing Delay

The longer the delay between the error and the detection of the error, the more difficult it is to detect the error. Early detection of an error tends to reduce the consequence of the error. (Failures with long delays are called **latent failures.**)

A short time between the error and its detection is one of the key features of the control charts used in statistical quality control. For example, if a defective part is detected before it leaves the department in which it is made, correction is easier than if the error is detected 2 weeks later when it is being assembled or 2 months later when the customer uses the equipment. Many cars have warning devices that make a sound if you remove the keys from the ignition while the headlights are on. In this case, you may forget (to turn off the lights), but you are able to make a correction before damage occurs. Finally, user-friendly word processing programs that use "WYSIWYG" technology—what you see is what you get—help users identify errors while working.

Guideline 9: Improve Error Detectability

Considering an error as a "signal" and the background as "noise," detectability is improved when the **signal/noise ratio** is high. Improved contrast can be achieved by amplifying the signal or reducing the noise, or both (refer back to Box 19.1).

Amplify Signal

One way to enhance the signal is to match it. This **paired comparison** improves detection of differences. Inspectors, for example, often use a comparator that superimposes two images. Also, when someone gives you a message, you can match it by repeating it back to them (preferably with paraphrasing) to ensure that you understood it.

Alternatively, the size of the signal can be increased. The position of a switch is in itself a display, but not a very obvious one. As one way to improve the display, when the switch is actuated, not only does the switch position indicate ON but an indicator also is turned on, creating a redundant display. Chapter 17 discusses control labeling.

The signal should not conflict with **population stereotypes** (expected relationships). For example, by

---

| BOX | **19.7** | *Error Message Guidelines* |

(Liu, 1997 adapted from Schneiderman, 1992)

- Try to reduce or eliminate the need for error messages.
- Be as specific and precise as possible.
- Be positive; avoid condemnation.
- Be constructive; tell user what needs to be done.

- Be consistent in grammar, terminology, and abbreviations.
- Use user-centered phrasing.
- Use consistent display format.
- Test the useability of error messages.

convention, decaffeinated coffee is placed in containers with an orange or a green stripe. Thus, do not place decaffeinated coffee in a nonstriped container or regular coffee in a decaffeinated container. Another example is putting caustic materials in or near food containers. In Topeka, Kansas, 12 people drank lye because it was stored in a container adjacent to a drink mix and the bartender picked up the wrong container (Casey, 1993). Do not keep chemicals in refrigerators or other locations where people expect to find food.

Location or time may affect the ease and cost of error detectability. For example, on a new car, a low level of brake fluid can be detected quite easily by checking the level in each vehicle before shipment. Once the vehicle is delivered and driven, the driver would notice a warning indicator and take the vehicle to the garage for service, but the cost of the error would be magnified manyfold by not detecting it at the factory.

The brain must recognize the error. A person might write "the box weight is 40 kg" when it is 40 lbs. Use of a spelling checker will not detect use of the wrong unit. One solution is to have the material checked by a person who initially did the work.

For components such as lug nuts and screws, dispense the components in batches to fit the assembly. If 10 screws are to be added, dispense exactly 10. Then, if after assembly, there are not enough screws or some left over, the operator knows something is wrong.

Reduce Noise

In addition to increasing the signal, contrast can be improved by reducing the noise. A large noise (variability, standard deviation) makes it difficult to detect changes in the signal. Noise can have many dimensions. For example, improve the visibility of a target through various visual techniques, such as color-coding (see Chapter 23). If the target is a sound, reduce background noise (see Chapter 24). See Guideline 7 of this chapter for comments on distractions.

Guideline 10: Minimize Consequences of Errors

With computer-based systems, it may be possible to indicate the consequences of a decision or action and ask for confirmation before execution. That is, important decisions or actions should (1) have multiple steps and (2) be reversible. The more important the decision or action, the more steps (and people) should be necessary to implement it.

Ideally, equipment/procedures should be **fail-safe** so errors are impossible. But equipment and procedures also can be designed so they are less sensitive to errors. See Table 19.5. An example is window envelopes for return mail—people may put the letter in

TABLE	19.5

Design equipment and procedures so they are less sensitive to errors.

ERROR	POSSIBLE COUNTERMEASURE
Power failure	Emergency power supply
Power surge	Circuit breaker
Bearing/tire wears out	Preventive maintenance
Instrument fails	Redundant information; more reliable instruments
Light bulb fails	Multiple light sources; spare bulbs
Air conditioning fails	Windows that open; portable fans
Address incorrect	Return address; notify sender
Untrained operator	Trained operator
Operator heart attack	Dead-man control; "co-pilot"
Intoxicated operator	Multiple operators
Spill on carpet/chair	"Scotchguard"; patterned (not plain) fabric
Glass container dropped	Plastic container
Container tipped over	Lid on container
Graffiti	Graffiti-resistant surface
Red-eye on photo	Red-eye pen

the envelope so that the address doesn't show. One solution is to print the firm's address on the envelope so that only the department shows through the window. Thus, the mail always will be delivered— although the firm may have to sort it to the correct department.

In a Concorde accident, the plane rolled over a strip of titanium on the runway, which burst a tire. A piece of the tire ruptured a fuel tank and severed electrical wiring, which ignited the massive fuel leak. What was done to prevent a future accident? The fuel tanks were lined with Kevlar, which, if punctured, limits leaks to a trickle. Wiring in the undercarriage is now wrapped in shielding to prevent it from being severed. The new tires expand only a little when inflated and, if punctured, lose air more like a football than a balloon.

In South Africa, a different patient died in the same bed on several Fridays. Finally it was discovered that the janitor polished the floor every Friday morning. She would unplug a cord in the only outlet, polish the floor, then unplug her cord and replace the original cord. Unfortunately the cord she removed was to the patient's life support system! What countermeasures could have been taken?

Ease of recovery also is important. Designers should analyze the error recovery path to be sure that recovery doesn't cause additional problems. For example, if a mistake is made in computer input, can the error be corrected easily? What if a box jams on a conveyor turn? What if a paycheck is lost?

Design the system to minimize the spread of the error throughout the system. If the computer fails, it should not affect the local area network. If the power plant fails, it should not cause the power grid to fail. If the tire has a blowout, it should not cause the auto to crash.

Longer time available for recovery from the error helps. For example, it is better if an overflow tank or a fire door has a 1 h capacity than a .1 h capacity since this permits more time for error correction. Thus, one strategy is to increase the permitted recovery time.

Many accidents and catastrophes result from combinations of failures. For example, the *Herald of Free Enterprise* sank because a worker was sleeping (and didn't close the bow doors), there was no instrument to show the captain that the doors were not closed, the sea was heavy, the ship was going relatively fast, and the bow was down because of the load.

Error effects can be minimized by guards. Guards can be on equipment (auto seat belts, air bags, roof on lift truck, rubber handles to prevent burns and electrical shocks), in the environment (stair railings), on people (hard hats, gloves), or in procedures (putting a stop on a check you don't want cashed).

Review Questions

1. What are the two primary justifications for ergonomics?

2. What is the point of the story about the poisoned grain in Iraq?

3. What is the point of the story about salting your food at an interview lunch?

4. What is the difference between a slip and a mistake?

5. What is the difference between an error of omission and an error of commission?

6. The 10 error reduction guidelines are divided into what three general categories?

7. What is the point of the story about the Bhopal disaster?

8. If a critical message is to be transmitted through a loop of several people, what is a good procedure?

9. What is the point of the story about the Patriot missile failure?

10. Discuss "anti-ergonomics."

11. Is a flammable or a combustible liquid more dangerous? What point did discussion of this information make?

12. What did the operators at Chernobyl, Three Mile Island, and the Airbus 320 crash at Mulhouse all do?

13. Why did 12 people in Topeka drink lye?

References

Andre, A. and Koonce, J. Spatial orientation and wayfinding in airport passenger terminals: Implications for environmental design. *Proceedings of the Human Factors and Ergonomics Society,* 561–65, 1991.

Benden, M. Creating the painless inspection station. *Ergonomics in Design,* 22–29, July 1994.

Butler, D., Acquino, A., Hissong, A., and Scott, P. Wayfinding by newcomers in a complex building. *Human Factors,* Vol. 35, No. 1, 159–73, 1993.

Casey, S. *Set Phasers on Stun.* Santa Barbara, CA: Aegean Publishing, 1993.

Drury, C. Human factors and automation in test and inspection. In *Handbook of Industrial Engineering,* 3rd ed., Salvendy, G. (ed.), Chapter 71. New York: Wiley, 2001.

Eastman Kodak. *Ergonomic Design for People at Work.* Belmont, CA: Lifetime Learning Systems, 1983.

Gallwey, T. Evaluation and control of industrial inspection: Part I—Guidelines for the practitioner. *Int. J. of Industrial Ergonomics,* Vol. 22, 37–49, 1998a.

Gallwey, T. Evaluation and control of industrial inspection: Part II—The scientific basis for the guide. *Int. J. of Industrial Ergonomics,* Vol. 22, 51–65, 1998b.

Hahn, H. and Price, D. Assessment of the relative effects of alcohol on different types of job behavior. *Ergonomics,* Vol. 37, No. 3, 435–48, 1994.

Kirwan, B. Human error identification in human reliability assessment. Part 1: Overview of approaches. *Applied Ergonomics,* Vol. 23, No. 5, 299–318, 1992a.

Kirwan, B. Human error identification in human reliability assessment. Part 2: Detailed comparison of techniques. *Applied Ergonomics,* Vol. 23, No. 6, 371–81, 1992b.

Kleiner, B. and Drury, C. Design and evaluation of an inspection training program. *Applied Ergonomics,* Vol. 24, No. 2, 75–82, 1993.

Koenig, S., Liebhold, G., and Gramopadhye, A. Training for systematic search using a job aid. *Proc. of Human Factors and Ergonomic Society,* 1457–61, 1998.

Konz, S. and Redding, S. The effect of social pressure on decision making. *Journal of Industrial Engineering,* Vol. 16, No. 6, 381–84, 1965.

Lee, D., Jung, E., and Chung, M. Isoresponse time regions for the evaluation of visual search performance in ergonomic interface models. *Ergonomics,* Vol. 35, No. 3, 243–52, 1992.

Littlewood, B. and Strigini, L. The risks of software. *Scientific American,* 62–75, November 1992.

Liu, Y. Software user interface design, 1689–1724. In *Handbook of Human Factors and Ergonomics,* 2d ed., G. Salvendy, (ed.). New York: Wiley, 1997.

Martinez, B. Employers group to unveil plan to reduce medical errors. *Wall Street Journal,* Jan. 17, 2002.

Nielsen, J. *Designing Web Usability.* Indianapolis, IN: New Riders Publishing, 1999.

Orasanu, J., Fischer, U., McDonnell, L., Davison, J., Haars, K., Villeda, E., and VanAken, C. How do flight crews detect and prevent errors? Findings from a flight simulation study. *Proceedings of the Human Factors and Ergonomics Society,* 191–96, 1998.

Oxenburgh, M. *Increasing Productivity and Profit through Health and Safety.* Chicago: CCH International, 1991.

Patkin, M. Anti-Ergonomics. *Ergonomics Australia,* Feb. 1998.

Proctor, R. and van Zandt, T. *Human Factors in Simple and Complex Systems.* Needham Heights, MA: Allyn and Bacon, 1993.

Rasmussen, J., Duncan, K., and Leplat, J. *New Technology and Human Error.* New York: Wiley, 1987.

Root Cause Network Newsletter. Knoxville, TN: Sept. 1997.

Salminen, S. and Tallberg, T. Human errors in fatal and serious occupational accidents in Finland. *Ergonomics,* Vol. 39, No. 7, 980–88, 1996.

Schneiderman, B. *Designing the User Interface: Strategies for Effective Human-Computer Interaction,* 2d ed. Reading, MA: Addison-Wesley, 1992.

Sinclair, M. The use of performance measures on industrial examiners in inspection schemes. *Applied Ergonomics,* Vol. 10, No. 1, 17–25, 1979.

Suresh, A. and Konz, S. Movement and part orientation in paced visual inspection. In *Advances in Industrial Ergonomics and Safety III,* Das, B. (ed.), 597–600. London: Taylor and Francis, 1991.

Sweats, J., Dawes, R., and Monahan, J. Better decisions through science. *Scientific American,* Vol. 283, 4, 82–87, 2000.

Tufte, E. *The Visual Display of Quantitative Information.* Cheshire, CT: Graphics Press, 1983.

Websites

Information about "root cause" training, www.taproot.com

John Snow information, www.cedc.gov/ncidod/dbmd/snowinfo.html

Leapfrog Group evaluation of hospital quality, www.leapfroggroup.org

Overview

Safety deals with accidents and short-term injuries. Focus on reduction of unsafe conditions rather than unsafe acts. Five reduction approaches are: reduce equipment failure; design the proper control, display, and environment; use distance; use guards; and use time. Medical management can reduce the effect of an injury.

Key Concepts

AND gates/OR gates

fail-safe

fault trees

ground fault circuit
   interrupter

guarded by location

layered defense

let go current

lockout/tagout

machine guards

mean time between
    failures (MTBF)

open manhole analogy

OSHA recordable
   accidents

parallel/standby

Pareto analysis

unsafe acts/unsafe
   conditions

warning

zero mechanical state

INTRODUCTION

Safety deals with accidents and injuries. (Of course, in a specific industrial organization, accidents and injuries may all be the responsibility of the safety department or the industrial hygiene department or some other department, or may be split between departments.)

1.1 Which Problem   The safety goals are to (1) reduce errors, (2) reduce the proportion of errors that become accidents, (3) reduce the proportion of accidents that become injuries (i.e., injury frequency), and (4) reduce the lost days/injury (i.e., injury severity). Because injuries are relatively rare events, it is easiest to work on the accidents. However, even accidents occur relatively rarely (they are the tip of the iceberg).

Expand the database to consider near accidents, hazardous disturbances, and even nondangerous disturbances. The worker should record, each day, all incidents that, at worst, could have resulted in personal injury; this should be done for at least 10 days. Laughery and Vaubel (1993) confirm that there is a great deal of similarity between the circumstances of minor and major **OSHA recordable accidents.** Therefore, minor accidents are a useful database in prevention of major accidents. If incidents are compared between locations, be sure that incidents have the same definition at each location.

The injury rate for a department or plant is calculated as the rate for 100 workers working a "year" (assumed to be 2,000 h, from 40 h/week $\times$ 50 weeks):

$$IR = I(200,000)/H$$

where IR = Annual injury rate/100 workers

I = Injury cases/yr

H = Hours (actual) worked/yr in the unit

The severity rate is $SR = D/I$

where SR = Days/case

D = Days charged. Include days on another job if the occupation change was due to an accident/illness.

I = Injury cases/yr

Occupational injury rates are reported by Standard Industrial Classification (SIC) code. See Table 20.1 and the OSHA and Bureau of Labor Statistics Web pages.

To decide which problems to work on, for each type of accident multiply the frequency rate by the severity rate (sometimes further refined by including the dollar cost/case); then rank-order the annual costs. Consider using a **Pareto analysis** (insignificant many, mighty few).

TABLE 20.1

Occupational nonfatal injury and illness incidence rates for selected industries in 2000 (*Injury Facts,* 2001). The data are from the OSHA 200 log; the "Lost workday cases with days away from work" is from checkmarks in columns 3 and 10 of the OSHA log; "Total lost workday cases" is from columns 2 and 9; the "Cases without workdays" is from columns 6 and 13; "Total case" is from columns 2, 6, 9, and 13. *Injury Facts* gives the data at different SIC code levels. For example, the household (251), office (252), and public (253) categories are subdivisions of furniture (25).

INDUSTRY	SIC CODE	LOST WORKDAY CASES WITH DAYS AWAY FROM WORK	TOTAL LOST WORKDAY CASES	CASES WITHOUT LOST WORKDAYS	LOST WORKDAYS
Manufacturing: Durable Goods					
Furniture	25	2.3	5.4	5.5	11.5
Household	251	2.3	5.5	5.5	11.0
Office	252	2.2	5.3	5.0	10.3
Public	253	3.1	8.2	6.7	14.9
Primary Metal	33	3.1	6.3	6.7	12.9
Industrial Machines	35	2.0	3.7	4.8	8.5
Instruments	38	0.9	1.8	2.2	4.0
Manufacturing: Nondurable Goods					
Food	20	2.8	7.3	5.3	12.7
Paper	26	1.8	3.7	3.3	7.0

Source: From National Safety Council. *Injury Facts,* 2001. Copyright © 2001 National Safety Council, Itasca, IL. Used by permission.

For example, if your organization over the last 5 years had X dollars of accident expense in the shipping department, 1.5 X dollars in the packaging department, and 9 X dollars in the machining department, focus your safety program in the machining department. Pareto analysis also can be done by type of injury—for example, electrical, cuts, slips and falls, and so forth. In addition, nonroutine tasks (construction, maintenance) have a higher risk. For example, Helander (1991) pointed out that construction (versus manufacturing) has 6 times as many fatalities/h and 2 times as many disabling injuries. Another possibility is to ask the workers where the safety problems are.

High risk also is associated with use of high-energy sources. Focus on energy sources (electrical, chemical, biological, physical) and (1) eliminate the source, (2) substitute for the source, (3) isolate the source, or (4) reduce exposure to the source.

1.2 Management Approach   As with any other activity, results occur where emphasis is placed. Management commitment to safety (time, resources) is the dominant factor in an outstanding safety program.

Operators want to be concerned with safety but may be "deprived of speech"; joint worker/management committees let everyone be heard. Laitinen et al. (1997) describe a technique used to improve "housekeeping" in hundreds of Finnish companies. Although one goal of the process was improved housekeeping (e.g., tools cleaned and returned after use, aisles kept clean), the primary goal was to form small groups of workers and supervisors to improve communication and reduce the workers' distrust of the management. As this distrust was reduced, technical improvements such as ergonomics were easy to implement. See Box 20.1. The degree of emphasis

can be observed by the following: Is safety discussed at production meetings? Is safety listed first on meeting agendas? Do supervisory bonuses and raises depend upon safety performance of supervised employees? How large is the safety budget?

Accidents can be categorized as caused by **unsafe conditions** (equipment failure) and by **unsafe acts** (human failure). Supervisors tend to blame an accident on unsafe acts rather than unsafe conditions. Unsafe conditions reflect on them; unsafe acts can be blamed on "irresponsible" or "stupid" workers. The ergonomic approach is to consider all accidents as due to unsafe conditions, and thus to focus on reducing unsafe conditions. Commercial aircraft safety is a good example of what can be done in an inherently unsafe situation.

More attention is focused on safety when Worker Compensation costs, medical costs, and the like are charged directly to the responsible department rather than to plant or division overhead.

Employee attention on the safety program can be focused a number of ways. For example, a large green light at the plant entrance can change to red when there is a lost-time accident, or workers can play "Safety Bingo," in which one number is drawn each day until there either is a winner or a lost-time accident. The prize might be 4 h off with pay.

The **open manhole analogy** is an easy way to remember which approach to use. The warning approach to safety is to put up signs that state, "Don't step into open manholes." The guarding approach is to have a guard around the open manhole. The engineering approach is to put a cover on the hole. The engineering approach is best because it is the most effective and because it is permanent rather than temporary (i.e., has endurance). Thus, the sequence is (1) design out the problem, (2) guard against the problem, and (3) warn about the problem.

BOX 20.1 | *Health and Safety Committee*

Health and safety are not just the responsibility of the technical staff or of management: they are the responsibility of everyone—including blue-collar workers. See Chapter 32 for more comments on "small groups," "teams," and "industrial democracy."

Marsicano (1996) described the health and safety committees at Bethlehem Steel. Some achievements include:

- Injuries reduced by 2/3 in the last 5 years
- Reduced lost work time
- Decreased OSHA recordables dropped

The committee has four health and safety professionals and representatives from management and labor. Some of its activities include:

- Further delegation to 21 local safety groups
- Involvement of workers
- Setting challenging safety goals
- Developing safety guidelines

2 REDUCTION OF UNSAFE CONDITIONS

Deal with unsafe conditions five ways: (1) reduce equipment failure; (2) design the proper control, display, and environment; (3) use distance; (4) use guards; and (5) use time.

2.1 Reduce Equipment Failure

2.1.1 *Failure rate*

Reduce the failure rate (that is, increase the **mean time between failures, or MTBF)** through failure locations, safety factors, redundant equipment, and maintenance policies.

Failure locations act as a "series circuit." Therefore, reduce the number of failure locations. For example, leaks on pipes usually occur at joints and valves, so reduce joints and valves. For highway safety, reduce the number of railroad–highway grade crossings. In a work or home environment, reduce the number of sharp edges and protruding objects.

Safety factors (ratio of strength/stress) involve designing so that the unit can take a greater stress (load) than the anticipated stress (load). Examples of more strength are extra-thick insulation, a larger than required motor, and a stronger than required brace.

Warehouse workers (and office workers also) can be injured when a cabinet tips over when a drawer is pulled out. The solution is to attach cabinets to the wall or to each other with an L-shaped bracket at the top of the back so the torque from open drawers won't cause the cabinet to tip.

In Singapore, spillage of liquids at a workstation was eliminated by putting the bottle of liquid in a "cup holder." A steel plate was placed on the table, and a magnet placed on the bottom of each cup holder. Thus, the cup holder—and thus the bottle—couldn't be tipped over.

Examples of less stress are reducing heat on electronic equipment and running a motor at less than full load. Derating is using a component with a design life greater than the equipment life (such as an auto transmission that would last 50,000 miles beyond the expected vehicle life).

Redundant equipment can be in **parallel** (e.g., two batteries in a car, either of which will start it) or in **standby** (diesel-powered electrical generator in a hospital). The parallel system has the characteristic that the redundant unit is in service and is wearing out (although the stress on the unit may be low due to the use of two units, thus giving a long MTBF for each unit). In the standby design, the unit isn't wearing out from use (although some units deteriorate without use). The disadvantage is that the standby unit must be switched in and out of the system (giving time delays plus the possibility of switching failures).

Humans using the buddy system can use either a parallel (both work) or standby (one works and one is "lifeguard") mode.

Decisions also can be made redundant. For example, there are voting circuits in some computers (the problem is solved in three independent circuits and, if the answer is not the same, the output of the circuits that agree is used). Another example is a second opinion from a physician concerning an operation.

Maintenance can replace a component before it fails. This preventive maintenance can be open loop (such as changing an engine based on hours of use) or closed loop. The closed loop utilizes feedback from built-in signals (noise from metal in brake pads when pads are worn) or failure signals observed by the operator ("It's running hot today" or, "It seems to shake more than usual"). A trained operator usually is required to take the signal and convert it into an action.

2.1.2 *Hazard*

Even if equipment fails, hazard can be eliminated or reduced.

An example of an eliminated electrical hazard is use of a **ground fault circuit interrupter** (GFCI). Even if a grounded person contacts the line, the GFCI breaks the circuit before injury occurs. See Box 20.2. Another example is replacing the glass in storm doors with plastic, which, even if shattered, has no sharp edges. Auto safety glass provides another example. **Fail-safe** design (fuse in electrical circuit, deadman throttle on locomotive or lift truck) is another example of eliminating the hazard.

Examples of reducing hazards include a battery-powered electric drill instead of a 110 V drill; a compressed air drill instead of an electrical drill; a less caustic chemical in place of a more caustic chemical; a high-mounted light lowered on a pulley so

---

BOX 20.2 **Electrical Safety**

Table 20.2 gives the effect of various levels of current, and Table 20.3 gives some electrical safety tips.

Ohm's Law says:

$$I = V/R$$

where

I = Current, amps

V = Voltage, volts

R = Resistance, ohms

Although the principles for electrical safety are well known, there are still many deaths and injuries.

T A B L E	2 0 . 2

Effects of 60-cycle AC current (Hammer, 1989). DC currents, for the same effects, are 3 to 5 times the AC value. Frequencies of 20–200 Hz are especially danger-ous because they cause ventricular fibrillation. See also Section 6.3 of Chapter 16.

MILLIAMPERES	EFFECT
1	Perceptible shock
5–25	Lose muscle control. For 60 Hz, **let go current** (the current at which people can still let go) depends on weight. Typical values are 6 for women and 9 for men.
25–75	Very painful and injurious. Death if paralysis lasts over 3 min.
75–300	Death if over 1/4 s (due to ventricular fibrillation)
2,500	Clamps (stops) heart. Causes burns to skin and internal organs. Immediately applied resuscitation may succeed.

T A B L E	2 0 . 3

Electrical safety tips (Hammer, 1989).

De-energize the circuit. Don't forget to discharge capaci-tance-stored charge.

Use ground fault circuit interrupters (GFCIs). A GFCI monitors the circuit. If it senses imbalance in the current, it breaks the circuit. It does not work for a line-to-line contact, only line-to-ground.

Insulate with distance (isolate). Put distance between people and current. Barriers can replace physical distance.

Insulate the person. Provide insulating material to stand and/or sit on, such as nonconductive shoes, rubber gloves.

Warn people. Active warning = lights, sounds; passive = signs, colored backgrounds.

when it has to be changed, it is lowered instead of having a person climb a ladder; and a small amount instead of a large amount of a dangerous material. Radial tires and front-wheel drive give better vehicle control than bias tires and rear-wheel drive.

2.2 Design the Proper Control, Display, and Environment
As shown in Figure 17.1, a person communicates to a machine through controls, receives information through displays, and does the task in an environment.

2.2.1 Controls See Chapter 17 for a discussion of controls, and especially Section 3, "Prevent Unintended Activation."

2.2.2 Displays Chapter 18 discusses instrument displays; Chapters 18 and 31 display of words; and Box 20.4 and Table 31.9 discuss warnings. In trans-portation environments, a locomotive or an emergency vehicle may signal its presence with a siren or horn. However, this horn (which typically has an intensity of 118 dBA at 10 m) may not be heard (Miller and Beaton, 1994; Seshagiri and Stewart, 1992). Why not?

Figure 20.1 shows the sound pressure at the oper-ator's ear as a function of distance. In addition to the distance effect, the sound will be attenuated by the vehicle (20 dBA is assumed). There also may be inte-rior noise (radio, conversation), and for detection of an auditory signal, its sound pressure level should exceed the background noise by 8–12 dBA. Since a vehicle with windows up and radio off has a typical noise of 70 dBA, the siren level at the driver's ear has to be 78–82 dBA. Assuming 78 dBA, the driver would hear the warning only when the distance from the noise source is about 32 m. Thus, auditory alarms should be complemented by other methods (e.g., flashing lights, crossing gates). Drivers of emergency vehicles should realize that other drivers may not hear the siren.

F I G U R E	2 0 . 1

Sound pressure level of an emergency siren (assumed at 118 dBA at 10 m) at the driver's ear. The closed vehicle window attenuates 20 dBA so the driver would hear only 98 dBA at 0 distance. For more or less attenuation, move the entire curve vertically.

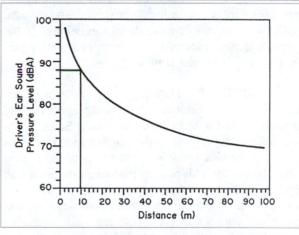

Source: Figure adapted from "The Alarming Sounds of Silence" by Michael E. Miller and Robert J. Beaton. *Ergonomics in Design,* Jan. 1994. Michael E. Miller, Image R&D, Eastman Kodak Co., 1700 Dewey Ave., 6/69/RL/01916, Rochester, NY 14624; phone 716/477-2972, fax 716/722-1193; mmiller@image.kodak.com. Reprinted with permission from *Ergonomics in Design,* 1994. Copyright © 1994 by the Human Factors and Ergonomics Society. All rights reserved.

2.2.3 *Environment/task* Housekeeping is a potential problem. Examples are lubricants (water, grease, oil, product) on the floor, projecting nails from scrap lumber and pallets, and sharp edges from machining chips. Poor housekeeping can cause fires. The key to good housekeeping is prevention, not cleanup. A good housekeeping campaign should have goals and regular inspections (perhaps random). A light touch ("Your mother doesn't work here—you must clean up after yourself"), and small rewards (free doughnuts at break on Friday if the area is clean) work well.

Solutions include "a place for everything and everything in its place" and organized scrap and waste disposal. Reduce congestion with shelving and drawers (use cube of space). Aisles, exit doors, access space to controls, and so forth should be identified with yellow markings on the floor or the space will soon be filled with boxes, pallets, and more. Drains and sloped floors reduce standing liquids and, thus, falls. Overwaxed floors can be a problem, especially at entrances where people can track in snow and rain. Use mats at entrances for people to dry their feet. Saari and Nasanen (1989) reported that an improved housekeeping program in a shipyard not only decreased accidents associated with housekeeping but also decreased other accidents substantially. In the office, appliance power cords (radio, coffeepot, etc.) are a common trip hazard.

The operator can be "overloaded" either from the job or the environment. A job overload can be due to an incentive workpace or just working at the top of the specific operator's capability (i.e., there is no margin). The overload also could come from the environment; it may be continuous (e.g., heat stress, cold stress, blowing dust, glare, noise) or intermittent (a visual or auditory distraction). The environment/process can be monitored for deviations in temperature, pressure, chemical composition, and so on. Feedback then can reduce these deviations. If the feedback is not automatic, an alarm can alert a person, who then can take action.

2.3 Use Distance

Distance (isolation) is a powerful protective technique. Separating people and equipment reduces the chance of injury. Some examples are locating a machine that throws sparks or chips away from the aisle (or at least changing its orientation) so the objects don't hit people; putting a dike around all chemical tanks and a drain under all valves (sooner or later all tanks and valves leak); not permitting people to walk under cranes that are carrying a load; separating people from a process by automation (e.g., automated warehouses, machine-loading of a press, remote manipulators for radioactive materials); and using a push–pull jig for loading machines and saws.

An example is divided highways (guard is the increased distance between opposite lanes or even concrete barriers). If the person or dangerous object is moving, reduce the speed so as to increase the effective distance. That is, driving 60 mph in a construction zone is better than driving 70 mph.

For people, provide enough vertical clearance under beams, pipes, and conveyors. For vehicles, provide enough vertical clearance from obstacles (use tie-downs for antennas to prevent contact with power lines) and provide sufficient horizontal clearance (e.g., people on sides of railroad cars may be squeezed in insufficient space between the car and a building).

A fence (barrier, wall) can increase the effective distance without changing actual distance. A fence is a type of guard.

2.4 Use Guards

Ergonomics normally makes equipment easier to use; but, in some cases, you want to make it more difficult to use; examples include guards. Guards are not acceptable if (1) the guard can be defeated easily or (2) the guard defeat or failure is not easily detectable by the user *and* the user organization. For example, if a press is designed to be operated by two separate buttons to keep the hands out of the die, but one button is tied down, this defeat should be obvious to any observer.

Another example is an electrical guard (such as insulation) that might fail and so pass a lethal current. A third example is a fire extinguisher that appears to be functional but is not. Another non-functional example is a sprinkler head shadowed by a wall. A poor guard may be a hazard in that it gives an impression of protection that doesn't exist.

Trees close to a highway illustrate that often there are multiple safety strategies. An environmental approach would be to remove the trees. A distance approach would plant the trees farther from the road. A guard approach would be to put a guardrail between the road and the trees.

Guards should not present a hazard. Notice how the ends of guardrails on highways are designed to reduce "spearing" the car.

Guards are divided into machine guards and people guards.

2.4.1 *Machine guards* Machine guards are attached to equipment to prevent people from dangerous contact. Occasionally a designer considers a danger point "inaccessible" and omits a guard, saying the danger is **"guarded by location."** Do not accept this, as it is extraordinary how people can put themselves in harm's way.

Some examples of machine guards are a barrier to prevent reaching into run-in or nip points (rotating machinery, shears) or entering an area (electrical substation, robot workspaces), guards on sharp objects (saws), guards to prevent electrical shocks, guards (e.g., insulation) to prevent burns, guards to catch falling objects under overhead conveyors or protect lift truck drivers, guards to intercept flying material (chips, sparks, splashes), and guards to prevent escape of liquid or vapor (enclosures). Building examples are guards and handrails on stairs, catwalks, ramps, and docks, and cages around fixed vertical ladders; they prevent falls to a lower level.

Another type of guard does not prevent contact but de-energizes equipment in certain circumstances. For example, on a lift truck where the driver should sit, power is cut off if the driver is not seated; if the driver should stand, power is cut off if the driver is not standing. On locomotives, the "dead man's switch" stops the locomotive if a handle is not gripped.

Note that guards and barriers are not perfect. People drive around railroad grade crossing barriers; children go through gates to swimming pools; maintenance people often remove machine guards to do maintenance; and so on. Consider guards and barriers as part of a layered defense.

An example of a **layered defense** is the Occupational Safety and Health Administration (OSHA) confined space regulation. (As a side note, in government documents, the word *shall* means required and *should* means recommended.) A confined space is dangerous due to oxygen deficiency, combustibility, or toxicity. Defenses include (1) employer evaluation of such spaces, (2) written permits required to enter such spaces, (3) establishment of safe procedures for safe entry, (4) attendants outside the space while it is occupied, and (5) trained rescue workers.

Lockout/tagout procedures require machine controls to be locked so the machine cannot be turned on by someone else while maintenance is being performed; see OSHA 1910.147. Preventing re-energizing of the system protects not only "authorized" people (operators) but also "affected" people (people affected by the machine operating). Note that turning off the electrical power is not sufficient; the machine should be in a **zero mechanical state** (have zero potential energy); there might be energy stored in hydraulic lines, compressed air, springs, or suspended parts. Lockout/tagout has an engineering aspect—subdivided into hardware (locks, hasps, tags) and software (procedures)—and a management aspect (lockout/tagout is implemented). See Section 3, Prevent Unintended Activation, in Chapter 17.

Purchase machine guards from the equipment manufacturer when the machine is purchased; locally manufactured guards tend to be poorly designed and constructed. (Tip: Have someone from purchasing on the safety committee.) Guards should not impair machine function (operator vision, maintenance) or they will tend to be removed. For example, if an opaque guard interferes with vision, make the guard transparent. Well-designed guards will be sufficiently rugged to withstand predictable events (impact from lift trucks, bursting of abrasive wheels, stock kickback).

Guards should: (1) benefit the worker (e.g., prevent splashes on clothing), (2) not hinder the worker (e.g., be easy to replace), (3) have convenient handles, and (4) not impair vision.

Thompson (1989) gave the safe object distance from seven heights of barriers for 99% of British males. He emphasized the need to test barriers with people instead of manikins.

In addition to their function of protecting the body, guards also reduce or amplify noise. See Chapter 24 for comments on noise reduction.

Sullman (1998) demonstrated that an improved seat belt increased compliance 36%; his conclusion was, "When safety is made easier, compliance is increased."

2.4.2 People guards If you don't use machine guards, there remains, as a last line of defense, putting guards on people—that is, protective clothing. OSHA regulations (29 CFR 1910.132) require conducting a hazard assessment before assigning personal protective equipment. Examples are safety shoes for the feet, aprons and leggings for the legs and torso (including clothing to protect against heat, cold, chemicals, welding, radiation), gloves and gauntlets (nonpermeable for chemicals; tough for abrasion resistance) for the hands, respirators to protect the lungs, earmuffs and earplugs to protect the ears against noise, helmets to protect the skull, and hairnets to protect the hair from rotating machinery. Special precautions have to be taken for loose clothing (such as neckties, sleeves, gloves) near rotating machinery. In addition, workers should remove jewelry such as rings, watches, and earrings.

There are two problems with protective clothing as the last line of defense. *First,* it is the last line; if it fails, injury results. *Second,* much protective clothing decreases the comfort or performance of the person and thus causes a temptation not to use it. Comfort of the protective device (e.g., helmet, safety glass, glove) has to be emphasized when it is purchased, as there are many examples of nonuse of uncomfortable safety equipment.

One-size-fits-all items tend to be less comfortable than garments in a variety of sizes. For example, a leg guard for forestry workers was improved (better dimensions, improved fastening, improved materials); in the test firm, annual injuries dropped from 10 injuries/day to 0; savings to the industry were $4,000,000/yr (Hendrick, 1997).

To encourage compliance, safety-conscious managements impose severe penalties on employees who are not using safety equipment (e.g., one day off without pay on the first offense, one week off on the second offense, and dismissal on the third offense). Unions strongly support such policies (as long as they are administered fairly), as unions are very safety-conscious. A positive approach to protective equipment is to consider them as a "mark of the expert, used with pride"; cite examples of folk-heroes such as football players and race-car drivers using protective equipment.

Since workers rarely have the technical knowledge to select safety equipment properly and may be tempted to purchase inferior protection to save money, organizations should purchase protective clothing and give it to the employees at no cost. Organizations should also control its maintenance.

2.5 Use Time   The final approach is to limit exposure time to the harmful energy (electrical, chemical, biological, physical). Limit time of electrical exposure (e.g., use ground fault circuit interrupters). Limit chemical injury by quickly washing caustic chemicals off the skin. For people working with animals, limit time where there is no barrier between the animal and the person. A physical example is limiting exposure time to knives (such as in a meatpacking plant) by minimizing the distance walked while holding a knife or by furnishing scabbards (knife holders).

3 UNSAFE ACTS

As discussed previously, for accident-prevention purposes, treat all accidents as unsafe conditions. Unsafe acts may result from lack of knowledge, deliberate risk, and drug effects.

3.1 Lack of Knowledge   Generally, someone somewhere in the organization knows what to do; the problem is to get this knowledge to the person at risk. The person at risk usually is the operator but can be an "affected" person (maintainer or passerby).

To minimize risk, make a fault analysis of all possible failures. See Box 20.3. Exactly what should be done by whom to return the system to normal? This fault analysis should consider not only operator errors but also equipment failure. For example, in the famous Three Mile Island nuclear accident, the system had a failure. A backup system was bringing the system back to normal, but a display did not present the proper information to the operator and the operator turned off the backup system, which then allowed the primary system to fail catastrophically.

What should be done if a valve or tank ruptures? A decision structure table (see Chapters 9 and 31) is a good tool for the safety analyst to use to record what should be done.

Next, this information has to be communicated to the people at risk, either through training (i.e., memorization) or a job aid (i.e., information always available); see Chapter 31. One of the problems with training is that it is not permanent. Not only do operators change jobs, but people also forget. Thus, practice makes perfect (fire drills, aircraft simulators). See Box 20.4 on warnings. Job aids (such as instruction books) may be helpful in some circumstances, but instruction manuals never seem to be around when you are looking for them, and in an emergency you may not have time to read the manual.

3.2 Deliberate Risk   Workers may take a deliberate risk because the risk is low, cost of compliance is high, and the rewards are large and immediate. People also tend to be poor at estimating how risky something is. Verhaegen et al. (1985) report a relation between accidents and absenteeism. People who have more accidents are absent more. Verhaegen et al. (1985) attribute the accidents to greater risk taking due to a more negative attitude toward the firm and its rules.

Risk homeostasis is the concept that people modify their behavior to take more risks when a device reduces

---

BOX | **20.3** | *Fault Trees*

Table 20.4 shows fault tree symbols, and Figure 20.2 shows a **fault tree.** The concept, originally developed at Bell Laboratories, shows how a "top event" (a potential accident) can occur. A fault tree shows the complexity of a situation, in a graphical form, which improves communication among those investigating the problem. It includes not only equipment failures but also personal factors.

Although fault trees are usually used without mathematics, it is possible to quantify and calculate probabilities of the various top events. The key problem is determination of the underlying probabilities. For example, what is the probability that an operator will drop a part during an 8-h shift? Is it .01, .001, .0001, or what?

However, the nonmath tree still is useful. Remembering that **AND gates** attenuate probabilities and **OR gates** multiply probabilities, try to redesign the situation to increase the number of AND gates and decrease OR gates. Another technique is to look for "single-point failures"—that is, situations in which failure at a single event will cause the top event. Usually this is through a series of OR gates. Another way a single-point failure could occur is at an AND gate if the other input is a normal event.

T A B L E	2 0 . 4	

Fault tree symbols.

SYMBOL	TITLE	COMMENTS
▭	EVENT	Event resulting from an AND or OR gate. An event is a dynamic change of state that occurs in a system element.
⬠	NORMAL EVENT	"House" symbol represents the event that "normally" occurs.
◇	EVENT	The diamond (sometimes a circle) is an event that will not be analyzed further but is included for completeness.
△	CONNECTOR (TRANSFER)	The triangle shows remote connections in the diagram (for ease of drawing).
AND gate (OUTPUT/INPUT)	AND gate	Output occurs if **all** inputs occur. $F_0 = f_1 f_2 \ldots f_n$. Thus, for three inputs with probability of .01 each, output probability = (.01) (.01) (.01) = .000 001. The *AND gate attenuates* probabilities.
AND gate with inhibiting (OUTPUT/INPUT)	AND gate with INHIBITING CONDITIONS	Hexagon depicts special case of AND gate. Oval shows **inhibiting** inputs (conditions).
OR gate (OUTPUT/INPUT)	OR gate	Output occurs if **any** inputs occur. $F_0 = 1 - (1 - f_1)(1 - f_2) \ldots (1 - f_n)$. Thus, for 3 inputs with probability of .1 each, output probability = $1 - (1 - .1)(1 - .1)(1 - .1) = 1 - (.9)(.9)(.9) = 1 - .729 = .271$. The *OR gate multiplies* probabilities.

F I G U R E	2 0 . 2	

Fault trees show which events lead to the top event. Even with the AND gate, a single-point failure could occur with a low friction floor, as highly waxed tile is a normal event.

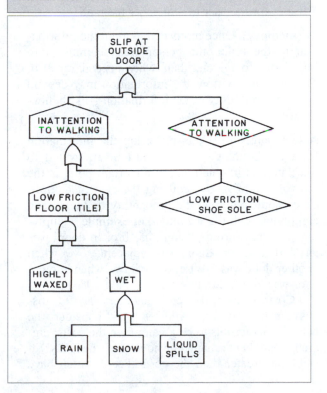

the risk. For example, people wearing seat belts drive more recklessly than people not using seat belts.

Low-probability events (accidents) are ineffective in controlling present behavior. The worker may even consider the accident as due to bad luck, instead of bad behavior.

Management must reinforce safe behavior with positive rewards and punish unsafe behavior with negative rewards. Some positive rewards are praise, public recognition of a group's behavior, free T-shirts or hats with safety slogans, and so forth. Negative rewards include verbal reprimand by supervisor, disciplinary action, and social pressure by colleagues. A good attention-getting device is a "safety traffic light" at the plant entrance. It stays green as long as there is no accident, is yellow whenever there is an accident but no lost time, and flashes red whenever there is a lost-time accident.

3.3 Drug Effects Unfortunately some accidents occur when the person is affected by drugs. Probably the primary drug present in accidents is alcohol. Kroemer et al. (2001) say that "alcohol is a contributing factor to deaths in 30 to 50% of motor vehicle accidents, 40% of falls, 26% of fires, 49 to 70% of homicides, and 25 to 37% of suicides."

In regard to motor vehicle accidents caused by drug and/or alcohol use, society has passed laws, spent considerable money on enforcement and punishment, tried moral pressure (e.g., Mothers Against Drunk Driving), and so forth. Yet the problem continues, as do falls,

BOX 20.4   *Warnings*

A **warning** is information about a possible negative consequence. For more information on warnings, see Laughery et al. (1994) and Miller and Lehto (2001). There is little evidence that product warnings work—that is, change people's behavior (Lehto and Miller, 1987; Arndt et al., 1998). Any cigarette smoker illustrates this point. There have been many warnings about the dangers of smoking, yet some people continue to smoke. Vredenburgh and Cohen (1995) demonstrated that high-risk activities increased readings of warnings but not compliance with warnings. Although useful change probably should focus on the individual (user knowledge and knowledge requirements), there has been considerable effort to improve the warning itself. The key point of this effort is the belief that an effective warning *changes behavior.*

The need for warnings increases when: (1) injury potential increases, (2) the danger is less obvious, (3) the injury onset is not obvious, and (4) more people are exposed (Kroemer et al., 2001). Although most warnings are visual, there also are auditory warnings (e.g., police and fire sirens) and vibratory warnings (rumble strips on highway shoulders).

The acronym PRUMAE from Lehto and Miller (1986) points out some of the problems.

P (present). The information must be present. If the warning is in an instruction manual that is never seen, the warning can't work. If the warning label is no longer on the machine, it can't be read.

R (read). The next problem is to get the warning read. People find many excuses not to read material. We are all subject to information overload, and people learn to filter out extraneous information. (Although an organization's lawyer may prefer to have detailed warnings about every possible problem placed on products, the resulting information overload would probably decrease reading of the warnings.) Since most warnings concern rare events, there is little penalty from not reading the warning.

The person needs to be "information seeking." It helps if the warning stands out from the background. Borders around the entire warning (not just signal word) help; red borders are best, followed by yellow, green, blue, and black; wider borders are better than thinner ones; complex borders (e.g., black/red stripes, blue inward arrows) are very good (Rashid and Wogalter, 1997).

U (understand, comprehend). Language problems can occur when the reader does not understand the warning language (e.g., native Spanish-speaker reading English). Even for a native English reader, problems can occur with long or complicated words. Pictographs are an attempt to reduce this problem; unfortunately, some of them are as intelligible as hieroglyphics. See comments on pictographs in Chapter 18.

Understandability can be improved with sentence construction and layout of the message. Make the signal stand out from the noise. Some people recommend that the warning be divided into four statements: signal word, hazard, consequence, and instruction. Examples: DANGER, HIGH VOLTAGE WIRES, CAN KILL, STAY AWAY or WARNING, CONTAMINATED WATER, ILLNESS MAY RESULT, DO NOT DRINK. The hazard statement is the most important; the other statements may be redundant information for informed users. In general, "danger" indicates potential death, "warning" indicates serious harm or injury, and "caution" indicates minor harm or injury. Canzola and Wogalter (1998) demonstrated quantification of warnings improved warning recall ("63% of all power tool injuries involve lacerations and amputations of hands and fingers" was better than "Holding a workpiece with your hand while using power tools is dangerous"). ANSI (1997) has detailed recommendations for safety signs.

If the message has multiple warnings, it is more difficult for the user to remember them all.

M (memory). Once motivated to input the information to the brain, the person must commit it to long-term storage and then, when needed, recall it. The decision to store the information may depend upon the credibility of the information—its "believability."

A (act, comply). Upon retrieving the information from the brain, the person must be motivated to translate this into action. An important point is the cost of compliance. Reducing the cost of compliance should improve the probability of the person complying with the warning. For example, complying with the warning "Don't use broken door" was 94% if another door was adjacent, 6% when another door was 50 ft away, and 0% when another door was 200 ft away (Wogalter et al., 1987).

Cost of compliance is another way of discussing benefit/cost. Athletes may consider the benefits of steroids to be greater than the costs; cigarette smokers may consider the benefits of smoking greater than the costs. People often have

20.4   *Warnings, continued*

poor estimates of the true probabilities of rare events. In addition, they often have the opinion that rare events won't happen to them.

People also may not consider the risk relevant; for example, instead of telling teenagers that smoking increases the risk of cancer, consider an appeal to vanity: "Smoking makes you smell bad." For alcohol: "Drinking inhibits sexual performance." Malstrom (1998) emphasizes the importance of short-term consequences. Which of these three equally true statements do you think is most effective? (1) Surgeon General's Warning: Cigarettes cause cancer; (2) Smokers live seven years less than nonsmokers; or (3) For a pack a day smoker, each pack you smoke shortens your life expectancy by 4.2 hours.

E (effective). The person must have the ability to perform the desired behavior. This involves both task characteristics and the person's skill and training. Consider packages falling from an overhead bin in an aircraft when the bin is opened. One hand is on the latch; the other hand may have to catch a package anywhere in a 60-inch bin length. Because the person doesn't do the task repeatedly, it would be best to focus on bin redesign. For a task done repetitively, operator practice would be an alternative.

For a warning to work, all of the above conditions must be met. Thus, warnings should be considered a last line of defense. If a warning message is important, field-test it on representative users under representative conditions to determine whether it modifies behavior.

---

fires, homicides, and suicides. These are representative of the basic conflict between freedom to use alcohol/drugs and the consequences of it. What to do? From an ergonomics viewpoint, attention must be focused on the system/machine rather than changing the individual. Changing the individual is not our mission.

4 MEDICAL MANAGEMENT

Although accident prevention is the first goal, provide good medical management to reduce the effect of an injury.

The first level is emergency care. This includes a plant nurse, first aid training for employees, first aid equipment, provision of emergency phone numbers, arrangements with local hospitals, and so forth.

The second level is rehabilitation and return to work. The rehabilitation work is done by specialists such as physicians, occupational therapists, physical therapists, and others. The consensus is that injured workers should return to work as soon as possible (often in light-duty jobs) rather than stay at home.

Box 20.5 describes Worker Compensation.

Review Questions

1. State the open manhole analogy, and explain which approach to safety is best and why.
2. For a department with 5 injuries in a year, 30 days charged, and 100,000 h worked in a year, calculate (1) the injury rate, and (2) the severity rate.
3. Discuss "guarded by location."
4. What is a ground fault circuit interrupter?
5. Why should accidents be considered as due to unsafe conditions rather than unsafe acts?
6. Briefly discuss the acronym PRUMAE.
7. Draw a fault tree for slipping on the floor.
8. Why might "Smoking makes you smell bad" be an effective warning?
9. Do AND gates attenuate probabilities? Do OR gates multiply probabilities?

BOX 20.5 *Worker Compensation*

The Worker Compensation system actually is more than 56 independent systems (50 states, District of Columbia, federal employees, longshore and harbor workers, and U. S. territories). In addition, railroad workers are covered by the Federal Employees Liability Act and sailors on the high seas by the Jones Act. These systems have diverse and ever-changing policies. Not everyone is covered; some excluded people include agricultural employees, domestic employees, temporary workers, and employees of small firms.

The concept is to have a "no-fault" system in which money goes to injured workers and not to lawyers. Workers are barred from monetary recovery suits against their employer by the Worker Compensation statutes; however, litigation abounds! The primary challenges are whether an injury arose "out of and during the course of an employee's job" and whether a particular work-related injury or disease "resulted in some permanent impairment of an employee's functional capacity that results in economic losses related to job opportunity or performance."

The employer pays for (1) replacement of income and (2) rehabilitation of the injured employee. Income replacement tends to be 2/3 of current and future income (less taxes). Rehabilitation involves medical care, including vocational training, at no expense to the employee until the employee is pronounced fit to return to work.

Since worker compensation is a cost to employers, the concept is that employers will have a financial motivation to reduce their worker compensation costs. Although some firms are self-insured, the majority have insurance; the insurance rates depend, to some extent, on the firm's injury costs.

Compensable injuries fall into four categories: (1) temporary partial disability, (2) temporary total disability, (3) permanent partial disability, and (4) permanent total disability. Temporary partial disability means the worker is capable of light or part-time duty; temporary total disability means the worker is incapable of any work for a period of time but is expected to recover fully. Permanent partial disability means the worker is not expected to recover fully; he or she may have to be retrained for another job. Permanent total disability (e.g., from the loss of both eyes or both arms) means the person cannot compete in the normal job market.

Physicians use the word "impairment" to mean the anatomic or physiological loss of function. There are published guidelines, such as AMA (1993), but disability relates to the job. For example, an office worker with an injured knee might return to work even when the knee is not fully functional. But a telephone lineman who has to climb poles may be unable to do previous work. In addition, there are psycho–social factors (will and motivation, job satisfaction/dissatisfaction, family and medical support systems, economic needs, etc.) that must be considered.

References

American Medical Association. *Guides to the Evaluation of Permanent Impairment,* 4th ed. Chicago, IL: Author, 1993.

American National Standards Institute (ANSI). Standards Z535.1 (Safety Color Code), Z535.2 (Environmental and Facility Safety Signs), Z535.3 (Criteria for Safety Symbols), Z535.4 (Product Safety Signs and Labels), and Z535.5 (Accident Prevention Tags for Temporary Hazards); available from NEMA, 1300 N. 17th St., Rosslyn, VA 22209.

Anderson, L. Biological effects of extremely low-frequency electromagnetic fields: In vivo studies. *Am. Ind. Hygiene Assoc. J.,* Vol. 54, No. 4, 186–96, 1993.

Arndt, S., Ayres, T., McCarthy, R., Schmidt, R., Wood, C. and Young, D. Warning labels and accident data. Santa Monica, CA: *Proceedings of the HFES,* 550–53, 1998.

Bracken, T. Exposure frequency for power frequency electric and magnetic fields. *Am. Ind. Hygiene Assoc. J.,* Vol. 54, No. 4, 165–77, 1993.

Canzola, V. and Wogalter, M. Consumer product warnings: Effects of injury statistics on recall and subjective evaluations. *Proceedings of Human Factors and Ergonomics Society,* 559–63, 1998.

Carter, N. and Menckel, E. Near-accident reporting: A review of Swedish research. *J. of Occupational Accidents,* Vol. 7, 41–64, 1985.

Cleary, S. A review of in vitro studies: Low-frequency electromagnetic fields. *Am. Ind. Hygiene Assoc. J.,* Vol. 54, No. 4, 178–85, 1993.

Ferro, W. Electric and magnetic field management. *Am. Ind. Hygiene Assoc. J.,* Vol. 54, No. 4, 205–10, 1993.

Hammer, W. *Occupational Safety Management and Engineering,* 4th ed. Englewood Cliffs, NJ: Prentice Hall, 1989.

Helander, M. Safety hazards and motivation for safe work in the construction industry. *Int. J. of Industrial Ergonomics,* Vol. 8, 205–23, 1991.

Hendrick, H. The economics of ergonomics. In *Advances in Occupational Ergonomics and Safety II,* B. Das and W. Karwowski (eds.). Cincinnati: IOS Press and Ohmsha, 3–8, 1997.

Horst, D., McCarthy, G., Robinson, J., McCarthy, R., and Krumm-Scott, S. Safety information presentation: Factors influencing the potential for changing behavior. *Proceedings of the Human Factors Society,* 111–15, 1986.

Injury Facts 2001. Chicago, IL: National Safety Council, 2001.

Janssen, W. *Accident Analysis and Prevention,* 26, 249–61, 1994.

Kroemer, K., Kromer, H., and Kromer-Elbert, K. *Ergonomics.* Upper Saddle River, NJ: Prentice Hall, 2001.

Laitinen, H., Saari, J., and Kuusele, J. Initiating an innovative change process for improved working conditions and ergonomics with participation and performance feedback. *Int. J. of Industrial Ergonomics,* Vol. 19, 299–305, 1997.

Laughery, K., Wogalter, M., and Young, S. *Human Factors Perspectives on Warnings.* Santa Monica, CA: Human Factors and Ergonomics Society, 1994.

Laughery, K. and Vaubel, K. Major and minor injuries at work: Are the circumstances similar or different? *Int. J. of Industrial Ergonomics,* Vol. 12, 273–79, 1993.

Lehto, M. and Miller, J. *Warnings: Vol. 1 Fundamentals, Design and Evaluation Methodologies.* Ann Arbor, MI: Fuller Technical Publications, 1986. See also Miller, J. and Lehto, M. *Warnings: Vol. 2 Annotated Bibliography.* Ann Arbor, MI: Fuller Technical Publications, 1987.

Malstrom, F. The rational consumer label. *Ergonomics in Design,* Vol. 6, No. 4, 23–28, 1998.

Marsicano, L. Working together for safety. *Synergist, Am. Ind. Hygiene Assoc.,* Washington, DC, 24–26, May 15, 1996.

Miller, M. and Beaton, R. The alarming sounds of silence. *Ergonomics in Design,* 21–23, January 1994.

Miller, J. and Lehto, M. *Warnings & Safety Instructions: Annotated and Indexed,* 4th ed. Ann Arbor, MI: Fuller Technical Publications, 2001.

Myung, R. and Smith, J. The effect of load carrying and floor contamination on slip and fall parameters. *Ergonomics,* Vol. 40, No. 2, 235–46, 1997.

Rashid, R. and Wogalter, M. Effects of warning border color, width, and design on perceived effectiveness. In *Advances in Occupational Ergonomics and Safety II,* B. Das and W. Karwowski (eds.). Louisville, KY: IOS Press, 455–58, 1997.

Saari, J. and Nasanen, M. The effect of positive feedback on industrial housekeeping and accidents: A long-term study at a shipyard. *Int. J. of Industrial Ergonomics,* Vol. 4, 201–11, 1989.

Savitz, D. Overview of epidemiologic research on electric and magnetic fields and cancer. *Am. Ind. Hygiene Assoc. J.,* Vol. 54, No. 4, 197–204, 1993.

Seshagiri, B. and Stewart, B. Investigation of the audibility of locomotive horns. *Am. Industrial Hygiene Association J.,* Vol. 53, No. 11, 726–35, 1992.

Sullman, M. Increasing seat belt usage in logging machinery. *Int. J. of Industrial Ergonomics,* Vol. 21, 397–405, 1998.

Thompson, D. Reach distance and safety standards. *Ergonomics,* Vol. 32, No. 9, 1061–76, 1989.

Verhaegen, P., Strubbe, J., Vonck, R., and van den Abeele, J. Absenteeism, accidents, and risk-taking. *J. of Occupational Accidents,* Vol. 7, 177–86, 1985.

Vredenburgh, A. and Cohen, H. High-risk recreational activities: skiing and scuba—What predicts compliance with warnings? *Int. J. of Industrial Ergonomics,* Vol. 15, 123–28, 1995.

Wogalter, M., Godfrey, S., Fontenelle, G., Desaulniers, D., Rothstein, P., and Laughery, K. Effectiveness of warnings. *Human Factors,* Vol. 29, No. 5, 599–612, 1987.

Websites

Bureau of Labor Statistics (including international comparisons), www.bls.gov

Ergonomic ideas for making work in a mine safer, from the Pittsburgh Research Laboratory, www.cdc.gov/niosh/pit/ergoidea.html

European Union Occupational Health and Safety, http://osha.eu.int

Health and Safety Executive, www.hse.gov.uk

IRSST (Canadian research on safety, ergonomics, and occupational health), www.irsst.qc.ca

Liberty Mutual Safety and Health Center, www.liberty-mutual.com/research/index.html

National Safety Council, www.nsc.org

NIOSH, www.cdc.gov/niosh

TEMPORAL ERGONOMICS

21

Overview

Fatigue and shiftwork are two temporal aspects of job design. Seven guidelines are given.

Key Concepts

active and passive rest

allowances

augmented crew

circadian rhythm

compressed workweek

concentration and attention

cross-trained people

fatigue half-life

job rotation

machine time

microbreak

micropauses

moonlighting

overload

rest time

shiftwork

sleep divisions

sleep inertia

underload

VDT work

working rest

zietgebers

![FATIGUE icon] FATIGUE

1.1 Problem Reduce fatigue so workers can (1) maintain/increase productivity and (2) have "optimal" stress. To optimize these two goals, the designer must consider both goals, not just productivity or just worker stress. "Optimal" stress implies that health/safety are not reduced, fatigue is not accumulated between shifts, and there is reasonable productivity. (After all, the purpose of work is to produce.) In general, resting time is not productive time.

The different kinds/locations of fatigue are:

- general body fatigue (cardiovascular system, physiological)
- muscular fatigue (muscles, physiological)
- mental fatigue (brain, psychological/physiological)

Ahsberg and Gamberale (1998) divide fatigue into five factors:

1. Physical exertion (e.g., bicycle ergometer work; described as warm, sweaty, out of breath; breathing heavily, palpitations)
2. Physical discomfort (e.g., static load on small-muscle groups; as tense muscles, aching, numbness, hurting, stiff joints)
3. Lack of energy (mental + physical; adjectives such as exhausted, spent, overworked, worn out, drained)
4. Lack of motivation (mental; described as listless, passive, indifferent, uninterested; lack of initiative)
5. Sleepiness (mental; described as sleepy, yawning, drowsy, falling asleep, lazy)

Jobs will have different combinations of fatigue; the combinations often will vary during the shift. For example, a material handler will have physical exertion stress, while an airline pilot will have lack of energy, lack of motivation, or sleepiness. A truck driver may have physical discomfort or sleepiness while driving and physical exertion while unloading. A VDT operator may have lack of energy and two different kinds of physical discomfort fatigue (static loading in the back from posture and repetitive strain on the fingers).

Fatigue generally is overcome by rest (recovery). **Resting time** can be classified as "off-work" (evenings, weekends, holidays, vacations) and "at-work." These are further divided into "formal breaks" (lunch, coffee), "informal breaks" (work interruptions, training), "microbreaks" (short pauses of a minute or less) and "working rest" (doing a different task using a different part of the body, such as answering the phone instead of keying data). From a viewpoint of financial cost, some resting time is paid and some is unpaid, but from a fatigue viewpoint, a rest is a rest.

The recovery value of a rest is a function of:

- how fatigued the muscle (cardiovascular system, brain) is when the rest (the "dose") begins
- length of the rest (the "response")
- what happens to the muscle (cardiovascular system, brain) during the rest (the "response")

The following will be given as axioms:

- Most jobs have peaks and valleys of demand within the shift. Most jobs do not have "constant" loads.
- Fatigue increases exponentially with time.
- Rest is more beneficial if it occurs before the muscle (cardiovascular system, brain) has "too much" fatigue.
- The value of a rest declines exponentially with time.
- Different parts of the body have different recovery rates.
- **Active rest** (improving blood circulation with exercise, heat, or massage) and **working rest** (working with a different part of the body while the fatigued part recovers) are alternatives to **passive rest.**
- Generally there is "output" during work and "no output" during rest. But the rest may permit greater output during work (not just prevent decline). Also, during "working rest," the person shifts to another task and so rest and work occur simultaneously. In addition, rest from one job may mean the operator is working for another employer (**moonlighting**) so the rest may not really be a rest. (According to the Bureau of Labor Statistics), approximately 5.7% of workers were moonlighting in 2000 (WSJ, 2000).

1.2 Work Hours To generalize about working hours is difficult as there are large differences, even in one country, depending on type of work (office versus factory versus services versus agriculture), full- versus part-time work, season of the year, overtime, absenteeism, etc. Nonetheless, some general statements can be made:

- Most countries have achieved a typical workweek of 40 h. In many European countries, the standard workweek is less than 40—even as low as 35.

- The typical number of hours worked per year also has declined—not in the U. S., but in Europe. The annual hours worked in 1980 and 1997, respectively, were: United States 1,883 (1,966), Japan 2,100 (1,889 in 1995), France 1,809 (1,656), and Germany 1,742 (1,574). The decrease in other countries came about through more and longer holidays and vacations as well as through fewer hours worked per week. In addition, more and more people seem to be working part-time. (In the United States, during the 90s, about 13% of people worked fewer than 30 h/week.)

■ The hours worked per lifetime has declined to about 70,000–85,000. This is due to the reduction in annual hours as well as working fewer years (entering the workforce later (more education), and leaving it sooner (early retirement)).

■ There seems to be a change in the daily hours, too, from the 8 h "standard." One reason is the economic pressure on employers to get good utilization of facilities and equipment as well as provide service to customers "around the clock." Most facilities do not use their equipment for 24 h/day for 365 days/year. In general, facilities are shut down for about 10 holidays/year. Some facilities shut down for vacation (e.g., 10 working days) and some stay open during vacation and have the employees substitute for each other. Assuming a single shift operation of 8 h/day for 5 days/week, 10 holidays, and staying open during vacation, gives 40 h × 52 weeks/yr = 2080 − 80 = 2000 h/year. This is a utilization of 2000/8760 = 23%. If breaks of 30 min/shift are considered, output hours are 37.5 × 52 = 1950 − 75 = 1875/8760 = 21%.

Note that partial shifts also can be used. For example, a 4 h shift can be scheduled for Saturday or, more popular, the 8 h shift can be extended to 9 h. But the year has 8,760 h! This has resulted in an "uncoupling" or "decoupling" of hours a specific person works and the hours the firm operates, and often results in shiftwork (second and third shift) and weekend work.

■ Firms desire minimum inventories. Firms now try to use fluctuation in worker hours (e.g., overtime) instead of building large inventories.

■ Firms use part-time workers. One type is job-sharing (in which two people share one full-time job).

■ A **"compressed workweek"** is coming into increased use. The daily hours worked are increased while the days are "compressed." This provides more "weekend time" and less commuting. Examples are 4 days of 10 h/day, 4 days of 9 h plus 4 h on Friday, 4 days of 9 h in week 1 and 5 days of 9 h in week 2, and 3 days of 12 h in week 1 and 4 days of 12 h in week 2.

In summary, although weekly, annual, and lifetime hours are decreasing and thus present fewer health/productivity problems, daily hours may be a problem—especially for people working more than 8 h/day and without proper sleep.

1.3 Rest Hours (Allowances) Engineered time standards have a normal time (the time for an experienced operator), developed either from time studies or

from predetermined time studies. This normal time is adjusted by **allowances** (often subdivided into personal, fatigue, and delay) to yield standard time. The fatigue allowance is obtained from the table entries given in Chapter 27.

Allowances are based on an 8 h day and 5 day week. Since they assume recovery is complete before the start of the following shift, they also do not consider the extra recovery time of weekends, holidays, or vacations. Further, allowances consider only the *duration* of the rest and not what happens during the rest. Each minute of rest is equally valuable.

1.4 Body Parts: Cardiovascular System The cardiovascular system is fatigued during "heavy" work. The most common task stressing the cardiovascular system is manual handling.

Murrell (1965), for the now unusual situation where a person works at high metabolic rates for 8 h, developed the following formula:

$$RESTP = (WMET - 5.33)/(WMET - 1.33)$$

where

RESTP	=	Percent of time of shift required for rest
WMET	=	Work metabolism, kcal/min
5.33	=	Assumed limit of metabolism for an 8 h shift
1.33	=	Assumed metabolic rate during rest

A key question is the length of the work shift. Mital (1984a, 1984b) determined that male material handlers could sustain, without overexertion, for 8 h workdays, 29% of their maximal oxygen uptake (bicycle aerobic capacity); the value for females was 28%. For 12 h shifts, the values declined to 23% and 24%. However, Mital et al. (1994) found workers in an air-cargo firm's package-handling area working, for a 2 h shift, at 40%–53% of the treadmill aerobic capacity, demonstrating that the percent of capacity depends on the work duration. (Note that if aerobic capacity is used as an indicator of when rest is needed, the calculation would be based on the individual, not the job.)

The NIOSH Lifting Guideline (Waters et al., 1993, 1994) adjusts the lifting frequency multiplier by a "lifting duration/session." The three categories are:

1. short   = .001 h to ≤ 1 h, with recovery time of at least 1.2 (duration)
2. moderate = ≥ 1 h but ≤ 2 h, with recovery time of at least 0.3 (duration)
3. long   = > 2 h but ≤ 8 h

1.5 Body Parts: Musculoskeletal System See Box 21.1. This section is divided into static work, dynamic work, and VDT work.

BOX 21.1 *Muscle Fatigue*

Muscles can be divided into two types:

1. *Slow-twitch* (type I) muscles are smaller, have a high capacity for aerobic metabolism (and thus are good for sustained or endurance activities), and have a long (e.g., 100 ms) rise time to peak tension. When stained with ATP-ase, they are dark. An example is the leg's soleus muscle—a postural muscle. Slow-twitch fibers are richly surrounded by capillaries and have great potential to store and use oxygen.

2. *Fast-twitch* (type II) muscles are larger, depend mostly on anaerobic metabolism (and thus are good for power such as that needed for sprinting or weight lifting), and have a short (e.g., 10 ms) rise time to peak tension. When stained with ATP-ase, they are light. An example is the eye muscle. Fast-twitch fibers provide short bursts of high exertion.

Strength training increases the thickness of fibers. Endurance training increases the muscles' ability to store and use oxygen.

During muscle contraction, the muscle requires nourishment and oxygen; it produces waste products. During static contractions, the blood flow drops drastically, so little nourishment is furnished or waste removed. In dynamic work, the interruption in the blood flow is intermittent, not continuous. Thus, static work is more fatiguing than dynamic work.

Figure 21.1 shows muscle recovery time as a function of work duration (x axis) and work intensity (% MVC), where MVC = maximum voluntary contraction. It points out the inefficiency of sustained heavy work.

Figure 21.2 also shows how endurance is low when load is high.

1.5.1 Static work

Dul et al. (1991) developed a work/rest model for static postures; this model was challenged by Mathiassen and Winkel (1992). Miedema, Douwes, and Dul (1997), for 19 different standing postures, compared maximum holding time (MHT). MHT depended on hand position. If hand position was less than 50% of shoulder height, posture was terminated by lower back and leg pain; if hand position was between 50% and 100% of shoulder height, posture was terminated by shoulder and arm pain.

For a forward bent posture, for low stress, recovery is rapid; for high stress, recovery is slow. Kilbom et al. (1983) suggested that it takes several days for recovery from maximal effort. Bystrom et al. (1991) reported that, after a continuous handgrip exertion, maximum voluntary contraction (MVC) was significantly reduced 24 h later. Bishu et al. (1995) reported that recovery after MVC was "asymptotic after 120 min"; they also reported that MVC for an individual has a coefficient of variation about 8%.

There is a great difference in the fatigue resistance of different muscles. For example, using the same protocol, endurance time of the soleus was 7 times greater than that of the quadriceps (Bigland-Ritchie, 1986).

For the legs and back, Van Dieen and Vrielink (1998) reported that subjective discomfort and swelling in the distal lower leg for inspectors were worst for 60 min standing followed by 15 min sitting—a work/rest ratio of 4. Three other superior conditions (45–15, 30–15, and 30–30) did not differ among themselves; the work/rest ratios are 3, 2, and 1. They recommend short breaks and dynamic leg activity (such as walking).

Pure static work is not common in most tasks. Usually there are small movements or the body parts are partially supported.

1.5.2 Dynamic work

In dynamic work, the muscles automatically create **micropauses** (in contrast to the constant load of static work). For example, when reaching out with the arm, the set of muscles for reaching out work while the set for reaching in have a rest. Thus, inherently, dynamic work has some recovery "built in." Pollack and Wood (1949) reported mean venous pressure at the ankle was 56 mm Hg during sitting and 87 mm Hg during standing. After 8 steps of walking, venous pressure dropped to 23 mm Hg.

Bhatia and Murrell (1969) studied industrial workers who had either 6 breaks of 10 min or 4 breaks of 15 min; 6 breaks of 10 min were preferred. Ramsey et al. (1974) reported that inspectors did better with short (0–24 min) work sessions than with long (50–74 min) sessions. Genaidy et al. (1995) had meat packers use microbreaks of prolonged static stretching when they perceived discomfort; break frequency was 2/shift with a mean duration of 48 s. Perceived discomfort was lower when microbreaks were used. Dababneh et al. (2001) reported chicken-processing workers preferred 4 breaks of 9 minutes over 12 breaks of 3 minutes.

Davis and Konz (1995) reported that, after 1 min of pushups, hand steadiness had not returned to basal levels within 6 h.

Nakamura et al. (1996) reported that, after pedaling, recovery was fastest in a 30°C bath, then a 38°

F I G U R E   21.1

Muscle recovery time as a function of work duration and work intensity. Heavy work is inefficient, especially for "long" times (Rodgers, 1984). If a person works at 20% of capacity (maximum voluntary contraction) for 1.0 min, the person would need a rest of .25 min. The person could work 1.0 min (80%) of the total time of 1.25 min. Still working at 20% of capacity, but for 2 min, the person then would need 1.2 min of rest. The person could work 2/3.2 min (62%) of the total time. The penalty is even higher for higher percents of capacity.

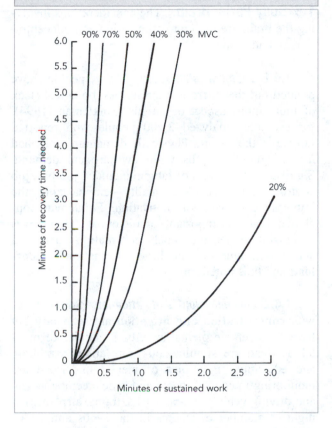

F I G U R E   21.2

Small decreases in load can yield big increases in muscle endurance time (Chaffin et al., 1999). For example, a load of 60% of muscle endurance can be done for about 1 min; a load of 20% for about 5 min, and a load of 10% with no limit.

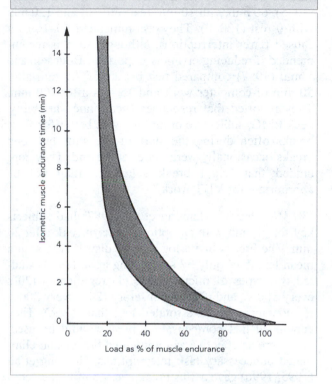

bath, and then in air. Fatigue sensation (1 = not tired, 2 = slightly tired, 3 = a little tired, 4 = tired, and 5 = very tired) had r^2 = 55% versus lactate concentration, mmol/L.

For more on fatigue with dynamic work (as well as static work), see Rodgers (1997).

1.5.3 *VDT work*

VDT work combines static load on the shoulders and back with dynamic work on the fingers. Four aspects are: time before a break, break length, microbreaks, and active/working/passive rest.

1. *Time before a break.* Zwahlen et al. (1984) concluded that, after 90 min, a 15 min break was not sufficient to control musculoskeletal discomfort. Misawa et al. (1984) studied VDT work for 120 min with 3 conditions: (1) 30 min with a 5 min break, (2) 60 min with a 10 min break, and (3) 120 min continuously. They suggested that VDT work should be < 60 min before a break. Floru et al. (1985) studied data entry for 120 min. Performance declined with time until it reached a bottom (about 50% of initial level) around 60 min. Then, however, performance climbed back to its initial level. Performance was correlated to EEG activity. In German industry, the rest break standard is 10 min of non-working rest after 50 min of continuous computer work (Boucsein and Thum, 1997). Galinski et al. (2000) reported reduced musculoskeletal strain for VDT operators when a supplemental 5-min break was given in the hours that the normal 15-min break did not occur; data entry performance was not reduced. Kadefors and Laubli (2002) emphasize that breaks from computer work must be frequent and allow for *mental* relaxation as mental load activates the same muscle motor units as does computer work.

2. *Break length.* Horie (1987) concluded that 10 min rest for 60 min work was best for <2 h/day of VDT work; for >2 h/day, have 15 min rest for 60 min work. Yoshimura and Tomoda (1994) studied 6 com-

binations: working 40, 50, or 60 min with breaks of either 10 or 20 min.; the best combination was 50 min of work with 20 min rest. Yoshimura and Tomoda (1995) studied a work period of 50 min with rest periods of 5, 10, 15, 20, and 25 min; they recommended 15 min. Kopardekar and Mital (1994) studied 30 min of work followed by 5 min of rest (30–5), 60 min with 10 min rest (60–10) and 120 min with 0 rest (120–0). They recommended 60–10 as it caused fewer interruptions, although 30–5 is recommended if reducing errors is important. Boucsein and Thum (1997) compared rest breaks of 7.5 min after 50 min of computer work and 15 min after 100 min. They reported that responses (heart rate variability, neck EMG, subjective opinions) were better for short breaks often during the start of the shift but long breaks occasionally were better at the end. They concluded that "rigid break schedules may not be appropriate for VDT work."

3. *Microbreaks.* Henning et al. (1987) had subjects key for 40 min with an optional **microbreak** after 20 min. The breaks had a log normal distribution with a mean length of only 27 s. Henning et al. (1994) studied two types of microbreaks: (1) regimented (20 s every 300 s), and (2) compensatory (20 s every 300 s, if spontaneous breaks totaled less than 17 s.). They concluded that compensatory breaks could be used; they were as effective as regimented breaks and eliminated unnecessary task interruptions. Henning et al. (1995, 1996) gave a 30 s break every 8 min; they concluded that feedback to the operators concerning breaks was desirable. In a field study, Henning et al. (1997) concluded that forced 30 s breaks were not desirable as they interrupted the work flow; they recommended breaks (of 3 min) but at operator discretion on timing. Many software packages now are available to remind VDT operators of breaks and microbreaks. A typical program counts time or keystrokes since the last break and then recommends when a break should occur. Usually, exercises are recommended. Kemp et al. (2002) recommend that users be given a choice of programs rather than specifying one program for everyone.

The physiological concept underlying the breaks is that the tense muscles squeeze the blood out of the capillaries, reducing oxygen input and removal of waste products. The breaks allow reestablishment of the blood supply.

4. *Active/working/passive rest.* **Active rest** varies from going to another area to doing gymnastics; no "work" is done. **Working rest** is other work activity such as going to the printer or doing handwriting. **Passive rest** tends to be sitting at the workstation, perhaps with conversation with coworkers. Asmussen and Mazin (1978) found active rest better than pas-

sive rest. Sundelin and Hagberg (1989) studied three types of rest: (1) passive, (2) active (seated gymnastics), and (3) active (walk in corridor). The 20 s breaks occurred every 6 min; the operators preferred active to passive rest. Thompson (1990) had exercise breaks of 5 min added twice a day for data entry operators; lost time due to injury decreased and productivity increased as a result. Swanson and Sauter (1993) found that "inconspicuous exercises taken at the workplace" may help prevent a decline in productivity. Henning et al. (1997) found working rest to be better than passive rest.

1.6 Body Parts: Brain The considerations involving the brain are optimum stimulation and concentration and attention.

1.6.1 *Optimum stimulation* Many people have pointed out that there is a strong psychological (lack of motivation) aspect of fatigue. Finkleman (1994), for example, analyzed 3,700 people who reported fatigue in their work. Physically demanding jobs had *less* fatigue than jobs with low physical demand. Significant predictors of fatigue included job pay, job control, and supervisor quality—emphasizing the importance of lack of motivation. Finkleman concluded that an important predictor of fatigue was processing either too much information—**overload** and thus fatigue—or too little information—**underload** and thus boredom.

1.6.2 *Concentration and attention* Some tasks with **concentration and attention** are sedentary but have considerable mental activity. Examples of mental overload are simultaneous translation, gambling, and education. Examples of mental underload are monitoring in control rooms and watchkeeping at sea, and driving vehicles (cars, trucks, trains, airplanes) at night. A number of studies in the 1960s and 1970s showed that machine-paced work requires more rest than operator-paced work (Konz, 1979). Megaw (1995) reviewed 95 articles on visual fatigue and concluded we do not know much about visual fatigue. Meijman (1995) pointed out that people can maintain mental performance by exerting more effort; as an index of mental effort, he used the .1 Hz component in the heart beat.

Translation. Simultaneous translators work in pairs; one translates while the other rests. In Quebec (French/English) they switch every 30 min; in Japan (Japanese/English) they switch every 20 min. Sign language translators for hearing impaired people also work in pairs; they switch every 30 min.

Gambling. In casinos, blackjack dealers (standing work with intense concentration and finger activity) work for 60 min and then have a 20 min nonworking rest.

Education. The typical schedule at universities in the U. S. is 50 min of lecture with a 10 min break before the next class. However, the typical student schedule is 15 class hours/week, so there is considerable recovery time between classes. Professors tend to have 6 to 12 teaching "hours" (each of 50 min) each week; typically they teach for 32 weeks/year.

High school students in the U. S. typically have 6 to 7 periods/day (often 1 period is physical education); each period is 60 min, which includes 5 min break. Lunch is an additional break. Typically they go to school <190 days/yr.

Bennett et al. (1974) studied college students doing arithmetic for 180 min. The three conditions were no rest, passive rest (sit quietly), and active rest (go to another room and have a soft drink). Active rest was superior to no rest and passive rest. In a second experiment, performance with two 10 min changes of task was superior to working without any change.

Henning (1987) had subjects make choice reaction time responses. They could take a microbreak between the 4 min trials. However, they took a mean break of only 10 s, which Henning concluded was too short.

While translation, gambling, and education are examples of overload, monitoring and driving are examples of underload.

Monitoring/vigilance. Example tasks are process-control monitoring, hospital patient monitoring, radar monitoring, and industrial inspection. Smith (1981) reviewed 50 references on boredom and found a change in task was as good as stopping work.

Table 21.1 gives the recommended work hours for control operators in nuclear power plants; a concern was the large amounts of overtime (400 h/year), but the primary concern was operator alertness/safety. The Nuclear Regulatory Commission (NRC) did not adopt these recommendations. Table 21.2 compares the NRC values to some other guidelines. For nuclear plant control room operators, Table 21.3 gives recommendations for 8 h shifts and Table 21.4 for 12 h shifts.

Flight attendants in the U. S. must be provided at least 9 h of scheduled rest within a 24 h time span—if they have been on duty for up to 14 h. Attendants must have a 24 h rest every 7 calendar days (Phillips, 1994).

In June 2002, the Accreditation Council for Graduate Medical Education, in an effort to reduce medical errors, set new standards for doctors-in-training. They will be limited to 80 h workweeks and they must get at least 10 h of rest between shifts. They will not be allowed to be on duty for more than 24 h continuously. Table 21.5 gives recommendations for watchkeeping at sea. Watchkeeping at sea implies the use of permanent shifts; at sea this may be reasonable since there are fewer social pressures outside work and thus circadian inversion may occur. Colquhoun et al. (1988) surveyed merchant shipping from 30 countries; 52 ships followed a 4 h on/8 h off system, 27 a 6 h on/6 h off system, and 3 a 12 h on/12 h off system.

T A B L E	2 1 . 1	

Limits of hours of work (including overtime) in nuclear power plant control rooms (Lewis, 1985). The limits exclude shift turnover time (typically 30 min/turnover). Shift turnover time is the time when the old shift communicates with the new shift.

PERIOD, DAYS[a]	MAXIMUM H UNLESS UNUSUAL CIRCUMSTANCES[b]	MAXIMUM H UNLESS VERY UNUSUAL CIRCUMSTANCES[c]
1	12[d]	–
2	24	–
7	60	72
14	112	132
28	192	228
365	2260	2300

[a] A "day" is any period of 24 consecutive hours.

[b] Deviations from this column must be approved by the plant manager; the authorization must be documented and available for Nuclear Regulatory Commission (NRC) inspection. An extended shutdown shall not be considered unusual circumstances.

[c] Deviations from this column shall be authorized, up to specific limits, by the NRC.

[d] In the case of a problem during operation (such as the unexpected absence of an operator), overtime may be worked on an individual basis. No individual should be allowed to work more than 16 hours straight, more than 1 period of 16 hours in a 7-day period, or more than 2 periods of 16 hours in a 28-day period.

T A B L E	2 1 . 2

Comparison of limits of hours of work (adapted from Lewis, 1985).

PERIOD, DAYS	NRC POLICY	LEWIS RECOMMENDATION		U. S. AIR FORCE	NON-NUCLEAR INDUSTRIES		
		Unusual	Very Unusual		Truck	RR	Airlines[d]
1	16	12	–	12[a]	10	12	8
2	24	24	–	24[b]	(20)	(24)	(16)
7	72	60	72	–	60	–	30
14	(144)	112	132	–	(120)	–	(60)
28[c]	–	192	228	125[a]	–	–	100
91	–	(626)	(734)	330	–	–	300
365	–	2260	2300	(1320)	–	–	1000

[a] In 1991, during Desert Shield and Desert Storm, duty days of 16 h for unaugmented crews often were extended to 20 h; duty days of **augmented crews** (e.g., two crews in the same plane) were 24 h. Because some preflight activity was not counted as part of a duty day, time continuously awake at the end of a duty day (i.e., at landing) was as much as 29 h for unaugmented crews and 33 h for augmented crews. The 125 h/month was increased to 150 (Neville et al., 1994). Neville et al. report the critical variable was the sleep in the previous 48 h; the increase from 125 to 150 for the month had no effect on fatigue.

[b] Numbers in brackets are extrapolations from one time period to the next longer time period.

[c] For U. S. Air Force and airline pilots and crew, the time period is 30 days.

[d] The current FAA rule is that, in any 24 h period, a pilot must have at least 8 h of rest and be scheduled for no more than 8 h of flight time; thus, pilots legally can be on duty for 16 h.

T A B L E	2 1 . 3

Routine 8-h schedule recommendations for control rooms (Lewis, 1985).

1. The schedule should be limited to a maximum of 7 consecutive days of work.

2. In any 4-week period, the schedule should not exceed 21 days of work (including training).

3. In any period of 9 consecutive days, the schedule should include at least 2 consecutive full days off.

4. A series of night shifts should be followed by at least 2 full days off.

5. The schedule should rotate forward, not backward.

T A B L E	2 1 . 4

Routine 12-h schedule recommendations for control rooms (Lewis, 1985).

1. The schedule should contain a maximum of 4 consecutive 12 h workdays.

2. Four consecutive 12 h workdays should be followed by no fewer than 4 days off.

3. The basic 12 h day schedule should be "2 on, 2 off," "3 on, 3 off," "4 on, 4 off" or a systematic combination of these such as the "every other weekend off" schedule (which combines the "2 on, 2 off" with "3 on, 3 off").

4. The general safety record of the plant should be satisfactory.

5. The plant should have the capability to cover unexpected absences satisfactorily without having any individual work more than 12 h/day.

6. The round trip commute time for the operators should not exceed 2.5 h. (Commute time reduces time available for sleep.)

All the regulations assume the hours of the day are equal and interchangeable. In addition, the regulations do not reflect the scientific consensus that fatigue is affected more by lack of sleep than hours spent working.

Craig (1985) summarized some field studies on vigilance. Changes that reduced boredom were beneficial. One example was loading/unloading (10 min) as well as inspecting coins (14 min). Another example was 30 min of inspection followed by 60 min of other tasks. This "task variety" can be considered working rest.

Driving/conducting/piloting. In their survey of fatigue among locomotive drivers, Buck and Lamonde (1993) reported that locomotive drivers tended to have irregular schedules that interfered with sleep. Failures to respond were more likely to occur close to 0300 and

Recommendations for watchkeeping at sea. (Buck et al., 1995).

- A duty schedule must be published before sailing. This schedule must be observed during the voyage.

- The cycle of repetition should be 24 h.

- The duty schedule could be varied from day to day. Hours on duty and off duty could begin no more than 1 h before the scheduled starting time; they could be extended up to the limits imposed by maximal hours on duty and minimal hours off duty.

- Watchkeepers should not be permitted to spend more than 18 h on duty in any period of 24 h and not more than 24 h in any period of 48 h. All hours spent working should be counted as being on duty and not just hours spent watchkeeping.

- Watchkeepers should spend not less than 6 consecutive hours off duty in any one period of 24 h and not less than 24 h off duty in any one period of 48 h.

Source: From L. Buck, M. Greenley, D. Loughnane, and R. Webb. "Statutory Regulations for Optimizing Work Schedules." *27th Annual Conference of the Human Factors Assoc. of Canada,* 245–50, 1995. Used by permission of the authors.

1500 h. Young and Hashemi (1996) proposed a two-tier fatigue model; some drivers arrive at work fatigued and have accidents early in the work period; other drivers start rested and become fatigued during the task. Fatigue may be more of a problem when the driver is "externally scheduled"—for example, when tired, a bus driver or a pilot cannot stop and take a break, whereas a car or truck driver, being self-paced, can stop. Japanese taxi drivers typically work a 16 h day and then have the following 1 or 2 days off.

Meijman et al. (1992) studied workload of driving examiners. Recovery time (including lunch) between exams decreased as more drivers were examined. It was 26% for 9 driver exams/shift, 20% for 10 driver exams/shift, and 15% for 11 driver exams/shift. Perhaps most interesting is that stress (blood pressure, adrenaline) was higher after the shift, as well as during the shift. This points out that stress effects may continue after work.

1.7 Sleep/Biological Clock

Three divisions are sleep, biological clock (circadian rhythm), and countermeasures.

1.7.1 Sleep

Sleep restores the functions of the brain. Only sleep allows some form of cerebral shutdown. Two **sleep divisions** are Rapid Eye Movement (REM, dreaming) sleep (15–20% of total sleep) and non-REM sleep. REM sleep occurs in bursts through-out the night at approximately 1.5 h intervals, and its duration tends to increase during the night.

The remaining sleep is divided into Stages 1, 2, 3, and 4. Stages 1 and 2 (about 50% of time) are light sleep. Stages 3 and 4 are called delta sleep or slow-wave sleep due to the slow brain waves. Stages 3 and 4 are most important to the restorative aspects of sleep (Monk and Follard, 1992).

Sleep duration follows a normal distribution with young adults having a mean of 7.5 h and a standard deviation of 1 h. However, females tend to need more sleep than males. Middle-age (>50) people tend to have more "fragile" sleep (shorter, more easily disrupted, more fragmented, lighter). So, females and middle-age people are more prone to night-sleep problems.

The sleepiness/alertness of a person can be tested with the Multiple Sleep Latency Test (MSLT). It measures the amount of time between trying to fall asleep and falling asleep; maximum sleepy = 0 min, and maximum alert = 20 min.

Many people have mild but chronic sleep deprivation. A typical MSLT score after 8 h of sleep is 15 min. However, if the two previous nights have 10 h of nighttime sleep, the MSLT = 20 (i.e., maximum alertness). Conversely, restricting sleep to 4 h/night for 2 nights gives a daytime MSLT = 5 (Coleman, 1986, p. 165).

Sleep deprivation of 24–48 h primarily affects motivation to perform rather than ability to perform; thus uninteresting, undemanding, simple tasks are the most affected. Longer sleep deprivation begins to affect more "cognitive" tasks. However, "ranger" soldiers could perform their duties even with only 6 h sleep in a 72 h mission (Ball et al., 1984).

1.7.2 Circadian rhythm

Various physiological functions in the body vary in a **circadian rhythm** (Latin *circa dies,* "about a day"). See Figure 21.3 for the circadian rhythm for internal temperature. The brain's central clock is the superchiasmatic nucleus. It works like a water clock, in which a bowl gradually fills until at last it tips, beginning a new cycle. The clock genes construct proteins that eventually accumulate to the point where they switch off the genes. The cycle takes 24 h (*Tyranny of Time,* 1999). Both internal temperature and potassium peak during the day and bottom at night. Cortisol (the "wake-up" hormone) peaks around 9 A.M.; melatonin (the "go-to-sleep" hormone) peaks around 2 P.M. Melatonin can be suppressed by daylight levels of illumination (e.g., >2000 lux) so night-shift workers driving home should wear sunglasses. If they wish to maintain their nocturnal orientation, they should wear sunglasses during the day to reduce the effect of outdoor illumination. Without external clues, the rhythm is about 25 h rather than the 24 h we get from time givers

Circadian rhythm for internal temperature. Oral temperature of 59 male seamen peaked around 4 P.M. (Colquhoun et al., 1968). They slept from 2300 to 0630 and performed light duty (primarily short tests) from 0800 to 1600; they had meals at 0700, 1200, and 1700. As body temperature drops, the pineal gland begins to secrete a hormone (melatonin), that tells the body it is time to sleep.

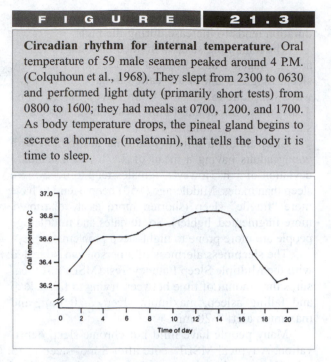

(German **zietgebers**). Outdoor light and darkness is the primary zietgeber. When shifting phases with coherent zietgebers (such as time zone shifting), the phase shift is about 2 h/day. When shifting phases with incoherent zietgebers (e.g., time of dawn is not changed but time of going to bed changes), the phase shift is about 1 h/day (Moog, 1987).

The two most common remedies for jet lag are bright light therapy (resetting the internal clock by exposing the eyes to bright light, such as outdoor daylight) and over-the-counter melatonin tablets. Melatonin tablet doses are complicated to figure, as the effects depend on when you take it. Edwards et al.(2000), in a study of the British Olympic team going to Australia, reported melatonin had no benefit. Alcohol, sleeping pills, sedatives, and caffeine worsen the symptoms of a scrambled body clock.

(Another problem of jet travel is dehydration; cabin humidities are 5–15%. Drink nonalcoholic beverages.)

Alertness peaks in the late afternoon and bottoms during 2300 to 0600. "Morning type" people—larks—have about a .9°C difference between maximum and minimum body temperature, while "evening types"—owls—have a difference about 1.0°C. A number of studies (e.g., Moog, 1987; Gander et al., 1993) show morning types to be less tolerant to shiftwork.

1.7.3 *Countermeasures* Three countermeasures to sleep deprivation are rest, drugs/food, and environmental stimulation.

1. *Rest.* Naps typically occur between 1430 and 1700 h and last about 90 min (Gillberg, 1985). Although naps taken at night (say, 0300) are of some benefit, people tend to think of them as inadequate opportunity to sleep rather than an opportunity for partial recuperation.

2. *Drugs/food.* The most common drug to decrease sleepiness/increase alertness is caffeine (see Box 21.2). Amphetamines also work well.

BOX   21.2   *Caffeine*

Caffeine, a drug with primarily stimulating effects, has a metabolic half-life of 3–7 h. Some factors influencing the half-life are pregnancy (increases half-life to as much as 18 h) and smoking (decreases half-life) (Evaluation of Caffeine Safety, 1987; Grice and Murray, 1987). Caffeine has no day-to-day accumulations as it almost completely disappears from the body overnight (Ensminger, 1994).

A pharmacologically active dose is about 200 mg (about 3 mg/kg), depending upon the individual (body weight, body tolerance). Rosenthal et al. (1991) reported increased sleep latency with doses as low as 75 mg.

Caffeine:

1. Stimulates the central nervous system (brain), thereby prolonging wakefulness with alert intellectual facilities.

2. Stimulates the heart action.

3. Relaxes smooth muscle (digestive tract, blood vessels).

4. Increases urine flow (a diuretic).

5. Stimulates stomach acid secretion.

6. Increases muscle strength and the amount of time a person can perform physically exhausting work.

A dose of 1,000 mg generally will produce adverse effects (insomnia, restlessness, excitement, trembling, rapid heartbeat with extra heartbeats, increased breathing, desire to urinate, ringing in the ears, heartburn). Daily consumption of about 800 mg will cause user dependence on caffeine.

Table 21.6 gives the caffeine content in some foods and drugs.

T A B L E 21.6

Caffeine content in selected items. 1 ounce = 30 mL.

ITEM	MEASURE	CAFFEINE, MG
Alertness tablets		
NoDoz	tablet	100
Vivarin	tablet	200
Pain relievers		
Excedrin	tablet	65
Anacin	tablet	32
Cold allergy relief	tablet	15–32
Weight-control		
Dexatrim	tablet	200
Dietac	tablet	200
Coffee (percolated)[a]	240 mL	21–148[b]
Coffee (instant)	240 mL	66
Tea[a] (black)	240 mL	50
Tea[a] (green)	240 mL	30
Tea[a] (instant)	240 mL	15
Tea[a] (decaf)	240 mL	2
Soft drinks with caffeine	375 mL	36–54
Chocolate, baking	30 mL	70
Chocolate, sweet or dark	30 mL	40
Chocolate, milk	30 mL	12

[a] Longer brewing increases caffeine content.

[b] 58 different people prepared coffee ranging in caffiene from 21 to 148 mg/cup (Eisenberg, 1989).

Zwyghuizen-Doorenbos (1990) demonstrated that caffeine increased daytime alertness; however, people begin to develop a tolerance to caffeine after just 4 administrations of caffeine. A 200 mg dose of caffeine attenuated the vigilance decrement during sentry duty (Johnson and Merullo, 1996). Although a common recommendation is to avoid caffeine during the last 2–4 hours of the shift (to allow good sleep after the shift), real shiftworkers, especially if they have little problem sleeping, may prefer to drink caffeine to maintain work alertness and alertness on the drive home.

Caffeine or naps? Bonnet and Arand (1994) advocate use of an "investment" nap (taken before the period of sleep loss) in combination with caffeine. They recommend, for hospital physicians, a secure afternoon nap and availability of coffee at night. If physicians take naps during the night, if workload permits, they cannot take caffeine, as it would interfere with potential sleep. Another nap at night problem is **sleep inertia** (poor performance for about 15–30 min after being awakened) (Dinges et al., 1985).

To improve daytime sleep, while not interfering with nighttime alertness, Walsh (1990) recommends a short-acting sedative such as benzodiazepine (trizolam) rather than a long-acting one (flurazepam). If a person must work immediately upon awakening, a sedative is not recommended, as the drug effect outlasts the sleep period.

Alcohol and some of the older antihistamines (e.g., diphenhydramine) increase sleepiness. At high blood alcohol concentrations, the enzyme dehydrogenase is saturated and the half-life of alcohol in the blood is increased (Paustenbach, 1994, p. 244).

The physiological effect of some compounds is affected by circadian rhythm. For example, ethanol (alcohol) affects a person more in the evening than the day (Coleman, 1986, p. 27); .4 g/kg of ethanol had the same effect after 5 h of sleep as .8 g/kg produced after 8 h of sleep (Roehrs et al., 1989). Ethanol has less effect on daytime alertness for fully rested subjects than for people with sleep deficits (Lumley et al., 1987). Alcohol has more effect on alertness in the early afternoon or early morning, as the alcohol then will reinforce the body's natural sleep tendencies.

Walsh et al. (1991) postulate that alcohol-related vehicle accidents at night may be "as likely due to reduced alertness as to impaired motor function or reaction time." Schwing (1990) reported that after-midnight hours, especially on weekends, are risky for vehicle accidents in the U. S.; 4.5% of the travel yields 32% of the fatalities. The combination of alcohol and fatigue is a powerful predictor of death on the highway. Evening-shift workers probably have the most danger in the drive home. First, their circadian rhythm is anticipating sleep. Second, it is dark (when accidents are more likely). Third, there are more drunks on the road. Problems two and three usually are minimal for the night-shift worker.

To overcome fatigue, many truck drivers recommend eating (possibly while still driving). A moderate intake of food with carbohydrates (rather than fats or proteins) may be best (Akerstedt and Landstrom, 1998). Another temporary solution is having a drink with caffeine.

3. *Environmental stimulation.* A recent approach is to have very bright lights in a control room during the night shift (Czeisler et al., 1990; Bovian et al., 1994). This gives a quicker adaptation of the circadian rhythm with better nighttime alertness and better daytime sleep. At the beginning of a block of shifts, light (level 4) is 4,000 to 5,500 lux. (A cloudy day is about 10,000 lux.) During the block of shifts, the light is decreased to level 3 (2,000 to 3,000 lux), to level 2

(800 to 1,200 lux) and then to level 1 (default) with 50 lux. (Detailed attention has to be paid to glare.)

To overcome fatigue, truck drivers often adjust the ventilation. Another method is to decrease their isolation by listening to the radio/tape/CD or talking on the radio (CB) or cell phone.

Physical activity (say walking 100 m) can be useful.

2 SHIFTWORK

2.1 Extent Although definitions of shift-work vary by country, the U. S. Bureau of Labor Statistics classifies people as being on **shiftwork** if they do not start work between 7 A.M. and 9 A.M. The percentage of people on some kind of shiftwork is somewhere between 20% and 30%.

One reason for shiftwork is economic. Equipment is available 168 h/week. Use for 8 h/day for 5 days/week gives only 24% utilization. Shiftwork is especially appropriate if capital is relatively expensive compared to labor, or if the equipment becomes obsolete quickly.

Another reason for shiftwork is "social need" for the service. Police and hospitals obviously have to be available 24 h/day, 7 days/week. But the trend has been for other service operations (restaurants, entertainment, retail stores, transportation) also to be available more hours/day.

2.2 Shiftwork Problems
The problems fall into categories of economic, social, and health/safety.

2.2.1 Economic People tend to dislike shiftwork; this may require extra pay for shiftworkers (night shift premium). There does not seem to be any firm evidence that productivity is lower with shiftwork. Since production records are available in many firms with shiftwork, this lack of evidence against a productivity penalty for shiftwork is convincing.

2.2.2 Social There are many social problems with shiftwork. Our society is not only daytime-oriented but also weekend-oriented. Most social, religious, and leisure activities occur during the evenings and weekends. Three spouse roles affected by shift work are care giver, social companion, and sexual partner. The social companion role affects not only the shiftworker, but also the spouse. The divorce rate is considerably higher for night-shift workers. The parenting role is probably worst for the evening-shift worker.

Childcare is a difficult problem for people doing shiftwork—especially for single parents and when both parents do shiftwork. A lack of relatives living in the area increases the problems. Rotating shifts (i.e., evening and night shifts) are especially difficult for childcare. Thus, some shiftworkers may prefer perma-

nent shifts. Childcare facilities are beginning to stay open for longer hours—even 24 h in some cases—but demand far exceeds the spaces available.

2.2.3 Health/safety As with productivity, there does not seem to be any firm evidence of safety problems related to shiftwork; that is, the safety records of the evening and night shifts, on average, do not differ from the day shifts. However, the Bhopal chemical leak, the Chernobyl meltdown, and the Exxon Valdez oil spill all occurred at night. Night workers at Three Mile Island received a warning of a malfunction at 4 A.M., but addressed the problem incorrectly.

There does not seem to be any generalized health decrement with shiftwork, but this may be due to self-selection of workers. Shiftworkers are a "survivor" group and tend to be noncomplainers (stoics). There tends to be fewer people over age 50 in shiftwork (Gander et al., 1993); this self-selection (change in "level of commitment") could be for economic, social, or health reasons. There have been some scattered reports of gastrointestinal problems among shiftworkers, because shiftworkers tend to have poor eating habits.

There definitely is a sleep problem if the shiftwork requires work during the night ("graveyard shift") (say midnight to 6 A.M.). When people work a permanent night shift, they gradually (in about 20 days) adjust their circadian rhythm—but only if they follow the same schedule on days off as workdays. However, most people conform to the rest of society on days off, and, since re-entrainment is fast (1–2 days), they never really adjust; their bodies are characterized by internal temporal disorder.

The gastrointestinal systems normally rest during the night—it is a time of fasting and energy depletion. Meals during the night shifts should be light. The main meal should be after day sleep. But food availability and quality tend to be poor during the night shift—primarily convenience food from vending machines. So part of the problem is biological and part managerial (both for the individual and the firm). See Table 21.7 for additional suggestions.

2.3 Shiftwork Criteria
Given the decision to have shiftwork, the shiftwork plan can be evaluated with various criteria. Table 21.8 gives some general guidelines (adapted from Knauth, 1993). Schonfelder and Knauth (1993) give the math model in Box 21.3. One of the virtues of a math model is the explicit statement of the variables and the coefficients. Thus, you can evaluate the effect of each variable (and perhaps challenge the coefficients!). Wedderburn and Scholarios (1993) demonstrated that shiftworkers do not agree with all the recommendations of shiftwork experts. A key factor in accepting a specific plan

T A B L E	21.7

Tips for day sleeping.

- Develop a good sleeping environment (dark, quiet, cool, with a bed). Have it *dark* (e.g., opaque curtains). Have it *quiet* since it is difficult to go back to sleep when daytime sleep is interrupted. Minimize changes in noise volume. Consider earplugs, unplugging bedroom phones, turning down phone volume in other rooms, reducing TV volume in other rooms, using a fan to make noise. Train your children. Have the sleeping area *cool*. The *bed* normally is OK but may be poor if the sleeper is not sleeping at home (e.g., is part of an "augmented crew" for trucks, aircraft). Then provide a good mattress and enough space.

- Plan your sleeping time. Tell others your schedule (minimize interruptions). Consider sleeping in two periods (5–6 h during the day and 1–2 h in the late evening before returning to work). Less daytime sleep and more late evening sleep not only make it easier to sleep but also may give a better fit with family/social activities. Night workers should go to sleep as soon as they get home because the sooner they go to bed, the less adjustment their biological clock must make (Czeisler et al., 1980).

- Have a light (not zero or heavy) meal before sleep. Avoid liquid consumption, as it increases the need to urinate (which wakes you up). Avoid caffeine (see Box 21.2). A warm drink before your bedtime (perhaps with family members starting their day) may help meet your social needs. Avoid foods that upset your stomach—and thus wake you up.

- If under emotional stress, relax before going to bed. One possibility is light exercise.

T A B L E	21.8

Shift system design recommendations (Knauth, 1993).

- Permanent night work does not seem to be advisable for the majority of shiftworkers. Full entrainment of physiological functions to night work is difficult. Even permanent night workers have problems due to readapting to day cycles during weekends, holidays, and vacations. If shifts rotate, rapid rotation is preferable to slow (weekly) rotation.

- Shift durations of 12 h have advantages and disadvantages. Some potential problems are: fatigue, covering absentees, overtime, limitation of toxic exposure, and possible moonlighting when workers have large blocks of leisure time.

- Avoid an early (before 7:00 A.M.) start for the morning shift.

- Distribution of leisure time is important. Have sufficient time to sleep between shifts (e.g., during shift changeovers). Limit the number of consecutive working days to 5–7. For every shift system, have some nonworking weekends with at least 2 successive full days off.

- Rotate forward (day, evening, night).

- Make the schedule simple and predictable. People want to be able to plan their personal lives. Make work schedules understandable. Publicly post them in advance so people can plan; 30 days in advance is a good policy.

Source: P. Knauth. "The Design of Shift Systems," *Ergonomics,* Vol. 36, Nos. 1–3, 15–28. Copyright © 1993 by Taylor & Francis, London. Used by permission. www.tandf.co.uk/journals

---

seems to be worker participation in the decision making. Also see Monk and Folkard (1992).

2.4 Shiftwork Plans
Shift and rest periods will be coded:

A = A (day) shift, usually 7 or 8 A.M. to 3 or 4 P.M.

B = B (afternoon, evening, swing) shift, usually 3 or 4 P.M. to 10–11 P.M.

C = C (night, graveyard) shift, usually 11–12 to 7–8 A.M.

D = Day shift for 12 h, usually 6–7 A.M. to 6–7 P.M.

N = Night shift for 12 h, usually 6–7 P.M. to 6–7 A.M.

R = Rest day

There are a number of decisions to be made. Probably most important is the hours/day—typically 16 or 24. Since there are 168 h/week, 16 h × 7 days gives 66.7% utilization and 24 h gives 100%. Of course, there are other possibilities, such as 2 shifts of 10 h (83.3%) or 2 shifts of 8 h + a 4 h shift (83.3%). In the service industries, there are many individuals who work less than "full-time." Thus, you might get 24 h of coverage but with 5 different people—who don't all work the same number of hours. In addition, service industries usually do not have a constant customer load—some times are busy and some are slack. Thus, even if the firm is open for 24 h, there may be 3 people on a task between 10 A.M. and 10 P.M., 2 from 8 A.M. to 10 A.M. and 10 P.M. to 12 A.M., and only 1 during the remaining time. Wal-Mart has shifts that start as often as every 15 minutes!

Many industries that adopt continuous (non-stop) schedules of 24 h/day also adopt 12-h shifts rather than 8-h shifts.

In some industries, there is another option—no weekend work. Some examples are manufacturing industries that do not have continuous processes (e.g., automobiles) and some financial markets (oil and currency trading). The traders have an interesting

BOX 21.3 *Shiftwork Criteria* **(Schonfelder and Knauth, 1993)**

The following criteria for evaluating shiftwork are based on "health" and "social life" standards from a German perspective. The larger the number, the worse the shiftwork system. Factors 1 to 9 (total weight = 70%) involve avoidance of health disturbances; factors 8 to 14 (total weight = 30%) involve disturbances in social life.

FACTOR 1: Consecutive night shifts

Night shifts	Cost	Night shifts	Cost
0	0	4	44.1
1	7.4	5	51.4
2	22.0	6	61.2
3	29.4	≥7	73.5

FACTOR 2: Quota of night shifts

$$F2 = n_n/n_s$$

where n_n = number of night shifts

n_s = number of days in the shift cycle

Factor 2	Cost	Factor 2	Cost	Factor 2	Cost
0	0	$.21 < F2 \leq .35$	68.6	$.56 < F2 \leq .63$	137.2
$\leq .07$	17.2	$.35 < F2 \leq .42$	85.7	$.63 < F2 \leq .70$	154.4
$.07 < F2 \leq .14$	34.3	$.42 < F2 \leq .49$	102.9	$.70 < F2 \leq 1$	171.5
$.14 < F2 \leq .21$	52.4	$.49 < F2 \leq .56$	120.0		
$.21 < F2 \leq .35$	68.6				

FACTOR 3: Number of consecutive working days

Consecutive working days	Cost	Consecutive working days	Cost	Consecutive working days	Cost
1	0	5	35	9	70
2	8.8	6	43.8	10	78.8
3	17.5	7	52.5	>10	87.5
4	26.2	8	61.2		

FACTOR 4: Weeks with >40 h working time

$$F4 = n_{>40}/n_w$$

where $n_{>40}$ = Number of weeks with >40 h working time

n_w = Number of weeks in the shift cycle

Factor 4	Cost	Factor 4	Cost	Factor 4	Cost
0	0	$.3 < F4 \leq .4$	35	$.7 < F4 \leq .8$	70.0
$F4 \leq .1$	8.8	$.4 < F4 \leq .5$	43.8	$.8 < F4 \leq .9$	78.8
$.1 < F4 \leq .2$	17.5	$.5 < F4 \leq .6$	52.5	$.9 < F4 \leq 1.0$	87.5
$.2 < F4 \leq .3$	26.2	$.6 < F4 \leq .7$	61.2		

FACTOR 5: Ratio of unfavorable shift sequences

$$F5 = n_u/n_w$$

where n_u = Number of forbidden or unfavorable shift sequences

Forbidden = N/M, M/A, A/N, N/A, A/M, M/N

e.g., N/M means night shift is followed by morning shift

N = night, M = morning, A = afternoon

BOX   **21.3**   *Shiftwork Criteria, continued*

Unfavorable = N/–/M, N/–/N

n_w = Number of weeks in the shift cycle

Factor 5	Cost	Factor 5	Cost	Factor 5	Cost
0	0	$.3 < F5 \leq .4$	84	$1.5 < F5 \leq 2.0$	168
$F5 \leq .1$	21	$.4 < F5 \leq .5$	105	$2.0 < F5 \leq 2.5$	189
$.1 < F5 \leq .2$	42	$.5 < F5 \leq 1.0$	126	$2.5 < F5 \leq 7.$	210
$.2 < F5 \leq .3$	63	$1.0 < F5 \leq 1.5$	147		

FACTOR 6: Index of shift rotation order

$F6 = (F - B)/(F + B)$

where   F = Sum of forward rotation (M/A/N)

B = Sum of backward rotation (N/A/M)

Factor 6	Cost	Factor 6	Cost	Factor 6	Cost
$F6 = 1$	0	$-.2 < F6 \leq .2$	17.5	$-.8 < F6 \leq -.6$	28
$.8 < F6 \leq 1.$	3.5	$-.4 < F6 \leq -.2$	21	$-1.0 < F6 \leq -.8$	31.5
$.6 < F6 \leq .8$	7.0	$-.6 < F6 \leq -.4$	24.5	$F6 = -1.0$	35
$.4 < F6 \leq .6$	10.5				

FACTOR 7: Start time of morning shift

Start time	Cost	Start time	Cost	Start time	Cost
After 8:00	0	6:31–7:00	21	5:01–5:30	31.5
7:31–8:00	3.5	6:01–6:30	21	Before 5:01	35
7:01–7:30	7	5:31–6:00	28		

FACTOR 8: Weekend leisure time index

$F8 = (n_{ss} + .43\, n_s)/n_w$

where n_{ss} = Number of weeks without free Saturday and Sunday

n_s = Number of weeks with free Saturday or free Sunday

n_w = Number of weeks in the shift cycle

Factor 8	Cost	Factor 8	Cost	Factor 8	Cost
$F8 = 0$	0	$.3 < F8 \leq .4$	50.4	$.7 < F8 \leq .8$	100.8
$0 < F8 \leq .1$	12.6	$.4 < F8 \leq .5$	63	$.8 < F8 \leq .9$	113.4
$.1 < F8 \leq .2$	25.2	$.5 < F8 \leq .6$	75.6	$.9 < F8 \leq 1.0$	126
$.2 < F8 \leq .3$	37.8	$.6 < F8 \leq .7$	88.2		

FACTOR 9: Index of working time adjustment

$F9 = (n_z + .25\, n_p)/n_w$

where n_z = Number of additional shifts beyond collective agreement

n_p = Number of paid days off

n_w = Number of weeks in the shift cycle

Factor 9	Cost	Factor 9	Cost	Factor 9	Cost
$F9 = 0$	0	$.8 < F9 \leq 1.0$	12	$1.6 < F9 \leq 1.8$	21.6
$F9 \leq .2$	2.4	$1.0 < F9 \leq 1.2$	14.4	$1.8 < F9 \leq 7$	24.0
$.2 < F9 \leq .4$	4.8	$1.2 < F9 \leq 1.4$	16.8		
$.4 < F9 \leq .6$	7.2	$1.4 < F9 \leq 1.6$	19.2		

BOX   **21.3**   *Shiftwork Criteria, continued*

FACTOR 10: Ratio of weeks with evening leisure time

$$F10 = n_{we}/n_w$$

where n_{we} = Number of weeks without free evening
n_w = Number of weeks in the shift cycle

Factor 10	Cost	Factor 10	Cost	Factor 10	Cost
F10=0	0	.3<F10≤.4	50.4	.7<F10≤ .8	100.8
F10≤.1	12.6	.4<F10≤.5	63	.8<F10≤ .9	113.4
.1<F10≤.2	25.2	.5<F10≤.6	75.6	.9<F10≤1.0	126
.2<F10≤.3	37.8	.6<F10≤.7	88.2		

FACTOR 11: Weeks in shift rotation

Weeks	Cost	Weeks	Cost	Weeks	Cost
1	0	5	2.4	9	4.8
2	.6	6	3.0	10	5.4
3	1.2	7	3.6	>10	6
4	1.8	8	4.2		

FACTOR 12: Number of changes between working days and days off in the basic pattern

Changes	Cost	Changes	Cost	Changes	Cost
1	0	3	2.4	5	4.8
2	1.2	4	3.6	≥6	6

FACTOR 13: Number of different types of shifts

Number	Cost	Number	Cost	Number	Cost
1	0	3	2.4	5	4.8
2	1.2	4	3.6	≥6	6

FACTOR 14: Shift sequence index

L_b = Length of shift blocks for each type of shift (morning, evening, night), maximum minus minimum; for individuals, 5 consecutive morning shifts is a block of 5; minimum always equals 1.

I_b = Interval (days) between shift blocks for each type of shift (morning, evening, night), maximum minus minimum; minimum always equals 1.

Determine F14 from the following matrix:

			L_b			
		0	1	2	3	≥4
I_b	0	1	1.5	2	2.5	3
	1	1.5	2	2.5	3	3.5
	2	2	2.5	3	3.5	4
	3	2.5	3	3.5	4	4.5
	≥4	3	3.5	4	4.5	5

Factor 14	Cost	Factor 14	Cost	Factor 14	Cost
F14=1	0	2.2<F14≤2.6	2.4	3.8<F14≤4.2	4.8
1<F14≤1.4	.6	2.6<F14≤3.0	3.0	4.2<F14≤4.6	5.4
1.4<F14≤1.8	1.2	3.0<F14≤3.4	3.6	4.6<F14≤5	6

strategy to cover the 24 h—they have one office in the United States, one office in Asia, and one in Europe. Then, allowing some time overlap, the Chicago branch might be open from 7:30 A.M. to 5:30 P.M., the Singapore branch might be open from 4 P.M. to 1 A.M. Chicago time (but 10 A.M. to 6 P.M. Singapore time) and London from 12 P.M. to 9 A.M. Chicago time (but 9 A.M. to 6 P.M. Singapore time).

Companies with incoming 800 numbers (computer help lines, airline reservations, etc.) avoid having to hire people for the night shift by hiring people in different time zones. For example, 11 P.M. to 8 A.M. in Chicago is 9 A.M. to 6 P.M. in New Delhi, India and 3 P.M. to midnight in Dublin, Ireland. (They even have training sessions in these countries so workers can improve their American accent!)

See Tepas et al. (1997) and Burns (2001) for more plans than those discussed next.

2.4.1 *5-day plans*   For 16 h/day:

- fixed shift (A and B only)
- alternate A and B shifts (usually weekly)

For 24 h/day, see Table 21.9:

- fixed shifts of A, B, C
- fixed C, weekly alternating shifts A and B
- rotating rapidly

Supervisors who work only days tend to prefer a rotating system as they get to know people on all three shifts. Weekly rotation is difficult for the workers; rapid rotation has fewer disadvantages. Note that Wednesday C shift is worked Saturday morning. An alternative is to work the C shift only 32 h/week. If machines are operated 24 h/day, when do they get maintained?

2.4.2 *7-day plans*   In addition to the problems of the 5-day shift, with 7-day plans, there is the loss of weekends and even less time available for maintenance. An additional option is 8 h or 12 h shifts.

- *Fixed 8-h shifts.* Assuming 2 days off/week, you need 12 crews. See Table 17.4 in Eastman Kodak (1986) for an example schedule.

- *Weekly rotating 8-h shifts.* Table 21.9 gives a plan for 4 crews, using a limit of 5 continuous shifts.

- *Rapid rotating 8-h shifts.* Table 21.10 gives a plan for 4 crews, using a 2-2-3 rotation and a 2-2-2 rotation. Although the 2-2-3 schedule has 2 rest days coinciding with a weekend only 1 weekend in 4 (and the 2-2-2 even less), they usually are preferred over the fixed or weekly rotating schedules due to better opportunities for social interaction with families and friends. The general consensus now is that a weekly

TABLE	21.9

7-day, 24-h shift schedule with 8-h shifts (Kodak, 1986). The schedule is shown for crew 1; crews 2, 3, and 4 start at weeks 6, 11, and 16.

			DAY OF THE WEEK	
		Week	MTWTF	SSu
Four crews,	Crew 1	1	CCCCC	RB
5-day work-		2	BBBBR	RA
week, 20-week		3	AAAAR	RC
cycle		4	CCCCR	BB
		5	BBBRR	AA
	Crew 2	6	AAARR	CC
		7	CCCRB	BB
		8	BBRAA	AA
		9	AARRC	CC
		10	CCRBB	BB
	Crew 3	11	BRRAA	AA
		12	ARRCC	CC
		13	CRBBB	BB
		14	RRAAA	AA
		15	RRCCC	CC
	Crew 4	16	RBBBB	BR
		17	RAAAA	AR
		18	RCCCC	CR
		19	BBBBB	RR
		20	AAAAA	RR
Return to week 1				

rotation is the worst possibility—you are better off with either a quicker rotation or a longer rotation.

- *Fixed 12-h shifts.* The 12-h shift (versus 8-h) is becoming more and more popular with shiftworkers. Comparing Table 21.10 (2-2-3 rotation) with Table 21.11 (EOWEO, rotating) shows that in both systems, they work the night shift 7 times in 28 shifts. The 12-h shift requires 14 shifts $\times$ 12 h = 168 work h/cycle, while the 8-h shift also requires 21 $\times$ 8 = 168 h. But, with 12 h, they have 50% of days off (14 days of 28) instead of 25%, they get 50% of weekends off instead of 25%, and they have to commute only 14 days/cycle instead of 21. This better distribution of nonwork time greatly improves family and social life as well as health (Mitchell and Williamson, 2000). Johnson and Sharit (2001), in a 10-year study of 2,433 workers, reported no significant change in occupational injury rate when shifting from an 8-h to a 12-h shift.

TABLE   21.10

7-day, 24-h shift schedules with 8-h shifts, rapid rotation (Eastman Kodak, 1986).

		WEEK 1		WEEK 2		WEEK 3		WEEK 4	
Schedule	Crew	MTWTF	SSu	MTWTF	SSu	MTWTF	SSu	MTWTF	SSu
2-2-3 rotation	1	RCCAA	BB	BRRCC	AA	ABBRR	CC	CAABB	RR
four crews	2	BRRCC	AA	ABBRR	CC	CAABB	RR	RCCAA	BB
	3	ABBRR	CC	CAABB	RR	RCCAA	BB	ABBRR	CC
	4	CAABB	RR	RCCAA	BB	BRRCC	AA	ABBRR	CC

Schedule	Crew	Week	MTWTF	SSu					
2-2-2 rotation,	1	1	CCAAB	BR					
four crews,		2	RCCAA	BB					
8-week schedule	2	3	RRCCA	AB					
		4	BRRCC	AA					
	3	5	BBRRC	CA					
		6	ABBRR	CC					
	4	7	AABBR	RC					
		8	CAABB	RR	Return to week 1				

- *Special weekend-only shifts.* For example, a nurse may work a 12-h shift only on Saturday and Sunday and not work during Monday–Friday. This permits the other nurses to avoid all weekend work.

- *Rotating 12-h shifts.* See Table 21.11. The conventional approach is 4 crews. However Karazman et al. (1998) describe an innovative shiftwork system with 5 crews. It used 8 h shifts but had more days off (basic schedule was 5 workdays followed by 3 days off). Employees on the 4 crew system would theoretically lose 9% pay, but the firm reduced this loss to 4%.

- *Service occupations* (police, hospitals, restaurants). Because customer workload is not constant, service organizations may use a mix of 8- and 12-h shifts for a specific team. For example, a hospital might have a team of 5 start work at 6 P.M., but 3 of them leave work at 2 A.M. and only 2 continue on

TABLE   21.11

7-day, 24-h shift schedules with 12-h shifts (Eastman Kodak, 1986). Assuming 3 breaks of 15 min and a 30 min lunch, productive time is 10.75 h/shift.

		WEEK 1		WEEK 2		WEEK 3		WEEK 4	
Schedule	Crew	MTWTF	SSu	MTWTF	SSu	MTWTF	SSu	MTWTF	SSu
EOWEO, every	1	DDRRD	DD	RRDDR	RR	DDRRD	DD	RRDDR	RR
other weekend	2	RRDDR	RR	DDRRD	DD	RRDDR	RR	DDRRD	DD
off, fixed shift	3	NNRRN	NN	RRNNR	RR	NNRRN	NN	RRNNR	RR
	4	RRNNR	RR	NNRRN	NN	RRNNR	RR	NNRRN	NN
EOWEO, every	1	DRRNN	RR	RDDRR	NN	NRRDD	RR	RNNRR	DD
other weekend	2	RDDRR	NN	NRRDD	RR	RNNRR	DD	DRRNN	RR
off, rotating	3	NRRDD	RR	RNNRR	DD	DRRNN	RR	RDDRR	NN
shift	4	RNNRR	DD	DRRNN	RR	RDDRR	NN	NRRDD	RR

until 6 A.M. The 8-h personnel could also work from 5 P.M. to 1 A.M. There could even be one person working just from 5 P.M. to 9 P.M.

3 GUIDELINES

The seven guidelines are divided into fatigue prevention (1, 2, 3) and fatigue reduction (4, 5, 6, and 7).

Guideline 1: Have a Work Scheduling Policy

The problem is insufficient rest. Two aspects are: (1) too many work hours, and (2) work hours at the wrong time.

3.1 Too Many Hours Count all the hours in "duty time." For example, jobs such as train crews and flight crews often have waiting and preparation time required before and after the "primary" job. Watchkeepers at sea often are assigned duties besides watchkeeping. There may be "shift turnover" time (the old shift stays to communicate with the new shift). Split-shifts (work, break—say 4–6 h—then work again) can lead to sleep problems.

People may work overtime. The entire group may work more hours, or individuals might work more hours when other individuals have to be replaced (illness, absenteeism). In such cases, shifts for individuals can be very long. There probably should be some organizational restriction on prolonged overtime (say, over 12 h/day and over 55 h/week). Lack of sleep can increase if the individual moonlights or has a long commute time. See earlier discussion in this chapter for some recommendations.

3.2 Work Hours at the Wrong Time Lack of sleep can result from sleeping at the "wrong time" or having irregular hours of work. This circadian rhythm problem affects both health and social life. See Tables 21.7, 21.8, and Box 21.3 for some recommendations.

Guideline 2: Optimize Stimulation During Work

The problem for the brain may be too much stimulation (overload) or too little stimulation (boredom). Stimulation comes from both the task and the environment.

3.3 Too Much Stimulation The usual solution is to reduce environmental stimulation. For example, for office tasks, increase visual and auditory privacy.

3.4 Too Little Stimulation Increase stimulation for either the task or the environment or both. Tasks are more stimulating if there is physical activity. Add variety within the task or schedule a variety of tasks done by the same person. For example, at the EPCOT Center, the tour guide stays with a group through the entire tour rather than just showing a single attraction and passing the group on to another guide.

Add environmental stimulation by (1) encouraging conversation with others (this may require two-way radios for those who are physically isolated), (2) varying the auditory environment (talk radio, stimulating music), (3) varying the visual environment (e.g., windows with a view), or (4) varying the climate (change temperature, air velocity). Also consider chemicals such as caffeine. See Box 21.2.

Guideline 3: Minimize the Fatigue Dose

The problem is that the "dose" of fatigue may become too great to overcome easily. Two aspects are intensity and work/rest schedule.

3.5 Intensity Good ergonomic practice reduces high stress levels on the person. For example, use machines and devices to reduce hold-and-carry activities. Static work is especially stressful, as specific muscles are activated continuously. The alternation of muscles that occurs in dynamic work is not there.

3.6 Work/Rest Schedule The effect of fatigue increases exponentially (not linearly) with time. Thus, it is important to get rest before the fatigue level becomes too high. (If piece rate incentives are used, insist that workers take their breaks.) The normal approach is to schedule a break. Another approach is to use part-time workers (as with sorting express packages).

Guideline 4: Use Work Breaks

The problem with a conventional break is that there is no productivity during the break. A solution is to use a different part of the body to work while resting the fatigued part.

If a machine is semi-automatic, the worker may be able to rest during the automatic part of the cycle—**machine time.** (Machine time may decrease physical fatigue but increase boredom.) **Job rotation** has the worker shift tasks periodically. Fatigue recovery is best if the alternative work uses a distinctly different part of the body—for example, loading/unloading a truck versus driving a truck; word processing versus answering a telephone.

Not quite as good, but still beneficial, is alternating similar work, as there would be differences in body posture, force requirements, mental activity, and so on.

One example is inspectors inspecting items on a belt conveyor; they shift jobs with other inspectors (doing a different kind of inspection) every hour. An assembly team of 6 rotates jobs every 30 min. In a packaging operation with 14 products on 14 different lines, workers shift lines every 60 min. Checkout clerks could use a left-hand station and then a right-hand station. In one warehouse, for half a shift, the workers picked cases from pallets to a conveyor; the second half they unloaded cases from the conveyor into trucks.

Job rotation, in addition to reducing fatigue, reduces the feeling of inequity among workers, as everyone shares the good and bad jobs; it also reduces boredom and monotony. In one warehouse, order pickers alternate picking large orders and small orders. (The large orders are considered more difficult.) Job rotation requires **cross-trained people** (able to do more than one thing). Cross-training gives scheduling flexibility to management.

Guideline 5: Use Frequent Short Breaks

The problem is how to divide break time. The key to the solution is that fatigue recovery is exponential; see Box 21.4 and Figures 21.4 and 21.5. If recovery is complete in 60 min, it takes only 4 min to drop from 100% fatigue to 75% fatigue but it takes 42 min to

drop from 25% fatigue to no fatigue. Thus, give break time in small segments. Ideally, breaks should be in the middle of the work period rather than at the beginning or the end. An additional benefit of frequent breaks is that they may reduce the exponential growth of fatigue (see Guideline 3).

Machine-paced work does not allow for individual differences between people (Mary versus Betty) and within people (Mary on Monday versus Mary on Tuesday). Operator-controlled breaks are better. However, people may not take enough breaks, so reminders may be necessary.

Some production is lost for each break. Reduce this loss by not turning the machine off and on, by taking the break near the machine, and the like.

Guideline 6: Maximize the Recovery Rate

The problem is to recover as quickly as possible. In technical terms, reduce the **fatigue half-life.**

For environmental stressors, reduce contact with the stressor. For heat stress, use a cool recovery area (see Figure 25.7); for cold stress, use a warm recovery

---

BOX   **21.4**   *Recovery/Work Ratio*

Both the amount of recovery (rest) and the distribution are important.

■ *Amount.* Recovery (repair, rest) time can be calculated as a ratio of exposure time; that is, as a recovery/work ratio. For example, in a 24-h day, if a specific joint on a person is used for 8 h, there are 16 h available for recovery. That is, there are 16/8 = 2 h of recovery for 1 h of exposure. If the joint is used only 4 h/day (say by alternating with the other arm), there is 20/4 = 5 h of recovery for 1 h of exposure. Overtime or long shifts can cause considerable reduction of the ratio; 12 h of work gives 12/12 = 1 h of recovery for 1 h of exposure. Weekends, holidays, and vacations increase the time available for recovery for the total body. Working rest (job variety) allows rest for part of the body.

See Box 21.5 for a discussion of exposure/recovery for chemicals.

Guideline: Increase recovery time.

■ *Distribution.* The above assumes that each minute of recovery (repair, rest) time is equally effective. That is, recovery rate versus time is a horizontal line. But recovery rate declines exponentially with time. See Figures 21.4 and 21.5. That is, the amount of recovery for minutes 6–10 is much less than for minutes 0–5. Thus, for the same total

length of break, many short breaks are better than occasional long breaks. A single break of 15 minutes is not as effective as 3 breaks of 5 minutes. An 8-h break is not as effective as 4 breaks of 2 h. Thus, it is better to rotate jobs within days rather than between days.

For example, have Joe work on job A in the morning and have Pete work on it in the afternoon. This is better than Joe working for 8 h on job A on Monday and then on job B for 8 h on Tuesday. Waersted and Westgaard (1991) suggest rotation probably should be after 1 or 2 hours rather than after 4 h.

In general, workers should be required to take breaks. They should not be permitted to omit breaks (say, to increase incentive earnings or to bring output up to standard).

There is a time penalty for breaks (e.g., operator turns off equipment, goes to rest area, rests, returns from rest area, powers up equipment); thus, very short breaks may not be cost-effective. An alternative is the microbreak: the operator takes a break (say, 20 s) at the workstation and leaves the equipment on, thus eliminating the travel cost and the on/off cost.

Guideline: Take frequent short breaks rather than occasional long breaks.

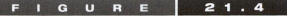

Recovery time from fatigue is exponential, so when time is low, the percent change in "concentration" is greater than the percent change in time. When time is high, the change in concentration is less than the change in time. There is more recovery in the first part of the break than in the latter. See Figure 21.5. Fatigue (while working) increases exponentially (curve is reversed). When time is low, a change in concentration is less than a change in time; when time is high, a change in concentration is greater than a change in time. Thus, 3 breaks of 5 minutes have more benefit than 1 break of 15 minutes as (1) recovery is better and (2) fatigue has not increased as much (Konz 1998).

Source: Reprinted from *Int. J. of Industrial Ergonomics,* 22. S. Konz. "Work/Rest Part II—The Scientific Basis (Knowledge Base) for the Guide." Copyright © 1998, pp. 77–99, with permission from Elsevier Science.

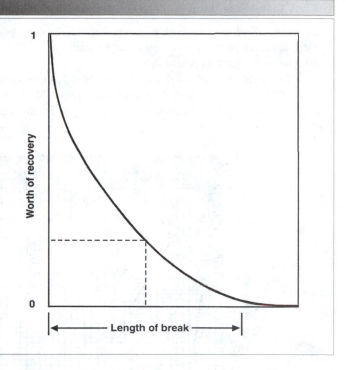

area. Use a quiet area to recover from noise, no glare to recover from glare, no vibration to recover from vibration.

For muscle stressors, good blood circulation carries away fatigue products and brings nutrients. Athletes use heat (hot showers, hot tubs, saunas, whirlpools) and massage. Workers usually don't have the time or facilities available during their breaks for these approaches. Muscles elevated above the heart (e.g., when the arm is raised) recover more slowly than when below the heart. In general, blood circulation is best for prone postures, then sitting, and then standing.

It helps to have a good circulation system. That is, a person in good physical shape will recover from muscle fatigue faster than a person in poor shape. People with heat-acclimatization recover from heat faster than people without heat-acclimatization.

Active rest seems to be better than passive rest. The active rest may be just walking to the coffee area (blood circulation in the legs improves dramatically

BOX | **21.5** | *Biologic Half-Life*

The concentration of a compound in the body will decline exponentially with time. Exponential curves with a negative exponent (as is our concern) have a value of $Y = 1$ at $X = 0$ and approach $Y = 0$ as an asymptote. However, exponential curves also can be approximated as a straight line for log Y versus X. An interesting characteristic of log scales is that the same physical distance along the axis represents a constant *ratio;* that is, the distance from 100 to 50 is the same as 50 to 25 or 25 to 12.5. See Figure 21.5 and Box 26.3.

This leads to the concept of biologic half-life. The half-life is independent of the concentration for a first-order process (elimination is a function of concentration); it is the time needed to eliminate 50% of the absorbed material. The longer the half-life, the slower the elimination rate.

The potential for the body burden to exceed normal levels during unusually long work periods exists whenever the biologic half-life for the chemical in humans is in the range of 3–200 h (Paustenbach, 1994, p. 231). A rule of thumb: Steady-state body burden occurs when exposure occurs for a period of greater than 5 biologic half-lives. For moderately volatile substances (e.g., solvents), which have half-lives from 12–60 h, and for most work schedules, the steady-state tissue burden will be reached in 2–6 weeks. For volatile chemicals (e.g., low molecular weight solvents) with shorter half-lives, steady-state will be reached in 2–4 days (Paustenbach, 1994, p. 274).

F I G U R E   21.5

Approximating an exponential curve. This can be done by a straight line on semi-log paper. In theory, an exponential curve approaches 0 concentration asymptotically (i.e., never reaches zero). An approximation of the end point is the time at which concentration reaches 1%.

If concentration is 1% at 60 min, the 50% level was reached in 9 min. The concentration took only 4 min to drop from 100% to 75% but took 42 min to drop from 25% to 1% (Konz, 1998). The time at which the response of an exponential curve reaches 50% (9 min in this example) is called the half-life. See Figure 30.6.

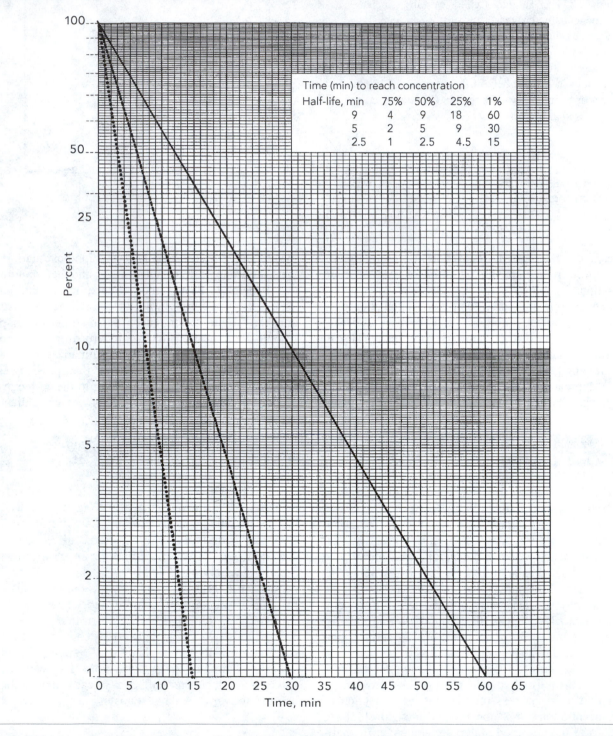

Time (min) to reach concentration			
Half-life, min	75%	50%	25%	1%
9	4	9	18	60
5	2	5	9	30
2.5	1	2.5	4.5	15

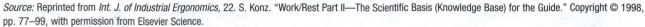

within <20 steps). For exercises done at the workstation (for "warm-up" and during short breaks), consider social acceptability (some people may be embarrassed to do some exercises).

For working rest, to encourage walking and using alternate muscle groups, consider cell layout (see Chapter 12) and having the operator do the material handling for the workstation (obtaining supplies or disposing of finished components).

Guideline 7: Increase The Recovery/Work Ratio

When the problem is insufficient time to recover, the solution is to increase the recovery time or decrease the work time. See Box 21.4. For example, if a specific joint is used 8 h/day, there are 16 h to recover; hence, 2 h of recovery/1 h of work. If the work of the two arms is alternated so one arm is used 4 h/day, there are 20 h to recover; 5 h of recovery/1 h of work. Overtime, moonlighting, or 12 h shifts can cause problems. Working 12 h/day gives 12 h of recovery, so there is 1 h of recovery/1 h of work.

Consider all break time, both paid and unpaid. In particular, consider machine time and job rotation as well as coffee and lunch breaks. Holidays, weekends, and vacations are valuable in reducing long-term fatigue (long half-life) where there is still a fatigue effect at the start of the day.

Review Questions

1. Give five factors into which fatigue can be divided.
2. Define "working rest."
3. What is a "compressed" workweek?
4. Why does static work tend to be more fatiguing than dynamic work?
5. To improve circulation of blood in the leg after standing or sitting, about how many steps are needed?
6. Briefly describe active, passive, and working rest.
7. Give some mental overload tasks and some mental underload tasks.
8. What are the two divisions of sleep? Which do you lose when you don't get enough sleep?
9. Give a zietgeber.
10. What is sleep inertia?
11. Does alcohol make you sleepier at night than during the day?
12. How do you know if you are on "shiftwork"?
13. Why is it recommended that night shift workers rotate rather than being on a fixed shift?
14. What is the difference between work time and duty time?
15. Give four different approaches to adding environmental stimulation.
16. What happens to the recovery/work ratio when a person goes from an 8-h shift to a 12-h shift?

References

Ahsberg, E. and Gamberale, F. Perceived fatigue during physical work: An experimental evaluation of a fatigue inventory. *Int. J. of Industrial Ergonomics,* Vol. 21, 117–31, 1998.

Akerstedt, T. and Landstrom, U. Work place countermeasures of night shift fatigue. *Int. J. of Industrial Ergonomics,* Vol. 21, 167–78, 1998.

Asmussen, E. and Mazin, B. Recuperation after muscular fatigue by "diverting activities." *European J. of Applied Physiology,* Vol. 38, 1–7, 1978.

Ball, C., Funk, T., Noonan, D., Velasquez, J., and Konz, S. Degradation of performance due to sleep deprivation: A field study. *Proceedings of the Human Factors Society,* 570–74, 1984.

Bennett, C., Marcellus, F., and Reynolds, J. Counteracting psychological fatigue effects by stimulus changes. *Proceedings of the Human Factors Society,* 219–24, 1974.

Bhatia, N. and Murrell, K. An industrial experiment in organized rest pauses. *Human Factors,* Vol. 11, No. 2, 167–74, 1969.

Bigland-Ritchie, B., Furbush, F., and Woods, J. Fatigue of intermittent submaximal voluntary contractions: Central and peripheral factors. *J. of Applied Physiology,* Vol. 61, No. 2, 421–29, 1986.

Bishu, R., Hallbeck, S., King, R. and Kennedy, J. Is 100% MVC truly a 100% effort? In *Advances in Industrial Ergonomics and Safety VII,* Bittner, A. and Champney, P. (eds.), 545–52. London: Taylor and Francis, 1995.

Bonnet, M. and Arand, D. The use of prophylactic naps and caffeine to maintain performance during a continuous operation. *Ergonomics,* Vol. 37, No. 6, 1009–20, 1994.

Boucsein, W. and Thum, M. Design of work/rest schedules for computer work based on psychophysiological recovery measures. *Int. J. of Industrial Ergonomics,* Vol. 20, 51–57, 1997.

Bovian, D., Duffy, J., Kronauer, R., and Czeisler, C. Sensitivity of the human circadian pacemaker to light. *Proceedings of the APSS.* Boston, 1994.

Buck, L., Greenley, M., Loughnane, D., and Webb, R. Statutory regulations for optimizing work schedules. *27th Annual Conference of the Human Factors Association of Canada,* 245–50, 1995.

Buck, L. and Lamonde, F. Critical incidents and fatigue among locomotive engineers. *Safety Science,* 16, 1–18, 1993.

Burns, R. Personnel scheduling. In *Handbook of Industrial Engineering,* 3rd ed., Salvendy, G. (ed.), Chapter 64. New York: Wiley, 2001.

Bystrom, S., Mathiassen, S., and Fransson-Hall, C. Physiological effects of micropauses in isometric handgrip exercise. *European J. Applied Physiology,* Vol. 63, 405–11, 1991.

Chaffin, D., Anderson, G., and Martin, B. *Occupational Biomechanics,* 3rd ed. New York: Wiley, 1999.

Coleman, R. *Wide Awake at 3:00 A.M.* New York: W. H. Freeman, 1986.

Colquhoun, W., Blake, M., and Edwards, R. Experimental studies of shift work, I: A comparison of rotating and stabilized 4-hour shifts. *Ergonomics,* Vol. 11, No. 5, 437–53, 1968.

Colquhoun, W., Rudenfranz, J., Goethe, H., Neidhart, B., Condon, R., Plett, R., and Knauth, P. Work at sea. *Int. Archives of Occupational and Environmental Health,* Vol. 60, 321–29, 1988.

Craig, A. Field studies of human inspection: The application of vigilance research. In *Hours of Work,* Folkard, S. and Monk, T. (eds.). New York: Wiley, 1985.

Czeisler, C., Johnson, M., Duffy, J., Brown, E., Ronda, J., and Kronauer, R. Exposure to bright light and darkness to treat physiologic maladaptation to night work. *New England J. of Medicine,* Vol. 322, 1253–59, 1990.

Cziesler, C., Weitzman, E., and Moore-Ede, M. Human sleep: Its duration and organization depend on its circadian phase. *Science,* Vol. 210, 1264–67, 1980.

Dababneh, A., Swanson, N., and Shell, R. Impact of rest breaks on the productivity and well-being of workers. *Ergonomics,* Vol. 44, 2, 164–74, 2001.

Davis, R. and Konz, S. Effects of muscular exertion on hand steadiness. In *Advances in Ind. Ergonomics and Safety VII,* Bittner, A. and Champney, P. (eds.). London: Taylor and Francis, 1995.

Dinges, D., Orne, M., and Orne, E. Assessing performance upon abrupt awakening from naps during quasi-continuous operations. *Behavior Research Methods, Instruments and Computers,* Vol. 17, No. 1, 37–45, 1985.

Dul, J., Douwes, M., and Smitt, P. A work-rest model for static postures. In *Design for Everyone,* Vol. 1, 93–95. Queinnec, Y. and Daniellou, F. (eds.). London: Taylor and Francis, 1991.

Eastman Kodak. *Ergonomic Design for People at Work,* Vol. 2. New York: Van Nostrand-Reinhold, 1986.

Edwards, J., Atkinson, G., Waterhouse, J., Reilly, T., Godfrey, R., and Budgett, R. Use of melatonin in recovery from jet-lag following an eastward flight across 10 time zones. *Ergonomics,* Vol. 43, 10, 1501–13, 2000.

Eisenberg, S. Looking for the perfect brew. *Food Technology,* Vol. 43, 42–45, 1989.

Ensminger, A. et al. *Foods and Nutrition Technology,* 2d ed., Vol. 1. Boca Raton, FL: CRC Press, 289–91, 1994.

Evaluation of Caffeine Safety. *Food Technology,* Vol. 41, 105–13, 1987.

Finkleman, J. A large database study of the factors associated with work-induced fatigue. *Human Factors,* Vol. 36, No. 2, 232–43, 1994.

Floru, R., Cail, F., and Elias, R. Psychophysiological changes during a VDU repetitive task. *Ergonomics,* Vol. 28, No. 10, 1455–68, 1985.

Galinski, T., Swanson, N., Sauter, S., Hurrell, J., and Schleifer, L. A field study of supplementary rest breaks for data-entry operators. *Ergonomics,* Vol. 43, 5, 622–38, 2000.

Gander, P., Nguyen, D., Rosekind, M., and Connell, L. Age, circadian rhythms, and sleep loss in flight crews. *Aviation, Space and Environmental Medicine,* Vol. 64, No. 3, 189–95, 1993.

Genaidy, A., Delgado, E., and Bustos, T. Active micro-break effects on musculoskeletal comfort ratings in meatpacking plants. *Ergonomics,* Vol. 38, No. 2, 326–36, 1995.

Gillberg, M. Effects of naps on performance. In *Hours of Work,* S. Folkard and T. Monk (eds.). New York: Wiley, 1985.

Grice, H. and Murray, T. Caffeine: A perspective on current concerns. *Nutrition Today,* Vol. 22, 36–38, July–August 1987.

Henning, R. Worker-terminated micro-breaks and perceptual-motor performance. In *Proceedings of the 4th Mid-Central Ergonomics/Human Factors Conference,* 374–80. New York: Springer-Verlag, 1987.

Henning, R., Kissel, G., and Maynard, D. Compensatory rest breaks for VDT operators. *Int. J. of Industrial Ergonomics,* Vol. 14, 243–49, 1994.

Henning, R., Callaghan, E., Guttman, J., and Braun, H. Evaluation of two self-managed rest break systems for VDT users. *Proc. of Human Factors and Ergonomics Society,* 780–84, 1995.

Henning, R., Callaghan, E., Ortega, A., Kissel, G., Guttman, J., and Braun, H. Continuous feedback to promote self-management of rest breaks during computer use. *Int. J. of Industrial Ergonomics,* Vol. 18, 71–82, 1996.

Henning, R., Jacques, P., Kissel, G., Sullivan, A., and Alteras-Webb, S. Frequent short rest breaks from computer work: Effects on productivity and well-being at two field sites. *Ergonomics,* Vol. 40, No. 1, 78–91, 1997.

Horie, Y. A study on optimum team of work hour with rest pause for VDT workers. *Japanese J. of Ergonomics,* Vol. 23, 373–83, 1987.

Johnson, M. and Sharit, J. Impact of a change from an 8-h to a 12-h shift schedule on workers and occupational injury rates. *Int. J. of Ind. Ergonomics,* Vol. 27, 303–19, 2001.

Johnson, R. and Merullo, D. Effects of caffeine and gender on vigilance and marksmanship. *Proc. Human Factors and Ergonomics Society,* 1217–21, 1996.

Kadefors, R. and Laubli, T. Muscular disorders in computer users: An introduction. *Int. J. of Industrial Ergonomics,* Vol. 30, 203–10, 2002.

Karazman, R., Kloimuller, I., Gartner, J., Geissler, H., Horwein, K., and Morawetz, I. Participatory development of age-adjusted optional shift time schedules in industrial workers in a plant. In *Advances in Occupational Ergonomics and Safety,* S. Kumar, ed. Amsterdam: IOS Press, 139–42, 1998.

Kemp, E., Phillips, D., Hedderley, D., Dickson, B., and Chan, M. Software selection for the management and prevention of RSI injuries in a diverse user community. *Int. J. of Industrial Ergonomics,* Vol. 29, 1, 1–14, 2002.

Kilbom, A., Gamberale, F., Persson, J., and Annwall, G. Physiological and psychological indices of fatigue during static contractions. *European J. of Applied Physiology,* Vol. 36, 7–17, 1983.

Knauth, P. The design of shift systems. *Ergonomics,* Vol. 36, 1-3, 15–28, 1993.

Konz, S. Endurance and rest for work with concentration and attention. *Proc. of the Human Factors Society,* 210–13, 1979.

Konz, S. Work/rest: Part II—The scientific basis (knowledge base) for the guide. *Int. J. of Industrial Ergonomics,* Vol. 22, 73–99, 1998.

Kopardekar, P. and Mital, A. The effect of different work-rest schedules on fatigue and performance of a simulated directory assistance operator's task. *Ergonomics,* Vol. 37, No. 10, 1697–1707, 1994.

Lewis, P. *Recommendations for NRC Policy on Shift Scheduling and Overtime at Nuclear Power Plants.* Washington, DC: NUREG/CR-4248, U. S. Nuclear Regulatory Commission, 1985.

Lumley, M., Roehrs, T., Asker, D., Zorick, F., and Roth, T. Ethanol and caffeine effects on daytime sleepiness/alertness. *Sleep,* Vol. 10, No. 4, 306–12, 1987.

Mathiassen, S. and Winkel, J. Can occupational guidelines for work-rest schedules be based on endurance time data? *Ergonomics,* Vol. 35, No. 3, 253–59, 1992.

Megaw, E. The definition and measurement of visual fatigue. In *Evaluation of Human Work,* 2d ed., J. Wilson and N. Corlett (eds.). London: Taylor and Francis, 1995.

Meijman, T. Mental fatigue and the temporal structuring of working times. *Proc. Human Factors and Ergonomics Society.* Santa Monica, CA, 789–93, 1995.

Meijman, T., Mulder, G., van Dormolen, M., and Cremer, R. Workload of driving examiners: A psychophysiological field study. In *Enhancing Industrial Performance,* Kragt, H. (ed.). London: Taylor and Francis, 245–58, 1992.

Miedema, M., Douwes, M., and Dul, J. Recommended maximum holding times for prevention of discomfort of static standing postures. *Int. J. of Industrial Ergonomics,* Vol. 19, 9–18, 1997.

Misawa, T., Yoshina, K., and Shigeta, S. An experimental study of the duration of a single spell of work on VDT performance. *Japanese J. of Industrial Health,* Vol. 26, 296–302, 1984.

Mital, A. Comprehensive maximum acceptable weight of lift database for regular 8-hour work shifts. *Ergonomics,* Vol. 27, 1127–38, 1984a.

Mital, A. Maximum weights of lift acceptable to male and female industrial workers for extended work shifts. *Ergonomics,* 27, 1115–26, 1984b.

Mital, A., Hamid, F., and Brown, M. Physical fatigue in high and very high frequency manual materials handling: Perceived exertion and physiological factors. *Human Factors,* Vol. 36, No. 2, 219–31, 1994.

Mitchell, R. and Williamson, A. Evaluation of an 8-hour versus a 12-hour shift roster on employees of a power station. *Applied Ergonomics,* Vol. 31, 83–93, 2000.

Monk, T. and Folkard, S. *Making Shiftwork Tolerable.* London: Taylor and Francis, 1992.

Moog, R. Optimization of shift work: Physiological contributions. *Ergonomics,* Vol. 30, No. 9, 1249–59, 1987.

Murrell, K. *Human Performance in Industry.* New York: Reinhold, 1965.

Nakamura, K., Takahaski, H., Shima, S., and Tanaka, M. Effects of immersion in tepid bath water on recovery from fatigue after submaximal exercise in man. *Ergonomics,* Vol. 39, No. 2, 257–66, 1996.

Neville, K., Bisson, R., French, J., Boll, P., and Storm, W. Subjective fatigue of C–141 aircrews during Operation Desert Storm. *Human Factors,* Vol. 36, No. 2, 339–49, 1994.

Paustenbach, D. Occupational exposure limits, pharmacokinetics and unusual work schedules. In *Patty's Industrial Hygiene and Toxicology,* 3d ed., Vol. 3A, *The Work Environment,* Chapter 7, 222–348, Harris, R., Cralley, L. J., and Cralley, L. V. (eds.). New York: Wiley, 1994.

Pasztor, A. and Gruley, B. FAA, in safety move, to seek to toughen limits on shifts of commercial pilots. *Wall Street Journal,* Dec. 14, 1995.

Phillips, E. FAA mandates rest for cabin crews. *Aviation Week and Space Technology,* Vol. 29, 22 August 1994.

Pollack, A., and Wood, E. Venous pressure in the saphenous vein at the ankle in man during exercise and change in posture. *J. of Applied Physiology,* Vol. 1, 649–62, 1949.

Ramsey, J., Halcomb, C., and Mortagy, A. Self-determined work/rest cycles in hot environments. *Int. J. of Production Research,* Vol. 12, No. 5, 623–31, 1974.

Rodgers, S. Work physiology—fatigue and recovery. In *Handbook of Human Factors and Ergonomics,* 2d ed., G. Salvendy (ed.). New York: Wiley, 1997.

Rodgers, S. *Working with Backache.* Fairport, NY: Perinton Press, 1984.

Roehrs, T., Zwyghuizen-Doorenbos, A., Timms, V., Zorick, F., and Roth, T. Sleep extension, enhanced alertness and the sedating effects of ethanol. *Pharmacology Biochemistry & Behavior,* Vol. 34, 321–24, 1989.

Rosenthal, L., Roehrs, T., Zwyghuizen-Doorenbos, A., Plath, D., and Roth, T. Alerting effects of caffeine after normal and restricted sleep. *Neuropsychopharmacology,* Vol. 4, 103–08, 1991.

Schonfelder, E. and Knauth, P. A procedure to assess shift systems based on ergonomic criteria. *Ergonomics,* Vol. 36, 1–3, 65–76, 1993.

Schwing, R. Exposure-controlled highway fatality rates: Temporal patterns compared to some explanatory variables. *Alcohol, Drugs and Driving,* Vol. 5, No. 4, 275–85, 1990.

Smith, R. Boredom: A review. *Human Factors,* Vol. 23, No. 3, 329–40, 1981.

Summala, H. and Mikkola, T. Fatal accidents among car and truck drivers: Effects of fatigue, age, and alcohol consumption. *Human Factors,* Vol. 36, No. 2, 315–26, 1994.

Sundelin, G. and Hagberg, M. The effect of different pause types on neck and shoulder EMG activity during VDU work. *Ergonomics,* Vol. 32, No. 5, 527–37, 1989.

Swanson, N. and Sauter, S. The effects of exercise on the health and performance of data entry operators. In *Work With Display Units,* 288–91, Luczak, H., Cakir, A., and Cakir, G. (eds.). Amsterdam: Elsevier, 1993.

Tepas, D., Paley, M., and Popkin, S. Work schedules and sustained performance. Chapter 32 in *Handbook of Human Factors and Ergonomics,* 2d ed., G. Salvendy (ed.). New York: Wiley, 1997.

Thompson, D. Effect of exercise breaks on musculoskeletal strain among data-entry operators: A case study. In *Promoting Health and Safety in Computerized Offices,* Sauter S. et al. (eds.). London: Taylor and Francis, 1990.

The tyranny of time. *The Economist,* 72–74, Dec. 18, 1999.

Van Dieen, J. and Vrielink, H. Evaluation of work-rest schedules with respect to the effects of postural workload in standing work. *Ergonomics,* Vol. 41, No. 12, 1832–44, 1998.

Waersted, M. and Westgaard, R. Shoulder muscle tension introduced by two VDT-based tasks of different complexity. *Ergonomics,* Vol. 34, No. 2, 265–76, 1991.

Walsh, J. Using pharmacological aids to improve waking function and sleep while working at night. *Work and Stress,* Vol. 4, No. 3, 237–43, 1990.

Walsh, J., Humm, T., Muehlback, M., Sugerman, J., and Schweitzer, P. Sedative effects of alcohol at night. *J. of Studies on Alcohol,* Vol. 52, No. 6, 597–600, 1991.

Wedderburn, A. and Scholarios, D. Guidelines for shift-workers: Trials and errors? *Ergonomics,* Vol. 36, 1–3, 211–17, 1993.

WSJ. Moonlighting is on the wane. *Wall Street Journal,* September 19, 2000.

Young, S. and Hashemi, L. Fatigue and trucking accidents: Two modes of accident causation. *Proc. Human Factors and Ergonomics Society,* 952–56, 1996.

Yoshimura, I. and Tomoda, Y. A study of fatigue estimation by integrated analysis of psychophysiological function—Relating to continuous working time and rest pause for VDT work. *Japanese J. of Ergonomics,* Vol. 30, No. 2, 85–97, 1994.

Yoshimura, I. and Tomoda, Y. A study on fatigue grade estimation for VDT work—Investigation of the rest pause. *Japanese J. of Ergonomics,* Vol. 31, No. 3, 215–23, 1995.

Zwahlen, H., Hartman, A., and Rangarajulu, S. Effects of rest breaks in continuous VDT work on visual and musculoskeletal comfort/discomfort and on performance. In *Human Computer Interaction,* G. Salvendy (ed.). Amsterdam: Elsevier, 315–19, 1984.

Zwyghuizen, A., Roerhrs, T., Lipschutz, L., Timms, V., and Roth, T. Effects of caffeine on alertness. *Psychopharmacology,* Vol. 100, 36–39, 1990.

MANAGING AN ERGONOMICS PROGRAM

22

Overview

rgonomics programs can be established to address many different aspects of the work environment (i.e. human–computer interaction, lighting, product design). This chapter discusses the development, implementation, and management of ergonomics programs that address work-related musculoskeletal disorders (WMSD). An effective ergonomics program can significantly reduce financial costs to employers and the costs to the individuals who experience these disorders. In addition to reducing the risk of injuries and illnesses, an effective ergonomics program also increases the productive efficiency of the workers, product quality, and the quality of working life.

Key Concepts

active/passive health surveillance

administrative controls

American National Standards Institute, ASC Z-365

buildability

engineering controls

ergonomics committee

Ergonomics Program Management Guidelines for Meatpacking Plants

General Duty Clause (5a-1)

health care provider

medical management

narrative analysis

National Institute of Occupational Safety and Health (NIOSH)

proactive effort

program evaluation

qualitative checklists

quantitative checklists

work-practice controls

Worker Compensation insurance

■ HISTORY OF ERGONOMICS PROGRAMS

Ergonomics program efforts have been very effective in many different industries. For example, ergonomics teams at automobile companies have made large contributions to the comfort and functionality of automobile interiors. The potential for errors that could have serious consequences at nuclear power plants has been reduced by groups of ergonomists that assist in the design of the control room controls and displays. Although decreasing errors and improving efficiency is the focus of many ergonomics programs, this chapter focuses on programs that are designed to improve occupational safety and health in manufacturing and service industries.

1.1 Focus on Musculoskeletal Disorders
There is a long history of musculoskeletal disorders associated with both work and non-work environments (National Research Council and Institute of Medicine, 2001); however, there has been a significant increase in the attention given to work-related disorders by industry, governmental agencies, and the media during the past 20 years. In particular, the Occupational Safety and Health Administration (OSHA) in the United States has devoted extensive resources to this area. This has resulted in controversy in both the technical and the political spheres.

In 1993, OSHA published the *Ergonomics Program Management Guidelines for Meatpacking Plants.* This guideline document was published due to the "significant increase in the reporting of cumulative trauma disorders (CTDs) and other work-related disorders due to ergonomic hazards." The publication of this document provided "due notification" to U.S. industry that certain job characteristics increase the risk of work-related musculoskeletal disorders. This guideline formed the basis of a number of **General Duty Clause (5a-1)** citations in many industries during the 1990s that involved millions of dollars in penalties (Purswell and Purswell, 2001). The *general duty clause* of the Occupational Safety and Health Act (1970) states that "an organization shall furnish to each of his employees a place of employment which is free from recognized hazards that are causing or are likely to cause death or serious physical harm to his employees."

The **National Institute of Occupational Safety and Health (NIOSH)** conducted health hazard evaluations associated with ergonomics in many industries (Bernard, 1997). The conclusions drawn by those government agencies responsible for safety and health from the research studies and hazard evaluations led to the development of a federal ergonomics program standard. The promulgation of the standard was politically volatile during the 1990s. Organized labor strongly supported the development of the standard, while business groups actively opposed it (Scalia, 1994).

1.2 Development of Ergonomic Standards
OSHA issued the *Ergonomic Program Standard* in November 2000, at the end of the Clinton administration; however, in early 2001, with the support of the new Bush administration, Congress rescinded the regulatory rule. Although there is currently no federal ergonomics standard, the basic elements of the standard, discussed in this chapter, have been implemented by many organizations in the United States. OSHA continues to apply the "General Duty Clause" to workplaces that exhibit those risk factors that increase the risk of musculoskeletal disorders. In addition, some state regulatory agencies have developed standards that address workplace ergonomics (e.g., California, North Carolina, and Washington).

During the 1990s, a parallel effort to develop a voluntary standard was conducted by the National Safety Council (NSC). The objective of the Accredited Standards Committee on Control of Cumulative Trauma Disorders, accredited by the **American National Standards Institute (ANSI),** was to develop the standard by forming a consensus among stakeholders from business, labor, academia, and professional societies (**ASC Z-365,** 2000). To accommodate the change in terminology, the standard was subsequently re-titled *Management of Work-Related Musculoskeletal Disorders.* This title is more descriptive of the issues addressed than is the OSHA title. There are many similarities between the elements of the OSHA Ergonomics Program and the ANSI standard that are discussed in detail later in this chapter.

Many companies are independently implementing ergonomics programs that have been found to reduce occupational injuries (GAO, 1997). Rather than simply being concerned with being in regulatory compliance, many of these programs focus on the benefits of ergonomics programs for increasing productivity and product quality, as well as improving the quality of working life for the employees.

■ ORGANIZATIONAL FUNCTIONS INVOLVED IN AN ERGONOMICS PROGRAM

2.1 Ergonomics Program as a System
There are two related objectives of an ergonomics program that specifically address work-related musculoskeletal disorders. One is to reduce or eliminate the potential for the disorders. The second objective is to provide treatment to reduce the effect of a disorder, if one does occur. Without the participation and contributions of each of the following functions, an

ergonomics program cannot be successful. The type of program and the functions involved also depend upon the size of the organization. A large facility with many employees has different functional responsibilities than does a small facility. For example, a large facility may have an on-site **health care provider** (e.g., occupational nurse or physician), whereas a small facility may use the local hospital or emergency medical facility to handle injuries and illnesses. Similarly, manufacturing operations have different personnel and responsibilities than do service industries (e.g., retail store, hospital, etc.). Although the various responsibilities may be assigned differently within the various organizations, the performance of each of the basic functions is necessary for any successful ergonomics program. The activities associated with a successful ergonomics program can be divided into three functional areas: human resources, engineering and operations management, and workers.

2.2 Human Resource Activities

The human resource function is responsible for collecting and maintaining the information that relates to the individual employees. This includes the occupational safety and health data, the medical records, and the health insurance and Worker Compensation records.

2.2.1 *Occupational safety*

The occupational safety function is usually located within the human resources department. The safety staff is responsible for maintaining the injury and illness database that is required in order to be in regulatory compliance. In addition, the safety staff analyzes those data to improve occupational safety and health. Due to the emphasis placed on ergonomics by OSHA, the safety function often has the responsibility of maintaining and documenting the ergonomics program. One of the disadvantages of this organizational structure is that management often considers safety programs as a cost to the company and does not consider the benefits that ergonomic activities can provide to the company's bottom line. Another disadvantage of assigning the responsibility for the ergonomics program to the safety staff is that such ergonomics programs tend to be solely focused on compliance with federal and state occupational safety laws, rather than being a good business practice.

2.2.2 *Medical*

For larger organizations that have resident health care providers (e.g., physicians, occupational health nurses, or emergency medical technicians), these individuals have direct interaction with those workers who experience biomechanical discomfort or disorders. They are able to address both the worker's general health and the job-related factors that impact the person's health.

The health care providers are generally responsible for making decisions as to alternative assignments, sometimes referred to as "light duty" jobs, when workers are unable to perform their normal tasks due to medical problems. For example, when a person has discomfort in her lower back and cannot experience prolonged standing, an alternative assignment to a seated inspection or assembly task might be appropriate. It is important that the health care providers have some understanding of the various task characteristics when specifying work restrictions.

Another reason that the health care providers are important participants in an ergonomics program is that they are generally responsible for the initial documentation of an occupational injury or illness (using OSHA 300 logs). It is natural for them to be responsible for some of the health documentation for the ergonomics program. They are also responsible for the medical management of any injuries or illnesses that do occur. As discussed later, medical management is an important aspect of an effective ergonomics program.

2.2.3 *Worker Compensation insurance*

The human resources department is also responsible for the administration of the Worker Compensation insurance programs (see Box 20.5 for a description of Worker Compensation). The payment of Worker Compensation costs is often directly related to ergonomic issues in the workplace. For example, when there is a disproportionately high number of Worker Compensation cases involving the hands or wrists associated with a particular workplace, it often indicates that the task characteristics should be modified to reduce the biomechanical stress. Worker Compensation programs are administered by the individual states, and each state's statutes determine the financial remuneration for workers who have experienced an occupational injury or illness. The Worker Compensation records are a valuable source of information for an ergonomics program. A reduction in Worker Compensation costs is one measure of the effectiveness of an ergonomics program that management can easily understand and appreciate. In addition, the Worker Compensation costs associated with a particular workstation can contribute to the cost justification necessary to make modifications to improve the workstations, work methods, tools, and equipment.

2.3 Engineering

The engineering function is responsible for designing, installing, and maintaining the workplace layout, work methods, tools, and equipment. Whether the environment is manufacturing or office operations, the design of the operator's task and equipment can have important implications for both task efficiency and the potential for biomechanical stress and disorders. In addition, product design engineers can often have an important impact on the production methods and potential problems.

2.3.1 *Process engineering* In manufacturing or process industries, the design or specification of the workplace layout, work methods, tools, and equipment is performed by engineers. Organizations use different labels for these process engineering functions (e.g., manufacturing engineering, industrial engineering). The engineers involved in process engineering generally have received their formal education in the fields of mechanical, electrical, or industrial engineering. They are involved in setting the initial design requirements for equipment and often work directly with the engineers at the vendors of equipment. Purchasing and installing systems that employ ergonomic design principles is a critical part of controlling the occurrence of musculoskeletal disorders. This component of an ergonomics program frequently does not receive sufficient attention. The avoidance of problems is preferable to requiring re-design or modification after installation. The individuals who are responsible for process design are usually very qualified in the mechanical and electrical disciplines; however, they often have little or no formal training in how the human is integrated into the system.

2.3.2 *Maintenance* Although production engineers design or specify the equipment and workplace layouts, the maintenance function is responsible for the installation and modification of equipment. The maintenance of the equipment is critical to the operators' ability to perform their jobs effectively. When operators are asked what characteristic of their job affects them the most, they frequently respond that it is the maintenance of the equipment. In particular, the maintenance of power tools used in assembly operations affects the employees' effort, fatigue, and potential for disorders.

2.3.3 *Product engineering* The **buildability** of a product can also affect the amount of biomechanical stress. For example, the type of fabric used in clothing, decorative pillows, or even automobile interiors can significantly affect the stress on operators during assembly process. Frequently, when there are work-related musculoskeletal disorders observed during fabrication, assembly, or packaging, it is necessary to modify the design of the product to address the problem. For example, self-tapping screws are beneficial because they eliminate the task of drilling a pilot hole. However, some operations found that the increased difficulty of driving self-tapping screws led to significantly increased medical costs related to disorders. Eliminating one operation was not found to be cost effective when all costs were considered.

2.4 Operations Management and Workers

2.4.1 *Upper management* The company's management, at all levels, must be dedicated to the ergonomics effort for it to be successful. In particular, upper management is responsible for setting the goals and committing the resources necessary to implement and maintain the program. In addition, upper management makes the assignments and identifies the parts of the organizations that have responsibility for the various elements of the ergonomics program.

2.4.2 *Production supervision* Production management, particularly first-line supervisors, are the most familiar with both the production processes and the individual operators performing the various tasks in their area of responsibility. If operators are experiencing a problem performing their job, the first-line supervisor is the first to be informed. They also have a direct interest in having an efficient operation, from the standpoint of productivity and product quality, as well as from the perspective of operator safety and health. If operators must perform the task in an awkward posture, their performance will deteriorate over time with respect to either the time required to perform the task or the quality of their work. In addition, if workers are uncomfortable when performing their jobs, the absenteeism and turnover rate will be high, having a negative impact on production.

2.4.3 *Workers* The operators are obviously affected by the work environment and are the beneficiaries of an effective ergonomics effort. Many studies have observed the advantage of having the employees participate in the problem-solving efforts to improve their workplace design, work methods, tools, and equipment (Lanoie and Tvenas, 1996; Moore and Garg, 1998; May and Schwoerer, 1994). The operators can often participate in process improvements that increase productivity and reduce the amount of effort, fatigue, and potential for disorders. The operators' ability to detect, and their willingness to report, early signs or symptoms of a disorder is important for a program to be effective at controlling work-related disorders.

3 PROGRAM ELEMENTS

As discussed in Section 1.2, a number of parallel efforts have addressed the development and maintenance of ergonomics programs. The program elements for some of these efforts are shown in Box 22.1. Although there are many similarities among the elements of these different programs, the basic goal of all of the programs is to provide a work environment (workplace layout, work methods, tools, and equipment) that can be used effectively by the human operator without biomechanical strain. In addition to

BOX **22.1** | *Program Elements*

Ergonomics Program Management Guidelines for Meatpacking Plants (OSHA, 1993)

- Worksite analysis
- Hazard prevention and control
- Medical management
- Training and education

Elements of an Ergonomics Program (NIOSH, 1997)

- Look for signs of WMSDs
- Set the stage for action through management commitment and worker involvement
- Provide training
- Gather and examine evidence of WMSDs by identifying risk factors and monitoring health and medical indicators
- Develop engineering and administrative controls
- Implement health care management
- Be proactive

OSHA Ergonomics Program Standard (OSHA, 2000)

- Management leadership and employee participation
- Hazard information and reporting
- Job hazard analysis and control
- Training
- MSD management
- Program evaluation

Management of Work-Related MSDs (ASC Z-365, 2000)

- Management responsibilities
- Training
- Employee involvement
- Surveillance
- Evaluation and management of WMSD cases
- Job analysis
- Job design and interventions

reducing unnecessary effort, fatigue, and the potential for disorders, a successful ergonomics program also results in increased productive efficiency and improved product quality. As stated earlier, however, the ergonomics programs discussed in this chapter specifically address only the issue of work-related musculoskeletal disorders.

Although every ergonomics program should include some form of each of the elements described in this section, the implementation of the elements has to be suitable for the size and characteristics of the specific organization. The program elements for larger organizations that have many types of operations would obviously be more extensive than the elements necessary for small organizations with only a few types of operations.

3.1 Policies and Procedures Document

For an ergonomics program to be effective, its objectives must be an integral part of the organization's goals. Ergonomics must be considered to be on the same level as production and product quality. This requires management involvement at all levels, from the first-line supervisors to the company's CEO. As previously discussed, the ergonomics program involves the coordinated effort of many functions within the organization (e.g., engineering, medical, operations management). Upper management must be actively involved to initiate and sustain this coordination. An ergonomics policy and procedures document is used to communicate the locations of authority and accountability within the organization, as well as to document the allocation of resources necessary to administer the program.

One of the primary purposes of an ergonomics policy and procedures manual is to provide the formal documentation of the program to fulfill OSHA regulatory requirements for occupational safety programs. Documenting the allocation of resources is one way that a company can illustrate its dedication to an effective implementation of ergonomics. To demonstrate the effectiveness of the program for both internal management and external regulatory agencies, organizations must document the modifications that have been implemented and the benefits of those modifications. Many organizations have an *Ergonomics Manual* that includes the program goals and objectives, policies and procedures, and documented improvements that have been accomplished. The minutes of the ergonomics committee meetings are included in this document, along with the prioritization of ergonomics projects with expected completion dates. Using photographs to illustrate the conditions both before and after a modification is an effective way to document the improvements that have been made. Some potential contents for an ergonomics manual are listed in Figure 22.1.

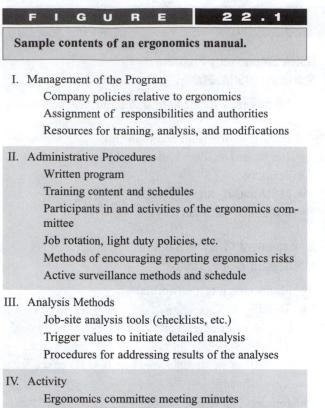

FIGURE 22.1

Sample contents of an ergonomics manual.

I. Management of the Program
  Company policies relative to ergonomics
  Assignment of responsibilities and authorities
  Resources for training, analysis, and modifications

II. Administrative Procedures
  Written program
  Training content and schedules
  Participants in and activities of the ergonomics committee
  Job rotation, light duty policies, etc.
  Methods of encouraging reporting ergonomics risks
  Active surveillance methods and schedule

III. Analysis Methods
  Job-site analysis tools (checklists, etc.)
  Trigger values to initiate detailed analysis
  Procedures for addressing results of the analyses

IV. Activity
  Ergonomics committee meeting minutes
  Schedule for modifications
  Before and after photos of modifications

V. Medical Management Program
  Treatment of various disorders resulting from risk factors
  Maintenance of health and safety records related to ergonomics

3.2 Ergonomics Committee   The ergonomics committee is an important element of an effective ergonomics program. The ergonomics committee should be separate from the safety committee, although they do interact and often have some members in common. The membership of the committee is made up of representatives from production (hourly and supervisory), safety, medical, human resources, maintenance, and engineering. As with other continuous improvement teams, the ability to communicate and interact effectively to develop consensus are important characteristics of the members. Although the committee members are generally appointed by the management, it can be beneficial for the hourly members of the committee to be voted onto the committee by their peers. It is very important that the hourly members have the support and confidence of their coworkers.

A "mission statement" would include the team goals (e.g., reduce musculoskeletal disorders, reduce

slip-and-fall accidents) and objectives (e.g., for reducing musculoskeletal disorders, to reduce carpal tunnel syndrome, to reduce shoulder problems, to improve return-to-work). The balance between the social aspects of health and safety and cost/benefit calculations should be specified. Standardized procedures such as "ergonomic concerns" logs, intervention tracking, and follow-up worksheets should be established.

When operating, there should be meeting agendas, action plans to accomplish objectives with individuals and due dates specified (e.g., "Joe and Betty will, by 15 November, investigate raising conveyer height at Mary's machine"), and minutes of the meetings.

One committee responsibility is to assist in the prioritization of the recommendations from the ergonomic surveys and job-site analyses. By performing periodic walk-through surveys of the facilities, the committee can both track the progress of the recommended modifications and identify other potential improvements for the future. An important responsibility of the ergonomics committee is to maintain the documentation for the ergonomics effort and to ensure that there is periodic review by themselves and upper management.

3.3 Proactive Measures   This element is often not part of the programs that derive strictly from regulatory compliance requirements; however, it is an important element of a successful ergonomics program. Part of the **proactive effort** is to integrate ergonomics into the design of workplace layout, work methods, tools, and equipment at the early stages of process design. Systems that are designed, installed, and used appropriately have a much lower chance of causing the worker to experience physiological or biomechanical stresses that increase fatigue and the potential for disorders. To accomplish this, it is important that engineers have an understanding of the ergonomic implications of their designs, as well as an understanding of the electrical and mechanical components of the system. In particular, understanding the constraints posed by human anthropometry and the implications of various motions and postures for human operators can ensure a proper interface between the human and the work. A system that is initially well designed can significantly reduce the cost of modifications when human interface problems arise.

Although it would be beneficial if equipment manufacturers could be relied upon to design and build equipment that adequately incorporates ergonomics, history has shown that this is often not the case. Significant attention has been given to ergonomic design in both the popular media and trade journals during the last two decades. However, there has actually been very little improvement in the ergonomic design characteristics of much of the production equipment currently being used. The responsibility to ensure that equipment incorporates ergonomic principles falls to the organizations that purchase and use the equipment. Engineers must be aware of the ergonomic implications of the equipment design when they document the specifications to be used by the purchasing department during the procurement process. The user organizations can also contribute to the process by providing feedback to the vendors of the equipment when modifications are necessary.

Some organizations have found it useful to have new equipment and process changes subjected to an ergonomic evaluation prior to purchase or implementation. This can often be accomplished by the ergonomics committee or a small subset of the committee. Most equipment and modifications can be evaluated and approved by a single individual who has the responsibility for the ergonomic considerations. If ergonomic issues are detected, the committee can also provide valuable input toward solving the problems before the equipment is purchased and installed. This is a much lower cost alternative.

3.4 Worker Involvement

The inclusion of the affected employees is an important component of an effective ergonomics effort. A suggestion system allows the operator to provide input as to perceived hazards and potential methods of improving the operation. This can be accomplished through a card/box system on the plant floor or in the cafeteria or break room. For an employee involvement system to be effective, feedback to the worker who makes the suggestion should be reliable and timely. When the recommendations are not feasible, it is still important that the worker be informed that the issue has been considered and that it will be addressed when a solution becomes technically or economically practical.

Feedback from workers can also be of assistance in documenting the positive effects of modifications that were previously suggested and instituted. The surveys must also be written at a level and in a language that the operators can understand.

3.5 Identification of Problem Jobs Through Surveillance

Surveillance methods can be divided into active surveillance methods that utilize surveys of current employees and passive surveillance methods that utilize archival safety and health records.

3.5.1 *Passive health surveillance*

Passive health surveillance methods of detecting jobs that have been associated with musculoskeletal discomfort involves the review of existing records such as the OSHA 300 logs. The OSHA 300 form is shown in Figure 22.2. Although these data are readily available and are often discussed in the context of an ergonomic analysis,

their usefulness is particularly limited when the incidence rate is low, as it is for musculoskeletal injuries at most facilities. The fact that the injury is cumulative and occurs over time makes the temporal nature of the worker's job history important. However, this information is not recorded on the log. The job that created or contributed to the problem may not be the job that the operator is performing when he reports to the medical facility. Other factors such as job rotation also make valid analysis of the safety and health records difficult. Finally, almost all current manufacturing and processing facilities go through continuous modifications in the process layout, equipment, tools, and methods. This can lead to erroneous conclusions as to the causal relationships that are based on historical data. Given these drawbacks, the archival data provide a starting point for establishing which tasks have been associated with problems in the past. However, the analysis of archival documents is no substitute for interactive discussions with health care providers, production supervisors, and the workers.

Another source of information that can be useful in interpreting the relative severity of disorders is the **worker compensation insurance** files. In addition, absenteeism records and the amount of turnover due to termination or transfer requests from particular jobs can assist in determining if jobs involve biomechanical stress. It is important to note that this information, which relates to individuals, is often confidential, and appropriate procedures for its use and storage should be documented and followed.

3.5.2 *Active health surveillance*

Active health surveillance methods involve the company soliciting information from the workers as to any discomfort they experience that is related to their work. OSHA has used the term "symptom survey" for the questionnaire used to establish whether workers experience discomfort when performing their jobs. The term *symptom survey* itself may have the unfortunate consequence of predisposing the workers to have "symptoms." A better approach is to use a term with a positive connotation, such as "job improvement survey" or simply, "ergonomics survey." In addition to collecting information about operator discomfort, the job improvement form shown in Figure 22.3 asks the operator for suggestions on how to improve the operation. The quality of the discomfort information collected is much better if the form imparts some amount of responsibility to the operator to evaluate potential improvements.

An issue with these surveys involves whether they constitute medical information, which has confidentiality constraints. The advantage of the form being completed anonymously is that the operators might be more comfortable responding, without fear of conse-

F I G U R E   22.2

OSHA 300 form.

OSHA's Form 300

Log of Work-Related Injuries and Illnesses

Year

U.S. Department of Labor
Occupational Safety and Health Administration

Form approved OMB no. 1218-0176

You must record information about every work-related injury or illness that involves loss of consciousness, restricted work activity or job transfer, days away from work, or medical treatment beyond first aid. You must also record significant work-related injuries and illnesses that are diagnosed by a physician or licensed health care professional. You must also record work-related injuries and illnesses that meet any of the specific recording criteria listed in 29 CFR 1904.8 through 1904.12. Feel free to use two lines for a single case if you need to. You must complete an injury and illness incident report (OSHA Form 301) or equivalent form for each injury or illness recorded on this form. If you're not sure whether a case is recordable, call your local OSHA office for help.

Attention: This form contains information relating to employee health and must be used in a manner that protects the confidentiality of employees to the extent possible while the information is being used for occupational safety and health purposes.

Establishment name

City   State

Identify the person

(A) Case No.	(B) Employee's Name	(C) Job Title (e.g. Welder)	(D) Date of injury or onset of illness (mo./day)

Describe the case

(E) Where the event occurred (e.g. Loading dock north end)	(F) Describe injury or illness, parts of body affected, and object/substance that directly injured or made person ill (e.g. Second degree burns on right forearm from acetylene torch)

Classify the case

Using these categories, check ONLY the most serious result for each case:

Death (G)	Days away from work (H)	Remained at work	
		Job transfer or restriction (I)	Other recordable cases (J)

Enter the number of days the injured or ill worker was:

On job transfer or restriction (days) (K)	Away from work (days) (L)

Check the "Injury" column or choose one type of illness: (M)

Injury (1)	Skin Disorder (2)	Respiratory Condition (3)	Poisoning (4)	All other illnesses (5)

Page totals   0   0   0   0 | 0   0 | 0   0   0   0   0

Be sure to transfer these totals to the Summary page (Form 300A) before you post it.

Page   1 of 1

Public reporting burden for this collection of information is estimated to average 14 minutes per response, including time to review the instruction, search and gather the data needed, and complete and review the collection of information. Persons are not required to respond to the collection of information unless it displays a currently valid OMB control number. If you have any comments about these estimates or any aspects of this data collection, contact: US Department of Labor, OSHA Office of Statistics, Room N-3644, 200 Constitution Ave, NW, Washington, DC 20210. Do not send the completed forms to this office.

quences. However, if the form is anonymous, the health care providers are not able to follow up on workers who indicate a physical problem but have not reported to the medical facility. The form shown in Figure 22.3 addresses this issue by placing a code on the form. The worker's name is placed on a similarly coded, tear-off signature sheet. Only the health care providers have access to the names of the workers so that they can follow up, if necessary. The forms, without the names, are reviewed by the appropriate personnel (i.e., ergonomics committee) to evaluate the technical and economic feasibility of the recommendations.

Some managers may have a natural concern that there will be a significant number of intentional or unintentional false indications of problems that result from simply administering the survey. This concern appears to be unwarranted. Although there is sometimes an initial transient increase in visits to the medical facility, this dissipates after the initial administration of the survey. In addition, some of the initial visits result in catching conditions very early, rather than much later when the cost to the company and the individual would be much higher. The survey provides valuable information about potential problem areas and possible solutions; however, it is the trend information developed from subsequent applications of the survey that is useful in evaluating the effectiveness of the ergonomics effort.

3.6 Identification of Problem Jobs: Job-Site

Analysis An ergonomic job-site analysis uses observations, interviews, and measurements to address the operations as they currently exist. Again, the issue is not simply to find the problem jobs from a health and safety perspective; rather, it is to make recommendations in the workplace design, work methods, tools, and equipment that can improve the effectiveness and efficiency of the process as a whole. There are four basic approaches to job-site evaluations that specifically address work-related musculoskeletal disorders: (1) mathematical/computer models, (2) qualitative checklists, (3) quantitative checklists, and (4) narrative text.

3.6.1 *Mathematical models* An example of a mathematical model approach is the use of the NIOSH lifting equations (Waters et al., 1993) discussed in Chapter 15. Similarly, computer-based, biomechanical models such as those developed and marketed by the University of Michigan provide estimates of the amount of risk for manual handling tasks. Liberty Mutual Insurance Company has developed a set of tables that help assess the tasks of lifting, lowering, pushing, pulling, and carrying (Snook and Ciriello, 1991). These tables are also discussed in Chapter 15. One significant advantage of these tables is that they provide the analyst with an estimate of the proportion of the working population that can perform various tasks. This is often a more valuable approach for matching the job requirements to operator capabilities than is providing a single "limit" that cannot be exceeded.

3.6.2 *Checklists* Two types of checklists are used for analyzing risk factors: qualitative and quantitative.

Qualitative checklists simply require categorical responses that provide flags to indicate where more in-depth assessment might be required. A qualitative checklist was developed by Keyserling, Stetson, Silverstein, and Brouwer (1993) to evaluate work-related musculoskeletal disorders (WRMD) risk factors for the upper extremity. The analyst indicates one of three levels of risk (zero, check, or star) to indicate the level of severity (insignificant, moderate, and substantial, respectively).

Other qualitative checklist systems include different levels of risk factors. For example, the UAW/GM Risk Factor Checklist (UAW-GM, 1998) includes the following item: standing stationary (no walking or leaning). The responses are: (1) never, (2) sometimes, and (3) more than 1/3 cycle. The Washington State Department of Labor and Industries system (2000) includes combinations of risk factors (see Box 14.1). For example, working with the neck bent more than 45° for more than 4 h total per day. This includes both the magnitude and duration of the stressor.

The Job Strain Index (JSI) is an example of a **quantitative checklist** in that it gives the analyst a scaled number to assess the existence or amount of risk (Moore and Garg, 1995). For example, the intensity of a grasping exertion would be documented as being "somewhat hard" if it required any of the following:

- 10 to 29% of maximum strength
- Borg Scale of 3
- Perceived effort of "noticeable or definite effort"

When the activity is determined to be *somewhat hard,* the analyst enters a coefficient of 2 toward the calculation of the Strain Index (SI). Combining the coefficients for different tasks provides an indication of the amount of risk. Preliminary testing revealed that jobs that were associated with distal upper extremity disorders had scores greater than 5, and scores less than or equal to 3 are probably safe. The authors do not address jobs that fall between these two values.

The checklist developed by Rogers (1992) is intended to allow the users to prioritize potential problems (see Table 22.1). Similar quantification systems are used for the Rapid Upper Limb Assessment (RULA) and the Rapid Entire Body Assessment (REBA) systems (see Chapter 14 and the ERGO disk).

FIGURE 22.3

Example job improvement form.

Ergonomics Survey

0867

Department: _____ Shift _____

Primary Job: _____

How long have you been doing this job?
☐ Less than 1 month ☐ 1-3 months ☐ 3 months-1 year ☐ 1 - 5 years ☐ more than 5 years

Do you regularly do any other jobs? No ☐ Yes ☐
If you do, what jobs do you do?
(1) _____
(2) _____
(3) _____

How can any of these jobs be improved?
_____

Check the areas below that could be improved.
☐ long forward reach ☐ high work level ☐ awkward postures ☐ quality of materials
☐ hand tools ☐ machine design ☐ machine maintenance ☐ job training

What other things make your job harder?

Have you had any soreness within the last month? No ☐ Yes ☐

If yes, put a check for each part of your body that has felt sore. [L- Left and R- Right]

Body Part		Barely Noticeable	Moderate	Very Noticeable
Neck				
Arm	L			
	R			
Wrist	L			
	R			
Hands	L			
	R			
Fingers				
Upper Back				
Lower Back				

Please answer all questions

When was the last occurrence?
☐ today
☐ yesterday
☐ last week
☐ more than a week ago
☐ more than a month ago

When does it occur?
☐ during the shift
☐ after work
☐ during the night
☐ all the time
☐ it varies

How often does it occur?
☐ every day
☐ once a week
☐ once a month
☐ less than once a month
☐ it varies

How long does it last?
☐ 1 hour
☐ all day
☐ 1-7 days
☐ 8-30 days
☐ more than 30 days

If you do more than one job, which one causes the most problems?

Ergonomics Survey
(page 2)

Have you reported this soreness to your? Supervisor ☐ Plant Nurse ☐ Not reported ☐

Have you seen a doctor about this? No ☐ Yes ☐
If yes, what treatment did you receive? _____

Were you put on another job because of this? No ☐ Yes ☐
If yes, what was that job? _____

Have you lost any time from work because of this? No ☐ Yes ☐
If yes, how long were you away from work? _____

What have you found that reduces the soreness?

What have you found that makes the soreness worse?

How many times have you worked 6 days a week in the last month? 0 ☐ 1 ☐ 2 ☐ 3 ☐ 4 ☐

How many times have you worked 7 days a week in the last month? 0 ☐ 1 ☐ 2 ☐ 3 ☐ 4 ☐

How many hours per day do you work?
Always 8 ☐   Sometimes less than 8 ☐   Sometimes more than 8 ☐

If you worked more than 8 hours a day in the last month, how long did you work?
9 hours ☐ 10 hours ☐ 11 hours ☐ 12 hours ☐ more than 12 hours ☐

How many days in the last month did you work more than 8 hours
0 ☐ 1 ☐ 2 ☐ 3 - 5 ☐ 6 - 10 ☐ 11-20 ☐ regularly ☐

☐ **Reviewed by Plant Nurse** Date __/__/__
☐ **Reviewed by Ergonomics Committee** Date __/__/__

(separate along perforated line)

This information is confidential and your name will be separated from the form. The medical staff will be the only individuals that will have access to your name.

Please Print Your Name _____ Date _____

Signature _____

0867

T A B L E	2 2 . 1

General ergonomic checklist to prioritize potential problems (Rodgers, 1992). After completing the "effort" (force), "continuous effort time" (duration), and "efforts/min" (repetition) columns, determine the priority for change.

Job title _____   Analyst _____

Specific task _____   Phone _____

Job number _____ Dept _____   Date of analysis _____

Location _____

Body part		Effort	Continuous Effort Time	Effort/Min	Priority
Back		_____	_____	_____	_____
Neck/Shoulders	R	_____	_____	_____	_____
	L	_____	_____	_____	_____
Arms/Elbows	R	_____	_____	_____	_____
	L	_____	_____	_____	_____
Wrists/Hands/	R	_____	_____	_____	_____
Fingers	L	_____	_____	_____	_____
Legs/Knees	R	_____	_____	_____	_____
	L	_____	_____	_____	_____
Ankles/Feet/	R	_____	_____	_____	_____
Toes	L	_____	_____	_____	_____

Effort

1 = light

2 = moderate

3 = heavy

Cont. Effort Time

1 = <6 sec

2 = 6 to 20 sec

3 = >20 sec

Efforts/min

1 = <1

2 = 1 to 5

3 = >5 to 15

Priority for change

332

331

323   Very high

322

321

313   High

223

312   Moderate

232

231

222

213

132

123

Source: Rodgers, S. A functional job analysis technique. *Occupational Medicine: State of the Art Reviews*, Vol. 7, No. 4. Philadelphia: Hanley & Belfus, Oct.–Dec. 1992.

Systems that provide a single, numeric assessment of combined risk factors to the analyst are very popular with operational personnel. When the amount of risk is documented by a specific number, prioritizing intervention projects is easier. In addition, it is easier to document and track the positive effects of making modifications intended to reduce the amount of risk.

The advantage of checklists, both qualitative and quantitative, is that they require less time to conduct and can be performed by individuals with less technical understanding of ergonomics. However, this simplicity inherently results in the checklist approach being less complete, which sometimes results in serious misrepresentations of the task requirements. In particular, the temporal nature of the task is very difficult to capture with a checklist (i.e., exposure across task elements, tasks, or even jobs, if rotation occurs). In addition, checklists are only descriptive, indicating whether there is a potential problem, rather than prescriptively indicating alternative methods of alleviating the problem. Although checklists appear to be very attractive from the standpoint of data collection, they still require a significant amount of judgment during both the documentation process and the interpretation of the results.

3.6.3 *Narrative approach* The fourth general method of conducting an ergonomic job-site evaluation is to document the conditions and recommendations in a narrative form (illustrated in Figure 22.4). The task requirements and risk factors are described in a report that generally uses photographs to illustrate the issues that are discussed. This method requires more time and is generally performed by an ergonomics professional. However, it is usually far more complete, valid, and useful in the process of improving the tasks that involve undesirable characteristics. It is often as important to document the positive characteristics of jobs that do not experience problems as it is to note the problem areas. The narrative approach provides this information, whereas the checklist does not. Another beneficial characteristic of the narrative form of analysis is that it includes a discussion of the technical and economic feasibility of alternative modifications. Conducting any ergonomic job analysis, particularly using a narrative, prescriptive approach, requires the analyst to have a relatively high level of technical expertise in ergonomics.

3.7 Methods of Controlling WMSDs

This element of an ergonomics program involves implementing controls that can reduce the risk of work-related musculoskeletal disorders by reducing the biomechanical hazards. There are three categories of controls: administrative, engineering, and work practice.

3.7.1 *Administrative controls* Administrative **controls** involve the way that the worker's job is structured to reduce the duration of the exposure to hazards. For example, one type of administrative control is to rotate workers from tasks that involve high muscle exertion (e.g., high grip force or lifting above shoulder level) to other tasks where different muscle groups are required. Job rotation is a very effective method of reducing discomfort by providing the opportunity of recovery from muscle fatigue. However, there is no evidence that job rotation reduces some soft tissue disorders such as carpal tunnel syndrome. As discussed in Chapter 4, the fatigue and recover mechanisms for tendons are very differ-

F I G U R E   22.4

Example of narrative analysis method. The photo illustrates a workplace layout that dictates that the operator's arms, shoulders, and neck be in an awkward posture. The reason for this design was to accommodate both small and large television sets. A movable fixture that allows the smaller televisions to be moved closer to the operator would be beneficial. In addition, by tilting the fixture (and the television) toward the operator, the angle of the tool would be improved, as well as visual access to the cavity.

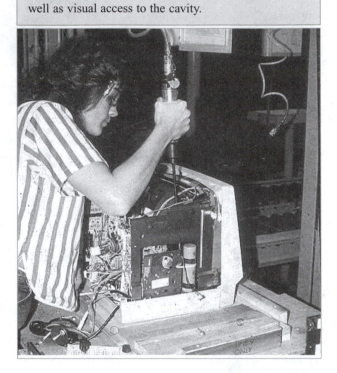

ent from those for muscles. Some workers prefer to rotate jobs and benefit from it. Others prefer to continue to work on the same task because they experience more discomfort when they are required to transition to other tasks.

Another administrative control is the use of "ramp-in" procedures that allow the workers to gradually increase their work pace as they become conditioned to a task. For example, the allowed time (i.e., work standard) for an individual worker performing an assembly task can be increased as the worker learns to perform the task more efficiently over time. This has been shown to be one of the most effective methods of reducing unnecessary discomfort for new employees who perform repetitive tasks.

3.7.2 *Engineering controls* Engineering con**trols** involve modifying the workplace design, equipment, and tools to accommodate the physical and physiological capabilities and limitations of the workers. Engineering controls have the advantage that they do not rely on adherence by the individual worker or manager, as do administrative controls. For this reason, regulatory agencies prefer engineering controls as a means of reducing biomechanical hazards. Many engineering controls address the postures and motion patterns used by operators when performing their jobs. For example, by using multiple scanners for grocery store checkout operations, the wrist motions necessary to orient the product when scanning can be reduced. This is illustrated in Figure 22.5. Providing fixtures to reduce the need to grasp a part during assembly operations can significantly improve the efficiency of the operation, as well as reduce the risk of disorders. The material covered in many of the chapters, Chapters 13, 14, and 15 in particular, address the factors that should be considered for effective engineering controls.

3.7.3 *Work-practice controls*

Work-practice controls address the correct methods of performing the task. In particular, task-specific training as to the correct use of handtools or fixtures can significantly decrease the biomechanical stress experienced by workers. Using the example of the cashier at the checkout station in a grocery store, the task can be performed by grasping and lifting items past the scanner. However, a preferable method is simply to slide the item over the scanner with a cupped hand. This decreases the time necessary to perform the task and also reduces the amount of biomechanical stress to the hand and wrist (see Figure 22.6). A further discussion of the supermarket checkout operation is presented in Box 13.2. For work-practice controls to be effective, both training and supervisor attention are necessary.

FIGURE   22.5

Scanning task with multiple scanners to reduce the need to grasp and manipulate items.

FIGURE   22.6

Using scanning method with straight wrist.

3.8 Training

Different parts of the organization require different types of training to make the ergonomics program effective. There are three basic categories of information to be presented:

1. Signs and symptoms that indicate that a musculoskeletal disorder might be developing.
2. Job-related risk factors that have been associated with an increase in the risk of disorders.
3. Procedures for addressing disorders, if they do occur.

Although each member of the organization should be aware of these three areas, the emphasis in the training varies for the different groups.

3.8.1 *Affected workers*

The most general training is presented to all employees who are exposed to biomechanical hazards. This general awareness training includes information on how to detect problems early—before they become permanent or disabling. The operator must be knowledgeable of the early signs and symptoms of disorders and be able to differentiate these from the normal sensations that are often experienced when becoming accustomed to a new job. If a worker can detect the onset of problems before they become more serious, it has a positive impact on both the operator and the company (which could incur the higher cost of a temporary or permanent disability). It is important to provide training that specifically addresses the procedures for reporting work-related discomfort and that assures the workers that there will be no negative repercussions resulting from the reporting. Although there is a general impression that this training will lead to a flood of workers "developing" symptoms, this generally does not occur if the presentation is adequate. In addition, to the extent that it does occur, some of the increase represents previously unreported, although real disorders. The others seem to dissipate quite rapidly.

Part of this training is to ensure that the workers understand the advantages of good biomechanics (postures, motions, etc.) and the personal consequences of using poor biomechanics when performing their tasks. The training provides job-specific instructions on the correct methods of performing particular tasks.

3.8.2 *Production management*   First-line supervisors can be the most effective "ergonomists" in the facility. It is very important that the supervisors receive training before the general training of the workers. An effective ergonomics effort can only occur when the supervisors understand the benefits of good biomechanics for both the company and the worker (occupational health, productivity, product quality, absenteeism, and turnover rates). In general, the supervisors can easily recognize biomechanical hazards (e.g., awkward postures) and, with the assistance of maintenance and engineering, they can frequently suggest very effective methods of reducing those hazards. It is a matter of viewing the production process with an "eye for ergonomics," as well the traditional concern for production numbers. When supervisors discover that absenteeism and turnover rates in their area are reduced, they become very positive toward ergonomics, independent of its contribution toward reducing injuries.

The supervisors' training should also help them learn to recognize problems early. Informing the supervisors of the benefits of providing an opportunity for the workers to become accustomed to the physical demands of the task can result both in retaining the employee and in reducing the potential of a disorder occurring. Another portion of the training deals with the OSHA reporting rules, as they pertain to the supervisors. For example, if the supervisor moves an operator from one job to another due to discomfort, this is an OSHA reportable event, even if the individual did not visit the medical facility. An important part of the supervisor's training addresses the benefits of the ergonomics survey and reinforces the policy that the information is used for improvements rather than in a punitive manner relative to either the supervisor or the worker (see Section 3.5.2).

3.8.3 *Engineering and maintenance personnel*   The training of the engineering and maintenance personnel addresses those characteristics of workplaces, work methods, tools, and equipment that can affect the risk of musculoskeletal disorders. One of the most important individuals who should be included in this training is the maintenance manager. Ergonomic modifications are only part of the many responsibilities that are balanced by the maintenance department. In addition to the factors that have been associated with musculoskeletal disorders, the engineering controls that have been shown to reduce the exposure of workers to these factors are also presented during this training. It is important to understand that the vast majority of modifications require very little time and virtually no capital expense. In particular, it is much easier and less costly to have a well-designed system initially, rather than retrofitting the configuration after installation.

The most effective training for engineers, as well as the production supervisors, involves the use of operational examples of good and bad ergonomics from their own facilities. Often, examples can be selected from the ergonomic job analysis and used as the basis for problem-solving exercises during the training sessions. For example, showing how a change in the work height can result in improved worker posture and performance can illustrate how many modifications are easily implemented and have significant benefits. The communication that occurs among different functions (e.g., process engineers and product designers) during the training is also a very profitable activity. As with the production supervisors, the benefits of the ergonomics survey need to be understood by the engineering staff.

3.8.4 *Health care providers*   The health care providers (both internal and external) require training as part of an ergonomics effort. It is important that there is consistency among all parts of the organization with respect to the protocol for detecting and treating musculoskeletal disorders. Specifically, the instruction includes a discussion of the signs and symptoms that are considered indicative of work-related disorders and the actions to be taken based on those signs and symptoms (e.g., restricted work, job reassignment, seeing a physician, etc.). To make work-relatedness and return-to-work decisions, it is important that the risk factors associated with each operation be consistently documented. For example, alternative assignments (often inappropriately referred to as light duty) should indicate the types of restrictions that can be accommodated (e.g., standing, bending, hand work, etc.).

3.8.5 *Ergonomics committee*   It is necessary that individual members of the **ergonomics committee** have in-depth training in all aspects of the ergonomics effort (job analysis, medical management, etc.). As with production management and engineering, the material generated during the ergonomic job-site analysis can be a good basis for the training of the ergonomics committee. The committee must be familiar with the engineering controls that can reduce disorders, as well as the technical and financial constraints that must be considered. Communication skills are also an important part of the training for any continuous improvement group.

Training is probably the most important component of an effective ergonomics effort. Without adequate and appropriate training, the ergonomics survey and job-site analyses are often rendered useless. A frequent scenario is that a company hires an external ergonomics consultant to perform an analysis and make recommendations that would reduce the incidence of disorders. Without the training discussed in this section, the analysis and the recommendations are likely to be placed (or misplaced) on a shelf. The management, however, feels that they have "done ergonomics." Again, performing an analysis, without making feasible modifications, can have more severe consequences than not having conducted the analysis. The support of the workers is lost and the company increases its risk of being cited by regulatory agencies for not addressing known hazards.

3.9 Medical management
Medical management of musculoskeletal disorders involves the prevention of disorders or disabilities through early detection and treatment. Although this is considered part of an ergonomics program from the standpoint of regulatory agencies (e.g., OSHA), it is often considered separate from the main ergonomics effort of reducing the risk of injuries in the first place.

A very important aspect of an effective medical management process is to have the individual workers understand the early signs and symptoms of disorders and readily report to the health care providers when these occur. As discussed in Section 3.8.1, this is a critical training element in an ergonomics program. It is also important that the management of the company effectively communicate to the workers that they are encouraged to report signs and symptoms of problems early without fear of punishment or reprisal.

It is often very beneficial to have the health care providers tour the production facilities to better understand the factors that could affect the workers' health. This is particularly important to help them make decisions as to alternative assignments, when workers are unable to perform their normal tasks due to medical problems. For example, when a person has discomfort in the lower back and cannot experience prolonged standing, an alternative assignment to a seated inspection or assembly task might be appropriate. It is important that the health care providers have some understanding of the various task characteristics when specifying work restrictions. The job-site analysis process can provide valuable information to health care providers and production supervisors to make sure that workers are appropriately placed.

3.10 Document and Evaluate the Program
To justify the ergonomics efforts, both internally to company management and externally to regulatory agencies, it is important to have complete and accurate documentation and evaluation. Part of the **program evaluation** procedure should be the periodic review of the documentation. With respect to documenting the engineering controls that result from the ergonomic job-site analysis or the ergonomics committee's analysis of the ergonomic survey, an "ergonomics casebook" has been used effectively by many organizations. Each operation for which modifications were suggested should be included, along with an evaluation of the technical and economic feasibility, and an estimate of the potential effectiveness. Based on this information, the proposed modifications are prioritized.

There are three categories into which the modification can be placed. The first category includes the changes that are easy, quick, and low in cost. For example, a change may involve improving the operator's posture by lowering the work height, which requires simply shortening the legs on a workbench. Many improvements in the facility that occur as part of normal operations are taken for granted and are not associated with ergonomics. Part of the training for supervisors and engineers is to ensure that these changes get recorded in the ergonomics documentation. The second category of modification involves changes that are prioritized and scheduled and for which an expected completion date is documented. Indicating that modifications are "in progress" is not sufficient. This category is probably the most important for the purpose of indicating to regulatory agencies that ergonomics is receiving serious attention and that continuous improvement is occurring. The third category involves modifications that are not technically or economically feasible at the current time. These should be included with an indication that they are recognized and that, if they become feasible (e.g., when expanding the facility or putting in a new production line), they will be implemented.

A part of the documentation that is often ignored or does not receive the required amount of attention is follow-up and evaluation to determine the effectiveness of the modification. It is not sufficient to make the modifications and assume that the problem has been corrected. In all likelihood, some of the changes will not have the desired results. In fact, as with any design effort, unexpected (and sometimes undesirable) consequences can arise. It is important to document that the modification was not successful and, to the extent possible, the reasons for the lack of effectiveness.

Program evaluation addresses both the administration of various elements and the quality of the results. A number of different measures can be used to determine the effectiveness of the program. The most obvious, and often the easiest to document, is a reduction in the worker compensation costs associated with musculoskeletal disorders (Alexander and Orr, 1992). Other measures that respond more quickly to changes are the number of restricted and lost days that result from poorly designed workplace layouts, work methods, tools, and equipment. Federal regulations dictate that these data are to be collected (OSHA 300 log). Some organizations have found that the turnover rate and requests for transfers are good measures of the effectiveness of the program. Studies have found that combining these various measures provides the best evaluation of an ergonomics program (Iridiastadi, 1998; Getty, 1993). As discussed throughout this chapter, an effective ergonomics program not only increases the occupational safety and health, but also provides corresponding increases in productivity and product quality. The effective implementation of ergonomics is a method of increasing company profits, not just a method of reducing costs.

Review Questions

1. What are the organizational functions that are involved in an ergonomics program?
2. How can Worker Compensation insurance payments indicate a problem that is related to ergonomics?
3. Explain the two types of surveillance.
4. What is the membership of an ergonomics committee?
5. Give examples of quantitative checklists.
6. What is the advantage of engineering controls over administrative controls?
7. What are the three types of modifications that result from an ergonomic analysis?

References

Alexander, D. Strategies for cost justifying ergonomic improvements. *IIE Solutions,* 30–35, March, 1998.

Alexander, D. and Orr, G. The evaluation of occupational ergonomics programs. *Proceedings of the 36th Annual Meeting of the Human Factors and Ergonomics Society,* 697–701, 1992.

Bernard, B. (ed.) *Musculoskeletal Disorders and Workplace Factors: A Critical Review of Epidemiologic Evidence for Work-Related Musculoskeletal Disorders of the Neck, Upper Extremity and Low Back.* DHHS (NIOSH) Publication No. 97-141. U. S. Department of Health and Human Services, Public Health Service, Centers for Disease Control and Prevention, National Institute for Occupational Safety and Health, Cincinnati, OH, 1997.

GAO. *Worker Protection: Private Sector Ergonomics Programs Yield Positive Results.* U. S. General Accounting Office Report to Congressional Requesters. Washington, DC: GAO/HEHS-97-163, 1997.

Gjessomg, C., Schoenborn, T., and Cohen A. (eds.). *Participatory Ergonomic Interventions in Meatpacking Plants.* DHHS (NIOSH) Publication No. 94-124. U. S. Department of Health and Human Services, Public Health Service, Centers for Disease Control and Prevention, National Institute for Occupational Safety and Health, Cincinnati, OH, 1994.

Iridiastadi, H. Measurement of ergonomic program in a workplace: A proposed framework. *Proceedings of the 42nd Annual Meeting of the Human Factors and Ergonomics Society,* 979–83, 1998.

Keyserling, W., Brouwer, M., and Silverstein, B. Effectiveness of a joint labor-management program in controlling awkward postures of the trunk, neck, and shoulders. Results of a field study. *International Journal of Industrial Ergonomics,* Vol. 11, No. 1, 51–65, 1993.

Keyserling, W., Stetson, D., Silverstein, B., and Brouwer, M. A checklist for evaluating ergonomic risk factors associated with upper extremity cumulative trauma disorders. *Ergonomics,* Vol. 36, No. 7, 807–31.

Lanoie, P. and Tvenas, S. Costs and benefits of preventing workplace accidents: The case of participatory ergonomics. *Safety Science,* Vol. 24, No. 3, 181–96, 1996.

May, D. and Schwoerer, C. Employee health by design: Using employee involvement teams in ergonomic job design. *Personnel Psychology,* Vol. 47, No. 4, 861–76, 1994.

Moore, J. and Garg, A. The effectiveness of participatory ergonomics in the red meatpacking industry: Evaluation of a corporation. *International Journal of Industrial Ergonomics,* Vol. 21, No. 1, 47–58, 1998.

NIOSH. *Work Practices Guide for Manual Materials Handling.* DHHS (NIOSH) Publication No. 81-122. U. S. Department of Health and Human Services, Public Health Service, Centers for Disease Control and Prevention, National Institute for Occupational Safety and Health, Cincinnati, OH, 1981.

NIOSH. *Elements of Ergonomics Programs.* DHHS (NIOSH) Publication PB97-144901. U. S. Department of Health and Human Services, Public Health Service, Centers for Disease Control and Prevention, National Institute for Occupational Safety and Health, Cincinnati, OH, 1997.

National Research Council and Institute of Medicine. *Musculoskeletal Disorders in the Workplace: Low Back and Upper Extremities.* Panel on Musculoskeletal Disorders and the Workplace. Commission on Behavioral and Social Sciences and Education. Washington, DC: Author, 2001.

National Safety Council. ASC Z-365, *Management of Work-Related Musculoskeletal Disorders.* Accredited Standards Committee. Itasca, IL: Author, Secretariat, 2000.

OSHA. *Ergonomics Program Management Guidelines for Meatpacking Plants.* Washington, DC: U. S. Department of Labor, Occupational Safety and Health Administration, OSHA Report 3123, 1993.

Purswell, J. and Purswell, J. OSHA's citation of ergonomic hazards under the "general duty" clause. *Proceedings*

of the 45th Annual Meeting of the Human Factors and Ergonomics Society, 1110–14, 2001.

Scalia, E. *Ergonomics: OSHA's Strange Campaign to Run American Business.* Washington, DC: National Legal Center for the Public Interest, 1994.

Snook, S. and Ciriello, V. The design of manual handling tasks: Revised tables of maximum acceptable weights and forces. *Ergonomics,* Vol. 34, No. 9, 1197–1213, 1991.

UAW-GM. *Ergonomics Risk Factor Checklist RFC2.* Auburn Hills, MI: United Auto Workers—General Motors Center for Human Resources, Health and Safety Center, 1998.

Washington State. *WAC 296-62-05174, Appendix B: Criteria for analyzing and reducing WMSD hazards for employers who choose the specific performance approach.* Olympia, WA: Washington State Department of Labor and Industries, 2000.

Waters, T., Putz-Anderson V., Garg, A., and Fine, L. Revised lifting equation for the design and evaluation of lifting tasks. *Ergonomics,* Vol. 36, No. 7, 749–76, 1993.

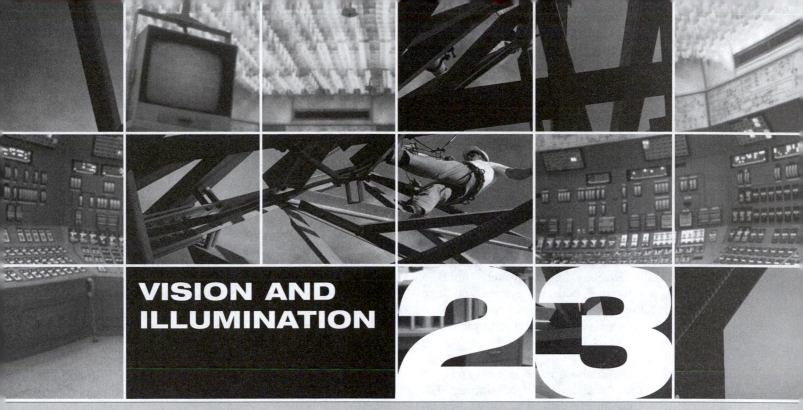

VISION AND ILLUMINATION

23

VISION AND ILLUMINATION

1 The Eye and Light

2 Reduction of Visual Problems

3 General Lighting

4 Special Lighting

Overview

This chapter explains the eye and light, provides specific recommendations for reducing visual problems, and then makes design recommendations for general and special lighting.

Key Concepts

accommodation	dark adaptation	lamp lumen depreciation	optical aids
astigmatism	diffuse/specular reflections	lumens	orientation of lights
bifocals/trifocals	diopters	luminaire dirt depreciation	polarization
coefficient of utilization	direct/indirect	luminance/brightness	presbyopia
color of light	dynamic visual acuity	luminance ratio	reflectance
color-weak	esthetics	lux/footcandles	restrike time
cones/rods	farsightedness	mirror test	Roy G. Biv
contrast	general/task lighting	near point	visual acuity
convergence	hue/brightness/saturation	nearsightedness	wavelength (color)
critical fusion frequency (CFF)	illumination cost	negative contrast	zonal cavity method
	indirect/direct glare	night vision	

THE EYE AND LIGHT

1.1 The Eye
First, the eye anatomy will be discussed, then vision.

1.1.1 *Anatomy*
Figure 23.1 shows the details of the eye, a 25-mm sphere. Light from the air enters through the transparent cornea. The cornea protects the eye and performs about 70% of the focusing required to produce an image on the retina. In addition, the change in refraction from air to the cornea permits the lens–fovea distance to be only 15 mm.

Next is the aqueous humor (watery fluid, in Latin), which nourishes both the cornea and lens. Glaucoma is a high pressure in the aqueous humor.

Next the light passes through the pupil of the biconvex lens. (*Pupil* is Latin for doll, since you can see a small, doll-like image of yourself reflected in the pupil.) The iris (rainbow, in Greek) expands and contracts to control the amount of light admitted. The iris tends to be blue in northern climates where sunlight is weak; in the tropics more melanin results in brown eyes, which are less sensitive to glare.

Pupil diameter varies from about 1.5 mm to 9 mm—a factor of 6. Since light admitted is proportional to area (that is, diameter squared), the maximum amount of light admitted is about 40 times greater than the minimum. The pupils expand with emotion and interest as well as light. Changes in pupil size reflect changes in attitude and can affect the attitude and responses of the person observing the pupil, even if the observer doesn't realize it is pupil size being reacted to (Hess, 1975).

The lens of the eye differs from a camera lens in that the ciliary muscle changes the lens shape to vary focal distance; this is called **accommodation.** This distance is measured in meters or, more commonly, the inverse—**diopters.** The resting state of the eye, dark focus distance, is .6 m (1.67 diopters). Accommodative insufficiency can be due to weakness of the ciliary muscle or hardening of the lens with age. Accommodation at ages 20, 40, and 60 changes from an average of 11 diopters to 5 to 1. Retinal illuminance changes from 1.0 at age 20, to .6 at 40, to .33 at age 60 (due to smaller pupil size and thicker lenses).

When viewing an object at infinity, "parallel" rays of light are focused on the retina. However, if the object is close to the eye, the light rays are not parallel; the lens thickens to maintain the focus at the same point (see Figure 23.2). The **near point,** the closest point at which you can focus, moves out as the lens hardens with age. Table 23.1 shows it is about .1 m at age 20 and 1 m at age 70. (Determine your own near point by bringing a printed page toward the eyes until the letters blur.) There is relatively little strain as long as work is done at over twice the near point.

Convergence, the act of aiming both eyes at a single point, is done by the 12 extraocular muscles. It is not needed for distances over 6 m (20 ft); that is why eye tests are set for that distance. Predetermined time systems include eye focus, convergence, and eye travel times.

After the lens, the light rays pass through the vitreous humor, a jellylike substance whose primary function is to maintain the eye shape. (If you see moving spots when you close your eyes, these may be red blood cells, which escaped from the retina, in the vitreous humor.)

Finally, the light strikes the retina, about the size and thickness of a postage stamp, which is attached to the sclera, the "white" of the eye. The retina, an extension of the brain, preprocesses the information before sending it through the optic nerve to the brain. The

---

F I G U R E   2 3 . 1

The human eye, a 25-mm sphere, has an iris to adjust the light admitted, a lens that adjusts focal length, and two "photographic films"—black and white and color. The films change "speed" as required.

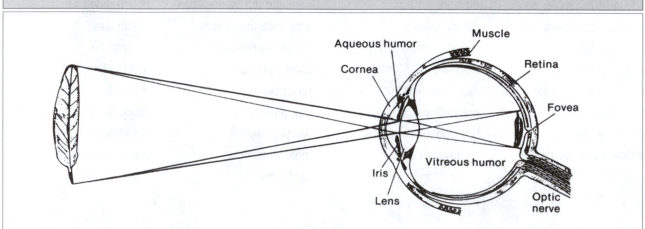

FIGURE 23.2

Eye problems and corrections. A and B show the normal eye at near and far vision. For normal far vision (B) the light rays are close to parallel and the eye is relaxed. As the object comes closer, the rays become less parallel and the lens is accommodated by the ciliary muscle to maintain the focus on the retina. C and D show **nearsightedness** (myopia) and its optical correction. E and F show **farsightedness** (hyperopia) and its optical correction.

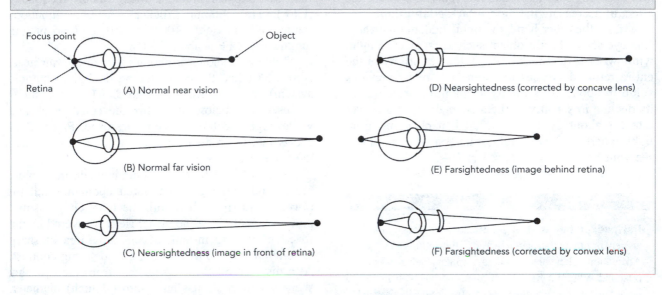

(A) Normal near vision

(B) Normal far vision

(C) Nearsightedness (image in front of retina)

(D) Nearsightedness (corrected by concave lens)

(E) Farsightedness (image behind retina)

(F) Farsightedness (corrected by convex lens)

TABLE 23.1

Age effects on the eye. Age affects speed of perception, dark adaptation time, ability to detect peripheral movement, resistance to disability glare, and luminance and contrast thresholds. The closest point at which the eye can focus, the near point, increases with age; visual acuity decreases. The increase in near point is called **presbyopia** (old man's vision, in Greek).

| Age, Years | PERCENT VISUAL ACUITY (6/6 = 100) | | | MEAN NEAR POINT | | Glare Borderline Between Comfort/ Discomfort, [†] nits |
	Best Refractive Correction	Actual Correction	Without Correction	Meters	Diopters*, 1/m	
10	—	—	—	.077	13.0	6900
20	100	83	75	.091	11.0	3100
30	99	83	60	.111	9.0	1900
40	96	82	50	.167	6.0	1400
50	90	68	25	.500	2.0	1050
60	85	60	20	.833	1.2	850
70	70	40	15	1.000	1.0	700

*The power of a lens is given in diopters:

$$P \text{ (diopters)} = \frac{1}{f \text{ (meters)}} = \frac{1}{S_1} + \frac{1}{S_2}$$

where S_1 = distance from light source to lens node, m
S_2 = distance from lens node to focal point, m

For normal viewing, S_1 = infinity and S_2 = .015 m, so the power of the eye is 67 diopters.
[†] BCD = 103,000 (age, yrs)$^{-1.17}$ from Bennett (1977).

retina not only has two different transducer systems (cones and rods) to convert light to an electrical signal, but it also changes the transducer's sensitivity with incoming light. This is analogous to having a camera with both black and white and color film, with the film also changing speed as required. Figure 23.3 shows the effect of decreasing the light—**dark adaptation.**

If, on the other hand, the light suddenly increases (the eye sees a bright object such as an electric light, window, or reflecting tabletop), the sensitivity of the entire retina decreases to about 20% of its previous value in about .05 s (alpha adaptation); it continues its decline in sensitivity (beta adaptation) at a slower rate for about 30 min. Thus, when changing from light to dark or dark to light, it takes a while until you see your best.

FIGURE 23.3

Dark adaptation is strongly affected by time. Time in an environment strongly affects the ability to see. Adaptation takes place with a pupillary/neural system (responds within a fraction of a second but with limited range) and a photochemical system (responds over several minutes but with a large range). The curve shows ability to detect a target vs. time. Initially exposed to a luminance of 3,400 cd/m², the eye requires a target to be 3 cd/m² to be detected. After 2 min of dark, the target need be only .03 cd/m² to be detected; after 40 min of dark, the target need be only .000 030 cd/m² to be detected.

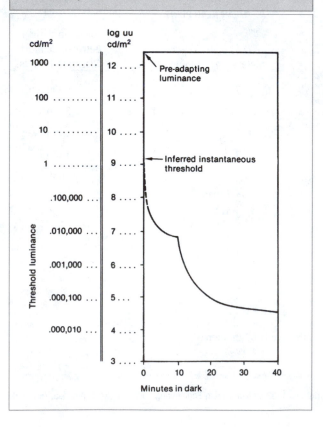

When looking at objects, the retina emphasizes changes in brightness more than absolute levels; the minimum detectable brightness difference between objects is about 1% to 2%. If an object oscillates in brightness, it will appear to flicker. This flicker will fuse or disappear at the **critical fusion frequency (CFF).** For optimum flicker detection situations (large, uniform fields, 100% on–off, high adaptation luminance), CFF is about 75 Hz.

Table 23.2 shows brightness for various surfaces. Above .001 lux, the **cones** (color, daylight, photopic system) are used; from .001 to .0001 both systems are used, and below .0001 lux the **rods** (black and white, night, scotopic system) are used. Figure 23.4 shows that the rods are more sensitive to light than the cones are.

The 7,000,000 cones (subdivided into blue, green, and red) are concentrated about a small pit (*fovea,* in Latin) in line with the lens. Only a small portion (about 1°) of the visual field is covered by the fovea at any one instant; beyond this area of sharp vision you detect only movement and strong contrast. At a distance of .5 m (20 inches) from the eye, this sharp vision circle has an 8 mm (.3 inch) diameter. The larger area we actually observe is due to the saccadic eye movement, as well as voluntary shifting of the focus point.

Figure 23.4 shows that the cones are more sensitive to some **wavelengths** (i.e., colors) than others. (The rods also are more sensitive to some wavelengths than others, but they don't respond to different wavelengths with different colors.) What color would you make an object if you wanted it to be very noticeable? From Figure 23.4, this is around 580 nm for daylight vision, and we use "hunter orange" and "highway orange." (On some backgrounds, a yellow-green color is more visible.) If you had a lamp emitting light at only one wavelength, what would be the wavelength to use?

Note that light above 650 nm (red light) does not affect the rods, so dark adaptation is maintained while the cones can see. One "red light" approach is to have the operator wear goggles with a filter for light below 650 nm; the other is to have lights that give light only above 650 nm. An example application is red light at night on a car instrument panel. Note that color discrimination is very poor with red light. Figure 23.5 shows that green, red, and yellow are not seen well if they are peripheral.

The 125,000,000 rods are scattered over the entire retina (except the fovea). Thus, for better night vision, look out of the corner of your eye. Rhodopsin, a chemical in the rods manufactured by the body from vitamin A, is bleached by light to give the photochemical effect for nerve excitation. See Figure 23.3 for dark adaptation time.

T A B L E	2 3 . 2

Luminance (cd/m²) of various surfaces.

APPROXIMATE BRIGHTNESS, CD/M²				
.000 001	to	.000 010	Absolute threshold of seeing	
.000 010	to	.000 100	Grass in starlight	
.000 100	to	.001	Snow in starlight	rod vision
.001	to	.010	Earth in full moon	rod + cone vision
.010	to	.100	Snow in full moon	
.100	to	1.0	White paper 1 foot from a 1 candela source	rod + cone vision
1.	to	10.		cone vision
10.	to	100.	White paper in good light, indoor movie screen, TV screen	
100.	to	1000.	Average sky on cloudy day, full moon	
	>	1000.	Average sky on clear day, instant-start cool white fluorescent tube (900–1150 for medium-loaded lamps, 1350 to 1800 for high-load lamps; preheat starting 500 to 1200)	

F I G U R E	2 3 . 4

Rod and cone sensitivity. Both rod and cone sensitivity vary with wavelength. Rods, the **night vision** system, have maximum sensitivity at 508 nm and require only 1% of the light required for the cones, the day vision system. The maximum sensitivity for cones is 555 nm (yellow-green). From 440–450, light is violet and indigo; from 450 to 500, blue; from 500 to 545, green; from 545 to 590, yellow; from 590 to 610, orange; and from 610 to 760, red. Remember this rainbow sequence by the name **Roy G. Biv.** Also remember to reverse the sequence since red is at 700 nm, not 460.

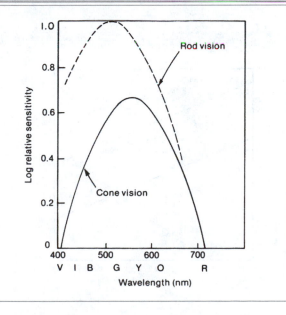

1.1.2 *Normal vision*   **Visual acuity,** the ability of the eye to distinguish detail, is:

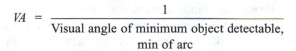

$$VA = \frac{1}{\text{Visual angle of minimum object detectable, min of arc}}$$

Table 23.3 shows the formula geometry. By expressing visual acuity in terms of the visual angle, any size target (dimension h) can be used at any distance from the eye (dimension d). The tangent of the visual angle, Θ, divided by 2 is equal to $d/2$ divided by h; since the angle is small, the approximation $\tan \Theta = h/d$ may be used.

By convention, "normal" vision is the ability to detect an object with 1 min of arc at 6 m (20 ft). This is expressed as 6/6 vision (20/20 in the United States). That is, you see at 20 ft what the normal person sees at 20 ft; 20/100 vision means you see at 20 ft what the normal person sees at 100 ft. If your vision in your better eye, after correction, is worse than 20/200, you are legally blind.

There are several kinds of visual acuity measurements: minimum separable (gap detection), minimum perceptible (spot detection), vernier (lateral displacement of two lines), and dynamic.

The minimum gap detectable is not 1 min of arc but is about 25 s for very good contrast, long viewing times, and high luminance. Squares and spots (dark and light) can be detected even if they are very small. A dark square of 14 s of arc against a bright sky can be detected 75% of the time; a star subtending .06 s of arc can also be detected. Vernier acuity, the ability to detect changes in the alignment of lines, is about 2

Peripheral color detection. The total field of view is about 150° for white light and is different for yellow, red, and green.

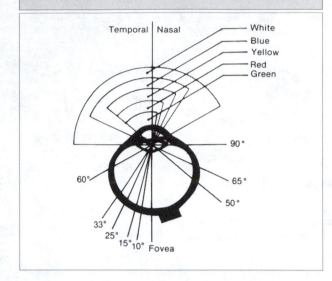

Visual acuity, the ability to discriminate detail, is calculated from the ratio of the minimum detectable gap or object *(h)* over the distance from the eye to the target *(d)*. $\Theta = 3438\ h/d$; visual acuity $= 1/\Theta_0$.

TAN Θ, H/D	Θ, MINUTES OF ARC	VISUAL ACUITY
.017 455	60.00	0.02
.001 000	3.43	0.29
.000 500	1.72	0.58
.000 241	1.00	1.00
.000 200	0.68	1.45
.000 100	0.34	2.90
.000 050	0.17	5.81

to 3 s of arc. Since the diameter of a single foveal cone is 10 to 40 s of arc, these acuities demonstrate the processing ability of the retina.

Dynamic visual acuity, the ability to discriminate detail in a moving target, is important for some inspection tasks. Unfortunately, an individual's static visual acuity (gap detection as measured on an eye chart) is not a good predictor of dynamic acuity; however, dynamic visual acuity can be improved with practice (Long and Rourke, 1989). Under most favorable conditions an object is detectable when it moves over 2 min of arc/s. Discrimination of detail in a moving target is satisfactory if the eye can lock onto the target. Boyce (1981, p. 58) says ability to lock-on

worsens rapidly beyond velocities of 50°/s. As any target shooter can tell you, it is easier to track a predictable target than a varying target.

Just because you can detect a small object doesn't mean that it is desirable to have objects you look at as small as possible—bigger is better. Figure 23.6 shows the ratio of object size (Θ) to the minimum object size detectable (Θ_0) versus contrast. Fortuin (1970), summarizing a lifetime of work, recommends $R = 2.5$ for "easy seeing." That is, for easy seeing, an object should be at least 2.5 times threshold size. If $R > 2.5$, easy seeing; $1 < R < 2.5$, strenuous seeing, resulting in eye fatigue; $R < 1$, the object is invisible. Note that the eye is not hurt by insufficient light just as a camera isn't hurt. Insufficient light causes eye muscle fatigue, bloodshot eyes, and headaches, but not permanent damage.

Unfortunately, most people do not have perfect eyes.

Visibility varies with both size (min of arc) and contrast of the target (Fortuin, 1970). The figure shows detectability of targets with a background of 10 cd/m². Below the threshold (area C), objects are invisible. Above the threshold in area B, they are visible but with considerable effort; in area A, they are visible with little effort. Duncan and Konz (1976) found that people could read light-emitting diodes and liquid crystal displays with no errors if they were 4–6 min of arc; however, the subjects preferred the displays to be 20–30 min of arc and, thus, preferred them to be about 5 times the minimum size.

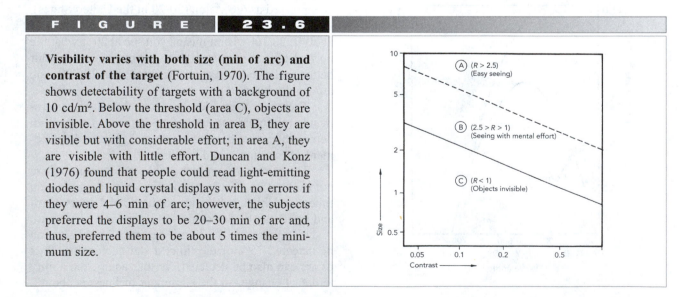

1.1.3 *Eye problems* Figure 23.2 shows two common eye problems and their optical solutions. A nearsighted person (myopia) has a long eyeball; the light rays from distant objects begin to diverge before hitting the retina. The solution is a concave external lens to bring the rays farther apart on the eye lens. A farsighted person (hyperopia) has the opposite problem—a short eyeball. The light rays from close objects meet behind the retina. The solution is a convex lens.

As you become older, your accommodation range decreases so you are forced to use bifocals, trifocals, or progressive focal length lenses. (With **bifocals,** there are two focal length lenses; with **trifocals** there are three focal length lenses; with progressive lenses, there is one lens with the focal length varying continuously from top to bottom.) The close lens for bifocals usually has a focal length of 16 inches; beyond 24 inches eyesight is blurred until the upper lens with a focal length of infinity is used. Thus, this lens has an intermediate area with poor vision for small detail (such as letters). Some people have football-shaped eyeballs with unequal radii of curvature in two axes. The result, a line focus instead of a point focus, is called **astigmatism** ("no point," in Greek). Astigmatism can be corrected by an external lens with unequal curvature. Laser surgery on the eye is the newest development in correcting eye problems.

Box 23.1 discusses eyeglasses for use with computers. Eyeglasses can be made impact-resistant, but note that any glass will break if it is hit hard enough. Polycarbonate lenses are lighter than glass but scratch easily. Many goggles have side shields; dust goggles have a fuzzy cloth next to the skin to give a better seal. Face shields protect the entire face from liquids and impact. Eyeglasses with chemicals in them to reduce light (either permanently as in sunglasses or temporarily as in lenses that automatically darken in sunlight) may present a safety hazard in welding areas. The chemicals probably will be designed only to cut off radiation in the visible spectrum. Thus, workers will think they are being protected, but the dangerous ultraviolet radiation is still hitting the eye. For that reason, use welding glasses in welding areas. Outdoor workers should reduce macular degeneration risk by wearing sunglasses and a hat with a brim.

Eyeglasses were not considered manly for Prussian officers. Monocles were not satisfactory, so the Germans developed contact lenses. Contact lenses support the cornea and thus retard the typical lengthening of the eyeball with age. The cornea is furnished with oxygen from the air instead of from inside the eye. Hard lenses prevent this breathing and so must be removed in a short time. Newer materials breathe better, so wearing time has been considerably extended. However, contact lenses do not provide eye protection against impact as eyeglasses do. They also tend to seal the surface of the cornea. Thus, they should not be worn where people are exposed to chemical fumes, vapors, splashes, or dusty atmospheres (even inside a respirator), as they tend to hold the irritant against the eye and not let the normal tears wash it out. Intense heat (e.g., furnaces) also can be a problem.

Some people have color perception deficiency. Cones specialize in detecting red, green, and blue. If your red cone pigment is defective, you cannot distinguish red or blue-green from gray; if your green cone pigment is defective, you cannot distinguish green or reddish-purple from gray. The X chromosome influences cone pigments. Since females have two X chromosomes, they have a "spare." About .4% of females and 8% of males have some color perception deficiency. Usually they are not completely deficient; consider them **color-weak,** not color-blind. Only about .003% of males are truly color-blind.

1.2 Light Definitions Table 23.4 gives the definitions of wavelength, polarization, luminous intensity, illuminance, luminance, reflectance, and brightness contrast. Wavelength and **polarization** describe the light. The key equation is:

BOX	**23.1**	*Glasses for Use with Computers*

Normal eyeglasses are "single vision" glasses; they have one focal point, generally infinity, that permits far vision (driving, TV watching, walking) and near vision (reading).

However, a person who has a prolonged need for near vision (reading, computer use) may use single-vision glasses ground for a specific near distance (say 16 inches for reading, 28 inches for computer monitors). But beyond this distance, objects are a blur. Another alternative is a VDT bifocal where the upper distance viewing segment is replaced with an intermediate viewing segment while the lower lens remains for close work. More recently, various progressive lenses have been developed for VDT viewing. These task glasses are useful while working with a VDT, but the user needs another pair of glasses for tasks such as walking or driving.

T A B L E	2 3 . 4	

Units and definitions of illumination.

QUALITY	UNIT	DEFINITION AND COMMENTS
Luminous flux, lm	lumen	Light flux, irrespective of direction from a source
Luminous intensity, I	candela	Light intensity within a very small angle, in a specified direction (lumen/steradian) Candela = 4π lumens
Illuminance, $d\text{lm}/dA$	lux	1 lumen/m^2 = 1 lux = .093 footcandle 1 lumen/ft^2 = 1 footcandle = 10.8 lux
Luminance	nit	Luminance is independent of the distance of observation as candelas from the object and area of the object perceived by the eye decrease at the same rate with distance 1 candela/m^2 = 1 nit = .29 footlambert 1 candela/ft$^2\pi$ = 1 footlambert = 3.43 nits
Reflectance	unitless	Percentage of light reflected from a surface

Typical Reflectance

Object	%
Mirrored glass	80–90
White matte paint	75–90
Porcelain enamel	60–90
Aluminum paint	60–70
Newsprint, concrete	55
Dull brass, dull copper	35
Cardboard	30
Cast and galvanized iron	25
Good-quality printer's ink	15
Black paint	3–5

Recommended Reflectances

Object	%
Ceilings	80–90
Walls	40–60
Furniture and equipment	25–45
Floor	20–40

Munsell Value	Reflectance (%)
10 =	100
9 =	100
8 =	78
7 =	58
6 =	40
5 =	24
4 =	19
3 =	6

QUALITY	UNIT	DEFINITION AND COMMENTS
Brightness contrast	unitless	$C = \|L_b - L_t\| / L_b$ where: L_b = Luminance of background L_t = Luminance of target
Wavelength	nanometers	The distance between successive waves (a "side view" of light). Wavelength determines the color hue. Saturation is the concentration of the dominant wavelength (the degree to which the dominant wavelength predominates in a stimulus). Of the 60 octaves of electromagnetic radiation, the human eye detects radiation in the octave from 380 to 760 nanometers.
Polarization	degrees	Transverse vibrations of the wave (an "end view" of the light). Most light is a mixture; horizontally polarized light reflected from a surface causes glare.
Coherence		Most light is incoherent, analogous to a stadium crowd roaring. Lasers produce coherent light—the crowd sings a song in unison.

Incident flux (Reflectance) = Reflected flux

That is,

Illuminance (Reflectance) = Luminance

Radiant power (radiant flux) is the time rate of flow of radiant energy; it is measured in watts. Luminous power, the visible part of radiant power from a source, is measured in **lumens** (lm). For exam-ple, a lamp may give 1,200 lumens. Luminous intensity, I, the luminous flux in a specified direction, is given in candelas (cd). A sphere subtends an angle in space of 4π steradians; thus the total flux emitted by a 1-candela uniform light source is 12.57 lm. The illuminance on a 1-m sphere by a 1-candela source is 1 lm/m^2 = 1 lux. In the SI system, lumens/m^2 is called **lux** (lx); in the U. S. system, lumens/ft^2 is called **foot-candles** (fc). Illuminance transmitted through a surface is called transmittance, *t,* unitless, with no transmittal = 0 and perfect transmittal = 1.

Luminance, or reflected luminous flux, in the U. S. system is lumens/ft^2, called foot lamberts (fl). However, in the SI system, luminance is measured in candelas/m^2, called nits, not lumens/m^2. Since candelas involve a spherical surface, a π term must be included for conversion to flat surfaces. Thus, for 1,000 lux incident on a 10% reflectance surface, the illuminance is 1,000 (.10)/π = 31.8 nits. Although often used interchangeably, technically luminance is a measure of the physical intensity of light while **brightness** is a measure of the intensity of the sensation perceived by the observer.

In both the U. S. and SI systems, **reflectance** applies only to perfectly diffuse reflection and is the ratio of reflected luminous flux to incident luminous flux.

Reflectance (in SI system)

$$= \frac{\text{Reflected flux}}{\text{Incident flux}} = \frac{\text{Luminance (nits)} \times \pi}{\text{Illuminance (lx)}}$$

Reflectance (in U. S. system)

$$= \frac{\text{Reflected flux}}{\text{Incident flux}} = \frac{\text{Luminance (fl)}}{\text{Illuminance (fc)}}$$

Brightness contrast, the difference in the amount of light reflected, is the ratio of two luminances. Color contrast differs with the composition of the light reflected.

The three attributes of color are **hue** (red, blue), related to wavelength of light; **brightness** (light red, dark red), related to intensity of light; and **saturation** (rich full red, pale red), related to purity of light.

Some color atlas systems (such as Munsell) use hue, value (lightness of a surface, how gray it is), and chroma (strength of a color). Using a paint-tinting analogy, value is like the amount of black paint added, and chroma is like the amount of colored paint added.

Light should be measured with a color- and cosine-corrected meter. Color-corrected means the reading is corrected for the sensitivity of the human eye. Cosine-corrected means the reading will not be affected by holding the sensor area at an angle to the light flux. The better meters give a digital output and have a "freeze" button so the last reading remains on the display even though the meter is moved.

2| REDUCTION OF VISUAL PROBLEMS

2.1 Criteria   The basic criteria for lighting a task are the following:

1. Have satisfactory visual performance.
2. Minimize cost of the lighting.

3. Have satisfactory esthetics.

Cost of illumination tends to be low in relation to labor costs, although it still has some absolute cost. **Illumination cost** can be divided into energy cost, fixture cost, and lamp cost. As a rule of thumb, energy cost is 80 to 90% of the total cost. Annual lighting cost in 2003 for an office or manufacturing area was about $.50/ft^2 (for an 8-h day).

Labor cost/ft^2 depends upon the labor cost and the worker density. Assume a wage rate of $15/h and fringe costs of 35% for a labor cost of 15 × 1.35 = $20.25/h. Assuming 1,800 h/year, annual cost is $36,450. Assume 1 worker/300 ft^2. Then annual labor cost is $121.50/ft^2; labor is 121.50/.5 = 243 times as expensive as lighting costs. The ratio will vary with labor cost, worker density, and type of lighting, but ratios usually are over 100 and often are over 300. Don't save a penny by reducing lighting costs if it costs a dollar in reduced labor productivity.

In general, performance in detecting small targets increases with increased illumination up to an asymptote; the exact asymptote depends upon many factors but is about 100 lux for easy tasks and about 1,000 lux for difficult tasks. The problem, of course, is to define easy and difficult!

Performance generally can be improved more by changing target size and contrast than by changing illumination. Regardless of the amount of illumination, performance on easy visual tasks far exceeds performance on difficult visual tasks; that is, more light will not change a difficult task into an easy one (Cushman and Crist, 1987).

Visual performance is affected by (1) individual differences, (2) quantity of light, (3) quality of the light, and (4) task requirements.

2.2 Individual Differences   People vary. Table 23.1 shows that visual acuity declines with age even with the best refractive correction. Resistance to glare and color discrimination also decline with age. Anshel (2001) says, to achieve good visibility, the 60-year-old worker requires 10 times more light than the 20-year-old worker. Table 23.1 also shows that many people do not have the best possible correction. For example, Ferguson, Major, and Keldoulis (1974) reported that 69% of workers without glasses needed glasses and 37% with glasses needed a new prescription. In addition, there are great differences in individual accommodation and convergence capabilities, so people may be able to do a task for a short time but prolonged performance results in fatigue and headaches.

An eye exam is recommended for everyone every other year up to age 55, then yearly. If employees have visual problems on a task, have their visual abilities checked—especially if they are middle-aged or older.

Jobs may require good vision at 20 to 40 inches (.5–1 m); a common example is VDT work. The plant nurse can check an employee's capability with a vision screener; a standard wall chart tests only far vision.

2.3 Quantity of Illumination

The recommended amount, sources, and fixtures will be discussed.

2.3.1 Recommended amount

Table 23.5 gives the **general lighting** recommendations by the IESNA. They also have detailed recommendations (with many subdivisions within each category) for Interior Lighting Locations and Tasks; Industrial Locations and Tasks; Outdoor Locations and Tasks; Sports and Recreation Locations and Tasks; Transportation Locations and Tasks; and Emergency, Safety, and Security.

For **task lighting** ("local lighting" with fixture on the floor or table), the amount of illumination depends on occupant age, speed and accuracy, and room reflectance. More light is needed for people over age 40, when speed or accuracy is important, or when room reflectance is insufficient. A common problem of task lights is that the lamp is located for convenience in mounting rather than convenience in vision. Task lights should not give direct or reflected glare (implies that the light should come from the operator's rear or side) and should light the *task*.

The lighting recommendations in this book are based on visual needs. The IES (2000, Chapter 5) has more on the non-visual effects of radiant energy, including discussion of the effect of ultraviolet radiation on the skin, light on vitamin D and calcium metabolism, biological rhythms, and phototherapy.

Phototherapy includes treatment of seasonal affective disorder (SAD), in which lack of sunlight in northern climates exacerbates depression. (In New Hampshire, about 10% of the population shows symptoms, while about 2% does in Florida.) Typical treatments are 2500 lux exposure for 2–4 h or 10,000 lux for .5 h; the light works by an ocular pathway, not a dermal pathway. Begemann et al. (1997) recommend that lighting also consider biological needs ("light as a vitamin"). Indoor lighting values of 1000 lux are "biological darkness" as outside daylight often exceeds 5000 lux. Perhaps people have a physiological need for windows and sunlight, not just a psychological need. For example, schizophrenia is related to a vitamin D deficiency in pregnant mothers (*The Economist,* 2002); vitamin D is "in" sunlight (as well as multi-vitamin pills).

TABLE 23.5

Illuminance categories. Adapted from Determination of Illuminance Categories (IESNA, 2000; Tables 10-9, 10-10, and 10-11). Low contrast: ≤.3 (but not near threshold); high contrast: >.3. Small size: ≤4 x 10⁻⁶ solid angle in sterradians; large size: >4 x 10⁻⁶ sr. For a reading task from 50 cm: 6-point type = 1.7 x 10⁻⁶, 8-point type = 3.1, 10-point type = 4.8, 12-point = 6.9, 14-point = 9.4, 24-point = 28, 36-point = 62. For a square object viewed from 30 m, a 7.5 x 7.5 cm object = 6.3 x 10⁻⁶. For a circular hole viewed from 40 cm, a .76 mm hole = 3.1 x 10⁻⁶.

Orientation and simple visual tasks. Visual performance is largely unimportant. These tasks are found in public spaces where reading and visual inspection are only occasionally performed. Higher levels are recommended for tasks where visual performance is occasionally important.

A	Public spaces	30 lux
B	Simple orientation for short visits	50 lux
C	Working spaces where simple visual tasks are performed	100 lux

Common visual tasks. Visual performance is important. These tasks are found in commercial, industrial, and residential applications. Recommended illuminance levels differ because of the characteristics of the visual task being illuminated. Higher levels are recommended for visual tasks with critical elements of low contrast or small size.

D	Performance of visual tasks of high contrast and large visual size	300 lux
E	Performance of visual tasks of high contrast and small size, or visual tasks of low contrast and large size	500 lux
F	Performance of visual tasks of low contrast and small size	1000 lux

Special visual tasks. Visual performance is of critical importance. These tasks are very specialized, including those with very small or very low contrast critical elements. Recommended illuminance levels should be achieved with supplementary task lighting. Higher recommended levels are often achieved by moving the light source closer to the task.

| G | Performance of visual tasks near threshold | 3000 to 10,000 lux |

2.3.2 *Sources* The ideal illumination source (which does not exist) would be free, give the desired amount of light on demand, and have high quality (color, no glare, highlighting, contrast).

A prime characteristic of sunlight is variability. The color temperature can range from 4,000 K (on an overcast day) to 40,000 K (with a clear blue sky). Light can range from effectively 0 lux at night to 1,000 lux (heavy overcast winter day) to 150,000 lux (sunny summer day).

Under normal circumstances, workplaces do not require daylight. See Box 23.2. Thus, the choice generally is among artificial sources.

Table 23.6 gives some lamp characteristics. Which lamp to use depends upon cost, convenience, and color.

Cost is primarily (about 90%) the cost of the energy, with about 10% for the fixture, lamp, and cost of replacing the lamp. Lumen output decreases with age, so for cost calculations, use mean lumens/watt rather than initial lumens/watt. Don't forget ballast losses. Lumens/watt are higher for bigger bulbs; often the advantage is over 25%. (In homes, compact fluo-rescent lamps should have, in theory, replaced incandescent lamps. Their high initial cost, however, has a breakeven point about 3 years into their 10-year life, and most people focus on the high initial cost and not the total cost over the 10-year life. The absence of a negative—higher utility bills—is a difficult concept.)

Convenience primarily involves the replacement frequency and restrike time. All bulbs except incandescent tend to have lives of over 10,000 h; mercury tends to last especially long. If there is a power interruption, when the power resumes, sodium, mercury, and metal halide lamps have a delay **(restrike time);** this may require supplementary fluorescent or incandescent lighting for emergencies.

Color of light of the low-pressure sodium lamp (LPS) is very poor; color of high-pressure sodium (HPS) is poor. In addition, Lin and Bennett (1983) recommended "Don't use sodium sources where there is substantial viewing of faces."

Fluorescent lamps vary both in Correlated Color Temperature (CCT) and Color Rendering Index (CRI). CCT is the color of the light source; cool-white lamps

---

| BOX | **23.2** | *Windows* | (Hanna and Konz, 2004) |

Windows are primarily a conflict of energy conservation vs. esthetics and a view. Tall windows let the light penetrate deeper into the room; broad windows give better views. Windows should allow a seated worker to see the view. Ideally, the horizon should bisect the window and the view should be of nature (such as water, foliage) rather than manufactured objects (such as a brick wall). To maximize the number of viewers, place windows in break rooms and at ends of corridors; use interior windows between windowed perimeter rooms and the interior core so people from the core can see through both sets of windows.

Windows in corridors and lounges have two advantages: (1) Being public, more people benefit from them; and (2) visual tasks are less critical. Interior windows (say, between an office and a corridor) seem to have a primary purpose of decreasing privacy; however, they do not have the disadvantages listed below of energy transfer, glare, and air transmission.

Disadvantages of windows (compared to solid walls) are the following:

- Windows cost more in both capital cost and operating cost (heat entry in summer, cold entry in winter, washing, and repair costs). A single-pane glass window has a U value of about 1 BTU/h / ft^2 / °F compared to .5 for a double pane, .4 for a triple pane, and .2 for a normal wall. Thus, a single-pane window transmits 5 times as much as a wall.

- Windows are a source of glare. Many windows are almost permanently covered with shades, drapes, or curtains. Glare is a special problem in computer areas for viewing monitors and in conference rooms for visual aids. Light interior colors near windows can be a glare source; dark colors absorb solar energy and thus send heat into the space. Windows also restrict the arrangement of nearby workstations.

- Windows are not a practical source of illumination in factories because the light is too variable (both in amount and in color), depending upon time of day, season, and weather, and because the light decreases by distance squared from the window. Work close to the window gets too much light and work far away gets too little. If you depend on sunlight through windows for illumination, equipment and workstations must be within about 20 ft (6 m) of a window, making maximum building width about 40 ft (12 m). Artificial illumination permits varied building size, shape, and layout.

- Windows may admit air. Exterior windows are not desirable sources of ventilation in industrial

(continued)

BOX   23.2   *Windows, continued*

buildings for the following reasons: (1) The air volume passing through a window is too variable because of wind velocity and direction, and is difficult to use in hot, cold, or wet weather; (2) the air admitted and released is not controlled; thus, you get low velocities at locations far from windows; if pollutants are being discharged, they are not controlled (e.g., passing through a filter); and (3) mechanical ventilation is relatively cheap and is easily controlled.

■ Windows pass noise and distractions from outside to inside, and inside to outside.

Window characteristics that can be good or bad are the following:

■ Windows decrease privacy for people on both sides of the window.

■ If windows can be opened, they allow air passage. If the heating, ventilating, and air conditioning (HVAC) system fails, either locally or totally, air passage may be useful. However, for normal operation of a HVAC system, open windows decrease system control and probably increase energy costs.

An advantage of windows is:

■ Windows permit a view. This view gives status. Some managements will not permit "lower-level" employees to have a window and, thus, a view.

Disadvantages of windows can be decreased by doing the following:

■ Maximize the view. Use windows with a long horizontal axis and a short vertical axis. Keep the sill low (.5 m above the floor) so that a seated person can see the view. Make windows public rather than private by placing them in common areas.

■ Have minimum surface area. Reduce area of existing windows with opaque insulated panels.

■ Use double panes and low-conductivity frames to reduce heat (and noise) transfer. Consider different glazing treatments for the south and west sides than for the north and east sides.

■ Shade windows from solar heat and glare. Permanent treatments include fenestration, recessed windows, and windows on enclosed courtyards (atriums). A semipermanent treatment is shading with deciduous trees. Adjustable insulation includes blinds, curtains, and shutters. Adjustment ease is important; if they are never adjusted, board up the window.

■ Decide whether the window will be permanently sealed, openable with a key, or openable anytime. Since openable windows leak air (even when closed), consider making only a few (e.g., 1/3) of the windows openable. Another option is a large sealed window and a small openable window.

■ If using skylights, make them vertical rather than horizontal (to reduce dirt and breakage), plastic rather than wired glass (better light transmission and less breakage), translucent rather than transparent (less glare), and openable (to supplement mechanical ventilation).

T A B L E   2 3 . 6

Characteristics of typical industrial lamps (Courtesy of General Electric Lighting Business Group).

TYPE OF LAMP	WATTS	LUMENS/WATT		LUMEN MAINTENANCE (%)	RATED LIFE (h)	RESTRIKE (Min)	RELATIVE COST
		Initial	Mean				
High-pressure sodium	35–1,000	64–140	58–126	90–92	24,000	1–2	Low
Metal halide	175–1,000	80–115	57–92	71–83	10,000–20,000	<10	Medium
Fluorescent	28–215	74–100	49–92	66–92	12,000–20,000+	Immediate	Medium
Mercury	50–1,000	32–63	24–43	57–84	16,000–24,000+	3–6	High
Incandescent	100–1,500	17–24	15–23	90–95	750–2,000	Immediate	High

*For basic lamp. Ballasting is required for all lamps except standard incandescent and tungsten-halogen.

have a CCT of 4100 K while warm-white have a CCT of 3000 K. CRI is the color appearance of illuminated objects under a given source; the minimum value permitted by code is 69; the maximum value is 100.

Veitch and McColl (2001) review the literature on fluorescent lamp CCT and CRI on preference and performance; CRI seems more important than CCT.

A new light source, light-emitting diodes, has begun to capture the market for red light (e.g., auto taillights, high-mounted brake lights, traffic lights); the advantages are low power consumption and a very long life.

Fluorescent lamps can be mounted among LPS lamps; the result is equivalent to HPS lighting—colors but not shades of colors are distinguishable. Metal halide gives good color (discriminate shades of colors); thus metal halide lamps often are mingled with HPS in high bays to get acceptable color and high lumens/watt. Fluorescent lamps not only give good color rendition but also permit you to select the color. In the United States cool white is the favorite. If you prefer a "warmer" (more red) light, use cool white deluxe. Warm-white gives the same color as incandescent. There also are specialized fluorescents to approximate spring outdoor daylight in northern Europe (the "standard" color).

Light may be important for inspection as well as esthetics. The perceived color of an object depends on (1) the color of the object, (2) the spectrum of the ambient light, and (3) the spectral characteristics of the viewer's eyes. Colored objects look white under light of their own color and black under light of a complementary color (e.g., red objects look white in red light and black in green light).

When inspecting the color of an object, specify whether the ambient light should be cool-white, incandescent, high-pressure sodium, or other, because perceived colors are quite different (Misra and Bennett, 1981). "Biological" inspection (e.g., grain, meat, cotton) should have a lighting source specified with a high color-rendering index (CRI). Metameric colors are colors that look different under differing light spectra. The "spectral power" of metal halide and sodium lamps is quite peaked, so they are questionable for precise color discrimination.

2.3.3 Luminaires (fixtures)

Although it is obvious, place the fixture close to the task rather than far away. Lamps can be put into a wide variety of fixtures. A fixture will release 50% to 80% of the light from the lamp to the room; in other words, it absorbs 20% to 50% of the light. Thus, using a fixture that absorbs less of the light means that the additional light is free. If a fixture's **coefficient of utilization** is .70, it means 70% of the lamp light inside the fixture is distributed to the work plane. The light distribution from a fixture (up vs. down) is in five categories:

direct (90% down), semidirect (90%–60% down), general diffuse (60%–40% down), semi-indirect (40%–10% down), and **indirect** (10%–0% down). Direct and semidirect are most used. Some uplight is good since (1) the light on the ceiling reduces brightness contrast, and (2) nondirect luminaires tend to stay cleaner (i.e., lose less light) as air can move upward through the fixture.

The downward component is further described by beam spread (highly concentrating, concentrating, medium spread, spread, widespread). Wider beam spreads give more overlapping (better illumination on vertical surfaces and less dependence on a single lamp). At high mounting heights, use narrower beams. The shielding angle (the angle between a horizontal line and the line of sight at which the source becomes visible) should be greater than 25°, preferably approaching 45°. The lighting distribution from linear sources (fluorescent and low-pressure sodium) tends to "batwing" (be emitted at a 45° angle downward, as viewed from the tube end).

Since it is difficult to foresee the future, fixtures should be selected that are relatively easy to relocate within the area. A variety of plug-in designs are available. Some fixtures have a disconnect feature that permits maintenance without shutting off the main circuit.

2.4 Quality of Illumination

In addition to the color of the light (mentioned above), consider the glare, orientation, and esthetics.

2.4.1 Glare

Glare is any brightness within the field of vision that causes discomfort, annoyance, interference with vision, or eye fatigue. Glare is divided into direct and indirect glare.

Direct glare. Four light sources in the field of view (thus causing **direct glare**) are windows, lamps (bulbs), incandescent objects, and backlighted objects.

Window brightness can be changed with louvers and curtains; see Box 23.2. An alternative is to change the "surround brightness"; see Figure 23.7. The effect of surround brightness (reduced contrast) can be observed by looking at auto headlights in the day (bright surround) versus night (dim surround). Also consider reorienting the individuals so they don't face the window.

Lamps (especially point sources such as incandescent and halogen) can cause direct glare. That is, since line sources have more area than point sources, the luminance/area is lower. Shield to at least 25° from the horizontal (45° is better). Increase the surround brightness of the ceiling by having some light go up from a luminaire. Translucent glass between the lamp and the eye reduces lamp brightness. Opaque shields (lampshades) prevent viewing the lamp.

"Surround brightness." Splayed recesses have an intermediate brightness between the window and the wall, which reduces luminance contrast (Konz, 1992).

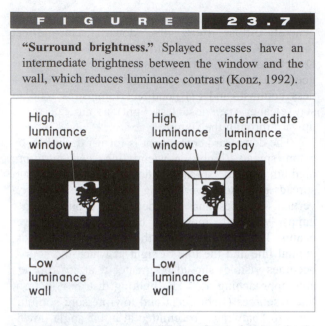

Source: S. Konz, "Vision at the Workplace: Part I—Guidelines for the Practitioner"; and "Vision at the Workplace: Part II—Knowledge Base for the Guide," *Int. J. of Industrial Ergonomics,* Vol. 10, pp. 139–60. Copyright © 1992 by Elsevier Science, Amsterdam, Netherlands. Reprinted with permission.

Incandescent objects (welding arcs, lasers, hot metal) are discussed in detail in Sliney and Wolbarsht (1980). Use specialized glasses for this type of source. Ordinary sunglasses are dangerous because they reduce visible light and the person has a false sense of security; however, the sunglasses transmit too much infrared and ultraviolet light.

Backlighted objects (such as microfilm and X-ray readers) occasionally are a source of glare. Use an opaque mask to cover the portion of the screen the film does not cover.

Indirect (reflected) glare. Caused by high luminance from a surface, **indirect glare** usually is horizontally polarized light.

One approach is to decrease the incoming light so less is reflected. Lion et al. (1968) reported better inspection performance when line sources (fluorescent) instead of point sources (incandescent) were used. In other words, increase the area of the incoming light so the lamp brightness is lower.

A second possibility is to use multiple low-powered sources instead of a single high-powered source. Matsushita puts curtains on the inside of inspection booths to reduce glare off objects. Consider filtering the light source with a multi-layer polarizer to minimize the horizontal reflection.

If the reflected glare is specular or directional (as in a mirror), try to reorient the reflecting surface or to reposition the glare source so the glare misses the eye.

A third approach is to decrease reflectance through matte finishes. Car dashboards and satin-fin-

ish chrome and stainless steel are examples. Psychologically, people tend to prefer matte blue, green, or brown over gray.

A fourth approach is to put the filter at the eye—sunglasses. Sunglasses reduce luminance but not contrast, so they reduce visual acuity. However, in most situations visual acuity is not critical, as capability far exceeds task requirements; thus, people trade off a reduction of surplus capacity for an increase in comfort. Polarized sunglasses, however, filter horizontally polarized light and improve both visual acuity and comfort (Mehan and Bennett, 1973).

A fifth possibility is to have people move their heads. However, to avoid the glare, operators may adopt a bad posture and thereby develop neck, shoulder, or back pain.

2.4.2 *Orientation* Orientation of lights to sharpen or blur the surface texture or form of an object is called modeling. For example, inspect bottles of liquid with light through the bottom. Back lighting may be useful for transparent materials. Low-angle lighting helps detect surface flaws. Figure 23.8 gives five different luminaire locations.

Orientation can be used to modify people's facial appearance. On the stage, light from below is used to

Five luminaire options. Place supplementary luminaires using 5 techniques: (a) luminaire located to prevent reflected glare (reflected light does not coincide with angle of view); (b) reflected light coincides with angle of view (it is in the "offending zone"); (c) low-angle lighting to emphasize surface irregularities; (d) large-area surface source and pattern reflected toward the eye; and (e) transillumination from diffuse source.

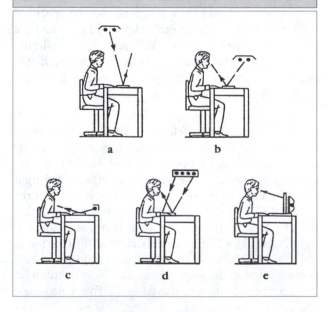

make a person look evil. Lighting of a speaker is best with a light 20° horizontally on each side of the face; vertically, lighting should be above 45° to reduce glare for the speaker but at 30° to improve audience impression (Golden, 1985). To emphasize the brightly lighted speaker, consider a dark background; fill light (even from a light-colored podium or podium light) also can help.

2.4.3 *Esthetics*   Light not only facilitates visibility of a task; it contributes in other ways to the visual quality—**esthetics**—of the space. Flynn (1977) and Flynn et al. (1979) did key studies showing that light also must be seen as a form of communication, evoking a perceptual response. Light communicates subjective impressions of the environment and also provides suggestions for behaviors.

Some research indicates which lighting results in various perceptions. See Table 23.7. Uniform supplementary wall lighting encourages perceptions of clarity. Nonuniform wall lighting, with its play of light and shadow, implies relaxation, privacy, and pleasantness. (Nonuniformity can be obtained by changing the wall texture and reflectance, as well as changing the lighting.) Dark surfaces (reflectances of 30–50%, saturated colors, and glossy finishes can maintain vital interest and stimulation but should be used to a limited degree.

Even underground areas can have good lighting esthetics. For example, have natural light from the ceiling and have a view (if the area is in a hill and thus permits window cutouts showing the horizon).

For outdoor esthetics, consider color variety (green from foliage, gray/white from stone, blue from water, and a brightly colored flower for contrast). Flowing water adds visual as well as auditory variety. A waterfall tends to produce more variety than an ordinary fountain (perhaps that is why many fountains are programmed to fluctuate).

Lighting controls can be set so that one switch can control a variety of lamps (with varying directions and intensities); each switch setting is called a "scene." Continuing the theatre analogy further, the pattern can change automatically with time—like a musical score. In theatres, lighting often is tied in with sound, which varies in intensity, pitch, and direction. Example industrial applications usually are in a room with multiple functions (e.g., conference rooms, lounges, food service areas).

In general, esthetic lighting design should consider the design of shadows as well as the design of light (Gordon, 1987)—emphasizing asymmetry and variability. Without shade or darkness, light loses much of its meaning. A cloudy, overcast day is bland; a bright, sunny day has bright highlights and sharp shadows.

Light also suggests behaviors. Orient user attention with a higher illuminance level than the surroundings (an extreme example is a spotlight on a stage; a subtle example is a display case in a store). "Points of interest" should have 3–5 times higher illuminance than surrounding areas. Lighting also can suggest a circulation pattern because, when following a path, people tend to follow the brighter path.

TABLE 23.7
Lighting influences on perceptions for various spaces.

PERCEIVED ILLUMINATION HAS	CANDIDATE SPACES	REINFORCING LIGHTING MODES
Visual clarity (clear, distinct vs. hazy, vague)	Offices, classrooms, laboratories, industrial space	■ High luminance on horizontal plane in central part of the space ■ Additional emphasis on peripheral surfaces ■ Cool, continuous spectrum light sources
Spaciousness	Corridors	■ Peripheral wall emphasis of a uniform nature
Relaxation	Lounges, some restaurants	■ Nonuniform lighting with peripheral emphasis ■ Warm color tones of white light
Privacy/intimacy	Private are intimate restaurants, reading areas Public are circulation areas, lobbies	For private: ■ Low intensity levels in immediate user area with higher intensities farther away ■ Nonuniform distribution patterns
Pleasantness	Lobbies, retail space	■ Nonuniform lighting with a peripheral emphasis

2.5 Task Requirements   Box 23.3 discusses reading. Improve the task by increasing the size of objects, the contrast, and the time available for viewing. If the object is the "signal" and the environment is the "noise," design a task with a high signal/noise ratio. The goal is to enhance the object so it emerges from its environment like an island from the sea.

2.5.1 *Increasing size*   One possibility is to increase the size of the object itself. An example is to use 20-point type instead of 9-point type on transparencies that people view at a meeting. Another is to use 10-point type instead of 8-point type in a book. Size can be increased mechanically. Examples are pantographs used in engraving and master/slave manipulators used in microscope work.

Another possibility is to bring the object closer to the eyes. This does present a conflict, however, because the hands usually are involved and holding objects close to the eyes becomes tiring. It is possible to support the arms with arm supports (see Figure 13.18). Another problem, however, is that the eye muscles (especially of older workers) become tired due to the efforts of accommodation and convergence.

An alternative is the use of **optical aids** (magnifiers). A 2X lens will double the size of the object while giving good depth-of-field. As magnification increases to 4X and more, depth-of-field becomes quite critical. A lens with a local lighting unit mounted on a swinging arm can be used in many tasks. When optics are used, visual clarity will decline due to light scattering in the lens and reduction of the visual field; however, the apparent size of the object will increase. For good targets, young eyes, less than 2-h inspection, and over 1,000 lux on the target, magnification probably will help if the targets are less than 2.5 min of arc (Wei and Konz, 1978).

If the target is to be magnified, the question is how much? Wei and Konz (1978) found 4X better than 2X magnification; increasing the target size (size after magnification) to the eye beyond 7 min of arc gave little benefit. Smith and Adams (1971), using microscopes, reported that time/correct inspection was minimum at 8 to 12 min of arc. A higher magnification, such as a microscope gives, has an additional problem in that it tends to put the operator in a fixed position—a "straight jacket."

Reduce static muscle fatigue of such workers by building working breaks into their job every 20 to 30 min. For example, when they finish with an assembly, have them carry it to a storage rack 10 m away or walk to get a supply of components. Magnification without the fixed posture is possible by using projection, such as with TV or optical comparators.

The microscope workstations at IBM in San Jose had ergonomic problems (static work posture, visual fatigue). When the engineers improved the ergonomics, costs and injuries were reduced; first year savings were about $1.1 million (Helander and Burri, 1995).

Another possibility is to mount the magnification device on the operator's head. The watchmaker's glass is an example that has the disadvantage of no biocular vision but the advantage of no accommodation strain. Another example is a surgeon's loupe, which fits on glasses and gives 2.5X magnification at 18 inches.

Alternatively, use magnifying lenses in spectacle frames. Usually they should be half-lenses (the top is omitted) so the operator can have normal distance vision. It also is possible to use glasses that cause the depth of the "stare point" to recede for close work (i.e., the object actually is .2 m from the eye but the eye through the lens perceives it as .3 m). The advantage is minimized accommodation and convergence effort.

BOX 23.3   *Reading*

Reading with normal vision. There is "reading-to-do" (looking up information and using it "soon") and "reading-to-learn" (reading for later use); in the workplace, the majority of reading is reading-to-do (Guthrie et al., 1991).

First, reading requires navigation (finding the desired information). For the "gross search," provide tables of contents, indices, and the like. Then aid the "local search" with typographic cues to make information noticeable through headings, type size, color, bold/italics, and the like.

After navigation is completed, reading requires object recognition. Reading has a fixation phase (mean of 200 ms; range of 100–500 ms). Then the eyes jump horizontally (saccades) about 8 characters in 20–40 ms. At the end of the line, the eye returns to the start of the next line (line saccades).

Reading for the visually-impaired. Partially-sighted people commonly magnify text with hand-held or spectacle-mounted loupes; the optical aid advantage is portability. A major improvement occurs with closed-circuit TV (CCTV) magnifiers; the advantage is large magnification (4X to 40X) (Den Brinker and Beek, 1996). Goodrich et al. (1980) reported people preferred CCTV magnifiers and had less fatigue with them, although mean reading rate was not faster than with optical aids.

Another example is VDT operators using prescriptions ground for the focal length of their task (typically about .5–.6 m) rather than a general-purpose prescription. Orchestra musicians habitually have their glasses ground for a distance of 1 m; this allows them to see their sheet music clearly (although the conductor is fuzzy). Eyeglasses can be considered as an effort-saving device rather than just as a defective vision correction device.

Finally, the task also might be improved by reorienting the object, since reorientation might improve visual size of a defect or improve contrast.

2.5.2 *Increasing contrast*

The art of camouflage consists of obliterating contrasts. We are concerned with anticamouflage. Improved **contrast,** which can be in either color or brightness, is especially helpful when the contrast is less than 30%. Attention to color contrast is especially useful. Seize any opportunity to modify target color. For example, use color-code file folders (Konz and Koe, 1969), tool handles, areas within a building, equipment, and worker clothing (to aid in identifying type of worker).

Use color in text and sign printing, photographs, and video displays. Some examples are "bluing" a piece of metal before scribing lines on it, bluing bearings before fitting, staining a tissue in a microscope slide, and painting a white line to differentiate the highway shoulder and pavement. A simple reflector under the task often makes viewing much easier.

Use light-color tabletops, as the reflected light improves viewing. For reading, use new printer cartridges, clear photo-duplications, pens not pencils, felt-tip pens not ballpoints, computer printouts on white paper not green paper, and white cardboard boxes not brown or manila. Spacing and grouping are also helpful. See the discussion of printed displays in Chapter 18. Fox (1977) reported that coin inspection was more accurate when the coins were presented in a standard array rather than a random array; the good coins provided a background against which the defective coins stood out. Just as a photographer often uses a plain backdrop behind a person to reduce the background "clutter," consider simple backgrounds around inspection stations to reduce visual clutter (and distractions).

For more on contrast, see Section 4.2.3 of this chapter.

2.5.3 *Increasing time*

Shoot sitting ducks. That is, work on or inspect stationary items rather than moving items.

A less desirable alternative is working on an object moving past the operator at a constant velocity. Cochran, et al., (1973) found that inspection performance was degraded at viewing times of .25 s but not at .5 s. In addition to time, consider angular velocity.

Values between 10 and 30 degrees/s will not affect performance too much if the worker has satisfactory dynamic visual acuity (Ludvigh and Miller, 1959). One solution technique is to have the operator face "upstream" to maximize viewing time. Removing visual obstructions is another.

If the operator is viewing randomly spaced objects on a fixed-velocity conveyor, there is a large variability in available viewing time. Some objects might be available for viewing for .2 s while others are available for 2.0 s. If the operator must occasionally make a motor movement (e.g., to remove a defective item), the next 10 items may not be inspected at all. With this fixed-pace system, the conveyor speed must be set for the worst performance level of the slowest operator.

A serious problem with some machine-paced conveyors or index tables is that the operator must make a positive action to prevent the departure of a defective unit to the next station. If it is necessary to use machine pacing, have the operator make a positive action to send the units to the next station. However, it is better to use operator-paced stations so the operator may vary viewing time to match viewing requirements.

3 GENERAL LIGHTING

3.1 Uniform Ceiling Lighting

One possibility is to light an entire area uniformly. Advantages include maximum flexibility in arranging the machines and workstations in the area, which eliminates the need to move fixtures if the area is rearranged and allows use of large lamps (which have higher lumens/watt than small lamps).

In most circumstances, uniform ceiling lighting has light fixtures mounted on the ceiling. Alternatively, lights can be mounted on stands and light bounced off the ceiling; this indirect lighting is relatively expensive but has low-glare characteristics.

Nonuniform lighting (i.e., low general lighting supplemented with task lights) has advantages of lower cost, more precise control of the light, and more esthetic appeal.

For uniform lighting, the basic **zonal cavity method** equation is

$$I(A) = (N_1)(N_2)(L)$$

where

$$
\begin{aligned}
I &= \text{Illuminance in area, lux} \\
A &= \text{Area illuminated, m}^2 \\
N_1 &= \text{Number of fixtures} \\
N_2 &= \text{Number of lamps/fixture} \\
L &= \text{Lumens/lamp}
\end{aligned}
$$

For example, if you wish to have 750 lux evenly in a 2,500 m² area and are going to use fixtures with

1 lamp/fixture with each lamp rated as 22,500 lumens, then $N_1 = 83$ fixtures are needed.

However, the equation has to be modified for three types of losses. The first loss, **coefficient of utilization** (CU), considers absorption of the light by the room surfaces. The second loss, **lamp lumen depreciation** (LLD), considers the loss of light output of a lamp with age. The third loss, **luminaire dirt depreciation** (LDD), considers the loss of light output due to dirt on the fixture.

The resulting equation is

$$I(A) = CU\ (LLD)\ (LDD)\ (N_1)\ (N_2)\ (L)$$

Detailed values for *CU, LLD,* and *LDD* along with N_2 and *L* for various fixtures are in the *IESNA Handbook* (2000) under "zonal cavity method." Lamp and fixture manufacturers also can furnish values, generally with a computer program to solve the equation for any design you suggest.

As a rule of thumb, assume *CU (LLD) (LDD)* = .5. That is, the space would need 166 fixtures instead of 83.

The next step is to locate the fixtures in the space. For uniform lighting on the worksurface, a checkerboard pattern with the fixtures on the same color squares is reasonably efficient. However, this does tend to overlight the center and underlight the room perimeter, so widen the spacing in the center and reduce it on the perimeter. End-to-end fixtures are an inefficient pattern.

Three guidelines for efficient uniform ceiling lighting are:

1. *A distant light is dim.* The farther the light has to travel to the worksurface, the less desirable it is. Thus, use low fixtures. A common error in factories is to mount the fixtures 10 ft or even 20 ft above the floor.

2. *Reuse the light.* The light that travels directly from the fixture to the worksurface is called direct light. However, light that first bounces off a surface (indirect light) helps. Light-colored ceilings, walls, floors, and furnishings give more indirect light.

3. *Use efficient fixtures.* Some fixtures trap as much as 30% of the light inside the fixture, while others trap only 5%–10%. In addition, some fixtures can direct the light better than others. Fixtures with some light going up (uplight) tend to be better than those with zero uplight because they permit airflow through the fixture (which keeps it cleaner); light on the ceiling gives better brightness contrast in the room.

3.2 Energy Conservation   As was pointed out in Section 2.1, labor costs far exceed lighting costs. It is important not to reduce labor productivity dollars in order to save a few pennies on lighting. In the United States, however, lighting consumes about 25% of electricity—about 20% directly and 5% for cooling of unwanted heat from lamps. The two basic conservation approaches are: (1) reducing lighting power, and (2) reducing lighting time.

3.2.1 *Reducing lighting power*   The four subdivisions are: the luminous environment, the physical environment, equipment selection, and design and maintenance procedures.

Luminous environment. See Table 23.5. Consider whether you will use: (1) high uniform ceiling lighting, (2) low uniform ceiling lighting supplemented with task lighting, or (3) nonuniform ceiling lighting supplemented with task lighting. For high-luminance areas, use lower levels from general lighting supplemented by task lighting. Generally, reducing task difficulty (Section 2.5) is more effective than adding more light.

Physical environment. Light is used more effectively when the ceiling fixture is low rather than high. Reuse the reflected light; avoid low-reflectance walls and partitions and floors; use translucent or transparent partitions rather than opaque ones. (For further savings, have a white roof in hot climates and a dark roof in cool climates.) Daylight may supplement artificial light (but see Box 23.2). New Wal-Mart stores have skylights to supplement the ceiling fluorescent lamps; as the outside light varies, the light from the lamps is automatically adjusted to compensate.

Equipment selection. Consider the lamp, the ballast, and the fixture. Since the lighting cost is about 90% for power and only 10% for the lamp and fixture, select efficient lamps, not just lamps with low capital cost. Perhaps you can overcome the poor color of high-pressure sodium lamps by mixing in a few metal halide lamps. Also consider high-efficiency ballasts; when replacing a failed ballast, their high efficiency may far outweigh their higher capital cost. Efficient luminaries have higher internal reflectance, allowing more light to escape from the fixture and staying clean longer.

Design and maintenance procedures. What brightness pattern do you want in the room? Consider a mixture of task and general lighting. Group tasks with high-brightness requirements. Have enough switches so lights can be turned off in unoccupied areas. To reduce the maintenance cost, consider group relamping (all lamps changed at once, even if they are still burning). Fixtures and lamps get dirty; clean lamps and fixtures periodically (say every 2 to 3 years). A dimming circuit with a sensor can increase lamp output as lamps get dirty, maintaining light level.

For further energy savings, automatically turn down heating or cooling systems approximately 1 h before the end of occupancy; the thermal inertia of the building will result in occupants not noticing.

3.2.2 *Reducing lighting time*   Three subdivisions are occupancy, cleaning, and daylight.

Occupancy. The last person leaving a room should turn off the lights but, as any parent knows, they don't always do it! Automatic occupancy sensors work well; they are especially useful in areas used occasionally, such as toilets and storage areas. Having fewer fixtures/switch helps, as people are reluctant to turn off lights that other people use.

Cleaning. The lights should be turned off when the regular workers leave, and turned on when the cleaning crew arrives. Cleaning, however, requires less light than most office or production work, so have a "cleaning" switch that turns on half of the lights. An alternative is to have the cleaning occur during the regular work time, not when the area is unoccupied.

Daylight. Certain non-work, "public" areas (lobbies, corridors, cafeterias) can be lighted by daylight, supplemented by artificial lighting. For energy conservation, however, the artificial lighting should be on a dimmer, connected to an illumination sensor (so the artificial light varies inversely with daylight).

4 SPECIAL LIGHTING

4.1 Lighting for VDT Areas   The following will discuss lighting for video display terminal (VDT) areas.

4.1.1 *Paper versus screens*   Until approximately 1980, the vast majority of tasks in offices involved working with paper. The paper tended to be relatively horizontal, and more light improved the ability to do the task. Now, however, practically all office workers use VDTs. The screen is relatively vertical but, more important, ambient light washes out the contrast on the screen. At present, we have not gone to the paperless office, so lighting must be designed for vertical screens, vertical paper (in document holders), and horizontal paper. In paperless offices, users often prefer quite low levels (say 100 lux) of ambient light.

If the light is uniform throughout the area, the amount of light is often too much for the screen and too little for the paper. A nonuniform alternative is task lighting. A further consideration is that, because most VDTs are in offices, there is considerable interest in esthetically pleasing solutions rather than just functional solutions.

Of the two tasks (paper and screen), the screen task tends to be the more difficult, as the electronic

characters are not as sharp as print, the letter/background contrast is worse, and there is some flicker. Reading rates are about 25% slower on screens than on print. Thus, if the lighting will be uniform, design for the screen, as it is the more difficult task.

Light below 100 lux enhances screen legibility; light above 500 lux enhances paper legibility. For uniform lighting, the Human Factors Society (1988) recommends 200–500 lux. The IESNA recommends that the light level for paper tasks not exceed 750 lux if there is uniform lighting.

If task lighting is used, illumination on the document can be relatively high (see Table 23.5) and relatively low illumination on the screen—assuming the task light is properly directional. The general lighting should not be too low. The IESNA recommends 200–300 lux—assuming proper shielding of glare sources. Yearout and Konz (1987b) reported that when VDT operators had general lighting of 350 lux supplemented by task lighting, the operators wanted their general view of the rest of the office to be much brighter (770 lux) and to be visually interesting. To solve this challenge, use light to "wash" a wall, use illuminated artwork, and so forth. For esthetic reasons, therefore, avoid "cavelike" offices.

Operators prefer the general lighting to be a mixture of indirect (uplight) and direct (downlight) rather than all downlight. Hedge (1991) reported, from a long-term field study of office workers, that both direct-parabolic and lensed-indirect lighting were preferred over recessed fluorescent luminaries with prismatic diffusers; the lensed indirect was preferred over the direct parabolic. The direct parabolic had recessed luminaries shielded with a grid of 18×10 cm parabolic louvers and provided 750 lux to the workplace. The lensed indirect had ceiling-suspended (pendant) luminaries that provided upward light, which then was reflected down to the workplane. It provided 500 lux to the workplace. Indirect light also can be supplied from floor lamps; halogen lamps are a popular light source but also furnish considerable heat.

VDTs occasionally are used in a paperless office (i.e., computer display only) environment. In such an environment with low ambient light levels (e.g., 10–30 lux), use indirect lighting (Krois et al., 1991).

4.1.2 *Reflections/glare*   Screen reflections can be reduced in eight ways. The first three ways reduce light from the source.

1. *Reduce light from windows.* Consider full or part coverage of the window. Common techniques are curtains and louvers. Vertical louvers can be positioned to block the sun, yet permit a view; horizontal louvers tend to restrict the view. Awnings and canopies reduce direct light, yet permit a view. A neutral-density film can be placed on the window to reduce transmission of light.

2. *Reduce ceiling glare.* One possibility is to use ceiling fixtures that have a restricted glare angle; for example, "egg-crate" fixtures have little glare, as most of the light goes vertically. Additional means of reducing ceiling luminance are diffusers, prismatic lenses, polarizers, and parabolic louvers.

Two other possibilities are: (1) Use indirect lighting, and (2) use task lights (local lights). Pure indirect lighting has no vertical downward component; light bounces off the ceiling and gives a "soft fog" of light with minimal glare. The lamp can be supported from below (floor or table) or above (ceiling fixture). Partial indirect lighting (combined lighting) can be provided by mounting the fixture below the ceiling (say 2 ft) and having some of the light go up as well as down. Task lights permit low light levels on the screen (from the ceiling) and higher levels on the non-screen environment (e.g., document, keyboard, aisles). The key to a task light is its ability to be directed to a "target" and away from "non-targets." Task lights also can be put on a dimmer so the user can control intensity, as well as direction and location, of the light.

3. *Reduce other brightness sources.* Have the operators wear dark shirts, not white shirts. Replace light-colored tabletops with dark-colored tabletops, and light-reflective vertical surfaces with darker, non-reflective vertical surfaces. Replace light "point sources" (such as white telephones behind the operator).

The next alternative is to intercept the light.

4. *Use barriers.* Partitions (hanging from the ceiling or rising from the floor) can block direct light from windows, ceiling lights, task lights at other workstations, and bright reflections. Detect these bright objects by using the **mirror test**—holding a mirror in front of the screen and looking at it from the operator's position.

The remaining four alternatives change the workstation.

5. *Tilt the screen.* Light comes in a straight line from the source, reflects, and hits the operator's eyes. Perhaps the screen can be tilted so the light ray does not hit the eyes!

6. *Change workstation orientation.* Lights (e.g., windows) behind the operator reflect off the screen; thus, don't have operators face away from windows. Facing the window, however, causes discomfort because of the large visual adjustments between the bright window and dark screen. Orient workstations so that windows (if any are present) are at the side (i.e., the screen is perpendicular to the window). Place the workstation, if possible, to minimize glare from ceiling fixtures. Since more light leaves fluorescent lamps laterally, brightness is less if the lamp is viewed from the end.

7. *Consider screen treatments.* Reflections on the screen can be diffuse or specular.

Diffuse (veiling) **reflections** are caused by ambient light, as well as the phosphor. Diffuse reflections increase the luminance of both the screen background and characters, thereby reducing the contrast ratio. The contrast can be improved with some types of filters. Their general characteristic is that the ambient light goes through the filter twice (in and out) but the light from the characters goes through the filter once (out). Thus, although the luminance is reduced for everything, the luminance is reduced less for the characters, so contrast improves.

If the filter has neutral density (gray), it reduces all energy of all wavelengths equally. A color filter (the color of the phosphor) will pass most of the phosphor color but will pass little of the ambient light (typically white), enhancing contrast.

Specular reflections (mirrorlike images) also occur. A matte treatment (frosting) reduces glare; unfortunately it also makes the characters fuzzy. A quarter-wavelength filter (like the frosting on camera lenses) is effective but expensive; fingerprints reduce its effectiveness.

8. *Change screen/character background.* Most word-processing programs give the user the choice of character and screen color. A common choice is white characters on a medium blue background; this is a positive-contrast screen. A **negative-contrast** screen (reversed video) might be black characters on a white screen. Negative contrast is often recommended but seldom used. An advantage is that glare is less noticeable on the white background; a disadvantage is increased flicker sensitivity (as a result of the larger luminous surface).

4.1.3 *Luminance ratios*   For a **luminance ratio** (characters-to-screen background), the Human Factors Society (1988) recommends at least 7:1 (that characters be at least 7 times brighter than the screen background). The IESNA (2000) says the ratio (for both positive and negative displays) should be between 5:1 and 10:1.

Does the eye have a problem looking at a bright surface (such as a document) and then at a dim surface (such as a screen)? The HFS (1988) says this is not a problem because the brightness within a workstation can vary as much as 20 to 1 with no problem.

For additional comments on characters, see Chapter 18 on displays and Section 2.5 of this chapter on how to improve the task.

4.2 Inspection
This section will consider inspection lighting in three areas: amount of light, color of light, and contrast.

4.2.1 *Amount of light*
Helander and Burri (1995) described how illumination was improved in an area at IBM in Austin, Texas, where automatic machines inserted components into circuit boards. Management had thought of the operators as "process monitors," but in fact they did considerable inspection for quality control. With the improved lighting, process yield improved dramatically, productivity improved, and quality improved; the company estimated a 1-week payback from these types of ergonomic improvements.

The amount of light on the inspection task may be insufficient. Inspection areas often are placed in an area with general lighting, which is sufficient for walking around and general seeing but not for inspection. In one situation, an inspector took items off a conveyor over which a fluorescent lamp was suspended. The lamp was moved 2 ft toward the inspector so that it lighted where the object was *inspected,* not where the object was *grasped.* In addition to improving direct lighting by moving the luminaire closer, consider improving indirect lighting by using light color (i.e., reflective) work surfaces, workstation dividers, and floors. See Table 23.5 for illuminance recommendations.

4.2.2 *Color of light*
Perceived object color is affected by color of the light. Color differences on red surfaces are emphasized by sources strong in blue light, and on blue surfaces by sources strong in red (Misra and Bennett, 1981). When designing areas for inspecting color, specify whether the lamp to be used is incandescent, cool-white fluorescent, HPS, or whatever, as colors appear quite different under different lamps.

4.2.3 *Contrast*
The object may be obscured by reflected glare. Figure 23.9 shows how lamps are tilted so the reflection is not into the inspector's eyes.

For color contrast, the inspection can be for the object shape or the object surface characteristics.

To detect shape, maximize the contrast of the task and the background. For example, if buttons on a table are inspected for holes, the table color should contrast with the button color. Another technique is a mask with the specified item shape; transillumination allows a thin border of light to show for a part that is in tolerance. When you are looking for shape, object orientation is critical. To demonstrate this, try to recognize a picture of a face turned upside down. For printed material, letters and background should have maximum contrast. Avoid "artsy" low-contrast letters

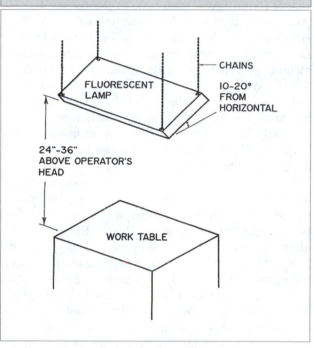

F I G U R E   2 3 . 9

Tilt lamps 10°–20° to prevent glare. Tilting also reduces directional noise coming from the workstation. An alternative is to tilt the worksurface.

(e.g., black on red, red on brown). They are not only less legible but also less attractive (Konz et al., 1972).

To detect surface characteristics such as color and texture, minimize the contrast of the task against the background. Pearls sold at retail are displayed on black velvet; the maximum contrast makes it difficult to detect color differences between pearls. When pearl merchants buy from each other, they display the pearls on white cloth to maximize color differences. Thus, if you are sorting green beans for color, sort on a table painted the green of a good bean.

Orientation of the lights may be important, both to reduce glare and to emphasize features. See Sections 2.4.1 and 2.4.2. It is good practice to have both the brightness and angle of incidence of inspection lighting adjustable by the inspector so performance can be maximized.

Peterson (1980) tested various homogeneous, opaque, colored backgrounds for the inspected object (versus a general heterogeneous background of conveyor and machinery); off-white resulted in the inspectors' detecting 4% more of the faults; white was judged to give too much glare.

See Cushman and Crist (1987) for a good discussion of inspection lighting.

4.3 Warehouse Aisle Lighting
In a warehouse, items are stored on racks with long, narrow access

aisles. The visual requirement is on the vertical plane (box sides) rather than the horizontal plane. If the stacking height is less than aisle width, treat the area as an open bay rather than a warehouse aisle.

The use of high racks makes high-intensity discharge (HID) lamps preferable to fluorescent lighting (fluorescent lighting can be used up to about 20 ft), as HID luminaries have better directional characteristics. Different directional patterns are available, such as medium symmetrical, wide symmetrical, and directional asymmetrical (4 lobes—2 up and down the aisle and 2 into racks). For luminaire mounting heights below 16 ft, the type of HID luminaire makes relatively little difference. However, at low mounting heights, a high-watt point source may be too bright. A high-reflectance aisle floor helps.

Mount the luminaries above the aisle instead of the racks. Protect the luminaries from impact by containers—items often are lifted several inches before being brought into the aisle. Shield HID sources for glare for operators looking at the top of the stacks. The HID spacing can be increased if there is substantial uplight and the ceiling has high reflectance.

A large number of low-watt sources will give a more even distribution of light than a small number of high-watt sources. If the aisle or rack locations are not permanent, mount the fixtures on tracks perpendicular to the aisles and make the wires plug-in instead of permanent. There are two strategies to save energy: (1) switch the light off when the area is unoccupied; this requires more switches so specific smaller areas can be switched off but, if HID lamps are used, the 10 min restrike time may be a problem; and (2) reduce the lamp output (using multilevel ballasts) during unoccupied times.

There often is considerable shadowing of boxes within the racks. If reading codes is required, consider strategies to reduce visual stress. Some possibilities are: (1) make the bin label larger with better contrast; (2) make the container label larger with better contrast; (3) supplement the light in the bin (e.g., with a vehicle floodlight), and (4) supplement the light in the vehicle for reading documents.

4.4 Emergency Lighting

Emergency lighting is designed to help people leave the building if the normal power supply fails. The minimum recommended illuminance is 10 lux along the centerline of the path of egress and 1 lux along a 1-meter band throughout the means of egress (IESNA, 2000, Chapter 29). Hazard areas (e.g., corridor intersections, abrupt changes of egress direction, staircases, changes in floor level, exits, obstructions along egress path) require more light. See Table 23.8. The levels in this table are the absolute minimums at any time and at any location on any plane where safety is related to

T A B L E	2 3 . 8

Minimum illuminance (lux) levels for safety (IESNA, 2000; Table 29.2).		
Hazards Requiring Visual Detection	**NORMAL ACTIVITY LEVEL**	
	Low	High
Slight	5	11
High	22	54

Source: Reprinted with permission, *IESNA Lighting Handbook,* 2000. IESNA, 120 Wall St., 17th Floor, New York, NY 10005.

seeing conditions. Example areas for 5 lux are conference rooms, closets, exterior floodlighting; for 11 lux, corridors, restrooms, exterior entrances; for 22 lux, freight elevators, offices, stairways; for 54 lux, elevators, escalators, computer rooms, stairways, and electrical and mechanical rooms.

Every flight of stairs should be illuminated by more than one luminaire to minimize shadows on nosings and treads. Photoluminescent paint can be used to supplement path delineation.

The Americans with Disabilities Act prohibits wall objects such as luminaires from projecting more than 10 cm (4 in) into walks, corridors, hallways, or aisles when these objects are mounted between 67 and 200 cm (27 and 80 in) above the finished floor.

The emergency lighting can be either completely separate lights with batteries or the normal lights with a backup power source. Separate lights tend to be projector and reflector (PAR) lamps, a battery, and a device to turn on the light when the power fails. Use PAR with wide horizontal patterns for open areas and with long narrow beams for corridors and stairs. The normal light can have a local battery (e.g., units in AC fluorescent fixtures) or a central battery. There also can be a motor generator. Note that HID lamps need 1 to 10 min restrike time (see Table 23.6) and another 3 to 5 min before coming to full intensity; thus, you may need some fluorescent lamps in HID areas.

Another option is a quartz lamp (about the size of a lipstick case) in some HID fixtures. After a momentary power interruption, the quartz lamp automatically lights until the HID lamp cools down, restrikes, and regains 60% of its full light output.

Exit signs can be self-powered but, in much of the country, codes permit the exit sign to be illuminated externally by the emergency lighting, which should be less expensive than having both emergency lights and internally powered exit signs.

The restrike problem of some lamps may make them unsatisfactory for emergencies, even with a backup power system. Some solutions include emergency fluorescents, a quartz lamp in the HID fixture, and dual-filament HID lamps (one filament is on "standby").

4.5 Security Lighting

4.5.1 *Target hardening* Target hardening increases the time, resources, and planning required of the perpetrator (IESNA, 2000, Chapter 29). Time is the enemy of the criminal. Hardening elements include fences, gates and locks, surveillance (personnel and cameras), response personnel, and established procedures for operations and maintenance. Lighting is part of the security system.

Stray light (light pollution) can be reduced by careful design, including the use of motion sensors.

4.5.2 *Offense versus defense* The purpose of security lighting is to prevent crime. The light should discourage intruders (reduce "offense") and improve detectability (improve "defense"). If a guard and/or TV camera is on-site, consider these as the "audience" and the intruder as the "actor." That is, the audience should have a good view of the actor; conversely, the actor should not be able to see the audience. If there is no on-site defender and if you depend upon outside police observers, make the site visible from off-site.

4.5.3 *Site considerations* Consider Table 23.9.

Large open areas. An increase in mounting height will reduce the shadows cast by obstructions. Every point in the area should receive light from at least two directions. Reflected light also decreases shadows, so a light-color surface is better than a blacktop surface.

Buildings. All entry points to the building (doors, windows, roof) should be lighted. High surface reflectance (stone chips, the building itself) help.

Perimeter fence. Opaque fences should be lighted on both sides. If people can see through the fence, use a low-reflectance fence material such as black- or green-coated chainlink instead of galvanized; if galvanized is used, aim the luminaires to reduce illuminance on the fence itself.

Entrances. The entrance to a secure site can be the most vulnerable area; crime by deception may be attempted. Lighting should have good color rendering so the color of people, documents, goods, and vehicles can be easily discriminated. A concrete road surface helps inspection of the underside of vehicles; luminaires set into the road surface are even better.

TABLE 23.9

Illuminance recommendations for security lighting (IESNA, 2000).

APPLICATION	ILLUMINANCE, LUX	COMMENTS
Large open areas	5–20	The greater the brightness of the surrounding area, the higher the illuminance required to balance the brightness in the space.
Buildings	5–20	Vertical illuminance on the building facade. The greater the brightness of the surrounding area, the higher the illuminance required to balance the brightness in the space.
Perimeter fence	5	Illuminance on the ground on either side of the fence.
Entrances	100	Illuminance on the ground in the inspection area.
Gatehouses	300	Illuminance on the workplane in the gatehouse. This light level must be dimmable to low levels at night so the guard can see outside the gatehouse.

Source: From IESNA, *Lighting Handbook: Reference and Application*, 9th ed. Copyright (c) 2000 by Illuminating Engineering Society of North America, New York. Used by permission.

Gatehouses. Light the inside of the gatehouse dimly (so people outside cannot see if the gatehouse is occupied or what guards are doing). Windows should be specular-reflecting, low transmission glass at a tilted angle (bottom closer to the guard). Paint the inside a dark color; make interior lighting dimmable.

4.5.4 *Public spaces* The lighting should make the space look attractive and safe. Through enhancing the visibility of people and spaces, suspicious behavior can be detected early enough for evasive action, and people can be identified and described with greater accuracy.

Pavement illuminance should be between 10 and 50 lux with a CRI>50; the CRI>50 requires high-pressure sodium lamps to deliver close to 50 lux on the pavement. Luminaires should provide illumination from more than one direction.

Parking garages are a serious problem and should have >60 lux on the pavement between the vehicles; these values should be maintained 24 h/day as daylight often does not penetrate well into parking garages. Non-enclosed parking should have >30 lux.

Parks and public areas should have >10 lux on the paved areas.

Review Questions

1. Sketch an eye, labeling the cornea, aqueous humor, lens, pupil, iris, vitreous humor, and retina.

2. At what wavelength (and color) are the cones most sensitive?

3. Define visual acuity with a formula.

4. Why is it dangerous to wear sunglasses in welding areas?

5. Do males or females tend to have more color weakness?

6. What is a lumen/m^2? A lumen/ft^2?

7. What are the three attributes of color?

8. What is a typical ratio, in an office, of labor cost to illumination cost? Give assumptions.

9. Rank incandescent, mercury, fluorescent, metal halide, and high-pressure sodium lamps for lumens/watt, life, and restrike time.

10. Is reflected glare horizontally or vertically polarized light?

11. Give three different ways (including examples) of how to increase visual size.

12. Give three examples of how glasses can be used as an effort-saving device.

13. What is the range of lux for outdoors?

14. Using the example of pearls, discuss whether the contrast of the object and background should be high or low when inspecting for surface characteristics such as color.

15. Discuss the advantages/disadvantages of uniform lighting vs. nonuniform lighting.

16. Discuss the esthetics of lighting.

17. Give three different ways of increasing the chances of lights being turned off.

18. Briefly discuss why filters on VDTs improve legibility.

19. Discuss search for items on a conveyor belt.

20. Discuss warehouse aisle lighting.

21. Discuss security lighting in terms of offense and defense.

References

Anshel, J. Visual ergonomics in the workplace. In *Applied Ergonomics,* Alexander, D. and Rabourn, R. (eds.), 193–98. London: Taylor and Francis, 2001.

Begemann, S., van den Beld, G. and Tenner, A. Daylight, artificial light and people in an office environment, overview of visual and biological responses. *Int. J. of Industrial Ergonomics,* Vol. 20, 231–39, 1997.

Bennett, C. The demographic variables of discomfort glare. *Lighting Design and Application,* Vol. 7, No. 1, 22–25, 1977.

Boyce, P. *Human Factors in Lighting.* New York: MacMillan, 1981.

Cochran, D., Purswell, J., and Hoag, L. Development of a prediction model for dynamic visual inspection tasks. *Proceedings of the 17th Annual Meeting of the Human Factors Society,* 31–43, 1973.

Cushman, W. and Crist, B. Illumination. In *Handbook of Human Factors,* Salvendy, G. (ed.), Chapter 6.3. New York: Wiley & Sons, 1987.

Den Brinker, B. and Beek, P. Reading with magnifiers. *Ergonomics,* Vol. 39, No. 10, 1231–48, 1996.

Duncan, J. and Konz, S. Legibility of LED and liquid-crystal displays. *Proceedings of the Society for Information Display,* Vol. 17, No. 4, 180–96, 1976.

Ferguson, D., Major, G., and Keldoulis, T. Vision at work. *Applied Ergonomics,* Vol. 5, No. 2, 84–93, 1974.

Flynn, J. A study of subjective responses to low energy and nonuniform lighting systems. *Lighting Design & Application,* Vol. 7 (2), 6–15, February 1977.

Flynn, J., Hendrick, C., Spencer, T., and Martyniuk, O. A guide to methodology procedures for measuring subjective impressions in lighting. *Journal of the Illuminating Engineering Society,* Vol. 8 (2), 95–120, 1979.

Fortuin, G. Lighting: Physiological and psychological aspects—Optimum use—Specific industrial problems. In *Ergonomics and Physical Factors.* Geneva: International Labour Office, 1970; pp. 237–59.

Fox, J. Quality control of coins. In *Human Factors in Work, Design and Production,* Weiner, J. and Maule, H. (eds.). London: Taylor and Francis, 1977.

Golden, P. The effects of lighting a public speaker upon observer impression. *Lighting Design + Application,* Vol. 15, No. 12, 37–43, December 1985.

Goodrich, G., Mehr, E., and Darling, N. Parameters in the use of CCTVs and optical aids. *American J. of Optometry and Physiological Optics,* Vol. 12, 881–92, 1980.

Gordon, G. The design department. *Architectural Lighting,* Vol. 1, No. 1, 53–54, January 1987.

Guthrie, J., Schafer, W. and Hutchinson, S. Relation of document literacy and prose literacy to occupational and societal characteristics of young black and white adults. *Reading Research Quarterly,* Vol. 26, 30–48, 1991.

Hanna, S. and Konz, S. *Facility Design: Manufacturing Engineering,* 3rd ed. Scottsdale, AZ: Holcomb Hathaway, 2004.

Hedge, A. The effects of direct and indirect office lighting on VDT workers. *Proceedings of the Human Factors and Ergonomics Society,* 536–40, 1991.

Helander, M. and Burri, G. Cost effectiveness of ergonomics and quality improvements in electronics manufacturing. *Int. J. of Industrial Ergonomics,* Vol. 15, 137–51, 1995.

Hess, E. The role of pupil size in communication. *Scientific American,* Vol. 233, 110–15, November 1975.

Human Factors Society. *American National Standard for Human Factor Engineering of Visual Display Terminal Workstations.* Santa Monica, CA, 1988.

IESNA, *Lighting Handbook: Reference and Application.* New York: Illuminating Engineering Society of North America, 2000.

Konz, S. Vision at the workplace: Part I—Guidelines for the practitioner, and Part II—Knowledge base for the guide. *Int. J. of Industrial Ergonomics,* Vol. 10, 139–60, 1992.

Konz, S. and Koe, B. The effect of color coding on performance of an alphabetic filing task. *Human Factors,* Vol. 11, No. 3, 207–12, 1969.

Konz, S., Chawla, S., Sathaye, S., and Shah, P. Attractiveness and legibility of various colors when printed on cardboard. *Ergonomics,* Vol. 15, No. 2, 189–94, 1972.

Krois, P., Lenorovitz, D., McKeon, P., Snyder, C., and Tobey, W. Air traffic control facility lighting. *Proceedings of the Human Factors Society,* 551–55, 1991.

Lin, A. and Bennett, C. Lamps for lighting people. *Lighting Design & Application,* Vol. 13, No. 2, 42–44, February 1983.

Lion, J., Richardson, E., and Browns, R. A study of industrial inspectors under two kinds of lighting. *Ergonomics,* Vol. 11, No. 1, 23–24, 1968.

Long, G. and Rourke, D. Training effects on the resolution of moving targets. *Human Factors,* Vol. 31, No. 4, 443–51, 1989.

Ludvigh, E. and Miller, J. Study of visual acuity during the ocular pursuit of moving test objects. *J. of the Optical Society of America,* Vol. 48, No. 11, 799–802, 1959.

Mehan, R. and Bennett, C. Sunglasses—Performance and comfort. *Proceedings of the 17th Annual Meeting of the Human Factors Society,* 174–77, 1973.

Misra, S. and Bennett, C. Lighting for a visual inspection task. *Proceedings of the Human Factors Society,* 631–33, 1981.

Parker, J. and West, V. *Bioastronautics Book.* Washington, DC: Supt. of Documents, 1973.

Peterson, G. Improvement of Inspection Performance, MS Thesis, Dept. of Industrial Engineering, Kansas State University, 1980.

Sliney, D. and Wolbarsht, M. *Safety with Lasers and Other Optical Sources.* New York: Plenum, 1980.

Smith, G. and Adams, S. Magnification and microminiature inspection. *Human Factors,* Vol. 13, No. 3, 247–54, 1971.

The Economist, Let the sun shine in. Vol. 71, Feb. 9, 2002.

Wei, W. and Konz, S. The effect of lighting and low power magnification on inspection performance. *Proceedings of the Human Factors Society,* 196–99, 1978.

Veitch, J. and McColl, S. A critical examination of perceptual and cognitive effects attributed to full-spectrum fluorescent lighting. *Ergonomics,* Vol. 44, 3, 255–79, 2001.

Yearout, R. and Konz, S. Illumination levels in offices with visual display units. *Proceedings of the Human Factors Society,* 1113–15, 1987a.

Yearout, R. and Konz, S. Task lighting for visual display unit workstations. *Proceedings of IX Int. Production Engineering Conf.,* 1862–66, 1987b.

Overview

The noise scale, decibels, confuses the general public because a doubling of the noise level gives an increase of only 3 dB. Noise control at lower levels (55 to 80 dBA) is primarily to eliminate annoyance; noise control at levels of 90 dBA and up is to protect hearing. Under most circumstances, noise does not affect productivity.

Noise reduction is relatively inexpensive if you plan ahead. It calls for some ingenuity and expense to modify the noise source; it requires considerable ingenuity and greater expense to modify the sound wave. Use of personal protective equipment requires day-after-day selling, motivation, and supervision.

Key Concepts

acoustic glare

audiogram

confine/absorb

dBA

decibel

dosimeters

earmuffs/earplugs

equal energy/equal pressure

free field

frequency

hearing impairment

impulse sound

inverse square law

masking noise

octave band

outer/middle/inner ear

permanent threshold shift
  (PTS)

power watt level (PWL)

pure tone

resonance

sones

sound pressure level (SPL)

speech interference

speech interference level
  (SIL)

temporary threshold shift
  (TTS)

turbulence

vestibular system

white noise

459

THE EAR

1.1 Anatomy of the Ear

Figure 24.1 gives an overview of the ear. Figure 24.2 gives a detail of the cochlea. Figure 24.3 gives a detail of the organ of Corti.

The outer part of the ear serves as a collector of sound vibrations in the air and funnels them to the eardrum. The auditory canal has a resonant frequency (which multiplies sounds) around 3,000 Hz. The eardrum is extraordinarily sensitive and will move in response to changes of as little as .000 02 N-m^2 and then will move only .000 000 001 cm! (And .000 000 001 cm = 1/2 the diameter of a hydrogen molecule.)

In the middle part of the ear, the vibration of the eardrum (tympanic membrane) is transmitted to the oval window through three small bones (ossicles) known as the hammer (malleus), anvil (incus), and stirrup (stapes).

The hammer "handle" is connected to the eardrum and the head to the top of the anvil. The base of the anvil is connected to the top of the stirrup. The baseplate of the stirrup moves the oval window leading to the inner ear.

The ligament of the stapes also dampens loud impulse noises and thus protects the inner ear. This acoustic reflex occurs after a short delay (.1 s), so it is not much protection against one sudden noise impulse but helps against steady loud impulsive noise (e.g., punch press area). The original vibration in air has now been transferred to a vibration of a second membrane. The signal is magnified, as the eardrum area is 14 times larger than the oval window area (gain 23 dB) and by a 1:3 lever arm ratio for the 3 bones (gain 2.5 dB) for a total gain of 25.5 dB.

The eardrum will be most efficient if the air pressure is the same on both sides, so the Eustachian tube

---

FIGURE 24.1

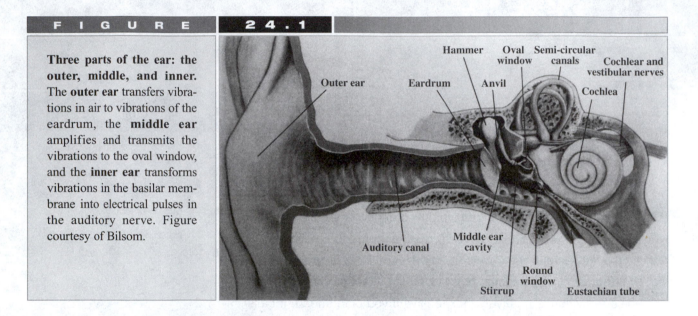

Three parts of the ear: the outer, middle, and inner. The **outer ear** transfers vibrations in air to vibrations of the eardrum, the **middle ear** amplifies and transmits the vibrations to the oval window, and the **inner ear** transforms vibrations in the basilar membrane into electrical pulses in the auditory nerve. Figure courtesy of Bilsom.

FIGURE 24.2

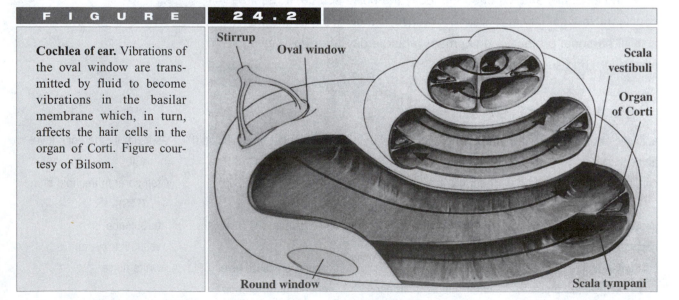

Cochlea of ear. Vibrations of the oval window are transmitted by fluid to become vibrations in the basilar membrane which, in turn, affects the hair cells in the organ of Corti. Figure courtesy of Bilsom.

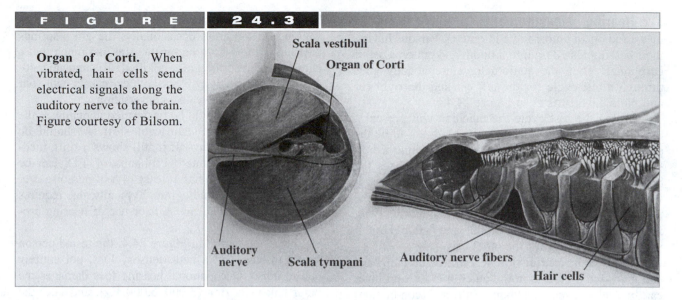

Organ of Corti. When vibrated, hair cells send electrical signals along the auditory nerve to the brain. Figure courtesy of Bilsom.

Scala vestibuli

Organ of Corti

Auditory nerve

Scala tympani

Auditory nerve fibers

Hair cells

comes in handy. One end is in the middle ear and the other end in the top of the mouth. If it becomes plugged and pressure is changing rapidly (jet descent or elevator descent), hold your nose, close your mouth, and "blow" gently.

The inner ear is the most interesting of all. The vibrations of the oval window set up vibrations in the fluids of the cochlear duct. The duct's upper passage (scala vestibuli) starts at the oval window; the lower passage (scala tympani) ends at the round window. Connecting the two is a small gap (helicotrema). The round window bulges out when the oval window bulges in, so the vibrations are not dampened. The basilar membrane divides the two passages. Now the noise has become a wave traveling in the fluid of the inner ear.

The basilar membrane vibrates with the frequency of the fluid vibration. The basilar membrane is narrow and stiff near the oval window and wide near the gap. High-pitched sounds travel only a short distance along the membrane before they die out, so the end near the oval window detects high-frequency sounds; low-pitched sounds are detected near the gap.

On top of the basilar membrane is the organ of Corti, which has about 16,000 hair cells. As the wave goes through the tympanic chamber, it deflects the vestibular membrane down into the cochlear duct. This, in turn, deflects the basilar membrane down into the tympanic chamber. This pulls down the hair cells in the organ of Corti. The hair cells are supported at both ends, so the pulling makes the hair cells send out an electrical pulse, which goes to the brain by way of the cochlear nerve.

The brain then decides that the muffler in your car either has holes in it or has a pleasant throb. The brain also is able to detect the slight difference in time that the sound takes to travel to each ear and so identify whether the sound came from the left or right—auditory localization. This can be demonstrated by placing yourself between two speakers; by adjusting the volume of one speaker, you can make the apparent sound location move. Tran et al. (2000) report that auditory beacons should: (1) be non-speech instead of speech, (2) have a repetition rate of 1–2 rep/s, (3) be continuous instead of pulsed.

Conductive hearing loss occurs in the outer or middle ear from wax, punctured eardrum, or corrosion of the bones, among other causes. Often it can be cured with medical or surgical treatment. Nerve loss in the inner ear is rarely curable; it can be caused by old age, viruses, drugs, and noise.

In addition to hearing, the ear provides a sense of balance through the pea-sized **vestibular system,** which is subdivided into the utricle and the semicircular canals. The utricle has "pebbles" (otoliths) resting on a bed of hairs (cilia); the pressure tells you which way gravity is operating. The three semicircular canals (one for each axis) are mutually perpendicular; they sense acceleration through movement of liquid in the canals. The utricle (static system) monitors the position of the head in space; the semicircular canals (dynamic system) monitor the movement of the head in space.

Motion sickness (seasickness) is caused by vertical acceleration in the range of .1 to .63 Hz; the greatest sensitivity is in the range .125 to .25 Hz (Griffin, 1996). The incidence of seasickness is presented by the following equation:

$$PVOM = .33\,(a^2_{rms}\,t)^{.5}$$

where $PVOM$ = Percent of unadapted adults who vomit

a = Frequency-weighted rms acceleration, m/s^2

t = Exposure duration, s (20 min < t < 360 min)

1.2 Hearing Measurement Hearing usually is measured on an automatic audiometer. Persons having their hearing tested go into a booth and put on a set of earphones. Then the audiometer automatically goes through a test cycle for the left ear and the right ear and plots the results as in Figure 24.4.

During the test cycle the machine will present a tone at 250 Hz that increases in loudness until the person indicates sound perception by pushing a button. It then decreases until the person releases the button. After 3 or 4 tests for a specific frequency, it will index to the next higher frequency and repeat the tests until it has completed all seven frequencies (250, 500, 1,000, 2,000, 4,000, 6,000, and 8,000 Hz); it then repeats the test for the other ear.

The typical **audiogram** tests the "air pathway" and gives the total loss in the outer, middle, and inner ear. In a refined test, the "bone pathway" (conduction) is tested; this omits the outer and middle-ear losses and gives the inner-ear (sensorineural) loss.

Hearing loss from noise can be temporary (recover overnight) or permanent. **Temporary threshold shift (TTS)** is measured 2 minutes after the end of exposure. With repeated exposure, TTS becomes **permanent threshold shift (PTS)** or noise-induced permanent threshold shift (NIPTS). Think of

hair cells as grass that is being walked on. TTS is walking on the grass occasionally; the grass springs back up. PTS is walking on the grass so much that a path is worn and the grass is killed. To simulate a 40-dB hearing loss, firmly block both ear canals with your fingers and try to carry on a conversation.

Audiograms should be performed annually; if the audiogram shows a significant shift, it should be repeated within 30 days. If it still shows a shift, medical review is warranted. Problems of TTS can be avoided if the person has at least 14 h of no noise over 80 dBA before the audiogram. Typically, this requires testing at the start of the shift or use of hearing protection devices (HPD).

From the output in Figure 24.4, the tested person seems to have had a neurosensory loss, not entirely due to noise. Occupational hearing loss damages the inner hair cells first (3,000–6,000 Hz), and later the farther hair cells. It almost always occurs on both sides equally and develops gradually.

Not all hearing loss is occupationally related. A series of audiograms over the years will help establish whether the occupation is responsible for the loss.

Yearout et al. (1996) reported that workers working in occupational noises over 85 dBA set their car stereos 6.5 to 9 dBA higher after work than before work. Thus,

---

F I G U R E   2 4 . 4

Audiograms show hearing ability. Plotted at each of 10 bands is the right ear of a 47-year-old male with 7,700 hours of flying time. Zero dB indicates normal hearing. Hearing loss due to noise usually starts with a small dip of 20 to 30 dB at 4,000 Hz before progressing to the severe loss of this pilot. Recreational noise causes problems also. A target shooter often has a 40 dB to 80 dB loss at 4,000 Hz. Since nonvoiced consonants (p, t, k, s) have frequencies of 2,000–8,000 Hz, they are the first to be lost. Next lost are the voiced consonants (b, d, g, z) and, finally, the vowels. Because female voices have a higher pitch, a person with auditory nerve damage has more difficulty hearing females than males.

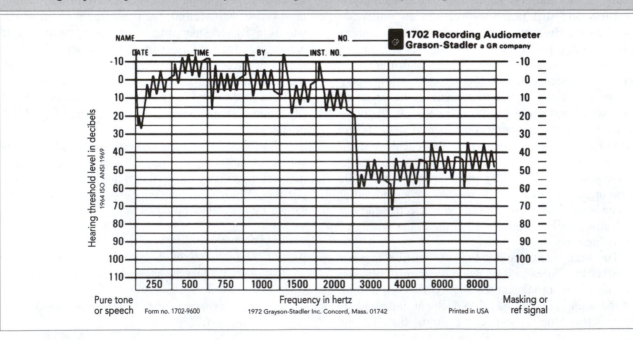

hearing testing during or after work would probably show 6.5 dBA to 9 dBA more loss than the workers actually had.

2 NOISE

2.1 Noise Definitions Absolute levels of sound pressure detectable by the human ear vary by 1,000,000,000,000 to 1. This scale is too large to use conveniently. The scale was compressed by using a log ratio (originally called the Bell, after Alexander Graham Bell, but since a smaller measure was needed, it was divided by 10 and called the deciBel or **decibel**). There are two relationships: sound pressure and sound power. The relation between sound pressure and sound power is analogous to temperature and heat. Another analogy is a lightbulb, with sound pressure akin to the amount of illumination and sound power to the bulb's watts.

$$SPL, dB = 10 \log_{10}\left(\frac{P}{P_0}\right)^2 = 20 \log_{10}\left(\frac{P}{P_0}\right)$$

where SPL = **Sound pressure level,** decibel

P = Sound pressure level of the noise, N-m² (the 2 reflects the effect of area of the eardrum)

When first measured, 0 dB was the minimum level of hearing. With more refined measurements, the mean minimum of the population with unimpaired hearing is now given as 4 dB.

P_0 = Reference sound pressure level

= .000 020 N-m² = 0 dB = 20 μ N-m²

= .000 200 dynes/cm² = .000 200 μ bar (approximately the minimum level of hearing of a young person)

The power level of a noise is:

$$PWL, dB = 10 \log_{10}\left(\frac{W}{W_0}\right)$$

where PWL = **Power watt level** of the noise, decibel

W = Acoustic power of the noise, watts

W_0 = Reference power level

= 1 x 10⁻¹² watt

Since 1 x 10⁻¹² watts = −120 dB, it can be expressed as:

$$PWL = 10 \log W + 120$$

That is, 120 dB of power corresponds to 1 W, 110 to .1 W, 100 to .01 W, and so on. The decibel scale, although giving a small range, confuses the public since it is not linear; it also requires "new math." Most confusing is that 100 dB + 100 dB is not equal to 200 dB! When combining or subtracting noises with the formula, we use the power formulas, not the pressure formula. Consider a machine generating noise with a PWL = .01 W (i.e., 100 dB) and with an SPL of 1 N-m² (94 dB) at a location 5 m from the machine. Now add another identical machine.

$$
\begin{aligned}
PWL &= 10 \log .020 + 120 \\
&= 10 \log 2 \times .010 + 120 \\
&= 10 \log 2 \times 10^{-2} + 120 \\
&= 10 (-2 + .3) + 120 \\
&= -17 + 120 = 103 \text{ dB}
\end{aligned}
$$

Thus, adding 100 dB of power to 100 dB of power gives 103 dB. The corresponding $SPLs$ are 94 + 94 = 97.

In addition to 94 + 94 = 97, we also have 74 + 80 = 81, and 80 + 95 = 95! Ten identical sound sources have an SPL 10 dB louder than just one source! If we have two noisy machines, then, each generating at 80 dB, and we completely silence one machine, the noise level drops from 83 to "only" 80. Rather than use the formulas, use Figure 24.5, a quick graphic technique.

It will be emphasized that the use of Figure 24.5 is the theoretical addition in a **free field.** In practice, most fields are not free. Outdoors, the wind can have a substantial effect, as well as reflections from reflectors such as brick walls. The noise might even be attenuated slightly by passing through intervening shrubbery. Indoors, there are many reflecting surfaces as well as solid paths to conduct the noise. Occasionally some of the indirect noise is reduced by absorbent materials on the floor, wall, or ceiling.

$$\text{Wavelength} = \frac{\text{Speed of sound}}{\text{Frequency}}$$

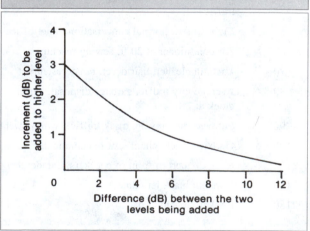

F I G U R E   2 4 . 5

Graphic technique to calculate dB. Add decibels in a free field from the figure. Take the difference between levels, read increment from graph, and add increment to higher level. For example: 80 − 80 = 0; 80 + 3 = 83. For example: 86 − 80 = 6; 86 + 1 = 87.

The speed of sound is 770 miles/h, 1,238 km/h, and 344 m/s. **Frequency** (the rate of oscillation of the sound) is in Hertz (cycles/second). Thus, a low-frequency sound (20 Hz) has a wavelength of 344/20 = 17 m. A high-frequency sound (20,000 Hz) has a wavelength of 344/20,000 = .017 m = 1.7 cm. A low-frequency sound (long wavelength) easily travels around corners and through openings. A high-frequency sound (short wavelength) behaves like light. It does not turn corners well, and it can be reflected. High-frequency noise is more attenuated by distance traveled in air than low-frequency noise. High-frequency noise is more annoying.

A **pure tone** is a one-frequency sound. Most industrial noise is a mixture of frequencies known as broadband noise. If the frequencies are equally distributed throughout the audible range, this is known as **white noise,** which sounds like rain.

If a sound has a duration of <1 s, it is known as **impulse sound.**

Reverberation is the reflection of sound from surfaces; see Table 24.10 for sound coefficients. Tables 24.1 and 24.2 give example noise levels. Table 24.2 shows that leisure noise levels can be quite high. Hayne et al. (1997) reported that students listened to car stereos an average of 12 h/week at 91 dBA, and to personal stereos for 15 h/week at 97 dBA. Clark (1991), however, says that, although rock concerts may present some hazard, the primary nonoccupational hazard is noise from gunfire. For a right-handed person, the stock protects the right ear, so the difference in hearing level of the two ears can be used as an index of gunfire hearing loss. Females have fewer problems because they tend to use smaller-caliber guns. For males, the ear differential may be greater than 15 dB. Hearing loss also can be caused by ototoxic chemicals (e.g., organic solvents, lead) and drugs.

2.2 Noise Measurement   Measuring the sound pressure level is not sufficient since the ear is more sensitive to sound at some frequencies than at others. That is, from a physiological judgment viewpoint, 80 dB at one frequency does not sound as loud as 80 dB at another frequency. The unit of loudness, the phon, equates loudness at other frequencies with the sound pressure level of a 1,000 Hz tone; thus, 60 dB at 1,000 Hz = 60 phons, and 68 dB at 100 Hz = 60 phons. See Figure 24.6. The curves show that the number of decibels to cause sounds that are equally loud varies considerably with the frequency of the sound. What makes the situation even more complicated is that the curves at various loudness levels (60, 80, 100, etc.) are not parallel.

The range of human hearing extends to approximately 20,000 Hz for children and young adults; most adults have an upper limit of less than 10,000 Hz. See Figure 24.7. The ear is most sensitive from approximately 600 to 4,800 Hz. The frequency range of telephones is about 200 to 3,600 Hz. The range of frequencies on a piano is from 27 to 4,186 Hz; "middle C," which is 2^8, is 256 Hz. The reader can simulate this frequency by singing the musical note "do." As you progress through the 8 notes—an **octave band**—of the

TABLE	24.1
Noise level examples.	

DECIBEL LEVEL, DBA	EXAMPLE
30	Quiet library, soft whisper
40	Living room, refrigerator, bedroom away from traffic
50	Light traffic, normal conversation, quiet office
60	Air conditioner at 20 ft, sewing machine
70	Vacuum cleaner, hair dryer, noisy restaurant
80	Average city traffic, garbage disposal, alarm clock at 2 ft
90	Subway, motorcycle, truck traffic, lawn mower
100	Garbage truck, chain saw, pneumatic drill
120	Rock concert in front of speakers, thunderclap
140	Gunshot blast, jet plane
180	Rocket launching pad

TABLE	24.2
Noise levels of leisure activities (Brown and Yearout, 1991).	

MEAN, DBA	ACTIVITY
90	Woodcutting, rough terrain driving
92	Motorcycling
94	Farming
95	Powerboating
96	Powered lawn equipment
98	Woodworking
101	Stock car races
110	Concerts (rock), hunting/target shooting
121	Drag races

Source: P. Brown and R. Yearout, "Impacts of Leisure Activity Noise Levels on Safety Procedures and Policy in the Industrial Environment," *Int. J. of Industrial Ergonomics,* Vol. 7, pp. 341–46. Copyright © 1991 by Elsevier Science, Amsterdam, Netherlands. Reprinted with permission.

song (from a female deer to a drop of golden sun to a name I call myself and back to "do") you have completed an octave (doubling of frequency) to 512 Hz.

Singing the notes again through a second octave will demonstrate 1,024 Hz (as well as a remarkable voice). When Figure 24.6 is used, the reader can see

---

FIGURE 24.6

Equal loudness curves (free field) for pure tones. The number of phons (loudness level of a sound) equates numerically with the sound-pressure level of a 1,000 Hz tone that sounds as loud as the sound being described. Note that not only does subjective loudness vary with frequency (curve is not horizontal) but also that the curve shapes vary with intensity (curves are not parallel). The 40-phon curve corresponds to dBA, the 70-phon to the B scale, and the 100-phon to the C scale.

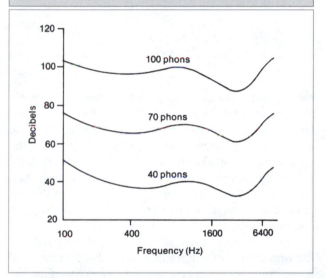

---

that the high-pitched whine of a jet engine or saw is worse than the rumble of an engine due to the ear's greater sensitivity to high-pitched noise.

As a rule of thumb, a sound will be "twice as loud" when noise increases 6 to 10 dB. Thus, eliminating one of two identical noise sources (a drop of 3 dB) will not cut "loudness" in half; subjectively, a change of 3 dB is "just noticeable"!

Loudness of a sound (in pure tones) is measured in **sones.**

$$S = 2^{(P - 40)/10}$$

where S = Loudness, sones

P = Phons

What the sones equation (which seems to be valid for nonpure tone sounds also) shows is that apparent loudness doubles only when noise increases by 10 dB (i.e., P changes by 10). A change of 3 dB is just noticeable.

How then to measure and report noise? First the instrument makers standardized measuring noise by octave band. See Table 24.3.

With an octave band analyzer, you could report to your boss that the noise level of a machine was 76 dB at 31.5 Hz, 77 dB at 63 Hz, 79 dB at 125 Hz, 83 dB at 250 Hz, 82 dB at 500 Hz, 86 dB at 1,000 Hz, 85 dB at 2,000 Hz, 82 dB at 4,000 Hz, and 77 dB at 8,000 Hz. This type of detailed analysis is quite useful when doing noise reduction work, as it enables you to pinpoint exactly where the problems are. For example, a tone at 29.2 Hz (1,750 rpm) probably indicates an electric motor (their shafts often rotate at 1,750 rpm).

For most work, however, you would be swamped in data. This led to the sound-level meter (see Figure 24.8). The sound-level meter gives just one number for noise. What it does is combine—inside the

---

FIGURE 24.7

Ear sensitivity varies with frequency and volume. The threshold of feeling (pain) is relatively independent of frequency at about 120 dB. Very low frequencies (infrasound) may affect organs of the body other than the cochlea. The brain, for example, is especially sensitive to a frequency of 7 Hz, the frequency of the brain's alpha waves. Figure courtesy of Bilsom.

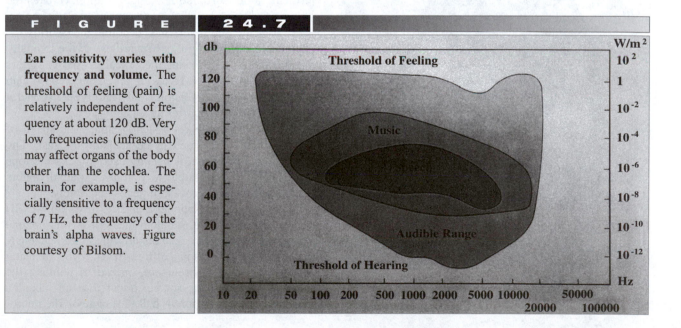

TABLE	24.3

Octave band center frequency, lower limit, upper limit, and adjustment for dBA. The octave band center frequency is the geometric mean of the lower and upper limits; the upper limit is twice the lower limit. Octave bands double in width for each successive band. White noise has a continuous frequency spectrum with equal energy/Hz over the band; thus, the energy in a band doubles in each successive band. Pink noise has a constant energy per band. The energy profile is sloped 3 dB per octave.

CENTER FREQUENCY, HZ	LOWER LIMIT, HZ	UPPER LIMIT, HZ	PHON dBA ADJUSTMENT, dB
31.5	22	44	−39
63	44	88	−26
125	88	177	−16
250	177	355	−9
500	355	710	−3
1000	710	1420	0
2000	1420	2480	1
4000	2840	5860	1
8000	5680	11,360	−1

FIGURE	24.8

Sound level meter. These meters usually use the A scale and the slow setting. When recording sound, stand with the instrument in front of you with the sound coming from the side. Point the microphone in a direction perpendicular to the noise path, keeping your body out of the path.

meter—the various frequencies. Table 24.3 shows how the meter adjusts the actual noise for each octave band. For the A setting, 39 dB are subtracted from the octave band measurement for 31.5 Hz, 26 from the measurement for 63 Hz, and so on. The adjusted band readings then are averaged and the result is displayed on the dial. The A adjustment corresponds to the 40-phon equal-loudness contour, the B to the 70-phon contour, and the C to 100-phon contour.

Some meters have a D scale that not only reduces the importance of the frequencies outside the speech range but also increases the importance within the critical 1,000 to 10,000 Hz range. It approximates the "perceived noise level" used to appraise aircraft noise. The A scale, however, has become the worldwide standard for reporting noise regardless of the intensity level. Report values using the A scale as **dBA.** Meters are available in three levels of precision: type 0 (lab standard), type 1 (precision field), and type 2 (general purpose). OSHA requires at least a type 2.

Noise is not always a steady state. The speed of response of the meter can be set slow or fast. The dBA slow setting that is usually used knocks the tops off spikes. It is possible to purchase special meters (impulse meters) to measure peaks accurately.

The American National Standards Institute (ANSI) requires use of a random-incidence microphone (responds equally to sounds arriving simultaneously from all directions, as in a diffuse field). If you are using it in a free-field environment, instead of pointing the instrument toward the source, orient it at an included angle of 70°–80°. A porous ball of sponge on the microphone will reduce wind noise. Hold the meter at arm's length to avoid sound reflections from your body.

Measured noise will be the machine noise (signal) plus the background noise. To determine the machine noise:

1. Measure noise level (L_{S+N}) with machine running.
2. Measure noise level (L_N) with the machine off.
3. Calculate the difference in the two levels. If the difference is <3 dB, the background noise is too high for an accurate measurement.

With the passage of noise legislation permitting 85 dBA for 16-h exposure, 90 dBA for 8-h exposure, 95 for 4-h, 100 for 2-h, and so on, many people wonder how long an employee is exposed to each level of noise. One way to find out would be to make an occurrence sampling study, but this tends to cost too much. Manufacturers have developed devices that record in proportion to the noise standard; that is, when noise is at 90 dB, it records at 100%, when at 95 at 200%, when at 100 at 400%, when below 85 at 0%, and so on. Then, when the **dosimeter** (see Figure 24.9) is read at the end of any period of exposure, it is known whether the person was exposed to too much noise. Some devices have a light that is activated if there is any exposure over the 115 dBA limit.

Note that noise readings, whether on a meter or a dosimeter, are a sample from a population. A single estimate is not as good as multiple observations. In addition, consider whether you wish to use the mean of the observations (i.e., protect 50%) or a value that would protect a higher percent of the population (e.g., 90%).

3 EFFECTS OF NOISE

3.1 Comfort and Annoyance

Noise reduces comfort because the workers must increase their concentration; this tends to increase fatigue. Annoyance with noise has increased over the years. There is some evidence that our environment is noisier than our parents' environment. The point to remember is that noise reduction may be required even if the costs are high and the economic and health benefits are small or negligible.

Epp and Konz (1975) made a study of annoyance and speech interference as a function of noise level for appliances; Figure 24.10 shows the results. If you measure a noise level of 80 dBA for an appliance, the vote could be predicted graphically as 3.7 where 5 = extremely annoying, 4 = quite annoying, 3 = moderately annoying, 2 = slightly annoying, and 1 = not annoying. The vote can be predicted also from the equation

$$\text{Vote} = -4.798 + .1058 \text{ dBA}$$

in which case the predicted vote would be $-4.798 + .1058 (80) = 3.7$. Speech interference in percent of words missed could be predicted from the graph as 4.7% or could be predicted from the equation

$$\% \text{ missed} = -11.17 + .1989 \text{ dBA}$$

as $-11.17 + .1989 (80) = 4.7\%$.

It should be noted that the subjects were college females, and that people with higher education levels make more complaints than those with less education. Expectations also might vary for offices, factories, stores, and so forth, rather than homes. See Table 24.4. (For appliance noise, it should be noted that some people associate noise with power, so noisy appliances may be considered good, not bad.)

Community reaction to industrial noise is highly variable. It also depends strongly on the history and background of the community. Expect more complaints from those with clout. Table 24.5 is based on the adjustments for composite noise rating curves and may give the reader an idea of some of the variables. Variability of noise generally increases annoyance.

The adjustments are independent, so if the noise is in a heavy industrial area and only during the daytime, you could (on the average) expect the same community reaction at another factory with noise level 20 dBA lower but located in a quiet suburb and making noise at night.

| F I G U R E | 2 4 . 9 |

Noise dosimeter. The latest versions can be programmed to sample noise at various times (e.g., 7 A.M. to 11:30, then 12:00 to 3:30 P.M.) and can be locked to prevent tampering. The output can be interfaced with a computer. Photograph courtesy of GenRad, Inc., Concord, MA.

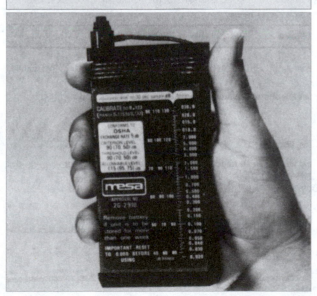

F I G U R E   24.10

Annoyance and speech interference predicted from dBA (Epp and Konz, 1975).

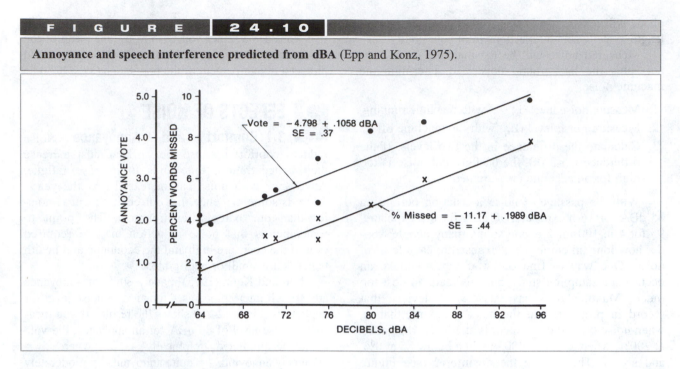

Mital and Ramakrishnan (1996) report that the federal noise limit from highway noise is 67 dBA. A noise barrier along the highway reduced noise by 5–10 dBA—more attenuation closer to the barrier. The wall should curve slightly at the top toward the road.

3.2 Performance   There is no firm evidence that productivity is lower when work is done in high-level noise (say 100 dBA) unless the person is working at maximum mental capacity (Kjellberg, 1990). For reference, conversation at 1 m with a normal voice is 55

T A B L E   24.4

Tolerable limits (dBA) in various rooms for noise continuously present from 7 A.M. to 10 P.M.

DBA	TYPE OF SPACE
28	Broadcast studio, concert hall
33	Theaters for drama (500 seats, no amplification)
35	Music rooms, schoolrooms (no amplification). Very quiet office (telephone use satisfactory), executive offices, and conference rooms for 50 people
38	Apartments, hotels
40	Homes, motion picture theaters, hospitals, churches, courtrooms, libraries
43	"Quiet" office; satisfactory for conferences at a 5 m table; normal voice 3 to 10 m; telephone use satisfactory; private or semiprivate offices, reception rooms, and small conference rooms for 20 people
45	Drafting, meeting rooms (sound amplification)
47	Retail stores
48	Satisfactory for conferences at a 2 to 2.5 m table; telephone use satisfactory; normal voice 2 to 6 m. Medium-sized offices and industrial business offices
50	Secretarial offices
55	Satisfactory for conferences at a 1 to 1.5 m table; telephone use occasionally slightly difficult; normal voice 1 to 2 m; raised voice 2 to 4 m; large engineering and drafting rooms, restaurants
63	Unsatisfactory for conferences of more than 2 or 3 people; telephone use slightly difficult; normal voice .3 to .6 m; raised voice 1 to 2 m. Secretarial areas; accounting areas, blueprint rooms
65	"Very noisy"; office environment unsatisfactory; telephone use difficult

Source: K. Kryter, *The Effects of Noise on Man,* 2d ed. (New York: Academic Press), 1985.

TABLE	24.5

Noise level adjustments attempting to predict community annoyance to noise (Goodfriend, 1973).

SITUATION	ADJUSTMENT IN dBA LEVEL, dBA
Very quiet suburban	+ 5
Suburban	0
Residential urban	− 5
Urban near some industry	− 10
Heavy industrial area	− 15
Daytime only	− 5
Nighttime	0
Continuous spectrum	0
Pure tone(s) present	+ 5
Smooth temporal character	0
Impulsive	− 5
Prior similar exposure	0
Some prior exposure	− 5
Signal present 20% of the time	− 5
5% of the time	− 10
2% of the time	− 15

to 68 dBA; in a 90-dBA environment, you must shout to be understood at 1 m. The "no loss in productivity" has an important assumption: Speech communication is not an important part of the job. Hartley, Boultwood, and Dunne (1987), in an interesting experiment, suggest that 95-dBA noise *helps* when following written instruction and *hurts* when following pictorial instructions.

3.2.1 *Speech interference* See Kryter (1985) or Sanders and McCormick (1993) if you wish to dig deeper.

The usual criterion for **speech interference** is the percent of words missed. "Words" are quite specifically defined. Single-syllable phonetically balanced words (are, bad, bar, bask, box) or two-syllable words, called spondees (airplane, armchair, backbone, bagpipe), are used.

The most refined index is noise criteria (NC) curves; articulation index (AI) is not quite as good, although it uses 20 frequency bands. **Speech interference level (SIL)** is the arithmetic mean of the dB readings in 3 octave bands centered at 500, 1,000, and 2,000 Hz. Figure 24.11 gives the SIL as a function of distance and voice level. In general, SIL is about 7 dB lower than dBA for most common noises.

FIGURE	24.11

Speech interference levels (SILs) vary with the level of the speaker's voice as well as the distance from the speaker to the ear. The figure is based on males, with average voice strengths, facing the listener, no reflecting surfaces nearby, and the spoken material not being familiar to the listener. Maximum permissible speech interference level (PSIL) = SIL + 3. The masking effect of a sound is greatest upon sounds that are close to it in frequency. At levels above 60 dB, the masking spreads to cover a wider range, mainly for frequencies above the dominating components. For U. S. telephones, telephone use is satisfactory when SIL is less than 65 dB, difficult from 65 to 80, and impossible above 80. Subtract 5 dB for calls outside a single exchange.

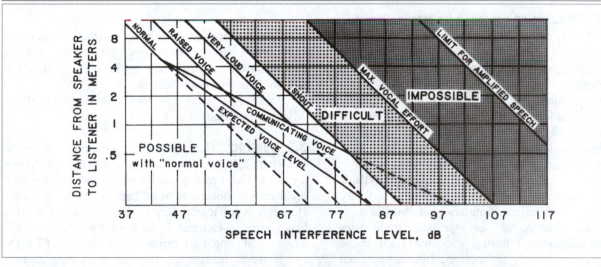

Source: A. P. G. Peterson and E. Gross, *Handbook of Noise Measurement* (Concord, MA: GenRad, Inc.), 1972.

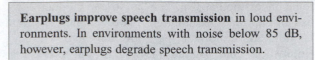

Earplugs improve speech transmission in loud environments. In environments with noise below 85 dB, however, earplugs degrade speech transmission.

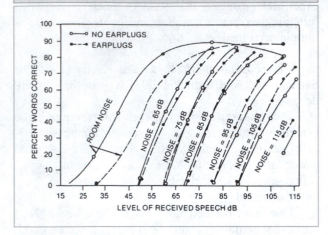

Source: K. Kryter, *The Effects of Noise on Man,* 2d ed., (New York: Academic Press), 1985.

Figure 24.12 gives speech interference at various levels of noise for earplugs and no earplugs (Kryter, 1946). Note that in high-level noise (greater than 85 dB), intelligibility is improved with earplugs or earmuffs since the ear is not overloaded and can better discriminate the signal from the noise. As an analogy, sunglasses reduce excess glare and thus improve vision.

In low-level noise, however, speech as well as noise is reduced to a level below the listener's threshold of hearing, so intelligibility is reduced. An interesting point is that speakers wearing hearing protective devices (HPD) lower their voices by 3–4 dB, which, of course, makes it more difficult for *listeners* to hear.

3.2.2 *Reduction of speech interference* In addition to reducing the noise, there are four other stages at which speech transmission can be improved: the message, the speaker, the transmission system, and the listener.

If the possible vocabulary is limited, with only certain words and sequences of words being permitted, intelligibility improves. Table 24.6 gives the international aviation alphabet as interpreted in a French pilot-training manual (David, 1974).

Intelligible talkers have longer average syllable duration, speak louder, have fewer pauses, and vary their pitch more often (Sanders and McCormick, 1993). Nontransmission of various frequencies reduces intelligibility. Filtering below 600 Hz or above 4,000 Hz has relatively little effect; filtering between 1,000 and 3,000 Hz degrades speech severely.

TABLE 24.6

International aviation alphabet as interpreted in a French pilot-training manual (David, 1974).

LETTRE A IDENTIFIER	MOT DE CODE	PRONONCIATION DU MOT DE CODE
A	Alfa	*AL* FAH
B	Bravo	*BRA* VO
C	Charlie	*TCHAH* LI (*CHAR* LI)
D	Delta	*DEL* TAH
E	Echo	*EK* O
F	Foxtrot	*FOX* TROTT
G	Golf	GOLF
H	Hotel	HO *TELL*
I	India	IN DI AH
J	Juliett	*DJOU* LI *ETT*
K	Kilo	KI LO
L	Lima	*LI* MAH
M	Mike	*MAIK*
N	November	NO *VEMM* BER
O	Oscar	*OSS* KAR
P	Papa	PAH *PAH*
Q	Quebec	KE *BEK*
R	Romeo	RO MI O
S	Sierra	SI *ER* RAH
T	Tango	*TANG* GO
U	Uniform	*YOU* NI FORM (*OU* NI FORM)
V	Victor	*VIK* TAR
W	Whiskey	*OUISS* KI
X	X-ray	*EKSS* RE
Y	Yankee	*YANG* KI
Z	Zulu	*ZOU* LOU

The listeners should have normal hearing and know the various messages they may receive. Repeating the message back to the speaker in different words is a desirable check.

Table 24.7 gives guidelines for auditory alerts. Also see Wolfman et al. (1996).

3.3 Hearing Hearing loss is an example of repetitive trauma, of cumulative strain. If your employees are not to lose hearing just because they work for your organization, noise has to be kept as low as possible. How low is sufficient? Kryter (1985) said that hearing loss begins to increase faster than it would from age alone when people are exposed to noises over 67 dBA.

However, hearing loss depends upon many factors. The following is a simplified version of the procedure

T A B L E   2 4 . 7

Auditory alerts (Cardosi and Murphy, 1995).

1. Use auditory alerts only:
   - when necessary.
   - when immediate action is required.

2. Auditory alerts should:
   - have readily apparent meaning.
   - be tested and evaluated in a realistic environment by a representative set of users.
   - be easily discernible from other signals or noise.
   - be consistently implemented throughout the system.
   - always have the same signal to indicate the same information.
   - have a visual display to back up the auditory alert.
   - be sufficient in number; they are used wherever needed.
   - terminate automatically when the problem is corrected.
   - be cancelable by the user.

3. Auditory alerts should not:
   - provide more information than necessary.
   - nag, or otherwise annoy, the user.

4. Signals should:
   - be at least 10 db above ambient noise or have been demonstrated to be sufficiently intense for a specific working environment.
   - be between 500 and 3000 Hz (so that they are well within the frequency band to which most humans are sensitive).
   - sound for at least .5 s.
   - if a repeating signal, have a pause between signals of < 3 s.
   - if a modulated signal, from 1 to 8 beeps/s.
   - if a warbling signal, vary from 1 to 3 times/s.

5. For any situation, only a few auditory alerts can be presented simultaneously.

6. The number of auditory signals (warnings, signs) that have to be identified should be less than 5.

---

given by Burns and Robinson (1970); it applies only to steady noise without any peaks at any frequency.

Given   Noise level = 85 dBA

Exposure = 250 days/yr of 8 h for 25 years

To Find   Hearing loss at 1,000 Hz for 25th percentile of population

Solution

Step		Value
1. Determine noise emission level		
A. Determine dBA for environment		85 dBA
B. Correct for *duration* of exposure, D		
D, dB = $10 \log_{10} T$		
T = Years of exposure		$D = 14$
	$85 + 14 = 99$	

C. Adjust for *gender*, G

Group	G Noise Adjustment, dB
Female	−1.5
Mixed	0
Male	+1.5

$$G = 0$$
$$99 + 0 = 99$$

D. Adjust for *frequency* at which ear will lose hearing, F

Frequency Hz	F Noise Adjustment, dB
500	−5
1,000	0
2,000	+7
4,000	+15

$$F = 0$$
$$99 + 0 = 99$$

2. Predict noise-induced permanent threshold shift *(NIPTS)* measured on audiometer, dB

A. Read value H for population median from Figure 24.13 $H = 2$ dB

B. Adjust for percentile of population, P

Percentile Losing Hearing	P Audiometric Adjustment, dB Emission at 1,000 Hz		
	85	95	105
10	+8	+9	+11
25	+4	+5	+6
50	0	0	0
75	−4	−5	−6
90	−8	−9	−11

$$P = 4$$
$$2 + 4 = 6$$

C. Adjust for age *(A)*

$A = cT^2$

c = Frequency constant = .0043

T = Years of exposure

Audiometric Frequency, Hz	c
500	.0040
1,000	.0043
2,000	.0060
4,000	.0120

$A = .0043\ (25)^2 = 3$

$6 + 3 = 9$

Predicted *NIPTS* = 9 dB

As the reader can see from the example solution of the model, the really critical adjustment is *D*, duration of exposure. Burns and Robinson (1970) said the coefficient in the equation should be 10 (the **equal energy** principle) (see Figure 24.13); summarizing more than 4,000 references, Kryter (1985) said it should be 20 for noise (the **equal pressure** principle) but 10 for recovery. A 10 means a doubling (or halving) of time changes *D* by 3 dB; a 20 changes *D* by 6 dB. Thus, Kryter would add 28 dB instead of 14 for 25 years of exposure. On the other hand, if the noise were for 4 h/day instead of 8, Kryter would subtract 6 from the 85 while Burns and Robinson would subtract only 3. The U. S. adjustment from the Occupational Safety and Health Administration (OSHA), MSHA, FRA, and DOT is 5; however, the EPA, DOD, most recent ACGIH recommendation, the OSHA 1996 draft standard, and many other countries use a 3-dBA tradeoff versus time.

Determining *P*, the percentile effect, is another problem. Kryter, to protect 75% of the population, would give *P* a value of –10 instead of –4 to –6. Burns and Robinson, in their detailed calculations of their Figure 10.17, give *P* = –6 for a noise emission level of 105 dBA and *P* = –5 at 95 dBA. This sensitivity of the ears of some of the population means that some people, if exposed for many years, start to lose hearing at some frequencies at noise levels below 70 dBA; Kryter says 67 dBA.

There still is no technique that can identify the sensitive ears before the hearing loss. A pre-employment audiogram can demonstrate whether hearing loss occurred before start of employment. Periodic audiograms also can identify sensitive ears by noting employees who have lost some hearing so they can be transferred before the hearing loss becomes too large. The decision of whether to ignore sensitive ears often depends on whose ears are going to be ignored.

The effect of gender is controversial. Some experts agree, and others don't, that noise affects females less and that women have better hearing. Some believe that reduced exposure to noise or reduced ear diseases rather than reduced susceptibility is what affects the value of *G*.

Even the value of *A* is not agreed upon. For 1,000 Hz, Burns and Robinson give *A* = 3, 5, and 9 at 45, 55, and 65 years, while the American Industrial Hygiene Association (1966) gives 3, 6, and 11 at the same ages. Part of the effect of aging (presbycusis) is poor blood circulation in the ears. Vasodilators (such as niacin and other B vitamins) are good for circulation; vasoconstrictors (such as nicotine and caffeine) hinder it.

Another problem is to define **hearing impairment.** Every definition starts with normal hearing values from the International Standards Organization (ISO) as a reference, but from there they differ. OSHA defines material impairment of hearing as a "25-dB hearing level at 1,000, 2,000, and 3,000 Hz." The meaning of this obscure but vital statement is that you have a "25 dB deductible."

The hearing loss also is not in the speech frequencies. Kryter (1973) proposed "an increase of 10 percentage points on the number of people to suffer average hearing losses of greater than 25 dB at 500, 1,000, and 2,000 Hz because of noise rather than aging."

The American Academy of Otolaryngology (1979) and the American Medical Association (1973) specify a mean loss of 25 dB at 500, 1,000, 2,000, and 3,000 Hz as "the beginning of slight impairment for the understanding of spoken English." Kryter (1985) says that if the three bands were 1,000, 2,000, and 4,000 instead of 500, 1,000, and 2,000, the NIPTS would be 10 dB higher.

FIGURE 24.13

Predicted hearing loss caused by noise can be calculated from this simplified adaptation of Burns and Robinson's (1970) Figure 10.17. Noise emission level and audiometric frequency determine the predicted noise loss for the population median.

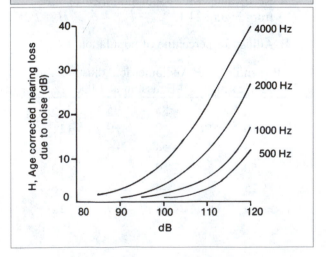

Kryter (1973) says the "slight impairment" of the AAO and AMA can be defined more precisely as "a person could understand but 90% of the sentences and 50% of the monosyllabic phonetically balanced (PB) words in the quiet, uttered at a normal conversational level of effort by a person one meter from him." However, there is considerable redundancy in everyday speech, so should we be concerned with the unexpected message?

Note that all the foregoing assumes that the noise was continuous and broadband, and important factors such as pre-exposure hearing, general health, and drug effects were not considered. However, one of the virtues of a math model is the explicit statement of the coefficients.

As you might surmise from the above, setting a legal standard for noise is not simple. The occupational standard in the United States is 90 dBA for 8 h of exposure/day with a 5-dBA tradeoff versus time during the day (the EPA uses a 3-dBA tradeoff versus time). Table 24.8 gives the resulting standard. There is no adjustment for years of exposure, G, or F. All noise below 85 dBA is assumed to have 0 effect. Beyond 115 dBA, 0 exposure is permitted. Fay (1991) summarized the effect of noise on health.

Ultrasound is noise above 10 kHz. It is very directional and only a small portion of sound will enter the ear canal unless the sound is transmitted directly toward its entrance. Because of its directionality, barriers can create a "sound shadow." For more on ultrasound, see Bruce et al. (1997). Table 24.9 gives ultrasound noise recommendations.

T A B L E	2 4 . 8

Maximum daily noise exposure in the United States. OSHA values (29 CFR 1910.95) are the legal values; the American Congress of Governmental Industrial Hygienists (ACGIH, 1993) values are recommendations. The tradeoff of exposure time vs. noise is 5 dBA for each doubling (halving) in each column. OSHA ignores noise below 85 dBA while ACGIH ignores noise below 80 dBA. Neither permits noise above 115 dBA.

| DURATION/DAY, H | NOISE, DBA | |
	OSHA	ACGIH
16	85	80
8	90	85
4	95	90
2	100	95
1	105	100
.5	110	105
.25	115	110
.125	–	115

T A B L E	2 4 . 9

Ultrasonic noise, threshold limits (American Congress of Governmental Industrial Hygienists, 1988).

1/3 OCTAVE BAND, kHz	NOISE, dB
10	80
12.5	80
16	80
20	105
25	110
31.5	115
40	115
50	115

4 NOISE REDUCTION

In offices, coworker conversation is a significant source of noise; it tends to be distracting because of its intelligibility. One possibility is to reduce the absolute level received (treating ceiling, floor, and walls with sound-absorbents). Another possibility is to reduce the signal/noise ratio by increasing the noise—to mask the signal with **masking noise.**

In some cases, noise masks a signal. Thus, masking noise can be bad as well as good. Masking-noise examples are fountains, background music, fans, air-conditioners, and fluorescent ballast hum. Firms even sell white noise generators, which make a sound like rain or static.

However, in most cases, we are interested in reducing the cumulative trauma on hearing and so will reduce noise. Bruce et al. (1997) give detailed calculation procedures for reduction of noise and vibration. Use the following sequence: (1) plan ahead, (2) modify the existing noise source, (3) modify the sound wave, and (4) use personal protection.

4.1 Plan Ahead   An ounce of prevention is worth a pound of cure. The four subcategories of the *ounce* are to substitute less noisy processes, purchase less noisy equipment, use quieter materials and construction, and separate people from equipment.

4.1.1 *Substitute less noisy processes*   Three examples of substitution are (1) reducing the use of impact tools (e.g., welding, not riveting) and chipping (by using grinding), (2) replacing internal-combustion engines with electric motors (lift trucks, lawn mowers), and (3) replacing gear transmissions with belt transmissions.

4.1.2 *Purchase less noisy equipment* Include noise levels in equipment purchase specifications. A specification must include three things: units, levels, and conditions. For example, "SPL for machines with auxiliary equipment shall not exceed 85 dBA (slow response) at the operator location when installed as specified." Ask vendors to include silencers and sound-damping devices in their quotes. Buy noise-suppression equipment (such as mufflers) from the manufacturer on the original requisition. It is much easier to get these low-cost items approved then than as a separate requisition later.

Certain types of equipment are quieter than their alternatives. Bevel gears are quieter than spur; nylon gears are quieter than metal; belt drives are quieter than gear drives; V-belt drives are quieter than toothed-type belts; reinforced rubber belts are quieter than leather or canvas belts; electric handtools are quieter than pneumatic tools; electrically operated valves and solenoids are quieter than air-powered ones. In drilling concrete, use carbide or diamond-tipped drills since star drills and air hammers create both noise and dust. Cast aluminum vibratory feeder bowls may be 15 dBA quieter than fabricated sheet metal bowls. Bearings with less clearance and higher finish make less noise.

Squirrel-cage fans are quieter than propeller fans. Properly sized fans (i.e., running at their peak efficiency) are quieter since undersize fans have high rpm whereas oversize fans have low rpm but separation of air flow over the blades. For the same capacity, large, slow fans are quieter than small, fast fans. A low-speed, multi-bladed fan is quieter than a high-speed, two-bladed fan. Thermoplastic fan blades have high inherent damping and are poor resonators and thus are quieter than metal blades. ASHRAE (2000, Chapter 42) has detailed design suggestions on how to reduce fan and duct noise for HVAC systems.

For manually operated punch presses, a pin-type clutch contributes about 70% of the total sound energy at the operator's ear; therefore, buy presses with hydraulic drives or air-actuated clutches.

4.1.3 *Use quieter materials and construction* Use quieter construction and materials to reduce impact, vibration, turbulence, and noise transmission.

Impact. Wood-block floors are easier on the feet than concrete; carpet is easier than tile; both are quieter also. (Carpet has an additional advantage over tile of lower maintenance.) Avoid metal-to-metal contact. Chutes and hoppers should be wood or plastic instead of metal; if metal is required for wear, back it up with wood. Cover the inside of chute tops with sound-absorbent material. Have products slide rather than drop onto chutes (e.g., change chute angle). When two dies register on each other, can one of the impact

surfaces be nonmetal (such as a plastic)? Line walls of tumbling barrels. Buy plastic or fiberglass tote pans. They weigh less and are quieter. Cover metal conveyor rollers with rubber, plastic, or carpet. Replace metal wheels on vehicles with tires. In kitchens, rubber mats on sinks and drainboards reduce noise and breakage.

Vibration. Figure 24.14 shows the isolation of pipes. Pipe noise also can be reduced by using bends in pipes, flexible couplings, and vibration isolators. Machine guards should be designed for noise control as well as safety. Reduce guard vibration by selection of material or shape. Encourage use of rubber or flexible plastic; discourage sheet metal and hard plastic. Encourage sheets with corrugations or holes (see Figure 24.15); discourage thin, flat sheets supported on one side. Drums make noise by vibration of the drumheads. Reduce vibration by modifying the drumhead. Figure 24.15 shows that one approach is to poke holes in the drumhead.

FIGURE 24.14

Isolation of pipes.

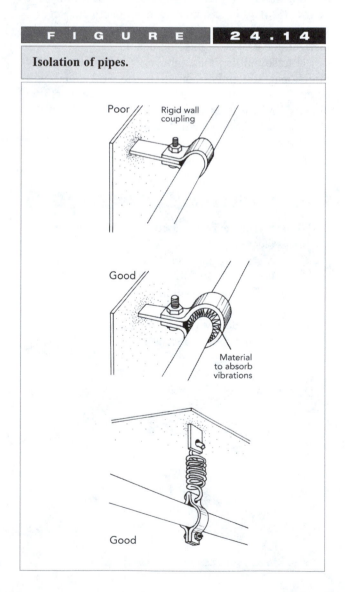

F I G U R E   24.15

Drumhead with holes. A perforated guard has less vibration and, thus, less noise than a solid one.

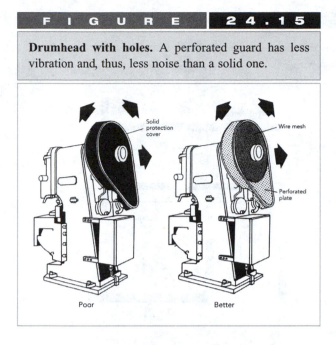

Poor   Better

F I G U R E   24.16

Add stiffeners to dampen vibration. Damping also can be done by material selection—plastic vs. metal bins. Or damping can be done by both shape and material. See the "sandwich" of the blade, rubber washer, and sheet metal.

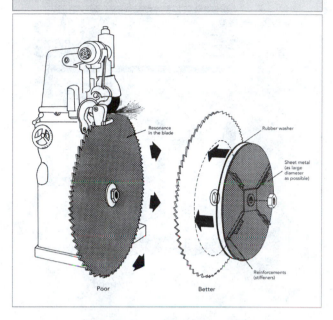

Poor   Better

Another approach is illustrated by hitting a hammer against a concrete wall and against a brass gong. This demonstrates the effect of **resonance.** Reduce resonance by damping—either by using material such as lead or sand or by stiffening the physical structure of the device (adding ribs). The ability of materials to amplify vibration (given as Q, the magnification ratio) is 1,000 for steel and aluminum, 500 for reinforced plastics, 200 for concrete, 100 for plywood, 50 for cast iron, and 10 for steel with polymer damping compound. For example, the screech of subway wheels was reduced 34 dB by adding polymer coating to the steel rim.

Adding ribs to the surface can reduce vibrations; Figure 24.16 illustrates this for saws. Flat sections of sheet metal can be backed with wood, felt, lead, or elastomers—making a "sandwich." Clamp items being machined or riveted.

Increasing the mass is another option. For example, fill the base of a machine with sand.

Turbulence. Smooth flow makes less noise than **turbulent** (non-smooth) flow, for both liquids and air. See Figure 24.17 and Section 4.2.3.

Transmission. Double doors and double walls with mineral wool or other insulation between walls reduce sound transmission and conserve heat; double windows with 100 mm (4 inches) air space do the same. Put an airlock between the office and the shop so shop noise doesn't come into the office when someone opens the door. Figure 24.18 shows how vibration transmission through the floor is reduced.

Quiet air ducts have large cross-sections to give low velocity, have several elbows, have internal insulation after elbows (before and after elbows is better),

use parallel or staggered baffles, have vibration breaks, and are not placed to produce the megaphone effect. If it is not possible to modify a duct, put a plywood baffle in front of the room air supply grille. The baffle (50% larger than the grille) should be surfaced with fiberglass on the grille side and should be placed far enough from the grille that it does not restrict air flow. When a machine cannot be totally enclosed because it is necessary to supply air (e.g., for cooling), have the passage make several right-angle bends and line the passage with acoustic material.

Arched ceilings convey sound from remote locations. One Italian cathedral has a spot worn in the marble floor. People could stand there and eavesdrop on conversations from a remote confessional.

If a workstation is lit by suspended fluorescent fixtures (see Figure 23.9), tilt the fixture so sound is directed away from the person.

4.1.4 *Separate people and noisy equipment* Mechanical equipment (e.g., pumps, boilers, fans), for heating, ventilating, and air-conditioning is inherently noisy; locate such equipment in an isolated room. Penetrations of the mechanical room by ducts, pipes, and so forth should be sealed airtight with a nonhardening sealant. The key number is 6; the **inverse square law** says 6 is the reduction in dB from a point source in a free field with each doubling of distance (provided the initial measurement is at a distance several times

Smooth flow makes less noise than turbulent flow. Smooth flow requires (1) no abrupt directional changes, (2) no abrupt volume changes, and (3) distance for turbulence to die down.

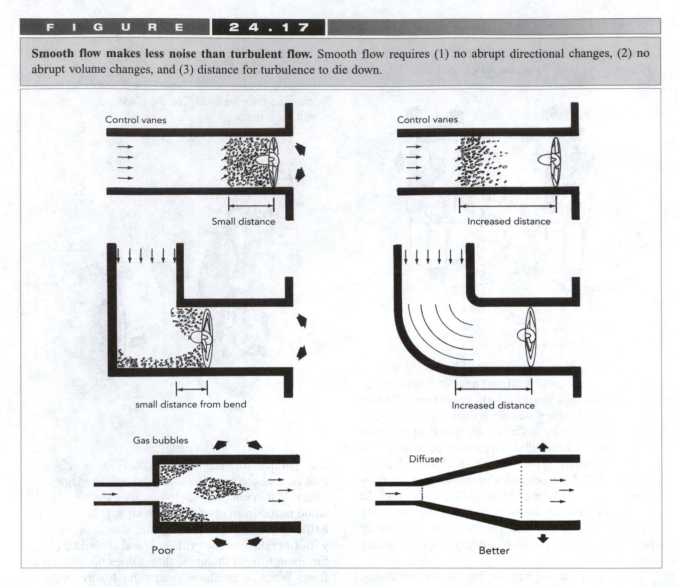

the longest dimension of the source). With absorbent material and good design, this can be increased to 8 dB or even more, even in an open-plan office.

In an open space, sound flows in all directions, so the direction factor (magnification ratio), Q, equals 1. See Figure 24.19. On a wall, sound can flow in only 1/2 of a sphere, so $Q = 2$. At a junction of two walls $Q = 4$ and in a corner $Q = 8$. Higher frequency sound waves have a high Q factor even if the source is in an open space. Therefore, don't put noisy equipment in a "megaphone" by locating it in a corner or at the end of a corridor. Supervise noisy equipment by TV rather than in person.

4.2 Modify the Noise Source

The pound of cure is more expensive than the ounce of prevention. Because of the way decibels add, always start with the loudest noise first. Three noise sources of 90, 85, and 101 dB combine to 102 dB. If the 90 dB noise is completely eliminated, the 95 and 101 still combine to

102 dB. The three ways to modify the source are to reduce the driving force, change the direction of the noise, and minimize velocity and turbulence of air.

4.2.1 *Reduce driving force* Step one is maintenance. Sharpen tools. Tighten screws and bolts. Lubricate bearings. Greasing and oiling equipment and replacing worn parts reduce noise as well as wear. Rebalancing rotating equipment reduces wear and noise and improves quality. Replace leaky compressed air valves to save air as well as reduce noise.

Use reducing valves when full shop pressure is not needed (e.g., when blowing off dirt) to improve safety as well as reduce noise. When drills, mills, and taps are under heavy load, cutting compounds reduce noise while they lubricate. A rake angle on punches lets the punch hit the work gradually, so the same energy is expended over a longer time. See Figure 24.20.

Stagger punch lengths when punching several holes at one stroke. Because of the reduced impact

F I G U R E   24.18

Machine foundations transmit vibrations and thus noise. Lighter machines can rest on various vibration isolators. Heavier machines need the slab itself to be isolated. If the ground is clay, it may be necessary to have the slab rest on pilings.

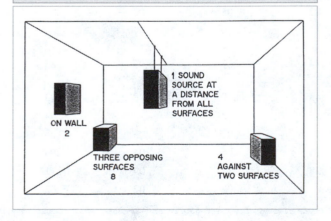

peak, noise is reduced and smaller presses can be used. The same principle works for shears. Spreading energy over a longer period also can be used to quiet diesel engines. Increase the turbulence of the fuel-air mixture (by bouncing it off the walls) so ignition occurs over a longer time; set the ignition timing to minimize peak pressures. Turn down the paging system volume at lunch.

4.2.2 *Change the direction of the noise* Since sound waves have a longer wavelength than light waves, they are not quite as directional as light. Yet (especially for high-pitched noise) turning a machine or exhaust 90

F I G U R E   24.19

Radiation of noise. Depending upon where the source is located, noise radiates to a whole sphere, to 1/8 of a sphere, or something in between. A noise source located in the room center radiates through the entire space. A source located in the corner radiates through 1/8 of a sphere; therefore, this is a good loudspeaker location

F I G U R E   24.20

Exert force over a longer time. Examples are angles on punches, staggering multiple punches, helical and bevel gears vs. spur gears, and standard vs. progressive shears.

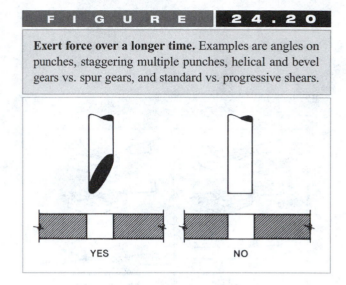

degrees often reduces noise as much as 5 dB. Gaseous jet noise is very directional. The best direction to turn it is up if no one is above the machine. The same 5-dB benefit can be obtained if the operators face the sound so the sound grazes their ears rather than hitting them from the side. Changing the hinge location on windows and doors so they open in a different direction may help.

4.2.3 *Minimize the velocity and turbulence of air* Can a vacuum hold-down (clamp) be replaced with a mechanical hold-down? It would not only reduce noise but also save compressed air (which commonly costs $.20–.30/1,000 cu ft). Avoid sonic velocities. Cutting air velocity in half can reduce dB by 15. (Dispersive mufflers work by reducing air velocity.) To air-dry objects, use a large number of low-velocity nozzles since volume, not velocity, is desired. Furnace noise has been cut by using additional burners to reduce gas flow per burner.

For air ejection, use a multiple-opening nozzle at low line pressure and place it close to the part. Since the high-velocity portion of the jet is only 2 jet diameters wide, accurate aiming of the jet permits lower velocities. Halving the distance between the jet and the part permits a 30% reduction in velocity, which will reduce noise by 8 to 10 dB. Jet exits should be designed to give laminar (not turbulent) flow.

Since many operations do not require full line pressure, use pressure regulators. (The OSHA requirement limiting air pressure for cleaning equipment to 30 psi is frequently cited for violation.) Automatic shutoffs save compressed air as well as reduce unnecessary noise; since the noise is intermittent, hearing loss is less. To make a whistle, blow across a sharp edge. On vacuum clamps, jigs, fixtures, and dies used with air ejection, streamline the sharp edges upstream of the part with fillets and chamfers. See Figure 24.21 for ways to reduce sharp edges. If you didn't plan ahead

Reduce sharp edges. Air-jet noise is increased greatly whenever the jet blows on a sharp edge. Filling in cavities or redirecting the jet can reduce noise levels as much as 7 dBA (Olivatt, 1981).

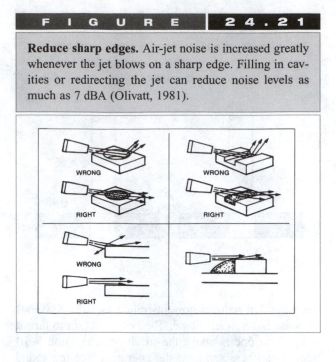

and can't reduce the noise at the source, you can try to modify the sound wave on its path to the ear.

4.3 Modify the Sound Wave
Confine and **absorb** the sound wave. Unfortunately, these are expensive procedures that often reduce dB very little.

4.3.1 *Confine* For confinement, the problem is the long wavelength. Any sound will escape even through a small opening. So, for confinement to work, enclosures must be total. Holes amounting to as little as .01% of the total area of the enclosing structure will transmit more than half the sound energy, lowering the total reduction by 3 dB. For a barrier reducing noise 40 dB, openings of .01%, .10%, 1%, and 10% reduce attenuation to 37 dB, 30 dB, 20 dB, and 10 dB. Access openings are the weak points in an enclosing structure.

The first goal is to confine and absorb before the sound gets out. Light, porous materials (fiberboards, cork, foam rubber, cloth, mineral wool) absorb sound but also transmit with little attenuation of sound. Hard, massive materials (brick, concrete) reflect and prevent transmission but absorb little (see Table 24.10 and Figure 24.22). Double-wall construction (see Figure 24.23) can help.

Transmission is less for frequencies over 1,000 Hz. The ideal is a heavy wall of brick to prevent transmission, with an inner lining of foam rubber to absorb. A compromise is a thin sheet of lead with a layer of foam. Note that not all foams are acoustical foams, so just because a foam is cheap does not mean it is a good buy. Unglazed brick absorbs 3 times as much as glazed brick; unpainted concrete block absorbs 3 to 5 times as well as painted block; a wood floor absorbs 3 to 15 times as well as concrete, while a heavy carpet

Sound absorption coefficients (α) of typical surfaces (α is the ratio of sound energy absorbed by the surface to sound energy incident). Note the effect of frequency. (Simplified from Table 37–3 of Hill, 1973.)

Material	FREQUENCY (HZ)			
	125	500	1000	4000
Brick: glazed	.01	.01	.01	.02
Brick: unglazed	.03	.03	.01	.07
Concrete block: coarse	.36	.31	.29	.25
Concrete block: painted	.10	.06	.07	.08
Floor: carpet, heavy with 40-oz pad	.02	.14	.37	.65
Floor: linoleum, rubber, or cork tile on concrete	.02	.03	.03	.02
Floor: wood	.15	.10	.07	.07
Glass fiber: mounted with impervious backing, 3 lbs/cu ft. 1 inch thick	.14	.67	.97	.85
Glass fiber: mounted with impervious backing, 3 lbs/cu ft. 3 inch thick	.43	.99	.98	.93
Glass: window	.35	.18	.12	.04
Plaster on brick or tile	.01	.02	.03	.05
Plaster on lath	.14	.06	.04	.03
Plywood paneling, 3/8 inch	.28	.17	.09	.11
Steel	.02	.02	.02	.02

FIGURE 24.22

Resonant frequency vs. material thickness. Resonant frequency depends upon both wall thickness and material. A 50-mm (2-inch) concrete wall has a resonant frequency of about 500 Hz.

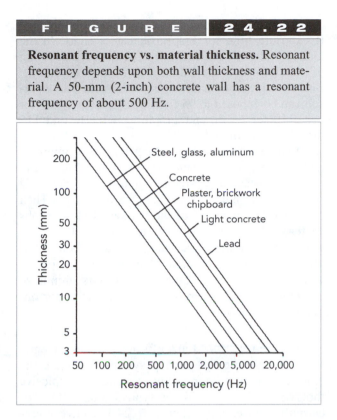

can absorb 30 times as much as concrete at some frequencies. Carpeting office walls is effective.

Complete enclosure of single-source noise such as motors and gearboxes is sometimes worthwhile but, as the noise source gets larger, the enclosure volume (and, therefore, material required and cost) increases rapidly. Temperature rises may be a problem. Treat ventilation ducts with sound-absorptive material; orient to prevent direct line of sight into the enclosure. Line the enclosure inside (not outside) with material that has an absorption coefficient of at least .7 (see Table 24.10 and Figure 24.23).

In offices, noise often is transmitted through air conditioning ducts. See Chapter 43 of ASHRAE (2000) for some duct treatments. Sound flows through small cracks, so use gaskets on doors and shafts. Total enclosure of the operator tends to be expensive because of working space requirements, door seals, provision of air for breathing, and access for maintenance.

Partial enclosure typically will reduce noise by <10 dB. It is easier to reduce high frequency noise (with its shorter, more directional waves). Noise paths from the enclosure to the outside should be convoluted; the openings should be directed away from people. As with full enclosures, have sound absorption material on the inside and sound barrier materials on the outside. A shield of auto safety glass between high-frequency noise (such as air jets) and the operator will permit seeing the task; both the noise and the operator should be close to the glass; the "acoustical shadow" should extend a meter beyond the head; a shield over the machine will reduce noise reflection from the ceiling.

Another possibility is to accept that the area is noisy but prevent the noise being transmitted to adjacent areas. For example, accept that the "shop" (Dept.

FIGURE 24.23

Double-wall construction is more effective than single. Air gaps give good transmission losses (TL). Note the penalty when the stud contacts both walls.

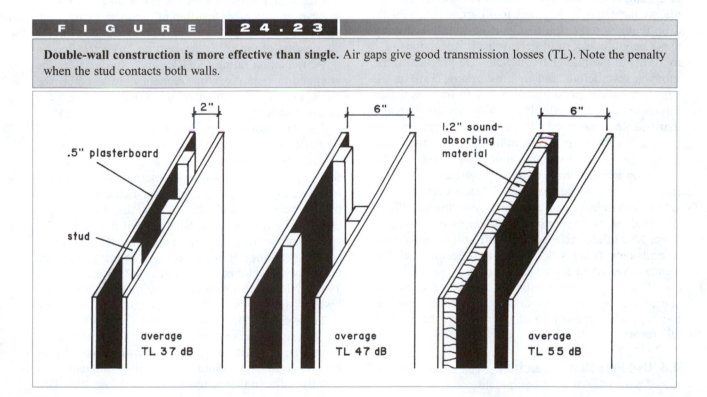

A) is noisy, but reduce noise transmission to the "office" (Dept. B) areas with insulation on common walls, airlocks with double doors, and the like.

If the sound can't be confined and absorbed directly at the source, it can be dissipated by a muffler. Muffle intakes and outlets. Use the proper design, and don't forget that mufflers wear out. Resonance mufflers are effective for specific frequencies. Be sure they are designed by an expert. Check that the operator doesn't remove the muffler. (Most motorcycle violations are due to failure to use the manufacturer's muffler.) A relatively ineffective (but cheap) shield can be created by storing work in process between the noise and the operator.

The discussion has assumed enclosing the noise and allowing the operator to be mobile. Another possibility is to create a noise refuge for the operator so that the operator supervises the equipment through a window or by TV. The enclosure need not be total. Three walls and a glass roof give some noise attenuation with minimum ventilation, lighting, and access problems.

Open-plan offices can have small (hold 1–2 people) conference rooms where people can escape office noise (rooms need a phone and an outlet for laptop computers). Cubicle partitions should be ≥62 inches high—perhaps even to the ceiling.

4.3.2 Absorb

Absorbing the sound once it is "out" (that is, the ear is between the noise source and the absorbent) by using absorbent panels on the walls or ceiling is not cost-effective. To reduce noise by 20 dB, we have to drop intensity to 1 part in 100; a 30 dB drop requires reduction to 1 part in 1,000. Achieving these magnitudes is not economical. Reductions of 7 to 10 dB in the higher frequencies are practical if the room is reverberant, but in most rooms 5 dB is the best that can be accomplished. (Note that insulation for noise generally will also insulate for temperature; that is, noise insulation should reduce energy costs!)

Put the absorbent on the walls if the minimum floor dimension is less than 4 times the room height. Carpeting a cinder block wall may be useful—especially if the wall is an outside wall and the carpet can therefore act as thermal insulation also. In classrooms and offices with multiple noise sources, soft surfaces will help until about 50% of the surfaces are soft. Flush-mounted fluorescent lamp fixtures act as sound reflectors and thus negate the effect of acoustical ceilings.

If you didn't plan ahead, couldn't modify the source, and found that modifying the sound wave was too expensive, protection of the receiver, the ear, is a last resort.

4.4 Use Personal Protection

The ear can be protected with time or with equipment.

4.4.1 Time

Higher noise levels can be tolerated if exposure time for a specific ear is short. In the United States the tradeoff is 5 dBA for each doubling of time instead of the 3 dBA used in most of Europe. Since our present maximum is 90 dBA for 8 h, a person can be exposed to 95 for 4 h, 100 for 2 h, 105 for 1 h, 110 for 1/2 h, and 115 for 1/4 h. Beyond 115 dBA is not permitted.

Reduce exposure by making the noise intermittent. For example, use automatic shutoff of tools and machines when they are not in use; this not only reduces noise but also reduces use of energy. Then minimize the exposure of the worker. Redesign jobs so that noisy areas are inspected by TV. Provide a quiet area for other work that can be done before and after work in the noisy area (blueprint reading, paperwork). Modules and quick disconnects minimize downtime as well as exposure of maintenance personnel. Consider job rotation within the day.

4.4.2 Equipment

Earmuffs and **earplugs** attempt to totally enclose the hearing system. They are the only realistic protection against gunfire and explosive tools. See Figure 24.24 for typical attenuations of earmuffs and earplugs. See Box 24.1. Active noise-cancellation headphones are commercially available for $40–$75; they are used to permit listening to music in high constant-noise environments.

In general, hearing protectors give a greater dB attenuation of higher-frequency noise. But, because many purchasers of hearing protectors don't know the frequency spectrum of the noise and don't want to have to remember 9 different numbers (1 for each of the 9 octave bands from 125 to 8,000 Hz) for attenuation of the protector, hearing protectors have a noise reduction rating (NRR), which summarizes the attenuation regardless of frequency. In general, the NRR exceeds the attenuation at the worst of the octave bands.

A laboratory comparison (Berger, 1983) showed an NRR of 8 for fiber plugs, 14 for premolded plugs, 17 for partially inserted (20% of plug in ear canal) foam plugs, and 31 for deeply inserted (100% of plug in ear canal) foam plugs; NRR for two different earmuffs were 21 and 25. When the muffs were combined with the plugs, NRR ranged from 25 to 35.

A number of studies have shown that actual noise reduction to the ear is not as good as implied by the laboratory-developed NRR values (Park and Casali, 1991). NIOSH recommends reducing the NRR rating by 25% for muffs, 50% for formable earplugs, and 70% for premolded earplugs (Franks, et al., 1994).

Rarely is the noise environment so loud that noise cannot be reduced to a safe level with personal protective equipment. Note that 15-dB attenuation is usually sufficient since most noise is below 105 dBA.

F I G U R E   2 4 . 2 4

Earmuffs tend to give more protection than earplugs. However, as with any other product, some models are better than others. The reported attenuations were from ANSI Z24.22–1957 standard. The ANSI S.19–1974 test standard uses a different test methodology and averages 5 dB less attenuation than the Z24.22–1957 test. Earmuffs can be designed to be worn with the band over the head, behind the head, or under the chin. One manufacturer reported, for its model, 2–8 dB less attenuation in the speech frequencies when behind the head and 5–8 dB less attenuation when under the chin. Wearer-molded (plastic foam) plugs probably will give attenuations in practice equal to the manufacturer's test data, but premolded plugs may give only 50% of their attenuation potential due to poor fitting by the users. Derate earplugs to about 50% of the manufacturer's NRR rating (Casali, 1992).

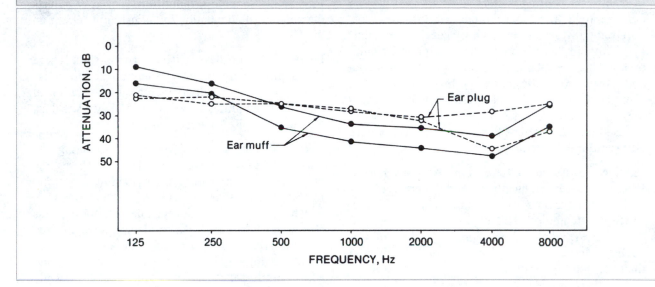

Note also that since ear protectors work best in the high-frequency range, it may be more desirable to reduce low-frequency components of the source noise if ear protectors will be worn anyway. For rockdrills, the low-frequency exhaust noise is dominated by the high-frequency piston and drill noise. It is worthwhile to reduce exhaust only if the high-frequency noise is also eliminated (e.g., by earplugs).

The problem of personal protective equipment is not bad design but, rather, bad application. Workers often are fitted with the wrong size, seals no longer seal with age, and, worst of all, workers refuse to wear the device at all due to the gradual onset of the hearing disability, and thus their lack of a feeling of danger. It is probably desirable to make wearing of hearing protection a part of the job description and a condition of employment. Emphasize to the employees that the employer is helping them; there is no need to lose the enjoyment of speech, music, and television. The most effective hearing protector is the one that is worn.

Earmuffs are advantageous in that one size fits almost everyone, and they are visible from a distance; a supervisor can tell who is wearing personal protective equipment. But they are hot and heavy, and they mess up curly locks; glasses reduce their seal, and the head is within a spring.

Earplugs should be individually fitted because ear canal sizes and shapes differ. Often the right ear is not the same size or shape as the left ear. Acceptance is increased considerably if employees can get earplugs molded to their ears or can try four or five sizes and models until they find plugs that are comfortable to their individual ears. You can hear better in noise with earplugs than without earplugs! (See Figure 24.12.) Forbid use of dry cotton wads as earplugs. Good quality earplugs are light and compact, and do not affect appearance. However, the supervisor can't tell if they are being worn, and they get lost. Reduce lost plugs by having the plugs connected with a cord. Be sure to have spares. In very high noise levels, have workers wear earmuffs over their earplugs.

Getting workers to wear earplugs is a serious problem, but some strategies to improve usage have been reported. Casali and Epps (1986) reported that noise attenuation of some earplugs tripled when revised donning instructions were given. Zohar et al. (1980) gave employees audiometric tests on two successive days. On one day employees wore hearing protection, and one day they didn't. Thus, the nurse could show specific evidence of the benefit of the protectors. Harns (1980) gave another technique. Before arriving for work, workers are asked to set their radio or tape player volume at a just-audible level and then turn it off (without changing the volume control). If, upon leaving work and turning it on, they cannot hear it, they need more hearing protection.

Reduction of noise is not a difficult problem if you plan ahead. It calls for some ingenuity and expense to modify the noise source. It requires considerable ingenuity and expense to modify the sound wave. It requires day-after-day selling, motivation, and supervision to get people to use personal protective equipment. The goal is, "Ears alive at 65!"

BOX 24.1 | *Noise Control Technology* (Casali, 1992)

Conventional hearing protective devices (HPDs) do not improve the speech/noise ratio—the most important factor for improving speech intelligibility—although they do improve speech intelligibility by lowering the total incident energy of both speech and noise. **Acoustic glare** is therefore reduced. (Sunglasses improve visual performance by reducing visual glare.)

Some modifications to the conventional passive HPDs are the following.

Passive, uniform attenuation. A conventional HPD increases attenuation with increased frequency. This "colors" the sound in a spectral sense. Uniform-attenuation HPDs have been developed that give the same attenuation, regardless of frequency. However, they give less total attenuation than conventional HPDs.

Passive, frequency-sensitive attenuation. The attenuation is reduced at low frequencies.

Passive, adjustable attenuation. The user adjusts the amount of attenuation by adjusting a setting on the HPD.

Passive, amplitude-sensitive attenuation. These HPDs provide minimum attenuation at low noise amplitudes but switch to increased attenuation at high noise amplitudes. At present, they work best for impulse noise such as gunfire.

Active. Rather than just passively accepting the noise vibrations, active noise control senses the noise vibration and cancels it by adding noise that is 180° out of phase—giving a constant pressure, which is perceived as silence. The concept depends on the much higher speed of electronics compared to the relatively slow speed of sound in air.

A microphone detects the incoming noise and adds noise to cancel it. The speech signal typically is pre-emphasized so the cancellation does not destroy the speech signal.

Review Questions

1. What is the purpose of the Eustachian tube?
2. What is the total dB change from 70 dB to 70 dB? From 70 to 75? From 70 to 90?
3. What is the noise level standard in the United States for 8 h of exposure? What is the tradeoff for each doubling or halving of time? What is the maximum permitted level?
4. How can you reduce resonance?
5. List in sequence the four major approaches to noise reduction.
6. Why should you put a rake angle on a punch? Why is a helical gear quieter than a bevel gear?
7. Why would you try to eliminate the loudest noise first? Discuss using an example of a 100-dBA and a 90-dBA noise.

References

ACGIH, *Threshold Limit Values and Biological Exposure Indices for 1988–1989.* Cincinnati: American Congress of Governmental Industrial Hygienists, 1988.

ACGIH. *1993–1994 Threshold Limit Values and Biological Exposure Limits.* Cincinnati: American Congress of Governmental Industrial Hygienists, 1993.

American Academy of Otolaryngology. Guide to the evaluation of hearing handicap. *J. of American Medical Association,* Vol. 241, 2055–59, 1979.

American Industrial Hygiene Association. *Industrial Noise Manual.* Detroit, MI: AIHA, 1966.

ASHRAE. *HVAC Applications and Equipment.* Atlanta, GA: American Society of Heating, Refrigeration and Air Conditioning Engineers, 2000.

Berger, E. Laboratory attenuation of earmuffs and earplugs both singly and in combination. *American Industrial Hygiene Association J.,* Vol. 44, No. 5, 321–29, 1983.

Brown, P. and Yearout, R. Impacts of leisure activity noise levels on safety procedures and policy in the industrial environment. *Int. J. of Ind. Ergonomics,* Vol. 7, 341–46, 1991.

Bruce, R., Bommer, A. and Moritz, C. Noise, vibration and ultrasound. In *The Occupational Environment— Its Evaluation and Control,* S. Dinardi, ed., Fairfax, VA: AIHA, 1997.

Burns, W. and Robinson, D. *Hearing and Noise in Industry.* London: Majesty's Stationery Office, 1970.

Cardosi, K. and Murphy, E. *Human Factors Checklist for the Design and Evaluation of Air Traffic Control Systems* (DOT/FFA/RD-95/3.1). Springfield, VA: National Technical Information Service, 1995.

Casali, H. Technology advances in hearing protection. *Proceedings of the Human Factors Society,* 258–62, 1992.

Casali, J. and Epps, B. Effects of user insertion/donning instructions on noise attenuation of aural insert hearing protectors. *Human Factors,* Vol. 28, No. 2, 195–210, 1986.

Clark, W. Noise exposure from leisure activities: A review. *J. Acoustical Society of America,* Vol. 90, No. 1, 175–80, July 1991.

David, H. French version of alphabet. *Ergonomics Research Society Newsletter,* March 1974.

Epp, S. and Konz, S. Appliance noise: Annoyance and speech interference. *Home Economics Research J.,* Vol. 3, No. 3, 205–208, 1975.

Fay, T. (ed.). *Noise and Health.* New York: New York Academy of Medicine, 1991.

Franks, J., Themann, C., and Sherris, C. *The NIOSH Compendium of Hearing Protection Devices* (NIOSH Pub. No. 94-130), Cincinnati, OH: NIOSH, 1994.

Goodfriend, L. Control of community noises from industrial sources. In *The Industrial Environment—Its Evaluation and Control,* Chapter 46. Washington, DC: Supt. of Documents, 1973.

Griffin, M. Occupational human vibration. Chapter 30 in *Occupational Ergonomics,* Bhattacharya, A. and McGlothlin, J. (eds.). New York: Marcel Dekker, 1996.

Harns, D. Combatting hearing loss through worker motivation. *Occupational Safety and Health,* 38–40, March 1980.

Hartley, L., Boultwood, B., and Dunne, M. Noise and verbal or spatial solutions of Rubik's cube. *Ergonomics,* Vol. 30, No. 3, 503–509, 1987.

Hayne, M., Schulze, L., and Quintana, L. Personal and car stereo volume levels: hazards of leisure listening activities. In *Advances in Occupational Ergonomics and Safety II,* B. Das and W. Karwowski (eds.). Cincinnati: IOS Press and Ohmsha, 1997.

Hill, V. Control of noise exposure. In *The Industrial Environment—Its Evaluation and Control,* Chapter 37. Washington, DC: Supt. of Documents, 1973.

Kjellberg, A. Subjective, behavioral and psychophysiological effects of noise. *Scand. J. Work Environ. Health,* Vol. 16 (suppl. 1), 29–38, 1990.

Kryter, K. Effects of ear protective devices on the intelligibility of speech in noise. *J. of Acoustic Society of America,* Vol. 18, 413–17, 1946.

Kryter, K. *The Effects of Noise on Man,* 2d ed. New York: Academic Press, 1985.

Kryter, K. Impairment to hearing from exposure to noise. *J. of Acoustic Society of America,* Vol. 53, No. 5, 1211–34, 1973.

Mital, A. and Ramakrishnan, A. An evaluation of interstate highway noise abatement efforts. In *Adv. in Occupational Ergonomics and Safety,* 671–74, 1996.

Olivatt, M. Energy conservation and noise control in pneumatic devices and systems. *Plant Engineering,* 116–18, August 6, 1981.

Park, M. and Casali, J. A controlled investigation of in-field attenuation performance of selected insert, earmuff and canal cap hearing protectors. *Human Factors,* Vol. 33, No. 6, 693–714, 1991.

Peterson, A. and Gross, E. *Handbook of Noise Measurement.* Concord, MA: GenRad, Inc., 1972.

Sanders, M. and McCormick, E. *Human Factors Engineering and Design,* 7th ed. New York: McGraw-Hill, 1993.

Tran, T., Letowski, T., and Abouchacra, K. Evaluation of acoustic beacon characteristics for navigation tasks. *Ergonomics,* Vol. 43, 6, 807–27, 2000.

Wolfman, G., Miller, D., and Volanth, A. An application of auditory alarm research in the design of warning sounds. *Proceedings of Human Factors and Ergonomics Society,* 1002–06, Santa Monica, CA: Human Factors and Ergonomics Society, 1996.

Yearout, R., Kwiatkowski, C., Lisnerski, D., Sprague, K., and Davis, S. Continuous exposure to noisy work environments does affect preferred leisure noise levels. *Int. J. of Industrial Ergonomics,* Vol. 17, 499–511, 1996.

Zohar, D., Cohen, A., and Azar, N. Promoting increased use of ear protectors in noise through information feedback. *Human Factors,* Vol. 22, No. 1, 69–79, 1980.

CLIMATE

CLIMATE

1 Air Volume and Quality

2 Comfort

3 Heat Stress

4 Cold Stress

Overview

Air volume and purity for office and shop environments are discussed. The thermal comfort zone depends primarily on dry bulb temperature and humidity; adjustments are given for some other variables. In heat stress, physiological responses can be predicted well, but performance effects are difficult to predict. Cold stress depends on air velocity as well as temperature.

Key Concepts

area/local ventilation	effective temperature (new)	percent people dissatisfied (PPD)	temperature index
Botsball temperature	evaporative heat transfer	prescriptive zone	threshold limit values (TLVs)
circadian rhythm	heat stroke	psychrometric chart	vapor pressure
clean rooms	homeostasis	radiant heat transfer	wet bulb globe temperature (WBGT)
clo	lower explosive limit (LEL)	relative humidity	
comfort zone	mean radiant temperature	setpoint	wet bulb temperature
convective heat transfer	mechanical efficiency	sick building syndrome	wind chill index
core temperature	natural wet bulb	source downwind	
dehydration	new effective temperature	static electricity	
dry bulb temperature	open loop/closed loop		

AIR VOLUME AND QUALITY

1.1 Clean (Office) Environments The volume of air required generally is proportional to the local contaminants; that is, outside air is used to dilute contaminated air. Contaminants can be defined a number of ways.

Generally, lack of oxygen is not a problem since a sedentary person (met = 1) has oxygen requirements of about .006 L/s. Assuming oxygen is 21% of the air and 25% of the air breathed is consumed, air requirements are only .12 L/s.

Carbon dioxide may be limiting. Outside air is about .03% carbon dioxide. In inspired air, carbon dioxide equals .03 + .52/V, where V = ventilation rate, L/s-person. The American Society for Heating, Refrigeration and Air Conditioning Engineers (ASHRAE, 2000) uses .25% as the maximum allowable carbon dioxide. Using CO_2 as a criterion, for a 1.0 met task, recommended V = 2.5 L/s-person since .03 + .52/2.5 = .24% carbon dioxide. For 1.5 met, V = 3.5 L/s; for 2.0 met, V = 5 L/s; for 2.5 met, V = 10 L/s.

Body odors and cigarette smoke also can be contaminants. In addition, there may be odors from the materials in the workspace and from the ventilation system itself. See Box 25.1.

ASHRAE, recognizing the health dangers and cognitive effects (Oborne, 1983) of passive smoking (breathing tobacco smoke fumes), sets higher limits for rooms where smoking is permitted; for 1.0 met, V = 10 L/s and for 1.5–2.5 met, V = 17.5 L/s.

Fanger (1988a) gives the following formula to estimate the percentage of people dissatisfied with indoor air quality:

$$PD = 395 \exp(-3.25/P^{.25})$$

where PD = Percentage of people dissatisfied

P = Perceived air pollution, decipols

For 10% dissatisfied, P = .7; for 25% dissatisfied, P = 2; for 50% dissatisfied, P = 6; and for 100% dissatisfied, P = 31. If Fanger's formula is used for ventilation requirements, ventilation volumes might be quite high as he defines 10 L/s-person of unpolluted air (and assuming no ambient odors) as P = 1.

ASHRAE (2001, Chapter 28), based on odor detection by 80% or more of visitors, recommends 8 L/s (15 cfm) of outside air/person.

Higher humidity reduces odor intensity. For minimum odor perception and irritation, keep air water vapor pressure between 10 and 15 torr. (1 torr = 1 mm Hg.)

For forced-air heating and cooling, the ventilation volume also may be determined by the room temperature. That is, to keep the temperature up in winter, warm air has to be added, and to keep the temperature down in summer, cold air has to be added.

BOX 25.1 *Odor Perception*

Professor P. O. Fanger of the Technical University of Denmark developed two units (the olf and the decipol) to quantify how humans perceive air quality. The *olf* is the pollution emission rate; it is analogous to lumen (light) and watt (noise). The *decipol* is the perceived level; it is analogous to lux (light) and decibel (noise).

One olf (from the Latin "olfactus" = olfactory sense) is the emission rate of air pollutants (bioeffluents) from a standard person (an average adult working in an office or similar nonindustrial workplace, sedentary, and in thermal comfort with a hygienic standard equivalent to 0.7 bath/day). Measurement of olf values requires a panel of judges and a measurement of the supply of outside air to the space. Fanger (1988a) estimates olf values as:

Olf Value	Source
0–5/m² of floor	Materials in office
1	Sedentary person, 1 met
5	Active person, 4 met
6	Smoker, average
11	Active person, 6 met
25	Smoker, when smoking

One decipol (from the Latin "pollutio" = pollution) is the pollution caused by 1 olf ventilated by 10 L/s of unpolluted air. That is:

1 decipol = 1 olf/10 L/s = .1 olf/L/s

In a study of 15 Copenhagen offices (Fanger, 1988b), there was an average of 138 olfs, although there was an average of only 17 people. That is, the people themselves contributed only 17/138 = 12% of the olfs. The remaining 121 olfs were from smokers (35), materials in the space (28), and the ventilation system (58). Fanger believed that the 28 olfs from materials and 58 olfs from the ventilation system were important findings, as the typical assumption is that the building is perfect and all indoor air pollution comes from people. See ASHRAE (2001) for more on odors (Chapter 13) and air contaminants (Chapter 12).

If the space is not occupied, ventilation requirements change drastically, as odors no longer are a consideration and temperatures can drift (higher in summer, lower in winter) from the thermal comfort values. Thus, since the typical office is occupied fewer than 50 of the week's 168 h, there is great potential for reduction of ventilation (and thus saving of energy) during the time the space is not occupied.

Exhaust air also can be recycled. For example, electronic precipitators are used to remove cigarette smoke and odors from the exhaust air; the purified air then is mixed with outside air to furnish supply air. The primary advantage is that the purified air does not have to be conditioned (brought to desired temperature and humidity levels).

The emphasis on energy conservation has led to relatively low ventilation rates ("tight" buildings), but sometimes this leads to **sick building syndrome** since interior pollutants and mites and fungi are not dispersed; allergic reactions may increase. Example pollutants are cigarette smoke, cleaning compounds, hydraulic elevator fluid, ozone (from copiers), and even emissions from new furniture. Carbon monoxide (from cars) can enter through supply air ducts located near busy streets or through infiltration (e.g., elevators from underground parking garages leading to the building).

Reducing the pollutants is better than increasing the ventilation, as higher ventilation costs will continue for many years. There is no evidence that plants can clean the office air (Hedge, 2000).

Box 25.2 considers a special type of "pollutant"—static electricity.

1.2 Dirty (Shop) Environments

An environment may become polluted through a local contaminant such as welding and solder fumes, solvent evaporation, smoke from ovens, and a variety of others. Here the problem is worker health rather than odors.

The first strategy should be decreasing the concentration of the airborne contaminant (containment, isolation, substitution, and change of operating procedures). Then, through administrative control, reduce worker exposure duration. Finally, consider ventilation.

A key goal is to remove pollutants from the ventilation air. The capital cost of most ventilation systems over their life is relatively small compared with the operating cost. The operating cost is twofold: (1) the direct cost of electrical power for the fan, and (2) the hidden cost of replacing the conditioned air (heated or cooled and humidified and purified to desired values) with new conditioned air. Thus, consider energy-recovery devices such as rotary wheels, fixed plates, heat coils, and runaround coils.

There are two general approaches: area ventilation and local ventilation. If the contaminant source is discrete, local ventilation usually is best.

1.2.1 Area ventilation

Area ventilation usually is used when contaminant sources are diffuse. The design rule is to keep the contaminant source between the person and the exhaust—that is, keep the **source downwind** from the person. In a multiple-source room, the air inlet and exhaust locations usually are fixed. The things that can be varied easily are (1) the orientation of the equipment relative to the exhaust and (2) the location of the equipment in the room.

| BOX | **25.2** | *Static Electricity* |

Static electricity is a voltage transient generated when materials of high electrical resistance are moved against each other (such as the human body and a synthetic fiber rug). In addition to annoyance, static electricity can interfere with electronic equipment. Solutions include:

- Raise humidity above 40%. This permits the moisture to form a film on surfaces, allowing a voltage to flow to ground. Also, the moisture is a lubricator, reducing friction between moving bodies.

- Make carpets conductive. "Total electronic capability" carpets have carbon fibers that conduct electricity. Topical treatments can be added to existing carpets but last only a couple of months and increase carpet soiling.

- Put an antistatic floor mat under the operator's chair; a cord connects the mat to ground. A typical price is $150–$200. A cheaper alternative ($30) is a desk mat, connected to ground, under a computer terminal and keyboard. Another technique, often used for electronic assembly, is to ground the operator with a static-bleed wrist strap.

- Discourage the use of nylons, slips, and polyester clothing. Cotton T-shirts and jeans or chino slacks discourage static electricity. Shoes also can have static-dissipating soles.

- Remove dust held by static electricity by blowing deionized air from an air gun.

Therefore, try to locate the workstation so the source is downwind from the operator. Try to locate the source as close to the exhaust as possible.

Some processes (usually electronic or pharmaceutical) require very clean environments; these processes can be done in **clean rooms** where the input air is specially filtered, the air-flow direction is specially controlled, and local contamination (such as from worker hair and hands) is carefully controlled. See Box 25.3. See also Chapter 26, Sections 6.1.5 and 6.1.6.

1.2.2 *Local ventilation* With **local ventilation,** the concept is direct capture of the contaminant with a duct and local exhaust. The contaminated exhaust air can be dumped into the outside air or can be filtered and recycled into the work area. Be sure that any filter system is fail-safe. That is, if the filter fails, the exhaust must not be recycled into inhabited space.

Air volume sufficient to remove explosive substances such as acetone, ethanol, or xylene usually is not sufficient to prevent health problems, as the **threshold limit values (TLVs)** are 1% to 3% of the **lower explosive limit (LEL).** For example, the LEL for acetone is 25,500 ppm while the TLV is 750 ppm. Thus, the TLV usually is limiting. See Chapter 26 for more on TLVs.

Office exhaust air often is recycled. For example, the exhaust air from the office can be part of the supply air for the paint booth or ovens.

Contaminant removal techniques include particle removal control (mechanical filters and electronic air filters) and gas and vapor removal (activated charcoal). Since dumping contaminated air out the window is not considerate of those downwind, you may as well reuse the air yourself. For more on ventilation, see ASHRAE's *HVAC Applications* (1999, Chapter 24) and ASHRAE's *Handbook of Fundamentals* (2001, Chapter 6) and George and DiNardi (1997).

2 COMFORT

Box 25.4 gives environmental standards for comfortable, hot, and cold environments.

2.1 Psychrometric Chart ASHRAE defines comfort as "that state of mind which expresses satisfaction with the thermal environment." However, specifying a comfortable environment is difficult since comfort is influenced by 7 major factors. Four are environmental (dry bulb temperature, water vapor pressure, air velocity, and radiant temperature) and two are individual (metabolic rate and clothing); the seventh is time of exposure.

The **psychrometric chart,** Figure 25.1, gives the relation between adjusted **dry bulb temperature** (mean of air temperature and radiant temperature) on the horizontal axis and water vapor pressure on the vertical axis.

BOX 25.3 *Clean Rooms*

Airborne particles can be a source of contamination to the product (electronics and pharmaceuticals). Reducing the number of particles requires controlling external and internal sources.

Provide clean air

- Make entrances an airlock (door, space, inner door).
- Use windows that cannot be opened. (Windows for a view should be separated with a corridor from the outside window.)
- Seal pipe openings and electrical outlets.
- Provide a vertical shower of air (plenum on floor).
- Maintain positive pressure in the clean room.
- Recycle the exhaust air after filtering.

Minimize contamination

Personnel

- Clean hands and face before entering the area.

- Use lotions and lanolin soap to lessen skin particle emission.
- Forbid cosmetics and skin medications.
- Forbid smoking and eating.
- Wear lint-free smocks, coveralls, gloves, and head and shoe covers.

Materials

- Clean materials and equipment before entry.
- Do not use pencils or erasers. Use nonshedding paper.
- Handle work parts with gloved hands, finger cots, tweezers, vacuum wands, and the like to reduce transfer of skin oils and particles.
- Shield and exhaust grinding, welding, and soldering operations.
- Use containers to store and transfer materials.

BOX 25.4   *Environmental Ergonomic Standards*

USA Standards   (Adapted from Ramsey, 1997 and Parsons, 2000)

Organization/number	Comment
ANSI/ASHRAE 55	Thermal environmental conditions for human occupancy.
ASTM	Thermal measurements. Skin (C1057), Medical applications (E859), Psychrometry (E334, E337), Clothing insulation (E1291)
ACGIH	TLVs for chemical substances. Also biological and physical agents.
Military	Handbook 759

ISO Standards

ISO 7243	Hot environments: WBGT index
ISO 7726	Thermal environments—measurements
ISO 7730	Moderate thermal environments; thermal comfort
ISO 7731	Auditory danger signals
ISO 7933	Hot environments—sweat rate
ISO 8995	Lighting of indoor work systems
ISO 8996	Metabolic heat production
ISO 9886	Thermal strain—physiological measurements
ISO 9920	Thermal environment—insulation of clothing
ISO 9921	Speech communication—SIL method
ISO 10551	Thermal environment—subjective scales
ISO 11079	Cold stress—clothing
ISO 11399	Visual danger signals—general requirements
ISO 11429	Danger signals—sound and light

2.2 Comfort for Standard Conditions

Figure 25.1 gives a simplified psychrometric chart (mechanical engineers use a more complicated one) that has a cross-hatched area giving the ASHRAE standard **comfort zone.**

The standards are based on studies on several thousand subjects at Kansas State University. Subjects voted their thermal sensation (TS): $TS = 1 =$ cold; $2 =$ cool; $3 =$ slightly cool; $4 =$ comfortable; $5 =$ slightly warm; $6 =$ warm; $7 =$ hot. This vote can be predicted from the following (Rohles et al., 1975):

$$TS = -1.047 + .158\, ET^*   \qquad ET^* < 20.7$$
$$TS = -4.444 + .326\, ET^*   \quad 20.7 < ET^* < 31.7$$
$$TS = 2.547 + .106\, ET^*   \qquad ET^* > 31.7$$

where TS = Thermal sensation vote for sedentary activity and .60 clo

ET^* = New effective temperature, C

It must be emphasized that you can't satisfy *all* of the people *any* of the time. For the conditions within the crosshatch, none of the 1,600 subjects voted hot (7) or cold (1) but 3% were warm (6) or cool (2); 94% were slightly warm (5), slightly cool (3), or comfortable (4); the mean vote was 4.0, and standard deviation was .7 (Rohles and Nevins, 1973). This variability occurred in spite of 3 hours of exposure, standard clothing (0.6 **clo**), and standard metabolic rate (sedentary sitting).

$$1\ \text{clo} = \frac{.155\ \text{m}^2 \times \text{C}}{\text{W}} = \frac{.18\ \text{m}^2 - \text{h} \times \text{C}}{\text{kcal}}$$

The **percent people dissatisfied (PPD)** can be calculated (Rohles et al., 1980).

PPD = Percentage of people dissatisfied (voting other than 3, 4, 5), corresponding to cumulative area from negative infinity for $CSIG$ or $HSIG$

$CSIG$ = Number of standard deviations from 50% for cold conditions ($< 25.3\ ET^*$) for sedentary activity, and .5–.6 clo

= $10.26 - .477\,(ET^*)$

$HSIG$ = Number of standard deviations from 50% for hot conditions ($> 25.3\ ET^*$) for sedentary activity and .5–.6 clo

= $-10.53 + .344\,(ET^*)$

ET^* = New effective temperature, C

FIGURE 25.1

Psychrometric charts show that a dry bulb temperature of 25°C and **vapor pressure** of 15 mm of Hg (i.e., 15 torr) identifies a specific point. Use the curve coming from the left vertical axis to read 64% **relative humidity** (23.5 torr is the maximum water vapor pressure in 25°C air; 15/23.5 = 64%). Move horizontally to the left to read dewpoint temperature of 17.5°C. Move to the left using the solid slanting lines to read psychrometric **wet bulb** of 20.2°C. Move up on the dashed line at a steep angle to read effective temperature *(ET)* of 24°C when the dashed line reaches 100% humidity. Any point along a dashed line has approximately the same skin wetness and gives approximately the same comfort. In 1971 the number attached to each dashed line was changed to be the intersection with the 50% rh line (rather than the 100% line); the line was named **"new effective temperature"** or *ET** (rather than effective temperature, which is *ET*); the weather reporters call *ET** the **temperature index.** Move down on the dashed line to read *ET** = 25.5°C. For an exact conversion between F and C, use the ERGO program or the formulas F = 9/5 (C + 32) and C = 5/9 (F − 32).

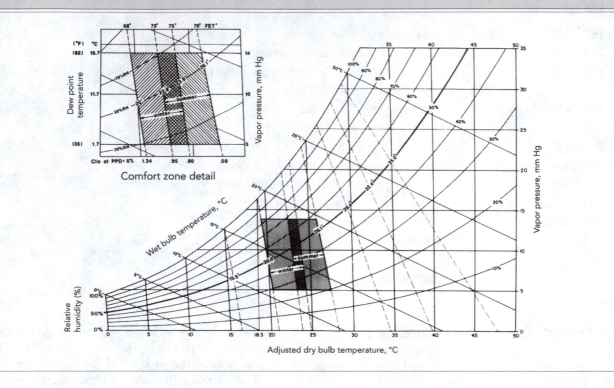

For example, for *ET** of 18° C, *CSIG* = +1.67; from a normal table, 95% are dissatisfied. For *ET** of 30°C, *HSIG* = −.21, and 42% are dissatisfied. At 25.3 *ET**, the minimum (6%) are dissatisfied.

The comfort temperature with a *PPD* of 6% and amount of clothing are related as follows:

$$ET^*6 = 29.75 - 7.27 \,(ICL)$$

where

ET^*6	=	ET^* temperature (C) at which 6% will be dissatisfied
ICL	=	Insulation value of clothing ensemble, clo $ICL < 1.1$
	=	.82 (Σ ICLI)
$ICLI$	=	Insulation values of individual clothing items, clo (see Table 25.1)

For example, 6% will be dissatisfied with .8 clo at 23.9 and with .95 clo at 22.8°C.

The standard (parallelogram) is valid for persons dressed with 0.5 to 0.7 clo and a metabolic rate of "sedentary sitting." The assumption is that people will wear more clothing in the winter than the summer. That is, clothing worn inside is affected by outside weather. Table 25.1 gives the clo values for various garments. Figure 25.2 shows various clothing factors.

Engineers should remember that sweating to remove heat is not considered "comfortable." That is, a wet skin is not acceptable for comfort. (Ingredients in old ink recipes include salt as mold-retardant and a few drops of brandy as antifreeze—a reminder of the days when climate control was crude.)

Fanger (1973a) reported, for air temperature over 10°C, that during comfort:

$$TSKIN = 35.7 - .0276\,M$$
$$\text{and } ESWEAT = .42\,(M - 58)$$

T A B L E	2 5 . 1	

Garment insulation values *(ICLI)*. Ensemble clothing, $I_{CL} = \Sigma$ *(ICLI)*. Thin garments are made of light fabrics worn in the summer; thick garments are made of heavy fabrics worn in the winter. To account for additional heat loss due to clothing ventilation caused by body movements, decrease I_{CL} by 10% for metabolic rates up to 100 W/m^2 and by 20% for metabolic rates over 100 W/m^2 (ISO/TR 11079).

ICLI, clo	GARMENT DESCRIPTION		*ICLI*, clo	GARMENT DESCRIPTION
Underwear			**Dresses and skirts (knee length)**	
.01	Bra		.14	Skirt, thin
.03	Panties		.23	Skirt, thick
.04	Men's briefs		.23	Thin, sleeveless, scoop neck
.08	T-shirt		.27	Thick, sleeveless, scoop neck (jumper)
.14	Half-slip		.29	Shirtdress, thin, short-sleeve
.15	Long underwear—bottoms		.33	Shirtdress, thin, long-sleeve
.16	Full slip		.47	Shirtdress, thick, long-sleeve
.20	Long underwear—top		**Sweaters**	
Footwear			.13	Vest, thin, sleeveless
.02	Socks, ankle-length athletic		.22	Vest, thick, sleeveless
.02	Pantyhose		.25	Thin, long-sleeve
.02	Sandals, thongs		.36	Thick, long-sleeve
.03	Slippers, quilted, pile-lined		**Suit jackets and vests (lined)**	
.03	Socks, calf-length		.10	Vest, thin, sleeveless
.06	Socks, knee-length (thick)		.17	Vest, thick, sleeveless
.10	Boots		.36	Single-breasted, thin
Shirts and blouses			.42	Double-breasted, thin
.12	Blouse, sleeveless, scoop-neck		.44	Single-breasted, thick
.17	Shirt, sport, knit, short-sleeve		.48	Double-breasted, thick
.19	Shirt, dress, short-sleeve		**Sleepwear and robes**	
.25	Shirt, dress, long-sleeve		.18	Gown, thin, short, sleeveless
.34	Shirt, sweat, long-sleeve		.20	Gown, thick, long, sleeveless
.34	Shirt, flannel, long-sleeve		.31	Gown, hospital, short-sleeve
Trousers and coveralls			.34	Robe, thin, short, short-sleeve
.06	Shorts, short		.42	Pajamas, thin, short-sleeve
.08	Shorts, walking		.46	Gown, thick, long, long-sleeve
.15	Trousers, thin, straight		.48	Robe, thick, short wrap, long-sleeve
.24	Trousers, thick, straight		.57	Pajamas, thick, long-sleeve
.28	Sweatpants		.69	Robe, thick, long wrap, long-sleeve
.30	Overalls			
.49	Coveralls			

Source: ASHRAE, "Physiological Principles and Thermal Comfort" in *Handbook of Fundamentals*, R. A. Parsons (ed.). Copyright (c) 2001 by American Society of Heating, Refrigeration and Air Conditioning Engineers. Used with permission.

where $TSKIN$ = Mean skin temperature, C

M = Metabolic rate, W/m^2

$ESWEAT$ = Evaporative sweating rate, W/m^2

2.3 Adjustments for Nonstandard Conditions

Nevins and Gorton (1974) and Fanger (1973b) gave the following recommendations for adjustments to achieve comfort.

2.3.1 Clothing Nevins (1975) said dry bulb temperature (DBT) decreases .6° C for every .1 clo increase. Nevins and Gorton (1974) said DBT decreases .6° C for every .1 clo increase from .6 clo when total metabolism is less than 225 W but DBT decreases 1.2° C/.1 for over 225 W.

2.3.2 Activity For each 30 W increase in total metabolism above 115 W, decrease *DBT* by 1.7° C.

Clo values for industrial clothing ensembles. I_{CL} = intrinsic clothing insulation, clo. Insulation total, I_T = I_{CL} + insulation of air layer above clothing. F_{CL} = clothing area factor. I_M = permeability index (0 = totally impermeable; 1 = totally permeable).

Shirt 111
Leno Weave
152.6 G/M²
65% Polyester
35% Cotton
Durable Press
Soil Release

Pants 207
Twill Weave
254.3 G/M²
65% Polyester
35% Cotton
Durable Press

Underwear   Shoes
Socks   Belt

I_T = 1.16 I_M = 0.39
F_{CL} = 1.20 I_M/I_T = 0.34
I_{CL} = 0.57

Coverall 313
Twill Weave
230.6 G/M²
100% SEF Modacrylic
Anti-Static
Acid Resistant

T-Shirt
Underwear
Socks
Shoes

I_T = 1.41 I_M = 0.39
F_{CL} = 1.25 I_M/I_T = 0.28
I_{CL} = 0.84

Shirt 104
Twill Weave
447.6 G/M²
100% Cotton
Flame Retardant

Pants 204
Twill Weave
451.0 G/M²
100% Cotton
Flame Retardant

Underwear   Shoes
T-Shirt   Belt
Socks

I_T = 1.51 I_M = 0.32
F_{CL} = 1.39 I_M/I_T = 0.21
I_{CL} = 1.00

To permit sweat evaporation, keep relative humidity below 60% (15 torr).

2.3.3 *Air velocity* There is a 4–8 mm thick boundary layer that moves upward over a person's body at about .2 m/s. Higher velocities whirl the layer, breaking through it, and enforce local heat convection. Not only air velocity but air turbulence (variation about the mean) is also important as the peaks can cause discomfort. Thus, to minimize drafts, use laminar (non-turbulent) air flow. The most sensitive area on the body is the uncovered arms and the neck. For seated office-type work, Griefahn et al. (2000) recommend a maximum mean air velocity with a turbulence (coefficient of variation) of less than 30%.

The air can come from the front, rear, side, above, or below. Airflow from above interferes with the heat rising from the body, causing turbulence; air from below gives a more laminar flow. For heating, bring warm air in at the bottom of people, as they will be comfortable at a lower air temperature; for cooling, bring in air from above as they will be comfortable at a higher air temperature.

For spot cooling of workplaces, 0.5 to 1.0 m/s are common for intermittent exposure and high work rates; 5 m/s to 10 m/s is a maximum. Using a box fan (i.e., turbulent flow), Rosen (1982) found that .1 m/s offsets a .3°C increase in air temperature. Nevins (1975) reported that a .1 m/s increase in air velocity (up to .6 m/s) increases DBT by .3°C; for velocities from .6 to 1.0 m/s, a .1 m/s increases DBT by .15°C. For more on evaporative heat transfer, see Section 3.3.6.

2.3.4 *Mean radiant temperature (MRT)* MRT is the average radiant temperature coming from all directions; it depends on the shape presented to each direction. For each 1°C deviation of *MRT* from dry bulb temperature, change the *DBT* 1°C in the opposite direction. For example, 25°C is a comfortable *DBT* when *MRT* also equals 25. But if *MRT* equals 27, then *DBT* should be 23.

2.3.5 *Time of exposure* The standard values are based on the vote after 3 h of exposure. Males voted .5 vote warmer and females .2 warmer at the end of the first hour than they did after 3 h. At present, it is recommended that you use the 3-h values and not compensate for actual occupancy time.

2.3.6 *Time of day* Even though core temperature is on a 24-h cycle, thermal comfort conditions do not differ with time of day (Fanger et al., 1974).

2.3.7 *Season of year* To most people's surprise, comfort temperature does not vary with season of the year even for different ethnic groups—if clothing and metabolic rate are standardized. Fanger (1973b) found that Nigerians who had just arrived by jet in Copenhagen had the same comfort temperatures as Danes, Danes who swam in the sea in winter, Danes in cold meat packing jobs, and Americans.

Humidity control becomes a problem in winter. Vapor pressures above 12 torr may cause condensation problems and affect the glue from boxes in the warehouse. A vapor pressure of 7 torr can still fit within the comfort zone. Cold outside air could have an 80% relative humidity but still have only 7 torr.

When warmed air with the low vapor pressure passes a nose or respiratory tract (with moisture at about 45 torr), the 38 torr driving force transfers water from the person to the air. The person gets a sore throat although the room temperature is comfortable. Green (1974) found, for indoor climates in the winter, that colds and upper respiratory infections increase as humidity drops below 50% (about 12 torr). In general, for comfort, .1 torr is equivalent to .10 CDB.

2.3.8 *Gender of occupant* If men and women have the same clothing insulation values, they have the same comfort temperature. Women's skin temperature at comfort is about 0.2°C lower, and their evaporative loss during comfort is about 4 g/m^2–h less; these characteristics balance women's lower basal metabolic rate (Fanger, 1972). Table 25.1 shows that women tend to wear clothing with lower clo values.

2.3.9 *Age of occupant* If the occupants have the same clothing insulation values and the same metabolic rates, they have the same comfort temperature. However, since activity level tends to decline with age, older people usually prefer warmer rooms than younger people do.

The decline in basal metabolic rate with age seems to be compensated for by a lower evaporative loss during comfort (19 g/m^2–h at age 23; 15 at 68; and 12 at 84) (Fanger, 1973b).

2.4 Individual Adjustment The conventional approach to comfort in the office is to set the conditions so they result in the comfort zone of Figure 25.1. But this assumes that everyone is the same: they wear the same clothes, have the same metabolic rate, and so on. A recent concept is to allow each individual to set their own environmental conditions through "desktop controls" of temperature, lighting, and airflow. Some units even have white noise generators. There is an occupancy sensor, which turns off the fan, local lighting, and equipment after 15 min of nonoccupancy. In addition to allowing individuals to fine-tune their environmental comfort, the energy savings typically have a payback of 6 months.

3 HEAT STRESS

3.1 Criteria of Stress In the previous section, comfort was the criterion. For more extreme environments the problem becomes the effect on performance (both physical and mental) and on health.

The most serious of heat-induced illnesses is **heat stroke,** which has the potential to be life-threatening or result in irreversible damage. Other heat-induced illnesses include heat exhaustion, heat cramps, and heat disorders (dehydration, rashes). If, during the first trimester of pregnancy, a female worker's core temperature exceeds 39°C for extended periods, there is a risk of fetus malformation. In addition, core temperatures above 38°C may cause temporary infertility in males and females alike (ACGIH, 1993).

Wyndham and Strydom (1965) gave Figure 25.3 as the temperature–time tradeoff for physical work (8.7 W/kg). Wing and Touchstone (1963) compiled a 162-reference bibliography on the effects of temperature on human performance. Wing (1965), summarizing 15 different studies of sedentary work in heat, gave Figure 25.4 as the temperature–time tradeoff for mental performance. He noted that human performance deteriorates well before physiological limits have been reached. Hancock and Vercruyssen (1988) show the effect of heat on different tasks in Figure 25.5. When people exercise, equilibrium body temperature rises (see Figure 25.6) and the exercise equilibrium body temperature may become the floor level from which the changes described in Figure 25.5 occur. In the zone of thermal equilibration, body temperature of sedentary workers (seated with metabolic rate up to 180 kcal/h) will not rise and performance will not be affected by heat. In the inertial interval, the body temperature will rise (and performance will drop) as the body heats up. The dashed lines indicate combinations of time and environmental temperature, which will give a constant rise in body temperature. The physiological tolerance limit implies a 1.7°C rise in core temperature above a resting threshold for a sedentary worker. Hancock (1981) reported breakdowns in dual task performance with a deep body temperature rise of .2°C, psychomotor performance with a rise of .9°C, and mental performance with a rise of 1.3°C. Ramsey (1995) reports that perceptual motor tasks show an onset of performance decrements when the environment is in the 30°C to 33°C *WBGT* range; mental tasks and simple tasks show little effect of heat.

A difficulty in using performance criteria from short-run situations (such as experiments) is that motivation seems to increase during experimental stress situations. Performance is *higher* in a heat-stress environment than in comfortable conditions. Meese et al. (1984) studied approximately 1,000 people working for

Temperature–time tradeoff for physical work. Physical work (shoveling) was reduced as temperature increased; however, the decline was less with higher air velocity; 100% was at 27.2°C WB (Wyndham and Strydom, 1965).

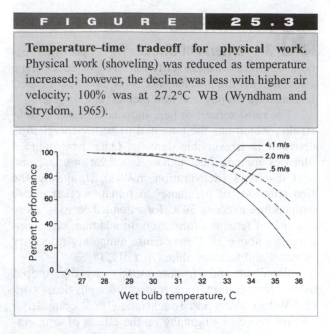

Sedentary worker performance is divided into three zones (Hancock and Vercruyssen, 1988).

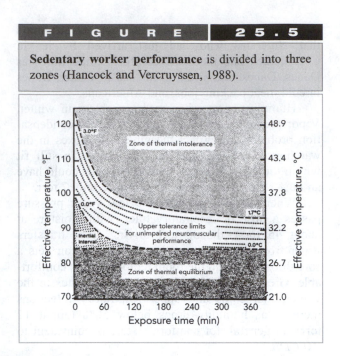

a day and found that performance improved up to 32°C, even though comfort decreased. It can't be entirely coincidence that all the developed countries are in the temperate zone, not the tropics. Ramsey et al. (1983) report that experimental evidence of 17,000 observations shows safe working behavior is best when

Summary of sedentary mental performance in 15 studies (Wing 1965). The curves give the upper limit. Above the curve some performance decrement should be expected. Grether (1973), ignoring exposure time, gives 35°C ET* (29.5 ET) as the point at which performance begins to deteriorate.

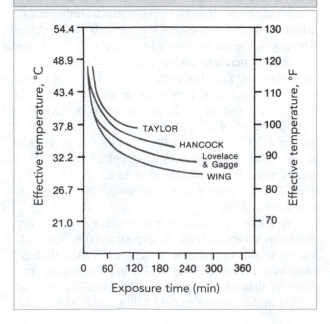

at comfort conditions. Therefore, design using comfort as the criterion, realizing that motivated people can work in hot environments but the ordinary worker in a hot environment will work at a low efficiency.

For health, increase in heart rate or systolic blood pressure could be the criterion. During physical exercise in the heat, the effect of heat is reflected in increased skin blood flow up to about 7 times basal skin blood flow. Pirnay, Petit, and Deroanne (1969) reported that the heart rate increases 32 beats/min for every °C increase in body temperature.

For a single criterion, most experts recommend maximum body **core temperature** as the best. The National Institute for Occupational Safety and Health (NIOSH) set 38°C as the maximum core temperature. Core temperature usually is measured as rectal temperature, although ear canal and esophageal temperature also are used. Rectal temperature = brain temperature = liver temperature = right heart atrium + .6 C = esophageal + .6 C = mouth + .4 C. Rectal temperature represents the temperature of 20% of body mass, while esophageal represents the temperature of 80% of the body (Minard and Copman, 1963).

Based on extensive experimental evidence (Konz et al., 1980; Konz et al., 1983), we recommend using multiple criteria rather than just body temperature i.e., body temperature, heart rate, and also subjective feelings of illness or faintness.

3.2 Environmental Limits   To set limits, there are two possible strategies: (1) measuring physiological responses during work and (2) predicting the stress on average people beforehand based on predicted environments and tasks.

Body temperatures as a function of exercise. Rectal temperature remains constant at lower environmental temperatures. In this nonstress zone, rectal temperature = 37.0 − .0038 (metabolic rate, W) (Berenson and Robertson, 1973). Nielsen (1938) made the original discovery that rectal temperature varies with metabolic rate in the nonstressed zone. However, as environmental temperature rises, eventually body temperature also begins to rise due to the environment. This environmentally driven zone, beginning about 26–29° C ET, is called the **prescriptive zone.**

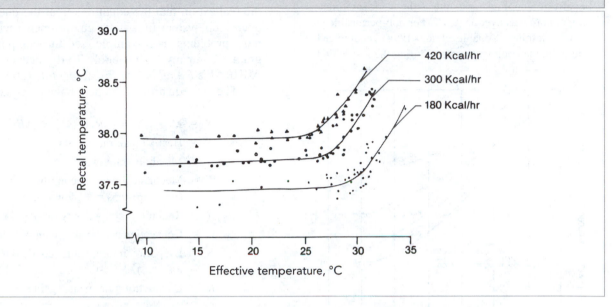

There are now personal monitors that monitor heart rate and body temperature and beep when the criteria levels are exceeded. Stay time at work was 50% to 100% longer when wearing the monitor over standardized prediction times (O'Brian, et al., 1996; Cohen, 1988).

For standardized predictions, Lind (1963) presented the critical concept of the prescriptive zone (see Figure 25.6). At lower environmental temperatures the body remains in thermal equilibrium, although the set point temperature is higher for higher metabolic rates. The point at which rectal temperature begins to rise is a function of metabolic rate as well as the environment. In addition, at higher metabolic rates there is little margin before rectal temperature reaches 38°C. Nielsen (1994) says people are exhausted (unable to continue) when their core temperature is 40°C.

Wyndham and Strydom (1965) remark that under compulsion (e.g., military training), heat stroke may occur at 28.5°C ET, whereas industrial workmen in Australian mines have worked without heat stroke at 32°C ET since they slow down in the heat.

NIOSH took Lind's concept and the idea that a small amount of heat storage is not harmful (i.e., as long as core temperature is below 38°C) to get the values given in Figure 25.7, which shows threshold limit values for heat. ACGIH (1993) recommends the following adjustments: 0°C for summer work uniform (.6 clo), −2°C for cotton coveralls (1.0 clo), −4°C for win-

ter work uniform (1.4 clo), and −6°C for water barrier, permeable (1.2 clo); also −2.5°C for unacclimatized workers. The values protect 95% of the workforce; it was assumed that the 5% of heat-intolerant individuals would not be working on hot jobs. It is essential to note that these are not heat *limits;* these are values at which precautions (provision of adequate drinking water, annual physical examinations, training in emergency aid for heat stroke) should begin to be taken.

The recommendations are expressed in a specific index called **wet bulb globe temperature (WBGT),** which attempts to combine into one number the effect of dry bulb temperature *(DBT),* water vapor pressure, air velocity, and radiant temperature. *WBGT* "probably exaggerates the danger of heat stress in medium and low-humidity environments" (Gagge and Nishi, 1976).

For an environment in which radiant temperature is close to air temperature, indoors or outdoors, with no solar load:

$$WBGT = .7\,NWB + .3\,GT$$

For an environment in which radiant temperature is not close to air temperature, outdoors with solar load:

$$WBGT = .7\,NWB + .2\,GT + .1\,DBT$$

where *WBGT* = Wet bulb globe temperature

    NWB = **Natural wet bulb** temperature (temperature of a sensor with a wet wick

Threshold limit values for heat (ASHRAE, 1999, Chapter 28) for heat-acclimatized people. The rest area is assumed to have the same *WBGT* as the work area. If the rest area *WBGT* is below 24°C (75°F), reduce resting time by 25%. Konz et al. (1983), however, found no benefit of a cool rest area unless the work environment temperature was over 35°C *ET.* For non-permeable protective clothing, Conable et al. (1994) recommended microclimate cooling garments during the rest period.

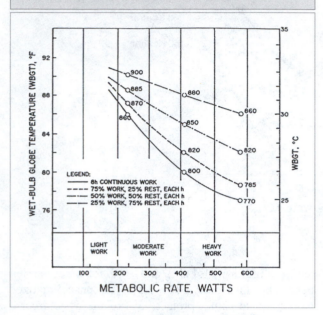

Source: From *ASHRAE. HVAC Applications.* Copyright © 1999 American Society of Heating, Refrigeration and Air Conditioning, Atlanta. Used by permission.

exposed to natural air currents). Don't confuse it with *WB,* **wet bulb temperature,** also called psychrometric wet bulb, which is the temperature of a sensor with a wet wick exposed to high (3 m/s) air velocities. $WB = NWB$ for air velocity > 2.5 m/s; for $.15 < V < 2.5$, $NWB = .1 \, DBT + .9 \, WB$ (Gagge and Nishi, 1976).

GT = Globe temperature (temperature at the center of a 15-cm diameter black sphere)

DBT = Dry bulb temperature (sensor shielded from radiation)

Rather than measuring *WBGT* directly with the expensive and cumbersome *WBGT* apparatus, many people use the inexpensive and simple Botsball device. Then either the **Botsball temperature** can be used directly or the *WBGT* temperature calculated. A good conversion equation ($r^2 = .90$) (Beshir, 1981) is:

$WBGT, C = 0.80 + 1.07$ (Botsball Temp., °C)

3.3 Reduction of Heat Stress Box 25.5 discusses homeostasis and control systems.

Solutions for various environments are complex due to the many feedback loops, but solutions can be found by computer simulation (Haslam and Parsons, 1994). For the person concerned with reducing heat stress, examination of the heat storage equation (with the realization that the equations treat the body as an open-loop system in a static environment) will solve most problems. For example, see the computer program accompanying this book. To dig deeper, consult ASHRAE's *Handbook of Fundamentals* (2001).

The key equation is the heat balance equation:

$$S = M - (\pm W) + (\pm R) + (\pm C) + (\pm E) + (\pm K)$$

where S = Heat storage rate, watts

M = Metabolic rate, watts

W = Mechanical work accomplished rate, watts (walk up steps = +; down = −)

R = Radiation rate, watts (gain = +; loss = −)

C = Convection rate, watts (gain = +; loss = −)

E = Evaporation rate, watts (condensation = +; loss = −)

K = Conduction rate, watts (gain = +; loss = −)

3.3.1 *Storage* Human body heat storage is:

$$S = 1.15 \, m \, C_p \, (MBT_f - MBT_i)/t$$

where S = Storage gain (+) or loss (−), watts

m = Weight of body, kg

C_p = Specific heat of body = .83 kcal-kg/C

MBT_i = Initial mean body temperature, C

MBT_f = Final mean body temperature, C

t = Time, h

Mean body temperature is calculated by weighing skin temperature and core temperature—usually with coefficients of .33 and .67, although in the heat, some experts recommend .3 and .7 and others .2 and .8 as the skin "shell" becomes thinner.

MBT = .33 (skin temperature)

 + .67 (core temperature)

3.3.2 *Metabolism* Reducing metabolic rate can be done by mechanization or by working more slowly. Since working more slowly usually reduces productivity, look for other alternatives first.

3.3.3 *Work* When the body accomplishes mechanical work such as walking stairs or pedaling a bicycle, this energy must be subtracted from M to determine the net heat within the body core. The ratio of W/M is the **mechanical efficiency** of the

BOX **25.5** | *Homeostasis*

Interior human body temperature is maintained at a constant value even though the environment varies. This is called **homeostasis.** (In Greek, *homoios* = similar and *stasis* = position, standing.) Other variables (blood sugar, water balance) also are maintained in homeostasis.

However, the body really does not maintain these values at a fixed point, the **setpoint.** There is a biological rhythm. Figure 21.3 shows the biological rhythm for body temperature. Since it is a 24-h rhythm, it is called a **circadian** (*circa die* in Latin) **rhythm.** Menstrual cycles are an example of a lunar rhythm. Although the moon's cycle is a precise 29.5 days, menstrual cycles are not so precise.

In addition, the setpoint for body temperature can change due to exercise.

Control systems can be **open loop** or **closed loop.** For a mechanical example, a traffic light controlled by a timer is an open-loop system. A traffic light controlled by a magnetic presence sensor in the pavement (feeding back the presence of a vehicle) is a closed-loop system.

Figure 25.8 depicts the human thermoregulatory system—a closed-loop system. The schematic has two portions: the controlling system (regulator) and the controlled system (regulated system). Body temperature is fed back to the comparator (anterior hypothalamus for heat and posterior hypothalamus for cold), where it is compared with the reference setpoint (around 37°C). The difference (error) triggers release of hormones, which actuate one or more of three controllers (muscles, sweat glands, blood vessels). Muscle activity adds heat; sweat gland activity increases heat loss; blood vessel vasodilation or vasoconstriction fine-tunes convective heat loss from the skin. The resulting body temperature is fed back to the comparator, where the cycle repeats. External events (metabolic work or change in environmental conditions) act as disturbances.

Since the system attempts to reduce the error, it is called a negative feedback system. The response (e.g., sweat) is proportional to the error (more sweat when you are hotter). Most mechanical systems use a discrete response. For example, a furnace turns on when you need heat but does not run at different levels of heat. It just runs for a longer or shorter time.

F I G U R E | **25.8**

Human thermoregulatory system. This closed-loop system can be divided into the controlling system and the controlled system (body temperature). Many of the problems associated with setting work limits in hot environments are due to using open-loop equations rather than closed-loop equations with individual variation in equation coefficients.

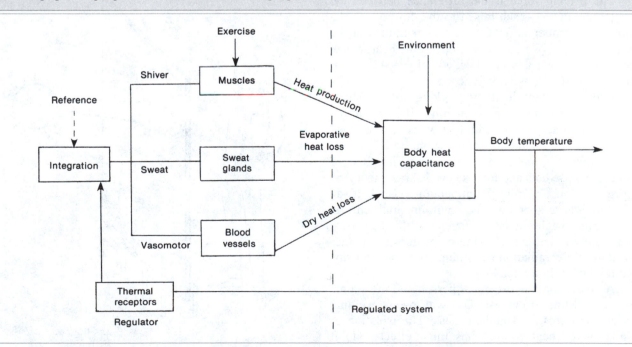

body when performing work. It is about .2 for pedaling and .06 for repetitive lifting, and is considered 0 for most activities.

3.3.4 *Radiation* Radiant heat transfer is:

$$R = \sigma A f_{eff} f_{cir} F_{cir} e(T^4_{mrt} - T^4_{skin})$$

where R = Radiant gain (+) or loss (−), watts

σ = Stefan-Boltzmann constant

= 5.67×10^{-8} watts/(m^2 – K^4)

A = Skin surface area, m^2 (see Chapter 5)

f_{eff} = Effective skin radiation area factor (.725 for standing, .696 for sitting) (Fanger et al., 1970)

f_{cir} = Increase in radiant area due to clothing

= $1 + .155 I_{clo}$

I_{clo} = Insulation value of clothing, clo (see Table 25.1)

F_{cir} = Multiplier to radiant heat transfer coefficient to adjust for clothing barrier

= $1/(1 + .155 (5.2) I_{clo})$ where 5.2 W/(m^2 – C) is the reference radiant heat transfer coefficient

e = Emissivity (nonvisible radiation: .95 for skin, clothing; visible radiation: .8 for black skin and dark clothing, .65 for pastel clothing, .6 for white skin, .5 for white clothing)

T_{skin} = Temperature in K of the skin, K = C + 273

T_{mrt} = Mean radiant temperature in K of environment, K = C + 273

The driving force is the difference between the two temperatures—each raised to the 4th power. The important number is 35°C—skin temperature in the heat. For T_{mrt} above 35°C, the body gains heat; below 35°C, it loses. For a typical task with T_{mrt} = 43°C, R = 60 watts; with T_{mrt} = 37.8°C, R = 5.

Reduce radiant load by working in the shade since heat radiation behaves much like light radiation. Working in the sun can add 170 watts to a clothed person and 220 to an unclothed person.

Clothing (a mobile shield) is the first line of defense, so use hats and long-sleeved shirts. As a first approximation, clothing temperature is halfway between skin temperature and environmental temperature. For visible radiation (such as the sun), use light-colored clothing; clothing color does not matter for nonvisible radiation. Clothing material, density, and thickness do matter.

A fixed shield between the person and the source is a second line of defense. Use with ovens, welding torches and arcs, and molten glass. The isolation or insulation of heat sources has three effects: (1) It

keeps heat in; (2) it reduces fuel costs; and (3) it improves comfort of workers. To protect against solar radiation through windows, paint the upper part with a water-based solution of blue dye or laundry blue. External louvers on the windows can be vertical or horizontal. Reflecting heat shields tend to be more effective and economical than absorbing shields or water-cooled shields. The air on the source side of the shield becomes heated and rises—giving a welcome current of supply (makeup) air to the worker. See Figure 25.9.

Aluminum is a good shield since it has high reflectivity and doesn't corrode. If the operator must see the source, use a screen of chains or coated glass (glass, although more effective, tends to get broken or dirty). Cover an oven conveyor entrance and exit with a screen of hanging chains.

Oxenburgh (1991, case 21) described the protection of a control cabin for a shear operator in a steel mill. The cabin was moved much closer to the "orange hot" metal; this cut labor requirements in half but, more important, permitted more accurate cuts, reducing scrap. Insulation of the cabin required gold-laminated glass! But the payback was only 1 month.

F I G U R E   2 5 . 9

Radiant heat shields should have a gap at the bottom aiding convection airflow. Another approach is two parallel plates with a gap of about 25 cm between the plates. The heat shields also act as a barrier to splashes of metal and sparks.

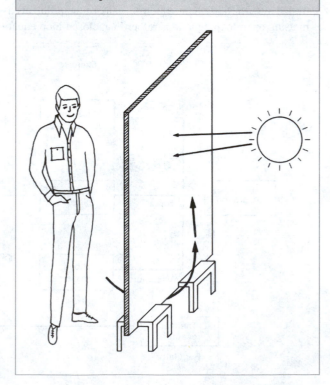

3.3.5 *Convection* Convective heat transfer is:

$$C = h_c A f_{clo}(t_{air} - t_{skin})$$

where C = Convection gain (+) or loss (−), watts

h_c = Convective heat transfer coefficient, watts/(m²-C)

= 4.5 $W/$(m²-C) for standing adults with velocity .05 to 2 m/s

= 8.3 $V^{.6}$ for seated adults

A = Skin surface area, m²

f_{clo} = Multiplier to h_c for clothing

= $1/(1 + .155 (2.9) I_{clo})$ where 2.9 $W/$(m²-C) is h_c in still air (.15 m/s)

I_{clo} = Insulation value of clothing, clo (see Table 25.1)

V = Air velocity, m/s

t_{air} = Air temperature, C

t_{skin} = Skin temperature, C

The driving force is the difference between the two temperatures. As with radiation, keep temperature of the environment below 35°C. Second, increase air velocity on the skin. Figure 25.10 shows that air velocity above 2 m/s has little additional benefit. It is important to note that air velocity drops very, very rapidly with distance. The primary effect of clothing is not obvious in the equation—it drops air velocity next to the skin to effectively zero. Therefore, to max-imize convective loss, wear little clothing if the temperature is below 35°C and insects, radiation, and social considerations are not a problem. If clothing is worn, don't restrict air circulation at the neck, waist, wrist, or ankles.

Convective cooling is effective if air temperature is sufficiently below 35°C, perhaps at 15°C. The problem is to get the cool air. One solution is to pass air through water, which will normally be about 10°–15°C. The air then is 15°C but humidity is 100%, say 12 torr. The worker then is cooled by convection. The technique works best with relatively high air velocities (.5 m/s).

3.3.6 *Evaporation* Evaporative heat transfer is:

$$E = h_e A W F_{pcl}(VP_a - VP_s)$$

where E = Evaporative gain (+) or loss (−), watts

h_e = Evaporative heat transfer coefficient
= 2.2 h_c

A = Skin surface area, m²

W = E/E_{max} (mislabeled the proportion of the skin that is wet, this actually is the proportion of actual sweat to maximum possible sweat. Values of .7 are a reasonable maximum and of .5 are much more common.)

F_{pcl} = Decrease in evaporative efficiency for permeable clothing

= $1/(1 + .143 (2.9) I_{clo})$ where 2.9 $W/$(m² − C) is h_c in still air (.15 m/s) for a sedentary person

I_{clo} = Insulation value of clothing, clo (see Table 25.1)

VP_a = Vapor pressure of water in air, torr

VP_s = Vapor pressure of water on skin (45 torr if t_{skin} = 35°C)

Evaporation can be limited by the body or the environment.

Body limitations. The capacity of the body to sweat is great, especially after acclimatization. Each kg of sweat gives about 580 kcal/kg if evaporated from the skin. Unacclimatized females have a maximum sweat rate of .7–.9 kg/h; males have 1.5–2.0 kg/h; after acclimatization, the maximum rate for females increases to .9 to 1.0 kg/h; for males it is still 1.5 to 2.0 kg/h (Torii, 1995). Mehnert et al. (2002) report that in heat stress, even after adjusting for their smaller body size, women sweat less than men and have higher body temperatures. With acclimatization, sweating starts at a lower core temperature than before acclimatization so the total amount sweated increases. Skin lotions can restrict sweat evaporation.

Acclimatization to heat requires exercise in the heat. People living in a hot climate who do not exer-

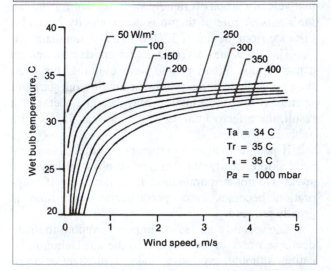

F I G U R E   2 5 . 1 0

Lines of equal cooling power. The lines show the effect of air velocity and metabolic rate when air and radiant temperature and vapor pressure are held constant. The person is assumed to be nude (Mitchell and Whillier, 1971). Note that increasing air velocity on the skin beyond about 2 m/s has little benefit.

cise do not get the benefits of acclimatization. In his work with gold miners in South Africa, Strydom (1976) demonstrated that vitamin C deficiency slows the rate of acclimatization; vitamin C aids sweating; use of 250 mg of vitamin C/day permitted acclimatization in an average of 5.2 days instead of 8.7 days.

Acclimatized people are able to eliminate heat by sweating rather than vasodilation. The reduced skin blood flow results in heart rates 30–40 beats/min less for acclimatized people when exercising. Unfortunately, acclimatization can be lost in as little as 10 days, so workers returning from vacation must be careful of heat stress. For each day of nonexercise in the heat (such as vacations), the equivalent of .5 day of acclimatization is lost (Givoni and Goldman, 1973).

As long as water is replaced, sweating can continue without health problems, but **dehydration** of 3% causes physiological performance changes, 5% gives evidence of heat exhaustion, and at 7% hallucinations occur. Losses totaling 10% are extremely hazardous and lead to heat stroke; if not treated immediately, death will result. See Figure 25.11.

Dehydration potential is greater when under forced ventilation (fans, vortex tube cooling, air jets). However, the thirst drive is not sufficient to replace water loss during heavy sweating. Supervisors must insist that workers drink water; frequent, small amounts are better than occasional large amounts. Drink from a container because volume drunk from a water fountain tends to be small (30–60 ml/drink) if in a comfortable-temperature environment (Coetzee and Bennett, 1978). An insulated mug keeps the water

cool, which increases palatability. Cool water is more important than flavorings (Konz et al., 1983; Johnson and Strowman, 1987). "Tank up" before exposure. Organizations have a responsibility to make access to cool water very convenient.

Sweat is .2% to .4% salt (.4% at high sweat rates) whether you are acclimatized or not, as long as you are in positive salt balance. If salt balance becomes negative due to lack of salt intake or heavy sweating, the kidneys start to decrease urine salt content within 30 min. Sweat salt content declines after several days (Collins, 1963).

Salt tablets rarely are desirable. People take them excessively and get stomach problems and high blood pressure. Salt on food usually is sufficient. Whenever more than 4 liters of water/day are required to replace sweat loss, provide extra salt—2 g of salt for each liter over 4. A person doing heavy work under hot conditions may need an extra 7 g/day (Committee on Nutritional Misinformation, 1974).

The normal adult diet in the United States provides 4 g of sodium and 10 g of salt/day; requirements are 2 of sodium and 5 of salt. A typical well-salted meal has 3–4 g of sodium; 1 cup of beef or chicken broth, consomme, or bouillon has about 1 g of sodium. If additional salt is absolutely necessary during work, add salt to a lime drink to reduce its concentration and increase palatability.

Environmental limitations. Evaporation also can be limited by the environment: "It isn't the heat, it's the humidity." When water vapor pressure is over 32 torr, a 1°C increase in wet bulb is equal to a 10°C increase in dry bulb. Reduce environmentally limited evaporation by (1) increasing air velocity or (2) decreasing water vapor pressure.

Figure 25.10 showed that beyond 2 m/s air velocity had little benefit. However, achieving 2 m/s at the skin is difficult. Figure 25.12 shows a plan view of air velocity for a typical fan. Figure 25.13 also shows that velocity drops off rapidly with departure from the fan's axis. A rule of thumb is zero velocity beyond a distance from the fan of 30D, where D = fan diameter.

The clo values of Table 25.1 were determined on a mannequin. When people wear clothing, however, they move their limbs (pumping air through garment openings) and the clothing may become wet. As a result, the effective clo may be as low as 55% of the Table 25.1 values.

If people wear non-permeable clothing (to minimize skin contact with chemical or physical hazards), sweat will not evaporate (and, thus, not cool). If evaporation becomes zero, permissible work time is greatly reduced.

The second approach to improve evaporation is to decrease water vapor pressure in the air. Dehumidification, although expensive, makes a pleasant environ-

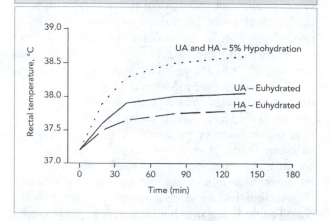

F I G U R E   25.11

Dehydration (hypohydration). Body temperature increases quickly, regardless of acclimatization; UA = unacclimated and HA = heat acclimated (Sawka and Montain, 1996). When fully hydrated (euhydrated), the increase is slower and to a lower asymptote, especially when acclimatized. Hydration level is the most important factor influencing exercise-heat performance.

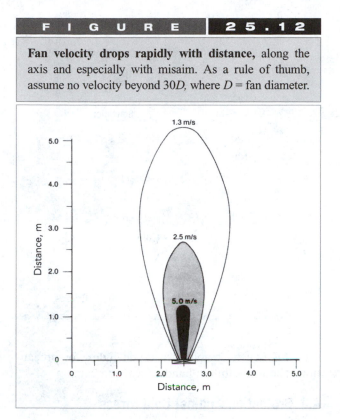

F I G U R E | 2 5 . 1 2

Fan velocity drops rapidly with distance, along the axis and especially with misaim. As a rule of thumb, assume no velocity beyond 30*D*, where *D* = fan diameter.

F I G U R E | 2 5 . 1 3

Fan placement is extremely critical because air velocity drops so rapidly with distance.

ment since sweat evaporates rapidly (discomfort is related to skin wetness).

3.3.7 *Conduction* Astronauts have metabolic heat that has to be removed. The early spacesuits used evaporative cooling to remove the metabolic heat, but blowers took considerable power and there was no place to dump the sweat-laden air. The solution was a network of small tubes on the torso through which small (1 L/min) volumes of cool (10°C) water were passed. Heat removal was excellent, and there were no physiological problems from removing heat from only a localized area of the body.

For earthbound applications, the problems with this personal cooling technique are the high capital cost/unit (about $1,500) and the weight of the associated pump, compressor, and battery. If the weight is not kept on the back, the worker must be connected with a lifeline to the source of water and power (Konz, 1984). Thus auxiliary cooling is most practical in aircraft and ground vehicles where operators are sedentary and power is available.

For mobility and minimum weight, the simplest approach is to immerse the vasodilated hands of a person with elevated body temperature into a bucket of cool (20°C) water; the heat removal is similar to that of an ice vest worn during work (House, 1996). Another technique is cooling with granulated dry ice placed in pockets next to the skin. But dry ice is difficult to store and handle. Cooling also can be done with

conventional ice in replaceable canisters. A pump circulates water by the ice and the warm skin. In another design, the ice is frozen in plastic packets and placed in pockets in a garment. There is no circulating liquid, pump, or battery, but the ice is not replaceable while the operator is working (Konz, 1984).

4 COLD STRESS

4.1 Criteria of Stress   At low levels of cold stress, we experience discomfort. Additional cold gives loss of mental performance and manual dexterity. Then comes pain and potential loss of extremities such as fingers, ears, and feet. Finally, death occurs. (At very low body temperatures (20°C), vital signs disappear but the brain oxygen supply may still be sufficient; therefore, death from accidental hypothermia should be defined as "failure to revive upon rewarming.")

However, cold is not all bad. Winter is the great friend of humanity—the silent white killer of insects and parasites. All the societies with long life expectancies are in climates with a frost.

Use the formulas in the section on comfort and Figure 25.1 to evaluate whether people will consider themselves slightly cool, cool, or cold.

Fox (1967), reviewing 68 references, said hand skin temperature (HST) critically affects dexterity and tactile sensitivity. Dexterity, assuming the core is warm, drops when HST reaches 15° to 20°C (Poulton,

1970). Fourt and Hollies (1970) report dexterity declines when HST reaches 12° to 16°C; tactile sensitivity declines when HST is below 8°C.

If the core temperature drops, vigilance decreases—Poulton (1970, p. 150) says at an oral temperature of 36.5°C. At a body temperature of 35°C, dexterity is so reduced that you cannot light a match or open a jack-knife. When body temperature drops below 35°C, the mind becomes confused; at about 32°C there is loss of consciousness. At deep body temperature of 26°C, death occurs from heart failure. Local tissue, such as fingers and ears, freezes at −1°C instead of 0 due to osmotic pressure.

The National Association of Building Contractors (Ramsey and Beshir, 1997) guidelines for reduction of motor skills are:

Eff. Temperature		Motor skill reduction, %	
°F	°C	Gross	Fine
0	−18	10	60
−10	−23	20	80
−20	−29	25	90

4.2 Environmental Limits Just as people want one number to combine all factors for heat and use *WBGT*, they want one number for cold and use the **wind chill index, I.**

$$I, \text{kcal/(m}^2\text{-h)} = h(t_{skin} - t_{air})$$
$$\text{where } h, \text{kcal/(m}^2\text{-h-C)} = 10.45 - V + (100 \ V)^{.5}$$
$$V = \text{Air velocity, m/s}$$
$$t_{skin} = 33°C$$
$$t_{air} = \text{Dry bulb air temperature, C}$$

Table 25.2 gives the sensation for various values of *I*. The concept of wind chill also can be presented in the format of Table 25.3. Values give the 1.8 m/s air temperature that has the same value of *I* as the moving air. The U. S. Weather Service reports wind velocity at 10 m above the surface; it blows harder there than at face level. Air velocity can be estimated as:

.8 m/s—paper on a desk moves

1.5 m/s—a noticeable breeze

2.5 m/s—light flag moves

5 m/s—light flag fully extended

7.5 m/s—raises newspaper sheet

10 m/s—blowing and drifting snow

Be cautious about rigorous use of the wind-chill index, as it is based on cooling a liter container of 33°C water at night, not a clothed human with a metabolism. A container of water does not have a metabolism, has no clothes, and has a much greater surface area/volume than a person. Wind-chill can be

TABLE	25.2

Sensations for various values of *I* (Newburg, 1968, p. 423).

I kcal/(m²-h)	Sensation
50	Hot
100	Warm
200	Pleasant
400	Cool
600	Very cool
800	Cold
1000	Very cold
1200	Bitterly cold
1400	Exposed flesh freezes

used for livestock and as a crude index for precautions about frostbitten hands, face, and ears.

4.3 Protection Against Cold Stress

4.3.1 *Clothing* Clothing is the primary defense in a heat-hungry environment. As clothing thickness increases, the insulation value increases to a point at which the increase is overcome by the increase in surface area. Thus, thin gloves may increase heat loss from a child's fingers! (If dexterity is not a problem, use mittens with liners rather than gloves.) The best insulator is air, so the Eskimos use two layers of fur. The Russian army since the Napoleonic War has issued winter boots one size too large—the soldiers stuff the extra space with straw or newspapers. The German army in World War II issued boots that fit exactly and many soldiers suffered frostbitten feet.

Thus, shoes for outdoor workers in cold environments should be big enough to fit an extra pair of thick socks. If the socks become wet, change them. Thick (8–10 mm) felt insoles restrict the contact cooling of the feet with the ground. The felt also tends to accumulate moisture and keep the feet dry; remove the insoles and dry them between work periods or overnight.

For clothing, a number of wind-proof layers tends to be more efficient than a single thick layer. One problem with layering is that many designs have an outer layer that protects against wind, rain, and snow; hence, this layer must always be worn and the inner layers added or removed as required. This, however, requires multi-step dressing/undressing. The Canadian military has a better system with three layers. The outer layer is added or removed to change the insulation level. The middle layer is worn at all times. The inner layer is worn only in extremely cold weather. Both the outer

T A B L E   2 5 . 3

Wind-chill "equivalent temperatures" to predict the effect of air velocity at various temperatures. The number in the table gives the temperature at 1.8 m/s, which has the same wind-chill as the dry bulb temperature at an air velocity. Thus, −12 @ 2 m/s, −6 @ 6 m/s, and 0 @ 8 m/s are approximately equivalent. A wind-chill of <30 has little danger (with exposed dry skin); 30<WC<56 has considerable danger (flesh may freeze in 1 min); and 56<WC has great danger (flesh may freeze in 30 s).

Dry Bulb Temperature, C	AIR VELOCITY, M/S							
	2	4	6	8	10	12	14	16
+ 4	+ 3.3	+ 1.8	− 5.0	− 7.4	− 9.1	−10.5	−11.5	−12.3
+ 2	+ 1.3	− 4.2	− 7.6	−10.2	−12.0	−13.5	−14.6	−15.4
0	− 0.8	− 6.5	−10.3	−12.9	−15.0	−16.5	−17.6	−18.5
− 2	− 2.8	− 8.9	−12.9	−15.7	−17.9	−19.5	−20.7	−21.6
− 4	− 4.9	−11.3	−15.5	−18.5	−20.8	−22.5	−23.8	−24.8
− 6	− 6.9	−13.7	−18.1	−21.3	−23.7	−25.5	−26.9	−27.9
− 8	− 9.0	−16.1	−20.0	−24.1	−26.6	−28.5	−29.9	−31.0
−10	−11.0	−18.5	−23.4	−26.9	−29.5	−31.5	−33.0	−34.1
−12	−13.1	−20.9	−26.0	−29.7	−32.4	−34.5	−36.1	−37.2
−14	−15.1	−23.3	−28.6	−32.4	−35.3	−37.5	−39.1	−40.4
−16	−17.2	−25.7	−31.3	−35.2	−38.2	−40.5	−42.2	−43.5
−18	−19.2	−28.1	−33.9	−38.0	−41.1	−43.5	−45.3	−46.6
−20	−21.2	−30.5	−36.5	−40.8	−44.0	−46.5	−48.3	−49.7

and middle layers have a water vapor permeable moisture barrier (Gore-Tex) (Frim, 1996). It is especially important to protect the head since it does not vasodilate or constrict. Froese and Burton (1957) estimated:

$$H = 285 - 7.55 \, T_{air}$$

where H = Head heat loss, kcal/(h-m² of head) (the head was approximately .12 m²)

T_{air} = Air temperature, C

Therefore at −4°C, heat loss from the head may be 50% of resting metabolism. Adding 2.4 clo units over the head gives the same result as increasing the insulation over the 1.7 m² of body by 4 clo units. A stocking cap gives good protection and is easily removed and stored when not in use. In severe cold, use a face mask.

Another technique is to warm the hands by putting on a jacket. The jacket reduces heat loss on the torso and thus lets warm blood rather than cold blood flow to the hands (Sundheim and Konz, 1990). (See Box 16.2 for comments on gloves.) Special precautions should be taken if a worker is handling evaporative liquids (gasoline, alcohol, or cleaning fluids) because of the danger of cold injury due to evaporative cooling.

One serious problem with clothing is exercise, because the exerciser becomes a tropical person in arctic clothing. Exercise causes sweating; the sweat

may accumulate in the clothing and freeze. Eskimos avoid this in two ways: (1) They constantly pull off their outer fur parka so that much of the time their skin is cool; and (2) the clothing is designed with many ventilation areas, gaps, and drawstrings. Eskimos bending over while wearing a parka show the bare skin of their backs. Breathable fabrics (such as Gore-Tex) prevent water from getting in but allow sweat to get out through wicking.

Reduce air velocity by providing windbreaks near the work. Relative humidity makes little difference since a 10% rh may give an absolute vapor pressure of 1 torr versus a 100% rh giving 7 torr. Skin vapor pressure is about 44 torr so 44 − 1 = 43 is not much more driving force than 44 − 7 = 37. A cold rain, however, puts cold water on the skin. Then, raising each kg takes 1 kcal/C. Thus, raising 1 kg of water from 5°C to the 33°C of skin temperature would require 28 kcal; if the water then is evaporated, it takes 80 more kcal/kg from the body.

4.3.2 *Other factors* People working indoors in cold environments should not be exposed to blowing air; cover vents with fabric or use diffusers or deflectors. Floors conduct heat (and cold) to the feet. Because of vasoconstriction, foot skin temperature usually is the lowest body skin temperature. Normal foot skin temperature is 33.3°C for males but 31.2°C for females (Oleson and Fanger, 1973).

Floors conduct cold (and heat) to the feet. When wearing normal shoes, optimal floor temperature is 23°C (73.5°F) for sedentary people (ASHRAE, 2001). Under-desk heaters may be requested when the problem is the chair design (too high with a sharp front), which cuts off circulation. Better chairs (lower and with a rounded front edge) and a footrest may eliminate the desire for a heater.

Obviously, avoid contact with cold metal such as metal seats and metal tool handles. Wood, because of its low thermal conductivity, is better than plastic.

Respiratory heat loss is one reason you can eat more calories in the cold weather. For 0°C air, dry loss is 3 kcal/h and wet loss is 10 kcal/h, so at the end of the day you can have an extra 8 spoonsful of sugar.

In the cold, urine production increases to about three times normal—leading to dehydration. Counter with warm drinks such as soup or hot chocolate. Avoid coffee with caffeine (which causes vasodilation).

Trauma sustained in freezing weather requires special attention because an injured worker is predisposed to secondary cold injury.

There is acclimatization to cold just as there is acclimatization to heat. The exact physiology is relatively unknown but probably involves improved nonshivering thermogenesis (increased heat generation without shivering). The location of the nonshivering thermogenesis in humans is debated but is probably the liver, the muscles, and fat. Metabolism in the muscles increases up to 50% before the physical movement of shivering begins. The cold-acclimatized person retains the ability to use shivering also.

Review Questions

1. Give five approaches to reduce the problems of static electricity.
2. Sketch the psychrometric chart showing: dry bulb temperature, absolute humidity, relative humidity, wet bulb temperature, effective temperature, and new effective temperature.
3. What is the clo value of the clothing you are presently wearing?
4. Sketch the core body temperature vs. environmental temperature for low, medium, and high metabolic rates.
5. What is the difference between wet bulb and natural wet bulb temperature? How is each measured?
6. Why did gold-laminated glass on a control cabin pay off?
7. Why should a radiant heat shield have a gap at the bottom?
8. How does heat acclimatization reduce heat stress?
9. Deficiency in which vitamin affects heat acclimatization?
10. What is the primary defense against heat stress? What is the primary defense against cold stress?
11. Why is it so important to protect the head in cold weather?

References

ACGIH. *1993–1994 Threshold Limit Values and Biological Exposure Limits.* Cincinnati: American Congress of Governmental Industrial Hygiene, 1993.

ASHRAE. *Handbook of Fundamentals.* Atlanta: American Society of Heating, Refrigeration and Air Conditioning Engineers, 2001.

ASHRAE. *HVAC Applications.* Atlanta: American Society of Heating, Refrigeration and Air Conditioning Engineers, 1999.

ASHRAE. *HVAC Systems and Applications.* Atlanta: American Society of Heating, Refrigeration and Air Conditioning Engineers, 2000.

Berenson, P. and Robertson, W. Temperature. In *Bioastronautics Data Book.* Washington, DC: National Aeronautics and Space Administration, 1973.

Beshir, M. A comprehensive comparison between WBGT and Botsball. *American Industrial Hygiene Association J.,* Vol. 42, No. 2, 81–87, 1981.

Coetzee, J. and Bennett, C. The efficiency of a drinking fountain. *Applied Ergonomics,* Vol. 9, No. 2, 97–100, 1978.

Cohen, J. Heading off heat stress. *EPRI Journal,* 22–28, July–August 1988.

Collins, K. Endocrine control of salt and water in hot conditions. *Federation Proceedings,* Vol. 22, 716–20, 1963.

Committee on Nutritional Misinformation. *Water Deprivation and Performance of Athletes.* Washington, DC: National Academy of Sciences, p. 2, 1974.

Conable, S., Bishop, P., Nunnely, S., and Chen, T. Intermittent microclimate cooling during rest increases work capacity and reduces heat stress. *Ergonomics,* Vol. 37, No. 2, 277–85, 1994.

Fanger, P. *Thermal Comfort.* New York: McGraw-Hill, 1972.

Fanger, P. Conditions for thermal comfort—A review. *Thermal Comfort and Moderate Heat Stress.* London: Her Majesty's Stationery Office, 1973a.

Fanger, P. Assessment of man's thermal comfort in practice. *British J. of Industrial Medicine,* Vol. 30, 323–24, 1973b.

Fanger, P. The olf and decipol. *ASHRAE Journal,* Vol. 30, No. 10, 35–38, October 1988a.

Fanger, P. Hidden olfs in sick buildings. *ASHRAE Journal,* Vol. 30, No. 11, 40–43, November 1988b.

Fanger, P., Angelius, O., and Kjeruf-Jensen, P. Radiation data for the human body. *ASHRAE Transactions,* (paper 2168, Part 1), 1970.

Fanger, P., Hojbjerre, J., and Thomsen, J. Thermal comfort conditions in the morning and in the evening. *International J. of Biometeorology,* Vol. 18, No. 1, 16–22, 1974.

Fourt, L. and Hollies, N. *Clothing Comfort and Function.* New York: Marcel Dekker, 1970.

Fox, W. Human performance in the cold. *Human Factors,* Vol. 9, No. 3, 203–20, 1967.

Frim, J. IECS: Successful implementation of the layering principle. *Environmental Ergonomics,* Y. Shapiro, Moran, D., and Epstein, Y. (eds.). London: Freund Publishing, 259–62, 1996.

Froese, G. and Burton, A. Heat losses from the human head. *J. of Applied Physiology,* Vol. 10, No. 2, 235–41, 1957.

Gagge, A. and Nishi, Y. Physical indices of the thermal environment. *ASHRAE Journal,* Vol. 18, No. 1, 47–51, 1976.

George, D. and DiNardi, S. An introduction to the design of local exhaust ventilation systems. Chapter 32 in *The Occupational Environment—Its Evaluation and Control.* Fairfax, VA: Am. Ind. Hygiene Association, 1997.

Givoni, B. and Goldman, R. Predicting effects of heat acclimatization on heart rate and rectal temperature. *J. of Applied Physiology,* Vol. 35, No. 6, 875–79, 1973.

Green, G. The effect of indoor relative humidity on absenteeism and colds in schools. *ASHRAE Transactions,* Vol. 80, Part 2, 1974.

Grether, W. Human performance at elevated environmental temperatures. *Aerospace Medicine,* Vol. 44, No. 7, 747–55, 1973.

Griefahn, B., Kunemund, C., and Gehring, U. The significance of air velocity and turbulence intensity for responses to horizontal drafts in a constant air temperature of 23°C. *Int. J. of Ind. Ergonomics,* Vol. 26, 639–49, 2000.

Hancock, P. The limitation of human performance in extreme heat conditions. *Proceedings of the Human Factors Society,* 74–78, 1981.

Hancock, P. and Vercruyssen, M. Limits of behavioral efficiency for workers in heat stress. *International J. of Industrial Ergonomics,* Vol. 3, 149–58, 1988.

Haslam, R. and Parsons, K. Using computer-based models for predicting human thermal responses to hot and cold environments. *Ergonomics,* Vol. 37, No. 3, 399–416, 1994.

Hedge, A. Where are we in understanding the effects of where we are? *Ergonomics,* Vol. 43, 7, 1019–29, 2000.

House, J. Reducing heat strain with ice-vests or hand immersion. *Environmental Ergonomics,* Y. Shapiro, Moran, D., and Epstein, Y. (eds.). London: Freund Publishing, 347–50, 1996.

ISO/TR 11079. *Evaluation of Cold Environments: Determination of required clothing insulation.* Geneva: ISO, 1993.

Johnson, R. and Strowman, S. Effects of cooling and flavoring drinking water on psychological performance in a hot environment. *Proceedings of Human Factors Society,* 825–29, 1987.

Konz, S. Personal cooling garments: A review. *ASHRAE Transactions,* 499–518, No. 4, 1984.

Konz, S., Rohles, F., and McCullough, E. Male responses to intermittent heat. *ASHRAE Transactions,* Part 1B, 79–100, 1983.

Konz, S., Rohles, F., Zuti, W., and Skipton, D. Physiological responses of 262 seated sedentary subjects in neutral and heat stress environments. *ASHRAE Transactions,* Part 2, 1980.

Lind, A. A physiological criterion for setting thermal environmental limits for everyday work. *J. of Applied Physiology,* Vol. 18, No. 1, 51–56, 1963.

Meese, G., Kok, R., Lewis, J., and Wyon, D. A laboratory study of the effects of moderate thermal stress on the factory workers. *Ergonomics,* Vol. 27, No. 1, 19–43, 1984.

Mehnert, P., Brode, P., and Griefahn, B. Gender-related difference in sweat loss and its impact on exposure limits to heat stress. *Int. J. of Ind. Ergonomics,* Vol. 29, 343–51, 2002.

Minard, D. and Copman, L. Elevation of body temperature in health. In *Temperature—Its Measurement and Control,* Hertzfield, C. (ed.). New York: Reinhold, 1963.

Mitchell, D. and Whillier, A. Cooling power of underground environments. *J. of South Africa Institute of Mining and Metallurgy,* 93–99, October 1971.

National Academy of Sciences. *Recommended Dietary Allowances.* Washington, DC: National Academy of Sciences, 90, 1974.

Nevins, R. Energy conservation strategies and human comfort. *ASHRAE Journal,* Vol. 17, No. 4, 33–37, 1975.

Nevins, R. and Gorton, R. Thermal comfort conditions. *ASHRAE Journal,* Vol. 16, 90–93, January 1974.

Newburg, L. (ed.). *The Physiology of Heat Regulation and the Science of Clothing.* New York: Hafner Publishing, 1968.

Nielsen, B. Heat stress and acclimation. *Ergonomics,* Vol. 37, No. 1, 49–58, 1994.

Nielsen, M. Die Regulation der Korpertemperaturbei Muskelarbeit. *Skandinavian Archives Physiologue,* Vol. 79, 193–230, 1938.

Oborne, D. Cognitive effects of passive smoking. *Ergonomics,* Vol. 26, No. 12, 1163–78, 1983.

O'Brian, J., Bernard, T., and Kenney, W. Personal monitor to protect workers from heat stress. *Proceedings of*

IEEE Fourth Conference on Human Factors and Power Plants, June 1996.

Oleson, B., and Fanger, P. The skin temperature distribution for resting man in comfort. *Archives des Sciences Physiologigues,* Vol. 27, No. 4, A385–93, 1973.

Oxenburgh, M. *Increasing Productivity and Profit through Health & Safety,* Chicago: CCH International, 1991.

Parsons, K. Environmental ergonomics: A review of principles, methods and models. *Applied Ergonomics,* Vol. 31, 581–94, 2000.

Pirnay, F., Petit, J., and Deroanne, R. A comparative study of the evolution of heart rate and body temperature during physical effort at high temperature (in French). *Internationale Zeitschrift fur Angewandte Physiologie Einschliesslich Arbeitsphysiologie,* Vol. 28, 23–30, December 1969.

Poulton, E. *Environment and Human Efficiency.* Springfield, IL: C. T. Thomas, 1970.

Ramsey, J., Burford, C., Beshir, M., and Jensen, R. Effects of workplace thermal conditions on safe work behavior. *J. of Safety Research,* Vol. 14, 105–14, 1983.

Ramsey, J. Task performance in the heat: a review. *Ergonomics,* Vol. 38, 154–65, 1995.

Ramsey, J. Environmental ergonomic standards: USA and international. In *Adv. in Occupational Ergonomics and Safety II,* B. Das and W. Karwowski (eds.). Cincinnati: IOS Press and Ohmsha, 553–56, 1997.

Ramsey, J. and Beshir, M. Thermal standards and measurement techniques. *The Occupational Environment—Its Evaluation and Control.* Fairfax, VA: AIHA, 1997.

Rohles, F., Hayter, R., and Milliken, G. Effective temperature (ET^*) as a predictor of thermal comfort. *ASHRAE Transactions,* Vol. 81, Part 2, 148–56, 1975.

Rohles, F., Konz, S., and Munson, D. Estimating occupant satisfaction from effective temperature (ET^*). *Proceedings of the Human Factors Society,* 223–27, 1980.

Rohles, F. and Nevins, R. Thermal comfort: New directions and standards. *Aerospace Medicine,* Vol. 44, 730–48, July 1973.

Rosen, E. Comfort and cooling with box fans. M. S. thesis, Kansas State University, 1982.

Sawka, M. and Montain, S. Hypohydration: Effects on body fluid redistribution, temperature regulation & exercise-heat tolerance. In *Environmental Ergonomics: Recent Progress and New Frontiers,* Shapiro, Y., Moran, D., and Epstein, Y. (eds.). London: Freund Publishing, 53–55, 1996.

Strydom, N. Effect of ascorbic acid on rate of heat acclimatization. *J. of Applied Physiology,* Vol. 141, No. 2, 202–205, 1976.

Strydom, N., van der Walt, W., Jooste, P., and Kotze, H. Note: A revised method of heat acclimatization. *J. South Africa Institute of Mining and Metallurgy,* Vol. 76, 448–52, 1976.

Sundheim, N. and Konz, S. Keeping bare hands warm with extra clothing on the body. In *Advances in Industrial Ergonomics and Safety II,* B. Das (ed.). London: Taylor and Francis, 1990.

Torii, M. Maximal sweating rate in humans. *J. Human Ergology,* Vol. 24, 137–52, 1995.

Wing, J. Upper thermal tolerance limits for unimpaired mental performance. *Aerospace Medicine,* Vol. 36, 960–64, October 1965.

Wing, J. and Touchstone, R. A Bibliography of the Effects of Temperature on Human Performance (Technical Report AMRL-TDR-63-13). Dayton, OH: Wright Patterson AFB, February 1963.

Wyndham, C. and Strydom, N. The effect of environmental heat on comfort, productivity and health of workmen. *South African Mechanical Engineer,* 208–21, May 1965.

Websites

American Society of Heating, Refrigeration and Air Conditioning Engineers, www.ashrae.org

TOXICOLOGY

26

Overview

Toxicology deals with the long-term effects of foreign chemicals on the body—it considers health. Although dermatitis is a common problem, toxins generally enter the body through breathing. Threshold limit values give the recommendations for permitted exposures. Toxicology controls are divided into engineering controls, administrative controls, and personal protective equipment.

Key Concepts

biological monitoring
biotransformation
dermatitis
excursions/peaks
industrial hygienists
leaky bucket

Material Safety Data
  Sheets (MSDSs)
permissible exposure limits
  (PELs)
poison targets
protective clothing

recommended exposure
  limits (RELs)
short-term exposure limits
  (STELs)
teratogens

threshold limit values
  (TLVs)
toxicology
work environment expo-
  sure limits (WEELs)

POISONS

Toxicology deals with long-term effects of foreign chemicals upon the body—it considers the effect of the chemical environment on health. A toxicology problem might be the effect of 10 years' exposure to a solvent. Safety deals with the short-term effects of physical agents upon the body—it considers accidents. A safety problem might be cutting off a finger in a punch press.

Toxicology is a complex subject, and this chapter touches the subject only briefly. Toxicology problems have been present for many years. The decline of the Roman Empire was due in part to the fact that, while poor people ate on pottery, the upper classes ate on lead plates—and thus became sterile. French hatters in the 17th century used mercuric nitrate to aid fur felting, and the resulting chronic mercury poisoning led to the expression "mad as a hatter."

Another example of Hg poisoning was at Minamata, Japan. Nippon Chisso discharged mercury into a bay of the sea; fish ingested the mercury; the local diet was high in fish; many people were therefore poisoned. Although the firm knew of the problem, it denied responsibility for approximately 15 years. The local government (heavily dependent upon Chisso's taxes and having many former Chisso employees as government employees) did nothing. Chisso finally lost a lawsuit in 1972 and paid a large fine. The case resulted in strict pollution laws in Japan.

Chemicals affect the body with doses producing a response. (**Industrial hygienists** are trained to deal with chemical hazards as well as physical hazards such as noise and radiation. See Chapter 24 for noise; see Box 26.1 for electrical and magnetic fields.)

1.1 Effect
An effect could be a permanent physical change, such as death, or could be reversible, such as change in dark adaptation of the eye. The **threshold limit values (TLVs)** given later in this chapter are based primarily on nonreversible functional changes in an organ (usually the liver and kidneys) and define maximum acceptable exposure to various materials.

A severe practical problem is that there may a 20-year lag between dose and response. For example, exposure to asbestos during the 1940s caused an increase in certain types of cancer in the 1970s and 1980s. In the 1940s, organizations did not realize that use of asbestos would impair the health of the employees many years later.

Another problem is that when there is such a long lag between exposure and the consequences (which are not certain, but just increased odds of poor health), many workers tend to ignore the hazard. A political problem is that the financial benefits accrue to organizations but the health costs to individuals.

1.2 Body
One technique of determining which chemicals are dangerous is to give the chemicals to humans and see what happens. This may be hard on the people! Thus, most TLVs are developed from studies on animals rather than humans. But there are marked species differences. For example, **teratogens** are substances that cause defects in fetal development. In rats and mice, thalidomide had no effect at a dose of 4,000 mg/kg of body weight, but a dose of .5 mg/kg in humans was teratogenic (Mastromatteo, 1981).

The TLV approach has been to consider that humans respond as the most sensitive animal species and then use a safety margin between the dose that produces the effect and the TLV. But you can see that the TLVs are not as precise as they may seem. In addition, the results from exposure to humans may indicate that a reduction in the TLV is needed. For example, some workers in polyvinyl chloride factories came down with a rare cancer many years later, and so the TLV was reduced. The point here is that if it had been a common cancer, the danger probably never would have been noticed.

BOX **26.1** *Electrical and Magnetic Fields*

Some concern has been raised about electrical and magnetic fields (emf) (Bracken, 1993; Cleary, 1993; Anderson, 1993; Savitz, 1993; Feero, 1993). In summary, there seems to be very little, if any, effect.

Magnetic field strength is measured in milliGauss (mG) or nanoTesla (nT); 1 mG = 100 nT. The ACGIH Occupational Standard at 60 Hz = 10,000 mG; the International Commission on Non-ionizing Radiation Protection Occupational Standard = 5,000 mG.

A typical U. S. home has a background field from .5 to 4 mG. Some example product emissions are:

300 mG	=	Electric hair dryer at 6 in.
200	=	Electric pencil sharpener at 6 in.
100	=	Electric shaver at 6 in.
60	=	Vacuum cleaner at 12 in.
2	=	Color TV or VDT at 24 in.
1	=	Digital clock at 12 in.

1.3 Dose/Response   With present technology, it is possible to detect chemicals in very low concentrations. Parts/million (ppm) is equivalent to milligrams/liter. One part/million is comparable to 1 min in 2 years. Parts/billion (ppb) is equivalent to micrograms/liter. One part/billion is equivalent to 1 s in 33 years. Mere detection of a chemical is not enough. What has to be considered is the dose in relation to the response. Water in excess will kill, as will salt, sugar, alcohol, sulfanilamide, or arsenic. The problem is to define "in excess."

Think of the human as a **leaky bucket** with components on shelves at various levels. See Figure 26.1. The problem is whether the liquid will rise high enough to cause corrosion. As in the analogy, poisoning depends upon the rate of poison input (liquid input), the kind of liquid, the body size (bucket size), target organ susceptibility (shelf level), and the poison removal capability (hole size).

Since the same amount of poison rises much higher in a small bucket (small person), the same dose is more dangerous for small people. For simplicity, the TLVs are given for a 70-kg adult rather than per kg of body weight. There also is a large individual range (5–10 fold or more) of susceptibility to toxins, just as there is a varying need for vitamins, the good chemicals. The hole size depends primarily on the ability of the kidneys and liver to transform the poison into a less toxic compound and to eliminate it from the body. Examples of people with less liver and kidney capacity are older people, people with hepatitis, and people who drink alcohol to excess.

2 POISON ROUTES

Figure 26.2 gives a schematic view of the body, making the point that entrance to the mouth or lungs is not entrance to the body. To enter the body, a poison must enter the blood. Thus, from a toxicology viewpoint, if your little brother swallows a penny and it goes through the stomach and is eliminated with the feces, it has not been in the "body." However, if he swallows or breathes an object or chemical that is broken down in the intestinal tract or is absorbed by the blood in the lungs, he has greater potential to be poisoned.

Thus, an important characteristic of potential poisons is their ability to penetrate the body's perimeter. In general, inorganic materials are slow to penetrate the barrier, polar organic materials penetrate more quickly, and nonpolar organic materials are absorbed most quickly.

The most important potential entrance points are the skin, the mouth, and the lungs.

2.1 Skin   The skin is a superb barrier; it can even resist even the vacuum of space. Common experience has shown that most compounds run off the skin rather than penetrate the barrier. Therefore, people can insert their hands into compounds that, if they would penetrate the skin, would kill them. In the TLV tables (Tables 26.1 and 26.3) the word *skin* is next to compounds that penetrate the intact skin. Clothing or shoes wetted with a toxic agent increase contact time with the skin and thus increase danger. Cuts and abrasions to the skin permit toxins (as well as germs)

FIGURE   26.1

"**Leaky bucket**" **analogy.** There are components on shelves at various heights. Will the liquid rise high enough to cause "corrosion"?

FIGURE   26.2

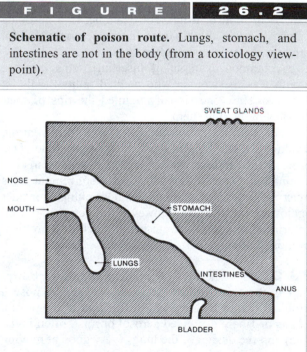

Schematic of poison route. Lungs, stomach, and intestines are not in the body (from a toxicology viewpoint).

TABLE   26.1

Five example compounds from the ACGIH 2002 Threshold Limit Values and Biological Exposure Indices (2002). In addition to the chemical substances, the booklet has recommendations for Biological Exposures Indices (BEIs), Physical Agents (Acoustic, Ergonomic, Ionizing Radiation, Lasers, Nonionizing Radiation and Fields, and Thermal Stress), and Biologically Derived Airborne Contaminants.

SUBSTANCE	TLV-TWA, ppm	TLV-STEL, ppm	Notations	Mol. Weight	TLV basis
Acetaldehyde	—	C 25	A3	44.05	Irritation
Acetic acid	10	15	—	60.00	Irritation
Acetic anhydride	5	—	—	102.09	Irritation
Acetone	500	750	A4; BEI	58.05	Irritation
Acetone cyanohydrin	—	C 17	Skin	85.10	Central nervous system; anoxia

C denotes ceiling limit.

A3 denotes animal carcinogen. See Appendix A in TLV/BEI booklet.

A4 denotes not classifiable as a human carcinogen.

BEI denotes there is also a Biological Exposure Index. (For acetone it is 50 mg/L in the urine.)

Skin denotes potential significant contribution to the overall exposure by the cutaneous route (including mucous membranes and the eyes) by direct skin contact or by vapors. Do not exceed this value during any part of the exposure.

Source: From *2002 Threshold Limit Value (TLVs®) and Biological Exposure Indices (BEIs®)* book. Reprinted with permission of ACGIH. The *TLV/BEI* booklet is updated annually.

to enter the body. However, in general, poisons entering the body through the skin do not pose a serious toxicology problem.

2.2 Mouth   The second entrance route is the mouth, by eating or drinking the poison. Although children often consume a poison by itself, the most common problem for adults in industry is toxic compounds in food or drink. For example, in a pesticide factory, dust in the air from the process may fall on sandwiches or in open coffee cups.

A famous example of inserting items into the mouth was the women who painted radium dials on watches. They occasionally pointed the tips of their brushes by licking them!

The best precaution seems to be to forbid eating, drinking, or smoking in work areas at any time. This protects the product, as well as the workers, from contamination. On the other hand, clean, convenient areas must be provided for eating and drinking; consider enclosing these areas. However, in general, poison entering through the mouth is not much of a problem in most industries.

2.3 Lungs   The biggest problem in poison absorption is the third route, the lungs. The lungs pose a problem due to both the physical nature of the poison (a gas or finely dispersed aerosol or mist, often invisible) and the design of the lungs (very good at moving molecules from the gas to the blood).

FIGURE   26.3

Distribution of airborne dust (solid line) (Frazer, 1973). The log-normal distribution has a peak about 2 μm. Particle penetration (dashed circle line) shows how the larger particles are filtered out (the line is lower than the solid line) (Carson, 1974). Retention (dashed triangle line) is even less (Carson, 1974).

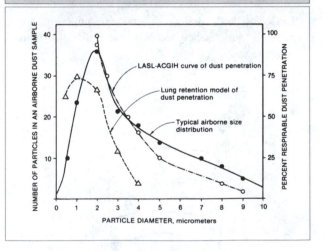

The most important characteristic of particles in regard to inhalation is their size. Figure 26.3 shows a typical log-normal distribution of airborne dust and respirable dust. The peak is about 2 μm. The next question is what sizes are retained in the lungs.

When lungs of 50- to 60-year-olds are dissected, about 50% of all particles are .5 µm or less in diameter. Effectively 100% are 5 µm or less; fewer than .002% are over 10 µm. (1 micrometer = 1 µm = 1 micron = .000 001 m. (A newspaper is 80 microns thick, a human hair diameter is 50 microns, and cigarette paper is 30 microns thick.) Particles in the air larger than 10 µm are removed completely in the nose and upper airways; particles between 5 and 10 µm or smaller are likely to be retained in the lung depths. (airborne particles from .1 to 1 µm significantly reduce visibility since their diameters are comparable to the wavelength of light in the visible region.)

A fiber will be defined as having a length more than three times the diameter. Almost all fibers will have a length shorter than 50 µm. Since fibers tend to orient their long axis to the airstream, straight fibers and short fibers penetrate deeper than curved, U-shaped, or long fibers.

(To better understand the physical dimensions, bring the objects to human scale by using 1 µm = 25 mm. Then a .1 µm particle is a BB, a 1 µm particle is a golf ball, and a 10 µm particle is a basketball. The trachea (actually 25 mm) becomes 625 m in diameter with the cilia (actually 10 µm long) becoming slightly longer than a pencil. The terminal bronchioles (actually 300 µm) and the alveolar sacs (actually 75 to 300 µm diameter) become like the walls of a small classroom. The three-layer membrane separating the gas from the blood (actually .2 µm) becomes the thickness of a book cover.)

3 POISON TARGETS

As discussed in the leaky bucket analogy, poison targets various organs. For discussion here, **poison targets** are divided into interior and exterior (skin).

3.1 Interior The first target is the respiratory system. One response might be an increase in airflow resistance (asthmatic response); this response usually ends when the mucociliary escalator removes the irritant. A second response (chronic bronchitis) might occur if there is continuing irritation to the mucosa due to high levels of irritant gas or particles. There is an increase in coughing and sputum. A third response (acute bronchitis or pneumonia) may occur if the cilia movements are paralyzed—thus leading to inadequate lung cleaning and possible improved colonization of bacteria. A fourth response (chronic interstitial lung disease) may occur from dusts containing microorganisms or animal proteins. In various forms, it is called bagassosis (from the baggasse, the fibrous material of sugar cane), farmer's lung (from moldy hay), cheesewasher's disease (from penicillium spores), malt worker's lung (malt dust in breweries), and grain worker's lung (weevils in flour).

(Cockburn et al., 1999, in an interesting study, report that workers given a nonsedating antihistamine prescription for allergic rhinitis were 5.2% more productive in their clerical work for the following three days, while workers given a sedating antihistamine prescription were 7.8% less productive for the following three days.)

Particles that penetrate the lung are engulfed by macrophages (big eaters) when they settle on the lung surface. The macrophages, having the power of independent motion, draw the particles through the tissues of the lung wall and (a) directly into the blood, or (b) to surrounding bronchioles for ciliary removal to the lymph system; the particles may (c) simply remain permanently attached to the wall. Inert particles present a problem. Free silica repeatedly kills the macrophages (silicosis); this leads to scar tissue and a loss of lung surface area (in effect, slow suffocation). Long asbestos fibers (over 5 µm) stick out of the macrophages and also cause scar tissue and loss of surface area. Cancer of the lungs is another possibility—especially from particles of chromium, nickel, uranium, and asbestos.

Finally, a compound may pass into the blood and attack other organs. Lead primarily affects nervous tissue, cadmium affects the kidneys, carbon monoxide and cyanide affect hemoglobin, and sulfur dioxide and hydrogen sulfide affect the lungs (cough). Hydrogen sulfide also causes pulmonary edema.

An unborn baby is especially endangered since the baby functions as a sponge to toxins; that is, it does not have a good ability to eliminate poisons. Substances that cause defects in fetal development are called teratogens. Thus, TLV standards that protect the normal adult are not strict enough for pregnant women. The most critical period is the first 3 months of pregnancy. Zenz (1984) discusses the following teratogens: lead and its compounds, benzene, carbon monoxide, DBCP, chlordecone, chloroprene (2-chlorobutadiene), epichlorohydrin, ethylene dibromide, ethylene oxide, mercury, vinyl chloride, anesthetic gases, ionizing radiation, and PCBs.

In 1975, General Motors was sued by the United Auto Workers for discrimination in a battery factory. General Motors had prohibited women of childbearing age from working there, although sterile women and women past childbearing age could work there. The lead concentrations varied from 1/2 to 3/4 of the TLV. The judge agreed with GM and said that, of the two competing social priorities of protection of health and equal opportunity employment, protection of health should take priority.

3.2 Skin

3.2.1 Dermatitis Dermatitis accounts for 35% to 40% of reported industrial disease. (Dermatosis denotes disease of the skin; **dermatitis** is more limited, referring to inflammation of the skin.) Birmingham (1973) reported that 1% of the working population has occupational skin disease during a year. Birmingham (1975) reported that 41% of occupational illnesses were skin ailments causing 25% of lost working days.

The skin is the largest organ system of the body. Structurally the skin is composed of two layers—the epidermis and the dermis. The epidermis has an outer layer of dead cells (horny layer, keratin layer, or stratum corneum), which provides a fair protection against chemicals (except alkalis and solvents). The epidermis also contains melanin, an inert protein that gives skin its color. Next is the Malpighian layer of living cells. The dermis or true skin has connective tissues, nerves, hair follicles, oil and sweat glands, and blood and lymph vessels.

Some people have a genetic predisposition to atopic dermatitis (AD). AD tends to flare up when a person is exposed to triggering factors, including:

- dry skin
- low humidity
- skin infections
- heat, humidity, and sweating
- emotional stress
- irritants and allergens

Irritants include solvents, industrial chemicals, detergents, some soaps and fragrances, fumes and tobacco smoke, paints, bleach, woolens, acidic foods, and astringents and other alcohol-containing skin-care products. Allergens are usually proteins from food, pollens, or pets (*All About Atopic Dermatitis,* 1989).

Contact dermatitis has two main categories of irritants: irritant contact dermatitis (75% of cases) and allergic contact dermatitis (25% of cases). With allergic contact dermatitis, an allergy takes 14 to 21 days to develop following initial contact. However, once sensi-

tized, response becomes obvious within 12 h of exposure; it may not even occur at the contact site. Medications that are notorious for sensitizing individuals include topical anesthetics containing benzocaine, topical antibiotics containing neomycin, topical antihistamine creams, fungi creams, and the skin disinfectant thimerosal (merthiolate) (Hogan, 1986).

Causes of occupational dermatoses are:

- *mechanical and physical*—abrasions or wounds, fiberglass, asbestos, and sunlight for outdoor workers (see Box 26.2).
- *chemical*—subdivided into strong irritants such as chromic acid and sodium hydroxide, and marginal irritants such as soluble cutting fluids and acetone, which require prolonged contact over time.
- *plant poisons*—woods such as West Indian mahogany, silver fir, and spruce (when being sandpapered or polished).
- *biological agents*—anthrax contracted by handlers of skins or hides from infected animals; grain or straw itch contracted by food and grain handlers from handling produce infected with mites, and the like.

In addition, some metals can sensitize the skin; for example, nickel. Nickel occurs in nickel plating and stainless steel. Example surfaces are earrings, tools, coins, and car door handles. The surface need not be metallic. Chromium is used to tan leather, so people allergic to chromium should avoid leather.

3.2.2 *Dermatitis prevention* Protective clothing helps—especially aprons and gloves. Aprons protect the chest and legs from liquids that might soak into the clothing and thus maintain contact with the skin for a long time. Gloves for chemicals naturally must not be permeable to that specific chemical.

BOX   26.2   *Ultraviolet Radiation*

The ultraviolet (UV) spectrum is divided into A (100–280 nm), B (280–315 nm), and C (315–400 nm); the visible spectrum goes from 400 to 780 nm; the infrared starts at 780 nm. Wavelengths around 300 nm are effective for bactericidal purposes. UV radiation increases 4%/1,000 ft of altitude.

B is the most dangerous ultraviolet radiation since it is the main cause of skin cancer; a fair skin greatly increases the risk of skin cancer. C goes 1 mm deep and ages and wrinkles the skin. There is also a consistent association between UV exposure and cataracts.

Control measures must address both the skin and the eye (Hitchcock et al., 1997). Engineering controls include welding curtains. Personal protection includes clothing, protective eyewear, sunscreens (absorb UV), and sunblocks (reflect rays away). For sunscreens and sunblocks, use a Sun Protection Factor (SPF) of 25–30 or more since otherwise you may not put enough on your skin. Caution: Some sunscreens and sunblocks cause allergies. The best sunscreen is a thick shirt.

Gloves also can protect the skin against dry irritants and against cuts and abrasions. Machinists tend to cut their hands by wiping them with rags contaminated with metal shavings; they should keep rags for wiping up separate from rags for hands—perhaps by using two colors of rags.

Exposure can be reduced by good housekeeping around the workstation, by designing machines with splashguards, and by educating the workers concerning the danger of various compounds (so they don't expose themselves unnecessarily).

Barrier creams, a substitute for gloves, are designed to prevent dermatitis, not to treat it. The two types are water-repellent and oil-repellent. Sunscreens can reduce the risk of nonmelanoma skin cancer by 90% (Hogan, 1986).

Personal cleanliness is the most important measure in preventing occupational skin disease (Birmingham, 1975). Younger workers and males develop more occupational dermatoses than older workers and females due to their lack of care in handling injurious materials and less personal cleanliness. Of course, engineers can help by providing adequate washing facilities near the work area.

When cleaning the hands, the cleaner should be specific for the substance to be removed. Powdered cleaners may be too abrasive; inorganic scrubbers (borax, silica) are more harsh than organic scrubbers (corn meal, rice hulls). Liquid soaps with a neutral pH are good when the soil is light and alkaline. Avoid soaps with perfumes. Waterless cleaners are better than a raw solvent but tend to dry the skin when used repeatedly. After using them, wipe the hands clean with a clean, dry towel, then wash and rinse the hands with mild soap and water, and then add a skin moisturizer.

Personal clothing worn on the job, including undergarments, should be washed thoroughly before reuse. Cohen and Positano (1986) found that unwashed shirts resuspended two to eight times more particles than washed shirts. A "bystander" (primarily the person who washes the clothing but also possibly children in the home) can be affected by the toxins (Grandjean and Bach, 1986). Two solutions are: (1) a double locker system with intervening shower, and (2) having the clothing cleaned professionally rather than at home. Zirschky and Witherell (1987) discuss the problems of cleanup of mercury contamination of thermometer workers' homes.

To summarize, consider poison ivy, a plant poison that causes a quick reaction. You can reduce the chance of contact by eliminating the poison ivy, using non-permeable gloves, detoxifying the handles of handtools that may have contacted the ivy, or using a barrier cream. If contact is made, eliminate skin contact with contaminated clothing and clean the skin. Finally, consider medications to reduce symptoms.

4 POISON ELIMINATION

Although the lungs eliminate carbon dioxide and sweat glands eliminate some salts, the primary organs for poison elimination are the liver and the kidneys.

The liver biotransforms the toxins in the blood through oxidation, reduction, hydrolysis, and conjugation; it converts fat-soluble compounds to water-soluble compounds. Figures 26.4 and 26.5 give schematics of the liver and kidney. After the compound has been transformed in the liver, it reenters the blood. Some transformed compounds are carried by the bile to the intestines for excretion. The blood with the transformed compound (as well as some of the original compound not yet transformed) goes to the various organs, including the kidney. The kidney, which receives 30% of cardiac output, takes the transformed compound and puts it into the urine, with which the transformed poison leaves the body.

Not all the blood goes to the liver, and not all of the compound is transformed each time; in some cases the liver even metabolizes a compound into something more toxic than the parent compound. This permits toxins to reach various target organs and cause ill effects before the liver eventually detoxifies

FIGURE   26.4

Sketch of liver and kidney. Liver cells are the primary means of biotransformations of poisons entering the body. About 30% of the liver's blood enters from the general circulation (through the hepatic artery) and 70% from the stomach and intestines (portal vein). Blood from the stomach and intestines must pass through the liver before entering the general circulation. Transformed materials leave the liver in bile (bile duct to small intestine) or in the blood to the general circulation (hepatic vein to vena cava).

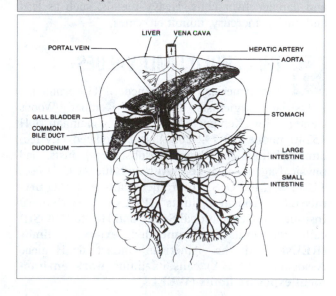

FIGURE 26.5

Schematic of biotransformation. The poison can enter the general circulation directly from the lungs or by penetration of the skin. If it comes from the intestines, it must pass through the liver. On each passage through the liver, a proportion of the poison is transformed. The transformed compounds in the blood are water-soluble and are transferred in the kidney to the urinary tract for elimination.

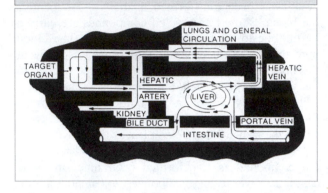

the body. The various metabolic reactions are complex, and interactions become important.

For example, two compounds (such as alcohol and barbiturates, or cigarette smoke and cotton dust or asbestos) may both compete for the same liver enzyme (and thus slow down **biotransformations**) or both act on the same or different target organs (e.g., lungs, brain).

Johns-Manville Corporation, citing a study reporting that smokers who are occupationally exposed to asbestos have a 92 times greater chance of developing lung cancer than the general population, banned smoking in its asbestos facilities. The policy was intended to give asbestos workers the same chance of lung cancer as the general nonsmoking population.

Alcohol and its products disturb liver metabolism and damage liver cells. Heavy metals, such as lead and methyl mercury, inhibit enzymes.

5 THRESHOLD LIMIT VALUES

The American Conference of Governmental Industrial Hygienists (ACGIH, Kemper Woods Center, 1330 Kemper Meadow Dr., Cincinnati, OH 45240; phone 513-742-2020) issues updated TLV recommendations for chemical substances, dusts, and physical agents each year. Although the ACGIH uses TLV-TWA, the U. S. government calls its limits **permissible exposure limits (PELs),** the National Institute for Occupational Safety and Health (NIOSH) calls its limits **recommended exposure limits (RELs),** and the American Industrial Hygiene Association (AIHA) calls its limits **work environment exposure limits (WEELs).**

Table 26.1 gives the TLVs for the first five chemical components listed. In addition to chemical substances, values are given for respirable dusts (fibrogenic dusts, which cause scar tissue in the lungs) and nuisance dusts (which cause insignificant scar tissue). Three different types of threshold limit values are given: a time-weighted average (TLV-TWA), a **short-term exposure limit (TLV-STEL),** and a ceiling (TLV-C).

The *TLV-TWA* is the concentration, for a normal 8-h workday and 40-h work week, to which nearly all workers may be repeatedly exposed, day after day, without adverse effect. It primarily recognizes chronic (long-term) effects.

The *TLV-STEL* is concerned with acute (short-term) effects of (1) irritation, (2) chronic or irreversible tissue damage, and (3) narcosis of sufficient degree to increase the likelihood of accidental injury, to impair self-rescue, or to reduce work efficiency. The STEL is a 15-min time-weighted exposure that should not be exceeded any time during the day even if the TLV-TWA is met. There should not be more than 4 STEL exposures of 15 min per day and there should be at least 60 min between each STEL exposure.

The *TLV-C* is the concentration that should not be exceeded during any part of the working day.

Excursions (peaks) are permitted above the recorded values of the toxin. They are permitted above the TWA and STEL but, of course, not above the C. For example, acetic acid has a TWA of 10 ppm. An exposure of 12 for 4 h can be balanced by an exposure of 8 for the remaining 4 h. You could even have an exposure of 80 for 1 h balanced by exposure of 0 for the remaining 7 h.

This, however, is where the STEL comes in. The STEL for acetic acid is 15. Thus, the exposure of 80 for 1 h is too high. An exposure of 80 for 1 min and exposure of 0 for 14 min would give an exposure of 6 for 15 min, which would be within the STEL.

Note that, for administrative simplicity, the TLVs assume that concentration × time = a constant. That is, you would get the same effect from 8 aspirins taken once in 8 h as from one aspirin taken each hour for 8 h. This is unlikely to be true, so don't push the excursions too far.

For TWAs with no STEL listed, ACGIH (2002) recommends, "STEL should exceed 3 times the TWA for no more than 30 min/day; under no circumstances should STEL exceed 5 times TWA, provided that TWA is not exceeded."

The TLVs in Table 26.1 are given both by volume and by weight. To convert (at 25°C):

$$\text{ppm} = \frac{24.45 \ (\text{mg/m}^3)}{\text{Molecular weight}}$$

The TLV is based on an 8-h exposure. The value has to be adjusted if (a) concentration varies during the day, (b) the day is not 8 h, or (c) exposure is to more than one substance.

First, assume a worker was exposed to acetone for 4 h at 500 ppm, 2 h at 750 ppm, and 2 h at 1,500 ppm. The equivalent exposure is:

$$TWA = \frac{C_a t_a + C_b t_b \ldots C_n t_n}{8}$$

where TWA = Time-weighted average (equivalent 8-h exposure)

C = Concentration of $a, b, c \ldots$, ppm or mg/m^3

t = Time of exposure to concentration $a, b, c \ldots$, h

For the above example, TWA = [500(4) + 750(2) + 1,500(2)]/8 = 6,500/8 = 812. Since 812 is more than the TLV-TWA of 750, the exposure is not acceptable (see Box 26.3).

Next, assume a worker was exposed to 1,250 ppm of acetone during the entire working day but worked only 6 h/day. Then TWA = [1,250(6) + 0(2)]/8 = 7,500/8 = 940. Since 940 is more than 750, the exposure is not acceptable. Assume that the worker was exposed to 900 ppm of acetone for a 10-h shift. Then TWA = 900(10)/8 = 9,000/8 = 1,125. Since 1,125 is over 750, the exposure is not acceptable.

The worker also might be exposed to a mixture of substances. The assumption is that the effects are additive, not independent. Assume exposure for 8 h to acetone at 500 ppm, 2-butanone of 45 ppm, and toluene of 40 ppm. The TLV-TWAs are 750, 200, and 100 ppm. Then

$$TWA_{mixture} = \frac{C_1}{TLV_1} + \frac{C_2}{TLV_2} + \frac{C_3}{TLV_3}$$

where

$TWA_{mixture}$ = Equivalent TWA mixture exposure (maximum of 1 permitted)

BOX 26.3   *Exposure/Recovery for Chemicals*

The Threshold Limit Value-Time Weighted Average (TLV-TWA) is the concentration, for a normal 8-h workday and 40-h workweek, to which nearly all workers may be exposed, day after day, without adverse effects. It primarily recognizes chronic (long-term) effects.

For example, the TLV-TWA for acetone is 750 ppm. If a person is exposed, for an 8-h day, to over 750 ppm, the exposure is not acceptable. If a person is exposed for periods different from 8 h, the permitted exposure is:

TLV Adjustment Factor = 8/Hours worked   (1)

For a 6 h shift, the TLV Adjustment Factor = 8/6 = 1.33; for a 12 h shift, it is 8/12 = .67. Thus, the permitted exposure for 6 h is 1.33 (750) = 1,000 ppm; for 12 h, it is 500 ppm. Equation (1) considers only the exposure time, not the recovery time.

Another possibility is to consider both exposure time and recovery time.

TLV Reduction Factor =   (2)

(8/h worked)(Hours off work/16)

(valid only for ≥ 8 h)

For a 6-h shift, the Equation (2) TLV Reduction Factor is not applicable. For a 12-h shift, it is 8/12 (12/16) = .67 (.75) = .5. Thus, this formula not only permits less exposure for periods over 8 h but also is more restrictive than Equation (3). Equation (2) is discussed at length as the "Brief and Scala" model by Paustenback (1994).

For chemicals whose half-life suggests that not all the chemical would be eliminated before returning to work the next day, a weekly formula is used. Examples whose biologic half-life is clearly over 10 h include PCBs, PBBs, mercury, lead, mineral dusts, and DDT.

TLV Reduction Factor =

40/Hours of exposure in one week   (3)

Equations (1) and (3) are the models the U. S. government uses (Paustenback, 1994).

If the TLV adjustment factor were used alone, very high exposures would be permitted for short work periods. These high exposures are restricted by the Short-Term-Exposure-Limit (TLV-TWA) and Ceiling (TLV-C). The STEL is a 15-minute, time-weighted exposure that should not be exceeded any time during the day even if the TLV-TWA is met. The TLV-C is the concentration that should not be exceeded during any part of the working day.

Equations (1), (2), and (3) do not consider the exponential decline in toxin concentration and, thus, tend to be conservative. See Box 21.5. If biological half-life (pharmacokinetic approach) is used for adjustment of TLVs, the adjustments are smaller than Equations (1) and (3) for longer work periods; they are larger for shorter work periods (Paustenback, 1994, p. 292). All the equations assume no exposure during non-work time; however, this assumption may not be valid if a person moonlights.

$C_{1,2,3}$ = Concentration (8 h) for a specific substance

$TLV_{1,2,3}$ = TLV for a particular substance

For the numbers above, $TWA_{mixture}$ = 500/750 + 45/200 + 40/100 = .667 + .225 + .4 = 1.292. Since 1.292 is over 1, the exposure is not acceptable.

The above calculations have been performed mathematically. The engineer should remember, however, the accuracy of the measuring equipment used in establishing the TLVs and the unknowns faced by the scientists. Thus, treat the TLV values as guides rather than precise numbers; that is, if the TLV is 5, then a value of 4.9 is not perfectly safe and a value of 5.1 not excessively dangerous. In general, the TLV standards are getting lower as more evidence is obtained.

In addition, there are measurement errors in obtaining concentrations at the job. For example, exercise makes a difference; Soderlund (1975) reported that the air in lungs contained twice as much toluene during light work as during rest. People with sedentary occupations inhale about 5 m^3 of air/8 h while those working very hard may inhale 20/8 h. Measurement of the contaminant concentration should be representative of the worker's breathing zone. The standard technique is to use a battery-powered pump with the sampling device in the breathing zone. Use of a direct readout unit (where sampling and analysis occur in one step) has the advantage that the second-by-second readout can be related to specific worker actions. This is much more useful than just knowing the total exposure over an 8-h period.

Although the TLVs are designed to protect the normal person during exposure for 40 h/week for the entire working life, they are not designed for hypersensitive people. Some examples of hypersensitive people are those with kidney and liver problems and the unborn babies of pregnant women (especially in the first 3 months).

6 CONTROLS

Controls are divided into engineering, administrative, and personal protective equipment.

Often the management staff tolerates working conditions for the employees that they would not tolerate if they had to do the work themselves. A key question is, "Would you let your own child work there?" If the answer is no, the employees shouldn't work there either.

6.1 Engineering Controls Engineering controls are the first priority for prevention. See Table 26.2.

6.1.1 *Substitute a less harmful material* For paints and cleaning compounds, replace organic-based compounds with water-based ones. Use solvents with higher TLVs (methyl chloroform with TLV = 350 instead of carbon tetrachloride with TLV = 5; toluene with TLV = 100 instead of benzene with TLV = 10). Glues often include solvents; this solvent drying time (and thus evaporation rate) can be controlled by the glue manufacturer. In addition, some substances are much more volatile than others. Table 26.3 gives the ratio of vapor pressure, ppm/TLV-TWA, ppm. Use substances lower rather than higher in the table.

6.1.2 *Change the material or process* Reduce carbon monoxide by using electric-powered instead of gasoline-powered fork trucks. Use safety cans instead of glass bottles (which can break). Reduce dust by using low-speed oscillating sanders instead of high-speed rotary sanders. Paint with a brush or roller instead of spray painting. Remove grinding particles or solder fumes with a vacuum cleaner instead of blowing them into the room with compressed air. When hand-grinding steel castings, workers are exposed to silica (sand) burned into the casting surface; reduce the risk of silicosis by coating mold surfaces to reduce sand burn-in, by shotblasting the castings, and by using high-velocity downdraft exhaust ducts. Reduce the

---

T A B L E   2 6 . 2
Controls for respiratory hazards (Revoir, 1973). Engineering controls are more desirable than administrative controls.

ENGINEERING CONTROLS	ADMINISTRATIVE CONTROLS
1. Substitute a less harmful material.	1. Screen potential employees.
2. Change the material or process.	2. Periodically examine employees (biological monitoring).
3. Enclose (isolate) the process.	3. Train engineers, supervisors, and workers.
4. Use wet methods.	4. Reduce exposure time.
5. Provide local ventilation.	
6. Provide general ventilation.	
7. Use good housekeeping.	
8. Control waste disposal.	

T A B L E	2 6 . 3

Comparison of toxicity (TLV) and vapor pressure (P_0) vs. vapor hazard ratio (VHR) for selected industrial solvents, rank ordered (Popendorf, 1984).

COMPOUND	1987 TLV, PPM	P0 AT 25°C, MMHG	VHR, PPM/PPM
Allyl chloride	1	365	480,300
Carbon disulfide	10 skin	361	47,500
Dichloropropene	1 skin	36	47,400
Carbon tetrachloride	5 skin	113	29,700
Chloroform	10	195	25,700
Benzene	10	95	12,540
1,2-Dichloroethane	10	79	10,400
1,1,2,2-Tetrachloroethane	1 skin	6	7850
Triethylamine	10	68	8910
Methylene chloride	100	431	5670
Hexane	50	151	3975
1,1,2-Trichloroethane	10 skin	24	3200
Trichlorethylene	50	74	1955
Ethyl ether	400	534	1760
1,1-Dichloroethane	200	227	1490
Cellosolve	5 skin	5.3	1395
Methanol	200 skin	122	800
Methyl ethyl ketone	200	95	625
Methyl isobutyl ketone	50	19	500
Perchloroethylene	50	18	484
1,1,1-Trichloroethane	350	121	455
Aniline	2 skin	0.67	440
Acetone	750	230	400
Toluene	100 skin	28	374
Styrene	50	6.1	160
Phenol	5 skin	0.35	92
o-Xylene	100 skin	6.6	87
Ethanol	1000	59	78
m- and p-Xylenes	100 skin	3.6	48
Cresol	5 skin	0.17	45
Diazinon	0.008[A] skin	2×10^4	33
Nonane	200	4.3	28
Parathion	0.008[A] skin	6×10^5	10
Dibrom	0.19[A] skin	3×10^4	2.1
Trichlorofluoromethane (Freon 11)	1000	0.8	1.1
Malathion	0.74 skin	4×10^5	0.07

[A]Value listed in 1982 TLV publication only as mg/m^3.

amount of solvent needed for cleaning by cleaning before the substance has time to harden or oxidize; an analogy is dishes in a dishwasher.

Many people now are allergic to latex; health-care workers can shift to non-latex gloves, but many precautions need to be taken for patients due to the presence of latex in so many places. In addition, certain foods (bananas, avocado, kiwi) increase the effect of latex allergies.

6.1.3 Enclose (isolate) the process Capture substances and vapors before they "get out" rather than after they have dispersed—it's cheaper. As a first approximation, cost of air handling is proportional to the volume moved. Two guidelines are: (1) physically enclose the process or equipment and (2) remove air from the enclosure (hood) fast enough so that air movement at all openings is into the enclosure (i.e., negative pressure). Heitbrink et al. (1994), for auto-body repair, demonstrated that ventilated sanders (which cost about $40 more than non-ventilated sanders) reduced dust exposure by a factor of 10. For paint booths, Goyer (1995) demonstrated the importance of reducing flow turbulence.

A mechanical supply of air (a fan) usually is better than depending on air infiltration. The operating cost is twofold: (1) the direct cost of electrical power for the fans, and (2) the hidden cost of replacing the conditioned air (heated or cooled and humidified and purified to desired values).

The plastic strips used for strip doors also can be used to enclose machines or processes (such as solvent tanks) that require passage of product on conveyors. Use lids on degreasing tanks; for compounds being stirred, use a lid with a small hole for the shaft of the mixer. The lid, in addition to reducing evaporation of vapors, can reduce energy consumption (especially when used with a thermostat).

Enclosure also reduces the number of workers exposed. When cleaners, glues, paints, and varnishes dry, solvents often are released. Most of the evaporation occurs in the first few minutes of drying, so isolate operators from the drying area, and for maximum ventilation efficiency, enclose this area. Normally the operator is "outside" and the machine is isolated. Some vehicles' cabins, however, should be isolated from exterior pollutants such as dust, fumes, and odors. Use fans to make the cabin environment positive pressure so flow is out, not in. Isolate pumps that could leak toxic compounds. A sealer coat on concrete floors reduces dust; less dust means fewer air changes/h and thus lower heating costs.

Maintenance workers need protection too. For example, an automotive plant found that maintenance workers were exposed to beryllium dust when repairing copper alloy welding tools.

Factories are not the only location of toxic compounds. Embalmers may be exposed to too much formaldehyde (Plunkett and Barbela, 1977). Asbestos fiber concentrations are high in some offices. Asbestos has been used as a fire retardant on steel beams. Over time, vibrations shake fibers loose to be circulated by the ventilation system. The problem is the worst when the area between the dropped ceiling and the floor above is used as a ventilating plenum.

6.1.4 *Use wet methods*
Water alone may not be enough, so use a wetting agent and dispose of the wetted particulate before it dries. Wet floors before sweeping. In rock drilling, use hollow drills through which water is passed. Steam cotton. Use moistened flint in potteries. Use a high-pressure water jet instead of abrasive blasting to clean castings.

6.1.5 *Provide local ventilation*
In the work area, the general sequence for the flow of air should be: input air, worker, contaminant, exhaust air. That is, the worker is upwind of the contaminant. The same sequence applies locally within the workstation: input air, worker, contaminant, exhaust air. Don't allow fumes to rise from the work area and pass the face before exiting the workstation. This may require downdraft ventilation.

For example, NIOSH improved manicure tables to control ethyl methacrylate exposure (Spenser et al., 1997). Among the improvements were increasing downdraft volume from .03 to .11 m³/s and removing the charcoal filter and exhausting the air outside (the filter had allowed the firm to reintroduce the "filtered" air into the room).

Local ducts are much more efficient if they have a flange (flat plate perpendicular to the duct axis) at the entrance. The flange should be equal to duct diameter; when length/width = 1 (square or round duct), focusing of the air increases duct velocity 25%; when L/W = 16 (slot), the flange increases centerline velocity 55% (Fletcher, 1982).

Dumping the exhaust "out the window" is not satisfactory. Clean the air with filters, cyclones, vapor traps, precipitators, and so forth. (Recycle the heat with rotary wheels, fixed plates, heat pipes, and runaround coils.) In some cases, this trapped waste product can be sold for a profit. One example is spraying alfalfa dust in a cyclone with liquid lard from a rendering company. The resulting mixture is sold at a profit as cattle feed. Paper mills formerly dumped sulfite liquor into the river. When forbidden to do this, they found they could sell it at a profit as a dust suppressor on roads.

When analyzing exposures, make a videotape of the operation. A first approximation is that toxin exposure is proportional to time exposed to the toxin. This estimate can be refined if a direct reading instrument can be used to estimate real-time exposure. For example, in a nonferrous foundry, lead exposure came primarily from moving an unvented ladle. It took 10% of the job time but gave 33% of the lead exposure (Edmonds et al., 1993). Edmonds et al. did not actually measure lead exposure but used an instrument that measured respirable aerosols. It was assumed that the lead concentration of the aerosol did not vary. The data were entered on a spreadsheet so average concentration, cumulative time, and cumulative exposure (product of average exposure and cumulative time) could be calculated.

6.1.6 *Provide general (dilution) ventilation* When the contaminant is released from nonpoint sources, use general ventilation; for point sources, local exhaust is more efficient. Forced ventilation (fans, blowers) is preferable to natural ventilation (open doors, windows) since air direction, volume, and velocity can be controlled. Inadvertent recirculation of exhausted air is a problem. Discharge exhaust air so that it escapes from the "cavity" that forms as a result of wind movement around buildings.

Also, take precautions when buildings are fogged with insecticides. The application should be done on Friday evening, and the building should be well-ventilated over the weekend. Before fogging, remove or store coffee cups, stationery, and clothing (Currie et al., 1990).

6.1.7 *Use good housekeeping* Remove dust from floor and ledges to prevent dust movement by traffic, vibration, and air currents. Eliminate piles or open containers of chemicals. Fix leaking containers. Immediately clean up spills of volatile chemicals.

6.1.8 *Control waste disposal* Consider each disposal problem separately. Specific procedures should be established for safe disposal of unused dangerous substances, toxic residues, contaminated wastes, material containers that are no longer needed, and containers with missing labels. Be sure the policies are followed under strict supervision.

In one GM plant, management had sewer covers tack-welded shut to prevent employees from dumping wastes down the sewer. Make provisions for leaking and broken containers. That is, the storage area should be fail-safe so that when a drum leaks, the contents are contained. Drain systems become chemical storage systems. Be sure you know what is going to mix in your drains.

6.2 Administrative Controls   See Table 26.2.

6.2.1 *Screen potential employees* Avoid using workers who are hypersensitive to the substance. Examples are people with allergic contact dermatitis, pregnant women who would be exposed to teratogens, and people with impaired livers or kidneys (they should be screened out just as a person with a bad back has lifting restrictions). Another example is screening out cigarette smokers from exposure to asbestos or cotton plant bracts.

6.2.2 *Periodically examine employees* So far, the concept has been to monitor the environmental air and compare the concentration of a substance to its TLV. Another approach is to monitor the body of an individual (**biological monitoring**) through measurement of a substance concentration in blood, urine, hair, fingernails, or expired air. Table 26.4 gives biological exposure indices (BEIs) for mercury and carbon monoxide (ACGIH, 2002).

As of 1996, 36 BEIs had been issued (Hee, 1997). Use biological monitoring when:

- it is mandated (e.g., blood lead)
- inhalation route is <70% (e.g., solvents penetrating the skin; hot, dusty environments where people lick their lips)
- personal protective equipment such as respirators, gloves, and protective garments are worn
- unanticipated exposures occur.

T A B L E 2 6 . 4			
Biological exposure indices (BEIs) from ACGIH (2002). Only two are given as an example.			

INDICES	TIMING	BEI	NOTATION
CARBON MONOXIDE			
Carboxyhemoglobin in blood	End of shift	3.5% of hemoglobin	B*, Ns+
Carbon monoxide in end-exhaled air	End of shift	20 ppm	B*, Ns+
MERCURY			
Total inorganic mercury in urine	Preshift	35 µg/g creatinine	B*
Total inorganic mercury in blood	End of shift at end of work week	15 µg/L	B*

*B indicates significant background levels usually are present in people not occupationally exposed.

+Ns indicates determinant is nonspecific. Nonspecific tests are preferred.

Source: From *2002 Threshold Limit Value (TLVs®)* and *Biological Exposure Indices (BEIs®)* book. Reprinted with permission of ACGIH. The *TLV/BEI* booklet is updated annually.

6.2.3 *Train the supervisors, engineers, and workers*

The U. S. government has published the Hazardous Communication Standard (29 CFR 191.1200), commonly called the "Worker's Right to Know." Manufacturers and distributors of hazardous chemicals must provide **Material Safety Data Sheets** (commonly called **MSDSs**) that identify the physical and health hazards of their products. Employers are responsible to inform their employees about the chemicals and to train them in safe use of the chemicals.

To meet training needs, give supervisors overviews with emphasis on costs and legal aspects; give technical principles and details to engineers and workers. Give the workers specific information rather than glittering generalities—for example, "Change your respirator filter once every four hours" rather than, "Change filter when needed."

6.2.4 *Reduce exposure time*

Reduced exposure time increases the recovery time/exposure time ratio. For example, if a worker is exposed 8 h/day, there is 16-h recovery or a recovery ratio of $16/8 = 2$. If two workers each are exposed for 4 h, the ratio goes to $20/4 = 5$. For more on work/recovery, see Boxes 21.4 and 21.5. In addition to job sharing, scheduling can help. For example, mines schedule blasting at the end of the shift so the dust can settle for 16 h before the next shift arrives. Schedule maintenance during off hours so the fewest possible people are exposed.

6.3 Personal Protective Equipment

Personal protective equipment is the last line of defense. Often it fits poorly, workers abuse it, it is not maintained, and workers are not taught how to use it. In addition, workers can get a false sense of security from the equipment.

Figure 26.6 shows some respirators (which cover the nose and mouth and provide filtered air). Another approach is to cover the entire head with a helmet and provide clean external air (which also can be cooled) through a hose. Dentists often wear a mask over their nose to reduce their breathing of metallic particles from the drilling of fillings.

As pointed out in Section 3.2.2, personal clothing after contamination is a risk to the spouse and family if it is brought home. Have the clothing cleaned professionally by people who know how to remove the toxins; have the worker shower before going home, especially if dealing with beryllium, asbestos, lead, PCBs, or chlorinated hydrocarbons (Bellin, 1981).

If cleaned at home (e.g., cleaning farming clothes contaminated with pesticides), do the following (*Farmsafe 2000,* 1994):

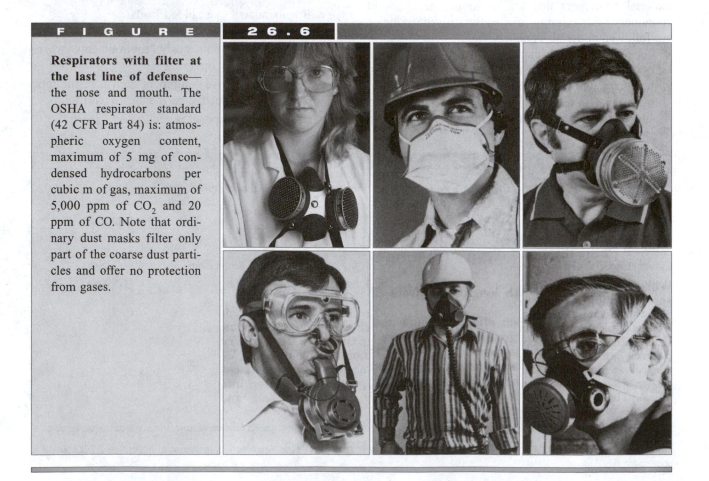

FIGURE 26.6

Respirators with filter at the last line of defense—the nose and mouth. The OSHA respirator standard (42 CFR Part 84) is: atmospheric oxygen content, maximum of 5 mg of condensed hydrocarbons per cubic m of gas, maximum of 5,000 ppm of CO_2 and 20 ppm of CO. Note that ordinary dust masks filter only part of the coarse dust particles and offer no protection from gases.

- If the clothing is saturated, throw it away.
- Wash clothing as soon as possible.
- Wash separately from other clothing.
- Wear rubber gloves.
- Prespot the toxin.

- Use hot water and 1.5 (normal amount) of heavy-duty detergent.
- Air-dry on an outside line.
- Run an empty cycle with hot water and detergent before using washer again.

Review Questions

1. Differentiate toxicology, musculoskeletal disorders, and safety.
2. Discuss the Hg poisoning at Minamata, Japan.
3. Discuss the body as a "leaky bucket."
4. Is the primary toxin entry point the skin, lungs, or mouth?
5. What do macrophages do?
6. How does silicosis kill?
7. What is a teratogen? List three.
8. Briefly describe the epidermis and the dermis.
9. What is a gauntlet?
10. Briefly describe how people in the home can be protected against toxins in work clothing.
11. What is the difference between TLV-TWA and TLV-STEL?
12. Assume that the TLV-TWA for acetone is 750 ppm. What exposure is permitted for 2 h? Show calculations.
13. List four engineering controls. Give an example for each.
14. Should the worker be upwind or downwind of the contaminant? Why?
15. Briefly discuss the concept of biological monitoring.
16. Show with an example how reducing exposure time improves the recovery/exposure ratio.

References

ACGIH. *2002 Threshold Limit Values and Biological Exposure Limits.* Cincinnati: American Conference of Governmental Industrial Hygienists, 2002.

All About Atopic Dermatitis. Eczema Association for Science and Education, 1221 Yamhill, Portland, OR 97205, 1989.

Anderson, L. Biological effects of extremely low-frequency electromagnetic fields: in vivo studies. *American Ind. Hygiene Association J.,* Vol. 54, No. 4, 186–96, 1993.

Bellin, J. Don't take your work home with you. *Occupational Health and Safety,* Vol. 5, No. 6, 39–42, 1981.

Birmingham, D. Occupational dermatoses: Their recognition, control and prevention. In *The Industrial Environment,* Chapter 34. Washington, DC: Supt. of Documents, 1973.

Birmingham, D. *The Prevention of Occupational Skin Disease.* New York: Soap and Detergent Association, 1975.

Bracken, T. Exposure assessment for power frequency electric and magnetic fields. *American Ind. Hygiene Association J.,* Vol. 54, No. 4, 165–77, 1993.

Carson, G. Sampling particulates in the industrial environment. *ASHRAE Journal,* Vol. 16, No. 5, 45–49, May 1974.

Cleary, S. A review of in vivo studies: low-frequency electromagnetic fields. *American Ind. Hygiene Association J.,* Vol. 54, No. 4, 180–85, 1993.

Cockburn, I., Bailit, H., Berndt, E., and Finkelstein, S. Loss of work productivity due to illness and medical treatment. *J. of Occupational and Environmental Medicine,* Vol. 41, 11, 948–53, 1999.

Cohen, B. and Positano, R. Resuspension of dust from work clothing as a source of inhalation exposure. *Am. Industrial Hygiene Assoc. J.,* Vol. 47, No. 5, 255–58, 1986.

Currie, K., McDonald, E., Chung, L., and Higgs, A. Concentrations of diazinon, chlorpyrifos, and bendiocarb after application in offices. *Am. Industrial Hygiene Association J.,* Vol. 51, No. 1, 23–27, 1990.

Edmonds, M., Gressel, M., O'Brien, D., and Clark, N. Reducing exposures during the pouring operations of a brass foundry. *Am. Industrial Hygiene Association J.,* Vol. 54, No. 5, 260–66, 1993.

Farmsafe 2000. Vol. 3, No. 1, NIOSH, 4676 Columbia Parkway, Cincinnati, OH 45226, 1994.

Feero, W. Electric and magnetic field management. *American Ind. Hygiene Association J.,* Vol. 54, No. 4, 205–10, 1993.

Fletcher, B. Centerline velocity characteristics of local exhaust hoods. *Am. Ind. Hygiene Assoc. J.,* Vol. 43, No. 8, 626–27, 1982.

Frazer, D. Sizing methodology. In *The Industrial Environment,* Chapter 14. Washington, DC: Supt. of Documents, 1973.

Goyer, N. Performance of paint booths equipped with down-draft ventilation. *American Ind. Hygiene Association, J.,* Vol. 56, 258–65, 1995.

Grandjean, P. and Bach, E. Indirect exposures: The significance of bystanders at work and at home. *Am. Industrial Hygiene Assoc. J.,* Vol. 47, No. 12, 819–24, 1986.

Hee, S. Biological monitoring. Chapter 13 in *The Occupational Environment—Its Evaluation and Control,* S. DiNardi (ed.). Fairfax, VA: AIHA, 1997.

Heitbrink, W., Cooper, T. and Edmonds, M. Evaluation of ventilated sanders in the auto-body repair industry. *American Ind. Hygiene Association, J.,* Vol. 55, No. 8, 756–59, 1994.

Hitchcock, R., Murray, W., Patterson, R., and Rockwell, R. Nonionizing radiation. Chapter 21 in *The Occupational Environment—Its Evaluation and Control,* S. DiNardi (ed.), Fairfax, VA, American Ind. Hygiene Association, 1997.

Hogan, D. Skin disorders are high on the list of occupational health hazards. *Occupational Health and Safety,* 42–45, October 1986.

Mastromatteo, E. On the concept of threshold. *American Industrial Hygiene Association J.,* Vol. 42, No. 11, 763–70, 1981.

Paustenback, D. Occupational exposure limits, pharmacokinetics and unusual work schedules. In *Patty's Industrial Hygiene and Toxicology,* 3d ed., Vol. 3A, *The Work Environment,* Chapter 7, pp. 222–348, Harris, R., Cralley, L., and Cralley, L. (eds.). New York: Wiley, 1994.

Plunkett, E. and Barbela, T. Are embalmers at risk? *American Industrial Hygiene Association J.,* Vol. 38, No. 1, 61–62, 1977.

Popendorf, W. Vapor pressure and solvent vapor hazards. *American Industrial Hygiene Association J.,* Vol. 45, No. 10, 719–26, 1984.

Revoir, W. Control of respiratory hazards. In *Safety Sentinel.* Southbridge, MA: American Optical Co., 1973.

Savitz, D. Overview of epidemiologic research on electric and magnetic fields and cancer. *American Ind. Hygiene Association J.,* Vol. 43, No. 4, 197–204, 1993.

Soderlund, S. Exertion adds to solvent inhalation danger. *Health and Safety,* 42–43, January 1975.

Spenser, A., Estill, C., McCammon, J., Mickelsen, R., and Johnson, O. Control of ethyl methacrylate exposures during the application of artificial fingernails. *Am. Ind. Hygiene Assoc. J.,* Vol. 58, 214–18, 1997.

Zenz, C. Reproductive risks in the workplace. *National Safety News,* 38–46, September 1984.

Zirschky, J. and Witherell, L. Cleanup of mercury contamination of thermometer workers' homes. *American Industrial Hygiene Association J.,* Vol. 48, No. 1, 81–84, 1987.

Websites

News about allergies (allergy database), www.absoluteallergy.com

American Conference of Governmental Industrial Hygienists (ACGIH), www.acgih.org

American Industrial Hygiene Association, www.aiha.org

Overview

After a good method is determined, determine how long the job takes. The measurement can be "quick and dirty" (type 2, nonengineered standards) or more precise (type 1, engineered standards). Allowances (personal, fatigue, and delay) are added to normal time to get standard time. Learning (both individual and organizational) improves operator performance versus standard time.

Key Concepts

acceptable day's work

audit

average cost/unit

delay allowances

discipline level

doubled quantities

earned hours

engineered estimates

fatigue allowances

going slowly less often

high-task/low-task

inside work

labor efficiency

learning

learning effect on time standards

log–log scale

machine time

manufacturing progress

measured daywork

nonengineered standards

normal time

observed time

occurrence sampling

performance ratios

personal allowances

restricted output

shift allowances/work allowances

short cycle

should-take/did-take standards

standard data

standard time

time logs

time study

unmeasured hours

work measurement

523

WHY DETERMINE TIME/JOB?

What you cannot measure,
your knowledge is of a
meagre and unsatisfactory kind.
                                    Lord Kelvin

So far, the emphasis in this book has been on job design. However, the four chapters in Part VI discuss how long a job takes (**work measurement**). Although industrial engineers should devote most of their effort to job design (as that is where productivity improvements are made), knowing time/unit is useful.

As an aside, the direct labor contribution to total cost has been dropping, so many firms are using **performance ratios** rather than direct labor; Table 27.1 gives some examples. The goal is to measure output and connect employee actions to the outputs.

MBNA, which has a large credit card business, uses (among others) the following standards: Customer

TABLE 27.1

Performance ratios other than direct labor (Engwall, 1987).

Engineering
- Number of software instructions/number of software engineers
- Cost of repair drawings/number of drawings produced
- Number of engineering change orders/number of engineers

Quality
- Cost of quality/cost of sales
- Total receiving inspection hours/lots received
- Production earned hours/quality engineered support hours

Procurement
- Purchasing department budget/number of purchase orders placed
- Lots received on time/total lots received
- Purchase order errors/purchase orders audited

Finance
- Number of pricing proposals/number of pricing people
- Operations budget/finance department budget
- Receivables over 60 days/total receivables

Information Systems
- Hardware uptime/total hardware time
- Out-of-service terminals/total number of terminals
- User complaints/hours of usage

Production
- Wait time/direct labor hours
- Indirect hours/direct labor hours
- Setup hours/earned hours

address changes must be processed within one day, the telephone must be picked up within two rings, and incoming calls must be transferred to the appropriate party within 21 seconds.

Time/unit is useful for five applications:

1. cost allocation
2. production and inventory control
3. evaluation of alternatives
4. acceptable day's work
5. incentive pay

1.1 Cost Allocation   Without time/unit, you can't determine costs. In Table 7.3, the cost of making a fan is discussed. One cost was direct labor of $1.00 with the notation "Time to stamp out blades, paint blades, assemble knob to shaft." In addition, burden (overhead) costs typically are determined by multiplying direct labor costs by a standard multiplier (e.g., 4) so that, if the direct labor cost is $1, burden is $1(4) = $4.

But, if you don't know the direct labor time, then how will you determine the direct labor and burden costs of the product? You may be losing money on every unit and not know it!

1.2 Production and Inventory Control   Without time/unit, you can't schedule or staff. For scheduling, when should components be made? How long will it take to make assemblies? For staffing, how many workers are needed for an order and for how long? Production and inventory control is impossible without time/unit.

1.3 Evaluation of Alternatives   Without time/unit, you can't compare alternatives. Should a part be made on a turret lathe or a screw machine? Should a part be repaired or be replaced with a new one? Note that when operations research people feed a_{ij} values into their computers, they need accurate estimates of the a_{ij} values; incorrect times result in incorrect decisions. Table 3.5 compares various motions; the point is that, without the time value, no comparison of methods can be made.

1.4 Acceptable Day's Work   Without time/unit, supervisors have difficulty in judging the performance of people working for them—an **acceptable day's work.** George made 29 widgits today—is that good or bad? Maria contacted 22 customers/h as part of her telemarketing job—good or bad? Juan picked 200 cases/h from the warehouse this week—good or bad? If a standard time is available, actual times can be compared to the standard, leading to more effective management.

Repetitive work is especially benefitted by time standards. Using standards to judge performance (but not determine pay incentives) is called **measured daywork.** See Table 27.2 for estimates of the potential benefits.

T A B L E		2 7 . 2

Productivity (%) as a function of work measurement and supervision (Sellie, 1992). The data are based on more than 1,000 productivity audits and work measurement installations.

PERFORMANCE	SUPERVISION		
MEASUREMENT	Poor	Average	Good
Measured	60–80%	70–90%	80–95%
Unmeasured	30–70%	50–75%	60–85%

Source: C. Sellie, "Predetermined Motion-Time Systems and the Development and Use of Standard Data," in *Handbook of Industrial Engineering,* 2d ed., G. Salvendy (ed.). Copyright © 1992 by John Wiley & Sons. Reprinted by permission of John Wiley & Sons, Inc.

1.5 Incentive Pay Without time/unit, you can't pay people based on the number of units they produce. Only a minority of firms use the pay-by-results (the positive reward) approach; the majority use the acceptable-day's-work (the negative reward) approach. For example, a warehouse might decide picking takes .33 h/pallet and pay Bill $5/pallet picked. If Bill picked 120 pallets in a 40 h week (i.e., worked at "standard speed"), then his pay would be 120(5) = $600. But if he picked 130, he would receive 130(5) = $650. If he picks less than standard, typically he would receive standard (100%) pay—unless a discipline level is reached (see Box 27.1).

Thus, a worker has everything to gain and nothing to lose. Why would a firm implement a policy that has direct labor costs increase at the same rate as output? Because overhead costs do not increase; thus, overhead cost/unit and total cost/unit decrease.

Boxes 27.2 and 27.3 give more on incentives.

BOX	27.1	*Consequences of Not Making Standard*

Organizations use different concepts of **standards.** See Figure 27.1. The curves show the potential long-range performance of the industrial population. Thus, for a low-task standard, over 99% of the industrial population would be able to reach standard.

Although it is tempting for the personnel department to attempt to prescreen those who "won't make it anyway," this approach has many possible legal problems. In the long run, having the individual try it and quit or try it and fail to make standard and thus not retain the job is the best policy.

The next question, however, is not what workers are potentially able to do but what they actually do. What if the standard is picking 100 cases/h and Joe picks only 50? It depends. See Figure 27.2.

If Joe is learning the job, he would be expected to achieve a certain percent of standard each week—for example, 50% the first week, 80% the second week, 90% the third week, 95% the fourth week, 98% the fifth week, and 100% the sixth week. Previously qualified workers returning to a job might be assumed to start part-way through a learner's standard. If Joe was assigned temporarily to the job, he could either be exempt from the **discipline level** or put on the learning schedule.

If Joe is a permanent, experienced worker, the performance could be considered "excused" or "nonexcused." (Performance usually is considered for a period of a week rather than a day so that random fluctuations average out.) Excused failures to meet standard are for temporary situations—bad parts from the supplier, back injuries, pregnancy, and so forth. For example, "Employees returning to work from Worker Compensation due to a loss-of-time accident in excess of 30 days will be given consideration based upon the medical circumstances of each individual case."

Nonexcused performances are those for which the worker is considered capable of making standard but did not achieve it. Generally, the first assumption is that training was not adequate. But if performance stays low, penalties begin to be imposed. See Table 27.3. Most organizations have a "forget" feature; for example, one month of unacceptable performance drops you down a step. The use of an established discipline procedure allows workers to self-select themselves on a job. The organization can have only minimal preemployment screening and thus reduces the risk of discrimination charges.

Standards are based on 8 h/day, but people sometimes work less than or more than 8 h/day. Examples of longer shifts are overtime and working 4 shifts of 10 h instead of 5 shifts of 8 h. Because of fatigue, in theory, people can produce more/hour when working shorter hours and less/hour when working longer hours. In practice, in today's society most standards are not very tight. People can pace themselves, and the output/hour tends to be constant over the shift. In addition, it is awkward to change the standard when people work longer or shorter hours because then it is not a standard. If an

BOX   **27.1**   *Consequences of Not Making Standard, continued*

adjustment is to be made, it is more practical to modify the discipline level.

Any change in discipline level for fatigue should be a function of the amount of fatigue allowance. That is, if a task has a 20% fatigue allowance, the task should be more subject to fatigue than a task with a 5% fatigue allowance. Fatigue also should be greater for longer shifts (e.g., 12 h versus 10 h versus 8 h) and longer periods of overtime (e.g., 4 weeks versus 1 week). Rodgers (1986) reports, for one study at Kodak, that performance for overtime was 5%–10% below the performance for 8 h. This implies that the discipline level for hours over 8 h might be 5%–10% below the discipline level for 8 h.

However, discipline levels should be based on longer time periods than just hours 8 and 9 of a day. Thus, if 95% discipline is used for 8 h and 90% for hours 8 and 9, the daily discipline level would be [8(95) + 2(90)]/10 = 94%. However, remember that performance should be compared to the standard on a weekly basis, not a daily basis.

The level at which discipline takes place is negotiable between the organization and the union. For example, it may be 95% of standard. That is, as long as workers perform above 95% of standard, they are considered satisfactory. However, this tends to get overall performance from the group running around 98% of standard. (As soon as the workers get above the discipline level, they take more leisure time.) The best long-range strategy probably is to set discipline at 100% of standard. Anything less will give a long-run loss in production—especially if a measured daywork system is used instead of incentives.

Organizations can use several strategies to improve the group performance and reduce output restrictions. Basically, they allow the employees as well as the organization to benefit from output over 100%.

The primary technique is to give money for output over 100%. A 1% increase in pay for a 1% increase in output is the prevalent system.

Another alternative is to give the employee time off for output over 100%. For example, allow individuals to "bank" weekly hours earned over 100%. These banked hours then can be used to compensate for weeks when their individual performance is less than the discipline level. Most people will run up a positive balance to use as "insurance." This can be combined with a plan in which all hours in the bank over (say) 20 h are given as scheduled paid time off. With the use of paid time off (taken in minimum amounts of 8 h), absenteeism tends to drop as employees can use the paid time for personal business.

Another possibility is to let the discipline level for individuals decrease when average performance of the group is over the discipline level. For example, if the group's performance is 98% and required = 95%, the discipline level for individuals that week is 95 − 3 = 92%. This allows the group to "carry" poor performers. Of course, management gets higher performance from many people while only 1 or 2 people are carried.

When discipline measures are taken, the standards themselves naturally begin to be questioned. These challenges typically can be resolved at the local level if the firm has been open and aboveboard in conducting the standards setting and has detailed records showing how each standard was set.

If conflicts cannot be resolved, the standard may go to arbitration (grievance procedure). Arbitration typically has several levels, with the lowest level being the plant, then division, and then outside-the-organization arbitration.

2 ESTABLISHING TIME STANDARDS

The next question is which time-measurement technique should be used? The choice depends on the cost of obtaining the information and the benefits of using the information.

A danger is using inaccurate information, thus, making the wrong decision. A product might priced too high or too low. A method or machine might be retained or replaced incorrectly. A work standard might be too tight or too low. In the common measured daywork system (a standard, but without financial incentive), people tend to work at 100% of standard but no more. If the standard is set at .1 h/unit when it should be .95 h/unit, then there is a 5% loss in productivity.

Techniques are divided into nonengineered and engineered.

2.1 Nonengineered (Type 2) Estimates
"Quick and dirty" information can be obtained with low cost; sometimes it is useful. **Nonengineered standards** are not preceded by methods or quality analysis; they are **did-take standards,** not **should-take standards.**

Normal pace (100% pace) is not the same from organization to organization. Different concepts of normal pace can be grouped into **low-task** paces and **high-task** paces. While it is difficult for many to maintain a 100% pace in the high-task concept (i.e., there is considerable worker selection), almost everyone can achieve the low-task pace. Karger and Hancock (1982) reported that "almost everyone" is 95% for MTM and time studies using MTM's definition of 100%. When allowances are added to the normal time, over 99% of the industrial population is capable of achieving standard. However, performance may not match capability.

The figure makes two points: (1) Times to do a job are not constant (i.e., the standard deviation is not zero!); and (2) normal pace (100% pace) is not the same from organization to organization.

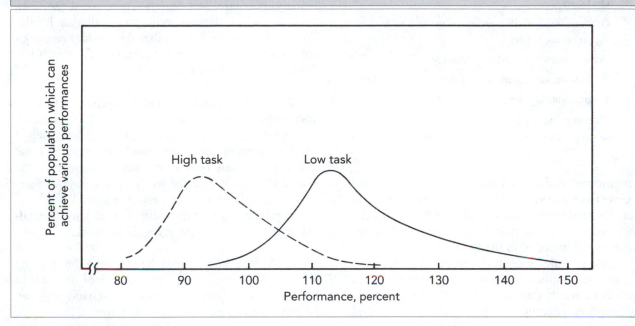

Restricted output has the characteristics of small variance and negative skewness (as a percent of standard). The key is a small amount of variation between or within individuals. The consistent achievement of the target over the reporting period (e.g., 1 week) may conceal wide fluctuations by period (days) but with the characteristic that, on the last day, cumulative actual performance for the period slightly exceeds cumulative required performance. For example, if the weekly goal is 100%, performance may be 95% on Monday, 90% on Tuesday, 90% on Wednesday, 100% on Thursday, and 125% on Friday. Often this pattern repeats as it becomes a game to the worker.

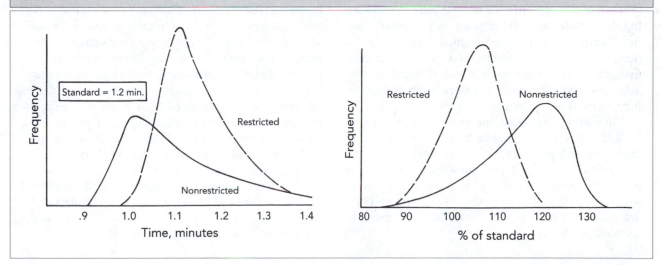

| T A B L E | | 2 7 . 3 |

Example discipline levels for not producing enough. A published set of rules ensures that everyone is treated fairly. Most organizations have a similar set of rules for tardiness and absenteeism.

STEP	DESCRIPTION
0	Normal operator, acceptable performance
1	Oral warning
2	Oral warning; detailed review of method with supervisor or trainer
3	Written warning; additional training
4	Written warning; some loss of pay
5	Written warning; larger loss of pay
6	Discharge from job

Nonengineered estimates have many subjective and few objective characteristics. All of the four techniques described below assume the worker works at a 100% pace. Also personal, fatigue, and delay allowances are included in the times.

Sometimes, the time study group is under pressure to determine standards on many jobs immediately, but it doesn't have the resources to do everything immediately. If type 2 standards are used in such situations, they should be identified as temporary and should expire automatically after a given date, say 60 days after issue. At the time of issue, the IE department should provide a schedule for upgrading the standard from type 2 to type 1.

2.1.1 *Historical records* Historical records may be used for "very dirty" estimates. For example, in a warehouse, how many cases can be picked per hour? You might count how many cases were shipped in January, February, and March. Then, count the work hours in each of these months; then, calculate h/case. You would have to assume that the product mix does not change, delays are reasonable, etc. The result is a did-take time, not a should-take time.

2.1.2 *Ask an expert* Another approach is to ask a knowledgeable person how long the job will take. Ask the maintenance department supervisor how long it will take to paint a room or install a conveyor system. Ask the sales manager how many customers can be visited in a week. Ask the traffic manager how many miles a driver of a semi can cover in a week.

A problem is that the estimate may vary depending on how "hungry" the group is for work.

2.1.3 *Time logs* It may be that time/job is being used for accounting purposes—time does not have to be known before the job is done. Then, **time logs** can be used. An engineer might write down:

| BOX | **27.2** | *Incentive Applications* |

At one time, individual incentive wages were common. Kopelman (1987, p. 37) reported that 75% of industrial organizations used wage incentives in 1935, 52% in 1939, 27% in 1958, and 20% in 1982. Wage incentives are becoming relatively rare, as it is more and more difficult to find jobs that (1) are highly repetitive, (2) are employee-paced, not machine-paced, (3) are performed relatively independently of other workers, and (4) have outputs that can be tested for quality and, if found acceptable, counted. The shift has been from individual incentives to group incentives.

In a group incentive, the group of workers may be told to produce 250 units/h. The concept is that the group will pressure the slower workers to work faster. Group incentives, however, can cause morale problems among the slower workers (due to social pressure) as well as the faster workers (who are getting less money because they are carrying the slow workers).

Another approach is to reward the entire factory based on standard costs of the entire product line; if standard costs go down X%, wages go up by Y% (where X may not equal Y).

An even more indirect incentive is an annual bonus that depends upon the firm's profit. (The U. S. auto industry has such a plan.) In this case the worker bonus depends not only on individual performance but also on management performance, product design and marketing, how tough the competition is, and other factors. Management has an advantage in this kind of plan since the worker income is not a fixed cost. That is, if profits are good, everyone can get a bonus, but if profits are bad, labor costs stay low. The workers benefit because management is more willing to give bonuses when times are good but strongly resists making them a fixed cost to be paid regardless of profits. (Of course, many people feel they are "just workers" and none of their income should be "at risk.")

BOX **27.3** *Financial Incentives for Nonincentive Employees*

By definition, nonincentive employees' wages do not vary with their output. However, it still is possible to use incentives to cut costs. (In addition, there are plans to increase revenue. Examples are employees on commission, dealers, and distributors.)

Example cost-reduction goals are to reduce standard maintenance downtime on company vehicles, reduce inservice accidents involving company vehicles, reduce tardiness, reduce absenteeism.

Each goal should have an objective and a performance level specified. For example:

Goal: Reduce tardiness

Objective: Reduce tardiness 30%

Performance level: No unexcused lateness each week

The rules of the game should be simple and specific (have written rules), attainable (every participant should have a chance of winning), and measurable.

Day	Project	Hours
Monday	A	4.0
	B	2.5
	C	2.0
Tuesday	C	3.5
	A	1.0
	B	4.0

Naturally, these are did-take times, not should-take times. Some reasons for possible inaccuracies are:

- Totals will be at least 8 h/day, even if the individual did not work 8 h/day. No idle time will be reported. This individual even carefully reported working more than 8 h/day.

- The person probably will try to complete the log at the end of the day, leading to considerable errors. In particular, small jobs tend to be omitted. A 10-min phone call on job P could be lumped with another project.

- The time estimate might be deliberately biased, based on the budget available. Assume the engineer has 500 h left on project B, but 0 h left on project D. But the engineer spent 4 h on Tuesday on project D. The easy solution is to charge project B.

A solution is to have a folder for each job. Each person working on the job writes down the time spent each day and initials it.

2.1.4 *Occurrence sampling* Occurrence sampling is described in detail in Chapter 10. The observer intermittently observes operations many times over a given period. For example, a study might establish that an office worker used the phone 40% of the workday. If the study was over a 3-week period and the work week was 40 h, this means that .4 (3)(40) = 48 h was spent on the phone. If there were 405 different calls during the time, it took 48/405 = .12 h/call.

Note that this is a did-take time, as the operation was not studied beforehand. Note also that the worker can bias the results by slowing down during the observation or by using poor methods.

2.2 Engineered (Type 1) Estimates
For more accurate estimates, use **engineered estimates.** Engineered estimates must be preceded by a methods and quality analysis so they give a should-take time, not a did-take time. Engineered estimates have few subjective and many objective characteristics.

If a facility, which formerly had no standards or had type 2 standards, is implementing type 1 standards, do the following:

1. Select a logical organizational unit; plan to set type 1 standards for all touch labor in the unit. Do not set standards for only a few people in multiple units.
2. Orient supervisors and workers.
3. Improve the work methods.
4. Determine the time, either through time study or standard data.
5. Calculate standards, including allowances.
6. Check and debug standards; implement for a trial period (say, 1 month).
7. Go to full implementation, including discipline.

(See also MIL-STD-1567A, Military Standards: Work Measurement.)

The two basic ways of determining time/job are stopwatch time study and standard data.

2.2.1 *Time study* Chapter 28 describes stopwatch time study in detail. Time is reported at three levels:

1. **Observed time:** The "raw" (unadjusted) time taken by the worker.
2. **Normal time:** The time an experienced worker should take. Normal time = (Observed time) (Rating).

3. **Standard time:** The normal time is increased to account for personal, fatigue, and delay allowances. See Section 3 of this chapter.

Stopwatch time study requires an operator doing the operation; thus, it cannot be done ahead of production.

2.2.2 *Standard data*

Standard data is described in detail in Chapter 29 (micro level) and Chapter 30 (macro level). The data elements are expressed in *normal time* (that is, rating is included); allowances are added to get *standard time*.

The analyst visualizes the work method and then (using either a table or a formula), determines the specific work elements and their associated times.

Compared with time study, the standard data method has three advantages: (1) cost of determining a standard is low (assuming you have a database with element times), (2) consistency is high, as everyone using the database should get the same times, and (3) standards can be calculated ahead of production. Two disadvantages are (1) you may not have the database and (2) the analyst must imagine the work method.

3 ALLOWANCES

3.1 Shift or Work Time?

It is a policy decision by the firm whether to give allowances as a percent of shift time or work time.

Shift allowances are expressed as a percent of shift time:

$$\text{Standard time} = \text{Normal time}/(1 - \text{Allowances})$$

Work allowances are expressed as a percent of work time:

$$\text{Standard time} = \text{Normal time} (1 + \text{Allowances})$$

Normal time has to be increased from standard time by personal, fatigue, and delay allowances.

3.2 Personal Allowances

Personal allowances are given for such things as blowing your nose, going to the toilet, getting a drink of water, smoking, and so on. They do not vary with the task—they are the same for all tasks in the firm. There is no scientific or engineering basis for the percent to give. A value of about 5% (24 min in a 480-min day) seems to be typical.

Most firms have standardized break periods (coffee breaks); for example, 15 min during the first part of the shift and the same during the second part. It is not clear whether most firms consider this time as part of the personal allowance or in addition to it.

The mid-shift meal break (lunch) is another question. This 20–60-min break obviously permits the

worker to attend to personal needs and recover from fatigue. Yet, lunch is not usually considered as part of allowances—even if the lunch period is paid.

Some firms give an additional break if work is over 8 h. For example, if a shift is 10 h, there is an additional break of 10 min after the 9th hour.

Some firms give additional allowances to all workers for cleanup (either of the person or the machine), putting on and taking off protective clothing, or for travel. In mines, the travel allowance is called portal-to-portal pay; pay begins when the worker crosses the mine portal even though the worker will not arrive at the work site until some time later.

3.3 Fatigue Allowances

The rationale for **fatigue allowances** is to compensate the person for the time lost due to fatigue. In contrast to personal allowances, which are given to everyone, fatigue allowances are given only for cause—for fatigue. No fatigue? Then, no fatigue allowance!

A challenge is the concept of **"machine time."** See Figure 27.3. With the increasing capabilities of servomechanisms and computers, many machines operate

---

FIGURE 27.3

Machine time allowance terms of 1 worker and 1 machine. OW = Outside Work = work that must be done outside the machine (process)-controlled time. IW = **Inside Work** = work that can be done within the machine time. UT = Unoccupied Time = operator not engaged in side work, attention time, or taking authorized rest. (UT usually has 0% allowance.) A = Allowances. Personal and environmental fatigue allowances must be taken away from the machine, but physical and mental fatigue allowances, in some cases, may be taken at the machine. It is difficult to use incentive pay when the outside work time is a small proportion of the total time. Generally, the goal is a 1% increase in pay for a 1% increase in output. But if the machine cycle dominates, even very good performance on the outside work has little effect on total time.

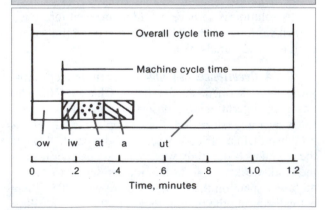

semi-automatically (operator is required only to load/unload the machine) or automatically (machine loads, processes, and unloads). During the machine time of the work cycle, the operator may be able to drink coffee (personal allowance), talk to the supervisor (delay allowance), or recover from fatigue. Thus, as a general principle, give a fatigue allowance only for the portion of the work cycle outside the machine time.

The following discusses the fatigue allowances developed by the International Labor Organization (ILO, 1992). They were supplied by a British consulting firm. The use of the ILO values is complex. Remembering that fatigue allowances are given for work time only (not machine time), sum the applicable fatigue allowance points. Then, using Table 27.4, convert points to percent time.

The fatigue factors are grouped into three categories: physical, mental, and environmental.

3.3.1 *Physical: Physical fatigue*   Table 27.5 shows how the ILO makes a distinction among carrying loads, lifting loads, and force applied. In the NIOSH lifting guideline (Chapter 15), the lift origin and destination, frequency of move, angle, and container are considered as well as load.

With heavy work (e.g., warehouse order picking), the time required for psychomotor motions does not adequately consider the problem of cardiovascular strain and fatigue (Garg, 1995). Two possible solutions are: (1) ensure that the time study covers a long period (say >4 h) of all potential workers (not just young men) and (2) give a large fatigue allowance.

3.3.2 *Physical: Short cycle*   Table 27.6 gives the fatigue allowance to permit time for the muscles to recover.

3.3.3 *Physical: Static load (body posture)*   Table 27.7 gives the allowance for poor posture. Also see Section 1 of Chapter 13.

3.3.4 *Physical: Restrictive clothing*   Table 27.8 gives the allowance for restrictive clothing. See Chapter 25 for more on clothing.

3.3.5 *Mental: Concentration/anxiety*   Table 27.9 gives the allowance for concentration/anxiety.

3.3.6 *Mental: Monotony*   Table 27.10 gives the allowance for monotony. Allowances for monotony, boredom, lack of a feeling of accomplishment, and the like seem questionable. These factors are unlikely to cause fatigue and increase time/cycle. Because these factors primarily reflect unpleasantness, they should be reflected in the wage rate per hour rather than the time/unit.

T A B L E   27.4

Conversion from points allowance to percent allowance for ILO. The second column (0) gives the 10s, and the remaining columns give the units. Thus, 30 points (0 column) = 15%; 31 points (1 column) = 16%; 34 points = 17%. The percent allowance is for manual work time (not machine time) and includes 5% personal time for coffee breaks.

POINTS	0	1	2	3	4	5	6	7	8	9
0	10	10	10	10	10	10	10	11	11	11
10	11	11	11	11	11	12	12	12	12	12
20	13	13	13	13	14	14	14	14	15	15
30	15	16	16	16	17	17	17	18	18	18
40	19	19	20	20	21	21	22	22	23	23
50	24	24	25	26	26	27	27	28	28	29
60	30	30	31	32	32	33	34	34	35	36
70	37	37	38	39	40	40	41	42	43	44
80	45	46	47	48	48	49	50	51	52	53
90	54	55	56	57	58	59	60	61	62	63
100	64	65	66	68	69	70	71	72	73	74
110	75	77	78	79	80	82	83	84	85	87
120	88	89	91	92	93	95	96	97	99	100
130	101	103	105	106	107	109	110	112	113	115
140	116	118	119	121	122	123	125	126	128	130

T A B L E	27.5

Carrying, lifting, and body force allowances (ILO, 1992). The ILO curves are straight lines when plotted versus percent allowances. Push includes foot-pedal push and carry on the back. Carry includes hand carry and swinging arm movements. Weight is averaged over time. A 15-kg load lifted for 33% of a cycle is 5 kg.

WEIGHT OR FORCE, KG	PUSH POINTS	CARRY POINTS	LIFT POINTS
1	0	0	0
2	5	5	10
3	8	9	15
4	10	13	18
5	12	15	21
6	14	17	23
7	15	20	26
8	17	21	29
9	19	24	32
10	20	26	34
11	21	29	37
12	23	31	40
13	25	33	44
14	26	34	46
15	27	36	50
16	28	39	50
17	30	40	53
18	32	42	56
19	33	44	58
20	34	46	60

T A B L E	27.6

Short-cycle allowance (ILO, 1992).

POINTS	CYCLE TIME, MIN
1	.16 – .17
2	.15
3	.13 – .14
4	.12
5	.10 – .11
6	.08 – .09
7	.07
8	.06
9	.05
10	< .05

T A B L E	27.7

Posture allowance (ILO, 1992).

POINTS	ACTIVITY
0	Sitting easily
2	Sitting awkwardly or mixed sitting and standing
4	Standing or walking freely
5	Ascending or descending stairs, unladen
6	Standing with a load; walking with a load
8	Climbing up or down ladders; some bending, lifting, stretching, or throwing
10	Awkward lifting; shoveling ballast to container
12	Constant bending, lifting, stretching, or throwing
16	Coal mining with pickaxes; lying in a low seam

3.3.7 *Environmental: Climate* Table 27.11 gives the allowance for climate.

3.3.8 *Environmental: Dust, dirt, and fumes* Table 27.12 gives the allowance for dust, dirt, and fumes.

3.3.9 *Environmental: Noise and vibration* Table 27.13 gives the allowance for noise and vibration. Also see Chapter 24.

3.3.10 *Environmental: Eye strain* Table 27.14 gives the allowance for eye strain.

3.3.11 *Overview of fatigue allowances* In general, the fatigue allowances seem to have inadequate ranges. In addition, note from Table 27.4 that points are not converted "1 for 1" to percent. A person with

0 points for fatigue gets a 10% fatigue allowance. A person with 30 points gets a 15% fatigue allowance—an increase of only 5%.

In addition, neither the length of the workday nor number of days/week are specified. Presumably, it is 8 h/day and 5 days/week. We do not recommend changing the allowances for working a shorter or longer time period. Any adjustment should be at the discipline level (see Box 27.1).

3.4 Delay Allowances Delay allowances should vary with the task, not the operator. They compensate for machine breakdowns, interrupted material flow, conversations with supervisors, machine maintenance and cleaning, etc. If the delay is long (e.g., 30 min), the operator clocks out (recording the start and stop times of the delay on a form) and works on something

TABLE 27.8

Restrictive clothing allowances. ILO (1992) considers clothing weight in relation to effort and movement. Also consider whether it affects ventilation and breathing.

POINTS	CLOTHING
1	Thin rubber (surgeon's) gloves
2	Household rubber gloves; rubber boots
3	Grinder's goggles
5	Industrial rubber or leather gloves
8	Face mask (e.g., for paint spraying)
15	Asbestos suit or tarpaulin coat
20	Restrictive protective clothing and respirator

TABLE 27.9

Concentration-anxiety allowances. ILO (1992) considers what would happen if the operator were to relax attention, responsibility, need for exact timing, and accuracy or precision required.

POINTS	DEGREE
0	Routine, simple assembly; shoveling ballast
1	Routine packing, washing vehicles, wheeling trolley down clear gangway
2	Feed press tool (hand clear of press); topping up battery
3	Painting walls
4	Assembling small and simple batches (performed without much thinking); sewing machine work (automatically guided)
5	Assembling warehouse orders by trolley; simple inspection
6	Load/unload press tool; hand-feed into machine; spray painting metalwork
7	Adding up figures; inspecting detailed components
8	Buffing and polishing
10	Guiding work by hand on sewing machine; packing assorted chocolates (memorizing patterns and selecting accordingly); assembly work too complex to become automatic; welding parts held in jig
15	Driving a bus in heavy traffic or fog; marking out in detail with high accuracy

TABLE 27.10

Monotony allowances. ILO (1992) considers the degree of mental stimulation and if there is companionship, competitive spirit, music, and so on.

POINTS	DEGREE
0	Two people on jobbing work
3	Cleaning own shoes for .5 h on one's own
5	Operator on repetitive work; operator working alone on nonrepetitive work
6	Routine inspection
8	Adding similar columns of figures
11	One operator working alone on highly repetitive work

TABLE 27.11

Climate allowances. ILO (1992) considers temperature/humidity, wet, and ventilation. For temperature/humidity use the average environmental temperature. For wet, consider the cumulative effect over a long period. For ventilation, consider quality/freshness of air and its circulation by air conditioning or natural movement.

POINTS FOR TEMPERATURE/HUMIDITY

Humidity, %	Up to 24° C	24–32°	Over 32°
Up to 75	0	6–9	12–16
76–85	1–3	8–12	15–26
Over 85	4–6	12–17	20–36

POINTS	WET
0	Normal factory operations
1	Outdoor workers (e.g., postal delivery)
2	Working continuously in the damp
4	Rubbing down walls with wet pumice block
5	Continuous handling of wet articles
10	Laundry washhouse, wet work, steamy, floor running with water, hands wet

POINTS	VENTILATION
0	Offices; factories with "office-type" conditions
1	Workshop with reasonable ventilation but some drafts
3	Drafty workshops
14	Working in sewer

T A B L E	27.12

Dust, dirt, and fumes allowances (ILO, 1992). For dust, consider both volume and nature of the dust. The dirt allowance covers "washing time" where this is paid for (e.g., 3 min for washing). Do not allow both time and points. For fumes, consider the nature and concentration; whether toxic or injurious to the health; irritating to eyes, nose, throat, or skin; odor.

POINTS	DUST
0	Office, normal light assembly, press shop
1	Grinding or buffing with good extraction
2	Sawing wood
4	Emptying ashes
6	Finishing weld
10	Running coke from hoppers into skips or trucks
11	Unloading cement
12	Demolishing building

POINTS	DIRT
0	Office work, normal assembly operations
1	Office duplicating
2	Garbage collector
4	Stripping internal combustion engine
5	Working under old motor vehicle
7	Unloading bags of cement
10	Coal mining; chimneysweeping with brushes

POINTS	FUMES
0	Lathe tuning with coolants
1	Emulsion paint, gas cutting, soldering with resin
5	Motor vehicle exhaust in small commercial garage
6	Cellulose painting
10	Molder procuring metal and filling mold

T A B L E	27.13

Noise and vibration allowances. ILO (1992) considers whether the noise affects concentration, is a steady hum or a background noise, is regular or occurs unexpectedly, is irritating or soothing. Consider the impact of the vibration on the body, limbs, or hands and the addition to mental effort as a result, or to a series of jars or shocks.

POINTS	NOISE CATEGORY
0	Working in a quiet office, no distracting noise; light assembly work
1	Work in a city office with continual traffic noise outside
2	Light machine shop; office or assembly shop where noise is a distraction
4	Woodworking machine shop
5	Operating steam hammer in forge
9	Riveting in a shipyard
10	Road drilling

POINTS	VIBRATION CATEGORY
1	Shoveling light materials
2	Power sewing machine; power press or guillotine if operator is holding the material; cross-cut sawing
4	Shoveling ballast; portable power drill operated by 1 hand
6	Pickaxing
8	Power drill (2 hands)
15	Road drill on concrete

else during the clocked-out time. Delays usually permit the operator to take some personal time and reduce fatigue; that is, they also serve as personal allowances and fatigue allowances.

How do you set a delay allowance? One possibility is to record the delays during a work sampling study or during a time study. For example, if there were 4 min of delay during 100 min of time study, then 4% could be used for the delay allowance.

Errors in delay allowances can occur from poor sampling or changing conditions. To obtain a valid sample of delays, the sample must represent the total shift, not just the middle of the shift. That is, in addition to the middle of the shift, the delays must be observed at the start and stop of the shift and just before and after lunch and coffee breaks. Also observe delays on the second and third shifts.

Conditions change over time. A reasonable procedure is to give delay allowances an expiration date; for example, 2 years after being set. After 2 years, they must be redetermined.

4 LEARNING

A person doing a task repetitively is a dynamic situation, not a static situation. That is, the amount of time to do a task depends on the amount of practice the person (and the organization) has. Fortunately, the amount of this learning can be predicted with reasonable accuracy.

The failure to adjust standard time for learning is the primary cause for incorrect standard times. Learning occurs both in the individual and in the organization.

TABLE	27.14

Eye strain allowances. ILO (1992) considers the lighting conditions, glare, flicker, illumination, color, and closeness of work and for how long strain is endured.

POINTS	DEGREE
0	Normal factory work
2	Inspection of easily visible faults; sorting distinctively colored articles by color; factory work in poor lighting
4	Intermittent inspection for detailed faults; grading apples
8	Reading a newspaper in a bus
10	Continuous visual inspection (cloth from a loom)
14	Engraving using an eyeglass

4.1 Individual and Organizational Learning

Individual **learning** is improvement in time/unit even though the product design doesn't change and the tools and equipment do not change. The improvement is due to better eye–hand coordination, fewer mistakes, and reduced decision time.

Organizational learning (**manufacturing progress**) is improvement due to changing product design, changing tools and equipment, and changing work methods; it includes individual learning.

Consider the example of Maureen serving breakfast. During the individual learning period, she learned where the coffeepot and cups were, the prices of each product, etc. The amount of time she took to do these tasks declined to a plateau. Then management set a policy to serve coffee in cups without saucers and to furnish cream in sealed, one-serving containers so the container need not be carried upright. These changes in product design reduced the time for the task. Other possible changes would include a coffeepot at each end of the counter. A different coffeepot may have a better handle so less care is needed to prevent burns. The organization may decide to have the server leave the bill when the last food item is served.

Organizational progress comes from three factors: (1) operator learning with existing technology, (2) new technology, and (3) substitution of capital for labor.

Factor 1 was just discussed. Examples of factor 2, new technology, are the subsurface bulblike nose on the front of oil tankers (which increased tanker speed at very low cost) and solid-state electronics. Moore's Law states that the number of transistors on a given chip size (roughly a gauge of chip performance) doubles every 1.5–2 years. Some example numbers are 3,500 transistors/chip in 1972, 134,000 in 1982, 3,100,000 in 1993, and 7,500,000 in 1997.

The use of two coffeepots by Maureen is an example of factor 3, substituting capital for labor. Another example is the use of the computer in the office, permitting the automation of many office functions. The ratio of capital/labor also can be improved by economies of scale. This occurs when equipment with twice the capacity costs less than twice as much. Then, capital cost/unit is reduced and fewer work hours are needed/unit of output.

4.2 Quantifying Improvement

"Practice makes perfect" has been known for a long time. Wright (1936) took a key step when he published manufacturing progress curves for the aircraft industry. Wright made two major contributions. First, he quantified the amount of manufacturing progress for a specific product. The equation took the form of Cost = a (Number of airplanes)^b; see Figure 27.4. But the second step was probably even more important—he made the data a straight line (by putting the curve in the axis!); see Figure 27.5. That is, the data are on a **log–log scale.**

On a log scale, the physical distance between **doubled quantities** is constant (i.e., 8 to 16 is the same distance as 16 to 32 or 25 to 50); see Figure 27.6. Wright gave the new cost as a percent of the original cost when the production quantity doubled. If cost at unit 10 was 100 h and cost at unit 20 was 85 h, then this was an 85/100 = "85% curve." Since the curve was a straight line, it was easy to calculate the cost of the 15th unit or the 50th unit. If you wish to solve the $y = ax^b$ equation instead of using a graph,

FIGURE	27.4

Practice makes perfect. As more and more units are produced, the fixed cost is divided over more units, so fixed cost/unit declines. In addition, variable cost/unit declines as fewer mistakes are made, less time is spent looking up instructions, better tooling is used, and so on. The variable cost data usually can be fitted with an equation of the form $y = ax^b$.

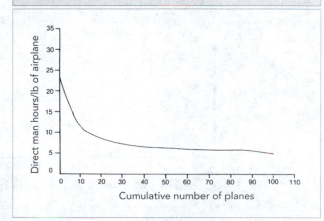

Log–log scale. Supervisors like straight lines. Plotting $y = ax^b$ on a log–log paper gives a straight line. The key piece of information supervisors desire is the rate of improvement—the slope of the line. The convention is to refer to reduction with doubled quantities. If quantity $x_1 = 8$, then quantity $x_2 = 16$. Then if cost at x_1 is $y_1 = 100$ and cost at x_2 is $y_2 = 80$, this is an "80% curve."

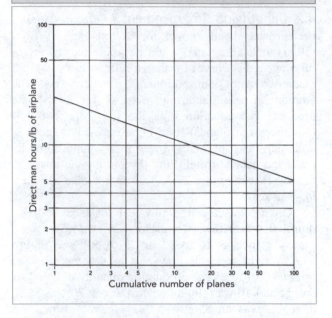

Cumulative number of planes

see Table 27.15. You also could use the program on the ERGO CD.

For example, assume the time for a (i.e., cycle 1) = 10 min and this is a 90% curve (i.e., $b = -.152$), then the time for the 50th unit is: $y = 10 \ (50)^{-.152} = 10/(50)^{.152} = 5.52$ min.

Table 27.16 shows how data might be obtained for fitting a curve. During the month of March, various people wrote on charge slips a total of 410 hours against this project charge number. The average work hours/unit during March then becomes 29.3. The average x coordinate is $(1 + 14)/2 = 7.5$. Because the curve shape is changing so rapidly in the early units, some authors recommend plotting the first lot at the 1/3 point $[(1 + 14)/3]$ and points for all subsequent lots at the midpoint.

During April, 9 units passed final inspection and 191 hours were charged against the project. Cumulative hours of 601 divided by cumulative completed output of 23 gives average hours/unit of 26.1. The 26.1 is plotted at $(15 + 23)/2 = 19$. As you can see from the example data, there are many possible errors in the data, so a curve more complex than a straight line on log–log paper (log x versus log y) is not justified. Figure 27.7 shows the resulting curve.

Although **average cost/unit** is what is usually used, you may wish to calculate cost at a specific unit. Conversely, the data may be for specific units and you want average cost. Table 27.15 gives the multiplier for various slopes. The multipliers are based on the fact that the average cost curve and the unit cost curve are parallel after an initial transient. "Initial transient" usually is 20 units, although it could be as few as 3. The multiplier for a 79% slope is $(.641 + .676)/2 = .658$. Thus, if we wish to estimate the cost of the 20th unit, it is $(24.9 \text{ h})(.658) = 16.4$ h.

Cost/unit is especially useful in scheduling. For example, if 50 units are scheduled for September, then work-h/unit (for a 79% curve) at unit 127 = $(13.4)(.656) = 8.8$ and at unit 177 = 7.8. Therefore, between 390 and 440 hours should be scheduled.

Cartesian coordinates, semi-log coordinates, and log–log coordinates. Cartesian coordinates have equal distances for equal numerical differences; that is, the linear distance from 1 to 3 is the same as from 8 to 10. On a log scale, the same distance represents a constant *ratio;* that is, the distance from 2 to 4 is the same as the distance from 30 to 60 or 1,000 to 2,000. Semi-log paper has one Cartesian axis and one log axis. Log–log (double log) paper has a log scale on both axes.

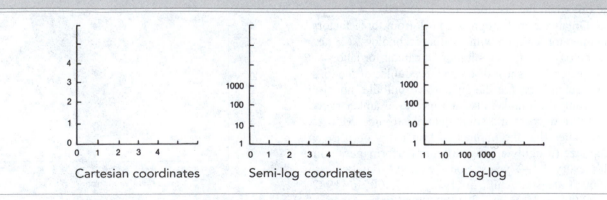

Cartesian coordinates   Semi-log coordinates   Log-log

T A B L E	27.15

Factors for various improvement curves. The multipliers in columns 3 and 4 are large-quantity approximations. For example, for a 90% curve, the table value in column 4 is 1.18. A more precise value at a quantity of 10 = 1.07, at 50 = 1.13, and at 100 = 1.17. A more precise value for an 85% curve at a quantity of 100 = 1.29; a more precise value for a 95% curve at a quantity of 100 = 1.077.

IMPROVEMENT CURVE, % BETWEEN DOUBLED QUANTITIES	LEARNING FACTOR, b, FOR CURVE $y = ax^b$	MULTIPLIER TO DETERMINE UNIT COST IF AVERAGE COST IS KNOWN	MULTIPLIER TO DETERMINE AVERAGE COST IF UNIT COST IS KNOWN
70	−.515	.485	2.06
72	−.474	.524	1.91
74	−.434	.565	1.77
76	−.396	.606	1.65
78	−.358	.641	1.56
80	−.322	.676	1.48
82	−.286	.709	1.41
84	−.252	.746	1.34
85	−.234	.763	1.31
86	−.218	.781	1.28
88	−.184	.813	1.23
90	−.152	.847	1.18
92	−.120	.877	1.14
94	−.089	.909	1.10
95	−.074	.926	1.08
96	−.059	.943	1.06
98	−.029	.971	1.03

Looking at Figure 27.7, you can see the extrapolated line predicts cost/unit at 200 to be 11.4 h, at 500 to be 8.3, and at 1,000 to be 6.6. If we add more cycles on the paper, the line eventually reaches a cost of zero at cumulative production of 200,000 units. Can cost go to zero? Can a tree grow to the sky? No.

The log–log plot increases understanding of improvement, but it also deceives. Note that cost/unit for unit 20 was 24.9 h. When output was doubled to 40 units, cost dropped to 19.7; doubling to 80 dropped cost to 15.5; doubling to 160 dropped cost to 12.1; doubling to 320 dropped cost to 9.6; doubling to 640 dropped cost to 7.6. Now, consider the improvement for each doubling. For the first doubling from 20 to 40 units, cost dropped 5.20 h or .260 h/unit of extra experience. For the next doubling from 40 to 80, cost dropped 4.2 h or .105 h/unit of extra experience. For the doubling from 320 to 640, cost dropped 2.0 h or .006 h/unit of extra experience. In summary, the more experience, the more difficult it is to show additional improvement.

The figures, however, would predict zero cost at 200,000 units, and products just aren't made in zero time. One explanation is that total output of the product, in its present design, is stopped before 200,000 units are produced. In other words, if we no longer produce Model Ts and start to produce Model As, we start on a new improvement curve at zero experience. A second explanation is that the effect of improvement in hours is masked by changes in labor wages/h. The Model T Ford had a manufacturing progress rate of 86%. In 1910, when 12,300 Model T Fords had been built, the price was $950. When it went out of production in 1926 after a cumulative output of 15,000,000, the price was $270; $200 in constant prices plus inflation of $70.

The third explanation is that straight lines on log–log paper are not perfect fits over large ranges of cycles. If output is going to go to 1,000,000 cumulative units over a 10-year period, you really shouldn't expect to predict the cost of the 1,000,000th unit (which will be built 10 years from the start) from the data of the first 6 months. There is too much change in economic conditions, managers, unions, technology, and other factors.

T A B L E	2 7 . 1 6

Time and completed units as they might be reported for a product.

MONTH	UNITS COMPLETED (PASS FINAL INSPECTION)	MONTH'S DIRECT LABOR HOURS CHARGED TO PROJECT	CUMULATIVE UNITS COMPLETED	CUMULATIVE WORK HOURS CHARGED TO PROJECT	AVERAGE WORK H/UNIT
March	14	410	14	410	29.3
April	9	191	23	601	26.1
May	16	244	39	845	21.7
June	21	284	60	1129	18.8
July	24	238	84	1367	16.3
August	43	401	127	1708	13.4

4.3 Typical Values for Organization Progress

The rate of improvement depends on the amount that can be learned. The more that can be learned, the more will be learned. The amount that can be learned depends upon two factors: (1) amount of previous experience with the product and (2) the extent of mechanization. Table 27.17 gives manufacturing progress as a function of the manual/machine ratio. Allemang (1977) estimates percent progress from product design stability, a product characteristics table (complexity, accessibility, close tolerances, test specifications, and delicate parts), parts shortage, and operator learning.

Tables 27.18 and 27.19 give about 75 manufacturing progress rates reported in the literature.

4.4 Typical Values for Learning

Assume learning has two components: (1) cognitive learning and (2) motor learning (Dar-El et al., 1995a, 1995b). Cognitive learning has a greater improvement (say, 70% curve), while motor learning is slower (say, 90% curve). For a task with both types, initially the cognitive dominates, then the motor learning dominates. Use values of 70% for "pure cognitive," 72.5 for "high cognitive," 77.5 for "more cognitive than motor," 82.5 for "more motor than cognitive," and 90 for "pure motor." Table 27.20 gives 43 tasks for which learning curves have been reported.

The improvement takes place through the reduction of fumbles and delays rather than greater movement speed. Stationary motions such as position and grasp improve the most, while reach and move improve little. It is reduced "information processing time" rather than faster hand speed that affects the reduction.

The range of times and the minimum time of elements show little change with practice. The reduction is due to a shift in the distribution of times; the shorter times are achieved more often and the slower times less often—"going slowly less often" (Salvendy and Seymour, 1973).

The initial time for a cognitive task might be 13–15 times the standard time; the initial time for a manual task might be 2.5 times the standard time.

4.5 Example Applications of Learning

Table 27.21 shows the effect of learning/manufacturing progress on time standards. The fact that labor h/unit declines as output increases makes computations using the applications of standard time more complicated.

4.5.1 Cost allocation

Knowing what your costs are is especially important if you have a make–buy decision or are bidding on new contracts. If a component is used on more than one product (standardization), it can progress much faster on the curve since its sales come from multiple sources. Manufacturing progress also means that standard costs quickly become obsolete.

Note that small lots (say, due to a customer emergency) can have very high costs. For example, if a standard lot size is 100 and labor cost is 1 h/unit and there is a 95% curve, a lot of 6 would have a labor cost about 23% higher (1.23 h/unit). Consider charging more for special orders!

4.5.2 Scheduling

Obviously, knowing how many people are needed and when is an important decision. Also, learning/manufacturing progress calculations will emphasize the penalties of small lots.

4.5.3 Evaluation of alternatives

When comparing alternatives, a pilot project might be run. Data might be obtained for 50–100 cycles. Note that the times after the pilot study should be substantially shorter, due to learning. In addition, the learning/manufactur-

F I G U R E   2 7 . 7

Average cost/unit from Table 27.16. Table 27.16 gives a 79% curve. Cost/unit is the cost of the nth unit; **average cost/unit** is the sum of the unit costs/n. Cost/unit can be estimated by multiplying average cost/unit by the factor from Table 27.16. The average cost of the first 20 units is estimated as 25.9 from the fitted line; the cost of the 20th unit is 25.9 (.658) = 17.0 h.

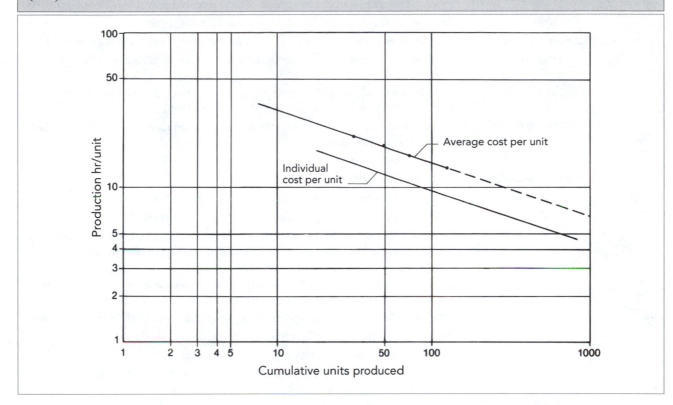

ing progress rate for alternatives A and B might differ, so what initially seems best may not be best in the long run.

4.6.4 *Acceptable day's work* *Learning* greatly affects *time standards.* Assume a time standard, *y*, is set at an experience level *x*. Assume further, for ease of understanding, that *y* = 1.0 min and *x* is 100 units. That is, a time study technician, Bill, made a time study of the first 100 units produced by Sally, calcu-

T A B L E   2 7 . 1 7

Predicting manufacturing progress from the manual and machine time.

PERCENT OF TASK TIME

Manual	Machine	Manufacturing Progress, %
25	75	90
50	50	85
75	25	80

lated the average time, and then left. Sally continued working. Let's assume a 95% rate is appropriate. Sally completes the 200th piece shortly before lunch and the 400th by the end of the shift. The average time/unit for the 1st day is about .9 min (111% of standard). On the second day, Sally completes the 800th unit early in the afternoon. She completes the 3200th unit by the end of the week. The average time of .77 min/unit during the week yields 129% of standard!

Point 1: The operators in your plant should turn in a time that improves as they gain experience.

Point 2: The magnitude of the learning effect dwarfs potential errors in rating. You might be off 5% or 10% in rating, but this effect is trivial compared to the errors in using a time standard without considering learning/manufacturing progress.

Point 3: Any time standard that does not consider learning/manufacturing progress will become less and less accurate with the passage of time.

Point 4: Since learning and manufacturing progress are occurring, output and number of work hours should not both be constant. Either the same number of people should produce more or fewer people should be able to produce a constant output.

T A B L E   27.18

Manufacturing progress rates reported in the literature with their references.

RATE, %	NUMBER OF CYCLES	EXAMPLES
60		Production work hours/cumulative units of steel produced since 1867 (Hirschman, 1964)
68	1000	Test and adjust time for product B (Conway and Schultz, 1959)
70	10,000,000 to 3,000,000,000	Average revenue/unit for silicon transistors industry accumulated volume (Conley, 1970)
	3,000,000	Price/unit for integrated circuits for industry total accumulated volume (1964–1968) (Conley, 1970)
	300,000,000 to 3,000,000,000	Price/lb of polyvinyl chloride (constant dollars) for industry accumulated volume; from 30,000,000 to 300,000,000 it was 95% (Conley, 1970)
	50,000,000 to 80,000,000	Average price/unit (constant dollars) for free-standing gas ranges for cumulative industry volume (1952–1967) (Conley, 1970)
		Overhead cost/airplane (Wright, 1936)
72	1,000,000 to 2,000,000,000	Price/unit of integrated circuits (1963–1972) (Noyce, 1977)
73	11,000	Electronic assembly of product A (Conway and Schultz, 1959)
75	8,000	Electro-mechanical assembly of product B (Conway and Schultz, 1959)
		$/ton for U. S. electric utility coal 1948 to 1971 (in 1970 prices), 1.5 to 5.5 billion tons. Sharp increase in price upon passage of Clean Air Act of 1970 (Fisher, 1974)
		Cents/kWh for electricity price in U.S. from 1926 to 1970 in 1970 dollars. 0.4 to 22 kWh $\times 10^{12}$. Price rose above trend during 1930s. Discontinuity in curve in 1971 due to effect of Clean Air Act of 1970 (Fisher, 1974)
76		Work hours/barrel of petroleum refined in United States since 1888 (Hirschman, 1964)
		Assembly labor/unit on 15 different models of machine tools (Hirsch, 1952)
		Maintenance work hours/shutdown in a General Electric plant
78–84		Production hours/unit for Liberty ships, Victory ships, tankers, and standard cargo vessels in United States during World War II (Hirsch, 1952)
79	1,000	Service time—IBM electronic machine (Kneip, 1965)
80		Cost/barrel of catalytic cracking unit capacity (inflation changed actual cost to 94%) (Hirschman, 1964)
		Work hours/airframe in United States during World War II (Hirsch, 1952)
		Labor cost/airplane (Wright, 1936)
		$/barrel of retail gasoline processing cost for United States 1919 to 1969. 1970 dollars. 2 to 37 C units where C = 10^{16} BTU (Fisher, 1974)
81	20,000	Service calls/150 machines (IBM electro-mechanical) (Kneip, 1965)
82		Total labor/unit on 16 different models of machine tools (Hirsch, 1952)
84	8,000	Final assembly labor/unit on product B (Conway and Schultz, 1959)
85	2,000	Labor hours/gun barrel on boring machines (Andress, 1954)
86	12,300 to 15,000,000	Cost/unit for Ford Model T. Price in 1910 when 12,300 had been built was $950. In 1926, when 15,000,000 had been built, price was $270 ($200 in constant prices) (Hirschman, 1964)
	1,000	Service time—IBM electronic machine (Kneip, 1965)
88	20,000	Machining labor/unit on 15 different models of machine tools (Hirsch, 1952)
		Cost of purchased subassemblies on airplanes (Wright, 1936)
90		Output of a fluid catalytic cracking unit
95		Lbs of raw material/airplane (Wright, 1936)
		$/barrel of price for crude oil at the well in United States 1869 to 1971. 1970 prices. .01 to 80 C units where C = 10^{16} BTU (Fisher, 1974)
96	11,000 to 120,000	Hours/unit for electronic assembly of product A (Conway and Schultz, 1959)

T A B L E	2 7 . 1 9

Japanese organization progress curves (Morooka and Nakai, 1971). Konz has estimated cumulative units, cumulative work time, early times, and late times from the Japanese figures and tables to give the reader a "feel" for each situation.

Industry	Firm & Product	Operation	Learning %	LEARNING % BASED ON Cumulative Units	Prod. Period, Days	"Early" Time/ Unit	"Late" Time/ Unit
Airline	V1	Maintenance/flying hr	91	396,000	2,000	4.45	2.44
Automobile	B1	Total	80		800	200.	45.
	B2		78		1,100	160.	95.
	J	Assembly	84				
	J	Lot work	87				
	J	Mechanical milling	93				
	J	Drilling	85				
	J	Lathe	87				
	Q	Assembly	83	3,892	300	1.52	0.24
	U1	Total, workers/unit	84	900,000		2.3	0.7
	U2	Engine	82		70	700.	150.
Chemical	D1	Paper (days/10,000 tons)	74	350,000 tons		800.	70.
	D2	Paper (days/10,000 tons)	75	1,300,000 tons		800.	40.
	F	Tire	89	1,146	21	276.	150.
Construction	E	Aluminum welding touchup, h	86	153	30	53.1	17.7
Electrical	C1	Assembly line, min	86		400	0.400	0.135
and	C2	Assembly line, min	88		300	0.090	0.037
Electronics	C3	Assembly line, min	89		280	0.080	0.037
	C7	Assembly line, min	82		28	0.15	0.055
	C8	Automatic lead insert machine, min	86		100	0.1	
	C9	Automatic lead insert machine, min	87		100	0.1	
	C4	Defect percent	81		100	0.65	0.17
	C5	Defect percent	90		100	0.45	0.18
	C6	Defect percent	70		70		0.15
	01	Total	83	26,200	220	9.2	4.4
	01	Total	83	26,200 to 106,800	180	4.4	3.1
	P	Tape recorder total	86	652	300	84.	16.
	Y1	Inspection	89	22,500	210	288.	164.
	Y2	Inspection	88	5,600	210	198.	117.
	Y3	Inspection	83	1,921	105	48.	30.
	Y4	Inspection	85	787	105	43.	33.
Food	T	Total	93	2,500	22	1.37	0.96
Processing	A	Lathe	84				
Machine	A	Drilling	90				
	A	Milling	87				
	H1	Grinding for casting	94	up to 8,000			
	H1	Grinding for casting	83	8,000 to 16,000	250	2.27	1.61

(continued)

T A B L E	2 7 . 1 9

Continued.

Industry	Firm & Product	Operation	Learning %	Cumulative Units	Prod. Period, Days	"Early" Time/ Unit	"Late" Time/ Unit
				LEARNING % BASED ON			
Food	H2	Grinding for casting	96	up to 8,000			
Processing	H2	Grinding for casting	87	8,000 to 16,000	250	2.25	1.74
Machine	L1	Mechanical cutting	93				
(continued)	L2	Assembly	87				
	N1	Total for cooling products	88	370			
	N2	Total for cooling products	91	350		505.	
	N4	Total for cooling products	91	400			
	N5	Total for cooling products	90	390			
	N6	Total for cooling products	85	400			
	N7	Total for cooling products	87	470			
	N8	Total for cooling products	91	450			
	N9	Total for cooling products	92	450			
	N10	Total for cooling products	89	650		970.	
	N11	Total for cooling products	93	500			
	Z	Machine assembly	87	700		350.	150.
Metal	X	Stainless steel	87		800	15.	11.
	W	Metal grinding	97	15,200		0.72	0.53
Precision	I2	Daily loss time, min (job 2)	76	110		250.	50.
	I2	Daily loss time, min (job 20)	83	20		11.	6.
	I2	Daily loss time, min (job 79)	79	80		200.	70.
	I2	Daily loss time, min (job 40)	79	80		38.	10.
	I3	Assembly (cash register A), h	96	40		190.	150.
	I3	Assembly (cash register B), h	93	35		170.	85.
	I3	Assembly (cash register C), h	92	90		50.	30.
	K1	Nut making	80	1,000		1.	
	K2	Nut making	81	1,000		1.	
	K3	Nut making	82	1,000		1.	
	K4	Nut making	86	1,000		1.	
	K5	Nut making	90	1,000		1.	
	K6	Nut making	95	1,000			
	K7	Nut making	98	1,000			
	S2	Thread	83	10,000		0.9	0.4
	S4	Thread	90	1,700		1.8	1.
Shipping	G	Total (small ships), h/ship	76	48,200 (53 ships)		3,320.	667.
	R1	Maching, %	86	460 (7 ships)		100.	66.
	R2	Boiler, %	88	480 (7 ships)		100.	69.
	R3	Tank and pipe, %	84	430 (7 ships)		100.	61.
	R4	Stringer, %	84	423 (7 ships)		100.	60.

T A B L E	2 7 . 2 0

Learning rates reported in the literature.

% RATE	NUMBER OF CYCLES	EXAMPLES
68		Truck body assembly (Glover, 1966)
70	12	Bag-molded aircraft cowls (Scheffler, 1957)
72	50	Complex, 300 h/unit assembly (Conway and Schultz, 1959)
74		Machining and fitting of small castings (Glover, 1966)
78	212	Complex cored large radrome (Scheffler, 1957)
80	400,000	Keyboard entry on business machines (Kilbridge, 1959)
		Precision bench assembly (Nadler and Smith, 1963)
	6,000	Press-molded housings (Scheffler, 1957)
82		Burring, sanding, and hand forming (McCambell and McQueen, 1956)
		Shearing plates (Titleman, 1957)
		Grinding (Nadler and Smith, 1963)
83		Fitting (Titleman, 1957)
		Power sawing (Nadler and Smith, 1963)
	40	Sorting cards into compartments (Crossman, 1959)
	4,000	Substituting letters for symbols (Crossman, 1959)
		Radio tube assembly (Glover, 1966)
		Servicing automatic transfer machines (Glover, 1966)
84	2,000,000	Cigar making (90% for cycles 2,000,000 to 10,000,000) (Crossman, 1959)
		Lathes (Nadler and Smith, 1963)
85		Gas cutting, thin plates — machines (Titleman, 1957)
		Work attendance hours — washing machines; effective hours were 88%, rate of wasted hours was 80% (Glover, 1966)
87	1,000	Drill, ream, and tap (Konz, 1960)
		Drilling (Nissley, 1949)
88		Welding — manual (Titleman, 1957)
89	10,000	Punch press (Conway and Schultz, 1959)
		4 2-cycle assembly (Barnes et al., 1940)
		Washers on pegs (initial cycle time = 20 s) (Daniels, 1966)
		Milling (Nadler and Smith, 1963)
90		Punch press (McCambell and McQueen, 1956)
		Bench inspection (Nadler and Smith, 1963)
91	8,000	Adding pairs of digits (Crossman, 1959)
92		Assembly with jig (Titleman, 1957)
	14,000	Assembly (70% from 14,000 to 25,000; 95% from 25,000 to 600,000 when put on piecework) (Youde, 1947)
		Gas cutting, thick plates — machine (Titleman, 1957)
		Welding (Nadler and Smith, 1963)
		Deburring, cleaning (Nadler and Smith, 1963)
94	300	Pegs in pegboard (Youde, 1947)
		Welding, submerged arc (Titleman, 1957)
95	450	Countersink (Konz, 1960)
	10,000	Punch press — average of 5 operators on 5 operations (range 89 to 98)
	450	Screwdriver work (85% for cycles 450 to 3500) (Barnes and Amrine, 1942)
		Reduction of running speed (m/s) vs. distance (km) for world-class male runner (94% for females) (Riegel, 1981)
96.5		Milling — no jig (Titleman, 1957)
98.5		Grinding — manual; chipping — pneumatic, blast cleaning; milling — with jig; assembly — no jig (Titleman, 1957)

T A B L E	2 7 . 2 1

Demonstration of the **learning effect on time standards.**

Learning Curve, %	TIME/UNIT AT			PERCENT OF STANDARD AT		
	2X	4X	32X	2X	4X	32X
98	.98	.96	.90	102	104	111
95	.95	.90	.77	105	111	129
90	.90	.81	.59	111	123	169
85	.85	.72	.44	118	138	225

Note: Even a small learning rate can have a major effect on performance. X = experience level of the operator when time study was taken, for example, 50, 100, or 500 cycles. The table gives time/unit based on a time standard of 1.0 min/unit; therefore, if actual time standard were 5.0 min/unit, then time/unit at 98% and $2X$ would be .98 (5.0) = 4.9.

5 DOCUMENTING, USING, AND MAINTAINING STANDARDS

5.1 Documenting Standards
Standards are part of a goal-setting system; control is essential to any such system. The attainment of goals must be monitored so performance can be compared to the goal.

5.1.1 *Quantification of output*
Generally, the operator would report completion of a lot, although, with barcoding and computers, even more detailed recording is possible. Be sure that quality is recorded as well as quantity.

When comparing output to the standard, note that the "standard" really isn't permanent. You would not expect a standard set 25 years ago to still be valid, as "things change." Thus, the standards should be updated periodically. The standard must have a detailed methods description so the amount of change can be determined. Another possibility is to have all standards (even type 2 standards) automatically expire at a set time (say, 5 years) after they are set.

5.1.2 *Audits*
The **audit** should determine the validity of the prescribed coverage, the percentage of type 1 and 2 coverage, use of labor standards, attainment of goals, and results of corrective actions on variance analysis. Audits encourage keeping the work measurement system up to date, accurate, and useful.

Which standards should be audited? Audit jobs with "major" methods changes. But many small changes can add up also. Auditing only for jobs in which the operators report performance over "X" percent of standard (e.g., 120%) doesn't work. As soon as the operators learn that 120 is the magic number, they never report performances over 120% again. They just take more breaks when given that job.

Audits should be periodic—that is, on a standard schedule. MIL-STD-1467A requires an annual audit. A recommended procedure is to set an expiration date (12 or 24 months) on each standard at the time it is set. Then, when the standard expires, if it is still active, an audit is made. If it is not active, the standard would be converted from permanent to temporary. Then, if the job is resumed, the temporary can be used for a short period (e.g., 30 days) until a new permanent standard is set. An advantage of a known expiration date is that if the standard is audited (and perhaps tightened), the operator will not feel "picked on."

When auditing time standards, keep track of the delay time over all the audits. This is a good check on whether the former delay allowance is still valid.

5.2 Using Standards
Feed information on actual performance versus standard performance back not only to management, but also to workers. Feedback to workers provides knowledge, motivation, and reinforcement. MIL-STD-1567A requires a labor performance report for each work center at least weekly.

Daily reports are useful to highlight delays and production problems. Weekly or monthly reports smooth the fluctuations and show the long-run trends.

Actual hours is the time reported by an operator. Two key indices are **earned hours** (time from the time standard) and **labor efficiency** (earned hours/actual hours). **Unmeasured hours** (time for tasks not on standard) also is useful. Percent coverage is the percent of standard hours that are type 1 standards; MIL-STD-1567A requires 80% coverage of touch labor hours.

Review Questions

1. List the five groups of applications for time/unit.
2. Briefly discuss the concept of a discipline level.
3. List four different ways of determining nonengineering (type 2) time estimates.
4. List two ways of setting engineering (type 1) time estimates.
5. Define observed time, normal time, and standard time.
6. Give three advantages and two disadvantages of standard data versus time study.
7. What is the difference between a shift allowance and a work time allowance?
8. Explain why you would or would not give fatigue allowances for machine time.
9. Are allowances based on the job or the person?
10. How did Wright make a curve into a straight line?
11. Is learning or inaccurate rating a greater potential source of incorrect time standards? Explain your answer.

References

Allemang, R. New technique could replace learning curves. *Industrial Engineering,* Vol. 9, No. 8, 22–25, 1977.

Andress, F. The learning curve as a prediction tool. *Harvard Business Review,* Vol. 32, 87–97, January–February 1954.

Barnes, R. and Amrine, H. The effect of practice on various elements used in screwdriver work. *J. of Applied Psychology,* 197–209, 1942.

Barnes, R., Perkins, J., and Juran, J. A study of the effect of practice on the elements of a factory operation. *University of Iowa Studies in Engineering Bulletin* 22, No. 387, 1940.

Conley, P. Experience curves as a planning tool. *IEEE Spectrum,* 63–68, June 1970.

Conway, R. and Schultz, A. The manufacturing progress function. *J. of Industrial Engineering,* Vol. 10, No. 1, 39–54, 1959.

Crossman, H. A theory of the acquisition of speed skill. *Ergonomics,* 153–65, 1959.

Daniels, R. Factors affecting industrial learning on interrupted production schedules. M. S. thesis, Kansas State University, 1966.

Dar-El, E., Ayas, K., and Gilad, I. A dual-phase model for the individual learning process in industrial tasks. *IIE Transactions,* Vol. 27, 265–71, 1995a.

Dar-El, E., Ayas, K., and Gilad, I. Predicting performance times for long cycle time tasks. *IIE Transactions,* Vol. 27, 272–81, 1995b.

Defense Civilian Personnel Center. MIL-STD-1567A, Military Standards: Work Measurement. Fall Church, VA: Author.

Engwall, R. Work measurement in the organization of the future. *IIE Integrated Systems Conference,* Nov. 1987.

Garg, A. Review of time standards with reference to work physiology. *Int. J. of Industrial Engineering,* 29–36, 1995.

Glover, J. Manufacturing progress functions II. Selection of trainees and control of their progress. *International J. of Production Research,* Vol. 5, No. 1, 43–59, 1966.

Helander, M. Design for manufacturing assembly. Chapter 17 in *A Guide to the Ergonomics of Manufacturing.* London: Taylor and Francis, 1995.

Hirsch, W. Manufacturing progress functions. *The Review of Economics and Statistics,* Vol. 34, 143–55, May 1952.

Hirschman, W. Profit from the learning curve. *Harvard Business Review,* 125–39, January–February 1964.

International Labour Office. *Introduction to Work Study,* 4th ed. Geneva, Switzerland: ILO, 1992.

Karger, D. and Hancock, W. *Advanced Work Measurement.* New York: Industrial Press, 1982.

Kilbridge, M. Predetermined learning curves for clerical operations. *J. of Industrial Engineering,* 203–09, 1959.

Kneip, J. The maintenance progress function. *J. of Industrial Engineering,* Vol. 16, No. 6, 398–400, 1965.

Konz, S. Learning curves for drill press operations. M. S. thesis, University of Iowa, 1960.

Kopleman, R. *Managing Productivity in Organizations.* New York: McGraw-Hill, 1987.

McCambell, E. and McQueen, C. Cost estimating from the learning curve. *Aero Digest,* 36–39, October 1956.

Morooka, K. and Nakai, S. *Learning Investigation.* Report by Committee of Learning Investigation to Japan Society of Mechanical Engineers, February 1, 1971.

Nadler, G. and Smith, W. Manufacturing progress functions for types of processes. *International J. of Production Research,* Vol. 2, No. 2, 115–35, 1963.

Nissley, H. The importance of learning curves in setting job shop standards. *Mill and Factory,* Vol. 44, 119–22, May 1949.

Noyce, R. Microelectronics. *Scientific American,* Vol. 237, No. 3, 63–69, 1977.

Riegel, P. Athletic records and human endurance. *American Scientist,* Vol. 69, 285–89, May–June, 1981.

Rodgers, S. *Ergonomic Design for People at Work,* Vol. 2. New York: Van Nostrand-Reinhold, 284, 1986.

Salvendy, G. and Seymour, W. *Prediction and Development of Industrial Work Performance.* New York: Wiley & Sons, 17, 1973.

Scheffler, F. Estimating for reinforced plastics. *Modern Plastics,* 135–50, 243, May 1957.

Titleman, M. Learning curves—Key to better labor estimates. *Product Engineering,* 36–38, November 18, 1957.

Wright, T. Factors affecting the cost of airplanes. *J. of Aeronautical Sciences,* Vol. 3, 122–28, February 1936.

Youde, L. A study of the training time for two repetitive operations. M. S. thesis, State University of Iowa, 1947.

TIME STUDY

TIME STUDY

1 Overview

2 Preparation

3 Timing

4 Rating

Overview

Time study should be preceded by a methods analysis so the resulting standard is a "should take" time, not a "did take" time. The time study is a sample from which the population is predicted. Better results are obtained if the sample is representative of the population, accurate measurements are taken, and data are carefully gathered. The observed time is multiplied by the rating to obtain normal time.

Key Concepts

allowances

continuous/snapback

elements

expectancy

flat ratings

foreign elements

irregular elements

machine time/manual time

micromotion

normal pace

normal time

observed time

present world/future
world

rating

sample/population

standard time

1 OVERVIEW

Stopwatch time study is one of the two methods to establish a type I time standard. (For standard data, the other method, see Chapter 30.)

After determining the proper method, the analyst will observe one or more operators continuously and record the time taken. This time is called **observed time.** Then this observed time is adjusted (given a **rating**) to obtain the time that a typical experienced operator would take.

(Observed time) (Rating) = **Normal time**

(In England, normal time is called basic time.) However, normal time is not representative of the time the experienced worker would take working all day. Additional time must be given for personal, fatigue, and delay **allowances.** See Chapter 27 for more on allowances. The resulting time is called **standard time.**

The basic time study procedure is to take a small sample of the times from the **present world** (now) and predict the times of the **future world** (then). There are potential inaccuracies in going from a **sample** of the present world to the **population** of the present world (i.e., from the person or persons studied to all people who have that job). There are also potential inaccuracies in going from the present world to the future world.

The procedures in this chapter attempt to reduce inaccuracies from the sample present world estimates of the population of present times. In addition, as the months pass, the present world changes and the relevance of the existing standard becomes more and more in question. General changes can be predicted from individual and organization learning. Specific changes should be observed through audits. See Chapter 27.

2 PREPARATION

Before the study, the analyst should do a methods analysis and select the operator to be studied.

2.1 Methods Analysis   The goal of a type I standard is a "should take" time, not the "did take" time of a type II standard. If a time study is done without a preceding methods analysis, the result is a type II standard.

Design of the job has been covered in the previous chapters of this book. Most of the book is devoted to job design, since that is where productivity changes are made and worker health is safeguarded. A poorly designed job can easily result in low productivity and poor quality. Having an accurate time standard for a low-productivity job doesn't give as much benefit to the organization and the workers as a type II standard on a well-designed job.

Thus, from a productivity viewpoint, supervisors of industrial engineering departments should devote most of the department's resources to job design and productivity and only a small portion to time standards. However, from a service viewpoint, many other groups need accurate time standard information. Thus, their needs for information must be balanced against the natural desire of the industrial engineering department to improve jobs.

The primary reason for doing a methods analysis before doing a time study is to establish a safe, productive job. A secondary, but still important reason is to leave a permanent record of the method so future audits will have a basis for comparison. Typical items that should be recorded are date of observation, person observed, person observing, machine used, tools/fixtures used, feeds, speeds, handtools, part number processed, and the like.

After a good method is established (say, by using the checklists given on the ERGO CD or the guidelines in Chapters 11 to 22, the job should be broken into **elements.**

For ease of understanding, consider the task to be polishing a pair of shoes. Rather than timing the entire task as a whole, the job might be divided into (1) get the shoes, (2) polish the shoes, and (3) put the shoes away.

There are five reasons to break a job into elements:

1. Elements make it possible to reuse the data. Assume the next job required the operator to get 4 shoes at a time instead of 2, or that someone else brought the shoes. Then a new time study would be required for element 1 only, not the entire task. In some tasks, elements may be used in different sequences, so having the job split allows the elements to be used for standard data. Think of the elements as bricks used to build a structure of times. We will reuse bricks instead of using new bricks.

2. Elements permit different ratings for different elements. The rating can be 90% for element 1, 100% for element 2, and 105% for element 3—but only if the job is broken into elements. Without elements, only one overall rating can be given. Elements should not combine machine time (which is always rated 100%) with manual time (which can have any rating). **Machine time** is time in which a machine can operate unattended. **Manual time** is time when an operator is required. Rating by element is especially important if the element will become a standard datum.

3. Elements permit consistency checks, within the study and between studies. For example, if getting the first pair of shoes took 1.2 min, the second took 1.3, and the third took 2.1, the long time of 2.1 stands out. When only the overall time is recorded, chance fluctuations in other elements may make the total time for all 3 elements be 4.1, 4.2, and 4.5. Then the long time in element 1 would not be noticed. Elements in this

study can be compared to similar elements in other studies. If the overall task had a different combination of elements, the overall times could not be compared.

4. Elements improve methods descriptions. A constant problem of audits is determining the method and quality of the original study so it can be compared to the present situation. Breaking the job into elements improves the methods description.

5. If you are studying a long-cycle task and the operator omits part of the task or changes the procedure for some operations, at least you have some useful data. If the task is not in elements, then none of the data can be used since it is incomplete.

After the task is broken into elements, record the element description with a description of its end point (EP). (It is also called termination point, TP.) Select a definite, easily defined point as the EP; an EP that makes a sound usually is best. For example:

Element	Description	EP
1	Get 1 pair of shoes from bedroom closet.	Release shoes
2	Polish shoes with dauber, brush, paste polish, and rag.	RL rag
3	Put shoes away in closet.	RL shoes

2.2 Operator Selection   Once the proper method has been developed, the next question is who should be studied. Under no circumstances should the timing be done without the knowledge of the worker and the supervisor. Treat the worker with dignity and respect.

Remembering that this is a sample from a population, try to make the sample as representative of the population as possible. In many cases there is no choice, as there is only one worker for the job.

If there is a choice (multiple shifts for the same job, multiple people doing the task on the same shift), select experienced rather than inexperienced workers. The standard will apply to experienced workers. Experienced means not only experienced in a specific type of work but also experienced doing this specific operation on this specific part or assembly—that is, reasonably far along the learning curve.

Work methods of novices have an unusually high number of delays, fumbles, hesitations, and slow decisions; it is quite difficult for the time study technician to determine the precise rating correction for these difficulties. Thus, the standard from studying inexperienced operators probably will be loose. If a standard is required now but the worker is at the start of the learning curve, establish a type II (i.e., temporary) standard until the worker has more practice.

If there are multiple experienced operators, it may be possible to do a time study on several of them. If possible, select average or typical workers rather than someone who is unusually slow or fast. (For methods analysis, study a fast worker, because the speed is likely to be due to a good method rather than a fast pace. For the time recording, however, it is better to use an average worker.)

There are two reasons to use an average worker for time study: (1) rating accuracy, and (2) worker acceptance.

Rating (discussed in more detail later in this chapter) requires the time study technician to normalize the observed time; this is to ensure that the *standard is based on the method, not the operator.* For example, assume the problem is to find the standard time for college males to run 1,500 m. If timing a world-class distance runner, the time might be 3.95 min; if timing Student A, the time might be 6.5 min; if timing Professor Konz, the time might be 12.0 min. When timing the expert, the analyst knows the runner is fast, but the question is how fast.

The rating might be 160%. The resulting normal time then would be $3.95 \times 1.60 = 6.32$ min. The rating on Student A might be 100%, so normal time $= 6.5 \times 1.00 = 6.50$ min. The rating on Professor Konz might be 50%, so the normal time $= 12 \times .50 = 6.00$ min.

Rating accuracy is greater if the performance is close to 100%. As performance gets farther and farther from 100%, the absolute error of rating increases. (Your firm may wish to set a policy of not using any time studies in which the operator performs at lower than 70% or higher than 130%.) Thus, to improve rating accuracy, study an average operator, if possible.

The second reason to study an average operator is to improve *worker acceptance* of the standard. Workers really don't trust ratings. The more the observed time is adjusted, the less they trust it. As pointed out in the previous paragraph, their mistrust of extreme adjustments is well founded.

To make the sample more representative, the time study should occur at different times of the day and week. That is, not all studies should be done on Monday or in the early morning or on the first shift.

3 TIMING

The normal technique is to time a live performance. However, some people like to make a videotape of the operation and then time the videotape.

Timing techniques, the number of observations to make, and irregular and external observations are covered in this section.

3.1 Timing Techniques

3.1.1 *The stopwatch*   There are two types of stopwatches: mechanical and electrical. First, assume that the watch is used in the **snapback** mode (at the end of an element, the timing starts from zero). The mechanical watch has been available for many years and is still used occasionally. Much more common now is the electronic watch. The electronic watch has three advantages. First, it has a digital display instead of an analog display so it is easier to read. Second, on a mechanical watch, when an element ends and the watch starts at zero, it takes a small amount of time to move the hand to zero (workers don't like to have this time omitted). On an electronic watch, there is no time required to move the hand. Third, on an electronic watch, the time at the end of an element can be "frozen" so the analyst observes a fixed display while the timing continues. On a mechanical watch, the analyst must remember where the hand was before it was reset to zero.

It also is possible to use watches in a **continuous** mode (the watch records constantly with the "display" changing constantly). However, this means the analyst is reading a "moving target" with consequent inaccuracies. In addition, to determine the element times, the sequential times must be subtracted from each other. The recommended technique is to use an electronic watch with snapback mode so the analyst records from a static display (although the timing is continuous) and no subtraction is needed. See Figure 28.1.

3.1.2 Videotape The primary advantage of the videotape is the permanent record of the method. Remember, however, to record feeds, speeds, operator's name, observer's name, and other relevant details; that is, the visual record by itself is not complete.

Multiple cameras can be used at the same time. Since the videotape is analyzed "off-line," the analysis can be done by a person other than the camera operator. The videotape also can be used to describe the method to people at other locations.

When individuals are being observed, they may change their behavior because they are being observed. This may be a problem when an analyst observes by using a stopwatch and a piece of paper but is likely to be even more of a problem when the observer is using a video camera.

When timing the videotape, use a stopwatch, as the tape counter does not give an accurate time (the counter may slip). Timing recorded automatically on the tape and displayed on the screen also can be used.

Videotapes can be performance-rated. Because the tape can be replayed, even elements can be rated, rather than giving just one overall rating for the whole task. As another advantage, if the rating is challenged, the method is a matter of record and all discussion can focus just on the rating.

3.2 Number of Observations There are two approaches to determining the number of observations: (1) statistical and (2) importance of decision.

3.2.1 Statistical A time study of sequential observations is a sample from a population of times. The goal is to estimate the population mean from the sample mean. Sample means are not precise (unbiased) estimators of the population mean. That is, if

---

F I G U R E   28.1

Snapback recording. Times usually are coded—that is 14, instead of .0014. The reverse side of the form would show a workstation sketch. See the ERGO CD for a copy of the form.

the mean time from a time study (a sample) is .1 h/unit, we cannot say that the population of times (time/unit over the weeks, months, and years) will have a mean of exactly .1 h/unit.

To minimize the difference between the sample and population means, increase the sample size; that is, make more observations. Unfortunately, increasing observations increases the cost of taking the sample. From statistics, the number of observations to record depends on (1) accuracy desired, (2) confidence desired, and (3) data variability. (The times vary primarily due to operator variations in grasp, position, and fumbles rather than moving or reaching faster.)

Accuracy desired. Accuracy can be given in relative or absolute terms. For a .2-h element, a ±5% relative accuracy is the same as an absolute accuracy of .2(.05) = .01 h. For a .02-h element, a ±5% relative accuracy is the same as an absolute accuracy of .02(.05) = .001 h. The limits of precision for the first case would be .19 to .21 h (a target width of .02 h). The limits of precision for the second case would be .019 to .021. Both have a ±5% relative accuracy, but the absolute accuracy is 10 times different! The size of the target determines the number of "shots" needed to hit it. It is more difficult to hit a smaller target, so more shots are needed. In a similar manner, more observations are needed for a small target (.002 h) than a big one (.02 h).

Unfortunately, people often are not precise in their statements. They may just say "5% accuracy" without specifying whether it is absolute or relative accuracy.

Confidence desired. Continuing with the target analogy, shots may not always hit the target. For 90% confidence, you want shots to hit the target 90% of the time; for 95% confidence, you want shots to hit the target 95% of the time. In terms of a time study, 90% confidence with ±5% accuracy for a .02-h element means that if there were 100 different time studies, then in 90 studies the time study mean would be between .019 and .021 h, assuming the population mean was .02 h. In actuality, only 1 time study is made, so the confidence is really the "long-run" confidence. Any individual time study could be wrong.

Data variability. The more variability in the data, the more observations are required to hit the target with confidence; that is, fewer shots are required with a good rifle, a good shooter, and no wind gusts than with a poor instrument, unskilled technician, and random variations in the task. To the time study technician, the data variability is unknown when the study begins. Therefore, it must be estimated.

Estimate the population variability by taking a subsample (e.g., 10 cycles), calculating the subsample's variability, and, from the subsample's variability, estimating the population variability. See Box 28.1.

TABLE	28.1

The range of a sample includes d_2 standard deviations, on the average.

SUBGROUP NUMBER, N	NUMBER OF STANDARD DEVIATIONS IN RANGE
2	1.128
3	1.693
4	2.059
5	2.326
6	2.534
7	2.704
8	2.847
9	2.970
10	3.078
11	3.173
12	3.258
13	3.336
14	3.407
15	3.472
20	3.735
25	3.931

3.2.2 *Importance of decision* The discussion in Box 28.1 assumes that the number of cycles should be determined solely from probability. However, in real life you can drown in a river that is only 1 meter deep on the average. Telling your boss you will be correct most of the time doesn't help when you have made a mistake on an important decision.

The same problem was faced in statistical sampling in quality control. The Military Standard 105 tables recommend larger sample sizes for larger lot sizes—that is, larger samples for more important decisions. (From probability, required sample size does not depend upon lot size.) That is, cost is not only the observer cost but also the cost of bad decisions from inaccurate information.

Tables 28.2 and 28.3 give three approaches to the concept of larger samples for more important decisions. Note that the tables do not agree. For example, for time/piece of .017 h (1 min), the Westinghouse recommendations are 20, 25, or 50 cycles (depending on quantity); GE recommends 40 (regardless of quantity); and Niebel recommends 25 to 40 cycles (depending on quantity). Thus, the recommendations should not be expected to apply exactly to all situations.

BOX 28.1   *Statistical Formula for Number of Observations*

Accuracy desired, confidence desired, and data variability are related by the following equation:

$$A = z\sigma'_{\bar{x}}$$

where A = Amplitude (absolute accuracy) of the target, that is, precision = $S\ (\Sigma X/N)$

S = Relative accuracy desired, decimal

z = Number of standard deviations corresponding to the confidence desired

$\sigma'_{\bar{x}}$ = Standard deviation of the population times

The standard deviation of the population times and subsample times are related by:

$$\sigma'_{\bar{x}} = \frac{\sigma'_x}{\sqrt{N^1}}$$

where N' = Number of observations required to meet the criteria of precision and accuracy

σ'_x = Standard deviation of the subsample

$$= \frac{1}{N}\sqrt{N\Sigma X^2 - (\Sigma X)^2}$$

N = Number of times (observations in subsample)

Substitution and solving for N' gives:

$$N' = \left[\frac{\sigma'_x}{\sigma'_{\bar{x}}}\right]^2 = \left[\frac{Z}{A}\sigma'_x\right]^2 =$$

$$\left[\frac{Z\frac{1}{N}\sqrt{N\Sigma X^2 - (\Sigma X)^2}}{A}\right]^2$$

Using the subsample size = N as an estimate of population variability gives a "biased" estimate. For an "unbiased" estimate, use $N - 1$ instead of N. (Think of the unbiased estimate as a factor of safety, since the formula using $N - 1$ makes the variance look larger and thus the user will be more cautious in using the data.) Then

$$N' = \left[Z\frac{\sqrt{\frac{\Sigma X^2 - (\Sigma X)^2/N}{N - 1}}}{A}\right]^2$$

The equation can be simplified in a number of ways. First, precision level, A, can be expressed in terms of X. Then 5% relative accuracy becomes .05 $(\Sigma X/N)$; 10% relative accuracy becomes .1 $(\Sigma X/N)$.

Second, the normal distribution can be assumed and 95% confidence rounded to 2 standard deviations instead of 1.96. Thus, for 5% precision and 2σ confidence:

$$N' = \left[\frac{40N\sqrt{\frac{\Sigma X^2 - (\Sigma X)^2/N}{N - 1}}}{\Sigma X}\right]^2$$

For 10% precision and 2σ confidence:

$$N' = \left[\frac{20N\sqrt{\frac{\Sigma X^2 - (\Sigma X)^2/N}{N - 1}}}{\Sigma X}\right]^2$$

Third, the population variability can be estimated from the range of the sample rather than the standard deviation of the sample. Although the range is not as efficient an estimator of the variability as the standard deviation, it is simpler to calculate.

$$R = d_2\sigma_x$$

so $$\sigma_x = R/d_2$$

where R = Mean range of a subgroup of specified size

d_2 = Number of standard deviations that the mean range includes, for a specified subgroup, sample size

σ_x = Standard deviation of individual times

For example, for a subgroup of 10 sample times, $d_2 = 3.078$ from Table 28.1. That is, the range of a sample of 10 will, on the average, include 3.078 standard deviations.

As given before:

$$A = z\sigma'_{\bar{x}}$$
$$= \left[\frac{z\bar{R}}{d_2 N}\right] \qquad \text{so } N' = \left[\frac{z\bar{R}}{d_2 A}\right]$$

For 5% precision, 2σ confidence, and a subsample $N = 10$:

$$N' = \left[\frac{2\bar{R}}{.05 d_2 \bar{\bar{X}}}\right]^2 = \left[\frac{40\bar{R}}{d_2 \bar{X}}\right]^2 = \left[\frac{40\bar{R}}{3.078\bar{X}}\right]^2 = \left[\frac{13\bar{R}}{\bar{X}}\right]^2$$

For 10% precision, 2σ confidence, and a subsample $N = 10$:

$$N' = \left[\frac{2\bar{R}}{.10 d_2 \bar{X}}\right]^2 = \left[\frac{6.5\bar{R}}{\bar{X}}\right]^2$$

In practice, the range of the sample is used instead of $\bar{R}$.

Assume 10 times were obtained in a time subsample: 20, 22, 20, 22, 20, 18, 18, 20, 19, and 21. The mean = 20. For 5% precision and 2σ confidence, $N' = 8$. That is, the subsample is sufficient and no more observations are needed. Using the range method, the

28.1 *Statistical Formula, continued*

subsample range is 4, giving $N' = 7$. In general, however, the standard deviation method gives a smaller N' than the range method (Hicks and Young, 1962).

Calculate N' for each element in the time study. If N' is equal to or less than the subsample size already taken, enough observations have been taken and the study can stop. If, for example, N' is 18 for element 3, then element 3 needs 8 more observations. In practice, it would be best to get 8 more observations on all elements and thus improve their accuracy and confidence also, rather than just studying 8 more cycles of element 3. Note also that the total of all the elements will have greater precision than individual elements.

T A B L E   2 8 . 2

Minimum number of cycles to study (Westinghouse and General Electric).

IF	AND WESTINGHOUSE ELECTRIC VALUES (WESTINGHOUSE, 1953)			OR GENERAL ELECTRIC VALUES (SHAW, 1978)
Time/piece or cycle is over	Activity/yr is under 1,000	Activity/yr is from 1,000 to 10,000	Activity/yr is over 10,000	Activity/yr is any value
.002 h (under)	60	80	140	200
.002	50	60	120	175
.003	40	50	100	125
.004	35	45	90	100
.005	30	40	80	85
.008	25	30	60	60
.012	20	25	50	40
.020	15	20	40	30
.035	12	15	30	18
.050	10	12	25	15
.080	8	10	20	13
.120	6	8	15	10
.200	5	6	12	9
.300	4	5	10	8
.500	3	4	8	5
.800	2	3	6	3
1.000	2	3	5	3
2.000	1	2	4	3

If accuracy of the time standard is especially important (as on a job with many hours/year), consider making two or three shorter studies rather than one long study. You will be estimating the population characteristics from several samples instead of one.

Generally, there is a fixed cost in making a time study (contacting the supervisor, analyzing the job, recording observations, making calculations, and writing it up). Therefore, it is probably worthwhile to spend at least 15 minutes recording times, regardless of the statistical calculations of Box 28.1. This seems to be the general approach of Tables 28.2 and 28.3. To make the benefits of the time study exceed its cost, increase sample size when (1) cycle time is short, (2) activity/year is large, and (3) cost of an inaccurate standard is high.

3.3 Irregular and Foreign Observations This section is divided into concept and recording technique.

3.3.1 *Concept* After initially analyzing the job, the observer will have recorded the elements in the

T A B L E	2 8 . 3

Minimum number of cycles to study (Niebel, 1992).

IF CYCLE TIME, min (h)	AND ACTIVITY IS LESS THAN			
	1,000/yr	1,000 to 5,000/yr	5,000 to 10,000/yr	Over 10,000/yr
<1 (.017)	40	45	50	60
1 to 2 (.017 to .033)	25	30	35	40
2 to 5 (.033 to .083)	18	20	22	25
5 to 10 (.083 to .167)	15	16	18	20
10 to 20 (.167 to .333)	9	10	11	12
20 to 40 (.333 to .667)	7	8	9	10
40 to 60 (.667 to 1.0)	5	6	7	8
>60 (1.0)	3	4	5	6

Source: B. Niebel, "Time Study," in *Handbook of Industrial Engineering,* 2d ed., G. Salvendy (ed.). Copyright © 1992 by John Wiley & Sons. Reprinted by permission of John Wiley & Sons, Inc.

order they should occur. But during the study, the operator may perform unexpected activities.

One possibility is that this is a rare or **irregular element**—at least the observer didn't anticipate it. It has to be included like any other element. The observer must determine how often the element should be allowed per unit produced.

Another possibility is that the data are not normal work but, rather, are **foreign elements.** (Foreign elements are not allowed directly as part of the recorded times, but the time for this delay may be allowed through an allowance.)

A delay can be avoidable (meaning the time will not be included in the standard) or unavoidable (meaning the time will be included in the standard). Examples of avoidable delay might be: stopping work to talk to friend, blowing nose, drinking a cup of coffee. Some time is allowed for these types of activities, but under the classification of personal allowances and fatigue allowances rather than work time. Examples of unavoidable delay might be: talking to supervisor about work, being idle because of lack of supplies, breaking a tool. Time is allowed for these types of activities under the classification of delay allowances.

Personal and fatigue allowances (see Chapter 27) are set from standard tables. The job gets a certain allowance, and the operator time spent in this type of activity during the study does not affect the allowance given. Delay allowances, however, should be determined from the delays occurring on the job. The delays occurring during a time study (especially longer studies lasting an hour or so) can give an estimate of the percentage of delays to allow for the standard. That is, if during the time study there was 5% unavoidable delay, then 5% may be a reasonable number to use for the delay allowance.

3.3.2 *Recording technique* At the time the unusual event begins, the observer does not know whether it is an irregular element, an unavoidable delay, or an avoidable delay. The data must be recorded as they occur; later the decision can be made whether to include them in the standard.

Figure 28.2 gives examples of the following problems.

Missed reading. The worker may be going through cycles in a standard manner and the observer just misses the end of an element. Put an M in the spot where the time should have been. See column 2 in Figure 28.2. Do not guess at the time, as this will bias not only the time of the missed element but also the time of the following element.

Omitted element. The worker may omit an element. Put a dash in the spot where the time should have been. See column 4 in Figure 28.2. An omitted element may indicate an inexperienced operator. More likely, the operator is trying to confuse the observer or the element is not needed 100% of the time.

Before a time study, workers may describe in detail many different things necessary to do the job. Then, during the time study, they may become engrossed in doing the job and do it the way they usually do it and forget to add the embellishments for the observer.

Element out of order. Operators may do an element out of the order the observer has on the form (say element 5, then 4 instead of 4, then 5) either because the

F I G U R E   2 8 . 2

Continuous recording technique showing various problems. Missed times are shown by an M as in column 2. When the worker omits an element, put down a dash, as in column 4. When an element is done out of order, as in columns 6–8, put a dash for the omitted element, record the next element over one column, and when the omitted element occurs, move over another column. If an unexpected element occurs, as in column 10, record the time and next to it a letter. Then, elsewhere on the form, write a short note describing the event.

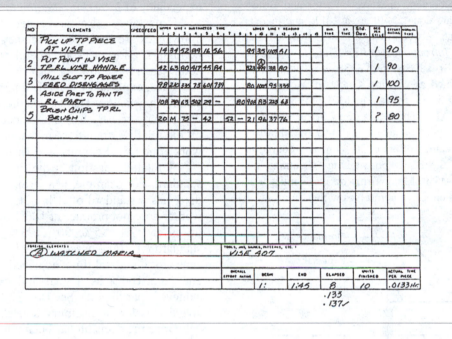

sequence isn't critical or because the operator is trying to confuse the observer. See columns 6–8 of Figure 28.2.

The simplest technique is to put a dash for the omitted element (4), put the time down for the next element (5) one column over, and then, when the skipped element (4) occurs, move over another column on the form and record it. Then element 5 is marked with a dash and the normal sequence resumes.

Unexpected element. As pointed out above, this may be an irregular element or avoidable or unavoidable delay. Record such elements as they occur; do not stop the watch. The decision of what to do with the time can be made later. See column 10 of Figure 28.2. As the events occur, move over a column and code them A, B, C, etc. Then, elsewhere on the form write a short note (1–3 words) defining the meaning of A, B, C codes.

4 RATING

4.1 Normal Pace

If rating is not used (as sometimes is advocated by worker representatives), then the analyst is at the mercy of the person being observed. Assume, for example, that a cleaning operation should take an experienced worker 1 min. But, if no rating is used, the person observed could take 2,

3, or even 4 min and the firm would have to accept the time. That is why all of the time study books for the past 100 years assume rating is used. During the time study, the observer will rate the worker, that is, determine the adjustment to convert the observed time to the time that a normal, experienced worker would take. If the standard deviation of the observed times is calculated, it should be greater than the standard deviation of the normal times. That is, there is less variability in the normal times.

Before this, a **normal pace** must be defined. This is not a trivial problem. Unless normal is defined, any time observation becomes a type II standard (i.e., a did-take time instead of a should-take time). Without a definition of normal pace, recording time is analogous to recording temperature without specifying whether the Fahrenheit or Celsius scale is being used.

It is recommended that the motivated productivity level (MPL) be defined first. Then, from this, a specified distance away (called **expectancy**) is acceptable productivity level (APL), also called normal. See Figure 28.3.

$$APL = MPL - \text{Expectancy}$$

Motivated productivity level (MPL) is the work pace of a motivated worker possessing sufficient skill and effort to do the job, physically fit to do the job after

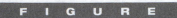

Establish motivated productivity level (MPL) as the "anchor." Then, a negotiated distance away (Incentive Expectancy) determines acceptable productivity level (APL), also called normal. Some researchers say that Work-Factor is at MPL, MTM is APL, and Expectancy is 25%. Others contend that Work-Factor and British Standard 3138 are equal, both are at MPL, and there is a 20% difference between them and MTM, which is at APL. However, *Introduction to Work Study* (1978) gives expectancy for British Standard 3138 as 33%, as incentive rate is defined as walking 4 miles/h. Work-Factor defines walking at 3.7 miles/h as MPL. MTM defines 3.57 miles/h as APL. The ratio of 3.57/3.7 is 96.5%, so expectancy is only 3.5% on walking; thus, MTM probably has an expectancy of about 30% on arm motions to counterbalance the 3.5% on walking—assuming the overall is 20%–25%. Many firms define 3 miles/h as 100% and don't concern themselves with MPL.

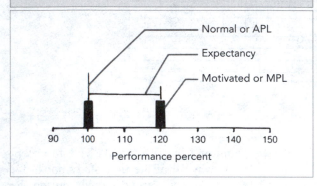

Performance percent

adjustment to it, and working at an incentive pace that can be maintained day after day without harmful effect.

Normal or acceptable productivity level (APL) is the work pace established by management or jointly by management and labor at a level that is considered satisfactory; it is established at a given relationship to motivated productivity level.

Expectancy = Incentive expectancy, percent

MPL is a function of human work capacity; it is the maximum at which average workers can be expected to work. APL, on the other hand, is a "discounted" value; it is how hard you expect workers to work. (If MPL were defined as 100%, the discount would be clearer but, by convention, APL is defined as 100% instead of MPL.) A smaller value of expectancy means workers are working closer to their limits; a larger expectancy means a looser standard.

Typical expectancy values were 10% to 15% during the 1930s and 20% to 25% during the 1940s. During World War II, the U. S. War Labor Board ruled that 30% was fair and equitable. Rice (1977),

surveying 1,500 U. S. firms, reported that target for daywork averaged 101% while target for incentive was 119%—a difference of 18%. Actual performance for daywork averaged 93% and for incentive averaged 123%—a difference of 30%.

British Standard 3138 defines incentive as walking 4 miles/h and daywork as walking 3 miles/h—an expectancy of 33% (*Introduction to Work Study*, 1978).

Expectancy also is related to allowances. If allowances are low, the expectancy discount tends to be high. If allowances are liberal, the expectancy discount tends to be low.

Thus, expectancy is really a political rather than a scientific decision. That is, whether a worker works at 20%, 25%, or 30% less than capacity really depends on the relative strength of management and labor, the work ethic of the country and firm, and so forth.

A related question is the discipline level versus standard. For example, if a firm, using an APL standard, has a standard of .1 h/unit, what happens if the worker does not produce at 100% of standard but produces at 99%, 95%, 90%, 75%, and so on? If a standard of 100% is considered as a minimum and cause for dismissal if not achieved, this is quite different from 100% as a goal and cause for praise if achieved (par in golf). See Box 27.1 for a more extensive discussion of discipline levels.

Once the decision has been made by management (with the formal or informal agreement of labor) on the definition of APL (say that walking 3 miles/h = 100 = APL), engineers can rate performance of specific individuals versus the defined standard.

Since most jobs involve more than walking and MTM is widely known, a practical strategy is to define an individual firm's APL in terms of MTM. That is, the firm's APL = MTMs or 90% of MTMs or 110% of MTMs. Then, on a specific job, the firm's standard could be compared to a standard set using MTM times.

4.2 Rating Techniques
Devotta (1988) surveyed the literature on rating. See also Niebel and Freivalds (1999). This section considers the problem and proposed solutions.

4.2.1 *Problem*
Tasks can be broken down into **micromotions.** Using MTM nomenclature (see Chapter 29), there are moves, reaches, grasps, positions, and so forth. The essential problem of rating is that each of these micromotions changes its proportion of the total task as the pace changes (Sakuma, 1975).

For example, at a 100% pace, the total task may take 1.0 min, composed of .1 min (10%) for reach, .2 min (20%) for grasp, .3 min (30%) for move, and .4 min (40%) for position. However, assume the worker speeds up so that the overall task takes only .8 min (i.e., overall pace is 1.0/.8 = 125%). The reach may have taken only .067 min (150% pace, 8.4% of total); grasp and move may take .16 and .24 min (125% pace, keeping at 20% and 30%); while position may take .333 min (120% pace, 42% of total).

The rater's problem is which micromotion to watch. The low-skill (difficulty) micromotions such as move and reach generally change less than the overall task; the high-skill (position, grasp) micromotions change more than the overall task. In addition, the proportion of low-skill to high-skill micromotions varies from element to element, so the rater cannot rate just one element and assume that the rating is valid for the entire task (Jinich and Niebel, 1970).

Table 28.4 shows levels of methods detail. Level 1, methods controlled by management, gives design details such as tools and equipment, fixtures and containers, workplace layout, and the material flow. Level 2, which management tries to control, gives the general motion pattern. Level 3, controlled by the skill and training of the worker, gives hand–hand coordination, unnecessary motions, fumbles and hesitations, and eye–hand coordination. The fine points of these level-3 micromethods are not detected by the usual rater even though they are critical to the time taken by the worker (Gershoni, 1969).

4.2.2 *Proposed solutions* Two approaches are pace rating and objective rating.

Pace rating. Pace rating (also called speed rating and tempo rating) is the simplest system. The observer estimates the pace, that is, primarily concentrates on the dynamic micromotions such as reach and move rather than the stationary micromotions such as position and grasp. This single-factor technique is the most common approach.

Objective rating. There are three steps. First, the observer rates the speed. Second, the observer estimates task difficulty, also called effort (in effect, estimates what proportion of the total time is composed of easy, average, and difficult micromotions). Third, the observer multiplies the speed factor by the difficulty factor to get the overall factor, pace.

Objective rating is a descendant of the original Westinghouse system, first used in 1925. The original Westinghouse system had four components: skill (proficiency at following a given method), effort (will to work), conditions, and consistency (low consistency went with low pace). See Matias (2001) for more on rating.

4.3 Improving Rating Accuracy After background comments, remarks will be given for rating procedures and rater training.

4.3.1 *Background* There have been a number of studies of pace rating. Investigators usually have a large number of raters (perhaps 100) from a number of different companies rate a number of different operations. When they calculate the variability of the total group, approximately 50% of the variability is within-company error and 50% is between-company error (Moores, 1972). That is, raters have been trained for their companies' definitions of APL, and the APL varies among companies. Excluding the between-company variability, Moores reports that 100 British raters had a mean standard deviation of 7%.

T A B L E	2 8 . 4	

Levels of methods detail. Divide methods into level 1, management-controlled; level 2, which management tries to control; and level 3, operator-controlled. Although level 3 greatly influences the operator's proficiency, most time study personnel have difficulty in detecting changes in level 3.

LEVEL	DETAIL OF METHODS DESCRIPTION
1. Management-controlled	Tools and equipment
	Fixtures and parts containers
	Workplace layout
	Material flow
2. Management attempts to control	General motion pattern
3. Operator-controlled (influenced by training)	Specific motion pattern, including hand coordination
	Unnecessary motions
	Types of motions (undesirable or highly refined)
	Amount of fumbling
	Eye–hand coordination
	Delay intervals between motions

However, the above assumes no variation in micromethods. For example, all reaches and moves are exactly the same distance for all operators. The level of worker skill is exactly compensated for by the rater. But Gershoni (1969) showed that most raters cannot detect these fine differences.

4.3.2 *Rating procedures* Perhaps the first question is whether to rate on each element, in individual cycles, or to give the same rating on all elements. Rating on individual cycles is not practical unless the cycles are fairly long (e.g., 1 min). On the other hand, giving the same rating to all elements can lead to problems. Consider an order-picking job in a warehouse that consisted of some mental elements (such as read list, decide how to stack different size boxes on pallet truck, etc.) and some manual elements (such as obtain box from rack, stack boxes on pallet truck, etc.). One worker might be good at the mental work and another at the physical work. Rating just overall performance would give biased estimates of the individual elements—a particular problem if the elements were used for standard data.

If the observer cannot rate each element, the observer should try to divide element rating into categories of mental, fine manipulative (finger work), and muscular (arm) work. Naturally, machine-time elements should be kept separate from operator-controlled elements.

A rating technique that should improve rating accuracy is to rate each element twice—once before starting the watch and once when the study is complete. Then use the average for the rating. For long elements, rating might even be done more often.

As mentioned previously, it is difficult to rate extreme pace. Thus, a firm may have a policy that if a time study has a rating of under 70% or over 130%, it will not be used.

Rating of inexperienced operators is difficult due to their many fumbles, delays, and hesitations. Although the rater may attempt to compensate, the resulting standard is likely to be loose. Then, with learning, the operator has a loose standard. Rather than exceed the informal production ceiling, the operator will take increased leisure time. Taking a time study on an inexperienced operator, therefore, may permanently restrict productivity on that operation.

Operators vary from cycle to cycle (see Section 3.2 of this chapter). That is, the observer is tracking a moving target. Thus, enough cycles have to be studied to estimate the mean pace. When observing movies of operations, Andrews and Barnes (1967) found no appreciable difference in rating accuracy whether the observation was for 5, 10, or 15 s. As a practical matter, the observer should be conscious of the pace throughout the time study although perhaps recording

it only at the end. In a longer study (e.g., 30 min total), the rating can be done several times during the study (every 15 min), and then averaged.

As mentioned before, the important differences in performance are due to skill in the stationary motions of position and grasp rather than the dynamic motions of reach and move. Gershoni (1969) found that raters did not detect very important differences in micromethods. His recommended solution was to use a predetermined time system of notation in the element description, assuming the system forces the rater to pay more attention to the exact motion pattern. Too much attention on reach and move results in "flat" rating (Moores, 1972; Wygant, 1984). See Figure 28.4.

Rating tasks requiring movement of heavy loads is especially difficult. The worker will move quickly so as to minimize the time with the load, probably more quickly than with a light load. Although the effect of the weight should be accounted for through the allowances, the rater has to be careful not to rate the pace high and thus negate the allowance.

Jobs that require high skill, application of pressure, cleaning, and inspection are difficult to rate. The analyst has trouble determining exactly what is being done and whether the operator is doing what is required or is embellishing it for the time study.

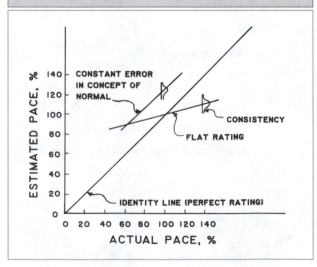

F I G U R E   28.4

Perfect pace ratings have each estimate fall on the identity line. If raters had no bias but had variability, values would fall randomly above and below the identity line. If they have a constant systematic bias (e.g., rating loosely), their values would fall around a line parallel to the identity line. If they pay too much attention to reaches and moves instead of positions and grasps, they will give **flat ratings**—being tight when the pace is fast and loose when the pace is slow.

In general, observers will do a better job rating if they are familiar with the job than if they are novices to it. Although it is not feasible in every job, it would be good practice for observers actually to do the jobs they study. In addition to teaching humility, it would give them a better understanding of the operator's problems.

Gambrell (1959) said raters trained to estimate to the nearest percent (97%, 109%) had less variability than those who rounded to the nearest 5% (95%, 110%).

4.3.3 *Rating training* Rating is a skill. As with any other skill, those with more experience and training do better than novices. Rating also is a subjective judgment in which the rater compares performance with a remembered standard. Therefore, the rater must know the standard and be calibrated with it.

The standard training procedure is to show the rater a movie or videotape of a reference operation.

Films of reference operations are available. Firms also can videotape 15 to 20 of their own operations to use as standards. (When studying different paces, have the worker speed up and slow down rather than speeding up or slowing down the projection speed, since the micromotion composition changes with pace.)

Das (1965) has studied the training procedure in detail. Most films mix operations (a scene of Form Rug Cups, then Cut Cork Tube, then Deburr, and so forth, each at a different pace). Das says this is good for testing but, for training, a number of paces should be shown for Form Rug Cups, then a number of paces for Cut Cork Tubes, and so on. After each scene, the rater should be given the true pace immediately after putting down the estimate; if the estimate is in error by more than 5%, back up and show the scene over. In training terminology, apply the principles of providing of results and giving immediate feedback.

Review Questions

1. If observed time = .1 h, rating = 110%, and shift allowances = 20%, what is standard time?

2. Is the goal of a type I standard a should-take time or a did-take time?

3. Give the five reasons to break a job into elements.

4. Does rating accuracy depend on the deviation from a 100% pace, or is it relatively constant for all paces?

5. From a statistics viewpoint, the number of observations depends upon what three factors?

6. Assume that, during a time study, the supervisor came by and gave some instructions to the worker. How would this time be incorporated into the standard time?

7. As a person improves performance, would you expect the proportions of time devoted to stationary micromotions to be increased or decreased? Why?

8. In pace rating, does the observer concentrate on the stationary or dynamic micromotions?

9. Justify why rating should be for each element rather than one rating for the entire task.

10. Using actual pace as the x axis and estimated pace as the y axis, show (1) the identity line, (2) consistent loose rating, and (3) flat rating.

References

Andrews, R. and Barnes, R. The influence of the duration of observation time on performance rating. *J. of Industrial Engineering,* Vol. 18, No. 4, 243–47, 1967.

Das, B. Applying programmed learning concepts to instruct in performance rating. *J. of Industrial Engineering,* Vol. 16, No. 2, 94–100, 1965.

Devotta, A. A survey of performance rating research in work measurement. M. S. thesis, Manhattan, KS: Kansas State University, 1988.

Gambrell, C. The independence of pace rating vs. weight handled. *J. of Industrial Engineering,* Vol. 10, No. 4, 318–22, 1959.

Gershoni, H. An analysis of time study based on studies made in the United Kingdom and Israel. *Am. Institute of Industrial Engineers Transactions,* Vol. 1, No. 3, 244–52, 1969.

Hicks, C. and Young, H. A comparison of several methods for determining the number of readings in a time study. *Journal of Industrial Engineering,* Vol. 13, No. 2, 93–96, 1962.

Introduction to Work Study, 3d ed. Geneva, Switzerland: International Labour Organization, 1978.

Jinich, C. and Niebel, B. Synthetic leveling—How valid? *Industrial Engineering,* Vol. 2, No. 5, 34–37, 1970.

Matias, A. Work measurement: Principles and techniques. In *Handbook of Industrial Engineering,* 3rd ed., Salvendy, G. (ed.). New York: Wiley, 1409–62, 2001.

Moores, B. Variability in concept of standard in the performance rating process. *Int. J. of Production Research,* Vol. 10, No. 2, 167–73, 1972.

Niebel, B. Time study. In *Handbook of Industrial Engineering,* 2d ed., Salvendy, G. (ed.), Chapter 62. New York: Wiley, 1992.

Niebel, B. and Freivalds, A. *Methods, Standards and Work Design,* 10th ed. New York: McGraw-Hill, 356–79, 1999.

Rice, R. Survey of work measurement and wage incentives. *Industrial Engineering,* Vol. 9, No. 7, 18–31, 1977.

Sakuma, A. New insight into pace rating. *Industrial Engineering,* Vol. 7, No. 7, 32–39, 1975.

Shaw, A. *Time Study Manual of the Erie Works of the General Electric Co.* Erie, PA: 1978.

Westinghouse Electric Corp. *Work Measurement Techniques and Application,* R-131-REV. Pittsburgh: Westinghouse Electric, 1953, p. 57.

Wygant, R. An analysis of performance rating. *Proceedings of Annual Ind. Engineering Conference,* 632–36, 1984.

29

PREDETERMINED TIME SYSTEMS

Overview

P redetermined time systems developed from therbligs. The most popular system at present is Methods-Time Measurement (MTM). It has several levels of detail, allowing a tradeoff between analysis detail versus analysis time. This chapter describes MTM-1, MTM-2, MTM-3, MOST, and MODAPTS.

Key Concepts

apply pressure	independence and	predetermined time
body motion	additivity	systems (PTS)
combined motions	limited motions	reach
disengage	move	release
efficient work method	MTM-1	therbligs
eye motion	MTM-2 and MTM-3	turn
grasp	position	

Predetermined time systems (PTS) are an excellent technique to analyze work methods, in addition to furnishing times. For information on standard data (i.e., times for macro elements), see Chapter 30.

HISTORY AND DEVELOPMENT

Frederic Taylor, developer of scientific management, first applied the scientific method to the mundane world of work rather than just to laboratory experiments. Frank and Lillian Gilbreth took a more detailed look at work than Taylor and broke work into 17 micro elements, called **therbligs.** Through micro-motion analysis of bricklaying, a task that had been performed for 2,000 years, the Gilbreths improved bricklaying productivity by 300%!

Step 1 is to determine an efficient work method. Step 2 is to determine the time/unit for the efficient work method. PTS can be used for step 2 as well as for step 1.

Therbligs were the first step in that they broke down work into elements. The second step was to assign time values to each of the elements. Then, to determine the total time for a task, the times for each of the elements are totaled.

In ordinary words, the concept is similar to constructing a building. A building is composed of elements—doors, walls, beams, bricks, plumbing. The structure is the sum of the elements. Likewise, a job is also considered to consist of elements, the total of which is the sum of the elements. In addition, each element does not affect what happens before or after it. In formal words, the assumption is that each job element is independent and additive—*independence and additivity.*

A number of critics of PTS have shown that these independence and additivity assumptions are not perfectly valid for all situations. That is, time for an element is affected by the preceding and following elements. The PTS do compensate for these assumptions—at least to some extent—since most elements occur in standard sequences. However, at the present state of knowledge, there is no realistic alternative to the PTS. They should be used with caution since their time values, especially in the hands of inexperienced users, often can depart from actual times by 25%–50%. Trained users do better. Furthermore, actual times vary, depending on worker and work pace on a specific day.

The concept of basic, universal units of work with accompanying standard amounts of time is an attractive idea. The most popular system (as of the present) is Methods-Time Measurement, described in this chapter. For other systems, see Sellie (1992).

METHODS-TIME MEASUREMENT

2.1 Basic Concept Methods-Time Measurement was developed by Maynard, Stegemerten, and Schwab (1948) in 1946 from motion pictures of sensitive drill press operations at Westinghouse. The MTM Association, which publishes news of research and applications in the MTM journal, has emphasized improving ease of application and development of simplified versions of MTM. MTM is probably the most widely used PTS in the world. For a detailed (503-page) explanation of MTM, see Karger and Bayha (1987).

This section describes the basic MTM system (MTM-1), as well as two simplified systems (MTM-2 and MTM-3). The MTM material was reviewed by Karl Eady, Director of Training Development of the MTM Association. The MTM tables are reprinted with the permission of the MTM Association, 1111 East Touhy Ave., Des Plaines, IL 60018; phone (847) 299-1111. People who wish to actually use MTM should take a training course approved by the MTM Association (approximately 24 to 80 classroom hours) in order to use the procedures accurately and consistently.

A popular simplified system is Maynard Operation Sequence Technique (MOST); see Section 3 of this chapter.

2.2 MTM-1 In the most detailed system, **MTM-1,** motions are broken down into 10 categories: Reach, Move, Turn, Apply Pressure, Grasp, Position, Release, Disengage, Body (leg–foot, horizontal, and vertical) Motions, and Eye Motions. Times for each of these are given in time measurement units (TMUs), which is a fancy name for .000 010 h. Thus, 1 TMU = .000 010 h = .000 600 min = .036 s. Conversely, 1 s = 27.78 TMU; 1 min = 1,667 TMU; and 1 h = 100,000 TMU.

The times are for an experienced operator working at a normal pace (100%). No allowances are included in the times. See Chapter 27.

Another question is how many cycles of practice it takes before a worker can achieve MTM standard. See Chapter 27 for a discussion of learning curves. Rivett (1972) developed learning curves for four tasks; MTM standard was achieved at 900, 135, 3,100, and 3,300 cycles. Karger and Bayha (1987) gave a complicated technique to apply learning curves to MTM. In their two examples, the worker achieved MTM standard after 1,900 cycles for method 1 and 2,300 cycles for method 2. For Rivett's four examples, at 200 cycles a worker would be expected to produce at 82%, 108%, 71%, and 74% of standard. Thus, complaints about inaccurate MTM times may be due primarily to failure to apply learning allowances. An important point is that the MTM standard will not be met for occasional work (for anything less than, say, 2,000 cycles).

2.2.1 *Reach* Reach is usually movement with an empty hand or finger while Move is generally movement with an object in the hand. Reach is subdivided into five cases (see Table 29.1), which can be modified in some instances by removing the effect of acceleration or deceleration, or both. The five cases of Reach are:

1. Reach to an object in a fixed location, or to an object in the other hand, or on which the other hand rests. (The concept is of minimum eye control and emphasis on proprioceptive feedback.)

2. Reach to a single object whose general location is known. Location may vary slightly from cycle to cycle. (The concept is that some visual control is necessary and that the following grasping motion will be simple and not slow down the reach.)

3. Reach to object jumbled with other objects in a group so that search and select occur. (The concept is that considerable visual, muscular, and mental control is necessary and that the following grasp motion will be complex, so the hand will slow down during the terminal portion of the reach to prepare for the complex grasp. It is the most difficult reach.)

4. Reach to a very small object or where accurate grasp is required. (The concept is that considerable visual control is necessary and that the following location grasp motion will be precise, so the hand will slow down during the terminal portion of the reach to prepare for the careful grasp.)

5. Reach to an indefinite location to get the hand in position for body balance or next motion or out of the way. (The concept is of minimum mental control. The movement often is "limited out" as other motions are done simultaneously.)

Table 29.1 gives the TMU for each case of Reach for various distances. The distances are for the motion path of the hand knuckle or fingertip rather than the straight-line distance between two points, although

---

TABLE 29.1

MTM-1 Reach times (TMU) for five cases at various distances. Case A and B Reaches also can omit an acceleration or deceleration. A typical code is R6B.

DISTANCE MOVED, INCHES	TIME, TMU A	B	C or D	E	HAND IN MOTION A	B	Case and Description
3/4 or less	2.0	2.0	2.0	2.0	1.6	1.6	A Reach to object in fixed location, or to object in other hand or on which other hand rests.
1	2.5	2.5	3.6	2.4	2.3	2.3	
2	4.0	4.0	5.9	3.8	3.5	2.7	
3	5.3	5.3	7.3	5.3	4.5	3.6	
4	6.1	6.4	8.4	6.8	4.9	4.3	
5	6.5	7.8	9.4	7.4	5.3	5.0	B Reach to single object in location, which may vary slightly from cycle to cycle.
6	7.0	8.6	10.1	8.0	5.7	5.7	
7	7.4	9.3	10.8	8.7	6.1	6.5	
8	7.9	10.1	11.5	9.3	6.5	7.2	
9	8.3	10.8	12.2	9.9	6.9	7.9	C Reach to object jumbled with other objects in a group so that search and select occur.
10	8.7	11.5	12.9	10.5	7.3	8.6	
12	9.6	12.9	14.2	11.8	8.1	10.1	
14	10.5	14.4	15.6	13.0	8.9	11.5	
16	11.4	15.8	17.0	14.2	9.7	12.9	D Reach to a very small object or where accurate grasp is required.
18	12.3	17.2	18.4	15.5	10.5	14.4	
20	13.1	18.6	19.8	16.7	11.3	15.8	
22	14.0	20.1	21.2	18.0	12.1	17.3	E Reach to indefinite location to get hand in position for body balance or next motion or out of way.
24	14.9	21.5	22.5	19.2	12.9	18.8	
26	15.8	22.9	23.9	20.4	13.7	20.2	
28	16.7	24.4	25.3	21.7	14.5	21.7	
30	17.5	25.8	26.7	22.9	15.3	23.2	
Additional	0.4	0.7	0.7	0.6			TMU per inch over 30 inches.

this fine point is often overlooked by users not intensively trained in MTM. Novices also tend to overlook the reduction in Reach distance due to shoulder movement and pivoting—called *body assist*.

If a movement is not given in the table, the user can interpolate (time for R15A is average of time for R14A and R16A) or just use the next higher value. The MTM Association recommends interpolation when the tables are given in inches but use of the next higher value when the tables are given in even cm or multiples of 5 cm.

In addition to breaking down Reach into five cases and a number of different distances, the effect of acceleration and deceleration also can be considered. The normal motion has the hand stopped at the beginning and end of the motion. Hands also could be in motion either at the beginning or end of the cycle, so either an acceleration or deceleration time can be omitted. The shortest time would occur in a situation in which the hand was in motion both at the beginning and end of the cycle and both acceleration and deceleration can be omitted. When one acceleration or deceleration can be omitted, time is decreased, as is shown by the hand-in-motion columns. When both acceleration and deceleration can be omitted, double this decrease is subtracted.

2.2.2 *Move* Move differs from Reach in that in Move the hand is usually holding something; occasionally the hand is pushing or dragging an object.

Move is subdivided into three cases (see Table 29.2). As with Reach, each Move can be refined to include the effect of acceleration or deceleration or both. There is also a refinement for object weight or resistance to movement. The three cases of Move are:

1. Move object to the other hand or against stop. (The concept is that there is little need to control the last portion of the move, except perhaps to prevent damage to the object.)

2. Move object to an approximate or indefinite location. (The concept is a move in which some control is needed at the end of the move, but not a great deal of control.)

3. Move object to exact location. (The concept is a move with considerable control needed at the end of the move. A case C Move very often is followed by a position.)

The three cases of Move thus differ (as did the five cases of Reach) by the nature of their destination. Thus, MTM, in effect, says that all elements are not purely independent but that both Moves and Reaches are influenced by the motions preceding or following them.

The shorthand for a 5-inch case C Move is M5C.

As with Reach, the hand acceleration or deceleration may not be needed for some Moves. If omitted, it

is indicated by "m" before or after the code—for example, mM6B, or M6Bm.

The last adjustment to Move is the effect of the weight of the object moved. Weight up to 2.5 lb/hand is included in the time shown in the Move table. Thus, if both hands move a 5-lb object, no extra time is allocated. If an object is slid rather than lifted, take the object weight times the coefficient of friction (0.4 for wood–wood and wood–metal, 0.3 for metal–metal).

Next, all weights between 2.5 and 7.5 lb are considered alike. First, the TMU value is multiplied by a factor and then a constant is added. For example, an M6B = 8.9. For a 5-lb weight, time would be M6B5 = 8.9 (1.06) + 2.2 = 11.8. For an 18-lb weight moved 12 inches with both hands, time for an M12C would be M12C9 = 15.2 (1.11) + 3.9 = 20.8.

MTM also has a more precise method of allowing for weights. Additional time for weight has a static component for obtaining control and a dynamic component for additional travel time. The static time component in TMU = .975 + .345 (weight, lbs). The dynamic time component is 1.1%/lb, at any given distance.

Table 29.3 gives the times for a variation of moving: *cranking*. For continuous cranking for 5 revolutions against a 1-lb load with a 6-inch diameter crank, the time would be $5 \times 12.7 = 63.5$ TMU plus 5.2 for start and stop = 68.7 TMU. Then the resistance is considered by multiplying by 1.11 (from Move table) and adding 3.9, giving a total of $68.7 \times 1.11 = 76.3 + 3.9 = 80.2$ TMU. The code is 5C6-10.

2.2.3 *Turn* The third type of motion with the hand is turn (see Table 29.4). **Turn** is a movement that rotates the hand, wrist, and forearm about the long axis of the forearm. The amount of time depends on the number of degrees turned as well as the weight of the object or the resistance against which the turn is made.

2.2.4 *Apply pressure* Apply Pressure (see Table 29.5) is the application of force without resultant movement. An APA is the basic element; an APB is an APA plus a Regrasp (G2).

2.2.5 *Grasp* The next four motions—Grasp, Position, Disengage, and Release—are the skill motions. Improvement in performance times usually is a result of reductions in times for these motions rather than increased speed of movement for Move, Reach, or Turn.

Grasp is the motion used when the purpose is to gain control of an object or objects; it almost always is followed by Move. Grasp is divided into five categories; Pickup and Select are subdivided further (see Table 29.6).

1. *Type 1:* Pickup Grasp. Usually follows an A or B reach.

T A B L E		2 9 . 2	

MTM-1 Move times (TMU) for three cases at various distances. Case B Moves can omit acceleration and/or deceleration. The effect of weight is calculated by multiplying effective net weight/hand by the dynamic factor and then adding the static constant. A typical code without weight is M8A; a typical code with a weight of 7 lb is M8A7.

Distance Moved, Inches	TIME TMU			Hand In Motion B	WEIGHT ALLOWANCE			CASE AND DESCRIPTION
	A	B	C		Wt. (lb) Up to	Dynamic Factor	Static Constant TMU	
3/4 or less	2.0	2.0	2.0	1.7				A Move object to other hand or against stop.
1	2.5	2.9	3.4	2.3	2.5	1.00	0	
2	3.6	4.6	5.2	2.9				
3	4.9	5.7	6.7	3.6	7.5	1.06	2.2	
4	6.1	6.9	8.0	4.3				
5	7.3	8.0	9.2	5.0	12.5	1.11	3.9	
6	8.1	8.9	10.3	5.7				
7	8.9	9.7	11.1	6.5	17.5	1.17	5.6	
8	9.7	10.6	11.8	7.2				
9	10.5	11.5	12.7	7.9	22.5	1.22	7.4	
10	11.3	12.2	13.5	8.6				
12	12.9	13.4	15.2	10.0	27.5	1.28	9.1	B Move object to approximate or indefinite location.
14	14.4	14.6	16.9	11.4				
16	16.0	15.8	18.7	12.8	32.5	1.33	10.8	
18	17.6	17.0	20.4	14.2				
20	19.2	18.2	22.1	15.6	37.5	1.39	12.5	
22	20.8	19.4	23.8	17.0				C Move object to exact location.
24	22.4	20.6	25.5	18.4	42.5	1.44	14.3	
26	24.0	21.8	27.3	19.8				
28	25.5	23.1	29.0	21.2	47.5	1.50	16.0	
30	27.1	24.3	30.7	22.7				
Additional	0.8	0.6	0.85					TMU per inch over 30 inches

EFFECTIVE NET WEIGHT

Effective Net Weight	No. of Hands	Spatial	Sliding
(ENW)	1	W	$W \times F_c$
	2	W/2	$W/2 \times F_c$

W = Weight in pounds
F_c = Coefficient of Friction

- Case 1A—small, medium, or large object by itself, easily grasped
- Case 1B—very small object or object lying close against a flat surface
- Case 1C1—interference with Grasp on bottom and one side of nearly cylindrical object; diameter greater than .50 inch
- Case 1C2—interference with Grasp on bottom and one side of nearly cylindrical object; diameter .25 to .50 inch

- Case 1C3—interference with Grasp on bottom and one side of nearly cylindrical object; diameter less than .25 inch

2. *Type 2:* Regrasp. This Grasp is used to change or improve control of an object that had previously been grasped. It often is performed during a Move and is "limited out."

3. *Type 3:* Transfer Grasp. This Grasp is used to transfer control of an object from one hand to the other.

TABLE 29.3

MTM-1 cranking motion times (TMU) for light resistance. A typical code is 6C5. With 10-lb resistance: 6C5-10. See also Table 17.4.

DIAMETER OF CRANKING (INCHES)	TMU (T) PER REVOLUTION	DIAMETER OF CRANKING (INCHES)	TMU (T) PER REVOLUTION
1	8.5	9	14.0
2	9.7	10	14.4
3	10.6	11	14.7
4	11.4	12	15.0
5	12.1	14	15.5
6	12.7	16	16.0
7	13.2	18	16.4
8	13.6	20	16.7

Formulas:

A. Continuous Cranking (Start at beginning and stop at end of cycle only)

$$TMU = [(N \times T) + 5.2] \times F + C$$

B. Intermittent Cranking (Start at beginning and stop at end of each revolution)

$$TMU = [(T + 5.2) F + C] \times N$$

C = Static component TMU weight allowance constant from move table

F = Dynamic component weight allowance factor from move table

N = Number of revolutions

T = TMU per revolution (type III Motion)

5.2 = TMU for start and stop

4. *Type 4:* Jumbled Grasp. Follows a C Reach.
   - Case 4A—object jumbled with other objects, so search and select occur; larger than 1 inch × 1 inch × 1 inch
   - Case 4B—object jumbled with other objects, so search and select occur; .25 inch × .25 inch × .12 inch to 1 × 1 × 1 inch

- Case 4C—object jumbled with other objects, so search and select occur; smaller than .25 inch × .25 inch × .12 inch
5. *Type 5:* Contact, sliding, or hook Grasp. This Grasp usually occurs between a Reach and a Move. No time is required to make contact with an object.

2.2.6 Position Original **position** is the collection of minor hand movements (distance moved to engage no more than 1 inch) for aligning, orienting, and engaging one object with another object. It usually follows a C Move. Align is orienting the longitudinal axes of the two items. Orient is rotation about the long axis to align mating features (key in lock). Engage is to move along the longitudinal axis to mate the parts. Disengage is the complement of the engage portion of position. It is assumed that the items are already aligned and oriented, so time for that is zero.

Position times (see Table 29.7) vary with amount of pressure needed to fit, with symmetry of the object, and with ease of handling. The three classes of fit are:

1. *Loose:* no pressure required (gravity sufficient); code = 1
2. *Close:* light pressure required (1 APA); most common fit; code = 2
3. *Exact:* heavy pressure required (3 APA + G2); code = 3

There also are three classes of symmetry:

1. *Symmetrical (Code = S):* This class is demonstrated by a round peg in a round hole. The concept is that, no matter in which orientation the part might happen to be, no rotation is necessary for assembly.

2. *Nonsymmetrical (Code = NS):* This class is demonstrated by a cylinder with a key. There is one and only one orientation in which the two parts will mate. A turn of 180° (either clockwise or counterclockwise) is the maximum rotation required. Because some preorientation is done during most moves, only 75° is considered to be typical (i.e., an extra 4.8 TMU is allowed).

TABLE 29.4

MTM-1 Turn (forearm swivel) times (TMU) vary with angle turned and weight in the hand. Typical codes are T30S and T45M.

WEIGHT	TIME, TMU FOR DEGREES TURNED										
	30°	45°	60°	75°	90°	105°	120°	135°	150°	165°	180°
Small: 0 to 2 pounds	2.8	3.5	4.1	4.8	5.4	6.1	6.8	7.4	8.1	8.7	9.4
Medium: 2.1 to 10 pounds	4.4	5.5	6.5	7.5	8.5	9.6	10.6	11.6	12.7	13.7	14.8
Large: 10.1 to 35 pounds	8.4	10.5	12.3	14.4	16.2	18.3	20.4	22.2	24.3	26.1	28.2

| | | TABLE | 29.5 | | | |

Apply Pressure times (TMU) have two categories. An APB is an APA plus a regrasp.

SYMBOL	TMU	FULL CYCLE DESCRIPTION	SYMBOL	TMU	COMPONENTS DESCRIPTION
APA	10.6	AF + DM + RLF	AF	3.4	Apply Force
			DM	4.2	Dwell, Minimum
APB	16.2	APA + G2	RLF	3.0	Release Force

| | | TABLE | 29.6 | | | |

Grasp times (TMU) given for five types of grasp. Pickup and Select are subdivided further. A typical code is G1A.

TYPE OF GRASP	CASE	TIME, TMU	DESCRIPTION	
PICKUP	1A	2.0	Any size object by itself, easily grasped	
	1B	3.5	Object very small or lying close against a flat surface	
	1C1	7.3	Diameter larger than 1/2"	Interference with Grasp
	1C2	8.7	Diameter 1/4" to 1/2"	on bottom and one side of
	1C3	10.8	Diameter less than 1/4"	nearly cylindrical object.
REGRASP	2	5.6	Change grasp without relinquishing control	
TRANSFER	3	5.6	Control transferred from one hand to the other	
SELECT	4A	7.3	Larger than 1" × 1" × 1"	Object jumbled with other
	4B	9.1	1/4" × 1/4" × 1/8" to 1" × 1" × 1"	objects so that search
	4C	12.9	Smaller than 1/4" × 1/4" × 1/8"	and select occur.
CONTACT	5	0	Contact, Sliding, or Hook Grasp	

3. *Semisymmetrical:* All positions that are neither symmetrical nor nonsymmetrical are considered semisymmetrical. An average turn of 45° is considered typical.

The two classes of ease of handling are: easy and difficult. They differ by a Regrasp, that is, 5.6 TMU. All flexible materials are considered difficult. A complete Position code includes all three variables; e.g., P1SE, P2SSE, P1NSD, P3SD. Alignment to a point or line (without engagement) within .25 to .5 inch requires only an M__C Move, within .06 to .25, an M__C Move plus a P1SE or P1SD, and less than .06, an M__C Move plus a P2SE or P2SD.

The middle table of Table 29.7 gives an alternative description for Position, and the lower table gives the times for Secondary Engage.

Secondary Engage is a component of Supplementary Position data, which is not a variable in original Position (top table of Table 29.7). It is the time required to insert an object into another for varying depths of insertion. It is used in analyses as a separate code when the radial clearance of two mating objects changes during insertion, as may be the case in chamfering or countersinking.

2.2.7 *Disengage* Disengage is the breaking of contact between one object and another. It includes the involuntary movement resulting from the sudden end of resistance (see Table 29.8). The three factors of class of fit, ease of handling, and care in handling are combined in a 2-factor table. The three classes of fit are given as:

1. *Loose:* very slight effort, blends with subsequent Moves (recoil up to 1 inch)
2. *Close:* normal effort, slight recoil (over 1 inch to 5 inches)
3. *Tight:* considerable effort, hand recoils markedly (over 5 inches)

Again there are only two classes of ease of handling: easy and difficult. A complete disengage code includes both fit and ease of handling—for example, D1E, D1D, D2D.

T A B L E   2 9 . 7

MTM-1 Position (align, orient, and engage) times depend on the pressure required, the symmetry, and the ease of handling. Using the top table (Original Position), a typical code is P2SSE, denoting close fit, semisymmetrical orientation, and easy handling. Insertion up to 1 inch is implied in all original Position codes. The middle table (Supplementary Position) classifies fit in terms of radial clearance between the mating objects as 21, 22, or 23. In addition to align, orient, and primary engage time, a secondary engage time is added to account for varying insertion depth. Select the Position time from one of the four Depth of Insertion columns. For example, to align, orient, and engage a semisymmetrical object with a radial clearance of 0.25 inch between the mating parts to a depth of 1 inch, coded P21SS4, requires 14.6 TMU. The Align Only column is used for surface alignments having no engagement depths, as when sliding a ruler to a point. The lowest table gives Secondary Engage times (TMU) as a function of class of fit and depth of insertion. It is used as a separate code when the radial clearance changes after the initial engagement and before completing the insertion. A typical code is E22-2 followed by a P21 Position.

CLASS OF FIT		SYMMETRY	EASY TO HANDLE	DIFFICULT TO HANDLE
1—Loose	No pressure required	S	5.6	11.2
		SS	9.1	14.7
		NS	10.4	16.0
2—Close	Light pressure required	S	16.2	21.8
		SS	19.7	25.3
		NS	21.0	26.6
3—Exact	Heavy pressure required	S	43.0	48.6
		SS	46.5	52.1
		NS	47.8	53.4

SUPPLEMENTARY RULE FOR SURFACE ALIGNMENT

P1SE per alignment: >1/16<1/4"   P2SE per alignment: <1/16"

*Distance moved to engage—1" or less.

CLASS OF FIT AND CLEARANCE	CASE OF SYMMETRY†	ALIGN ONLY	DEPTH OF INSERTION (PER 1/4")			
			0	2	4	6
			>0≤1/8"	>1/8≤3/4"	>3/4≤5/4"	>5/4≤7/4"
21	S	3.0	3.4	6.6	7.7	8.8
.150" to .350"	SS	3.0	10.3	13.5	14.6	15.7
	NS	4.8	15.5	18.7	19.8	20.9
22	S	7.2	7.2	11.9	13.0	14.2
.025" to .149"	SS	8.0	14.9	19.6	20.7	21.9
	NS	9.5	20.2	24.9	26.0	27.2
23*	S	9.5	9.5	16.3	18.7	21.0
.005" to .024"	SS	10.4	17.3	24.1	26.5	28.8
	NS	12.2	22.9	29.7	32.1	34.4

*Binding—Add observed number of Apply Pressures.

Difficult Handling—Add observed number of G2's.

†Determine symmetry by geometric properties, except use S case when object is oriented prior to preceding Move.

CLASS OF FIT	DEPTH OF INSERTION (PER 1/4")		
	2	4	6
21	3.2	4.3	5.4
22	4.7	5.8	7.0
23	6.8	9.2	11.5

T A B L E	2 9 . 8

MTM-1 Disengage times (TMU). Times depend on the class of fit and ease of handling. The lower table aids in selecting the proper category. A typical code is D2E.

SUPPLEMENTARY		
Class of Fit	Care in Handling	Binding
1—LOOSE	Allow Class 2	
2—CLOSE	Allow Class 3	One G2 per Bind
3—TIGHT	Change Method	One APB per Bind

Class of Fit	Height of Recoil	Easy to Handle	Difficult to Handle
1—LOOSE—Very slight effort, blends with subsequent move	Up to 1"	4.0	5.7
2—CLOSE—Normal effort, slight recoil	Over 1" to 5"	7.5	11.8
3—TIGHT—Considerable effort, hand recoils markedly	Over 5" to 12"	22.9	34.7

Source: Copyright by MTM Association for Standards and Research. No reprint permission without written consent from MTM Association, 1111 E. Touhy Avenue, Des Plaines, IL 60018.

2.2.8 *Release* **Release** is the relinquishing of control of an object by the hand or fingers. Table 29.9 shows that there are only two categories. The most common Release, a simple opening of the fingers, is given 2 TMU. In the contact Release, for which no time is allowed, the release begins and is completed at the instant the following Reach motion begins. The two codes are RL1 and RL2.

2.2.9 *Other motions* Other motions include (1) body, leg, and foot motions; (2) eye motions; and (3) combined and limited motions.

Body, leg, and foot motions. The previous tables gave motions of the hand and arm. Table 29.10 gives **body motions** (motions of the leg–foot, horizontal torso motions, and vertical torso motions). The descriptions of the motions in the tables are reasonably self-explanatory. A foot motion is hinged at the ankle, a leg motion is hinged at the knee or hip or both, and the body center-line doesn't move appreciably. In a sidestep, the time depends on the distance the centerline moves. A pace is considered to cover 2.8 feet, or 34 inches, at a relatively fast pace of 3.57 miles/h. For walking through obstructed areas, use 17 TMU/pace. Use 15 TMU/pace for stairs. For carrying a load up to 34 lb, use a 30-inch pace and 15 TMU/pace. For vertical torso motions, going up takes more time than going down.

Eye motions. In addition to motions of the limbs and torso, time is allowed, in certain cases, for activities of the eyes. Table 29.11 gives the two basic elements of **eye motions**: Eye Focus and Eye Travel, and the formula for Read. Eye Focus is the focusing of the eye once it has an object in its line of sight. Eye Travel is the movement of the eyes from one point to another. From geometry, when $T/D = 1$, the angle swept by the eyes is 45°; for $T/D = 2$, the angle is 90°; for $T/D = 3$, the angle is 135°. Thus, 15.2 TMU is allowed per 45° sweep (.33 TMU/degree) with the limitation, however, of a maximum allowable for Eye Travel of 20 TMU, because the eyes are generally restricted to a maximum movement of 70°. Reading 100 words takes 505 TMU (18.2 s).

T A B L E	2 9 . 9

MTM-1 Release times (TMU). Only two subdivisions. Normal release is coded RL1.

SUPPLEMENTARY		
Case	Time, TMU	Description
1	2.0	Normal release performed by opening fingers as independent motion.
2	0	Contact Release.

Source: Copyright by MTM Association for Standards and Research. No reprint permission without written consent from MTM Association, 1111 E. Touhy Avenue, Des Plaines, IL 60018.

TABLE   29.10

MTM-1 times (TMU) for motions of the leg and torso have three major subdivisions. Typical codes are W5P and SS15C1.

TYPE	SYMBOL	TMU	DISTANCE	DESCRIPTION
LEG–FOOT	FM	8.5	To 4"	Hinged at ankle
MOTION	FMP	19.1	To 4"	With heavy pressure
		7.1	To 6"	
	LM–	1.2	Ea. add'l inch	Hinged at knee or hip in any direction
HORIZONTAL			<12"	Use Reach or Move time when less than 12";
MOTION	SS–C1	17.0	12"	complete when leading leg contacts floor
Side		0.6	Ea. add'l inch	
Step	SS–C2	34.1	12"	Lagging leg must contact floor before next motion
		1.1	Ea. add'l inch	can be made
Turn	TBC1	18.6	–	Complete when leading leg contacts floor
Body	TBC2	37.2	–	Lagging leg must contact floor before motion can be made
Walk	W–FT	5.3	Per Foot	Unobstructed
	W–P	15.0	Per Pace	Unobstructed
	W–PO	17.0	Per Pace	When obstructed or with weight
VERTICAL	SIT	34.7	–	From standing position
MOTION	STD	43.4	–	From sitting position
	B,S,KOK	29.0	–	Bend, Stoop, Kneel on one knee
	AB,AS,AKOK	31.9	–	Arise from Bend, Stoop, Kneel on one knee
	KBK	69.4	–	Kneel on both knees
	AKBK	76.7	–	Arise from Kneel on both knees

Source: Copyright by MTM Association for Standards and Research. No reprint permission without written consent from MTM Association, 1111 E. Touhy Avenue, Des Plaines, IL 60018.

Combined and limited motions. So far the motions have been described as if the person performed one at a time. Often we have combined motions or simultaneous motions.

Combined motions are those that occur when the same body member performs two or more motions at the same time (Turn a part of the hand while moving it; Regrasp during a Move). The time to allocate is the greater of the two times. Thus, a Regrasp during an M3A would be given 5.6 for time, with a slash line through the M3A. A Regrasp during an M6A would be given 7.0 for time, with a slash line through the G2. See Figure 29.1 for a combined motion.

Motions also occur simultaneously, such as right and left hands, hands and feet, or eyes and hands. If they are *truly* simultaneous, allow only the longer time.

TABLE   29.11

MTM-1 times (TMU) for the eye are Eye Focus, Eye Travel, and Read. Eye Focus assumes eye travel is completed. Eye Travel is the movement from one point to another at .33 TMU/degree of motion. Reading time, TMU, = 5.05 N, where N = number of words.

Eye Travel Time	=	$15.2 \times T/D$, with a maximum value of 20 TMU.
where T	=	the distance between points from and to which the eye travels
D	=	the perpendicular distance from the eye to the line of travel T
Eye Focus Time	=	7.3 TMU

SUPPLEMENTARY INFORMATION

Area of Normal Vision	=	Circle 4" (100 mm) in diameter 16" (400 mm) from eyes
Read Formula	=	5.05 N where N = the number of words

Source: Copyright by MTM Association for Standards and Research. No reprint permission without written consent from MTM Association, 1111 E. Touhy Avenue, Des Plaines, IL 60018.

F I G U R E   · 2 9 . 1

A **combined motion** (such as the G2 during the Move to the hole) has a slash through it. This indicates it isn't included in the TMU total. Note how repeated steps can be described with the number column. Time to assemble 30 pegs in the pegboard = 1159.3 TMU = .70 min.

MTM FORM

Sheet: 1 of 1   System: Pegboard + 30 pegs / Assemble 30 pegs   Date: 21 July 1999
Study no.: 1A   Analyst: SK

Left Hand Description	No.	L H Motion	Time	R H Motion	No.	Right Hand Description
Reach to (1) peg in bin w/RH Pick up and place disk first in hole. See sketch up back for hole sequence. Repeat (30) times)						
			13.6	R11C	1	Reach to bin for (1) peg from table edge
			333.5	R8C	29	Reach to bin for (1) peg from pegboard center
			219.0	G4A	30	Grasp (1) peg
			354.0	M6C	30	Move (1) peg to hole
				G̶1̶	30	Regrasp during Move
			168.0	P1SE	30	Position (1) peg in hole
			60.0	RL1	30	Release peg
			11.2	R11E	1	Return hand to table edge
			1159.3			

If they are only *apparently* simultaneous, allow both times. Use Table 29.12 to decide between *truly* and *apparently* simultaneous. Truly or apparently depends on which combinations are considered, on whether they are in the area of normal vision (objects within 4 inches of each other at a distance of 16 inches from the eye), and the amount of practice (one common definition is 500 cycles, although others use 1,000 or 2,000).

Thus, for truly simultaneous motions such as an M8A with the left hand and an M10A with the right hand, allow only the 11.3 of the M10A. If apparently simultaneous but, according to Table 29.12 not actually simultaneous (such as an M8C with the left hand and an M8C with the right hand), allow 11.8 + 11.8—a total of 23.6.

In many cases where truly simultaneous motions are not allowed by Table 29.12, one hand can drift toward the target while the other does the motion. For example, while the right hand does an M8C, the left hand does an M8B. The M8B can be done simultaneously with the M8C and is "limited out"; it is conventional to circle **limited motions** (see Figure 29.2 for an example). Then, when the M8C is completed, the left hand has only a small distance (an MfC where f stands for fractional) remaining. The time allowed is 11.8 for the right hand plus a 2.0 for the left—a total of 13.8.

T A B L E   2 9 . 1 2

If motions are easy to perform simultaneously, allow just the longer of the two times. If they can be done without practice, use judgment on whether to allow both times. If difficult, allow both times.

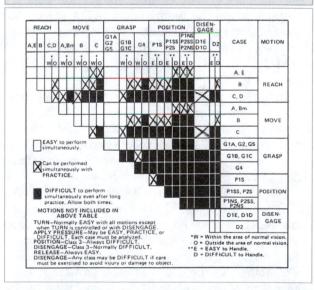

Source: Copyright by MTM Association for Standards and Research. No reprint permission without written consent from MTM Association, 1111 E. Touhy Avenue, Des Plaines, IL 60018.

FIGURE 29.2

Limited motions are circled to show they do not add to the TMU total. Note that working smart with two hands gives an assembly time of 809.8 TMU = .49 min or 70% of the one-hand method.

MTM FORM

Sheet: 1 of 1   System: 30 wooden peg + (1) pegboard   Date: 21 July 99
Study no.: 1B   Analyst: JK

Left Hand Description	No.	L H Motion	Time	R H Motion	No.	Right Hand Description
Reach into bin with BH.		Get (1) peg in each hand. Move peg to board with				
beveled end FIRST. See sketch on back for hole sequence						
To bin from table edge	1	R11C	13.6	R11C	1	To bin from table edge
To bin from board center	14	R8C	166.0	R8C	14	To bin from board center
Turn hand 60°	14	T60		T60	14	Turn hand 60°
Grasp (1) peg	15	G4A	109.5			
			109.5	G4A	15	Grasp (1) peg
Move (1) peg toward board *		M8B	177.0	M8B	15	Move (1) peg to board
Regrasp during move		G2		G2	15	Regrasp during move
Turn hand 60°		T60		T60	15	Turn hand 60°
			84.0	P1SE	15	Position peg in hole
Move (1) peg to hole	15	M8C	30.0			
Position peg in hole	15	P1SE	84.0			
Release peg	15	RL1	30.0	RL1	15	Release peg
Hand to table edge	1	R11E	11.2	R11E	1	Hand to table edge
			809.8			
* Although these rows are within area of normal vision, lack of practise						
precludes SIMO motion.						

2.3 MTM-2 and MTM-3

How much error can be tolerated in the time determined for a specific task: 1%, 5%, 10%, 30%? How much are you willing to pay for accuracy? The answers are not the same for all situations, so the International MTM Directorate (an association of 12 national MTM organizations) developed two simplified systems called **MTM-2 and MTM-3.** (The basic system described previously is called MTM-1.)

In MTM-1 it takes about 250 times the cycle time to analyze the task, while in MTM-2 it takes about 100 times, and in MTM-3 about 35 times (Sellie, 1992). Figure 29.3 shows expected error limits (95% confidence) as a function of the nonrepetitive manual time in a task and the level of analysis.

For example, for a specific task with a 1,000-TMU cycle time, an MTM-1 analysis would take about 3.5 h and would be expected to be accurate within ±7%; an MTM-3 analysis would take about .5 h and would be accurate within ±20%. Magnusson (1972) found that the use of MTM-2 gave times 0.1% higher than MTM-1 while MTM-3 gave values 0.9% higher than MTM-1. (This "bias" is considered to be insignificant.) The remaining random error (after this

systematic error) will decrease with increasing sample size or, in this case, with longer cycle times. A 10,000-TMU cycle with MTM-1 would therefore be expected to be accurate within ±2%.

However, Knott and Sury (1986) reported that accuracy was the same for MTM-1, MTM-2, and MTM-3, so the only tradeoff was the desired level of methods description with the increased time to calculate a time. MTM-2 and MTM-3 require considerable judgment by the analyst.

2.3.1 *MTM-2* Table 29.13 shows the MTM-2 table; there are only 37 times in all.

The two key motion categories are GET (combining Reach, Grasp, and Release) and PUT (combining Move and Position). Which of the 15 values of GET or PUT to use depends on the case of GET or PUT, the distance, and the weight or resistance to motion.

Figure 29.4 shows the decision tree for GET to determine case. Then the user estimates (not measures) the distance and uses one of the five rows. Third, if necessary, add 1 TMU/2 lb moved if the object to be moved weighs 4 lb or more per hand.

Predict analysis time and accuracy from the graph, using the lines for MTM-1, MTM-2, or MTM-3 (Magnusson, 1972). Magnusson estimated MTM-1 took 350 times the cycle time, so a 2,000-TMU (.02 h) task would take 350 (.02) = 7 h to analyze by MTM-1; predicted accuracy (with 95% confidence) is ±4.9%.

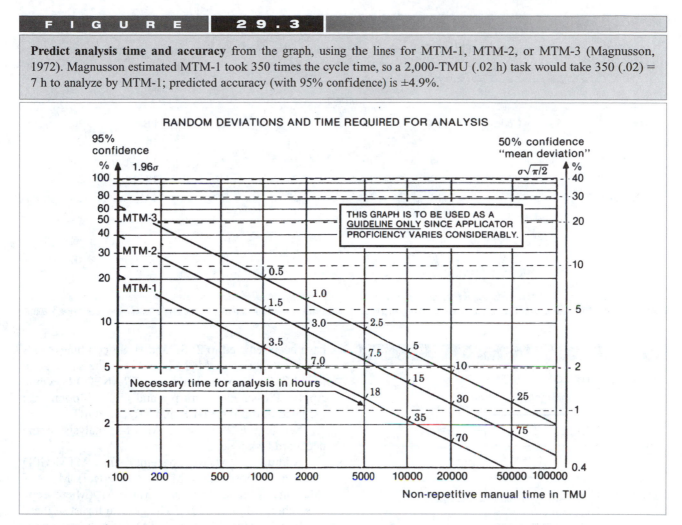

RANDOM DEVIATIONS AND TIME REQUIRED FOR ANALYSIS

Figure 29.5 shows the decision tree for PUT to determine case. Then the user estimates (not measures) the distance and uses one of the five rows.

Third, if necessary, add 1 TMU/10 lb moved if the object weighs 4 lb or more per hand.

There remain seven motions:

A. Apply Pressure—an action with the purpose of exerting muscular force on an object

R. Regrasp—a hand action performed with the purpose of changing the grasp on an object

E. Eye Action—an action with the purpose of either recognizing a readily distinguishable characteristic of an object or shifting the aim of the axis of vision to a new viewing area

C. Crank—a motion with the purpose of moving an object in a circular path of more than half a revolution with the hand or fingers

S. Step—either a leg motion with the purpose of moving the body or a leg motion longer than 12 inches

F. Foot Motion—a short foot or leg motion when the purpose is not to move the body

B. Bend and Arise—a bend, stoop, or kneel on one knee, and the subsequent rise

See Figure 29.6 for an MTM-2 analysis of the two-hand assembly of the pegboard.

2.3.2 *MTM-3* Table 29.14 shows the MTM-3 table. Now there are only 10 times.

The two key motion categories have been reduced to HANDLE (getting control over an object with the hand or fingers and placing the object in a new location) and TRANSPORT (placing an object in a new location with the hand or fingers). Which of the four values of HANDLE or TRANSPORT to use depends on the case and the distance.

Figure 29.7 shows the decision tree for both HANDLE and TRANSPORT. Distances are estimated as either equal to or less than 6 inches or over 6 inches. The seven additional elements of MTM-2

T A B L E   29.13

MTM-2 (simplified) version of MTM-1. Task analysis time should take about 150 times the cycle time. Times are in TMU.

				MTM-2			
RANGE	Code	GA	GB	GC	PA	PB	PC
Up to 2"	−2	3	7	14	3	10	21
Over 2" to 6"	−6	6	10	19	6	15	26
Over 6" to 12"	−12	9	14	23	11	19	36
Over 12" to 18"	−18	13	18	27	15	24	36
Over 18"	−32	17	23	32	20	30	41
	GW 1-per 2 lb						PW 1-per 10 lb
	A	R	E	C	S	F	B
	14	6	7	15	18	9	61

Source: Copyright by MTM Association for Standards and Research. No reprint permission without written consent from MTM Association, 1111 E. Touhy Avenue, Des Plaines, IL 60018.

F I G U R E   29.4

Decision tree for GET in MTM-2.

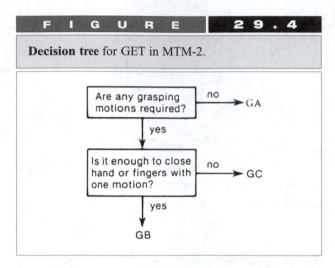

Source: Copyright by MTM Association for Standards and Research. No reprint permission without written consent from MTM Association, 1111 E. Touhy Avenue, Des Plaines, IL 60018.

F I G U R E   29.5

Decision tree for PUT in MTM-2.

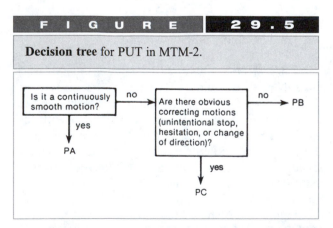

Source: Copyright by MTM Association for Standards and Research. No reprint permission without written consent from MTM Association, 1111 E. Touhy Avenue, Des Plaines, IL 60018.

have been reduced to 2: SF and B. SF combines the S and F categories of MTM-2 and B is the same as in MTM-2. Crank now would be a TRANSPORT, while Apply Pressure, Regrasp, and Eye Motion are included in the HANDLE and TRANSPORT.

See Figure 29.8 for an MTM-3 analysis of the pegboard task assembly.

Additional MTM systems are MTM-GPD (General Purpose Data), MTM-C (Clerical), MTM-V (Machine Tool Users), and MTM-M (Microscope Assembly) (Matias, 2001). The general thrust of these additional systems (versus MTM-1) is shorter application time and specialization by type of work.

3 MOST WORK MEASUREMENT SYSTEM

The MOST (Maynard Operational Sequence Technique) was developed in Sweden for the H. B. Maynard Company in the 1960s by Zandin (1980). It resulted from the observation that the vast majority of activities involved with the handling of an object were associated with a limited number of motion sequences. By analyzing the activities with respect to these sequences, the time required to perform an analysis was significantly reduced from that required by the traditional MTM system without a reduction in the precision of the analysis.

Beyond the basic MOST (which is the focus of this section), further developments resulted in modifications of the sequence-based system that accommodates particular situations. MiniMOST is used for short-cycle, highly repetitive operations. Although the accuracy is greater, this system requires more time to conduct an analysis and should be applied only when necessary. On the other end of the

F I G U R E	2 9 . 6

MTM-2 analysis of one-hand and two-hand assembly of pegboard previously analyzed in Figures 29.1 and 29.2. MTM-1 shows total time = 1,270 TMU = .76 min and 949 TMU = .57 min.	MTM FORM

Sheet: 1 of 1   System: (30) wooden pegs + (1) pegboard   Date: 21/July 99
Study no.: 1 C (MTM 2)   Analyst: SR

Left Hand Description	No.	L H Motion	Time	R H Motion	No.	Right Hand Description
Reach to (1) peg in bin w/RH. Pick up and place nose first in bin. Repeat 60						
times. See sketch on back for hole sequence.						
			690	GC12	30	Get (1) peg
			570	PB12	30	Put peg in hole
			R	30	Regrasp during Move
			1260			
Reach into bin w/BH time						
Get (1) peg from bin	15	G-	345			
Overlap Always Required.	15	GC2	210			
Put (1) peg into hole	15	Pm	285	PB12	15	Put into hole
		R		R		
Overlap outside Area						
of Normal vision	10	PB2	100			
Hand to table edge	1	GA12	9	GA12	1	Hand to table edge
			949			

T A B L E	2 9 . 1 4

MTM-3 has only 10 times; analysis time should take about 50 times the cycle time. Times are in TMU.

		MTM-3			
RANGE	CODE	HA	HB	TA	TB
Up to 6"	−6	18	34	7	21
Over 6"	−32	34	48	16	29
		SF	18	B	61

F I G U R E	2 9 . 7

Decision tree for both HANDLE and TRANSPORT in MTM-3.

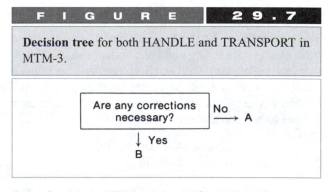

continuum are tasks that have very long cycle times and have many, non-identical operations. For this case, the basic MOST involves more detail than necessary and the MaxiMOST system provides an efficient method of establishing times that have the necessary accuracy. Other, task-specific MOST systems have also been developed, such as the MOST for Clerical Operations. The MOST systems are also computer-based. More information about these systems can be obtained from the H. B. Maynard and Company website listed at the back of the chapter.

The majority of operations performed in manufacturing/processing operations can be addressed using the basic MOST system. There are four sequence models within the basic MOST: general move, controlled move, tool use, and manual crane sequence. The general move sequence model is used to analyze the movement of an object through space where the

F I G U R E	2 9 . 8

MTM-3 analysis of one-hand and two-hand assembly of pegboard previously analyzed in Figures 29.2 and 29.6. Shows how you revert to MTM-2 if frequency is over 10 (except for SF).

MTM FORM

Sheet: 1 of 1   System: 30 wooden peg + (1) pegboard   Date: 21 July 99
Study no.: 1D (MTM 3)   Analyst: SK

Left Hand Description	No.	L H Motion	Time	R H Motion	No.	Right Hand Description
Reach to (1) peg in bin w/ RH Pick up and place Loose first in bins. Repeat 30 times						
See sketch on back for hole sequence.						
			1440	HB32	30	Get and position (1) peg
Since frequency is over 10, use MTM 2 instead. See Figure 30.6.						
Reach into bin w/BH simo.						
Get and place 1 peg	15	(H -)	48	HB32	15	Get and position 1 peg
Overlap always need	15	HB6	34			
			72			
Since frequency is over 10, use MTM-2 instead. See Fig 30.6.						

path is not restricted and there is no resistance to the movement. Table 29.15 illustrates how the sequence of activities is categorized and the index values (times) that are associated with each category. The general move sequence has three components: *get, put,* and *return.* These components are described by parameters related to actions/motions. The parameters are:

> A—action distance B—body motion
> G—gain control P—placement

The *get* action involves an action distance (i.e., two steps), a body motion (i.e., bend), and gain control (i.e., get heavy/bulky). The values for each parameter in the general move varies from 0 to 16, depending upon the time required to perform the action. For example, a *get* move might be characterized by the following parameters and index values:

$$A_3 \ B_6 \ G_3$$

To determine the time (in TMUs) the sum of the index values, 12, is multiplied by 10. In this case, the action requires 120 TMUs or 0.072 min.

The *put* action also involves an action distance and body motion; however, the third parameter is placement (i.e., position with precision). The last parameter for the general move sequence is the *return.* The *return* is represented by an action distance (A). Consider the simple example where an operator gets a washer (in reach) from a bowl of washers (grasp light object) and places it on a bolt (within reach, place with adjustments). The total sequence and values for the general move is as follows:

$$A_1 \ B_0 \ G_1 \qquad A_1 \ B_0 \ P_3 \qquad A_1$$
$$\text{(get)} \qquad\quad \text{(put)} \qquad\quad \text{(return)}$$

The total time for this simple action would be 0.042 min ($7 \times 10 = 70$ TMU).

The controlled move sequence model differs from the general move model in that the path of the object is restricted by contact with another object, attachment to another object, or a movement through a specific path. The sequence model involves three components: *get, move/activate,* and *return.*

The *get* and *return* activities for the controlled move sequence are the same as for the general move (A B G). The move/activate component has 3 parts: controlled move (M), process time (X), and alignment (I). The full sequence for a controlled move is as follows:

T A B L E   2 9 . 1 5

General move sequence model.

ṁ⟩ **ABGABPA**			GENERAL MOVE		
INDEX	**A** ACTION DISTANCE	**B** BODY MOTION	**G** GAIN CONTROL	**P** PLACE	**INDEX**
0	≤ 2 IN ≤ 5 CM			HOLD TOSS	0
1	WITHIN REACH		LIGHT OBJECT LIGHT OBJECTS SIMO	LAY ASIDE LOOSE FIT	1
3	1-2 STEPS	BEND AND ARISE 50% OCC	NON SIMO HEAVY OR BULKY BLIND OR OBSTRUCTED DISENGAGE INTERLOCKED COLLECT	ADJUSTMENTS LIGHT PRESSURE DOUBLE	3
6	3-4 STEPS	BEND AND ARISE		CARE OR PRECISION HEAVY PRESSURE BLIND OR OBSTRUCTED INTERMEDIATE MOVES	6
10	5-7 STEPS	SIT OR STAND			10
16	8-10 STEPS	THROUGH DOOR CLIMB ON OR OFF			16

A B G   M X I   A
(get) (move/actuate) (return)

Table 29.16 illustrates how the sequence of activities is categorized and the index values that are associated with each category.

The tool use sequence is made up of five "phases." These phases are:

1. get tool
2. put tool in place
3. use tool
4. put tool aside
5. return

The sequence model for the tool use sequence is:

A B G   A B P   Use*   A B P   A
(get tool) (put tool in place) (tool use) (tool aside) (return)

The parameters used for the *get, put, aside,* and *return* actions in the tool use sequence are the same as those in the general move. The parameters associated with using the tools are illustrated in Table 29.17.

The last sequence model making up basic MOST is the manual crane. This is a set of special sequences that were developed to address a frequently encountered class of material handling equipment. Table 29.18 illustrates the parameters that are associated with the use of cranes.

H. B. Maynard and Company have developed computer-based versions of MOST. The MOST for Windows® software includes basic MOST, MiniMOST, and MaxiMOST. The software allows the development and maintenance of a work element database. The computer-based system can also reduce the time required to conduct an analysis by using the work area layout to determine movement distances, eliminating redundant data entry (i.e., using drag and drop), and performing error checking that controls for the input of infeasible or conflicting data.

4 MODAPTS

The MODAPTS system was developed in the 1960s by Chris Heyde of Australia. Heyde's system is based on the concept that the body member used is the key variable. All body movements are multiples of a single unit of time called a MOD. 1 MOD = .129 s = .00215 min. For more information, see the website listed at the end of the chapter.

5 COMMENTS ON PREDETERMINED TIME SYSTEMS

In theory, MTM-1, MTM-2, MTM-3, and MOST, when applied by a trained analyst, can accurately predict the amount of time for a task. However, there is extensive evidence that the theory and reality don't agree. If the reader is interested in the extensive literature on the subject, see Frederick (1960), Schmidtke and Stier (1961), Bailey (1961), Sellie (1961), Taggart

(1961), Davidson (1962), Schmidtke and Stier (1963), and Sanfleber (1967). For data on angle of movement (a variable neglected by the PTS), see Konz, Jeans, and Rathore (1969); for data on weight allowances during moves, see Konz and Rode (1972). An impartial observer must conclude that the PTS cannot always accurately predict the time a worker will take for a task.

So, do you throw away your bowling ball because it gives strikes only 7 times in 10? In this imperfect world we must use the available tools—even though not perfect—until better tools come along.

One problem with the predetermined time systems is that they are not automatic; analyst judgment is required. Different analysts get different times for the same job because of different interpretations of the various rules. Very detailed rules have been found to be feasible if applied by a computer, but the programming is complex. At least two computer systems for applying MTM-1 and one for applying MTM-2 are in worldwide use.

The popularity of the quick and dirty systems such as MTM-2 and MTM-3 suggest that most managements do not need a great deal of accuracy and are quite concerned with cost of analysis. The point here is: "What is the purpose of making a PTS study?" The purpose is (1) to make a methods analysis of the job to determine an **efficient work method,** and (2) to determine the amount of time necessary to do the job.

PTSs force the analyst to consider use of both hands, whether a grasp is simple or complex, whether the distance moved is 6 or 9 inches, and so on. If a PTS system analysis results in an efficient work method, it has accomplished its most important task.

The second and less important task is to assign a time to the efficient work method. Time per unit is necessary for several purposes:

1. *Cost accounting:* How much should we charge for the unit?
2. *Scheduling:* If we want to be done by the 15th, when should we start?
3. *Evaluation of alternatives:* Should the job be done with one hand or two?
4. *Acceptable day's work:* How many should Joe do in a week?
5. *Pay-by-results:* What should Betty Jo's pay be today?

In most of these applications, a 10% deviation from the estimated time is not critical. This especially is true if the error is consistent. That is, if a PTS time system consistently estimates times that are 7%–12% shorter than an organization achieves, the supervisor can adjust without much difficulty by just adding 10% to the standard time.

T A B L E   2 9 . 1 6

Controlled move sequence model.

Basic MOST® System					A B G M X I A				CONTROLLED MOVE	
	M				**X**			**I**		
INDEX X 10	MOVE CONTROLLED				PROCESS TIME			ALIGNMENT		INDEX X 10
	PUSH/PULL/PIVOT	KEYWORD	CRANK (REVS.)	SECONDS	MINUTES	HOURS	OBJECT	KEYWORD		
1	≦ 12 Inches (30 cm) Button/Switch/Knob	PUSH PULL ROTATE		.5	.01	.0001	To 1 Point	ALIGN - POINT		1
3	>12 Inches (30 cm) Resistance Seat or Unseat High Control 2 Stages ≦ 12 Inches (30 cm)	SLIDE SEAT TURN UNSEAT OPEN SHIFT SHUT PRESS PUSH + PULL (INCHES,CM OR STAGES)	1	1.5	.02	.0004	To 2 Points ≦ 4 Inches (10 cm)	ALIGN - POINTS CLOSE		3
6	2 Stages >12 Inches (30cm) With 1 - 2 Steps	OPEN + SHUT OPERATE PUSH OR PULL WITH 1 or 2 PACES	3	2.5	.04	.0007	To 2 Points >4 Inches (10 cm)	ALIGN - POINTS		6
10	3 - 4 Stages With 3 - 5 Steps	MANIPULATE MANEUVER PUSH OR PULL WITH 3, 4 or 5 PACES	6	4.5	.07	.0012				10
16	With 6 - 9 Steps	PUSH OR PULL WITH 6, 7, 8 or 9 PACES	11	7.0	.11	.0019	Precision	ALIGN -PRECISION		16

TABLE 29.17

Tool use sequence model.

Basic MOST® System — FASTEN (F) or LOOSEN (L) — TOOL USE

Index X 10	Finger Action	Wrist Action				Arm Action				Tool Action	Index X 10
	SPINS	TURNS	STROKES	CRANKS	TAPS	TURNS	STROKES	CRANKS	STRIKES	SCREW DIAMETER	
	Fingers, Screwdriver	Hand, Screwdriver, Ratchet, T-Wrench	Wrench, Allen Key	Wrench, Allen Key, Ratchet	Hand, Hammer	Ratchet	Wrench, Allen Key	Wrench, Allen Key, Ratchet	Hand, Hammer	Power Wrench	
1	1	-	-	-	1	-	-	-	-	-	1
3	2	1	1	1	3	1	1	-	1	1/4" (6 mm)	3
6	3	3	2	3	6	2	-	1	3	1" (25 mm)	6
10	8	5	3	5	10	4	2	2	5		10
16	16	9	5	8	16	6	3	3	8		16
24	25	13	8	11	23	9	4	5	12		24
32	35	17	10	15	30	12	6	6	16		32
42	47	23	13	20	39	15	8	8	21		42
54	61	29	17	25	50	20	10	11	27		54

Basic MOST® System — Cut(C), Surface Treat(S), Measure(M), Record(R), Think(T) — TOOL USE

INDEX X 10	C — Cut				S — Surface Treat			M — Measure	R — Record			T — Think			INDEX X 10
	TWIST BEND	CUTOFF	CUT	SLICE	AIR-CLEAN	BRUSH-CLEAN	WIPE	MEASURE	WRITE		MARK	INSPECT	READ		
	Pliers		Scissors	Knife	Nozzle	Brush	Cloth	Measuring Device	Pencil		Marker	Eyes, Fingers	Eyes		
		WIRE	CUT(S)	SLICE(S)	SQ. FT. (0,1M²)	SQ. FT. (0,1 M²)	SQ. FT. (0,1M²)	IN. (CM) FT. (M)	DIGITS	WORDS	DIGITS	POINTS	DIGITS, SINGLE WORDS	TEXT OF WORDS	
1	GRIP		1	-	-	-	-		1	-	CHECK MARK	1	1	3	1
3		SOFT	2	1	-	-	1/2		2	-	1 SCRIBE LINE	3	3	8	3
6	TWIST BEND - LOOP	MEDIUM	4		1 SPOT POINT CAVITY	1 SMALL OBJECT	-		4	1	2	5 TOUCH FOR HEAT	6 SCALE VALUE	15 DATE / TIME	6
10		HARD	7	3	-	-	1	PROFILE - GAUGE	6		3	9 FEEL FOR DEFECT	12 VERNIER - SCALE	24	10
16	BEND - COTTER PIN		11	4	3	2	2	FIXED SCALE CALIPER 12 IN. (30CM)	9	2	5 SIGNATURE, DATE			38 TABLE VALUE	16
24			15	6	4	3	-	FEELER - GAUGE	13	3	7			54	24
32			20	9	7	5	5	STEEL - TAPE 6 FT. (2M) DEPTH MICROMETER	18	4	10			72	32
42			27	11	10	7	7	OD - MICROMETER 4 IN. (10CM)	23	5	13			94	42
54			33					ID - MICROMETER 4 IN. (10CM)	29	7	16			119	54

T A B L E	2 9 . 1 8

Manual crane sequence model.

Basic MOST® System			A B G M X I A					CONTROLLED MOVE	
	M				**X**			**I**	
INDEX X 10	MOVE CONTROLLED			PROCESS TIME			ALIGNMENT		INDEX X 10
	PUSH / PULL / PIVOT	KEYWORD	CRANK (REVS.)	SECONDS	MINUTES	HOURS	OBJECT	KEYWORD	
1	≦ 12 Inches (30 cm) Button/Switch/Knob	PUSH PULL ROTATE		.5	.01	.0001	To 1 Point	ALIGN - POINT	**1**
3	>12 Inches (30 cm) Resistance Seat or Unseat High Control 2 Stages ≦ 12 Inches (30 cm)	SLIDE SEAT TURN UNSEAT OPEN SHIFT SHUT PRESS PUSH + PULL (INCHES,CM OR STAGES)	1	1.5	.02	.0004	To 2 Points ≦ 4 Inches (10 cm)	ALIGN - POINTS CLOSE	**3**
6	2 Stages >12 Inches (30cm) With 1 - 2 Steps	OPEN + SHUT OPERATE PUSH OR PULL WITH 1 or 2 PACES	3	2.5	.04	.0007	To 2 Points >4 Inches (10 cm)	ALIGN - POINTS	**6**
10	3 - 4 Stages With 3 - 5 Steps	MANIPULATE MANEUVER PUSH OR PULL WITH 3, 4 or 5 PACES	6	4.5	.07	.0012			**10**
16	With 6 - 9 Steps	PUSH OR PULL WITH 6, 7, 8 or 9 PACES	11	7.0	.11	.0019	Precision	ALIGN -PRECISION	**16**

Source: Copyright © by H. B. Maynard and Company, Inc. Reproduced with permission.

Review Questions

1. What are the two purposes of making a PTS analysis?

2. What is the pace for MTM?

3. At which number of cycles is a worker predicted to achieve MTM time?

4. In MTM-1, what is the difference between a Reach and a Move?

5. In MTM some motions may or may not be simultaneous. How is the decision made whether the motion is simultaneous or not?

6. What type of screw head would you recommend for use with power screwdrivers? Phillips-head screws eliminate some positioning motions but require a push force to hold the bit to the screw (see Table 3.4).

References

Bailey, G. Comments on an experimental evaluation of the validity of predetermined time systems. *J. of Industrial Engineering,* Vol. 12, 328–30, September–October 1961.

Davidson, J. On Balance—The validity of predetermined elemental time systems. *J. of Industrial Engineering,* Vol. 13, 162–65, May–June 1962.

Frederick, C. On obtaining consistency in application of predetermined time systems. *J. of Industrial Engineering,* Vol. 11, No. 1, 18–19, January–February 1960.

Karger, D. and Bayha, F. *Engineered Work Measurement,* 4th ed. New York: Industrial Press, 1987.

Knott, K. and Sury R. An investigation into the minimum cycle time restrictions of MTM-2 and MTM-3. *IIE Transactions,* 380–91, December 1986.

Konz, S., Jeans, C., and Rathore, R. Arm motions in the horizontal plane. *AIIE Transactions,* Vol. 1, 359–70, December 1969.

Konz, S. and Rode, V. The control effect of small weights on hand–arm movements in the horizontal plane. *AIIE Transactions,* Vol. 4, 228–33, September 1972.

Magnusson, K. The development of MTM-2, MTM-V, MTM-3. *J. of Methods-Time Measurement,* Vol. 17, 11–23, February 1972.

Matias, A. Work measurement: Principles and techniques. Chapter 54 in *Handbook of Industrial Engineering,* 3rd ed., Salvendy, G. (ed.). New York: Wiley, 2001.

Maynard, H., Stegemerten, G., and Schwab, J. *Methods-Time Measurement.* New York: McGraw-Hill, 1948. (See also Maynard, H. (ed.). *Industrial Engineering Handbook,* McGraw-Hill.)

Rivett, H. Learning curve prediction development using MTM and the computer. *MTM Journal,* Vol. 1, 32–42, February 1972.

Sanfleber, J. An investigation into some aspects of the accuracy of predetermined motion time systems. *International J. of Production Research,* Vol. 6, No. 1, 25–45, 1967.

Schmidtke, H. and Stier, F. An experimental evaluation of the validity of predetermined elemental time systems. *J. of Industrial Engineering,* Vol. 12, 192–204, May–June 1961.

Schmidtke, H. and Stier, F. Response to the comments. *J. of Industrial Engineering,* Vol. 14, 119–24, May–June 1963.

Sellie, C. Comments on an experimental evaluation of the validity of predetermined elemental time systems. *J. of Industrial Engineering,* Vol. 12, 330–33, September–October 1961.

Sellie, C. Predetermined motion-time systems and the development and use of standard data. In *Handbook of Industrial Engineering,* 2d ed., Salvendy, G. (ed.). New York: Wiley, 1992.

Taggart, J. Comments on an experimental evaluation. *J. of Industrial Engineering,* Vol. 12, 422–27, November–December 1961.

Zandin, K. *MOST Work Measurement Systems.* New York: Marcel Dekker, 1980.

Websites

H. B. Maynard (MOST), www.hbmaynard.com

Methods Time Measurement, www.mtm.org

MODAPTS, www.modapts.org

30 STANDARD DATA

Overview

Once the database of standard data has been developed, use it for cost savings and consistency and because it can be done ahead of production. Data elements can be at either the motion or the element level of detail. Variable elements allocate time more accurately than constant elements do. Curve fitting has been simplified by having a computer do the calculations, but the analyst must select the proper equation from those investigated.

Key Concepts

coefficient of correlation

coefficient of determination

coefficient of variation

constant/variable elements

database

exponential curve

family of curves

half-life

hyperbola

imagine the task

least-squares equation

motion/element

parabola

polynomial

random error/constant
   error

residual

SAS

standard data

standard error

straight line

REASONS FOR STANDARD DATA

Rather than measure new times for each and every new operation, consider reuse of previous times—use of standard data. A popular application of standard data is to predict the cost of automotive repairs. Standard data have three advantages and two disadvantages.

1.1 Advantages
The three advantages of **standard data** are cost, consistency, and ahead of production.

1.1.1 *Cost*
It is cheaper to look up a number in a table or solve an equation than to make a time study to determine the same number. For example, assume you wish to know the time to reach 300 mm to a washer in a bin, grasp it, and move it to assembly. You could use the MTM tables in Chapter 29. Or you could set up a workstation and operator to do the task, have the operator do it while being timed, analyze the data, and determine the time.

Or assume you wish to know the amount of time required to load pallets into 15 trucks, each with 24 pallets, while you presently have available data for 16, 20, and 28 pallets/truck. You could solve an equation and estimate the time for 24 pallets. Or you could have operators load, for example, 15 trucks while you record the time.

In both examples, it is much cheaper to do the calculations or look up the figures in a table than to obtain new data.

1.1.2 *Consistency (fairness)*
Time values obtained from standard data are more consistent than time values obtained from one study since they come from a bigger database. In statistical terms, $\sigma_{\bar{x}}' = \sigma'/\sqrt{N}$. That is, the mean standard deviation of the average of multiple studies (represented by $\sigma_{\bar{x}}'$) is smaller than the mean of the standard deviation of N individual time studies (represented by the σ'). Any one time study has individual variability (hopefully corrected by rating) and, thus, possible error. Random errors will tend to cancel over many studies. Using standard data minimizes the random error due to individual operators or individual ratings.

Although it may seem to be heresy, it is more important in time standards to be consistent—small **random error**—than to be accurate—small **constant error.** (Error equals actual time minus standard time). It's nice, of course, to be both accurate and consistent. See Figure 30.1 for a sketch of random and constant errors.

For example, assume actual time for both job A and job B is 1.0 min. A consistent system might set time for A at .90 min and B at .91, or time for A at 1.05 and B at 1.05; this system has low random error

---

FIGURE 30.1

Random and constant errors are shown on a 2-dimensional bull's-eye (Error = Bull's-eye – Hit location). The lower figures on the side and bottom with the Xs show error in 1 dimension. Constant errors can be corrected by calibration. Random errors can be corrected by improved techniques, better devices, and by training the observer. Random error also can be compensated for by increasing sample size. That is, if you "fire enough shots," you can "hit the bull's-eye," since random error approaches zero as *n* approaches infinity.

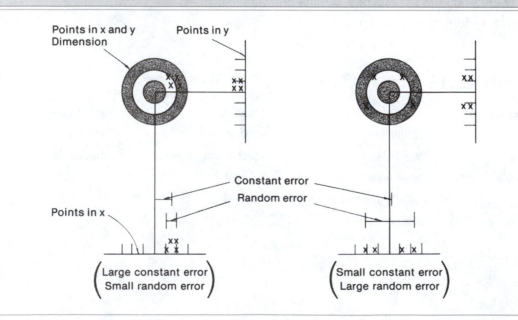

and high constant error. A random but accurate system might set time for A at .9 and B at 1.1, or B at .96 and A at 1.04; this system has a high random error and a low constant error. Best of all would be a system that sets time for A at 1.0 and time for B at 1.0; this system would have low random error and low constant error.

Constant errors are much easier to correct or handle administratively. For example, assume for the whole department that the standard averaged .90 min and performance averaged 1.0 min. Then department efficiency is 90%. The supervisor can make simple adjustments of the standards when doing schedules and evaluating employees, the cost accounting department can easily estimate product cost, and so on. However, if the standards were in error randomly, scheduling would be difficult, costs would be inconsistent, and other problems would surface. An important consequence is that everyone would lose faith in the time standard system since it gives incorrect answers.

1.1.3 *Ahead of production*

The third advantage of standard data is that the standard can be determined ahead of production. Timing an operation requires that the operation be observed. There must be a workstation with tools and equipment, parts to be worked on, and an experienced operator. But times often are needed for cost estimates on bids, for determining which method to use for scheduling of machines and operators—that is, before production.

1.2 Disadvantages

Among the three roses are two thorns: imagining the task and database cost.

1.2.1 *Imagining the task*

To visualize the task when doing a time study, the analyst simply goes to the workstation and watches the operator; the items worked can be "held in the hand." In addition, the operator can be consulted for information.

In contrast, with standard data the analyst must **imagine the task,** including each and every element to be done. There is no operator to consult, there are no items to examine, or quality levels to compare, and there is no workstation to examine. Thus, the analyst must be quite familiar with the task to be done. Even experienced analysts occasionally forget to include elements that are done rarely (e.g., machine maintenance elements, bin replenishment elements).

1.2.2 *Database cost*

As pointed out above, it is better to reuse data than continually have to develop new values. The problem is that you may not have the **database.**

If we are dealing with a database at the motion level (that is, use of MTM); the firm has to invest money in having its staff trained in the specific predetermined time system.

If we are dealing with a database at the element level (that is, elements such as "Load milling machine, using jib crane = .05 h" or "Load truck with 24 pallets = .33 h"), the firm has to invest money in developing the database (either from the micro-systems or from time studies), training staff in use of the system, and maintaining the information (typically in a computer and supporting notebooks). Developing the database requires both money and time. If your firm didn't do it in the past, you will not have a database by which to save the firm money in the future.

2 STANDARD DATA STRUCTURE

Two decisions that must be made about the database are whether to use motions or elements and whether to use constant or variable elements.

2.1 Motions versus Elements

The database can be built at various levels of detail. Using an analogy, the goal is to build a "house." The components may be at the micro, or **motion,** level (e.g., boards and nails) or at the macro, or **element,** level (panels, doors, cabinets). See Table 30.1.

MTM times are at the motion level. Here each component time is very small—.5 or even .1 s.

An element system has a collection of individual motions, and the elements might be "Transfer box from conveyer to pallet" or "Load fixture and clamp item." Here the component time is much larger—10, 100, or even 1,000 s. The elements can come from a buildup of motion times by an analyst, from time studies, from curve fitting, or from a combination.

Using the house analogy, it is easier to build the house from larger components than from individual boards and nails. However, in the house you must have the proper size and shape component or it won't work. In the same way, an element system is fine if the element is appropriate to the job; if not, you will either have to accept "sloppy construction" (errors in standard times compared to what worker actually takes) or build it from scratch (with time study or predetermined times).

2.2 Constant versus Variable

The element in the database can be considered as either a constant element or a variable element. See Table 30.1. **Constant elements** occur or don't occur; the time allowed is either "A" or "0." A constant element for an order picker in a warehouse might be "Drive truck from loading dock to dispatch station." If the operator did the element, a time of .01 h might be assigned. Constant elements are easy to apply but tend to have large random error. That is, they are reasonable, on

T A B L E	**3 0 . 1**

Levels of detail for standard time systems.

MOTIONS (TYPICAL TIME RANGE FROM .1 TO 1 S)

Element	Code	Time, TMU	
Reach	R10C	12.9	
Grasp	G4B	9.1	1 s = 27.8 TMU
Move	M10B	12.2	
Position	P1SE	5.6	1 TMU = .036 s
Release, etc.	RL1	2.0	

CONSTANT ELEMENTS (TYPICAL TIME RANGE 1 S TO 1000 S)

Element	Time, s
Assemble bracket to unit	8
Get equipment	90
Polish a shoe	130
Put away equipment	47
Load carton on pallet	15
Pack box	52

VARIABLE ELEMENTS (TYPICAL TIME RANGE 1 S TO 1000 S)

Assemble bracket	Time = f (number of holes, type of fastener)
Pack box	Time = f (type of component packed, number packed)
Walk	Time = f (distance traveled, load carried)
Repair computer	Time = f (manufacturer of computer, type of defect)

the average, in the long run but are inaccurate for specific operators doing specific cycles.

The element "Drive truck from loading dock to dispatch station" also might be made a **variable element.** The time might vary depending upon the type of truck used and from which dock the driver is coming to dispatching, but the random error would be smaller. The constant error also would tend to be smaller, as real applications (1) probably would not have exactly the same proportional use of truck J and truck K as the constant element assumes and (2) probably would not have the same average distance traveled as the constant element assumes. However, time is more difficult to calculate.

Difficulty of calculation will not be as large a problem as it was previously, however, if the calculations are done by computer. For example, the computer may look up in its memory that operator Joe is assigned truck J. The computer may also look up in its memory that the previous order picked was delivered to dock 7. Since it knows the location of dock 7, for the following order it obtains the distance traveled (say 90 m) and calculates an appropriate travel time (giving due allowance for acceleration and deceleration time).

When making a variable element, try to use variables that are easy to count (pages of drawings, meters of weld wire used, number of pieces made, tons melted). Try to use a variable that is known ahead of production. Consider dimensional categories (part, length, thickness), process categories (machining rev/min, distance from pan to machine), and material properties (tensile strength, difficulty).

Next you must see if the actual data vary with your variable. That is, you may assume walking time is a function of distance traveled and load carried. You need to plot your data versus the variable and determine the equation. See the following section on curve fitting. Naturally it is absolutely essential that the methods description on the time study include sufficient detail (length of cut, size of box, weight in box, etc.).

You may consider stepwise multiple regression. In this procedure, you give identifiers for all the "X" variables associated with a specific time. For example, a time of .1 h may be identified with a distance variable of 10 m, a weight variable of 5 kg, a temperature variable of 35°C, a container variable of sack, and so forth. You enter all data into the computer, and it attempts to fit a straight line for each variable; it identifies the variables that are promising for you to analyze further (perhaps with a different curve shape or family of curves).

If specific data points are not well described by the equation, you must use judgment on whether the data point is an outlier and an aberration or whether your predictive model lacks some variables.

All formulas should be valid only within specified ranges since extrapolation can lead to absurd numbers.

2.3 Developing the Standard
A series of steps has to be taken to convert motions (micro level) or elements (macro level) into the task standard (the house in the analogy). Keep elements in normal time; add allowances only after all elements have been totaled into a task.

2.3.1 *Plan the work*
First, plan what the standard data system will cover. Warehouse, factory or both? All assembly? All machining operations? Just lathe work? In general, use standard data when jobs/tasks are related and repetitive. In general, set up standard data one area at a time. For example, set up the standard data system for order pickers in a dry grocery warehouse. Then add order pickers in a perishable section of the warehouse or add the fork truck drivers who replenish the racks. That is, build a step at a time.

2.3.2 *Classify the data*
Code the data with identifiers such as types of machines, types of product. Examples would be to identify elements as lathe work, packing work, grinding work; machining with steel, plastic, or brass; machine shop work, electronics work, assembly work, warehouse work. The problem is similar to the coding problems of group technology. You are trying to find "relatives" so you can group them into "families." When making a time study, it is important to describe the element and environment in detail so the elements can be classified properly.

2.3.3 *Group the elements*
Now organize your data. It may be that data fit into only one category (e.g., machine shop), but many elements must be put in several categories (e.g., machine shop, maintenance, material handling). Being able to find a relevant element from several directions makes the database more useful.

2.3.4 *Analyze the job*
Make a preliminary breakdown of the job into elements. How many of these elements are in your database? You need not have 100% coverage of all the job elements from the standard data. If an element is missing, one possibility is to develop a new standard element for this job (either from a predetermined time or a time study) and then put it into the database after using it for this specific job. A second possibility is to give a blanket allowance for the nonspecified elements. For example, if time for elements 1, 2, and 4 (from the database) is .15 h, you might just add a blanket allowance (say, 25% additional time) for elements 3 and 5. A third possibility is to have the entire job done "off standard." That is, there is no standard set for this job.

2.3.5 *Develop the standard*
Using the selected elements, do the required table lookups and formula calculations. Add allowances. Note that computers can have decision rules built into them in addition to the normal programs permitting easy computation. That is, the program can have diagnosis and error-checking capability. Although these programs are expensive to develop, a number of firms have developed them. For example, the Micro-Matic Methods and Measurement (4M) system reduces the time to apply an MTM standard to 25% of manual time. In addition, it calculates a number of indices showing where methods might be improved:

- MAI—percent utilization of both hands
- RMB—percent of reach/move motions time in total cycle
- GRA—cycle time indicating grasp complexity
- POS—cycle time indicating position complexity
- PROC—ratio of waiting-for-process to total time

See Box 30.1 for a brief description of a warehouse standard data system.

3 CURVE FITTING
To analyze experimental data: (1) plot the data, (2) guess several appropriate curve shapes, (3) use a computer to determine the constants for the selected shapes, and (4) select which equation you want to use.

You can tell how well the **least-squares equation** (the sum of the Y deviations of the data points from the line squared) fits the data from two different indices: (1) the absolute error in Y (given by the standard error), and (2) the explained error in Y (given by the coefficient of determination, r^2). See Figure 30.2. That is, if you have plotted distance walked in meters as X and time in hours as Y, then the standard error (e.g., SE = .01 h) will give you the standard deviation of the points from the equation in hours. You can convert absolute error into relative error. Divide standard deviation by the mean value of Y; this ratio is called the **coefficient of variation.** In Figure 30.2, an SE of .01 h divided by a mean of .5 h gives a relative error of 6.7%.

The equation can explain anywhere from 0 to 100% of the variability of the data. If it explains 100%, all the points will fall on the line. The ratio of

30.1   *Order Picking in Dry-Grocery Warehouses*

Order pickers drive electric pallet jacks (each holding two pallets) along the aisles in a warehouse. The computerized picking list (with peel-off labels) indicates how many cases of each product to stack on a pallet. After the list is picked, the load is stretch-wrapped. The pallets are transported to a truck. Then the picker goes to a dispatch station and gets a new pick list.

Since the standard data system is computerized, an individual time is calculated for each specific order.

After allowing time for obtaining the order, the program calculates the distance to the first pick location and assigns a time for the travel. Then a pick time is assigned depending on the weight of the specific item, type of container, and whether it is on the first- or second-level rack. A weight allowance is calculated from a regression equation, entering the item weight to the closest pound. Then the distance is calculated to the next pick, and so on.

---

explained variation/total variation, r^2, is called the **coefficient of determination;** r is the **coefficient of correlation.** An r^2 value of .60 means that the equation explained 60% of the total variability.

Although it is possible to fit equations to data by eye, the ease of using computers and preprogrammed calculators makes it worthwhile to use the least-squares programs. A strong advantage of the programs is that, for a given set of data and equation form, everyone gets not only exactly the same answer (there is no judgment in the fit), but also the best answer. The only judgment required is the tradeoff between equation complexity and goodness of fit (indicated by r^2 or SE). Note that with increasing number of terms, r^2 always increases (as the curve can make more bends).

However, with increasing number of terms, SE will decrease for a while and then increase as the cost of dividing by a larger and larger N overcomes the benefit of a slightly lower unexplained error. If the equation will be stored and solved by computer, additional equation complexity is not the disadvantage it was with manual calculations. However, if the equation is so complex that you can't put it on a graph, simplify it.

Note also that the program will give you the best fit for the curve shape you specified. If you specified a **straight line** and the data are best fitted by a parabola, the program will give you a best-fit straight line. As a general policy, have the program print out the actual value of Y, the predicted value of Y, and the difference—also called **residual.** If the residuals have a pattern, consider another equation form. For example, consider 10 points and a fitted straight line. If the deviations are randomly + and −, the line is satisfactory. But if the first 2 deviations and the last 2 deviations are + and the middle 6 are −, then a curve would give a better fit.

3.1 Curve Shapes   Three possible results will be discussed.

3.1.1 *Y independent of X*   See Figure 30.3. It may be that Y is not related to X. Then the estimate of $Y = A$; that is, Y is a constant. You can determine that Y is not related to X by the value of SE (if SE is too high) or r^2 (if r^2 is too low). From an engineering viewpoint, what is too high or too low will vary with the situation. However, from a statistical viewpoint, the critical value of r^2 can be given for various risk levels. (Risk is defined as the chance that the equation predicting Y from X occurred by chance. That is, there is a 5% chance that the coefficients of X in the equation are really not significantly different from 0.)

3.1.2 *Y depends on X, one variable*   There are many possibilities.

F I G U R E   30.2

Goodness of fit of equations is determined by the spread of the points from the line or curve; the absolute error is given by the **standard error;** the relative error is the coefficient of variation; the ratio of explained variability/total variability is the coefficient of determination.

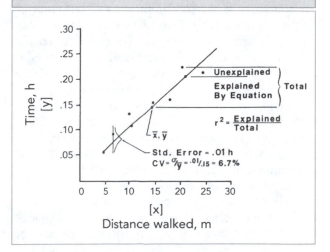

Distance walked, m

F I G U R E   3 0 . 3

If *Y* is not related to *X* (is independent of *X*), then $Y = A$, where *A* is a constant.

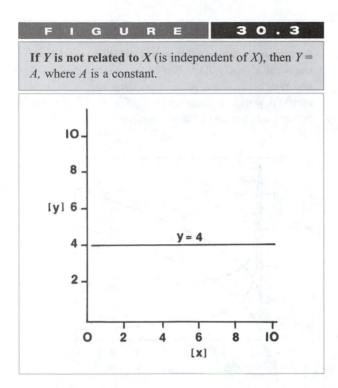

1. The equation has the form $Y = A + BX$, that is, a straight line. See Figure 30.4. If the value of $A = 0$, the line goes through the origin.

2. The equation has the form $Y = AX^B$; that is, a geometric curve. See Figure 30.5. Geometric curves can be approximated by a straight line if both the

F I G U R E   3 0 . 4

Straight lines have the form $Y = A + BX$. If $A = 0$, then the line goes through the origin. If *B* is positive, the line slopes upward; if *B* is negative, the line slopes downward.

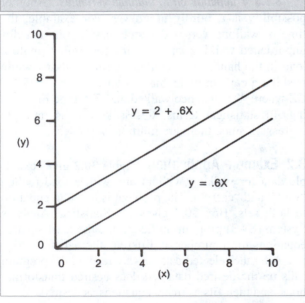

X and *Y* axes are logarithmic. Generally you would do this by using log–log paper and plotting *X* and *Y*, but it also could be done by using regular graph paper and plotting the log *X* vs. log *Y*.

3. The equation has the form $Y = Ae^{BX}$, that is, an **exponential curve** where $e = 2.178 \ldots$, the base of natural logarithms. See Figure 30.6. Exponential curves can be approximated by a straight line with a plot of *X* vs. log *Y*. (The equation also can be expressed as $Y = r^x$ where $x = eB$.)

4. The equation has the form $Y = A + BX^n$. If *n* is known or suspected, a plot of X^n vs. *Y* approximates a straight line.

5. The equation has the form $Y = X/(A + BX)$ or $X/Y = A + BX$, that is, a hyperbola with asymptotes $X = -A/B$ and $Y = 1/B$. See Figure 30.7. The hyperbola can be approximated by a straight line with a plot of *X* vs. *X/Y* or of *1/X* vs. *1/Y*.

6. The data may be best described by three coefficients *A*, *B*, and *C*. To show the **polynomial** relationship:

$$Y = AX^0 = A(1) = A$$
$$Y = AX^0 + BX^1 = A + BX$$
$$Y = AX^0 + BX^1 + CX^2 = A + BX + CX^2$$

F I G U R E   3 0 . 5

Geometric curves have the form $Y = AX^B$. All six curves have $A = 2$, but *B* has different values. The geometric curves with *B* positive all pass through the points $(0, 0)$ and $(1, A)$, and as one variable increases, so does the other. The curves with *B* negative all pass through the point $(1, A)$; they have $X = 0$ and $Y = 0$ as asymptotes, and as one variable increases, the other decreases.

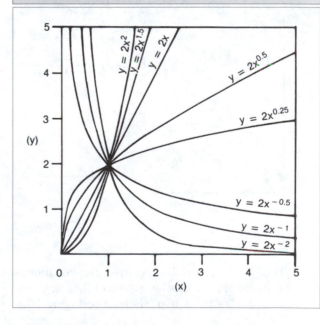

Exponential (logarithmic) curves have the form $Y = Ae^{BX}$**.** All six curves drawn have $A = 1$, but B has different values. The curves all pass through the point $(0, A)$. If the exponent is negative, they have $Y = 0$ for an asymptote. If $Y = .5$, the effect Y has declined to 50% of its original value, its **half-life.** But $Y = .5$ when the exponent $-BX = .6935$. For $B = -1$, the X value = .6935. For $B = -.1$, $X = 6.935$. For $B = -.01$, $X = 69.35$. The three equations would be $y = e^{-x}$, $y = e^{-.1x}$ and $y = e^{-.01x}$.

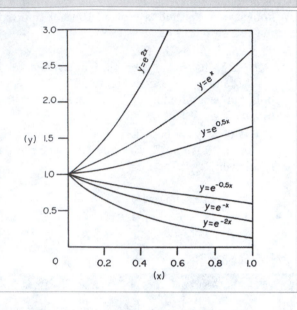

Hyperbolas with the form $Y = X/(A + BX)$ **or** $X/Y = A + BX$ **have asymptotes** $X = A/B$ **and** $Y = 1/B$**.** The four curves all have the value of $B = .2$, but A has different values.

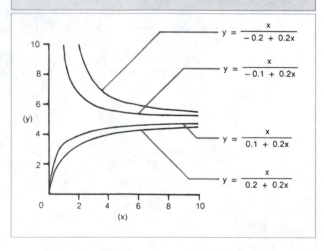

When the exponent 2 is positive, the equation is called a **parabola.** When the exponent 2 is negative, the equation is called a **hyperbola.** See Figure 30.8.

Parabolas or hyperbolas with a third constant have the form $Y = A + BX^n$**.** Two of the curves have $A = 0$ and two have $A = 2$. If n is positive, the curve is a parabola with a Y intercept = A. If n is negative, the curve is a hyperbola with asymptotes $X = 0$ and $Y = A$.

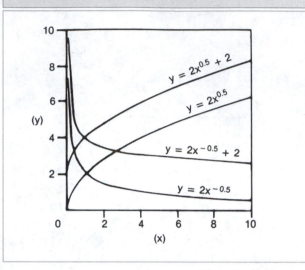

Each term in the polynomial beyond 2 gives 1 bend to the curve. That is, using coefficients A and B, the equation is a straight line; using coefficients A, B, and C, there is 1 bend to the curve; using coefficients A, B, C, and D, there are 2 bends to the curve; and so on.

In addition, the data may be fitted by 1 equation over part of the range of X and another equation over another part of X. Progress curves often have one straight line (on log–log coordinates) for beginning experience and another straight line for mature experience.

3.1.3 *Y depends on X, multiple variables*   Another possibility is a **family of curves.** For example, the time of walking versus distance may be one line for unburdened walking, another line for walking with a load in the hands, and another line for walking while pushing a cart. In mathematical terms: $Y = A + BX + CZ$ where X = distance walked and Z = type of walking. In statistical terms, this is known as multiple regression since there are multiple variables.

3.2 Example Application   Table 30.2 gives example data for walking without and with a load (called "walk" and "carry"). The problem is to fit an equation to both sets. Box 30.2 gives the Statistical Analysis System (SAS) program to determine the least-squares equations for a number of different alternatives.

After the selected data sets are read in, the program calls up the desired data set, does desired transformations, and then fits as many equations as desired.

30.2   *SAS Curve Fitting*

You will need three types of entry lines:

1. program lines
2. data lines
3. program lines

Program Lines		Comments
Line 1	DATA name;	Put your name in the location "name" (e.g., WALK).
Line 2	INPUT DIST TIME;	All program lines in SAS *must* end in a semicolon.
		The distance value will be entered first and then the time value with a space between entries.
Line 3	DISTSQ = DIST**2;	This creates a new variable, DISTSQ.
Line 4	DISTLOGE = LOG (OF DIST);	New variable is log base e of DIST.
Line 4a	DISTLTEN = LOG10 (OF DIST);	Alternative new variable is log base 10.
Line 5	IDIST = 1/(DIST);	Inverse of DISTANCE.
Line 6	ITIME = 1/(TIME);	Inverse of TIME.
Line 7	CARDS;	

Data Lines			One line per point; do *not* end with semicolon.
Line 8	5	.0553	
Line 9	5	.0590	
Line 32	20	.1980	

Program Lines		Comments
Line 33	PROC PRINT DATA=name;	Prints out your data.
Line 34	PROC REG DATA=name;	Uses Regression procedure on your data set.
Line 35	MODEL TIME=DIST/P;	Fits straight line TIME = A + B (DIST).
Line 36	TITLE 'ST.LINE OF name';	Labels output.
Line 37	PROC REG DATA=name;	Runs a new analysis of same data.
Line 38	MODEL TIME = DIST DISTSQ/P;	Fits Time = A + B (DIST) + C (DIST)^2.
Line 39	TITLE 'PARABOLA OF name';	Labels output.
Line 40	PROC REG DATA=name;	Runs new analysis of same data.
Line 41	MODEL TIME=DISTLOGE/P;	Fits TIME = A + B (log of DIST). You may wish to use alternative of line 4A.
Line 42	TITLE 'EXPONENTIAL OF name';	Labels output.
Line 43	PROC REG DATA=name;	Runs new analysis of same data.
Line 44	MODEL ITIME=IDIST/P;	Fits ITIME = A + B (IDIST).
Line 45	TITLE 'HYPERBOLA OF name';	Labels output.
Line 46	DATA name;	Use CARRY this time.
47–53		Repeat of lines 5 to 10.
54–78		Entries for CARRY.
79–88		Repeat of lines 36 to 48 with CARRY for name.
Line 89	RUN;	

T A B L E	3 0 . 2

Walk and carry normal times (min).

	DISTANCE, M			
Activity	5	10	15	20
Walk	.0553	.1105	.1654	.2205
	.0590	.1170	.1751	.2205
	.0550	.1105	.1660	.2090
	.0521	.1045	.1680	.2200
	.0541	.1080	.1625	.2080
	.0595	.1200	.1800	.1980
Carry	.0691	.1116	.1571	.1984
	.0732	.1158	.1681	.1962
	.0693	.1094	.1660	.1881
	.0651	.1066	.1626	.1958
	.0676	.1080	.1511	.1872
	.0737	.1188	.1674	.1762

In this example, the walk data set was fitted with the following equations:

$$\text{Walk time, h} = .0054 + .01 \,(\text{Distance, m})$$
$$r^2 = .986 \quad \sigma = .0073 \text{ h}$$
$$\text{Walk time, h} = -.01 + .014 \,(\text{Distance, m})$$
$$-.00013 \,(\text{Distance, m})^2$$
$$r^2 = .989 \quad \sigma = .0067 \text{ h}$$
$$\text{Walk time, h} = -.13 + .11 \,(\log_e \text{Distance, m})$$
$$r^2 = .966 \quad \sigma = .012 \text{ h}$$

$$1/\text{Walk time, h} = .24 - .96 \,(1/\text{Distance, m})$$
$$r^2 = .881 \quad \sigma = .021 \text{ h}^{-1}$$

The best fit is the parabola with $\sigma = .0067$ h, with the straight line a close second with $\sigma = .0073$ h. The user would have to decide whether the small gain in accuracy with the parabola is worth the additional equation complexity.

The carry data set was fitted with the following equation: Carry time, h = $A + B$ (Distance, m)

The results were:

$$\text{Carry time, h} = .030 + .0082 \,(\text{Distance, m})$$
$$r^2 = .975 \quad \sigma = .0077 \text{ h}$$
$$\text{Carry time, h} = .013 + .012 \,(\text{Distance, m})$$
$$-.00014 \,(\text{Distance, m})^2$$
$$r^2 = .981 \quad \sigma = .0069 \text{ h}$$
$$\text{Carry time, h} = -.078 + .087 \,(\log_e \text{Distance, m})$$
$$r^2 = .960 \quad \sigma = .0098 \text{ h}$$
$$1/\text{Carry time, h} = 2.36 + 60.8/\text{Distance, m}$$
$$r^2 = .981 \quad \sigma = .52 \text{ h}^{-1}$$

The best fits are the parabola and hyperbola. Again the user must decide between accuracy of fit versus complexity.

If the curves for walk and carry are parallel, the following form could be used:

$$\text{Time, h} = A + B \,(\text{Distance}) + C$$
$$\text{where } C = \text{Difference in time between the curves.}$$

For example, $C = 0$ for walk and $C = C_1$ for carry.

This also could be formulated as $A + B$ (Distance) with one value of A for walk and another for carry.

Review Questions

1. Give the three advantages and two disadvantages of standard data systems.

2. Assuming your true weight is 70 kg and you are weighing yourself on a scale, give an example of random error and systematic error.

3. Give an example of standard data at the motion level and at the element level.

4. For one element, give as a constant element and give as a variable element.

5. How is the standard error related to the coefficient of variation?

6. What is the definition of the coefficient of determination?

7. Give the equation (using a consistent format) for (a) Y unrelated to X, (b) Y related to X by a straight line, and (c) Y related to X by a parabola.

1 Problem

2 Medium and the Message

3 Training (Memorization)

4 Job Aids

Overview

The primary resources of any group are the skills of its people. The primary instruction medium is visual; the message can be pictorial or text. This chapter gives recommendations on how to improve messages. The worker can be trained or given a job aid. In either case, the training material is important.

Key Concepts

active/passive	grade level	no stupid students, just	scenarios
audio input	information repository	terrible teachers	self-instruction
AVO	job knowledge require-	pictorial messages	simulation
cross-training	ments	pilot testing	sit by Nellie
decision structure tables	kinesthetic input	plan/draft/revise	text message
distributed practice/	limit aids	programmed learning	visual input
massed practice	linear/branching mode	psychomotor information	
expert systems	memorization/job aid	routing sheets	

593

▌▌PROBLEM

1.1 Is Training the Solution?

Given the general need for people skills, the first question (step 1) is, "Is training the solution?" (Samways, 1997). Because training is temporary, health and safety problems normally should be solved with permanent engineering solutions rather than temporary training solutions.

There are considerable training/turnover costs among long-distance truck drivers; people do not like to be away from home so much. One engineering solution is to use a modified Pony Express concept, where the trucks keep moving but the drivers change. (In the historical Pony Express, the riders kept moving but the horses changed.) For example, a truck going from Detroit to Dallas (and returning) with one driver might require a driver to sleep away from home three days. By switching drivers at St. Louis, each driver sleeps away from home only one day.

1.2 Training Needs Assessment

Step 2 is "training needs assessment." It may help to identify what is driving this specific training need. The driver may be external—for example, regulation (e.g., meeting requirements of OSHA, EPA). The driver may be internal (e.g., health and safety audits, sickness reports, imbalance between **job knowledge requirements** and worker knowledge).

Imagine a physical gap between actual and desired level of performance. What knowledge and skills do people need to close this gap? This involves knowing your target audience. What is their average reading level? Minimum and maximum? Minimum, average, and maximum experience on the job?

Don't forget the "big picture." For example, "level 1" training might be completed in 30 days, level 2 in 90 days, level 3 in a year, and level 4 in 3 years.

The gap between actual and desired performance can occur four ways:

1. static job and static worker
2. static job and changing worker
3. changing job and static worker
4. changing job and changing worker

1.2.1 Static job and static worker   Use training to improve the worker's job knowledge. For example, Table 31.1 shows a better way to close the top of a cardboard box to reduce repetitive strain on the operator's shoulder. Use Table 31.1 as a training aid. Alternatively, have a word processor operator learn how to use a new software program. Office personnel could learn how to operate the new phone system, or an industrial engineer might learn about a new ergonomic technique.

TABLE   31.1

Closing the flaps on a cardboard box (see Figure 31.1) should be done close to the body to reduce repetitive strain on the shoulders. Use four playing cards or rectangular pieces of paper to visualize the pattern.

BAD:	TUCKING IN CORNER AWAY FROM BODY STRESSES SHOULDER.	GOOD:	TUCKING IN CORNER CLOSE TO THE BODY HAS BETTER LEVERAGE.
Left Hand	**Right Hand**	**Left Hand**	**Right Hand**
Reach to 1B	Reach to 2R	Reach to 2	Reach to 3B
Grasp 1B	Grasp 2R	Grasp 2	Grasp 3B
	Fold 2 flat under 1		Fold 3 flat under 2
Fold 1 flat over 2		Fold 2 flat over 3	Release 3
Release 1	Release 2	Release 2	
Reach for 4L	Reach to 3	Reach to 1	Reach to 4
Grasp 4L	Grasp 3	Grasp 1	Grasp 4
Fold 4 flat over 1			Fold 4 flat
	Fold 3 flat over 2 and over 4	Fold 1 flat over 2 and under 4	Release 4
Release 4	Hold 3 flat	Release 1	Reach to 3B
Reach for 2R		Reach to 4	Grasp 3B
Grasp 2R		Hold 4 flat	Pull 3B above 4R
Pull 2R above 3T		Release 4	Release 3
Release 2R	Release 3		

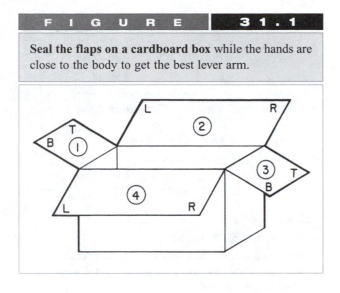

FIGURE 31.1

Seal the flaps on a cardboard box while the hands are close to the body to get the best lever arm.

1.2.2 *Static job and changing worker* Even though the job does not change, individual employees quit, get promoted, get demoted, are fired, go on vacation, or are absent for the day. The replacement worker has to know how to do the job. Well-managed firms will not wait until the job is vacant before doing the training; they train before the vacancy. Pretraining employees is called **cross-training**—each worker is able to do several different jobs. For example, the word processor operator can do filing, the auto transmission specialist can work on the auto electrical system, the assembler for station 4 also can do the work of stations 3, 5, and 6. Cross-training not only fulfills desires for job enlargement and allows resting individual muscles, but it also greatly simplifies the day-to-day administration of any group. Some firms also train potential employees, thus allowing better selection of employees from the applicants.

Even with constant technology, the number of workers may change as sales go up or down. Assume that a firm decides to hire 10 more people to expand production. Naturally there is the training requirement for that 10. But, in addition, most firms fill positions through a "bidding" or "posting" procedure. That is, the job is posted, and existing employees can bid on the new job. For example, a person who is now an assembler can bid on one of the new scheduling clerk jobs. But then the assembly job is open; it may be filled by an existing material handler. Then the material handler job is open; it may be filled by one of the new hires. Thus, for every new person hired, 3 or 4 people may have to be trained.

This movement of people also occurs with reductions in the workforce; the procedure is called bumping. In a layoff, a higher-seniority person can bump a lower-seniority person. For example, if a firm eliminates the second shift, a high-seniority press operator on the second shift may bump a low-senior-

ity material handler on the first shift. The material handler may bump someone else. Thus, if 10 people are laid off, 30 people may change jobs.

The number changing depends upon the rules of bumping at the firm. More will change if the seniority is plantwide instead of departmentwide and if required demonstrated proficiency requirements are low. For example, if a person with high seniority has 90 days to learn how to do another job, naturally the person will bid on the job because, at the minimum, the paycheck will continue for another 90 days. This can cause great quality problems during the 90 days. Previous cross-training can reduce these problems.

1.2.3 *Changing job and static worker* The technology of the job may change. For example, the packing station may be changed so that the boxes are taken away by conveyor instead of on pallets; a scanner might replace keying of customer information; an automatic loader might be installed on a machine to replace manual loading. Because of changing job requirements, it is a good idea to have a product designer learn about ergonomics so the designer can become a better engineer. In these examples, it is assumed that the same worker does the job as before; however, the worker has to be trained in the new technology.

1.2.4 *Changing job and changing worker* Here we are dealing with major changes in the job. This can occur in an existing job (for example, replace manual spray painting with robotic spray painting) or a new job (opening a new factory or office and hiring new people to do the job). The job skills for the new job differ considerably from those for the old job. One of the characteristics of "lean production" (also called just-in-time) is use of a skilled, cross-trained worker. Another trend is the increase in worker involvement in many decisions (see Chapter 32). For this reason, manufacturers are becoming more selective in their hiring. A high school diploma has become the minimum as firms increase the ratio of hourly to salaried workers. Chrysler, for example, had 25 hourly workers per each salaried worker in 1991 and 48 in 1994 and hopes to increase the ratio (Templin, 1994).

1.3 Specify Instructional Objectives
Step 3 is to decide what is needed to close the gap between actual and desired performance. A well-defined objective has three elements.

1. The desired performance must be observable.
2. The desired performance must be measurable.
3. The conditions under which performance occurs must be specified.

For example: Using a model XX word processor and software program YY, the operator will be able to determine the assembly sequence for product ZZ and print the sequence.

1.4 Develop Content Step 4 is to organize the information (message) to be presented through a medium.

2 MEDIUM AND THE MESSAGE

Organize the information (message) to be presented through a medium.

2.1 Organization Three parts of organizing information are (1) **planning,** (2) **drafting,** and (3) **revising.** (See Table 31.2.)

2.1.1 *Planning* What is the user's ignorance? What should be communicated? What are your goals? What do the users know *before* your communication? What happens *during* your communication? What will happen *after* your communication? How will your database be filled and organized?

A key point is that not all knowledge resides in the management/staff; considerable job knowledge resides only in the workers. In addition, not all staff have the same knowledge and not all workers have the same knowledge. In addition, as shown in Figure 32.3, some knowledge is factual and some knowledge is in the form of emotions/attitudes.

Then decide how to communicate. In particular, how much of your message will be text and how much will be graphics? After this strategic decision, you will have to decide on the tactics of specific types of text, graphs, tables, and so forth.

2.1.2 *Drafting* Table 31.2 gives some comments on drafts. Perhaps the most important thing to know is that the first version is not the final version. Multiple drafts are the mark of good communicators.

2.1.3 *Revising* The draft material requires **pilot testing** with the target audience; that is, the presentation needs a quality assurance test. Testing requires identifying the target audiences, finding a representative sample, and doing the test. Obtaining a sample of people who represent the target audience is important. In particular, they are unlikely to be similar to the people in the writer's office! A good test will evaluate at both the macro level (logic and structure of the presentation) and the micro level (specific adjectives and nouns used, use of a bar graph as opposed to a line graph). After the test, the material is revised, and then another test is administered to evaluate the revisions. Allow sufficient time for the testing and revisions.

The information (message) can be communicated to the trainee through many media.

T A B L E	31.2

Some guidelines for good instruction writing.

PLAN

- Know the user's ignorance. This requires knowing the user.
- Decide what will be communicated.
- Decide on strategy (medium; text vs. pictures).
- Decide on tactics (e.g., organization of message, types of tables, etc.).

DRAFT

- Plan on multiple drafts.
- Put the information in a logical order. Number steps.
- Have a specific objective for each instruction (who, what, where, why, when, how).
- Use both text and figures.
- Make the text at the appropriate reading level.
- Use two short sentences instead of a long sentence with a clause. Instead of, "After cleaning the part with solvent, dry in a ventilated location," say:
  1. Clean the part with solvent.
  2. Dry in a ventilated location
- Use **active** statements. Avoid **passive** or negative statements.
  Active: The large lever controls the depth of cut.
  Passive: The depth of cut is controlled by the large lever.
  Negative: The small lever does not control the depth of cut.
- For emphasis in sentences, use **bold** or *italics;* avoid underlining and CAPITALIZATION.

REVISE

- Identify the target audience (see PLAN).
- Select a sample population for testing.
- Run the test.
- Revise material.
- Continue the loop until satisfied.
- Allow sufficient time for testing and revision.

2.2 Media The three primary input channels are kinesthetic, audio, and visual.

2.2.1 *Kinesthetic* Learning by doing, primarily through touch and **kinesthetic** (movement) **input,** has a long-established reputation of success. Hands-on experience results in learning with long retention. For example, most teachers believe that students learn more when they write notes than when they just underline or read with no physical action. Motor movements, such as riding a bicycle, are resistant to extinction. Use kinesthetic input for highly repetitive psychomotor movements (skilled movement) so processing becomes automatic.

In some cases, hands-on learning is possible, but with dangers removed. For example, practice handling containers of acid with water substituting for acid.

2.2.2 *Audio*

2.2.2 *Audio* Auditory signals, or **audio input,** that are mechanical tend to be quite simple (a horn honking, a phone ringing). They present only one of a limited number of choices. In other words, they can be used for a signal but do not communicate much information. It is possible to get more elaborate in the mechanical signal through variations in pitch (a horn versus a buzzer), duration (Morse code), and even volume, but the number of alternatives that can be indicated mechanically probably will be 10 or fewer for most situations.

The human voice, of course, can present a wide range of alternatives (stop, go, turn right, slow down, call home, call Sally, drink Pepsi).

A problem of auditory messages is that they are transitory—they disappear with time. (An exception can be very simple audio messages such as buzzers, which can be continuous. However, an annoyance problem occurs within a few seconds.) What if someone tells you to call (785) 532-5606? Unless you write it down, you probably will forget the number within a few seconds. That is, there is no permanent reference. Complex information is difficult to communicate well by voice because people forget some of the details, which is why organizations have the rule **AVO**—avoid verbal orders.

Another problem with the audio message is its pacing effect. You can hear the message only at the rate it is being presented. One example is Morse code—a series of auditory dots and dashes presented as short beeps and long beeps. You can receive the code only at the rate the sender is transmitting it to you. If it is too fast for you, you will miss it; if it is too slow, you get bored and impatient. Audiotapes have been used to talk workers through an assembly task (Dickey and Konz, 1969). The problem was the fixed rate. For the initial cycles of the task, the tape was too fast in relation to the worker's ability. After practice, the workers had to wait for the messages; that is, the rate of output was limited to the tape speed. If audiotapes are used, they should be available at a variety of speeds.

Computer prompt (help) information should follow the same principle, varying the information with the user's skill level. That is, beginners want detailed information, and experts want no information because they already know it. The user should be able to select the desired prompt level.

In most situations the instruction medium will be visual. Many choices remain.

2.2.3 *Visual*

2.2.3 *Visual* The first choice when using the medium of **visual input** is whether the visual image will be text, a representation of the object, or a combination. All images are codes; codes must be decoded. Since many codes are easy to decipher (and for instructional purposes, that is the way it should be), the decoding (translation) problem often is forgotten. A pictorial message requires the least translation. (A word equals .001 picture!) For example, show an operator the correct location of solder joints by using a picture of the assembly with circles around the solder joints; teach how to load a camera with pictures showing the loading sequence. Translation from the image to the task is simple and direct. Although pictures can communicate the *how,* text is useful for communicating the *why.* The best approach seems to be not just a picture, not just text, but both pictures and text (Dickey and Konz, 1969; Stern, 1984; Nugent, 1987).

Another choice is whether the information will be presented in a linear or a branching mode. The traditional approach is the **linear mode.** An example is a movie. The information is presented in a standard sequence determined by the program designer. In a **branching mode,** the information branches, depending upon the needs of the learner. This textbook is designed for a branching rather than sequential reading of the chapters.

Much instruction now is presented on computers as they permit easy branching and can hold much information, including graphics. Branching is easy with computerized instructions; the decreasing cost of computers makes branching more and more competitive. Branching also is used with **scenarios** (interactive stories). In the opening scene, students are given several choices. Depending on their choice, different scenes are presented along with a rationale for why they should or should not have chosen that choice. They continue with choices until reaching the end of that "storyline" (path).

Another choice is whether the information will be communicated to individuals or to a group. Certain approaches lend themselves to group presentations (movies, slides and transparencies, lectures), some to small groups (TV, demonstrations), and some to individual instruction (books, printed photographs). Some approaches are flexible. Another determination to be made is the importance of social interaction and involvement between the instructor and students and among students.

Another choice is ease of modification. It is easy to replace a slide in a magazine or to rearrange the slides; it is difficult to modify the images of a filmstrip or movie. It is difficult to modify a book or printed material; it is easy to modify digital material.

Is distributed or massed practice best? Evidence for over 100 years indicates that, for the same total hours of instruction or practice, **distributed practice** (short training sessions) produces better learning than **massed practice** (long training sessions). Bradeley and Longman (1978), for example, emphasized the importance of the amount of training per day. They found that 1 session of 1 h/day was better than 1 session of 2 h/day or 2 sessions of 2 h/day. Bouzid and Crawshaw (1987) reported that 2 30-min sessions for word processing training were better than 1 60-min session.

Another choice is the location of the instruction. Classroom instruction permits use of machines requiring power, projection screens, space for demonstrations, and the like. Field instruction may not allow use of powered equipment (unless it is battery-powered), seats for the participants, or space to set up instructional equipment. In some field situations, no equipment may be available and the instruction site may be dirty, vibrating, noisy, or otherwise distracting. Computerized instruction allows great flexibility in scheduling and location. With home computers, CDs, and laptop computers, firms have begun to assume that training can be done at home during the employees' personal time.

Do not overemphasize mechanical devices. Our society—and especially engineers—tends to overemphasize the machine (the medium) and neglect the message.

2.3 Message   As mentioned previously, the message usually is visual. The primary divisions of visual messages are pictorial and text.

2.3.1 *Pictorial messages*   Pictures can be communicated in many ways. **Pictorial messages** include a live demonstration, sequential frames (film, video), still photographs (printed or projected), and line drawings (drawn, printed, projected, and even animated).

Moving or still? Still pictures, in addition to usually being cheaper, permit viewers to look at the pictures at their own individual pace; backing up or rearranging the pictures is easy. Movies and video, on the other hand, can show relationships such as sequences of hand–arm motions. However, freezing the image or backing it up requires the designer to plan ahead or provide special equipment for the viewer. Even if the special equipment is available, a specific viewer may not wish to interrupt the group to see a scene again.

Color or black and white? Color film and color video are so common that presenting the image only in black and white is more expensive. However, color printing and photoduplication may be expensive. In addition to being more interesting to view, a color image generally will be easier for the viewer to understand due to contrast, shading, and other features.

Image fidelity? A slide or printed photograph can be used in place of the physical object itself—if the representation gives all the relevant information. (Adequate representation is the basic principle of the simulator used for flight instruction.) Photographs may be out-of-focus, over- or underdeveloped, poorly lighted, and so forth; however, they do take little physical space (and thus are easy to store and transport), can be duplicated inexpensively, can be magnified, and can emphasize important features. Physical models (i.e., the real thing) can be manipulated by the operator for a better view, can be disassembled, touched, and so on. (If you use physical models of an assembly as a training aid, save workstation space by mounting the models on a turntable.)

Line drawings generally can communicate information better than photographs because they are carefully designed to emphasize important features and omit irrelevant details. Line drawings reproduce well, and exploded views can be used. (See the left-hand corner of Figure 25.1 for an exploded view.) If using a sketch, use isometric views because many people have difficulty understanding drafting conventions.

2.3.2 *Text messages*   The **text message** is discussed in categories of words, style, and format.

Words.   Don't write merely to be understood; write so you cannot possibly be misunderstood. The vocabulary of most workers is not as advanced as the vocabulary of university graduates (who often write the instructions). Workers are not comfortable with multiple-syllable or uncommon words such as "subsequent, prior, chartreuse, incorporate, and simultaneously"; they like "little" substitutes such as "after, before, yellow-green, put in, and at the same time." See Table 31.3. So eschew obfuscation! In general, use Anglo-Saxon-derivative words (such as pig, end, begin, first, and go) rather than their Latin equivalents (swine, finish, commence, initial, and proceed). Use "cuts and bruises," not "abrasions and contusions." Use specific numbers instead of the vague "few," "some," "many," and "numerous." See Table 31.4 for common writing problems.

In addition, remember that English may not be the first language of some of your workers.

Style.   Consider the complexity of your writing. Complexity can be quantified with the two following formulas. The first formula was developed by the Gunning-Mueller Clear Writing Institute:

$$GL = .4 (A + P)$$

where GL = **Grade level,** years (Readers at that grade level would be expected to score 75% on a comprehension test.)

A = Average words per sentence. Treat independent clauses (they start with the word

T A B L E	31.3
Use simple words.	

BAD	BETTER
parameters	values, variables
scrutinize	look at
incorporate	put in
verification	check
precede	before
prior	before
facilitate	help, make easy
subsequent	after
simultaneously	at the same time
via	by
inquire	ask
equivalent	equal
simulate	pretend
pulmonary	lung
perforation of	hole in

T A B L E	31.4
Common writing problems and solutions.	

STYLE

- Prefer the short word to the long.
- Prefer the Saxon word to the Romance.
- Prefer the familiar word to the far-fetched.
- Prefer the concrete to the abstract.
- Prefer the single word to the circumlocution.
- Every table and figure should have a number and title.

GRAMMAR

- Use computer spelling/punctuation checkers.
- Use numbers instead of words for 10 and up; below 10 use words unless two numbers are compared.
- Use 5 to 10, not 5–10.
- That vs. which: "that" introduces a clause that is essential to the sentence meaning; "which" introduces a modifying clause, which adds information incidental to the sentence meaning.
- *Data* is plural.
- *Cannot* instead of *can not*.

and, or, but, nor, or *yet* or with semicolons) as separate sentences.

P = Percent (not proportion) of words with three or more syllables.

For *P*, omit:

a. Capitalized words (except the first word in a sentence).

b. Easy combinations such as screwdriver and guestworker.

c. Verbs that reach three syllables with the addition of -es or -ed.

The Flesch-Kincaid Grade Level score is used in Microsoft Word (click Tools, Options, Spelling and Grammar tab):

$$GL = -15.59 + .39\ ASL + 11.8\ ASW$$

where ASL = Average sentence length

= number of words/number of sentences

ASW = Average number of syllables/word

= number of syllables/number of words

TV Guide has a *GL* of 6 and the *Wall Street Journal, Time,* and *Newsweek* average 11. People prefer to read below their grade level. You may wish to have more than 75% comprehension.

Consider job aids for your writing. Presently most people are rooted to TV, which emphasizes pic-

tures and hearing at the expense of reading. One simple aid is spell check programs. More advanced grammar programs are available on many computers. The Microsoft Encarta College Dictionary is designed for student writing with 600 usage notes (e.g., *disinterested* means "impartial," not "not interested"), 400 spellcheck notes (errors your computer's spellchecker won't catch), and 10,000 geographical and biographical entries.

Finally, realize that messages can be negative as well as positive. That is, negative examples often are a good teaching technique. However, the consequences of the negative example (the punishment) should not be severe. For example, if you make a mistake on a computer input, it should not be difficult to recover.

Format. See Section 2, Arrange Characters and Symbols, of Chapter 18 for comments on text, codes, abbreviations, formulas, menus, data tables, graphs, projected images, and symbolic messages.

Tabular formats are superior to narrative formats; flow charts give fewer errors than do narrative formats (Kammann, 1975; Wright and Reid, 1973). Table 31.5 shows how to improve the following text.

When time is limited, travel by Rocket, unless cost is also limited, in which case go by Space Ship. When only cost is limited, an Astrobus should be used for journeys of less than 10 orbs, and a Satellite for longer journeys. Cosmocars are

T A B L E		3 1 . 5	
Decision structure tables communicate with fewer errors than text or decision diagrams (boxes connected by lines). Use of the connective words (if, and, then) and verbs (is) aid communication. Single and double lines help also (Wright and Reid, 1973).			

IF TIME IS	AND COST IS	AND JOURNEY LENGTH IS	THEN TRAVEL MODE IS
limited	unlimited	any	Rocket
limited	limited	any	Spaceship
unlimited	unlimited	less than or equal to 10 orbs	Cosmocar
		more than 10 orbs	Superstar
unlimited	unlimited	less than or equal to 10 orbs	Astrobus
		more than 10 orbs	Satellite

recommended, when there are no constraints on time or cost, unless the distance to be traveled exceeds 10 orbs. For journeys longer than 10 orbs, when time and cost are not important, journeys should be made by Superstar.

Don't condense tables or force the user to make calculations. Use "white space" to show organization of information. Keep information in specific behavioral terms. See Table 31.6.

3 TRAINING (MEMORIZATION)

Assume that the decision has been made to train the worker in specific knowledge. More specifically, the worker is to use **memorization** to "know it by heart." See Box 31.1. Section 4 of this chapter, Job Aids, briefly covers an alternative method. With a **job aid,** the worker does not memorize the information but, rather, looks it up each time.

This "transfer of technology" has two aspects. Assume that the knowledge to be transferred has been developed. The knowledge has to be transferred locally and to "sister facilities." Transfer to sister facilities primarily requires a communication plan and procedures to implement the communication.

Locally, the challenge is to transfer knowledge to the mind of a specific worker. This requires:

- subject knowledge by the trainer
- knowledge of how to teach by the trainer
- training materials
- training time
- a trainee willing and able to learn

Assume that the trainee is not a problem. The following challenges remain.

3.1 Who?   The first challenge is who will be the trainer. Four possibilities will be discussed.

One possibility is what the British call **sit by Nellie;** that is, learn by observing a fellow worker. But Nellie may not know the *best* way of doing a job, although she may know *a* way of doing the job. Nellie probably has not been trained how to teach. Nellie will have access to some physical demonstration aids,

T A B L E		3 1 . 6	
Use specific behavioral terms.			

POOR	BETTER
Unlock box.	With left hand, hold the latch on the left side.
	With the right hand, insert key 14 and turn clockwise.
Inspect nameplate to ensure that it has been properly installed.	Inspect nameplate.
	Place 75 mm from top and 100 mm from left side of cover.
	Nameplate should not be able to be pried up with fingernails.

BOX **31.1**   *Memory*   (Anon., 1998)

Memory is divided biochemically into three types: short-term, intermediate, and long-term.

1. *Short-term memory.* Nerve cells modify existing proteins; the change is transient. When the need for the memory has passed, the cells return to their previous state and you forget the memory.
2. *Intermediate memory.* The cells make more proteins of the types they were making already. They do not make any different proteins.

3. *Long-term memory.* The nerve cells make new types of proteins. These new proteins create changes in the physical structure of the brain, by forming new connections between nerve cells. The important memories of the day are transferred from temporary storage in the hippocampus to permanent storage in the neocortex during slow-wave sleep.

---

such as the product and the workstation, but will not have any theory materials. If Nellie's time is used for training, it will decrease production.

A second possibility is to let the supervisor do the training. The problems of subject knowledge and teaching materials remain; the supervisor probably will have better knowledge of theory and poorer practical knowledge of the task. Teaching knowledge may be slightly better, but demands upon the supervisor's time are many, so time availability probably is worse.

A third possibility is to hire a teacher to teach the workers. Subject knowledge may be a problem because the teacher will have to know many subjects. Teaching knowledge should be adequate, but teaching materials are important since the teacher will not be familiar with each subject. Teaching time may be a problem because the teacher may be overworked one week and idle the next, since demands for teaching fluctuate. The cost of the teacher, however, now has become a budget item and becomes visible. Thus, the organization may want the teacher to teach a group of workers rather than an individual so teaching time can be prorated over more people. Yet, because specialized knowledge has limited requirements, industrial class sizes tend to be small—5 to 10 students. If workers are released from a job to attend classes (and, most important, are paid to attend), this attracts additional attention to the training costs.

This has led to a fourth approach: Eliminate the teacher. Self-service has been used in many fields, so why not education? In **self-instruction,** the trainer and trainee are the same person, but the trainer, of course, has no subject knowledge. Knowledge of how to teach is small, although it is possibly offset somewhat by knowledge of what has to be known. Scheduling problems are minimal. However, good training materials assume great importance since there will be no teacher to emphasize what is important, to answer questions, and to correct errors in the training materials. Self-instruction can benefit from the knowledge gained through research on pro-

grammed instruction by B. F. Skinner, a psychologist from Harvard.

3.2 Training Principles
Two divisions are programmed learning and enhanced training.

3.2.1 *Programmed learning*
Skinner trained rats and pigeons through programmed instruction. How? Consider teaching a pigeon to turn a clockwise circle. First, watch until it turns part of a clockwise circle. Then give it a piece of grain. Continue giving grain for turning, but gradually require more and more of the circle for the reward—that is, shape its behavior. As shown in the pigeon training by Skinner, five principles are involved in **programmed learning:**

Principle	Pigeon Example
1. Define specifically the exact behavior you wish the trainee to do.	Turn a clockwise circle.
2. Present the information in small increments, steps, or modules.	Small arcs first.
3. Present information at a pace determined by the trainee.	Pigeon sets pace.
4. Give immediate feedback of the correct answer (knowledge of results) to the trainee.	Grain for correct movement.
5. Observe trainee behavior. If not satisfactory, modify program.	If pigeon doesn't learn, try another technique.

Research indicates that, when applied to humans, steps 2 through 4, although desirable, are not essential. The essential steps are 1 and 5.

Step 1 (specific behavior) means we must specifically define which motor movements we want. Glittering generalities such as "know the job" or "understand the process" are replaced by "if the temperature on gauge 7 rises above 95°C, turn the red switch on column 7 to 'off' and call your supervisor." See Table 31.6. Give training programs the same attention as you give to computer programming. Poor teaching is often simply insufficient attention to detail. Training is best if the trainee is active rather than passive. Active would be doing an assembly while watching a video of the assembly procedure; passive would be just watching the video.

Step 2 (small steps) says that information is more digestible in small bites. Many studies have indicated better training when a large body of knowledge is divided so training is in parts. The best size of the bite may depend on the appetite.

Step 3 (self-pacing) lets trainees receive the message at their own rates rather than at some rate appropriate for the average. If average is defined as "between the 40th and 60th percentile," average includes only 20% of the group. Any presentation at a rate appropriate for the average is inappropriate for 80% of the group. Ideally, the level of difficulty can be varied along with the rate of presentation so instruction is personalized. Self-pacing is aided if the training is done "off-line" so the pressure of production does not conflict with the training. Off-line could mean training in a separate facility or using production equipment during evening or weekend hours.

Step 4 provides immediate feedback to the trainee. Delay of the correct answer for a previous question may mean that the trainee may be misled on much subsequent material. Even more important is the motivational value of quick confirmation of the correct response. Positive feedback tends to work better than negative feedback. Everyone likes praise.

Step 5, immediate feedback to the trainer, is important. Feedback distinguishes an efficient closed-loop system from an open-loop system in education just as it does in any other system; the feedback system reduces system error. Reduction of system error through program change can be summarized as "there are **no stupid students, just terrible teachers.**" It stems from Skinner's belief that he was smarter than any pigeon. If the pigeon did not learn, it was not the pigeon's fault; it was up to Skinner to develop a better teaching method.

This concept, that poor learning is the teacher's fault, is hard for many teachers to accept. They reply that some students could not learn nuclear physics no matter how well they were taught; they have neither the capability nor the motivation. True. Therefore, use the "no stupid students, just terrible teachers" concept to keep teachers doing the best possible job instead of looking for excuses.

3.2.2 *Enhanced training*
Three training principles are: (1) practice, (2) part-task, and (3) training wheels. "Practice makes perfect" has been known for a long time. Avoid "rookie" mistakes by practice. Chapter 27 has information on quantifying the effect of learning.

Part-task training is superior to whole-task training. The concept is that because some parts of the total task are harder than others, the focus should be on the difficult parts instead of overlearning the easy parts.

"Training wheels" permit the trainee to learn without injury or damage. In general, people learn best when permitted to make errors, but you don't want the errors to affect the system. Therefore, use "training wheels" to notify the trainee that the behavior was wrong without actually implementing the error.

3.3 Simulation
Most workers learn on the job. They produce product as they learn. However, there are some situations in which workers need a very high level of skill before they produce product. In that case, they can practice in a **simulation** of the environment. Some examples are the following:

- Athletes practice specific skills and also have scrimmages, games against easy opponents, and so on.
- Military personnel spend most of their time practicing, at the individual level and at various levels of group activities.
- Pilots have classroom training but also training on simulators. These simulators have considerable fidelity. The instruments respond, the simulator vibrates, and the visual and auditory environment of flight is simulated.
- Business planning simulation software models a business environment; multi-player simulations add a competitive edge.

In general, use simulation for training when the cost of an error in real performance is high. Simulation tends to reduce errors in the "real world." Computerized simulation has benefited greatly from the development of video games and the greatly reduced cost of computers.

3.4 Evaluation and Improvement
Step 5 is to conduct the training.

Step 6 is to evaluate the training. Five types of evaluation (Samways, 1997) are:

1. Participant satisfaction (opinion ratings of the training)
2. Learning outcomes (exam questions, job simulations)
3. Attitude changes (as observed in interviews and on the job)
4. Behavior or performance changes (observations of work, safety records, supervisor comments)

5. Accomplishment of organizational goals (widgets/h, errors/widget, lost workdays)

Step 7 is to improve the training. That is, in a feedback loop, use the evaluation to improve the training materials and training procedures. Training is a continuous process.

4 JOB AIDS

An alternative to memorizing information is to have the information constantly available for reference. The highest level of a job aid is an **information repository.** See Box 31.2. Job aids (also known as job performance aids) are divided into procedural and psychomotor. Some examples include "to do" lists and assembly instructions.

4.1 Procedural   Some examples are to-do lists, recipes, and assembly instructions. Present procedural (big picture) information in **decision structure tables** such as Tables 31.7 and 31.8 or a **routing sheet** such as Table 31.9. These tables give various decisions that have been made about processes. These decisions can be made in advance by experts rather than by inexperienced operators under time pressure, who lack all the relevant information. The tables also serve as a convenient storage location for tool numbers, standard costs, and so forth. They serve as a good training aid.

In computer-aided manufacturing (also called computer-integrated manufacturing), these tables, routing sheets, and the like are stored in a computer—a step toward the paperless office. The computer permits an easily updated central file and complex decision structure tables, and facilitates comparison with similar parts (group technology)—assuming the similar parts information also is in the database.

The tips in Table 31.10 were developed for emergency warning messages. Nevertheless, they apply to most job aids.

More complex versions of decision structure tables are called **expert systems.** The expert system may ask questions of a user and then suggest a solution (forward chaining), or it may take a solution suggested by the user and confirm or deny it (backward chaining). Development of the expert system through a number of iterations with users forces experts to refine their knowledge and reduces operator errors (Drury and Sarac, 1997)

Instruction manuals, whether on paper or computer, should be indexed. The indexing should be from the user's viewpoint, not from the author's viewpoint. Use organizing aids such as tab dividers, page headers, variable print size, and emphasis. Panel et al. (1993) point out that design of job aid documents should consider

1. *information readability* (typographic layout clues, including bold, italics, underlining, paragraphs, justification). Because the text may be farther than .3 m from the eyes or lighting may be poor (especially for maintainers and inspectors), consider larger print.

2. *information content* (appropriate content, balance between text and graphics)

3. *information organization* (classifying and layering information into categories; giving information in the format of the command verb, the action qualifier, and the objects)

4. *physical handling and environmental factors* (job aid must be rugged, lighting adequate, etc.). Consider mounting the job aid on a suspended pivoting holder so the worker can read an instruction, swing the aid

---

BOX   31.2   *Information Repositories*

Repositories come in all sizes and shapes. A letter, an article, a manila file folder, a file cabinet, a textbook, a library and the network of libraries all are repositories. These examples all contain printing on paper.

But the cost of computation continues to decrease. Thus, the wave of the future is electronic repositories such as files, directories, discs, hard drives, local area networks, and the Internet.

Some advantages of electronic repositories are virtually unlimited storage space, convenient access with no travel requirements, and search engines to locate the desired information. Additional advantages are ease of updating (compare with updating paper manuals on 1,000 shelves) and ease of distribution (compare with distribution of 1,000 paper manuals). Another advantage is that the repository can be "proactive" rather than reactive; that is, instead of information waiting in the repository until you ask for it, the computer can notify you when new information arrives that is relevant to you (such as a change in a client's e-mail address or an article evaluating computer keyboards).

One recent repository development is the Internet. It has two disadvantages: (1) there is a huge mass of information and (2) the information has not been "peer-reviewed," so how do you separate the trash from the treasure?

T A B L E	31.7	

Decision structure tables give explicit instructions. This example is of a check-cashing policy for a grocery store.

IF TYPE OF CHECK IS	AND AMOUNT OF CHECK IS	AND BANK OF CHECK IS	AND CUSTOMER ADDRESS IS	THEN CUSTOMER IDENTIFICATION REQUIRED IS	AND ON BAD CHECK LIST	THEN DECISION IS
Two-Party	Any	Any	Any			Reject
Company	Up to $25	Any		0		Accept
	$25.01 to $200	Any	Any	1		Accept
	$200.01 and up					Reject
Personal	Up to $25	Local	Local	1	Yes	Reject
					No	Accept
			Out of Town	1	Yes	Reject
					No	Accept
		Out of Town	Local	1	Yes	Reject
					No	Accept
			Out of Town	2	Yes	Reject
					No	Accept
	Over $25	Any	Any			Reject

out of the way for the task, swing it back for reading the next instruction, and the like.

4.2 Psychomotor Present **psychomotor** ("fine-grain picture") **information** in pictorial instruction sheets or on videotape. Emphasize grasp and position elements as these are the skill elements. Move and reach are less important. In general, using only words is fair, using only pictures is better, and using words plus pictures is best. Words explain the why; pictures explain the how. Words such as "element break-downs" (as with MTM) may communicate to other engineers but don't give workers the necessary details. If using videotape, have operators add audio comments with a voiceover while viewing themselves. For photographs, digital cameras work well. Then staple the picture to a sheet of paper and have the operator add supplementary words. Leave space for changes. See also Table 31.10.

Leave a copy of the instructions at the machine, as well as having a copy for the office. Avoid the "gold plating" of using professional photographers, typed instructions, elegant mounting, and so forth. Put in a looseleaf folder or laminate for protection. If an elegant copy is desirable, wait until instructions have been polished by the users; count on several drafts as most first drafts are poor. More polished instructions can be justified if the procedure is a stan-

T A B L E	31.8	

Decision structure table example for selecting drill size before tapping or clearance drill size. Assume that you wish a hole large enough so the drill will not touch the bolt threads.

	NATIONAL SPECIAL THREAD SERIES		
IF BOLT DIAMETER, INCHES IS	AND THREADS PER INCH IS	THEN DRILL SIZE FOR 75% THREAD IS	THEN CLEARANCE DRILL BIT SIZE IS
1/16	64	3/64	51
5/64	60	1/16	45
3/32	48	49	40
7/64	48	43	32

TABLE 31.9

Routing sheet example. Also called operations charts, routing sheets vary depending on the organization, but the table below is typical. Operation numbers are given in multiples of 10 so that operations originally omitted can be added without changing the numbers of the other operations. Some routing sheets also include bill of material information. The direct labor hours per unit should not include process time such as for drying.

Part name ___Punch___   Part number ___541-675___   Raw Material ___1040 10 mm Round___

Operations ___SK___   Date ___20 Jan 04___   Used on ___Model 80___

OPERATION NUMBER	OPERATION NAME	MACHINE	TOOLING	FEED, MM/REV	SPEED, REV/MIN	H/UNIT	REMARKS
10	Turn 4 mm dia	J & L	#642 Box	.225	318		
	Turn 3 mm dia	T. Lathe					
	Cut off to length	J & L	#6 cutoff	Hand	318	.008	
20	Mill 5 mm radius	#1 Milwaukee	Tool 84	Hand		.004	
30	Heat-treat	#4 furnace				.006	
35	Degrease	Vapor degreaser					
40	Measure hardness	Rockwell tester				.002	
50	Store						

TABLE 31.10

Tips for emergency warning messages (Johnson, 1980).

- Use pictures, not just words
- Use 3-dimensional, not 2-dimensional, pictures
- Use pictures rather than symbols (which require learning)
- Number sequential drawings
- Show both initial and final locations of controls
- Present what *not* to do as well as what to do
- Use drawings, not photographs (less irrelevant information, can emphasize important items, easier to change)
- Show time pressure with clockface; time changes in each picture
- Evaluate message with typical users (*not* equipment designer)

dard manufacturing process and the instruction is widely distributed. If the instruction sheets are in the office only and not at the point of use, they lose most of their effectiveness.

An alternative to paper-based instructions are instructions on a computer. Some advantages are the constantly decreasing cost of computers and newer technology such as digital cameras. For example, Motorola uses a digital camera to take pictures of each component and then puts the digitized images on the computer, supplemented with text. With a computer, on-screen highlighting and color-coding are easy. Updates are relatively easy.

The International Standards Organization requires manufacturers to demonstrate that every copy of every assembly instruction is up to date. With the instructions on a central computer server, a change there gives the same instructions to each terminal (which even can be in different cities). In addition, there are no old paper instructions to dispose of.

Note that after workers obtain the job knowledge (e.g., how to fold a cardboard box), they will need many repetitions before knowledge becomes a skill.

For inspections, human judgments are most accurate when they involve direct comparisons rather than memorized images. Photographic **limit aids** are useful in reducing inspection errors. The steps are as follows:

1. Establish a panel of experts to define what is acceptable and not acceptable for each type of defect.

2. Select parts with defects. These defects should range from very bad defects to just rejectable defects. In addition, select parts with perfect quality and just acceptable quality.

3. Arrange the parts in a column by descending quality with best on top. Put a gap between the just acceptable and just rejectable defect. Mount the parts on a display board or, if space is limited, as it usually is, photograph them.

4. Give each inspector and operator a set.

Review Questions

1. Give three advantages of cross-training.
2. Briefly discuss the transitory and pacing problems of audio messages.
3. Give an example of a linear presentation and of a branching presentation.
4. What are the Latin-derivative words for the following Anglo-Saxon–derivative words: *pig, end, begin, first, go?*
5. List the six things with which an independent clause may begin.
6. Rewrite the sentence, "The next step is to drill and chamfer the 50-mm hole," with two short sentences each starting with an action verb.
7. What is the difference between training and a job aid?
8. Using pigeon training for an illustration, list the five steps of programmed instruction.
9. Discuss the concept, "There are no stupid students, just terrible teachers."
10. In training of psychomotor movements, is it more important to emphasize the Grasp and Position elements or the Move and Reach elements? Why?

References

Anonymous, Memory building. *The Economist,* Vol. 348, No. 8083, 70–72, August 29, 1998.

Booher, J. Relative comprehensibility of pictorial information and printed words in proceduralized instructions. *Human Factors,* Vol. 17, No. 3, 266–77, 1975.

Bouzid, N. and Crawshaw, C. Massed versus distributed word processor training. *Applied Ergonomics,* Vol. 18, No. 3, 220–23, 1987.

Bradeley, A. and Longman, D. The influence of length and frequency of training sessions on the rate of learning to type. *Ergonomics,* Vol. 21, No. 8, 627–35, 1978.

Dickey, G. and Konz, S. Manufacturing assembly instructions: A summary. *Ergonomics,* Vol. 12, No. 3, 369–82, 1969.

Drury, C. and Sarac, A. A design aid for improved documentation in aircraft maintenance: A precursor to training. *Proc. of Human Factors and Ergonomic Society,* 1158–62, Santa Monica, CA: HFES, 1997.

Johnson, D. The design of effective safety information displays. *Proceedings of Human Factors and Industrial Design in Consumer Products,* Tufts University, 1980.

Kammann, R. The comprehensibility of printed instructions and the flowchart alternative. *Human Factors,* Vol. 17, No. 2, 183–91, 1975.

Nugent, W. A comparative assessment of computer-based media for presenting job task instructions. *Proceedings of the Human Factors Society,* 696–700, 1987.

Panel, S., Drawer, C., and Prabhu, P. Design and usability evaluation of work control documentation. *Proceedings of the Human Factors and Ergonomic Society,* 1156–60, 1993.

Rodgers, S. A functional job analysis technique. In *Occupational Medicine: State of the Art Reviews,* Vol. 7, No. 4, 679–711, Oct.–Dec., Philadelphia: Henry and Belfus, 1992.

Samways, M. Worker education and training (Chapter 30) in *The Occupational Environment—Its Evaluation and Control.* Fairfax, VA: AIHA, 1997.

Stern, K. An evaluation of written, graphic, and voice messages in proceduralized instructions. *Proceedings of the Human Factors Society,* 314–18, 1984.

Templin, N. Auto plants, hiring again, are demanding higher-skilled labor. *Wall Street Journal,* March 11, 1994.

Wright, P. and Reid, F. Written information: Some alternatives to prose. *J. of Applied Psychology,* Vol. 57, No. 2, 160–66, 1973.

Overview

A technical proposal is useless unless it is accepted and implemented. Change involves the sociopolitical world as well as the world of facts. Small group techniques, which move decision making lower in the organization, not only improve fact gathering but can also improve acceptance through resolution of emotional/attitudinal problems. Quality Circles are an example of a small group technique. Recommendations are given on how to improve the acceptance of proposals.

Key Concepts

area of freedom	force field analysis	passive approach/active	solution space
client's servant	frequent consultation	approach	Taylorism
defense before offense	industrial democracy	project scope	vertical barrier/horizontal
emotions and attitudes	local experts	Quality Circles	barrier
facilitator	ownership	quality versus acceptance	
fish diagram	Pareto diagram	reduction of uncertainty	

CHALLENGE OF CHANGE

Most of the chapters of this text discuss obtaining a technically excellent design. The book presents material concerning hand movement patterns, handtool design, workstation design, noise, toxicology, and so forth. However, when the engineer has decided upon a technically correct concept, the concept must be translated into practice. Technological change (e.g., adding a conveyor, changing workstation height) is easier to implement than organizational change (e.g., changing a wage payment system or what an operator's job is). Yet, even technological change interacts with social systems to produce a "soft system." Translation of a concept into practice involves the sociopolitical world as well as the technical world. Engineering students, raised on a diet of mathematics and physical science, often have difficulty adjusting to this sociopolitical world, which treats their technical "solution" as merely a "proposal."

$$\left(\begin{array}{c}\text{Technical \textbf{quality}}\\\text{of a proposal}\end{array}\right)\left(\begin{array}{c}\textbf{Acceptance}\\\text{of a proposal}\end{array}\right)=\left(\begin{array}{c}\text{Amount of}\\\text{improvement}\end{array}\right)$$

Leisman (1977), when reviewing this chapter in the first edition, commented:

> Without acceptance, nothing has happened. The technique or technology may be a thing of beauty, the analysis may be perfect and even foolproof, the proposal may be well written and well presented and overwhelmingly justified, with excellent payback. But it is nothing, zero, a total waste of time, unless it is acceptable to those who are impacted.
>
> Your skill at implementing change will determine how far and how fast you will be recognized by your supervision and your peers as having the potential for increased responsibility in your organization. This skill in total consists of 85% approach and 15% technical application.
>
> The bottom line of engineering is implementation—there is no other.

Change will occur eventually. If change is resisted, eventually there is great change (an "earthquake"). To prevent these earthquakes, consider a policy of continuous improvement (small changes often).

The statement that "where you stand depends upon where you sit" expresses the fact that whether you are for or against a change may depend upon which job you presently are holding. Staff units value change because that is how they prove their worth; line units value stability because change inconveniences them or reflects unfavorably on them. On the other hand, staff units are strongly committed to preserving control and rule systems (that's where they get their information and their power) whereas line units prefer flexible interpretation of control systems (we'll do the paperwork if we have time).

The following summarizes resistance to change:

- When a new idea is offered: "It is probably not true."
- When the idea is confirmed: "Yes, it may be true, but it is not important."
- When its importance is validated: "Yes, it certainly is important, but it is no longer new."

PROCESS OF CHANGE

2.1 Forces   Table 32.1 breaks the change process into five steps. The situation starts with stability, "unfreezes," "moves," "refreezes," and then is stable again. Only trivial technical changes arouse no resistance. The question, then, is how to overcome the resistance.

As an example, consider three workers (Joe, Pete, and Sam) rotating every 2 hours among jobs A, B, and C on the subassembly of product X. They are paid by the piece. The engineer proposed that Joe always do job A, Pete always do job B, and Sam always do job C. The engineer computes that their pay will increase 25% (due to increased specialization and thus more pieces/h) and the organization's cost/unit will drop (due to lower burden cost/unit even though labor costs/unit remains constant). However, the workers refuse to change.

Figure 32.1 gives a force diagram of this situation. The pointer can be pulled toward the present (the status quo) or toward what is proposed. Facts are shown as solid arrows and emotions–attitudes are shown as dashed arrows. Note: (1) the many arrows (i.e., how complex even small problems can be) and (2) the preponderance of emotions–attitudes over facts.

The pointer can be made to go to the proposed side by increasing the forces toward the proposed

T A B L E	3 2 . 1

Stages of the change process. When more individuals have to be unfrozen, moved, and refrozen, the challenge is greater. The longer a situation is frozen, the more difficult it is to unfreeze (Munson and Hancock, 1969).

STAGE	DESCRIPTION
1. Frozen	stability
2. Unfreeze	rethink goals; consider alternatives
3. Move	try new methods; feelings of insecurity
4. Refreeze	"I like it," "it really works"
5. Frozen	stability

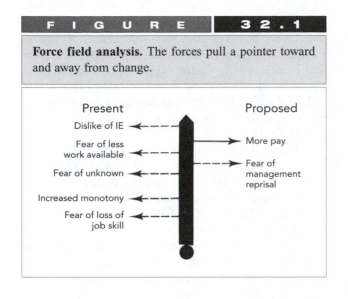

F I G U R E   3 2 . 1

Force field analysis. The forces pull a pointer toward and away from change.

(increase the +), by decreasing the forces toward the present (decrease the −), or by combining the two.

As a general strategy for dealing with **emotions and attitudes,** reduce the negative ones (pulling toward the present) rather than increase the positive ones (pulling toward change). People often resist the social aspects of change rather than the technical aspects. Emotions and attitudes are important factors in a potential change situation. Engineers tend to overlook the critical importance of the worker's social circle breakup, fears of the unknown, and so forth. One common technique for reducing financial fears is to have the organization guarantee no financial loss to the worker. If labor requirements are reduced, the worker is transferred to some other job (with no loss in pay) and the organization "eats" the cost of the surplus worker until attrition reduces the workforce. However, even with no financial loss, the workers may not approve of the social losses, the changes in power, and the disruptions, and may therefore resist change. Increasing emotions and attitudes toward the proposal may be counterproductive. For example, increasing the employees' fears of management reprisal for not making the change may just set up counter-emotions to resist the change ("it's them or us"; "solidarity forever").

Another example of counterproductive behavior can be bringing high levels of management into a problem when lower levels of management are "in error." The lower levels, then, in self-defense, become passionate defenders of the status quo. The change agent should try to avoid such defensive behavior by presenting the proposal in a way that avoids blaming individuals. Try to avoid the "culture of blame" and focus on "root causes" of problems. If, for example, Joe sent the wrong part to a customer, try to identify whether the problem was a misunderstood part number, poor lighting, or other problem; focus on Joe's act rather than Joe as an individual.

If methods used by other operators at the same facility or other facilities of the organization can be applied to the proposal, this should reduce negative forces. This may require a visit by the operators to the sister location so they can see for themselves.

Breaking a large change into a series of smaller steps usually will aid implementation. Many people fear (with reason) giant steps. A common technique is the test market, in which the change is implemented in one "market" and the results are studied before being implemented everywhere.

2.2 Area of Freedom

Figure 32.2 shows how the **solution space** is reduced (limited, constricted, restrained) by various economic, legal, technical, or policy factors to the net **area of freedom.** For example, an engineer might consider a particular task satisfactory, but corporate policy may say no due to the risk of injury. In addition to the moral responsibility to protect the workforce, there are severe economic penalties to a firm for injuries. For example, a back surgery may cost over $20,000.

More and more corporations are charging the medical expenses of injuries to the plant, rather than retaining the charge at the corporate level. Another

F I G U R E   3 2 . 2

Decisions are limited by the area of freedom. Limitations might be economic (keep capital cost less than $10,000), union rules (all maintenance work must be done by in-plant workers), company policy (all reductions in the workforce must be by attrition), legal (noise level must be less than 90 dBA), and so forth.

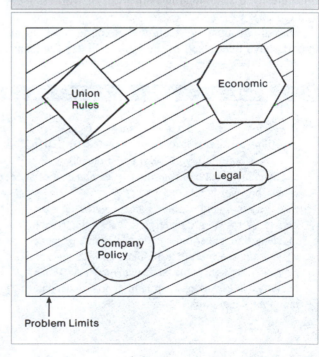

technique is to have corporate pay the actual expenses of an injury but charge a flat fee to the plant, such as $20,000 per permanent disability or $500/day for a lost-time injury. This is corporate's way of getting the attention of plant-level management.

2.3 Incomplete Communication   Resistance to change may be due to lack of knowledge of some of the facts and emotions. For example, an industrial engineer (IE) might not know all the details of the union contract and may be proposing changes not permitted by the contract. Important facts to communicate include the reason why the change is being proposed and what the expected consequences are. A challenge is that some workers may be reluctant to share their local knowledge with other workers and especially management.

Figure 32.3 makes this point more explicitly. People concerned with a problem include technical experts or outsiders (such as IEs) and **local experts** or insiders (those doing the job). Note: (1) The technical experts tend to be "long on information and short on emotions," and (2) not all facts or emotions are known to each party. Thus, coordination among people should increase the knowledge available to everyone. This should improve not only quality of the solution but also acceptance of the solution.

2.4 Teams (Small Groups)   If it is accepted that problems are complex, that emotions and attitudes are involved as well as facts, and that no one individual knows everything, teams are logical.

The Taylorism concept of workers blindly following the orders of their supervisors has been made obsolete by the increasing education of workers (see Table 32.3).

Small groups of technical experts and local experts have been used in the United States for many

years. The Hawthorne studies at Western Electric in the 1930s demonstrated the importance of worker involvement (as well as a placebo effect). See Coch and French (1948), Chaney (1969), the Scanlon plans (Frost et al., 1974) and the work simplification of Allan Mogensen. Safety and health committees usually involve local experts. A related topic is Quality of WorkLife (QWL).

Teams have many names (e.g., Productivity Circles, Effectiveness Teams, and Quality Teams). A popular form of these small groups is called **Quality Circles** (discussed in Section 3). Data General calls its groups PRIDE Circles (People Really Involved in Developing Excellence).

Teams can be considered **industrial democracy,** with many of the same benefits that come from democracy in the political arena. However, your desire for democracy may depend on your position. Many supervisors want to maintain their power; that is, they want to have special privileges. Power sharing with workers occurs mainly at the first-line supervision level; that is where there is the most resistance to industrial democracy.

William Brough of Washington Ergonomics gave a seminar for seven insurance companies (Hendrick, 1996). Six of the seven did a follow-up program emphasizing worker involvement. For the six, strain-type injuries dropped from 131 in the 6-month period before the seminar to 42 in the 6-month period following the seminar. Net savings were $1,300,000/yr. The one company that did not involve workers had 12 injuries in the prior 6-month period and 10, 16, and 25 in the three 6-month periods following the seminar.

2.4.1 *Team composition*   The best combination, from a factual information viewpoint and from a breaking-of-cultural barriers viewpoint, is a combination of technical experts and local experts. Rodgers

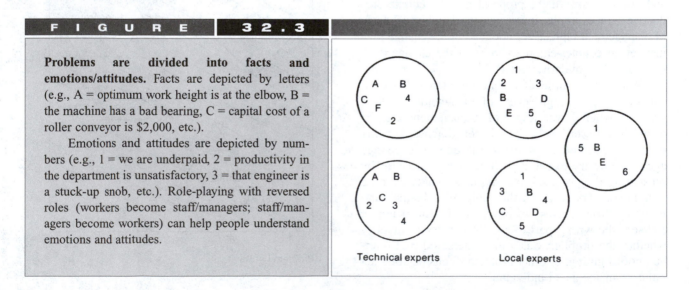

F I G U R E   3 2 . 3

Problems are divided into facts and emotions/attitudes. Facts are depicted by letters (e.g., A = optimum work height is at the elbow, B = the machine has a bad bearing, C = capital cost of a roller conveyor is $2,000, etc.).

Emotions and attitudes are depicted by numbers (e.g., 1 = we are underpaid, 2 = productivity in the department is unsatisfactory, 3 = that engineer is a stuck-up snob, etc.). Role-playing with reversed roles (workers become staff/managers; staff/managers become workers) can help people understand emotions and attitudes.

Technical experts   Local experts

(1992) recommends that the team consist of (1) people doing the job under consideration, (2) skilled-trades (maintenance) people, and (3) staff people such as process engineers, health/safety specialists, and first-line supervisors. The Design for Ergonomics teams at Ford have representatives from manufacturing (components, assembly), ergonomics, and engineering. In some situations, an outside technical expert becomes part of the team due to special knowledge, lack of time of the other technical experts, or lack of trust among the other participants. For more comments, see Section 3.2 of this chapter.

2.4.2 Team procedures See Table 32.2 for some tips. Successful decision making in a group requires (1) that all essential knowledge is within the group, (2) that this knowledge be available to be transmitted to the group members, (3) that this knowledge is transmitted, and (4) that the group members accept this knowledge. In practice, some knowledge is known to all people in the group but some knowledge is concentrated—perhaps only in one person, and that person may not even be in the group.

Thus, one strategy is to spread the knowledge among more of the group so that when decisions have to be made, the knowledge is more widely distributed. This should reduce transmission problems as well as acceptance problems. A common technique is training—especially on-the-job training for multi-skilling such as job rotation and job overlap. Another technique is the formal designation of experienced workers as "coaches"; one of their job responsibilities is to coach "rookies." Another approach is a formal policy of communication with crews on other shifts—especially for nonstandard situations such as "disturbances" in production and maintenance problems.

The situation being studied may occur in sister facilities of the same firm. The sister facility might be visited by team members to see how its decision makers approach the problem. In addition, if the team has a good solution, this "lesson learned" should be communicated to the sister facility.

T A B L E	3 2 . 2	
Key aspects of successful workplace teams.		

ASPECT	COMMENTS
1. Management commitment	▪ Leadership commitment and support is critical. This includes not only top management but also middle management and union leaders. ▪ Initial statements concerning the importance of worker participation are not enough; the statements must be followed by actions. ▪ Middle management personnel often feel threatened; they need support. Perhaps emphasize their mentor role.
2. Training	▪ Both management and worker members of teams will need training. Technical training would include items such as control charts and data analysis. Perhaps even more important, especially for the workers, is training on problem-solving skills and communication skills. ▪ Avoid lectures; use case studies and hands-on approaches.
3. Team composition	▪ Group size of 7–15 members works well. ▪ Should include workers as well as staff and management. Need to ensure that staff and management do not dominate or intimidate workers. Do this by restricting their number on the team and by instructing them. ▪ Whether to limit members to one part of the organization or to include supporting departments (e.g., maintenance, purchasing, inspection) depends on the situation, but some breadth is good.
4. Information sharing	▪ Teams will need access to information; management should not prevent access. ▪ Management has to be up-front about the potential consequences of team recommendations. Job security is a common concern. What are limits of capital expenditures?
5. Activities and motivation	▪ Have systematic procedures (e.g., bi-weekly meetings, minutes of meetings, assignment of meeting leader, agenda for meetings). ▪ Teams should set goals (major and minor); check progress toward goals. ▪ Management should give recognition and rewards to team.
6. Evaluation	▪ Evaluate team performance.

Source: From A. Cohen, "Worker Participation" (Chapter 10) in *Occupational Ergonomics*. Bhattacharya, A. and McGloughlin, J. (eds.). Copyright © 1996 by Marcel Dekker. Used by permission.

An advantage of participation is **reduction of uncertainty.** People naturally resist what they don't know. Communication within the group will reduce uncertainty, thereby reducing the resistance to change due to "fear of the unknown."

Another advantage of participation is the training of the workers in the various analysis techniques. This encourages continuous improvement by many people.

2.4.3 *Negotiation* Working with a diverse group of people with diverse backgrounds requires negotiation. Three negotiation advantages are: (1) negotiation takes time, thereby allowing people to change their concepts gradually, (2) clearly unacceptable designs are eliminated (these bad designs generally occur because the technical experts didn't understand the complete problem or the consequences of their proposal), and (3) negotiation improves the communication within the group.

Communication gives the technical experts better facts for the proposal as well as reducing unnecessary fears among the inside experts. It helps the technical experts understand the (usually sound) reasons given by inside experts when resisting the changes and permits the proposal to be modified to reduce the resistance. The value of a dissenting minority is not so much in the correctness of the minority position as it is in the thought process and attention necessary to refute the position. It may be that those opposing the change understand the situation better than those proposing the change. In particular, there often are differences in who pays the costs and who receives the benefits. There also may be a time gap between costs incurred and benefits received. While costs tend to occur quickly, benefits often are received over the long-run.

Participation by the local experts not only improves the distribution of facts but also reduces emotion–attitude problems (change imposed—change opposed). Being involved in the change process (as "partners in design," not as experimental subjects) allows people to have **ownership** of an idea; this makes them more willing to implement the idea because ownership reduces resistance to change. For example, Burlington Northern found local experts could be given a feeling of pride and accomplishment by painting worker-suggested ergonomic improvements (e.g., on handtools, lifting aids, workstations) a bright yellow.

Negotiations may take place in two stages. The first stage is within the group. The second stage is when the group negotiates with management.

3 QUALITY CIRCLES

3.1 Historical Background Quality Circles began in Japan in 1963, developing from the needs of Japanese industry and the characteristics of Japanese society and management.

The needs of Japanese industry concerned its long-range goals. Previously, Japan had competed on the basis of low labor costs. However, the Japanese wanted to improve their standard of living, and this required higher wages. In addition, there were millions of competitors in Asia willing to work for very low wages. The Japanese, therefore, decided to compete on the basis of quality and technology. To get that quality, they decided to get everyone to help, rather than just the elite group of engineers and managers—the idea being: for quality (of product), use quantity (of people).

Japanese society and management style aided this concept of mass participation in decision making. Japanese management also emphasizes gaining consensus by groups and setting a long-range goal.

The standard approach to job design in the developed societies since Frederick Taylor has been to have technical experts design the job and have the workers follow the instructions, a policy often called **Taylorism.** As pointed out in Chapter 2, it has been extraordinarily successful in improving productivity and the standard of living in many societies.

As Table 32.3 shows, education levels have been rising. Individuals with more education earn more. In 2000, workers age 30–44 had relative earnings of 65% if they had less than a high school degree, 100% with a high school degree, and 170% for a college degree.

The Japanese, however, have a highly educated workforce—even more educated than the United States workforce. Japanese industry decided that the elite groups of engineers and managers would still work on the major problems. However, the masses would work on the many minor problems. The emphasis would be on quality problems.

Training would be necessary to give ordinary blue-collar workers the ability to solve quality problems. This training would be at two levels: (1) specific technical techniques (how to plot a histogram, how to do a Pareto analysis), and (2) administrative skills (e.g., how to run a meeting, how to make a presentation). It also would be necessary to give the workers an

TABLE		32.3
Percent of population at age 25 that has graduated from high school or college.		

YEAR	HIGH SCHOOL	COLLEGE
1960	41	8
1970	52	11
1980	66	16
1990	78	21
2000	84	26

organizational mechanism through which to use the newly learned skills. The training materials and procedures and the organizational forms were developed. A massive program was implemented.

The result is that Japanese products have a reputation for quality. Almost all of Japan's 54,000,000 workers have some quality training. Approximately 8,000,000 have had technical courses in quality from the Union of Japanese Scientists and Engineers. Membership in Quality Circles rose explosively from 10,000 (in 1,000 Circles) in 1964 to 80,000 (in 10,000 Circles) in 1966 to 6,000,000 (in 600,000 Circles) in 1980; 6,000,000/54,000,000 was about 12% of the workforce in Quality Circles (Arai, 1979; Berger and Shores, 1986).

By the late 1970s the Quality Circle concept had spread to Korea, Taiwan, Brazil, Europe, and the United States. The technical group in the United States is the Association for Quality and Participation (AQP). In 1998, it had more than 7,000 firms as members. The AQP address is AQP, PO Box 2055, Milwaukee, WI 53201-2055 (phone: 1-800-733-3310, e-mail: aqp@aqp.org, website: www.aqp.org/).

3.2 Circle Design

Circles generally are coordinated by a supervisory committee (board of directors; steering committee). The committee is responsible for establishing program policies, procedures, objectives, and resources. This overview responsibility includes publicity, training programs, coordination with management, and the like. Generally, a diverse committee works best—that is, people from line management, engineering, purchasing, perhaps a union member, and others—because a large responsibility of the committee is to maintain acceptance of Quality Circles throughout the organization.

The steering committee normally delegates its detailed supervision of Circles to a **facilitator.** The facilitator's job is to train the Circle members, set up Circles, perhaps run their meetings for the first few times, and, in general, facilitate their operation.

Circles range from 3 to 25 members, but a typical size is 10. Membership is voluntary. Membership is primarily blue-collar workers.

First of all, the Circle should have approximately five core operators from a specific group; these members should "touch the product." Next, the Circle should consider the problems of the horizontal and vertical organizational barriers.

The **horizontal barrier** is the barrier between hourly and salaried workers—between blue-collar and white-collar workers. A Circle should have one or two white-collar workers. A common choice is the supervisor. This not only permits the Circle to break the horizontal barrier but also to allay the suspicions and mistrust supervisors might have if they are excluded from the group. In addition to bridging the horizontal barrier, another technique is to reduce it. For example, at a Cummings Engine plant in Columbus, Indiana, both production workers and managers wear company-issue khaki pants and dress shirts with no neckties.

The **vertical barrier** is the barrier between groups (Dept. A versus Dept. B, operators versus inspectors, operators versus maintenance, operators versus scheduling, and so on). The Circle should have members from these support groups. Thus, the Circle should have about five core blue-collar workers and five support workers (two white-collar, one being the supervisor).

Circles meet from once/week to once/month. The meeting can be either on company time or after work. In general, the members do not receive any additional pay for their work or any financial reward for cost savings. However, there is a heavy emphasis on praise, publicity, and public thanks.

For example, Ford Motor has a policy by which it picks the best projects from its Quality Circles. Ford then flies the team members to Detroit for several days, tours them around various plants, and has them make their presentations to the chairman of the board in a fancy conference room. They all receive T-shirts saying, "I made a presentation to the chairman of the board." They leave Detroit "feeling 10 feet tall."

Specific projects usually are selected by a Circle, with management and the steering committee having veto power. Projects primarily concern quality, although Eklund (1997) reported that several studies show that about 1/3 of the suggested improvements are ergonomics-related. In general, Quality Circles should stay away from cost-reduction projects, especially those involving reducing labor. That type of project should remain with the technical staff and management. Circles instead should focus on the "insignificant many" problems and let the staff and management work on the "vital few."

Project meetings have to be structured because most Circle members are not familiar with running a meeting. Some guidelines are:

- The meeting should be held at a standard time and place (say, every other Thursday at 4:00 in room 2).

- Someone has to be the secretary; someone has to run the meeting.

- Every member should receive a written agenda 24 h before the meeting.

- At the meeting, a "to do" list is developed with identification of specific tasks, dates, and people. (For example, Mary is to sketch the assembly workstation, including dimensions, by the next meeting.)

- A printed copy of the "to do" list is distributed within 24 h after a meeting.

3.3 Example Circle Project   The following example shows how Ms. F. Hashimoto's Quality Circle team at Matsushita Electric analyzed switches used for the volume control on stereos (Konz, 1979).

Step one was to select the project. Among the defects from the assembly line, the largest percentage was attributed to the volume switch. After consultation with management, the Circle decided to study switch defects.

Step two was to analyze present conditions. Figure 32.4 shows the Circle's **Pareto diagram** for defects over a 3-month period. The Y axis is percent defective. The X axis is a series of bars, arranged in descending magnitude, of various causes. They shaded the major cause for emphasis. Then they plotted cumulative defects (line with dots). Rotation caused 70% of the defects, so switch rotation was chosen as the way to reduce switch defects.

Figure 32.5 shows an analysis of the types of rotation defects. 87% were uneven rotation. Then the Circle used the **fish diagram** (cause–effect diagram) given in Figure 32.6 to organize the problem and improve communication. With Figure 32.6 as a guide, they collected defect data from the in-process inspectors, sorted it by cause, and developed Figure 32.7.

The third step was to establish goals. At their next Circle meeting they established three goals:

1. Reduce rotation defect rate from 1.3% (as of January) to 0.5% by December, while introducing a more stable control system.

2. Develop an overall Circle implementation plan (Figure 32.8).

3. Selectively attack the problems for improvement using the Pareto chart order.

The fourth step was to promote control activities. One activity was an *np* chart (Figure 32.9). For their production, a sample ($n = 400$) taken every hour was

---

F I G U R E   3 2 . 5

Another Pareto analysis, analyzing rotation defects. The study showed that 87% of the problems were a result of uneven rotation.

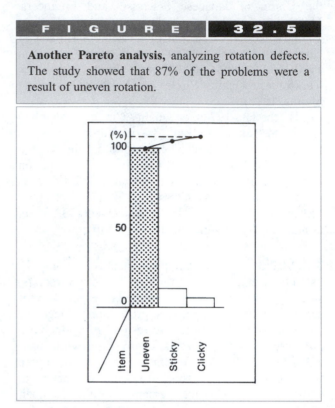

F I G U R E   3 2 . 4

Pareto analysis. Data over 3 months showed that switch rotation accounted for 70% of the defects. Thus, it was selected for further analysis.

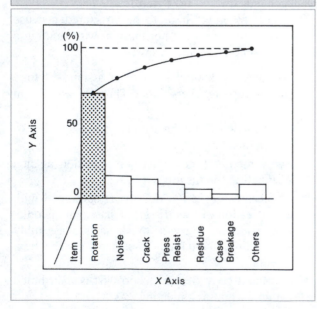

F I G U R E   3 2 . 6

Fish diagram (cause–effect diagram) of uneven switch rotation errors. The fish head is the goal, major bones are the major categories of the production process, and minor bones are the subdivisions of the major categories.

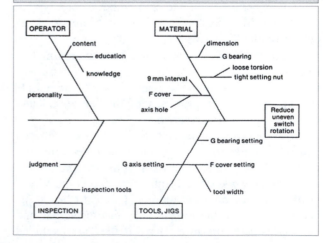

F I G U R E   3 2 . 7

Using the fish diagram in consultation with the in-process inspectors, the Circle developed a new Pareto diagram of causes of uneven rotation.

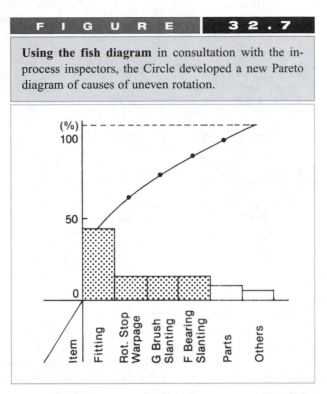

F I G U R E   3 2 . 9

An *np* chart identified when defects occurred. The first control limits describe the original process. The second set of limits describes the results after the second and third Circle meetings. The third set describes results after the fourth, fifth, and sixth meetings, and the fourth set after the seventh meeting.

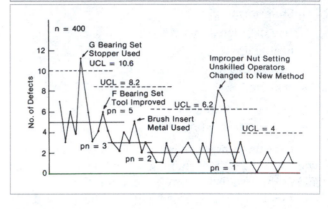

F I G U R E   3 2 . 8

Goals and a schedule were set by the Circle at their next meeting.

	O J F M A M J J A S O N D
1. Analysis of Present Conditions	△─○
2. Dev. and Imple. of Improvements	
• Improper Fitting	△─○─□
• F Rot. Stop Warpage	△─○─□
• G Brush Slanting	△─○─□
• F Bearing Slanting	△─○─□
• Parts	△─○─□
• Others	△─○─□
3. Introduction of More Stable Control System	△─○─□
	△─────○─□───□

appropriate. When an out-of-control condition developed (point beyond control limits), the Circle had a meeting. Depending upon the nature of the problem, members determined either the cause of the problem or a measure to prevent recurrence of the problem. To control common deficiencies in previous operations, checklists were developed for critical control points. The operators used these checklists to check their

own work. After improved procedures were put into practice and found workable, the standard procedure was revised to ensure continued use of the new method. Due to the smaller number of defects, the sample size was changed from 400 to 1,600.

As a result of these activities, by the end of a year the defect rate was reduced from 1.3% to 0.3% for an annual savings of 400,000 yen (about $1,000 at the exchange rate in 1965). In her paper, Ms. Hashimoto concluded that although the Circle had achieved its goal, it had not completely eliminated the problems. The members were determined to continue improvement to achieve a still better result. In addition, she commented that, as an inexperienced Circle leader, she had not worked enough with people from other departments.

A number of comments can be made about the example project. First, this was a small project with a $1,000 annual savings. Yet, a considerable amount of work was necessary to achieve the savings. In examining many examples of Japanese Quality Circles, I have not seen return on investment reported. Typically, the number reported is annual savings or percent defects. This implies that the engineering cost (that is, the cost of the time to make the analysis) and capital cost of making the change are not considered worth reporting. However, this analysis cost may be quite low, as analysis is done during normal work time; meeting time probably is charged to training or general quality costs. Thus, a quality improvement was made that many United States firms, with a heavy emphasis on cost accounting, would not undertake.

Second, the Japanese blue-collar Circle members used techniques in 1965 that, by U. S. standards in 2004, are sophisticated. Pareto diagrams, fish diagrams, and *np* control charts are not even known to many American engineers—much less used. The key here is management's emphasis on training Circle members in the use of these techniques and encouraging their use. In discussing the need for training for Circles in the United States, Gryna (1981) gave the following training modules:

- introduction to Quality Circles
- brainstorming
- fish diagrams
- histograms
- checklists and data recording
- case study
- how to make graphs
- how to make a presentation

In Cummins' Columbus, Indiana, plant, new workers get 250 h of training, including 72 h of math and 36 h of statistical process control. (Note that this requires considerable selectivity in who is hired.) In addition, there is a need to train Circle leaders in interpersonal skills.

Third, quality problems were considered to be technical problems, not motivational problems. The improvements implemented were modified handtools, modified assembly procedures, modified operator training, and operators' use of checklists.

Fourth, many quality problems are communication problems. Fukuda (1978, 1981) summarized the results of 87 groups at Sumitomo (see Table 32.4). Figure 32.10 is a modified version of one of his figures showing that information must be known to both the operator and the technical staff to be practiced. Knowledge alone is not sufficient; note also that both groups must want to apply the knowledge.

FIGURE 32.10

Many problems are communication problems. Area C, for example, shows that if information is known to the technical–managerial staff but not to the operator, the technique is not practiced.

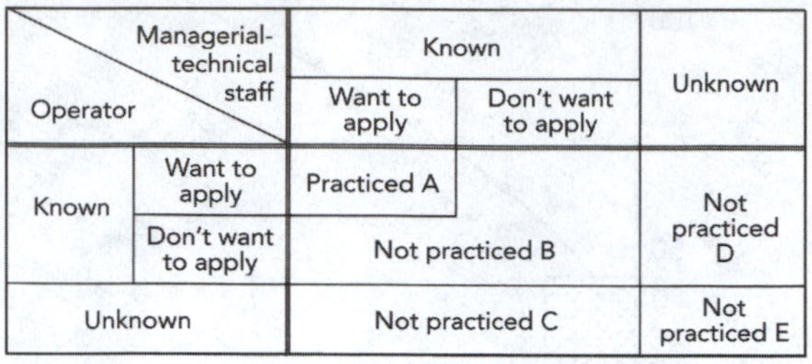

Fukuda summarized the figure in the saying, **"defense before offense."** In defense, try to move from categories B, C, and D to category A. Defense examples are to put warnings and suggestions into easily readable visible form, to clearly define standard operations, and to develop tools enabling less effort yet more skill to be put forth. Only when you are "farming as well as you know how" do you take the offense and make changes in equipment and manufacturing conditions.

One way to emphasize communication is to post the fish diagrams on the wall next to the machines and invite everyone to make comments and suggestions. You will have many detectives, rather than just one person, looking for clues. The goal is to get all workers to think beyond what they are told to do. The Circle then takes the best of these ideas for further investigation.

TABLE 32.4

Types of countermeasures found effective by Quality Circles at Sumitomo (Fukuda, 1978, 1981).

| COUNTERMEASURE TYPE | TYPE OF RESULT (%) | | | |
| | Limited | | Considerable | |
	Slow	Quick	Slow	Quick
Warnings and suggestions put into easily readable visual form—defensive	41	25	57	68
Clearly defining standard operations—defensive	24	35	24	53
Developing tools enabling less effort, yet more skill, to be put forth—defensive	12	5	37	32
Making improvement in equipment—offensive	5	5	30	12
Making changes in manufacturing conditions—offensive	0	5	20	5

Quick = within 3 months	Limited = Reduction of defects of less than 40%
Slow = over 3 months	Considerable = Over 40%

For investigation, you can use a **passive approach** (reactive approach) and a control chart such as that in Figure 32.9. When something on the chart changes, try to go back and find out what changed in the process. An alternative is to use an **active approach** (proactive approach) and use EVOP (see Chapter 9). In the active approach, variables are selected for investigation and the chart shows the result of the selected change. The active approach is preferable since it produces more knowledge in a shorter time with less effort. Remember, however, as was pointed out in the EVOP discussion in Chapter 9, to make evolutionary changes rather than revolutionary changes.

4 PROPOSING CHANGE

To accomplish change, the project has to be managed. Then a proposal has to be made to decision makers.

4.1 Project Management Five points will be emphasized (Hanna and Konz, 2004).

4.1.1 *Scope defined* The **project scope** should be agreed upon ahead of time: Who will do what by when? "Who" includes members of the project team, company management, outside experts (e.g., subcontractors and vendors), and users. Who will help you for how many h/week? What resources (budget) will be available? Who will evaluate the project and how? What is the "work product" (e.g., report, computer analysis)? A tentative schedule for the various events (milestones) helps focus the problem. It is important that the project scope be put in writing. If your supervisor will not put the scope in writing, you should do it and submit it for approval. It is important to minimize potential misunderstandings as soon as possible.

4.1.2 *Client's servant* Being your **client's servant** is an attitude. You are trying to help a client, a customer. You are not a master, giving commands. You are trying to satisfy client needs; the client is not trying to satisfy you.

4.1.3 *Frequent consultation* **Frequent consultation** not only provides you with more facts but also improves the attitudes and emotions of clients toward you. Consult with the user, not just with staff. Information can be obtained from face-to-face consultation and tours (take notes) and from videotapes of existing operations. For videotapes of existing operations, be sure to take several minutes of tape with multiple views. Views of multiple operators are good because operators often use considerably different micromotions. It also may be possible to view similar operations in other facilities. Inspection of records

tends to produce relatively little information, because recorded data generally are not complete or in convenient form. Written requests for information are fairly useless. No one wants to fill out forms, and if the forms are returned, you get "bare bones" answers.

The decision makers should be consulted at multiple approval points, not just at the end of the project. Consultation allows them to change their mind on various points early (rather than after you have done irrelevant work) and to change priorities. Early discussion of alternatives also tends to bring out potential problems that you may not have considered.

Discuss alternatives with users in short (30s) briefings. Prototypes and mock-ups aid communication. Putting information (such as primary owner, ergonomics contact, project schedule, and current status) on a website permits all stakeholders and customers to have current information even if they are at a remote location.

4.1.4 *Use of experts* Both line and staff people consider themselves experts in their jobs. Whether they are expert is not as important as their own concept of themselves as expert. You want them on your side, not against you.

Consult these experts during the project. For example, cost-accounting departments consider themselves expert in cost justifications. Even if you are able to do a cost justification by yourself, it is better to have the cost accountants go over your project. You want to go into the final decision stages with them on your side, not with their being unfamiliar with the project or, even worse, opposing you.

Don't forget indirect users (e.g., maintenance, inspection, production control). Although the official decision will be made at a formal meeting, the real decisions may be made beforehand with these informal contacts.

4.1.5 *Give the buyer a choice* All decision makers want to make decisions. They do not like to be confronted with no alternatives and just rubber-stamp something. The choices can be "yes" or "no" for the entire project, for pieces of the project, for the implementation schedule, and so forth, but if you make the alternative all or nothing, it may be nothing.

Making a tradeoff among multiple criteria may be easier for the decision makers if you present a summary such as Table 9.7. The table allows criteria with different dimensions (cost, quality, ease of supervision) to be totaled for various alternatives. Giving the best solution a value of 100% improves ease of comparison. Consult the decision makers ahead of time on how much weight each criterion has.

4.2 Written Proposal Eventually the project will come to the official decision-making stage. A formal written proposal is needed. The goal of the proposal is acceptance and implementation of the proposal recommendation. Thus, the proposal has to convey convincing information. The information itself is not sufficient. The proposal must convince the decision makers to accept the recommendation, and their decision will convert a recommendation into action, a deed.

Before writing the report, you need a plan—an outline. The outline not only aids the reader in following your logic but the sections also allow you to divide your writing into sections rather than writing the entire project at one time. You need to answer the following: What is the purpose of the report? Who will read it? What do they not know that the report will tell them?

Some decision makers tend to avoid risk; others emphasize economic gain. You need to know your decision maker. Generally, decision makers will be interested primarily in the economic aspects rather than the technical aspects of the proposal. Since they probably will accept the proposal as technically sound, avoid technical overkill. Remember that the decision maker will be reviewing many proposals. Not all will be accepted. Why should yours be?

Decision makers are busy. Thus, the report should present the proposal concisely. It also may present the proposal in depth, but the decision makers are unlikely to go through the detail. (They hired you to do the detail work!) They will want the detail to be available for their inspection, if they choose to inspect it. This leads to the concept of a short report, with the detail in appendices.

The following is a good general format with a logical structure obvious to both the reader and the writer: On the cover sheet, put the project title, the date, your name, and the word RECOMMENDATION, followed by 50–100 words giving the recommendations. At the top of the second page, write the word PROBLEM, followed by a 10- to 50-word statement of the problem. Next, write ANALYSIS, followed by the analysis. This section may take 3 to 10 pages. Reduce the material by putting the detail in appendices. The appendices should be preceded by a table of appendices, and each appendix should be identified by a letter. Pages should be numbered in each appendix (for example, B14 identifies page 14 in Appendix B). Finally, write CONCLUSIONS and give them briefly. Some decision makers also like an EXECUTIVE SUMMARY that summarizes the entire project in 200–400 words.

Determine the preferred writing style, and use it. Some people want an informal, active-voice style, such as, "We measured background noise levels" or even, "I measured background noise levels." Others want a formal, passive style such as "Background noise levels were measured."

Proposals should include the following economic information: annual cost of the present and proposed methods, capital cost of the proposed method (such as new equipment, installation costs, training costs), estimated project life, and expected savings. On simple proposals, an annual return on investment is sufficient, but expensive, long-range projects often require a cash flow analysis.

State your assumptions specifically (e. g., product life = 3 more years at 8,000 units/yr, no change in product design, the change will not affect sales of spare parts, quality is not affected). Good proposals also have a schedule of "milestones" (1 May: proposal accepted; 15 May: change schedule OK by facility manager; 15 June: all machines moved; 20 June: production back to normal).

Proposals should go through several drafts. Be sure to schedule enough time for multiple drafts. Consider handwritten material as notes rather than a draft; too many errors of spelling, composition, and structure lurk in handwritten material to dignify it with the word "draft." Plan to have the report redone at least twice for a small project and more for an important project.

The report must not have any spelling, grammatical, or typographical errors if it is to have a reasonable chance of being accepted. Spellcheck programs *must* be used, even though they won't catch all errors. Many word processing programs now have grammar subroutines that check the use of active versus passive voice, agreement of subject and verb, trite sayings, and redundant words; they also may suggest alternative adjectives and so forth. Unless you are a skilled writer, you should use a grammar program routinely—whether you take the program's advice or not.

Chapter 18 has eight guidelines for good table design and discusses features of good and poor graphs.

The decision makers will generally be poorly prepared to evaluate the technical merits of your proposal. After all, you are the expert and they are decision makers. However, they can judge typing, spelling, and grammar; if these are poor, they will consider the technical material to be poor also.

4.3 Oral Presentation The meeting or presentation audience should include those who can contribute, those who can make decisions, those with divergent views, and those who will carry out the decisions.

You will enhance your reputation if your presentation always has a clearly defined technical objective, always starts on time, always ends on time, and always reaches a conclusion.

You will appear more dynamic if you move around during the presentation, less dynamic if you stand in one place, and least dynamic if you sit. You also tend to project your voice better if you stand rather than sit. The presentation should focus on the benefit to the firm, not how clever you are.

An experienced consultant advises, "Spend only about one-third of your allocated time on your formal presentation. The remaining two-thirds should be for comments and discussion. During this critical time, use your ears, not your mouth. If silence develops, don't talk; make the audience talk."

Oral presentations usually are accompanied by visual aids. Speakers sometimes pay more attention to their clothes than their visual aids, but the audience will remember the visual aids, not the clothes.

Consider the medium and the message.

4.3.1 *Medium* Consider overheads, slides/Power-Point presentations, video, flip charts, and the presentation site. See Table 32.5 as well as Chapter 18.

Overheads. Some comments are:

- Consider simple use of color to show organization (e.g., red for disadvantages, green for advantages; blue for body of talk, black for recommendations).

- Mount frame borders on transparencies. They minimize fumbling by you and can also serve as a notecard—to the audience you appear to be speaking without notes.

- Face the audience, not the screen. If you stand on the left of the projector, point to the transparency with your right hand; if you stand on the right of the projector, point with your left hand. Point with a pointer or pen, not your finger. See Table 32.5. With a computer-projected slide or 35 mm slide, a laser pointer is best as it gives the speaker the ability to walk around.

Slides/PowerPoint presentations. Some comments are:

- Use light lettering on a dark background.

- Use color (simple, not excessive).

- Note slides can be 3 high × 2 wide (portrait) or 2 high × 3 wide (landscape). Design text in either a 3/2 or 2/3 format to use the slide area.

T A B L E	3 2 . 5	

Effective overhead transparency and slide presentations. An important characteristic of slides and transparencies is that they force you to organize your presentation.

OVERHEADS

- Stay within $7\frac{1}{2} \times 9\frac{1}{2}$ format, since projector platen is not $8\frac{1}{2} \times 11$.
- Use color to "outline" the talk as well as for figures and overlays.
- Organize your presentation so it has a beginning, middle, and end. Tell what you will tell them, tell them, tell them what you told them.
- Use high-contrast originals; be sure the transparency is easily readable from the farthest viewer position; check by projection, not hand-held viewing.
- For graphs, use grids or graph paper under paper originals to get proper scales and relationships.
- Keep projector on your left if you point with your left hand, on your right if you point with your right. Point to the transparency with a pointer or pen, not your finger. Face the audience, not the screen.
- Have material prewritten on the film. Handwriting speed is about .4 words/s, speaking is 2 to 4 words/s, and reading is 3 to 9 words/s.
- Mount frame borders on transparencies to serve as a notecard—to the audience you appear to be speaking without notes.

SLIDES

- Don't put too much onto one slide. Three guidelines are: 1 slide/min of presentation, 20 words maximum per slide (6–7 words/line; 5 lines; 3 vertical columns), and maximum of 9 double-spaced lines high and 54 elite (45 pica) characters wide.
- Use color, not black and white.
- Use only one font in a series of slides. Get text variety through color, boldface, and type size.
- Keep information/slide to one idea; no more than three curves/graph.
- Make material *easily* readable from the farthest viewing position. Graphs and tables that are satisfactory in print have to be simplified and lines emphasized for slides. Leave space—at least the height of a capital letter—between lines of text.
- Use duplicate slides rather than backing up during a presentation.
- Practice your talk. Do it *early* so you can make changes in the slides.

- Slides or an electronic presentation are the high-quality approach. Physical slides are high cost and have long lead times (and so are difficult to change quickly). Computer programs now allow you to develop slides; the programs permit varied text and backgrounds and slides can be changed easily.

- Slides can be presented through computers. This requires special equipment (both projection and screen) and can result in low-resolution images. However, special effects such as sound, fades, and blends can be used. In addition, changes in slides are relatively easy, both before the presentation (off-line) and during the presentation (on-line). An example of on-line use is to key the exact wording of a motion for voting and project it onto the screen; this is especially helpful for people whose first language is not English (as they can follow written English better than oral English).

Video. Unless professionally made, use videos sparingly because audiences will compare them with other, more professional videos and television they have seen. Video is effective for showing existing operations. If videotaping a "talking head," use a "mural" background, not a blank wall. If the video has a voice, dub the voice after filming rather than when filming. When presenting, use a remote control.

Flipcharts. Advantages of flipcharts are that they can be used in any room (e.g., a restaurant meeting room), multiple flipcharts can be used in the same room (say, when a larger group breaks up into focus groups), each sheet can be a "frame" (helps organize the material), and the large pad size allows 50 or more words/"frame."

Presentation site. Many presentation rooms have poor (excessive) lighting, either from windows or from ceiling lighting controlled with only one switch. Photographs on slides as well as text and graphics with poor contrast can be washed out or not visible at all. Try to turn off the lighting in the front 2/3 of room and dim the light in the rear 1/3.

Another choice is the number of screens. Although one screen is the easiest, multiple screens permit multiple images simultaneously instead of sequentially; this reduces mental effort by the audience. One image might show the talk outline while the other shows detailed information; one image might be graphic while the other is text; by alternating left and right for the new image, the viewer can always view the previous image as well as the present image.

A back-projection screen reduces noise in the presentation room.

See the Forms section of the ERGO CD for an oral-presentation checksheet.

4.3.2 The message   Consider organization, tables versus graphs versus figures, and legibility.

Organization. Some comments include:

- Organize your presentation so the audience can see its structure. It should have a beginning, a middle, and an end. (Tell them what you will tell them, tell them, tell them what you told them.)

- Note that presentation is not equal to communication. Long-term retention = p_1 (Short-term retention) $\times$ p_2 (Heard, Read) $\times$ p_3 (Presented) where p_1, p_2, p_3 = proportions less than 1. The important point here is to try to increase what the audience members retain. Just because you present information does not mean it is retained! Also the audience can read (and understand) better than it can listen. See Box 32.1.

- Don't put too much on a slide/transparency. Three guidelines:
  1. At least one slide per minute of presentation. This does not include the title slide. Using 2/min is high for text (but it could be higher if the slide is built item by item); pictorial scenes can have 4 or 5/min.
  2. 20 words maximum per slide (6–7 words/line, 5 lines, 3 vertical columns)
  3. Maximum height of 9 double-spaced lines and maximum width of 54 elite (45 pica) characters

- Use visual aids to permit covering more material in a time period. (Handwriting speed is about .4 words/s, speaking is 2 to 4 words/s, and reading is 3 to 9 words/s.) You need not speak every word that is on a slide.

- Practice your talk. Do it early so you can change items. Ideally, your practice would be in the room where you will present so you can check lighting, power cord lengths, light-switch locations, whether your slides are visible in the rear of the room, and the like. For important presentations, rehearse not only the talk but also the question and answer period (as politicians do before appearing at a news conference). (If you don't know the answer to a question, don't "wing it"— say, "I don't know but I'll find out.")

- Have someone else change slides and transparencies. This permits you to move around and appear more dynamic.

- After the presentation, you may wish to summarize the consensus or decision on a transparency, a flipchart, or a chalkboard. Anyone who disagrees with your written interpretation can give immediate feedback.

Tables versus graphs versus figures. Some comments are:

BOX | **32.1** | *Communication Skills* | (Adapted from Spaeth, 1997)

TV news commentators have shaped our expectations on how to present information. Some tips:

■ *Your job is to tell a story.* Your job is not to transmit a list of facts. A good story has a clear point of view. It has a beginning and an end, interesting characters, a plot, good dialogue, humor, and illustration. To tell a story well, rehearse.

■ *Eye contact is critical.* Good eye contact is deliberate and slow-paced; look at a person long enough for the person to realize he or she is being addressed. Look at each person in the audience to create a "one-on-one bonding."

■ *Show you are listening.* When listening, animate your face to show your interest. Japanese constantly say "Hai" when listening to someone, to show they are paying attention; you can nod and say, "Okay, yes, I see."

■ *Use a variety of visual elements to make your presentation more interesting.* A TV reporter reporting on price of cough medicine would use props (bottle of cough medicine), graphics (label and circling parts that changed), and testimony (video of customer complaining). Try to have at least two of the three (props, graphics, testimony).

■ *Make personal contact.* Move out from the podium and interact with the audience. In larger groups, this may require a wireless microphone.

■ *Appear spontaneous.* Your oral presentation is for the ear, not the eye; it will have pauses, half-sentences, repetitions, asides, and self-deprecating lines. Your printed speech will be quite different.

■ Tables give precise numbers for comparison; make the comparison easy.

■ Graphs show relationships.

1. Have simple scales on the axes; use a "break" in the scale if the scale doesn't begin at zero.

2. Label axes in a horizontal fashion to improve readability.

3. Use line graphs to show continuous-scale data, trend lines, or data versus time.

   ■ If data points are plotted, make them obvious; use only a few simple shapes for coding.

   ■ Indicate variability of the data behind the line (e.g., by indicating standard error).

   ■ When coding lines, use segmentation (dots versus dashes), line color (red versus black), and line thickness (thick versus thin). Use redundant coding.

   ■ Use bar graphs when the X axis is discrete, not continuous.

   ■ Use pie charts to represent portions of a whole.

   ■ For graphs, use overlays for multiple-line figures to build up the idea. Use light grids to show proper scales.

   ■ Figures (people, buildings, equipment) add interest to a talk. Consider a TV news program without any figures!

Legibility. Some comments are:

■ Do not use handwriting.

■ Have good contrast between the text and the background. Use color contrast (e.g., dark blue letters on a white background) and shape contrast (use a plain background, not a patterned background that camouflages the letter shapes). Avoid red and yellow.

■ Make characters large enough to be read easily from the rear of the room; check by projection, not hand-held viewing.

1. Make the figure type large enough
   ■ 20 to 26 points for slides
   ■ 22 (minimum) to 29 (preferred) points for transparencies

2. Make figure large on screen
   ■ Adjust knobs on the machine
   ■ Move the projector farther from the screen

■ Use double-spacing of text.

■ Use key words or bulleted statements, not complete sentences.

■ Center information on the visual aid; leave ample margins.

■ Simplify graphs and tables from printed media, and emphasize lines when projected.

Review Questions

1. Give the formula relating quality, acceptance, and amount of improvement.
2. Discuss the statement "Where you stand depends upon where you sit."
3. Briefly describe a situation with resistance to change. Sketch a force field analysis of the situation and discuss strategies to improve acceptance.
4. Give some examples of people who are considered to be local experts and technical experts.
5. Contrast the concepts of Taylorism and Quality Circles, relating them to education of the workforce.
6. Briefly discuss the five points of project management.
7. Give a sentence written in informal active voice. Give the same information written in formal passive voice.
8. When using a transparency projector, should you face the audience or the screen? Which hand should you use when pointing to the material on the projector?
9. In an oral technical presentation, about how much time should each transparency or slide be allotted?
10. List the four sections into which a written technical report should be divided.

References

Arai, J. Japanese productivity: What's behind it? *Modern Machine Shop,* Vol. 52, No. 4, 117–25, 1979.

Berger, R. and Shores, D. (eds.). *Quality Circles: Selected Readings.* New York: Marcel Dekker, 1986.

Chaney, F. Employee participation in manufacturing job design. *Human Factors,* Vol. 11, No. 12, 101–106, 1969.

Coch, L. and French, J. Overcoming resistance to change. *Human Relations,* Vol. 1, No. 4, 512–32, 1948.

Cohen, A. Worker participation. Chapter 10 in *Occupational Ergonomics,* Bhattacharya, A. and McGloughlin, J. (eds.). New York: Marcel Dekker, 1996.

Eklund, J. Ergonomics, quality and continuous improvement—conceptual and empirical relationships in an industrial context. *Ergonomics,* Vol. 40, No. 10, 982–1001, 1997.

Frost, C., Wakely, J., and Ruh, R. *The Scanlon Plan for Organizational Development.* East Lansing: Michigan State University Press, 1974.

Fukuda, R. The reduction of quality defects by the application of a cause and effect diagram with the addition of cards. *International J. of Production Research,* Vol. 16, No. 6, 305–19, 1978.

Fukuda, R. Introduction to the CEDAC. *Quality Progress,* Vol. 14, No. 11, 14–19, 1981.

Gryna, F. *Quality Circles.* New York: American Management Association, 1981.

Hanna, S. and Konz, S. *Facility Design: Manufacturing Engineering,* 3rd ed. Scottsdale, AZ: Holcomb Hathaway, 2004.

Hendrick, H. Good ergonomics is good economics. *Proceedings of the Human Factors and Ergonomics Society,* Santa Monica: HFES, 1–10, 1996.

Konz, S. Quality Circles: An annotated bibliography. *Quality Progress,* Vol. 13, No. 4, 30–35, 1979.

Leisman, F. An engineer-in-charge of manufacturing development, General Motors Corp.; personal communication, June 2, 1977.

Munson, F. and Hancock, W. Problems of implementing change in two hospital settings. *American Institute of Industrial Engineers Transactions,* Vol. 1, No. 4–12, 166-76, 1969.

Rodgers, S. A functional job analysis technique. *Occupational Medicine: State of the Art Reviews,* Vol. 7, No. 4, Oct.–Nov., Philadelphia: Hanley and Belfus. 679–711, 1992.

Spaeth, M. What you can learn from Brokaw & Co. *Wall Street Journal,* Jan. 6, 1997.

Thurman, J., Louzine, A., and Kogi, K. *Higher Productivity and a Better Place to Work.* Geneva, Switzerland: International Labour Organization, 1988.

Websites

Association for Quality and Participation, www.aqp.org

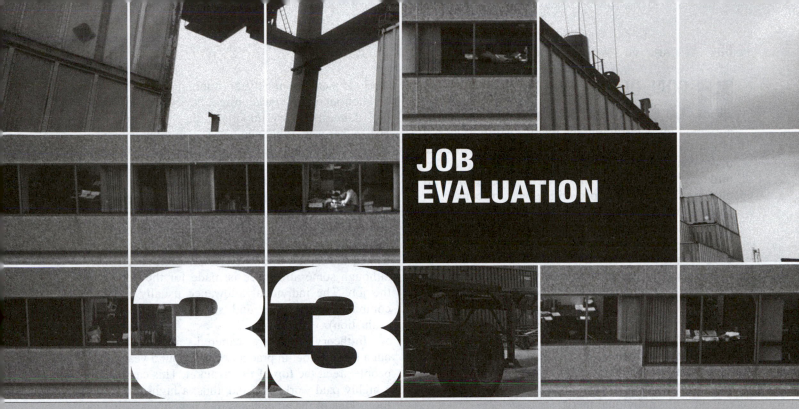

JOB EVALUATION

Overview

Job evaluation determines the relative worth of jobs. It is an analytical, consensus-building approach, not a procedure based on science. The first step is the job description. Then the jobs are arranged in sequence and a wage value is assigned. Labor grades simplify administration and permit paying for individual merit as well as the value of the job.

JOB EVALUATION

1 Goal of Job Evaluation

2 Job Description

3 Arranging Jobs in Order

Key Concepts

differential pay

effort factors

entry level

job condition factors

job descriptions

labor grades

pay for knowledge

responsibility factors

skill factors

top of the bracket

two-tier

work to rule

GOAL OF JOB EVALUATION

1.1 Comparable Worth   Job evaluation is a method for determining the relative worth of jobs. It is concerned with providing hard data on which to make conclusions about the rate for the job. The "formula for fairness" offers system and stability if planned for and developed on the basis of consensus, cooperation, and concord. It is a rational consideration of the more important differences among the inputs of human work. The crux of the problem of different pay for different people—**differential pay**—is assessing and agreeing on the fairness of differential pay—the problems of equity and acceptability. The systems are not perfect. At root they are judgments, a thread in a total fabric, a skeleton framework for a system of equitable payment.

There are three goals: (1) make wages for jobs consistent within the organization, (2) make job wages comparable to job wages paid by competitors, (3) allow for individual merit.

For more information, see Hannon et al. (2001).

1.2 Labor Grades   Wages should consider both the worth of the job and worth of the individual. See Figure 33.1. After determining the worth of the job (see Section 3 of this chapter), jobs similar in worth are grouped together into **labor grades.** For administrative purposes, all jobs in a labor grade are considered equal for pay purposes. The horizontal dimension of the labor grade considers job worth; the vertical dimension considers individual merit.

One important decision to be made is the relative importance of job worth compared to individual merit. If merit has relatively little importance, the top and bottom of the bracket might be 5% from the middle; if merit is very important, the limits might be 50% either way. What number do you think is best?

Another design decision is the slope and shape of the curve connecting the labor grade means. How steep should the slope be? Should the shape be a straight line or a curve?

Another challenge is how to determine individual merit. In many firms it is seniority, or time-in-grade. In Japan, age often is the determining factor. In the United States, however, the job is the primary factor, although some allowance is made for the holder of the job. The individual allowance usually is some combination of merit and seniority (performance evaluation).

In theory people are scattered vertically throughout a labor grade; in practice, after about 5 years most people are at the **top of the bracket.** This can lead to a highly paid workforce and, thus, a high-cost workforce. One of the advantages of a new plant is that its average labor costs are quite a bit lower because many people are at the bottom of the bracket instead of the top. In an effort to reduce this problem, some firms have instituted **two-tier** plans. In one form of the two-tier system, the top of the bracket is lower for new hires, called **entry level,** than for existing employees. For example, the top of the bracket for new hires is $15/h while it is $18/h for existing employees.

In another form, the existing wage structure is maintained, but it takes longer for the new hire to reach the top. For example, present employees may have been able to make $18/h after 3 to 5 years, but for new employees it will take 10 to 15 years.

FIGURE   33.1

Labor grades (the boxes) summarize the equation of wage compared to worth. All points (jobs) within a box are considered of equal worth for administrative purposes. The vertical dimension of the box permits adjustment for different individual contributions to the same job; it should be greater for more complex jobs. The boxes generally have a vertical overlap so a person at the bottom of the bracket in a higher grade may earn as much as a top-of-the-bracket person in a lower grade. Both the overlap and the vertical spread from the mean wage for the grade should increase with complexity so individual jobs can be modified with minimal effect on an incumbent's pay and so there is more scope for merit rating.

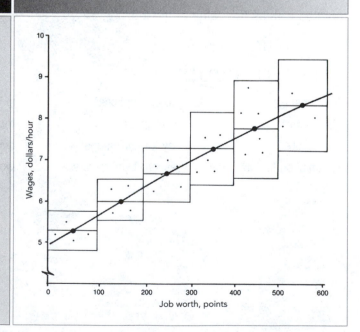

Under both forms of two-tier plans, the new hires feel like second-class employees. Two-tier plans have been implemented in only a few firms.

2 JOB DESCRIPTION

Job evaluation has four steps: (1) describe the class of job (e.g., office assistant), (2) specify the minimal hiring requirements, (3) arrange the jobs in order of worth, and (4) describe a specific job at a specific location—a "position description" (e. g., office assistant for electrical engineering). See Figure 33.2.

2.1 Describe the Job Class Describing the job class has two substeps: (1) securing the factual information, and (2) writing the information in standardized format. The information to obtain includes:

- duties and the percent of time devoted to each
- responsibilities
- knowledge and skills needed
- performance standards to be met
- what is used
- working conditions, including hazards

F I G U R E   3 3 . 2

Sample job description for an office assistant. Job descriptions should be accurate, brief, and clear statements of what the worker is expected to do. Begin sentences with verbs. Be specific. State duties rather than qualifications of the incumbent.

Section A: Position Purpose:

Explain concisely why the duties and responsibilities assigned to this position are essential to agency operations.

The person occupying this position functions as the receptionist, word processor, and clerk for the Electrical Engineering Department. Since this position is the only one of its type in the Department, it is obviously critical to the operation of the Department. This person is expected to meet students, staff, and the public, provide general information about the Department, and direct the visitor to the proper place or person for more information or help. Duties of this position include keying of research manuscripts, daily correspondence, and other material submitted by faculty and staff.

Section B: Duties and Responsibilities:

Instructions: (1) Number each duty and indicate approximate percent of time spent on each major duty or group of duties; (2) include specific data as to responsibility for direction of work of other employees; position numbers and class titles of employees supervised; degree of responsibility for funds or actions, decision making, and program and policy planning; nature, purpose, and level of contacts within and outside the agency; (3) indicate how independently of supervision this position functions or, conversely, how closely and directly the position is supervised.

DUTY NO. AND PERCENT OF TIME	DUTIES
1. 25%	Act as office receptionist, answer general questions about the Department, direct visitors, answer telephones, take messages. Person must have general knowledge about operation of the Department and University. Visitors include faculty, staff, students, and the general public.
2. 45%	Key research papers, proposals, correspondence, examinations, and forms. Most work submitted to this person is in the form of handwritten drafts. Work is checked by person submitting the material. Little supervision is required; work is checked when completed.
3. 3%	Use photocopy machine. Employee is responsible for meeting deadlines set by faculty, staff, and supervisor.
4. 25%	Maintain records of all students enrolled in Electrical Engineering. Related tasks include assigning advisors, transferring students, posting semester grades, recording drop-add slips, and filing all student-oriented transactions. Employee maintains line schedule, textbook lists, and course outlines. Little supervision is given. Results checked as files accessed.
5. 2%	Handle mail and maintain office supplies. Assist other staff members with clerical work. Perform other duties as assigned.

Section C: Minimum Qualifications (Education and Experience, Certificates, Licenses, Degrees, Skills Required)

Good oral and written abilities. Vo-Tech graduate with course emphasis on secretarial science, 1-year experience.

The human resources staff generally secures the information using some combination of questionnaires, interviews, and observation of the jobs. Questionnaires, if used, have to be checked and supplemented by worker interviews for better worker acceptance and improved accuracy. The most common approach is interviews with the workers. Use a structured interview. Observation is a good check but generally is not sufficient by itself.

Although the information gathering and write-up should be done by a trained person, the results should be checked for clarity and brevity by a committee of interested parties. For accuracy in the third step—ranking of the jobs—all job descriptions should be about the same length and contain about the same level of detail. Raters will be more consistent if the person writing the job description knows what types of information they want and includes them in the description.

Keep the number of job descriptions (and jobs) reasonably small. The most common problem is over-specification of jobs and resulting lack of flexibility as workers **work to rule** and refuse to do work that is not in their job descriptions. For example, a carpenter might refuse to turn on the power, as that would be an electrician's work. All job descriptions should therefore have a "miscellaneous duties" section. In Figure 33.2 it is "Perform other duties as assigned."

As firms began to realize that the world is dynamic rather than static, they started an aggressive program of reducing the number of job descriptions by broadening the language. Typically, the goal is 5 to 10 job descriptions for the entire blue-collar workforce in a plant, replacing the former 50 to 100 descriptions. For example, all maintenance personnel might fall into one category instead of jobs of carpenters, electricians, plumbers, millwrights, and so forth. All inspectors might be called inspectors rather than electrical inspectors, mechanical inspectors, and so forth. However, this means that more emphasis is being placed on individual worth than on just the job. This, in turn, means more training for employees who now must be able to do it all (multi-skilling). Some organizations give a bonus for more education (e.g., a Master's degree).

The big benefit for management is improved flexibility in shifting people among work assignments and, thus, reduced labor costs since there is less idle time. However, this policy of few labor grades and broadly trained workers—sometimes called **pay for knowledge**—is a sharp change from the conventional detailed job description approach and may be resisted by workers familiar with and comfortable with the concept of knowing just one job.

2.2 Specify Minimal Hiring Requirements
This step, job specification, has become a difficult task with the increased emphasis on equal employment opportunity, nondiscrimination, and hiring people with disabilities. In many situations, organizations are sued if they don't make a "reasonable effort" to modify the job to fit a disability (such as a bad back). See Table 33.1. If job requirements are too rigorous, the organization may be challenged in a court case to prove that these are relevant. For example, can it prove in court that a high school diploma is necessary for job X? Desire to hire well-qualified employees is not proof! On the other hand, putting no requirements

---

T A B L E	3 3 . 1

The Americans with Disabilities Act (see Box 6.1) has increased the need for functional job description elements (rather than general descriptions). The examples (Rodgers, 1992) are from different jobs.

GENERAL	FUNCTIONAL
Heavy lifting	Lifts 50-lb bags close to body from floor to waist level; 6/min for 30 min every 2 h.
Extended reaches	Procures parts at 25 in. in front of the body and 50 in. above the floor. Parts weigh .25 lbs each and are handled with a power grip. One part is handled every 5 min throughout the 8-h shift.
Standing	Work is performed while standing for approximately 75% of the 8-h shift. Minimal walking is required to access materials.
Bending	Low work while bending forward is performed for short (<15 s) intervals throughout the shift. About 50 bends are done per 8-h shift.
Exposure to heat	Operator has to monitor equipment in a 95° F/70% rh room for 5 min each hour throughout the 8-h shift.
Awkward postures	Operator works in tight spaces (<25 in. behind a console) while squatting for up to 1 h continuously in an 8-h shift.

Source: Rodgers S. "A Functional Job Analysis Technique." *Occupational Medicine: State of the Art Reviews.* Vol. 7, No. 4, 679–711. Philadelphia: Hanley and Belfus, 1992.

on a job doesn't help much either. Hiring people and then allowing them 30 to 90 days to prove they can do the job results in poor quality and may result in worker injury if the new hires aren't physically qualified. If an entry-level job is part of a job sequence (such as helper, apprentice, electrician), specify enough qualifications for the entry job, or soon you will have people in the entry job who cannot complete the normal sequence.

2.3 Arrange Jobs in Order of Job Worth

This major step is discussed in detail in Section 3, "Arranging Jobs in Order."

2.4 Describe a Position

After the general categories of jobs are described (clerk, office assistant, etc.), it is necessary to describe individual jobs at individual locations (the job in electrical engineering). Then it can be determined that this specific job should be an office assistant. Sometimes the positions are described first, and then the combinations are used to form a job description.

3 ARRANGING JOBS IN ORDER

3.1 Background

There are many different jobs: lion tamer, astronaut, cook, secretary, engineer, corporate executive, teacher, welder, truck driver, assembly operator, and so on. Fortunately, this variety can be reduced, because job evaluation has as a goal the arrangement of jobs within an organization, not between organizations. There still may be a great diversity, however. This diversity is reduced to a practical level by setting up multiple plans—for example, one plan for clerical/office, one for managerial/technical, and one for shop/maintenance. Different plans for the different groups are justified in two ways:

1. Factors vary in importance by group. For example, effort and working conditions have relatively little importance in distinguishing among office jobs but considerable importance in shop jobs. Responsibility and initiative might vary considerably among professional/technical jobs and little among clerical jobs.
2. Wage curves are the goal. Wages for the work are, to some extent, determined by competition with other employers.

In addition, professional/technical jobs have to compete on a national rather than a local basis. An engineer may look at wages all over the country, whereas shop people may compare wages only within the community; thus, the level of competition is higher for jobs in which people are more mobile, and organizations have to offer relatively higher wages to meet the competition. However, except for monopolies such as the government, organizations generally have a local wage curve (rather than a national curve) for both clerical and shop personnel.

There are four approaches to arranging jobs: (1) ranking, (2) classification (such as the Civil Service grades of the U. S. government), (3) factor comparison, and (4) point systems. This section will discuss only the most popular approach, point systems. For information on the others (and more detail on point systems), consult the references at the end of the chapter.

3.2 Point Plans

The general concept of a point system is to analyze the levels of the factors relative to a job. Each factor has a number of levels with points allocated for each level. The analyst just adds up the points to get job worth. Although simple in concept, this process requires judgment.

The first judgment step is in selection of the factors and levels for the plan. As a general consensus over the last 50 years, the various factors have been grouped into categories of skill, effort, responsibility, and job conditions. Typical **skill factors** are "education," "experience," and "initiative and ingenuity." Another breakdown of skill is "pre-employment training," "employment training and experience," "mental skill," and "manual skill." Typical **effort factors** are "physical demand" and "mental or visual demand." Typical **responsibility factors** are for "equipment or process," "material or product," "safety of others," and "work of others." Another breakdown of responsibility is for "materials," "tools and equipment," "operations," and "safety of others." Typical **job condition factors** are "working conditions" and "hazards." Another breakdown is "surroundings" and "hazards."

Most plans use 10 to 15 different factors within each of these four categories. Since some factors are more important than others and wider ranges of points are given for some factors than others, a smaller number of factors probably would be sufficient from a technical viewpoint. However, from an administrative (political) viewpoint, the larger number of factors permits the administrator to say "our plan covers everything."

Table 33.2 gives 11 factors and the points assigned for the Midwest Industrial Management Association plan for shop jobs; there is another plan for office jobs. Table 33.3 gives the levels of factor 10 (working conditions), and Table 33.4 gives the levels of factor 11 (hazards). If, for example, the job of a lathe operator were being evaluated, for working conditions it probably would be 2nd degree or 20 points; for hazards it probably would be 3rd degree or 10 points.

T A B L E	3 3 . 2

Scoring system for the MIMA job evaluation plan for shop jobs.

JOB FACTORS	DEGREES				
	1ST	2ND	3RD	4TH	5TH
Skill					
1. Education or Trade Knowledge	14	28	42	56	70
2. Experience	22	44	66	88	110
3. Initiative and Ingenuity	14	28	42	56	70
Effort					
4. Physical Demand	10	20	30	40	50
5. Mental and/or Visual Demand	5	10	15	20	25
Responsibility					
6. Equipment or Process	5	10	15	20	25
7. Material or Product	5	10	15	20	25
8. Safety of Others	5	10	15	20	25
9. Work of Others	5	10	15	20	25
Job Conditions					
10. Working Conditions	10	20	30	40	50
11. Hazards	5	10	15	20	25

GRADE RANGES

Score Range	Grades	Score Range	Grades
139	12	250–271	6
140–161	11	272–293	5
162–183	10	294–315	4
184–205	9	316–337	3
206–227	8	338–359	2
228–249	7	360–381	1
Maximum Points			500

In the interests of accurate job evaluation and acceptance of the job evaluation, an evaluation of any specific job never should be made by a single individual. Each allocation of points should be checked by a committee of diverse backgrounds and interests, and a consensus reached. Jobs should be re-evaluated periodically (every 5 or 10 years), because jobs change considerably over time. There should be a formal appeals process. The success of job evaluation plans has been founded on such analytical, detailed, consensus-building techniques to replace opinionated, general, whimsical approaches.

The basic question is how much weight should be given to experience and initiative (often found in white-collar jobs) and how much weight should be given to physical demand and working conditions (often found in blue-collar jobs). Remember that the points reflect, to some extent, not only the requirements of the job but also the desire of people to do the job. As extreme examples, consider the jobs of selling women's clothing at retail and collecting garbage. The amount of initiative, responsibility, and the like is relatively high for the salesclerk but the supply of people who want to do this job is very high, so it is a minimum-wage job. It is hard to find people who will collect the garbage, so the result is that they are relatively well paid.

T A B L E	3 3 . 3	
Factor 10: Working conditions.		

This factor measures the surroundings or physical conditions under which the job must be done and the extent to which those conditions make the job disagreeable. Consider the presence and relative amount of exposure to dust, dirt, heat, fumes, cold, noise, vibration, wetness, etc. When working conditions vary with specific work assignments, such as found in maintenance jobs, the degree selected must represent the weighted average of all the conditions encountered.

1st Degree	*Excellent working conditions* with absence of disagreeable conditions
2nd Degree	*Good working conditions;* may be slightly dirty or involve occasional exposure to some of the elements listed above
3rd Degree	*Somewhat disagreeable working conditions* due to exposure to one or more of the elements listed above to the extent of being objectionable; may be exposed to one element continuously or several elements occasionally, but usually not at the same time
4th Degree	*Disagreeable working conditions* where several of the above elements are continuously present to the extent of being objectionable
5th Degree	*Continuous and intensive exposure* to several extremely disagreeable elements; working conditions *particularly disagreeable*

T A B L E	3 3 . 4	
Factor 11: Hazards.		

This factor measures the hazards, both accident and health, connected with or surrounding the job, considering safety clothing, devices, or equipment that have been installed or furnished at the work location, the material being handled, the machines or tools used, the work position, and the probable extent of injury in case of accident.

1st Degree	*Accident or health hazards negligible;* remote probability of injury
2nd Degree	*Accidents improbable,* outside of minor injuries, such as abrasions, cuts, or bruises; health hazards negligible
3rd Degree	*Exposure to lost-time accidents possible,* such as severe injuries to hand or foot, loss of finger, or eye injury, etc.; some exposure to health hazards, not incapacitating in nature
4th Degree	*Exposure to incapacitating* accident or health hazards, such as loss of arm or leg, impairment of vision
5th Degree	*Exposure to accidents or health hazards* which may result in *total disability or death*

Review Questions

1. How is pay based both on the worth of the job and the worth of the person holding the job?

2. Why is it bad to have too many different job descriptions?

3. List the four major categories for the factors in the point systems.

References

Hannon, J., Newman, J., Milkovich, G., and Brakefield, J. Job Evaluation in Organizations. In *Handbook of Industrial Engineering,* 3rd ed., Salvendy, G. (ed.). New York: Wiley, 2001.

Rodgers, S. A functional job analysis technique. *Occupational Medicine: State of the Art Reviews,* Vol. 7, No. 4, Oct.–Nov., Philadelphia: Haney and Belfus, 679–711, 1992.

INDEX